Walter Barker

ocv
Dl Biol Gen

Developmental Psychology

A PSYCHOBIOLOGICAL APPROACH

Developmental

JOHN NASH, McGill University

Psychology

A PSYCHOBIOLOGICAL APPROACH

Prentice/Hall International, Inc.

The Prentice-Hall
Series in Developmental Psychology

JOHN C. WRIGHT, *Editor*

PIAGET AND KNOWLEDGE
  Hans Furth

PIAGET'S THEORY OF INTELLECTUAL DEVELOPMENT: AN INTRODUCTION
  Herbert Ginsburg and Sylvia Opper

THE COGNITIVE PROCESS: READINGS
  R. J. C. Harper, C. C. Anderson, C. M. Christensen, and S. Hunka

PSYCHOPATHOLOGY OF CHILDHOOD
  Jane W. Kessler

Developmental Psychology: A Psychobiological Approach

by JOHN NASH

Copyright © 1970
by PRENTICE-HALL, INC., *Englewood Cliffs, New Jersey*

Library of Congress Catalog Card Number: 74–86520

PRENTICE-HALL INTERNATIONAL, INC., *London*
PRENTICE-HALL OF AUSTRALIA PTY. LTD., *Sydney*
PRENTICE-HALL OF CANADA LTD., *Toronto*
PRENTICE-HALL OF INDIA PRIVATE LTD., *New Delhi*
PRENTICE-HALL OF JAPAN, INC., *Tokyo*

To Heather, Pippa, Alan, and Godfrey,
from whom I have learned so much

Preface

This book has evolved out of the lecture notes I prepared for courses in developmental psychology over the past dozen years. Looking back on earlier drafts I realize that my views on development have changed and that some of my interpretations of the facts are different from those I proposed to my original students. I have always had a markedly biological orientation, no doubt because I came to psychology from zoology and physiology, and also because I was reared in the British tradition of psychology which has retained more of an organismic approach than has North American psychology. However, despite my earlier training I found that the first courses I gave in Canadian universities took on the environmentalist ethos of North American psychology, and these early courses emphasized the role of learning in the development of behavior.

But I have come to the realization, not that this view is wrong, but that it is incomplete. The environment with its various influences is crucial to development, and the human organism with its considerable ca-

pacity for learning is subject to modification and even control by the environment. Nevertheless, man's biological nature has much to do with the kind of environment he creates: His capacities for learning are biological characteristics and are subject to the constraints of his physiology. There is thus a feedback loop in which the development of the child is to a large extent *organized* by biological influences: It is this aspect which this book seeks to emphasize.

When I considered a title, one that appealed to me as most appropriate was *The Organization of Development*, but that seemed too similar to the title of another, earlier McGill book. However, this is what much of the book is about—the manner in which man's evolution and his biological equipment direct and organize ontogenetic development. I have sought to do more than describe the biological nature of the child, by showing how the environment interacts with this biological substratum, eventually to produce the mature adult. The key phrase here is *interacts with*, since it seems to me that much of child psychology has been concerned with how the environment *acts upon* the growing child as if he were a passive recipient of these influences.

A decision to undertake the considerable labor of writing a book (and the responsibility of adding to the literature explosion) must rest on serious dissatisfaction with existing offerings. One such dissatisfaction of mine arose from the lack of gestalt already mentioned. Some books have dealt with the biology of development and many more have been concerned with the outside influences impinging upon the child. Some of the latter have made a token acknowledgment of biological influences with a chapter or two on genetics or maturation, to which no substantial reference is made in later chapters, for none of these books, to my knowledge, has made a serious attempt to integrate the extensive findings of what can be called "behavioral biology" with that of the social sciences to produce a comprehensive treatment of the psychology of development. Another dissatisfaction I have felt with the available books is that they have tended to treat child psychology as an isolated discipline, having little relation to general psychological theory or to the considerable body of knowledge on adult psychology. This is regrettable, since adulthood is what the child is developing toward. Also neglected have been the broad, general questions such as what kind of society we should prepare our children for. At this stage in history we should be thinking in terms of far fewer children reared with a much higher quality of care. I believe that developmentalists should be addressing themselves to the problem of defining the ideal child-rearing system, and I have attempted to present my views on this topic.

The plan of the book is to proceed from a description of the biology of human development to a discussion of the environment's interaction with this biological basis. Thus, the early chapters are predominantly biological in orientation, and the later ones are more social

and environmental. It is hoped that the whole presents a more complete account of human development than is given in either those few books that describe the biology, or those many which discuss environmental influences.

One feature that undergraduate students may find objectionable is that throughout the book numerous references are given for literature that is not cited in detail. The reading might be simpler with these references omitted, since some of the general references are not always essential to the immediate discussion. However, the advanced student who wishes to delve more thoroughly into a given topic will find these references of value in providing access to the literature.

In undertaking a work that attempts to encompass as many areas of psychology as this book does, one has to ask experts in the various fields for critical evaluations. It is a pleasure to recognize my indebtedness to the following who have read parts of the manuscript and offered their comments, to the improvement of the book. R. S. Rodger of the Psychology Department, University of Sydney, read an earlier version of the manuscript, and his astute criticisms saved me from a too hasty publication of ill-digested ideas. W. M. O'Neil also made a positive contribution by persuading me to omit some tangential topics which interested me but did not contribute to the argument. The following members of the faculty of McGill University have given generously of their time to discuss with me content and ideas in one or more chapters: John Blundell, neurology; Robert Lemon, zoology; Klaus Minde and Gert Morgenstern, psychiatry; John Southin, genetics; and at the Department of Psychology at McGill, the following: Dalbir Bindra, Don Donderi, Marcel Goldschmid, Karl Konrad, Ronald Melzack, and John McNamara.

I am also indebted to a considerable number of students, who perhaps more than anyone help pinpoint one's ideas. I must in particular mention Catherine Snow and Roger Barnsley, graduate students at McGill, who read the early drafts of several chapters and contributed many valuable comments, ranging from questions of clarity to criticism of ideas. Most of all I wish to thank James Mac-Dougall, who as a teaching assistant in my developmental course for three years was intimately concerned in the process of communication of my ideas to undergraduates. He read and criticized each chapter as it was written, and in many different ways has made a signal contribution to this work.

The staff of Prentice-Hall have been delightful, helpful people to work with. John C. Wright, as outside expert editor of The Prentice-Hall Series in Developmental Psychology, gave help which I much value to the final stages of the manuscript, and the production staff have been pleasantly efficient in dealing with the intricacies of bookmaking.

Marilen Picard helped with checking the manuscript, and Heather Nash put much effort into checking the bibliography. The long task of typing the various drafts of the manuscript was undertaken skillfully by Helga Leibhold and Elma Picher, to whom I am grateful for their patient help. Phoebe Prowse and Bonita Trent of the Medical Library of Montreal Children's Hospital gave invaluable help in obtaining the literature. Pippa Nash assisted in proofreading.

I wish also to give my thanks to the Faculty of Graduate Studies and Research at McGill University for financial aid to the work of preparing the manuscript, and to the Board of Management of the Montreal Children's Hospital for encouraging me in this undertaking.

JOHN NASH

Montreal, 1969

Contents

Developmental Psychology

A PSYCHOBIOLOGICAL APPROACH

Prologue

It seems appropriate to commence with a definition of *developmental psychology* as I use the term. An important point is that it is different from *child psychology*. The latter, as I understand it, attempts to describe the behavioral characteristics of the human child at various ages and stages and has a strong (if implicit) interest in the practical applications of this knowledge to the education and rearing of the child and to dealing with behavioral abnormalities.

The developmental psychologist (as I perceive him or her) is not uninterested in these questions but views them in a broader context than does the child psychologist. For one thing, he is interested not only in the development of the human individual, but also in the evolution of the human species and man's place in nature. This view of developmental psychology is not universally held. Some psychologists, for example, make a distinction, similar to the one proposed above, between child psychology and developmental psychology, but do not include phylogenetic considerations as part of the developmental science. For them, developmental psychology deals only with the investigation of behavioral similarities and behavioral differences occurring through ontogenesis.

I believe that the individual in maturity is the product not only of his own history, but also of the history of his species, and that to understand human development fully one must take human evolution into account. Hence a consideration of comparative data is properly part of a developmental psychology. (The qualifications and limitations on knowledge from this source are discussed in other contexts.) This approach is also a practical necessity, because ethics prevents the kinds of manipulations of humans required to answer many questions, and it is good to have logical justification for extrapolation from animal data to the human condition.

Throughout the book there is both implicit and explicit questioning of what might be called the "environmental position." In North America especially, and in developmental psychology in particular, there is a marked emphasis on the social influences on the human organism. Even though there is a steadily increasing group of specialists interested in various biological approaches to understanding psychology, it is generally true that most psychologists interested in *human* psychology regard themselves as social scientists. In particular, most of the work on human development has concerned itself with environmental influences and their outcomes. This position seems to imply that all neonates are essentially alike, a kind of "standard organism" that then becomes modified by its experiences. This standard organism is taken for granted, and its characteristics are not considered especially pertinent to psychological inquiry.

One has only to point out that without constitution, without the nervous system and all its built-in tendencies to function in particular ways, and without all the biochemical factors that influence functioning, there is no organism for the environment to work upon. If one wishes to make an epigram, he can claim that the organism can create an environment, but the environment cannot create an organism. Like most epigrams, this is only partly true, but it may serve as a contrast to the emphasis on experience made by the environmentalists. This is not to say that the environment should or can be ignored, and constant reference will be made to the organism-environment interaction. But a perspective needs to be brought into the discussion of this interaction.

Long ago J. J. Rousseau proposed what was in his time the novel idea that the child is not a miniature adult and that the child's mind is not some kind of reduced copy of the adult mind. It might be thought unnecessary to mention this at this stage of the history of psychology, but yet there are indications that a reminder may be required. As will be reviewed in later chapters, there is in some quarters the idea that adult mental processes, in logic, for instance, can be taught earlier and earlier in human development, to the point, presumably, where calculus can become a kindergarten subject. Implicit in this idea is the notion that the only difference between the child and the adult is in their experiences and

that one has only to provide these experiences early for the child to reach adult status early. As will be shown at several points in the argument of this book, the child is essentially different from the adult in a variety of ways, most pertinent of which to psychology are the neurological differences between early life and maturity. These differences are pervasive and mean that the child, who reacts distinctively to the environment and the experiences it provides, is an organism distinctive from the adult.

This book is to be considered as an essay in a specialized branch of biology; that is, it regards psychology as a biological science. It treats man as a biological organism interacting with a social environment. It may in a rough manner be possible to say that as he grows older man changes from a biological to a social organism, but this is really only partly true, because throughout life man does remain a biological organism: It is, indeed, this fact that eventually ends his course.

The progression from biological determinants of behavior toward the greater role of social influences might be taken as one of the most characteristic features of the developmental process, and instances of this shift will be seen in a number of aspects of development.

Man must be viewed not as a finished product, but as a species in evolution. Man at his present stage has certain features that are widely enough spread throughout the species to be considered characteristic, whereas others might be merely emerging and found (as yet) only in a minority. Such a view might be considered undemocratic, at least where valued characteristics are involved, but the concern of science is reality. Even democratic ideals must be tempered with realism.

The view of man as a stage of dynamic evolution rather than as static implies that certain characters in the gene pool are adaptive and desirable and should be encouraged by breeding until they are universal (or, conversely, that disadvantageous traits such as mental deficiency be eliminated by selective breeding). The impracticability of such eugenic measures even in a totalitarian society are widely known and need not be elaborated here. Psychologists cannot concern themselves directly with such matters and are forced to concentrate on those that fall within their scope—that is, to seek the environmental factors that are influential and to optimize the environment rather than try to change the gene pool. However, we must know where our biological limitations lie and must therefore keep in touch with such sciences as genetics. For instance, it is suggested later that an adaptive trait that is desirable but newly emerging and hence still uncommon in the gene pool is creativeness. If this is true, then it is wasted effort to attempt to inculcate creativity in all by vast educational changes that can benefit only a few. Rather, we need to know the realities with which we must work and must seek the geneticist's aid in doing this. If (as one anticipates he might) he tells us we *are* dealing with a genetically determined trait, then the psychologist's task becomes that of identifying individuals bearing this trait and of setting up an educational milieu *for them* that will permit the fullest growth. (Whatever possibilities the future may hold for the geneticist's manipulation of the gene pool are another matter.) Thus a knowledge of the biological limits has practical influences on the educational measures taken.

A point that is repeatedly emphasized throughout the book is that the human species (in common with most of the animal kingdom) really consists of two distinct types or subspecies—male and female. This is contrary to the general assumption in psychology that they are so much alike as to make it unnecessary to consider the two apart, except in minor details of functioning. It will be argued that the differences between males and females are so pervasive that they affect total functioning in subtle but nonetheless important ways.

Another feature of this book that some may find unusual, and that may lead them to ask if it is really about developmental psychology, is the considerable reference to studies of adults. The reason for this is that one must keep in mind what development is toward. Most of the existing works in the field may be criticized on the grounds that they are too isolated from general psychological theory and from the body of knowledge of adult psychology. (It is true that this body is a somewhat twisted one, resting heavily on a biased sample of college students, but we must use the data we have.) The attempt is made here to approach the task not as an exercise in an isolated field, but as one integrated with the general corpus of psychology—at least as we understand it today.

In addition, it is also the case that development does not cease at some arbitrary point, such as the twenty-first birthday. There is repeated emphasis in this book on the aim toward a realization for each individual of his fullest potential, a process of self-growth that should continue throughout life.

It is also suggested at various points that a proper task for the developmentalist is not only to investigate and theorize about development as it is, but also as it should be. The old dictum that "the proper study of mankind is man" is fully accepted. Though this may draw disagreement from some, it is insisted that it is both appropriate and a duty for the developmental psychologist to estimate the potential of the human organism and to enter into a wider domain by saying what changes in human societies are necessary to achieve the realization of this potential.

This involves one in some philosophical issues, but as it has been put in Brett's *History*,

It is an open question whether a psychologist can be an idealist or a realist. He should perhaps be simply a psychologist. But apart from collectors of detail and writers of monographs, history has failed to produce a psychologist who was not a philosopher of some kind, and it is notorious that the rejection of metaphysics is the most metaphysical of all positions [R. S. Peters, 1953, p. 573].

Julian Huxley has repeatedly urged that scientists must take responsibility for the effects on society of their discoveries (see, for example, his essays *Ends and Means,* 1937). He deplores how little is spent on the sciences of man as compared with the natural sciences, a lament that is still valid. He also deplores a trend, which still continues, toward an intensive specialization that reduces each branch of science to a condition approaching meaninglessness. Indeed, he reprimands some scientists for lauding specialized meaninglessness as a sign of true science. They indulge their whim for delightful and amusing researches but refuse to take responsibility for anything. These purists, he says, accuse of bad science and charlatanism those who attempt to relate the particular results of specialization to human life as a whole.

There are signs, which I regard as healthy that there is a general movement toward a much broader consideration of issues. For example, J. Paul Getty (1968) has spoken of a growing realization in the big corporations that the top executives need to be men able to understand the social implications of industrial change. The narrowly trained science graduate, he says, is suitable only as a technician. The higher echelons of the business world are being increasingly occupied by men trained in the humanities rather than in science, because the former are better able to deal with the broad issues on which they have to make decisions. The same realization is touching the scientific field, as, for instance, numerous articles and editorial comments in *Science,* the journal of the American Academy for the Advancement of Science, bear witness. Etzioni's article (1968) on the social implications of biological discoveries that may lead to sex control is but one of many indications of a concern with such broad issues. Developmental psychology must also be touched by this new awareness in science of broader considerations than those of mere data collection.

This book does make an attempt to relate a number of specialized areas of inquiry to some molar concept of the human condition. For this reason it contains a number of speculations, because an attempt must be made to bring a perspective to certain important issues in developmental psychology. There is an enormous mass of data from the research over the past half century or so but little in the way of a philosophy that can unify these masses of data into any sort of coherence. It would be both immodest and untrue to claim that this book will bring order into the field, though what it does do is to attempt to present a point of view that will enable a considerable proportion of this material to fall into place and that will also reveal the gaps in our knowledge and the kinds of data that are needed to bridge these gaps.

It is becoming quite clear that there is no simple statement that will unify biology, or even psychology, within the biological sciences. There is no equivalent for psychology of the formula $E = mc^2$, which has unified so much of physics.

To bridge gaps and to suggest new lines of inquiry, one must speculate. Speculation is in fact a respectable scientific occupation. As T. H. Huxley put it, "Anyone who is practically acquainted with scientific work is aware that those who refuse to go beyond fact rarely get as far as fact." And anyone acquainted with the history of science knows that all major advances have involved a speculative and intuitive leap beyond the facts into suppositions that in strict logic were not yet tenable. Logic can only operate deductively—that is, arriving at particular conclusions from established general statements. The creation of new generalizations requires *intuitive* processes that are illogical in the sense of going beyond facts.

This book is not primarily concerned with methodology; there is already at least one excellent work in this aspect of the field (Mussen, 1960). There is, however, one point that requires mention: There are many areas of human development in which strictly correct methodology is impossible to apply. Sometimes this is because suitable techniques of inquiry have not been devised, but this is a problem the creative imagination of investigators may yet solve. More often there is an unsurmountable difficulty that we must hope will remain so. That is, certain problems of human development can be solved only by the application of techniques that ethics and a respect for the rights of the individual prohibit. In these areas we must content ourselves with such data as we can derive from animal studies (with the question of their valid application to the human situation) or with observations of various social accidents (which it is our duty to prevent). In the latter case the conditions of observation and the clarity of the evidence are usually far short of what is desirable, but it is all we have to go on, or all we can conscientiously wish for.

There are many areas of development in which the psychologist has two clear choices. He can, on the one hand, insist on the elegance of experimental design that is taught by idealistic professors of the subject and that guides the decisions of journal editors; if he does this, he must admit that certain topics will forever remain unexplored in any reasonable human society. On the other hand, he can be prepared to compromise his experimental purity and accept evidence that not only fails to reach the arbitrary .05 minimum probability of chance occurrence, but that also is based on observations that have not been strictly controlled.

If he insists on methodological elegance, he must admit that psychology has little to say on most of the more pressing problems, such as juvenile delinquency or mental illness, that concern human societies. He must regard psychology as an academic pastime that does not have much contact with a real world and that for the most part can make statistically significant statements only on insignificant questions. Taking the less impeccable course (if he is vain enough to believe that psychology may have something to say that is useful in the real world in which men live) does not mean

throwing methodology to the winds. What it does mean is taking all possible pains with his methods, accepting only the most rigid standards of evidence so long as these can serve his purpose; only when these fail must he try to close the gap or reach out into the unknown on a less acceptable basis.

Most real-world decisions, in business or in private life, for instance, are made on statistically nonsignificant bases, and even the strictest of methodologists chooses his wife with much less confidence (in the statistical sense) than he accepts the results of an experiment. Some socially important changes in recent years have been made on the basis of psychological findings of dubious statistical validity. For example, the studies of the effects of institutional care of children (reviewed in Chapter 11) are almost all bad from the point of view of experimental design, yet one cannot deny that the decisions based on this scientifically shaky evidence have been wholly commendable. Had the matter been left to methodologists, we would still be unconvinced that orphanages are a breeding ground for later misery.

The aim of this book is to take valid knowledge as far as it will carry our understanding of human development, but it does not restrict itself to considering impeccable evidence only. Where sound studies fail, then (but only then) it is considered right to look to intuition for enlightenment. Even if none of the speculations made here prove to be valid on closer examination, they may still perform a useful function if they suggest lines of inquiry. They will have served the proper function of hypotheses in science.

This book is concerned with the determinants of development. It seeks to outline the manner in which development is organized. Organization is at first mediated almost exclusively by innate biological factors, but this pristine organizational system is soon modified by its own interactions with the environment. The importance of these environmental influences increases rapidly, but though reduced in their relative potency, the biological organizational principles remain operative over the developmental period. Because of maturational (biological) changes, the organism does in fact become *less* modifiable in certain important respects (this is seen, for one of innumerable examples, in the rapidly decreasing ability to recover from aphasia after about the fourteenth or fifteenth year). Not all these maturationally determined reductions in modifiability occur at the end of the developmental period: Some occur quite soon and impose relatively early constraints on the later course of development. (These are discussed as critical periods in Chapter 7.)

In the strict sense, it is not accurate, therefore, to describe development as progressing from the biological to the social. As already stated, it is true in a rough manner, as a kind of catchphrase epitomizing certain trends in development, but it oversimplifies the actual course. Man as a social organism is constrained both by his early history as a predominantly biological organism and by his contemporary biological nature in his mature interactions with the environment. Even the social environment that man has evolved for himself is to a considerable extent molded by his biological nature, and these biological determinants of culture are discussed in Chapter 18.

The structure of this book attempts to follow this progression from the biological to the social, though it does not seem possible (to me at least) to present the argument in a strictly logical manner—no doubt to some extent because the idea itself is not entirely logical. One would wish to start, like Euclid, with certain axioms and develop theorems of increasing complexity in strictly logical sequence (and hopefully be successful in crossing the *pons asinorum*). Human development simply does not lend itself to this tidy approach. Its complexity forces one into arbitrary divisions of the material, and however one arranges it, it seems unavoidable that he discuss some topics briefly in some contexts in anticipation of a fuller discussion elsewhere. Inevitably the threads of the argument become tangled, but it is hoped that this introduction will enable the reader to maintain a direction even if he occasionally loses the track as attention is focused on specifics.

One

Efficiency in Development

There are two main approaches to a study of child rearing. One is the *nomothetic* and the other the *idiographic*. These approaches have been discussed by G. W. Allport (1937), and as he says, psychology has been striving to make itself an exact science and to become a nomothetic discipline, one that endeavors to state the general laws governing behavior. The second approach, the idiographic, will be discussed in Chapter 2, in which the problems posed by individuality or uniqueness are raised.

As applied to the developmental field, the nomothetic discipline attempts to study the general principles underlying growth, unfolding of personality, and age changes in behavior. One means of approach is to study what actually occurs—the types of behaviors actually found in given populations of children, their manifest personality characteristics, and the kinds of child-rearing experiences that seem to be related to these behaviors and characteristics. The greater part of child psychology (as distinct from developmental psychology) is of this descriptive nature. One aim of developmental psychology is to attempt to look deeper than this and to

ask whether what is occurring is what *must* occur—to ask whether the actual child-rearing practices of a particular population best serve the developmental process. The word *best* here arouses many questions, and the task of this chapter is to take up some of these problems.

PROBLEM OF THE NORMAL

Implicit in any approach to development is the idea of what is *normal*. Either one is seeking to discover what normal development is or one has a concept of normality that is fitted into some frame of reference; the latter is the underlying assumption in works that make recommendations about educational or child-rearing procedures.

This question of normality poses a number of problems, which have been discussed by King (1945). He points out that the "average" or the "ordinary" is a misleading way to approach the question. Some things may be "average" in particular populations without necessarily being normal. Even if everybody has cancer (not too improbable an event if radiation and air pollution continue unabated), cancer would still not be normal. It would, of course, be "normal" in the statistical sense, and a reliance on average or statistical estimates of normality may mislead us into regarding as normal things that in other senses are not. As King says, if we calculate an average, we get an average, not a norm.

King proposes a biological concept of normality in which it is defined as "that which functions in accordance with its [the organism's] design" (p. 494). He points out that in nature design and function are inseparably correlated and that there is a *pattern norm* in which the functioning of the organism is consistent with its inherent design. King suggests, as a synonym of *normal*, the term *paradic*, which does not have the misleading connotations that have grown around the former. Unfortunately this suggestion has not been followed in the literature.

It may not always be easy to know what the design is, or what function is in accordance with it, and the average may often have to provide a first approach to the detection of the normal. A visitor from Alpha Centauri, where cancer is unknown, in performing autopsies on the human specimens he collects might conclude that growths are "average," especially if he has a preponderance of older subjects. But if he is smart enough to make the journey through space, he certainly will not be misled by his data. He will note, for instance, that these growths are distributed irregularly, rather than consistently, as are other anatomical features. He would probably not be long in concluding that these strange things were interfering with function rather than being consistent with it.

The attempt to discover the design of the human organism and how this design unfolds over childhood is the main purpose of this book. It attempts to suggest how man can best function in accordance with the human design and what child-rearing processes are consistent with this design. In King's terms, we seek the *anthroparadic*.

The task of defining the pattern norm is by no means straightforward. One might define the "normal" height of a population of men by taking the mean of a considerable number, and, as with cancer, in certain circumstances this may give misleading information. Thus in Germany during World War I the Allied blockade of food supplies led to a measure of malnutrition among growing children that was reflected in the final stature of young men in the immediate postwar years; therefore, the "normal" height as defined by the mean was below that which might have been expected in a better nourished population. However, although well-nourished children grow faster and taller than poorly fed ones, there is a limit to such growth. Children are not like plants that can be made to grow to prodigious heights (compared with the mean) by "overfeeding" and watering. There is a maximum growth determined by constitutional factors that no amount of "overfeeding" can exceed. Insofar as height is concerned, the pattern norm might be defined as that which is the maximum potential, though this is not necessarily so.

There are, of course, two pattern norms. One is the mean pattern norm for the species, and this could be the same as the statistical average. Insofar as height is concerned, the statistical average height of young adults in the middle and upper classes of North American society is probably close to it if not identical with the mean pattern norm.

The other pattern norm is the individual one, in this case the maximum height a given person's own genetic endowment enables him to attain. This individual pattern norm is a somewhat theoretical one, because in practice it may be difficult to estimate.

DESIGN AND EFFICIENCY

A concept being proposed in this book is one of *psychological efficiency*, that is, the idea that the design of the human organism makes certain modes of function easier to elicit and more effective in operation than others. These relate especially to the fundamental properties of the central nervous system (CNS), but also involve the whole constitution. Also implicit here is the idea of *developmental efficiency*, the notion that because of the inherent design of the developing organism certain ways of developing are more efficient than others.

Some of these modes of function are universal to the human species. While they may be absent in particular individuals, their absence must be considered either as resulting from a developmental abnormality or caused by a specific condition such as brain damage. An instance of this is the process of translation from short- to long-term memory storage, a fundamental property of the nervous system that must have an effect (as yet little studied) on long-range learning. It presumably underlies such phenomena as the relative efficiencies of spaced and massed trials in learning.

Other modes of function are sex-linked, which does not mean they are necessarily present only in one sex but rather that they are better represented in one. A question that does arise here is whether phenotypically similar behaviors are necessarily of the same genotype in both sexes. In many modes of function they probably are, but there may be some in which similar-appearing behaviors actually depend on different modes of both acquisition and operation. For example, males have been characterized elsewhere as field-independent (Chapters 10 and 16). Yet we know that some females are also field-independent; do they become so by the same process as males do? One difference might be that males become so maturationally: It is an innate aspect of masculinity. A girl, on the other hand, must *learn* field independence. Conversely, a male may learn field dependence, whereas for the girl it may emerge spontaneously unless modified by the environment.

Implicit in this idea is the notion that certain modes of functioning are more efficient

for males than for females. Males *can* acquire feminine modes of function, and vice versa, but perform less efficiently in them.

Not only are there general modes of function that are most consistent with the species design, and within the species certain functions that are more efficient for one sex, but also there are individual modes of maximally effective functioning. The ultimate task for a philosophy of child-rearing systems is not to propose blanket techniques of rearing that are universally applicable but to consider each individual as a unique constellation of potentialities, requiring his own special conditions for growth.

There is, however, one assumption here that needs to be questioned. Returning to our example of height, is the *maximum* height necessarily the "best" height, biologically defined? Perhaps the question is clearer if we take weight instead of height. A great many North Americans are concerned about a weight that is not only above the average but above the desirable. What is the optimum weight for a species or an individual? Dietitians attempt to define it in terms of height-weight ratio, but their tables are based upon averages for the population. The optimum height-weight ratio, that which makes for the healthiest functioning of an individual, may or may not approximate that derived from these tables, though we have at present no better way of determining it.

It is proposed, then, that in psychological functions there is a pattern norm, and part of the task of developmental psychology is to discover what the norm is and to suggest child-rearing conditions consistent with it. Psychological functioning will be most efficient under these conditions. It is possible, of course, for function to exceed the pattern norm, but only at the cost of greater effort, the efficiency of which must be assessed according to the circumstances. To revert to a physical analogy, there are optimum rates at which a man can run. The most efficient rate in particular circumstances depends on whether he has to cover 100 yards, 1 mile, or 10 miles. To attempt to apply the 100-yard maximum to a 1-mile track will be inefficient, because it will result in collapse before the quarter-mile mark.

Similarly, there are for man in general, and for particular individuals, optimum rates of psychological functioning that can be sustained indefinitely. The pattern norm may be exceeded for short spurts, but the attempt to maintain this rate over long periods is stressful and hence inefficient. Too long continued, it may lead to psychic collapse, but even if it does not do so, it must be considered inefficient in the sense that it drains energy from other functions. Thus it must be considered inefficient for a man to sustain a high level of intellectual productivity if it detracts from his emotional functioning. Or for a child to be submitted to an advanced rate of intellectual development is to be considered inefficient if emotional development is thereby inhibited. Thus one must have a concept of *total* functioning and assess efficiency in terms of it.

It is evident that a statement of the pattern norm for man can hardly avoid value judgments. Some may argue that intellectual productivity is sufficient and that emotional retardation is a small price to pay for it; others will argue differently. Judgments of this sort can be put to arbitration. If (as may be suspected) it can be demonstrated that the highest sustained rate of intellectual output comes from individuals who are emotionally well developed, then the choice is clear, assuming, of course, that intellectual productivity is desirable. Perhaps value judgments are inescapable after all.

The manner in which the developmental capacity of the child may be limiting on what can be efficiently achieved is illustrated by the well-known walking-talking conflict. The child who has just learned to walk often shows a regression in walking skill when he subsequently starts to talk (or vice versa if talking precedes walking). The beginning walker may actually fall down if he tries to say something while walking. At this stage the acquirement of one major skill fully taxes his capacities, and it is developmentally inefficient to impose both simultaneously.

Two

Individuality

Science deals with generalities and is embarrassed by uniqueness. With psychology's concern with being scientific, it is not surprising that a matter commonly ignored in psychological discussions is the uniqueness of the individual. There is perhaps some excuse for this: The problems of understanding psychological principles are difficult enough without the added complication of considering each case uniquely.

In dealing with organisms in general, the life sciences are taking their lead from the physical sciences, where unique instances are less common. Generally, in physics, if one knows all the factors entering a given system, he can then predict the outcome with certainty (this statement excepts the uncertainty principle of some special situations). For a considerable range of physical events it is already possible to have this knowledge.

In principle, of course, the same *may* be true of living organisms, but we are so far from any such complete understanding that at present its attainment is impossible, even *if* theoretically possible. The simplest of events impinges upon an organism of great complexity, especially if one deals with an animal as complex as the rat, as most psychological experiments do. Because we have only a naive understanding of many of the complexities of the organism, confounding factors that are unpredictable are introduced. The behaviorists chose to ignore these inexplicable mediating events, to study only the stimulus and the response to it, in the belief that these are the objective and measurable aspects of a psychological phenomenon. The fact that a given stimulus of accurately describable physical properties may not be the same to all observers spoils this simplicity: For instance, light of a certain wavelength in the region of turquoise may appear green to some observers, blue to others, and gray to a few. Similarly, even in simple response situations actual responses vary greatly, and for many experiments idiosyncratic responders are quietly dropped from the data. Even in uncomplicated situations the best one can say is that under certain conditions a particular kind of response occurs more often than not, but this means that it is a minority—often a sizable one—who do *not* respond as expected.

As Allport, among others, has insisted, sooner or later attention must be drawn from the laws governing the cases that do respond typically to devote more attention to those underlying the exceptions, that is, to the idiographic approach mentioned in Chapter 1. In the meantime we need to bear in mind that in dealing with organisms in general we grossly oversimplify. And we do not get a great deal nearer the truth by dealing with a species as if it were uniform.

Williams (1956) and Medawar (1957) are among those who insist strongly on biological individuality. They discuss the many ways in which the whole physiology of each organism differs from that of others. This biochemical and physiological distinctiveness must surely carry psychological consequences. As Williams et al. (1962) have put it, "The so-called 'behavioral sciences,' which most often merely bow to biology and then pass on their way, must sooner or later face the inborn individuality." One might bristle at "so-called" but still feel that the warning is well intended.

In spite of Williams, Medawar, and others, physiologists in general do not seem to have considered uniqueness to a great extent in the past, although recent work in immunological reactions and other matters are forcing this to their attention. An understanding of biological uniqueness will no doubt throw considerable light on psychological idiosyncrasies. For example, it is possible that unusual if not unique biochemical processes may underlie the psychological manifestations of some mental illnesses.

Not only is the individual unique within himself, but he also interacts with an environment that is unique to him. In the psychological domain, part of this uniqueness of the environment arises from the fact, mentioned elsewhere, that the individual *perceives* the environment differently even when the physical attributes are uniform. But each individual in his social environment interacts with others who are also unique. Hence one becomes far removed from the physicist's

world of uniform matter operating in standard systems.

It might be argued (and commonly is) that understanding of determinism is limited only by our ignorance. After we really understand color vision, we can predict whether a given individual will respond by saying "blue" or "green" to a given stimulus. When we fully understand protein synthesis, we will know why some transplants are rejected and will be able to predict accurately whether tissue from a particular donor will be acceptable to a given host. In this view the indeterminancy principle in psychology will apply only to very special circumstances, as in physics, and virtually all scientific psychology can proceed without the necessity of regarding this principle.

On the other hand, there are some who insist that the indeterminancy principle operates as an essential part of biological theory, with an appreciable range of phenomena being unpredictable. This indeterminancy arises from the fact that the act of observation changes the situation being observed: Often the experimenter cannot hold one variable constant without also influencing variables that he wishes to observe operating freely. This is a very familiar difficulty to the psychologist.

This does not mean that such events are unlawful, but merely that we cannot observe them under conditions that make possible the detection of these laws. However, whether or not life processes can with more sophisticated observations be reduced to ultimate explanations in terms of physical laws is at present a purely philosophical question and is a long way from becoming a practical one.

The neovitalists, like Driesch and von Uexküll, insist that the question can never become a practical one. Driesch (1914), as a biologist, concluded that the living organism is more than the aggregate of its parts and that in the last analysis life cannot be explained in terms of physical or chemical phenomena. The biologist von Uexküll (1934) also held that the life process is only partly understandable in mechanical terms. In his scheme, every animal has its peculiar world with different internal images of the external reality. Thus man as a species has a particular "world view" mediated by the perceptual equipment of his species. But one might go further and recognize that every individual also has his private view of reality.

Much of this book is concerned with mechanistic explanations of human development and functioning, and at a certain level of discourse their competence is undeniable. It must be admitted that certain external agents —an object rapidly approaching the face, for instance—have fairly definite effects on human behaviors. Similarly, internal agents, like androgens, have their influences on psychological functions. Perceptual processes are determined to a considerable extent by the nature and structure of the receptors and of the nervous system. As a parallel to von Uexküll's mechanistic biology we have a mechanistic psychology that deals with that part of psychological functioning that is mechanistically understandable. This book is concerned almost entirely with this extensive area but acknowledges that there may be a residual to which such explanations are not yet applicable. An individualistic psychology would certainly have to take cognizance of any principle of psychic indeterminance. While mechanistic psychology will describe the general effects of androgens or the general principles of perception, individualistic psychology will concern itself with single idiosyncratic reactions to androgens or sensory stimuli. Reference is made at many points to such individual differences, but this work does not aim to be a systematic account of individual psychology. The aim of this chapter is simply to show that there are raised by individuality certain problems that must be considered in attempting to provide a complete view of man and his development.

If one understands Buddhism and other oriental philosophies correctly (by no means an easy thing), then the idea of the individuality of personality is not universally shared. To the Buddhist, the individual is but a fragment of a supraordinate whole, the Great Self, and individuality is but fiction. Each of us is a moment of awareness in the flux of eternal time (Bouquet, 1950). Western thought maintains the "ego illusion" that each of us is "a separate ego enclosed in a bag of skin" (Watts, 1966.) The Buddhist, it appears, believes that the idea of a separate ego is false and feels himself as part of the pattern of life: There is no distinction between knower and known, between experiencer and experience; all are part of a single experiencing and knowing.

When the Westerner tries to understand what these statements really mean, he encounters such difficulty as to wonder whether the Buddhist really understands them, or if indeed he can really believe them. Most Westerners who think at all about their identity are faced with the loneliness of individuality, with the isolation rather than the merging oneness. Perhaps this is the secret, to seek communion with some Great Self rather than with one another. It would seem, moreover, that the Buddhist would blame our difficulties on our reliance on a limited set of symbols to express the truths of the universe. We tend to comprehend only what we can set out in either verbal or mathematical symbols, but both are systems of limited application. Only a part of truth (the Buddhist would say) can be communicated by these symbolic systems; they cannot be revealed to the mind, only to the spirit. Because we reject the spirit, we cannot comprehend the truth in its wholeness.

The idea of some union with the Great Self is not entirely lacking in Western thought. In certain religious beliefs, such as the inner light, or "God-in-every-man" of the Quakers, this idea is implicit, though in a different form. It is that man contains a fragment of God, rather than being a fragment of God.

Be that as it may, there are evidently cultural differences in the concept of *social* individuality. For the Russians, for instance, the idea of a scientist or anyone else making a personal comment as an individual is foreign: One can speak only as a member of a group. The trials of "deviationist" writers must be understood, even if not applauded, in this context.

This is not the place for metaphysical discussion, but merely for a comment on the implications of our metaphysical preconceptions for child rearing. Individuality is a biological fact and the immediate question is whether it is also a psychological fact. There is much evidence, that will be reviewed in later chapters, to suggest that it is.

There are trends in our society, just as there are in other cultures, toward a loss of individuality. One might see the mass media of communication as suppressive of individuality and trending toward the predictions of George Orwell's *1984*. On the other hand, it might be argued that individuality is a biological fact with psychological consequences that receives its most marked expression in the human species. It is a species-specific character, and because it has biological primacy, it is likely to be difficult to suppress. In this view any attempt at suppression, whether from communism, fascism, or Buddhism, is contrary to man's biological nature and in the long run is likely to fail.

Part of the aim of this book is to consider the optimum child-rearing system that will best elicit the human potential. If this insistence on individuality is valid, then there is no one ideal system. Each individual will have his own best conditions. Society must provide for variety in its care and nurture of children. One is, of course, making a value judgment in supposing that psychological individuality is a human trait to be fostered rather than minimized.

Our cultural attitudes to this question are ambiguous. On the one hand, we insist on the sanctity of the individual, yet this is in some senses opposed to the democratic ideal. The philosophy of the egalitarian society has a history, which at present is perhaps difficult to throw off. In eighteenth-century Europe individual differences were minimized: There were the aristocrats, who were believed to be uniformly gifted and intelligent, and the proletariat, who were uniformly unintelligent and of limited capacity. This philosophy is clearly referred to in novels such as *Jane Eyre,* though Jane's efforts at Lowood School were motivated by a questioning of this assumption. A protest against this inequality goes deep into the philosophy of the founding fathers of the American colonies. The noble sentiment that all men are equal under God was somewhat misinterpreted. The idea that God is not concerned with a man's IQ in valuing his soul was taken to mean that all IQ's are equal and all else is the same, and it became somewhat sacrilegious to point out that men are not in fact equal on earth, whatever their equal rights in facing St. Peter at those pearly gates. The same assumptions came to be applied to the question of sex differences, in which there has been the confused notion that sexual distinctiveness is incompatible with ethical equality.

This reluctance to face the full implications of individuality has affected psychological studies. The greater part—by far the greater part—of the literature on child rearing has sought to show that differing kinds of experiences produce different effects. The literature on the converse phenomenon, the same experience having differing effects with different individuals, is much less extensive. It is in fact difficult to make a systematic survey of this question because thinking does not move along these lines, and sources such as the *Psychological Abstracts* are not indexed to provide ready access to such studies.

It is true, of course, that a considerable body of literature is devoted to providing a single uniform experience, a test situation, and to showing that individuals react differently to it, but in this literature it is usually assumed that the differences observed fall into two (or more) fairly homogeneous groupings, and the results are also usually related to some differing antecedent experience. The ideal paradigm is that prior condition A produces score X on a test or measure, and condition B, score Y. The fact that X and Y range considerably is regarded as experimental noise, not the result of fundamental differences in the organisms constituting the groups. Certainly, few people deny the existence of these differences, but they are commonly taken as a nuisance to clear experimentation rather than as a fact of life to be accounted for. It may be that comparative psychologists are especially prone to this assumption, but developmental psychologists are by no means free of it.

One study that has considered the question of differing reactions to similar antecedents is by Thomas et al. (1960), who show that similar patterns of rearing and toilet-training practices are reacted to very differently by different infants. They point out that "every experience is an individualized one for each child and its psychological influence can be understood only in terms of the environmental context in which it occurs and the primary characteristics of reactivity of the child."

However, this same group then proceeds in a later study to categorize these individual reactions to experience (Birch et al., 1962), which illustrates nicely how ingrained the scientific habit of classification is and how difficult it is to avoid. In a longitudinal study of young children they show how reaction characteristics to various common experiences can be described under nine headings, which tended to be stable over time. These patterns of reactions tend to cluster, so that from their data five distinctive groupings were discernible. One is not criticizing Birch et al. for doing what is necessary in science. It is conceptually difficult to consider each case uniquely, and it is also highly uneconomical when there are in fact a considerable number of characteristics that individuals have in common.

At least for the present, developmental psychology must concern itself mainly with communalities. When the ground rules for common reactions are known more thoroughly, unique cases can be considered. We can

then seek to understand why a given individual deviates from the common reaction, and can hope to do this not merely by appeal to some group characteristic—by saying he is mentally defective, for instance—but by showing how his unique situation brings about an idiosyncratic response—by describing, for example, his unique pattern of deficiencies (and his assets) and the manner of their interaction in the incident in question. Even in this statement, it will be noted, there are implied general characteristics: In speaking of deficiencies, one implies comparison with a norm, a statement of what is expected of some average individual. The man in the street, the average person, may not exist, but his ghost is certainly ubiquitous.

In discussing uniqueness, it perhaps needs to be pointed out that the term itself is ambiguous. We are taught in school that unique is unqualifiable—an event or an object is either unique or it is not. Every individual is unique because nowhere and at no time is there to be found a precisely similar person with the same biological makeup and the same set of life experiences. This is true even of identical twins. But within this uniqueness there is much that is shared.

If one takes a so-called average child, for example, one who scores 100 on the Wechsler Intelligence Scale for Children (WISC), this child's subtest scores will vary from those of others who also score 100. Probably, however, one could find many other children with the same pattern of scatter on subtests, because the degrees of freedom permitted by the scoring of the test are limited. One might find uncommonness, or even uniqueness, in the manner in which a child describes what he should do if he is in the unlikely position of seeing a train approaching a broken track or in the exact movements by which he places the blocks in a design. In most instances and for most purposes these slight idiosyncratic variations are of little interest, and one can ignore them. Indeed, the attempt to consider them is merely confusing. There are, of course, certain contexts in which unique responses may be highly significant—if the child is schizophrenic or if one is interested in creativity, for example.

In other words, whether one concerns himself with uniqueness or not depends on the context and the questions he is asking. One does not have to consider uniqueness all the time, but one should not overlook it where it is relevant. Psychologists do frequently fall into the latter error. But even within the unique individual there is much that is shared with others, and it is these shared characteristics that are the main concern of science, and the burden of most of this book.

Three

Evolutionary and Genetic Influences on Development

As pointed out in the Prologue, developmental psychology is concerned both with the development of the individual, or *ontogeny,* and with the development of the species, or *phylogeny.* It is the second concern that is one important topic of this chapter.

The evolutionary approach to understanding human development assumes that there has been a continuous process from that time so many eons ago when, under the influence of ultraviolet light, molecules of inorganic substances first formed into self-reproducing molecules and life began. This progression through organisms of increasing complexity has led ultimately to man, as the most complex of living things upon this planet. In other words, man is an animal. Whether he is *only* an animal is another question, but the evolutionary approach assumes a continuity between all forms of life, from the least to the most complex. On this assumption it is, in general, competent to seek clues to understanding human development from an investigation of animals, which are for a variety of reasons more convenient to study. They are able to provide some evidence not available

to us from direct observation of humans because there is the overriding desire to treat humans as people and hence to refrain from the more extreme experimental manipulations to which we feel ourselves able to submit other animals.

In his basic physical characteristics man is similar to his immediate animal relatives, and many of his characteristics are much more distantly spread. For example, there are no neurophysiological processes known in any of the vertebrates (man included) that are not found in the invertebrates (Bullock, 1958). One can even account for man's fantastically complex neurological functions in terms of the ancient processes mightily magnified (Sperry, 1958). The embryological processes of development are essentially the same for all vertebrates, despite the apparent differences introduced by uterine development in the mammals. At certain stages fish and human embryos are well-nigh indistinguishable, even down to the primitive precursors of gills being clearly visible in both. Therefore one can multiply the instances of physical similarities between man and the animals, including the mechanisms of reproduction and of the genetic transmission of these characteristics. Many of man's genes come directly from his animal ancestors.

The physical continuity of man and the animals is quite generally accepted today (even if in some quarters evolutionary theory still carries some slightly wicked overtones). Some religious-scientific philosophers go even further than most scientists, who are either irreligious or nonphilosophical, or both. Teilhard de Chardin (1959) traces man's evolution back to the prelife, to the primeval stuff that preceded the solar system. Despite these liberal concepts of man's history, there is still a reluctance among social scientists to incorporate these ideas into *their* view of mankind. They do not like to think back beyond recorded history, and even when they think historically, they tend to do so in terms of the cultural transmission of man's characteristics rather than of genetic transmission. It is, of course, quite legitimate to restrict oneself in this manner, for cultural transmission is a fact and there is a whole range of topics in the social sciences that one can competently discuss without reference to man's body, let alone his genes or the ancestors from which he got them.

In using the comparative approach, one must not overlook its dangers. As Klopfer (1968) has insisted, extrapolations from the behavior of animals to that of man are frequently in error. One reason for this is the sometimes false assumption that the behavior under consideration is a unitary phenomenon. In Klopfer's example, territorial behavior differs markedly in its form and implications from species to species, and to explain such things as human attitudes to property in terms of the territorial behaviors of other species *may* be misleading. There must be similarity in the evolutionary progression and the physiological processes involved before we can safely make such extrapolations.

This warning is well taken. It is not to be assumed, however, that *no* extrapolation is valid, and Klopfer is not implying this. At a number of points in this work extrapolations are made—often, it must be admitted, in the absence of the certainty that underlying evolutionary continuities are present. However, these extrapolations are usually of a general nature and do not require a detailed continuity. For example, it is assumed that humans, like animals, have innate tendencies to respond in particular ways to specific stimuli. It is certainly not suggested, however, that these stimuli are the same in humans as in other species, nor that the responses are the same, except in a very general sense. It would be patently absurd to make such assumptions. Nor is it assumed that the genetic mechanisms involved in the transmission of these species-specific characters are the same across species. The assumptions made here are really quite modest—for instance, when the newly hatched gosling follows the first large, moving object that it encounters, and when the human infant smiles in response to the stimulus provided by a smiling human face, it is assumed that these behaviors are analogous and broadly similar in their consequences. It is assumed, furthermore, that both behaviors are inherited. But it is certainly not implied that the two phenomena are identical, except in the very general sense that both are forms of imprinting and significant to the social development of individuals in their respective species.

It is also necessary to draw attention to the distinction between the *genotype,* or the actual genetic material, and the *phenotype,* or the appearance of the material. A character, like mental deficiency, in which a number of individuals appear alike, may in fact be due to a variety of genetic (and nongenetic) mechanisms. That is, mental defectives are phenotypically alike, but may be genotypically different.

As Harlow (1958a) has stated, the *kinds* of learning are as old, phylogenetically, as learning itself. Yet there are many problems in learning that can be studied without reference to this fact. In psychology generally there are numerous topics that can be studied as contemporary phenomena without concern for their origins.

It will be insisted at several points in this book that in studying the *development* of behavior one must take the historical approach. The *origins* of behavior are the essential concern of the developmentalist. And to be thorough, one must be concerned not only with the origins of what one observes in the life history of the individual—ontogeny—but also with phylogeny, or the origins of behaviors in the individual's immediate and more distant ancestors.

It is not inconsistent with the evolutionary concept to find peculiar or even unique characteristics in a particular species. There are numerous characteristics that are special to certain groups of animals—the ability to extract oxygen from water, or to fly, or to sense the polarization of light. Man and numerous other species do not possess these particular characters. Whether man has in fact any characteristics that are exclusive to his species, different in kind and not merely in degree from anything found elsewhere in nature, is a difficult question that need not detain us for long. Self-consciousness and speech are possible candidates for consideration as uniquely human traits. Even if animals do have them, it is only in very limited degrees, and hence the human infant may be considered in this respect as more akin to the animals than is the human adult. A striking feature of the older human is an extensive capacity for learning: The human infant has not yet developed this potential, and in any case has not had opportunity to learn much. Such behavior as emerges in infancy is thus to be viewed as largely if not entirely the product of innate factors.

As will be discussed in later chapters, these innate behaviors form the basis upon which the child's first interchanges with the environment depend: They determine, for instance, some of the reactions of the parents toward him and may have profound effects on the kinds of social learning the child later does. Similarly the nature and range of later learning, and even the selection of its content, may be initially influenced by factors with genetic origins. Just as a slight difference in the slope of land at the headspring may have determined whether a mighty river flowed north or south, so the initial direction of a child's development may be determined by subtle inborn tendencies. For example, the fact of maleness or femaleness—initially a genetic difference—determines not only a whole range of physical events but also psychological ones. It is not merely that society teaches males and females different things but also that the sexes tend, even before society begins to impose its expectations, to react differently to the same stimuli, to select different stimuli for attention, and to excite different reactions from the environment. Within maleness or femaleness there is a host of individual idiosyncrasies of selection and reaction that tend to impose an imprint on what the child learns.

SOME MECHANISMS OF GENETIC CHANGE

Mutations

From the evolutionary point of view, mutations are of fundamental importance, because the whole idea of evolution depends on the occurrence of spontaneous change in genes. It is known that most such changes are disadvantageous or even lethal, but occasionally one occurs that confers an adaptive advantage on the organism in which it happens; the organism thus has a better chance of survival and of transmission of this improvement. According to this theory, the human species is the culmination of a long series of these fortunate genetic changes.

Mutations will occur, and some differences between individuals may arise from this cause. A child may be different in some genetic respects from either of his parents or any of his ancestors.

Effective mutation rates are probably higher in humans than in most species, because humans can survive better than most others with disadvantageous but sublethal changes. Thus some differences between related individuals may be due to a mutant gene, and even identical twins might differ in this manner. However, mutation rates are low, unpredictable, and often undetectable, and because we often have no means of knowing whether an observed behavioral peculiarity is due to a mutation, this theoretical possibility does not at present have much heuristic value.

It is possible, of course, that an exciting mutation may arise in the human species, conferring some new psychic advantage (telepathy, maybe?). But for the moment this possibility is more useful to authors of science fiction than to authors of developmental treatises.

Genes and Determinism

Part of the cultural reluctance to admit that there are inherited factors in personality springs, perhaps, from the idea that it implies determinism and is contrary to the North American ideal of the self-made man. We echo O'Shaughnessy's cry, "I am the master of my fate, I am the captain of my soul."

Allport (1937) has discussed determinism in relation to personality and points out that the idea of genetic determination of personality "does not state that personality is inherited but rather that *no feature of personality is devoid of hereditary influences*" (p. 105, italics his). He goes on to say that while the notion of a genetic basis to personality claims that every aspect of it is influenced in some manner by the genes, it also acknowledges the role of environmental influences. A high degree of drafting skill may be an inherited trait, but whether the individual uses this as a productive artist, as a clever drafts-

man in an engineering firm, or as a forger of banknotes is a matter influenced by the environment and, to some extent at least, decided by the individual.

On the other hand, we do have to face the realities of the situation. The carrier of a "schizophrenic" gene may have the expression of this potential determined by his environment: The measure of control he himself has over the manifestations of this genetic-environmental interaction is problematical. Or to take another case, in the genetic idiot the environment has little or no influence on the expression of his idiocy and certainly he has no control whatever over his intellectual status. However much it offends our aesthetic sensibilities or our philosophical ideals, we must accept the fact that our physical structures to a considerable extent, and our personalities to a lesser but still significant degree, *are* influenced by our genes.

We can modify personality by environmental manipulation, and even by the individual effort previous generations called "willpower," but we must do this within the constraints imposed by our evolution and present genetic endowment. This is not to discount the value of seeking better environments for man and for his development; it is merely to insist that our search must take realistic account of man's inherent potentials and his imposed limitations.[1]

Instincts are part of man's evolutionary inheritance. Although the concept of instinct has been passé in psychological spheres for two or three decades, they are now being freely discussed once again by a number of psychologists, largely because of the work of the ethologists. This question is dealt with extensively in Chapter 4. Here it suffices to claim that part of man's biological equipment includes certain innate tendencies to react in

[1] This statement ignores the possibility some biologists are seriously entertaining that we may eventually be able to alter genes or provide new ones at will. For the present at least, it remains true that man must be content with the genes nature has provided.

specific ways to particular stimulus patterns. These tendencies to behavior are deeply overlaid by learning in adults; nevertheless there are indications that these tendencies are present. They exert a subtle influence on emerging behaviors at various times in childhood, and some features of human cultures can be seen as institutionalizing them. For example, it is this fact—that man has powerful reproductive tendencies to behavior—that requires all human cultures to exert potent controls and to institute rules for the expression of these urges. If sex behaviors were solely a matter of learning, then man could learn *not* to act as easily as he learns to act, and the elaborate and pervasive system of controls to inhibit action found in all human societies would be unnecessary. Another potent urge that requires containment is aggressivity (especially in males), a tendency shared with many other species. In many species aggression between members is regulated by "appeasement" signals that are stereotyped and species specific. Some traces of these are to be found in humans, and these are reinforced by sanctions against violence within the group. It is a tragedy of man's incomplete social evolution that adequate means of allaying aggression on a wider group basis have not been satisfactorily developed before the technical means of total destruction.

It is part of the thesis of this book that there is a whole range of instinctive tendencies to behaviors that are part of man's species-specific inheritance. This inheritance exerts subtle but pervasive influences on human cultures and on the development of children within these cultures. There is a complex interplay between man's evolved nature and the nurturing processes that have further evolved from this nature. For instance, males, because of their nature, tend to act in certain ways that are distinct from females. This is expressed as a cultural expectation for males to act in these ways. These expectations have arisen from this basic fact of nature and in turn reflect back on and tend to reinforce the

basic tendencies to action. Nature and nurture are thus not mutually exclusive, but are mutually dependent directional forces on human evolution and on the development of the individual.

EVOLUTION OF CULTURE

Man as we know him is not, we must suppose, the final product of evolution. The rate of physical evolution is normally very slow, and there is no evidence of any significant evolutionary change in man in historical times, the past eight or ten thousand years. But in the terms in which species evolution is usually considered, this is a mere moment and too short a time in which to expect any noticeable change in a species so slow-breeding.

The special evolutionary innovation of recency in man is not so much physical as social. This social evolution was, of course, preceded by and is dependent on his physical evolution and notably on the upright gait, the forebrain development, and the capacity for speech. One of the results of this social evolution is that it has blunted the edge of the evolutionary tool: Man can evade the forces of natural selection that encourage the survival only of the fittest in the physical sense. He can, in fact, control his own evolution by circumventing the normal processes of evolution.

The evolutionary crisis that faces the species is that man has been too successful in his physical adaptation and has been able to control his environment in ways so as to evade the usual restraints on species populations. He has evolved a social adaptation that is effective for small groups with extensive terrain, but has not yet evolved a social organization that can cope adequately with the new environment of massive groups with ever-diminishing space per head and with food production lagging farther and farther behind.

It is obvious that a very rapid evolution into a new state of social adaptation is a vital necessity to survival of the species. This self-conscious evolution can be achieved only by having the clearest possible statement of man as he now is and the most accurate assessment of his potential for change, his weaknesses, and his assets. Current concepts in the social sciences are in danger of offering an inadequate assessment of man by overestimating the role of culture in transmission and underestimating both the liabilities and the assets of his biological nature as a factor in development.

It may be, for instance, that competition is an essential ingredient of both the evolutionary process and human nature. If this is so, then competition can be expected to increase between man and man as living space becomes smaller. It is a matter to be taken into account in any assessment of the current situation and in any attempt to control social evolution.

One must not oversimplify what is in fact an immensely complex situation. There is a nongenetic process of inheritance in which parental influences are transmitted (Rossler, 1966.) Thus environmental influences on the parents before conception may show up in the offspring, giving the appearance of genetic transmission, which in fact it is not. This might explain William McDougall's belief that he had experimentally demonstrated the inheritance of acquired characteristics. Such an effect is that (described in Chapter 11) by which the early infantile experiences (gentling) of female rats lower emotionality in their offspring, so that their litters perform better in test situations in which less emotionality is an asset. However, to admit this is to admit that development is complex: It is not to deny that genetic factors are important and should not be taken as a suggestion that *all* apparently genetic effects are artifacts of this kind.

Culture is a feature of human life that is unusual in its scope, even if a somewhat broad definition of the term enables us to see "cultures" in certain animal species. It is, in fact, this aspect of human life that has most interested the social scientists, and among them the developmentalists. However, culture may be viewed as a biological adaptation that man has evolved to cope with his environment (Huxley, 1958.) It introduces a vast second level of transmission that is nongenetic but that is founded on a biological basis, and its emergence can be viewed as part of the evolutionary process for the human species. The learning of complex social mechanisms is the adaptive survival technique man has developed (Freedman and Roe, 1958). This is, however, a biopsychological mechanism, being founded on the cortical control that man exercises over his instincts and more basic tendencies, but a control he can exercise only by virtue of the evolution of his extensive neocortex—a species-specific characteristic genetically transmitted.

In line with this argument is the suggestion by Medawar (1963) that human evolution since the introduction of techniques for environmental control and social organization has become Lamarckian in kind. We now depend, he says, on acquired change from the culture pool rather than on morphological change dependent upon changes in the gene pool. This kind of inheritance is reversible and can in fact be lost in a single generation. This evolution depends on the transmission of knowledge, skills, and understanding from father to son.

NATURAL SELECTION AND ADAPTATION

Under conditions of natural selection the genetic variance in a population favors evolution to accommodate change in the environment. Over a range of environmental conditions there are individuals available who will be optimally adapted to various points on the range. Some will be less than optimally adapted to the conditions actually existing at a given time, but even though disadvantaged they will represent a reserve of individuals as a kind of insurance against change. (Presumably in environments highly stable for some particular property, such as available food or temperature, the range of variation will tend to decrease if the more divergent individuals are markedly disadvantaged, but if the environment really is stable, this does not matter.)

This implies a unitary environment to which a proportion, and probably a majority, of individuals are well adapted, but in which some are marginal members. Their presence is useful to the species, but their conditions are not necessarily the most desirable for themselves. In human terms this is rather like the economic theory that sees a reserve of unemployed as a stabilizing influence on the labor market. It is difficult for them but is said to be good for society as a whole. If one is seeking the ideal society (and the ideal child-rearing practices within it), then each individual is entitled to *his* optimum environment, and the human environment should not be unitary, but diverse.

A lesson from controlled evolution in animals—that is, selective breeding—is that genetic homeostasis sets in as a contrary force (Lerner, 1954). In any given environment the characteristics of a species—the height, rate of maturation, and so on—are held in the population by natural selection at an optimum level for that environment. One can selectively breed individuals who are atypical (i.e., adapted to some different environment), but as soon as selection is discontinued, the stock begins to revert to the previous level. Thus if one is to consider a eugenic policy for man, one must also change his environment to correspond to the new genetic norm being established.

GENETICS OF BEHAVIOR

It is a regrettable fact that most of our knowledge of genetics applies to physical rather than psychological traits, and because of the impossibility of breeding experiments

with humans, most of the data are on animals (or plants). To a considerable extent we must act on the assumption that the genetic laws that apply to the inheritance of physical characteristics also apply to psychological ones. There is, however, enough evidence even at the human level to maintain the reasonableness of this assumption.

This chapter is not intended as a comprehensive review of behavioral genetics. Extensive reviews are provided by Fuller and Thompson (1960), McClearn (1962), and McClearn and Meredith (1966), among others. There is also a survey by Stern (1960). A selection of the more recent studies is given here, together with a discussion of some special topics necessary to developing the arguments of this book.

Genetics has become a highly sophisticated science that creates difficulties for the eclectic developmentalist who tries to understand all the factors contributing to the process of development from conception to maturity.

There is considerable literature on the genetics of behavior in mice and rats, the more recent of which has been reviewed by McClearn and Meredith (1966). Such matters as strain differences in activity, emotionality, social behavior, learning and alcohol preference have been demonstrated in a number of studies, together with investigations of "mechanisms," or the anatomical structures and physiological and biochemical processes that mediate between genotype and phenotype. These mechanisms include inherited neurological conditions leading to "staggering," "whirling," and other gait abnormalities, and brain serotonin levels that may underlie strain differences in activity and emotionality, as well as things such as adrenal hormone differences affecting reactions to stress.

A considerable part of the knowledge of human behavioral genetics concerns mental illness. The extensive work of Kallman on schizophrenia is well known and has been reviewed by Rainer (1966a). There is a well-established genetic component in the disposition to depressive mental illness, and the literature is discussed by Rainer (1966b). A number of investigators claim a genetic component in neuroticism, and obsessional traits in particular have been seen to run in families and are common among the relatives of obsessional-compulsive neurotics (World Health Organization [WHO], 1966).

The existence of a genetic contribution to neuroticism is also supported in a study by Vandenberg et al. (1966). Alcoholism, together with certain other personality traits including intelligence and sociability, shows considerable heritability, though not necessarily in concert (Partanen et al., 1966).

Two pieces of human behavior of considerable developmental import, which are discussed in later chapters, are the smiling response and the fear response to strangers, which follows the smiling response in development. There are individual differences in the precise age of onset of these behaviors and in the amount of smiling and in the degree of the fear reaction to strangers. There can be little doubt that these behaviors are innate, and D. G. Freedman (1965) has shown a high degree of concordance in the characteristics of these responses in identical twins.

In the first month of life there is often seen a spontaneous smile that has no specific external stimulus and that usually appears when the infant is satiated and about to fall asleep. This is apparently a kind of reflexive motor action and not the true social smile. This usually disappears in the second month to be replaced by a smile that is a response to an external stimulus, such as a touch to the lips or the tinkle of a bell. About this time the infant commences intent visual fixation of the adult face, and after about ten days of this kind of visual inspection the first social smile appears.

The smile may be observed in blind children and is also accompanied by orienting movements of the eyes toward the person holding the child (D. G. Freedman, 1965), which is evidence of its innate basis. It also suggests that the orientation going with smiling is determined by central rather than peripheral mechanisms. The biological adaptiveness of the smile is discussed in later chapters, in which it is suggested that it plays a part in forming the bond between parent and child and is the human analogue of the following response of birds.

Until about five or six months the infant smiles indiscriminantly, but at this age he begins to discriminate familiar faces from strange ones. The infant continues to smile to the former but to react fearfully to the latter. Just as there are individual differences in the amount of smiling, so there is in the nature of the fear response, and for some infants fear is almost too strong a term. The adaptive function of the fear response is perhaps to prevent the dilution of the primary relationship within the family by generalization to all and sundry (D. G. Freedman, 1965).

It has been suggested by Schaffer and Emerson (1964a) that the avoidance of close physical contact on the part of some infants may have an innate basis. This would presumably represent a failure of the normal "program" that mediates cuddling in normal infants. This pattern of noncuddling has, on mother-child interaction, an early influence that may produce widespread effects on later social behaviors of the child.

The role of genetics in communication disorders is discussed (but not clearly demonstrated) by several authors. Weiss (1967) has described central language imbalance (cluttering) as "exquisitely hereditary." It is characterized by a complete lack of concern on the part of the clutterer about his disorderly manner of speech delivery. Silver and Hagin (1967) also infer a constitutional basis to language disabilities.

Gottesman (1966), among others, has speculated about the inheritance of personality characteristics. He had produced some evidence from twin studies of the heritability of traits measured by the California Psychological Inventory (CPI), notably a "person orientation" or "introversion-extraversion" dimension. He wonders if this might not be derived developmentally from the noncuddling syndrome of Schaffer and Emerson.

Gene-to-Behavior Pathway

In speaking of the genetics of behavior, there is a logical quibble, for in a strict sense it is clear that behavior cannot be inherited. Only genes can be handed on from parent to offspring. What actually intervenes between the gene and the action is not known in detail. Certain of the kinds of intermediating processes are discussed in later chapters. In Chapter 5 we see that Sheldon has suggested that certain patterns of constitutional organization (related to body type) affect the manner in which the individual reacts to the environment and acts upon it. Elsewhere, autonomic differences (presumably in part, at least, innate) may mediate distinctive patterns of behaving. Endocrine balance and neural organization are other sources of variation in behavior. In none of these is it likely that there is a purely genetic effect. There is instead the possibility of a resultant of the interplay between genetic and environmental influences.

Although the mode of translation from gene to character is not always known, it is in the case of two physical conditions, albinism and phenylketonuria (PKU), and these illustrate some aspects of the matter. The color of most mammalian skin tissue and hair is due to the pigment melanin, produced in four stages from the amino acid phenylalanine, which is plentiful in the diet (see Figure 3–1).

Each of these conversion reactions is controlled by an enzyme and the conversion of dihydroxyphenylalanine to melanin is controlled by one called dopa oxidase.

Dopa oxidase is produced by a dominant gene (A). Almost everybody has at least one (AA or Aa) and hence can complete the production of melanin. Almost everyone, even the fairest, has some degree of pigmentation of hair, skin, and related tissues. The albino (aa)

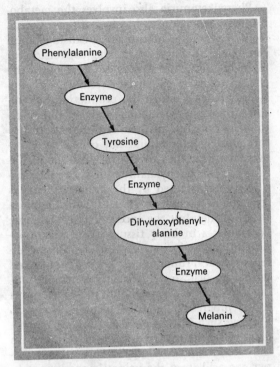

FIGURE 3–1. *Stages in the conversion of phenylalanine to melanin.*

cannot produce dopa oxidase and hence cannot complete the series of reactions leading to the production of melanin. Ectodermal tissue is thus totally unpigmented, the hair is completely white, and the skin and eyes are pink.

Albinism does not have direct psychological results, though, as with any other physical condition that marks an individual as different from his fellows, it may have indirect ones.

Phenylketonuria is due to a recessive Mendelian character that is carried by about 1 in 200 individuals. (Thus the chances of two individuals, each with a recessive gene, marrying are 1 in 40,000, ignoring such selective factors as regional incidence, though this occurs. Even when they do marry, the chances are 3 to 1 against the pure recessive appearing. Phenylketonurics themselves rarely produce offspring.)

Phenylketonuria also involves the metabolism of phenylalanine but at a different stage from that of the inborn error causing albinism. Here the first stage, the conversion of phenylalanine into tyrosine, is affected; the effect occurs in the liver. Actually, two enzymes are involved in the production of tyrosine from phenylalanine, and in phenylketonurics only one of them is deficient, and so the effect is relative and not complete. However, the deficiency results in a residue of unmetabolized phenylalanine that cannot adequately be excreted by the kidneys: Some is removed as phenylpyruvic acid (which appears in the urine), but the excess of phenylalanine accumulates in body tissues. This accumulation of the amino acid has an inhibiting effect on neural functioning. The infant appears normal at first, and apparently continues normal physical development, but in a few months shows progressive signs of mental deficiency. Feeding such infants on a diet low in phenylalanine results in a reduction of the level in the blood and a disappearance of phenylpyruvic acid from the urine; improvement in the mental symptoms has also been reported.

This condition is of interest not only in illustrating a mechanism by which genes are related to behavior, but also in demonstrating that inherited defects are not of necessity without the hope of cure.

It will be noted that the psychological effects of PKU are indirect and negative or inhibitory. Intellectual functioning is depressed by a kind of clogging or poisoning of nerves. Such a mechanism seems unable to account for other behavioral characteristics, for instance, highly intelligent functioning. It is possible that intelligence may be a function of efficient neural chemistry, the rapid formation perhaps of synaptic conductors, and the prompt removal of the waste products of neurochemical reactions. Efficient oxygen transport and utilization might be another aspect of this neurophysiology. Gene-derived enzymes could presumably be important in these reactions, the dominant genes in the genetic model for intellectual inheritance (see p. 38) mediating optimal chemical conditions.

Other sorts of inherited behaviors, for instance, the smiling response of the infant, would not seem to be adequately explained by such a model. Here it would seem more likely that the genetic mechanism determines some detail of the structure of the nervous system—the organism is, as it were, wired to make this kind of response when given certain stimulus conditions.

Gene Interactions

The old idea of a simple one gene-one character relationship is no longer tenable. The phenomena of *pleiotropism* and *modifier genes* make gene actions complex (see Figure 3–2).

Pleiotropism. All genes affect a number of characters, a phenomenon called pleiotropism. It is probable that each gene acts primarily on a specific character but also has a radiating subsidiary influence on cytoplasmic processes primarily influenced by other genes. There is thus an amazing complex of interactions. A gene derived from one parent may interact with one from the other to produce an effect that was found in neither. It is not possible at present to quote a confirmed example of this action in behavioral genetics, so it remains a theoretical consideration.

Modifiers. Some genes are known to be affected by other *modifier* genes. Cataract is a trait with simple dominant inheritance but with considerable variation in expressivity, and this expressivity is also an inherited characteristic. One gene determines the occurrence of cataracts and another the particular kind of opacity of the lenses; the latter operates as a a modifier of the former (Stern, 1960). If pleiotropy is universal, it would seem that in fact every gene is a modifier of some others.

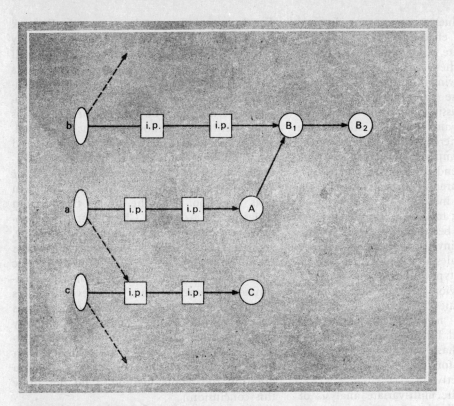

FIGURE 3–2. *Modifier action and pleiotropy. Modifier action of a gene refers to the influence of one gene (a) on some intermediate process (i.p.) between another gene and the character it mediates (c, C). Pleiotropy refers to the influence that the final character dependent upon one gene has on the actual outcome of the action of another gene (A → B). This effect is "mechanical" or post-genetic.*

Heritability

The concept of a genetic-environmental interaction is well imbedded in modern genetic theory in the idea of heritability. This is the ratio of the variance attributable to additive gene effects to the total phenotypic variance, or how much of the range can be attributed directly to genetic influences and how much to environmental ones.

A point that needs to be borne in mind is that heritability is an estimate for a population. The figure given for the heritability of a given trait is an average for this population, and it does not necessarily follow that all *individuals* will show this degree. It would, in fact, be surprising if they did, because variation about a mean rather than an absolute figure is well-nigh universal in biological measures. Thus some individuals may be, with respect to a given trait, more subject than others to environmental influences; or conversely, others will be more subject to genetic influences.

The whole question of trying to sort out the relative contributions of hereditary and environmental influences is complex. For example, birth-order effects (reviewed in Chapter 18) may operate, and Vandenberg (1966) points out that these effects may influence twin similarity: Twins with other siblings may receive less of the parental attention that might increase dissimilarity and hence be more alike than twins without. Similarly, the greater initial differences between dizygotic (DZ) twins as compared with monozygotic (MZ) twins may tend to promote greater differentiation in parental treatment of them and hence further increase differences.

A point relating to the environment-heredity interaction has been mentioned by Gottesman (1963a), who investigated the inheritance of sociability in males and females. In females the cultural stereotype imposes a pressure toward social behavior, and this pressure is less marked for males. Hence the heritability of sociability [as measured in adolescent twins by the Social Introversion Scale of the Minnesota Multiphasic Personality Inventory (MMPI)] is lower for females than for males (.60 and .84, respectively).

A method for the multivariate analysis of the relative contributions of environmental and genetic factors to personality characteristics was developed by Cattell et al. (1955). Using rating, questionnaire data, and objective test results, these authors obtained estimates of certain personality factors. Those that were predominantly environmental in determination were "tender-mindedness," "general neuroticism," "surgency-disurgency," "will control," and "somatic anxiety." Factors about equal as to the roles of heredity and environment were "energetic conformity," "dominance," "socialized morale," and "impatient dominance." Those showing a greater role for heredity than nurture were "cyclothymia vs. schizothymia," "adventurous cyclothymia vs. submissiveness," and "general intelligence."

The authors recognized that the study was a pilot rather than a definitive one, and some of the data raises questions of interpretation.

For instance, some authors, notably Eysenck and Prell (1951), have proposed a markedly genetic determinant of neuroticism. Cattell et al. explain the difference in their results as being caused by a different operational definition of neuroticism and another (better) statistical technique. They regard their results as more accurate than those of Eysenck and Prell.

The relative contributions of genetic and environmental influences to individual differences in personality was measured by Scarr (1966). Her subjects were MZ and DZ twin girls of school age. She found that certain scales of the Adjective Check List (ACL) notably n Change, n Affiliation, and Anxiety, showed greater than 50 percent heritability. Of the nineteen scales, nine showed genetic contributions, seven showed primarily environmental contributions, and several others showed more or less equal influences. (It is perhaps a warning that a few scales apparently showed neither genetic nor environmental influences, something which some might wish to interpret as an absurdity that calls into question the whole method. I do not draw this conclusion.)

Dobzhansky (1967) has stated that the intellectual, temperamental, or special abilities of parents mostly have low predictive value for these qualities in their offspring, but this does not mean that genetic effects are nonexistent. The heritabilities of these characters are in most cases rather low, and the environment provides most of the variance. In the case of intelligence at least, some authorities (notably Burt) disagree with this and claim that the heritability is high and the environmental variance low.

It might be argued that if there are traits of low heritability in which the environmental influences are relatively strong, why not ignore the former and concentrate on the latter. This in effect is the position the environmentalist takes. He assumes that the organism is to all intents and purposes constitutionally neutral so that a uniform environment has virtually equal effects on all.

This contention omits the fact that some or many individuals do not so respond and leaves the question of why this uniform environment produces varying developmental responses a mystery. Instead, one might propose the general thesis that every individual should (insofar as these tendencies are adaptive) develop according to his native potential. This is the most economical and harmonious manner of developing for him. Each individual has his own pattern norm. Some of the inherent tendencies that make up the pattern norm may be weak, but it is more efficient to follow these than to impose contrary directives on the organism.

Furthermore, some traits may be of more considerable heritability and even less economically overridden by an unfavorable environment. We need a great deal more information about the genetic ingredients of personality development.

Thus it is being insisted that rather than having a genetically neutral human organism, for whom we can prescribe (after we know enough) a uniform environment that will be equally conducive to the finest development of all, we have a native diversity of human organisms for whom a diversity of environments are needed for optimum development.

The question of environmental interaction was succinctly discussed in the well-known article by Anastasi (1958) under the title "Heredity, Environment and the Question 'How?'" In this paper she points out that the real question is not "Which?" or "How much?" but simply "How?" In other words, what are the mechanisms that mediate the interactions we confess must take place?

Penetrance and Expressivity

A source of bewilderment to both geneticists and developmental psychologists is that similar effects arise from different antecedents, and those who ignore genetics are bewildered because the similar effects seem to arise from nowhere. In discussing the work of a preschool program for emotionally disturbed children, Silverman et al. (1967) have remarked that some of their child patients "have demonstrated the devastating potentials of nature" as contrasted with others that show the effects of "noxious nurturance."

The genetical concepts of penetrance and expressivity are important ones in trying to understand the differential effects of nature and nurture. Stern (1950) has defined them thus: "Penetrance . . . refers to the all-or-none expression of a gene, regardless of degree of expression; expressivity applies to the variability of the kind of expression" (p. 272). Other writers use the term *incomplete penetrance* rather than *expressivity* (Snyder and David, 1953).

Penetrance is a statistical concept referring to the frequency with which phenotype corresponds to genotype. Thus a gene of 100 percent penetrance always shows when it is present. One of 50 percent penetrance manifests itself in half the individuals who carry it. Difference in expressivity (or incomplete penetrance) refers to the fact that the degree of manifestation of the trait may differ in different individuals.

Some genes differ not only in their penetrance and expressivity, but in the *time* of manifestations. Huntington's chorea is the classic example of this. It is a nervous degenerative disease carried by a dominant gene that usually manifests itself between about thirty to forty years of age in affected individuals but that may appear as early as age five or as late as age sixty.

The factors underlying the irregularities of genetic manifestations are twofold. Some relate to the internal environment; for instance, some genetic allergies are determined in penetrance by the amount of sex hormone circulating in the body. Other sources of influence relate to the external environment. Stern (1950) has quoted the case of identical twin brothers: One suffered mildly from diabetes mellitus; the other, though presumably carrying the same genetic constitution, was healthy. The affected brother was a restaurateur who also drank beer heavily. The other twin was not so unsuitably employed and did not subject his susceptible equipment to this strain.

Age may be a factor that induces change in dominance. Thus the child of one dark-haired parent and one light-haired parent may at first resemble the latter, but as he grows older, the dominant genes from the dark-haired parent become more assertive and the child's hair also darkens. Biochemical changes with maturation may account for this. Differences in singing voices among boys are genetically determined; the voice changes of puberty are independent of genes but dependent on the sex hormones.

It is believed that the determination of voice is polygenetic, there actually being a continuous gradation from the lowest to the highest singing voice, from bass to soprano. There is in the voice box, chest, respiratory organs, tongue, lips, and so on a whole range of variables that, together with physiological and psychological variables, determines voice (Stern, 1960). Among the physiological variables is androgen secretion, which is one factor in the deeper voice of males. The highest boys' voices become the deepest men's ones, and the deepest boys' voices develop into the highest adult ones (Stern, 1950).

The ideas of penetrance and expressivity are significant in explaining a source of individual variation. They also incorporate the notion of an interaction between gene effects and extragenetic factors, whether these are internal to the organism or outside in the environment, and underline the fact that development is an interplay between intrinsic and extrinsic factors.

Unfortunately not a great deal is known at present about these matters. It may be that some flaws in the arguments of the more environment-oriented psychologists arise from applying data relevant to traits of low penetrance or expressivity to traits that are high in them and hence follow different paths of susceptibility to environmental influence. For some psychological traits it may be true that the environment is the main or even the sole determinant of development; this may be less true or even totally untrue of certain other traits. Also, among individuals the susceptibility to environmental influence or the degree of genetic determination may vary.

Some traits that are of low penetrance and hence originally subject to environmental influence lose this susceptibility later in development. Thus the harelip is apparently a genetic tendency of low penetrance that depends on certain conditions in the uterine environment: After this environment has acted and the harelip is there, no further environmental change modifies the condition (excepting, of course, surgery, which is an environmental intervention of a different kind). This anticipates the discussion of critical periods (Chapter 7).

SEX LINKAGE AND SEX-RELATED TRAITS

In twenty-two of the chromosome pairs—the autosomes—one chromosome, and hence half the genes, is derived from each parent. It is the twenty-third chromosome set that contributes to sex-linked differences. The boy is like the father and different from the mother in the possession of the Y chromosome; he gets (needless to say) the Y chromosome from the father. The girl resembles the mother (and is different from the father) in having the two X chromosomes.

Despite these facts, there is a sense in which the boy may be said to inherit more from the mother. The Y chromosome is small and carries fewer genes than the X chromosome. Because the boy's X chromosome comes from his mother, he actually acquires in total more genes from her than from his father. Some of the genes on the X chromosome are unmatched by ones on the Y chromosome, and it is the mother's contribution in these instances that determines phenotype. Hemophilia and color blindness are the classic examples of this kind of contribution.

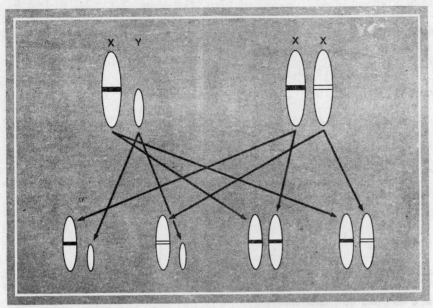

FIGURE 3–3. *Mechanism of sex linkage. Note how the mother provides the trait to both sons and daughters, but the father only to daughters.*

On the other hand, the girl acquires her second X chromosome from the father and in this sense gets more genes from him than does the boy. The girl in fact gets an equal complement of genes from each parent.

Y Linkage

It seems that very few of the many inherited traits in man are Y linked (Stern, 1960). This is in part a necessary consequence of the fact that the Y chromosome is small and presumably carries relatively few genes. Most of the known instances of Y linkage are rare abnormalities. The "porcupine men" (*ichthyosis hystrix gravior*), in which the skin becomes scaly and rough with bristle-like protrusions, are one example (Stern, 1960.)

Some (and perhaps most) of the genes on the Y chromosome are hemizygous; that is, they are not matched by a homologous gene on the X chromosome and exert their effect singly rather than in a paired allele as is usual.

According to Fuller and Thompson (1960), Y linkage has no immediate application to behavior genetics. They presumably mean that no relevance has yet been demonstrated, not that no mechanism is possible.

X Linkage

A majority of sex-linked traits are carried on the X chromosome (are X linked). When the X-linked mechanism operates, it may result in a zero correlation between fathers and sons for a character but a positive correlation between fathers and daughters. The mechanism here is illustrated in Figure 3–3 (the mother is heterozygous, though it also applies if she is homozygous, all female children then being homozygous). Stafford (1965) has mentioned two behavioral variables showing such correlational patterns in which he believes this mechanism applies: spatial visualization and quantitative reasoning ability. Thus some personality characteristics of the male might be like hemophilia, transmitted by the female but expressed in the male. In the realm of personality traits, Fuller and Thompson (1960) have reviewed several studies that show

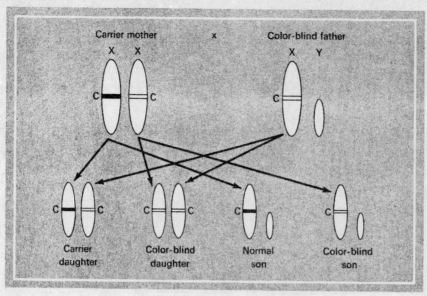

FIGURE 3–4. Inheritance of a sex-linked trait, color blindness.

a tendency toward greater similarity in certain personality traits (measured by such instruments as the Bernreuter Scale), either between mother and children of both sexes or in any familial relationship involving a female (i.e., mother-daughter, sister-sister, father-daughter, mother-son).

Certain forms of hereditary deafness are sex-linked, though the linkage differs. Some result in deafness in males and others in females. Deafness is also acquired; there is a rather marked tendency for its acquisition to occur more frequently in males because of the greater susceptibility of male infants to diseases such as meningitis, which may carry deafness as a sequel (Fraser, 1965). A sex-linked system disorder within the CNS is described by Baar and Gabriel (1966). It results in spastic paraplegia and mental deficiency and is carried by the female but expressed in the male.

X-linked recessive traits, such as color-vision anomalies, generally affect males more frequently than females, though they can be transmitted to females, as illustrated in Figure 3–4. If q is the frequency of the abnormal

X-linked allele, then $1 - q = p$ is the frequency of the normal allele. The probability of a man having the two kinds are thus q and p, respectively. Women, however, can be homozygous, heterozygous normal, or homozygous abnormal and, because of the greater range of possibilities, there is less chance of the last. The chances of both X chromosomes being normal is p^2; for the heterozygous normal it is $2pq$ and for homozygous abnormal it is q^2. Thus if the frequency of the abnormal gene is 1 in 20 (.05), then this is also the frequency of the abnormal trait in males, but for females it is 1 in 400 (.0025). The reported frequencies do not always correspond to these theoretical figures. For instance, women heterozygous for the color-blind allele may have a reduced color aptitude and be mistakenly considered color-blind if not carefully tested, hence inflating the statistics (Stern, 1950).

The matters discussed above need qualification by the fact that the Y chromosome is strongly determinant of the bodily characteristics of the male sex. The mammalian body is basically female and develops thus if the Y is absent, even in such conditions as Turner's syndrome (XO) in which only one X is present. But in sex chromosome polysomy (XXY or even XXXXY) the body is male; the individual may be disadvantaged by mental deficiency and other abnormalities, but is definitely male (if that is any advantage).

As will be discussed in later chapters, a number of psychological characteristics that tend to be associated with maleness—aggressivity, dominance, certain modes of cognitive style, and so on—are already known. The mechanism of this association is not known; it may in some cases be of the X-linked type. On the other hand, such characters may not spring directly from any specific gene, because some of the bodily characteristics of maleness do not depend directly on genes on the Y chromosome but on biochemical mechanisms. These mechanisms are initiated by genetic factors, but after they are started under the influence of the genes, they apparently operate independently (we do not know, of course, whether continued genetic influence is necessary to their maintenance, and hence we cannot yet claim that the independence is real). Thus some of the personality characteristics of the male might be associated with hormonal factors (Chapter 9) or with the male-type nervous system (Chapter 10), but they are only indirectly related to genetic factors in that the Y chromosome initiated the early developmental events on which these physiological features of the male depend.

It is also noteworthy that autosomal genes may express themselves differently in male and female bodies. The genetic type of baldness is a case in point, which expresses itself only in the presence of higher levels of androgen in the body and hence usually in males, though it may be expressed in females with adrenal oversecretion (Stern, 1960). A number of other genes are sex-limited; that is, they are expressed in one sex only. In mammals both males and females carry the genes for milk production, but these are female sex-limited in their effects. Similarly the genes for beard growth and distribution of body hair are male sex-limited. It is evident that it is the bodily environment (e.g., presence or absence of hormones) that controls the expression of these genes. It is possible that nervous system differences between males and females may influence the expression of behavioral genes carried by both and thus account for certain sex differences in behavior and psychological functioning.

As mentioned in another section, Gottesman (1963a) has described sex differences in the heritability of certain personality traits as measured by the CPI, though whether the effect here is sex linkage in the strict sense of being carried on the X or Y chromosome or whether it arises from a sex difference in the heredity-environment interaction, as he suggests, has not been proved (the latter seems the more probable in these particular instances).

A comment on apparently sex-linked behavioral traits of the kind reviewed by Fuller and Thompson and mentioned above: While the mother-son and father-daughter correlations are consistent with sex linkage, the mother-daughter correlation is not. The sister-sister correspondence might be explained by their both having acquired the trait from the father. None of the correlations were high (though those of the mother-child tended to be higher than those of the father-child) and inadequacies of the instruments used might be the explanation. However, leaving aside this possibility, some of the effects might be accounted for by supposing that the particular traits in question were of low heritability and that the results reflected the greater influence of the mother in an environment with a matricentric child-rearing system; this explains the mother-daughter correlation. This influence has worked on the considerable environmental susceptibility of these particular traits. Some other traits more strongly under genetic determination might not show this effect. Thus, especially in traits of low heritability, the relative genetic contribution of the two parents may not show up unless the environment is such as to give both equal influence. An environment favoring one or the other will distort the genetic contributions involved and needs to be taken into account in interpreting the data.

TWINNING

Multiple births are common in many species, but uncommon in most primates. Most of the multiple births in humans are fraternal or DZ twins, occurring in about one parturition in eighty-eight. They result from the separate fertilization of the two ova, not necessarily from the same copulation, and it is *possible* that they could have different fathers. Even when they have the same paternity, they are no more alike than other siblings.

A small proportion of twins are MZ, resulting from a single conception. The mechanism producing identical twins is not genetic. MZ twins result from the separation of two groups of cells at some stage after conception. Even though it is possible that the tendency for this to happen may be genetically influenced, it is not a genetic mechanism. These happenings are lucky ones for geneticists and have thrown considerable light on problems of inheritance, because here we have the unusual circumstance of two individuals with a very high degree of genetic similarity.

Particularly useful insights into genetic factors are provided by twin studies, notably, of course, those involving MZ twins, though comparisons of MZ twins with DZ twins and with other siblings often highlight the effects. The literature on the contribution of twin studies to an understanding of the genetics underlying psychological functions has been reviewed by Vandenberg (1966). He notes that after a period of neglect there has been a revival of interest in twin studies and remarks that the more sophisticated techniques now possible, together with a developmental approach to longitudinal studies, should produce fresh data.

The data so far available have been reviewed by Vandenberg under several headings. As might be expected, MZ twins are very similar in growth patterns, and this is consistent with other evidence showing a high degree of hereditary control of growth.

Twin studies, together with other evidence, also reveal a considerable hereditary component in a number of physiological measures. Heart rate, galvanic skin response (GSR), and electroencephalograms (EEG) are among those reviewed by Vandenberg. Even at birth, autonomic nervous system similarities can be detected in twins. It is suggested that differing reactions among people to stress may underlie patterns of grosser physiological response: For instance, individuals showing predominant heart-rate changes might later be subject to cardiac disease and those with GSR changes to allergic and other psychosomatic responses. In this connection Thomas (1966) has suggested that susceptibility to hypertension comes from an environmental interaction with an inherited tendency, those individuals with abnormal cholesterol levels reacting differently to stress from those with normal levels.

In the study of sensory functions there is the potential for considerable contributions to our knowledge of behavioral genetics, but Vandenberg has outlined some of the methodological problems that at present inhibit much progress in this area. There has not in fact been a great deal of research with twins. Such as there is suggests a hereditary component in the range of auditory response, in critical fusion frequency (CFF), and, of course, in color vision, which has long been a topic of interest.

In addition to the important role of learning in perceptual processes, Vandenberg has cited evidence from a number of studies of a marked influence of heredity on certain perceptual tasks. Such things as the autokinetic effect, the Mueller-Lyer illusion, and the size of afterimages have an inherited component. Of particular interest to the discussion of later chapters is the finding that the Gott-schaldt embedded figures and field dependency on the Witkin rod-and-form test are also influenced by heredity (Vandenberg, 1962).

Another study showing greater concordance between MZ as compared with DZ twins of preschool age is by Brown et al. (1967), who studied sleeping and feeding behaviors and similarity to the mother in temperament.

A further area of performance showing inheritable effects are motor skills. It is well known that there are wide individual differences in these skills, which are detectable at an early age. An aspect of this is handedness. Merrell (1957) has proposed that left-handedness is an autosomal recessive trait and that heterozygous individuals can learn to use either hand in childhood. Trankell (1956) has also suggested a genetic basis for left-handedness, a recessive trait with incomplete penetrance.

A note of warning appears in a study by Scarr (1966), who notes that parents of twins thought to be identical but not really so still tended to rate them as being much alike. The net effect of this phenomenon will be to reduce the dissimilarity between data on fraternal and identical twins. Of course, it is the case that some siblings *are* more alike than others, and it is not improbable that fraternal twins who look alike (have a rather large genetic commonality) will in fact tend to behave alike also. The reports may not be entirely due to bias from the expectations of the reporter.

A point that seems to be overlooked in twin studies of psychological traits is that genes may differ in penetrance between identical twins. Stern (1960) quotes an instance of a MZ twin pair in which one had a harelip, but in which there was lack of penetrance of this genetic trait in the other. (Presumably this reflected some difference of the uterine environment of the two boys, despite their simultaneous occupancy of the same uterus.)

Although in general there is a high degree of concordance between identical twins, in specific instances there may be marked discordance, and it is often difficult to account for this. For example, D. G. Freedman (1965) noted a considerable difference in fear of strangers between identical twin sisters. One showed only mild discomfort when handled by a stranger or in response to a strange object such as a jack-in-the-box, whereas the sister showed strong and persistent fear responses in the same situations. Freedman carefully rules out any differential handling by the parents or gross physical differences between them in their history but does suggest minimal brain damage in the fearful twin as a possible explanation.

INHERITANCE OF INTELLIGENCE

A review of the literature on the inheritance of intelligence up to the early 1950's has been given by W. R. Thompson (1954). He discusses animal experimentation, including the well-known studies by Tryon (1940) on the breeding of "bright" and "dull" strains of rats as measured by ability in maze learning. Thompson mentions the difficulties of interpreting the animal data. There is, for instance, the suggestion by Searle (1949) that Tryon's rats differed in emotionality rather than intelligence and that the results were caused by motivational differences. In all the animal studies one is uncertain of whether he is really dealing with intelligence.

The same objection can be applied to the human studies, because intelligence has never been adequately defined. This would be a somewhat finicky argument, as there is general agreement that intelligence tests do give at least an operational definition of intelligence. Thompson's review covers a number of the studies of human intelligence, including ones on identical twins, that show a strong inherent factor in transmission.

Like most authors on this topic, Thompson is careful to make clear the fact that inheritance is not the only factor in intellectual *performance.* The environmental influences will be discussed elsewhere.

Having reviewed the literature on the genetics of intelligence over the past half-century, Erlenmeyer and Jarvik (1963) have remarked on the consistency of the data relating mental functioning to genetic potential. From the literature they gleaned a total of over 30,000 correlation pairings, which show marked trends toward increasing intellectual resemblance as genetic relationship becomes closer, despite the variety of intellectual measures used. Moreover, the medians of the empirical correlations in most categories are close to the theoretical value that would be predicted if the genetic factor were the only one involved. They also note that the data do not support a hypothesis of sex linkage for overall intellectual functioning but do not preclude the possibility of sex-linked genes for specific factors of ability.

Erlenmeyer and Jarvik state that they do not imply that the environment is without effect on intellectual functioning. As two instances, they point out that early total deafness lowers the IQ by about twenty points (Salzberger and Jarvik, 1963) and that PKU produces even greater deficiencies, the expression of which is modifiable by early manipulation of the diet (Horner et al., 1962).

The expression of the genotype varies under different environmental conditions, producing differing phenotypes. Individual differences in *potential* stem from genotype differences; individual differences in behavioral *performance* result from the non-uniform recording of environmental stimuli by intrinsically nonuniform organisms.

One of the strongest proponents of the thesis that intelligence is an inherited trait is Burt, who insists that between individuals most of the variance in this quality is caused by genetic differences rather than environmental influences. This is a theme that has repeatedly appeared in his literature for over fifty years and that he has lately reiterated (Burt, 1966). While he believes that intelli-

gence is influenced far more by genetic constitution than by environmental conditions, he does not ignore the latter. Burt (1966) says that despite what his critics say he has always insisted that hereditary and environmental influences interact, though in the case of intelligence the contribution of the latter is relatively small. The strongest evidence for this is the remarkable similarities of intelligence of identical twins even when reared apart.

A qualification of this (to which Burt would no doubt agree) is that *given a reasonable environment,* genetics is the main determinant. The situation is no doubt analogous to that of body size (see Chapter 5), in which, after a certain optimum level of diet is reached for a population, differences in size between individuals in that population are genetically determined. In populations in which diet levels differ markedly among individuals, both environment (diet) and genetics contribute to differences. In other words, Burt's contentions may be true of populations in which all individuals receive an adequate level of early stimulation and are free from physical factors such as malnutrition or disease that may affect neural development. Hopefully this is the case with most privileged communities.

There have been numerous objectors to the thesis of Burt (and others) of a primarily constitutional basis to intelligence. This is understandable in the prevailing climate of psychological opinion, in which the influences of J. B. Watson are still strong. Stott (1966) is among the critics. He points out that because multiple pregnancies tend to create an unfavorable uterine environment, twins are disadvantaged and tend to be of inferior intelligence. Their similarities of IQ, he claims, are due to this factor. This is certainly a valid point, though whether it merely qualifies Burt's position in a minor degree or really introduces a major confounding factor is an open question. One might suppose the former. Stott also mentions a motivational factor, though without making it very clear how this applies to the situation. A comment on Burt's position has also been given by Lewis (1966), who says in effect that genetic constitution may indeed be a major influence on IQ but that the existing data do not satisfy all the conditions necessary to prove this. However, despite this element of uncertainty about conclusive proof, I see the evidence in support of a large genetic component to intelligence as very strong.

In connection with Burt's estimates of the heritability of intelligence, it should be noted that the measure used is apparently a variable in the degree of heritability found (Erlenmeyer and Jarvik, 1963; Vandenberg, 1966). It would seem from the available evidence that certain kinds of intellectual functioning are more strongly influenced by genetic factors than others.

Whether or not we accept Burt's high estimates of the role of genetics, we must admit that inheritance plays an important and possibly major role in differences of intellect among persons. Furthermore, the social

changes that are raising living standards, making them more uniformly available throughout the population, and that are making educational facilities available to all may be having the effect of reducing environmental sources of variability and hence increasing the relative genetic contribution.

As J. Hirsch (1962), among several others, has pointed out, it is more profitable to approach the study of behavior genetics by attempting to assess the contribution of genotype variation among individuals to phenotype variance than to ask the more naive question of whether a piece of behavior is inherited or not. Because not all behaviors of interest to psychologists are influenced by simple Mendelian actions of single alleles, polygenic models and the application of statistical genetic techniques are necessary for an understanding of behavior genetics.

Hurst's theory of the genetics of human intelligence is the only such theory based on experimental data (Hurst, 1932, 1934). Part of his data is taken from a study of European

HURST'S DATA ON THE GENETICS OF INTELLIGENCE

Intelligence of Parents	n (Families)	Intelligence of Offspring
1. Mediocre x mediocre	85	(i) All mediocre
Mediocre x mediocre	77	(ii) One-half mediocre, one-half high- or low-grade
2. Mediocre x high- or low-grade	39	(i) All mediocre
Mediocre x high- or low-grade	133	(ii) One-half mediocre, one-half high- or low-grade
3. High- or low-grade x high- or low-grade	72	(i) One-fourth mediocre, three-fourths high- or low-grade

SOURCE: J. L. Fuller and W. R. Thompson. 1960. *Behavior genetics.* New York: Wiley, Table 7-15, p. 224.

royalty (Woods, 1906), which made intelligence ratings of 424 regal parents and 588 of their offspring. The rest is derived from data collected by Hurst in Leicestershire (England). It is gleaned from 388 parents and 812 offspring.

The children in the latter group were all given the 1917 Stanford-Binet and the Healy Picture Completion Test, as were some of the lower-grade adults. The rest of the adults were not tested but were rated on available criteria. The data were grouped into eleven grades of intelligence, with class intervals of about twenty points of IQ. Hurst thus had a total of 406 families in which, as shown in the table, the parents could be classed in three ways and the offspring classified in five ways. He explained these data by assuming that mediocrity in intelligence is determined by a single dominant gene, N. If this were the only factor, the homozygous recessive would then be either high-grade or low-grade; but because about a quarter of the offspring of matings of high- or low-grade parents were mediocre, Hurst proposed that there are also modifier genes that act only in the absence of N. He suggested five such genes, in which A, B, C, D, and E might act as unit increasers, each of about ten points of IQ, while a, b, c, d, and e would be unit decreasers. Thus nn, AA, BB, CC, DD, and EE would represent the highest extremes of intelligence. Idiot levels would be represented by nn, aa, bb, cc, dd, and ee. Those with nn, but heterozygous for the modifiers (Aa, Bb, Cc, Dd, and Ee), would be mediocre, as would be those with NN and all other combinations of minor modifiers. By supposing the various intermediate combinations of these modifiers with nn, the range of intelligence could be ingeniously explained from high to low.

The theory does quite plausibly explain most of the data. It also shows how mediocre parents can produce both mediocre children and some offspring of exceptional grading. But the figure of 50 percent in the 77 families of mediocre parents [1 (ii) in the table] is, according to Fuller and Thompson (1960), surprisingly high, because at the most 25 percent would be predicted and that 25 percent only by ignoring the normalizing effects of the minor modifiers. However, if *all* offspring of mediocre parents are considered together, something nearer this ratio is obtained.

Another theory has been put forth by Pickford (1949), who suggests that the distribution of Stanford-Binet scores can be explained by ten equal and additive gene pairs. Bowles and Pronko (1960) have claimed that an adequate explanation of the range of intelligence can be given by a model of four gene pairs acting cumulatively. Neither of these theories has any factual basis other than an *ad hoc* explanation of the observed distribution of IQ's.

Conrad and Jones (1940) anticipated Pickford and Bowles and Pronko when they argued that a "blending" theory must be inadequate. Although such a theory might quite neatly explain some of the facts (notably that of distribution selected by later writers), it is unable to account for the equally important factor of regression of offspring means toward the population mean, nor does it predict the found value of sibling correlation. According to a "blending" hypothesis, one would expect a correlation between siblings to be as high as .71, but the consensus of a number of studies shows the observed value as approximately 50.

Conrad and Jones are also critical of Hurst's theory. It does not (they claim) properly account for regression in the case of offspring of nn parents (group 3 in the table). Here, they say, the average should not be at the mid-parent level, but at a regressed value. They also point out (and this is the more cogent criticism) that the theory lacks the independent test that would have been given by also observing the intelligence of the next (F_2) generation. Notwithstanding these points, Hurst's theory is the most acceptable of the three quoted and, even if imperfect, gives the best account of the genetics of intelligence so far offered.

It must be emphasized that it is not sug- gested that the Hurst model for the inherit- ance of intelligence is *the* mechanism in- volved; there is no proof of such an assump- tion. The model is merely a hypothetical one that mostly fits the facts. However, it seems likely that some rather complex mechanism is necessary (and this is a parsimonious one). Moreover, similarly complicated mechanisms may be involved in the inheritance of other psychological characteristics.

SEX CHROMOSOME ABNORMALITIES

It has long been known that anomalies of the chromosomes exist—for example, that mongoloids have forty-seven rather than the usual forty-six. It has also been known that sometimes there may be an extra or a missing sex chromosome. Until recently this matter was not easy to study or to relate to other variables.

A new tool in the study of genetics has been provided by the Barr test, or the sex chromatin test (Barr, 1957). A "spot" is dis- cernible in cells at certain stages of mitosis; normally it is present only in the cells of females. The rule is that there is one fewer chromatin spot than there are X chromo- somes; hence the male has no spot (is chroma- tin negative) and the female has one (is chromatin positive). To make the test, a sample of tissue is taken (commonly from a scraping of skin from inside the mouth) and examined histologically. Among any sample, some of the tissue will be in the requisite stage of division. This test is simple enough to perform to make possible more extensive studies of sex chromosomal anomalies, and greatly increase our knowledge of them.

The sex chromatin test has revealed that there is a range of chromosomal abnormalities; these have been reviewed in K. L. Moore (1966a, b, c). Although there are these reports of a variety of abnormal chromosome con- stitutions, they in fact concern only a very

small proportion of the population. Chromo- somal abnormalities of all known kinds affect a little less than 1 percent of newborn in- fants, and of these only about half affect the sex chromosomes, the rest being autosomal (WHO, 1966).

Among the commoner abnormalities are XO (in which the second sex chromosome is absent) and XXY. The latter type, Kline- felter's syndrome, are male in the sense of having testes (though these do not produce sperms). They frequently suffer handicapping conditions, of which mental deficiency is com- mon but not invariable, and also bodily ab- normalities such as atrophied testicles, a eunuchoid figure, and breast development (Ferguson-Smith, 1966). Their sex life is often unsatisfactory, though this is probably in part at least secondary to the feelings of inadequacy and inferiority that accompany the condition (Kvale and Fishman, 1965). There is usually a marked reduction of sexual activity, at least of a social kind, but some instances of psycho- sexual pathology have been noted (Money, 1966). Although some "Klinefelters" may be homosexual, the tendency does not appear to be an invariable or even usual accompani- ment of the condition. Certainly the syn- drome does not seem to represent any mech- anism that can account for the general run of homosexuals.

The XO type (Turner's syndrome) are fe- male, but their ovaries are degenerate and as adults they remain infantile in sexual devel- opment. These individuals also commonly show a number of bodily abnormalities and are frequently mentally defective (Moore, 1966b). Again, there is an absence or reduc- tion of sexual behavior rather than active psychopathology (Money, 1966).

A number of other kinds of genetic ab- normalities, such as "super-females" XXX and even XXXX), have been detected by this method and reported in the medical literature, but they are almost always indi- viduals with fairly gross abnormalities. It is a point of psychological interest that these conditions are far too rare to account for the number of psychosexually deviant individuals in the population.

Another form of genetic abnormality leads to hermaphroditism, in which there is either one ovary and one testis or a combined ovotestes. The hermaphrodites are genetic mosaics, in which some cells contain one chromosome pattern and other cells another. This state is common among invertebrates but is rare in higher animals and humans. Such human mosaics as XXX-XX, XX-XXX, and XO-XY have been reported in the literature (O. J. Miller, 1961; Moore et al., 1964). An XX-XY has also been reported (Josso et al., 1965). A review of a variety of types of hermaphroditism has been given by Lennox (1966). There are fairly gross abnormalities in both the external and internal reproductive structures, and unlike the mythological Greek deity from whom they get their name, hermaphrodites are rarely reproductive in either sex and certainly not in both. Some points of interest in the psychological development of hermaphrodites will be considered in Chapter 9.

It would, of course, be inaccurate to suppose that *all* criminality or mental illness is related to abnormalities of the sex chromosomes. MacLean et al. (1968) found that, in a large-scale survey of mental hospital patients and mental defectives, .5 percent of males showed sex chromosomal anomalies (which is about the same ratio as in the general population, according to WHO statistics). However, sex chromatin-positive males as a specific group are significantly more common in institutional populations than in the general population. In considering the overall picture of genetic mechanisms in aberrant development we should add the autosomal genetic factors underlying certain psychoses to the sex chromosome abnormalities.

The purpose of this review is not to suggest that all psychological aberrations are genetically determined but only to show that some may be. It is possible that other genetic mechanisms of which we are as yet ignorant may play a part in some of the effects we at present ascribe to the environment alone. A few years ago we had no proof of genetic factors at all.

It is also important to emphasize that genetics is almost certainly only one of several factors. It seems that having an XYY makeup may predispose an individual to criminality, but this is not to say that every XYY becomes a criminal no matter what the condition of his environment. We need to examine this question by identifying XYY individuals in the normal population (assuming they exist) and by studying the influences that have prevented the manifestation of their "delinquent potential."

GENETICS OF DEVIANCE

A concordance between identical twins in "criminality" is shown in a number of studies and has been discussed by Stern (1960). He recognizes that environmental factors could account for these findings but notes that the concordance is much lower in nonidentical twins, who also share a common home background. This fact weakens the argument that a "bad" home is a sufficient explanation for criminal tendencies, though undoubtedly such an environment does contribute to their expression.

The ideas of Lombroso and others, long discredited, are reemerging. Forssman and Hambert (1967) have discussed research findings that show a relationship between sex chromosome abnormalities and antisocial behaviors in both males and females. They suggest that the most probable explanation of these findings is that chromosomal abnormalities are associated with cerebral abnormalities (presumably developmental) of the type commonly called minimal brain damage.

An interesting series of nine cases of men with XYY-chromosome makeup all of whom were incarcerated in a Scottish maximum security prison, has been reported by Price and

Whatmore (1967). They all suffered severe degrees of personality disorder, without evident psychosis or brain damage. Seven of the nine were mentally subnormal (IQ between 60 and 80). They had long criminal records, commencing at unusually early ages, but without, in eight of the cases, any ostensible disturbance in their families (the remaining one had an alcoholic father). They were characterized by emotional instability and low tolerance of frustration; their crimes were against property rather than persons.

The incidence of XYY- and XXY-chromosomal abnormalities has also been noted by Telfer et al. (1968) in a male criminal population in the United States. Another study in England has also noted an unexpected proportion of XXY and XYY in an English maximum security institution (Bartlett et al., 1968). The two XYY individuals in this study were both homosexual and psychotic, though at least the former characteristic does not seem to be a necessary accompaniment of this chromosome type. An Australian study also notes XYY males among persistent offenders (Wiener et al., 1968).

An incidental observation is that individuals of the XYY type are characteristically tall. A variety of crimes, including arson, have been noted; whether the observation that nonviolent crimes are usual will be borne out remains to be seen. (A newspaper report states that Richard Speck, who murdered eight student nurses in Chicago, was found to be of the XYY type, but I have not yet seen this reported in a scientific article.) Price and Whatmore note that none of their cases had been at all amenable to the psychotherapeutic endeavors directed toward them before incarceration.

From a survey of over 2000 consecutive births, Sergovich et al. (1969) report an incidence of one XYY in 250 male births (which would make it the commonest form of aneuploidy in humans). These authors urge caution in regarding criminality as a necessary sequel of the condition, though a strong correlation certainly exists. They say that a spectrum of neurological deficits may accompany the condition, which might be manifest in overt forms of deviation—of which antisocial behavior is but one—and also more subtle forms of intellectual or behavioral abnormality. So far as criminal populations are concerned, the figure of 3 percent of XYY's given in the Price and Whatmore study, or 2.8 percent in the study by Bartlett et al., is well above the apparent incidence in normal populations.

The possibility that certain forms of antisocial behavior, or behavioral deviances, are inherited does not mean that all are. Even for those that are, the amount of environmental modification is problematical. Thus it may be well established that there is a genetic component to schizophrenia, but what does this really mean? The schizophrenic tends to misperceive and distort reality. In some cases (but not universally) there are perceptual disturbances similar to those that can be produced by lysergic acid diethylamide (LSD) or other hallucinogenic drugs. In others there are no perceptual distortions of this kind, but there are social ones, as in the paranoid schizophrenics. Are these distinct phenotypes different expressions of the same genotype? If so, what determines the difference? The influence of social factors is clearly seen in delusional systems. The "Napoleons" that once formed the stereotype of the lunatic have disappeared, replaced more recently by "Hitlers" and "Stalins" and today represented by "Maos" and "les grands Charles de Gaulles" (an interesting instance of remote *folie à deux*). Information on the detailed childhood experiences and longitudinal studies of the development of such delusional systems might be highly revealing of the kinds of interactions that take place between genetic factors and environmental pressures.

As mentioned, it should not be claimed that all deviant behaviors have a genetic basis. In a later chapter homosexuality will ·be discussed as a form of behavior once believed to be genetically determined, but now seemingly learned to a large degree. Certain constitutional factors may favor this particular learning, but they are probably not factors that can be related to any specific gene, and only indirectly perhaps to genetic mechanisms.

It would be naive to suppose that genetics provides an adequate explanation for all behavioral deviance. But it might be no less naive to suppose that environmental explanations always provide a sufficient explanation.

GENETICS AND INDIVIDUAL DIFFERENCES

In the popular mind genetics explains why people are alike, why children resemble their parents, and why certain traits run in families or in groups. This is, of course, one aspect of the science, but equally important is the fact that genetics explains why individuals are different. The major biological advantage of sexual reproduction is that it ensures that no two individuals are alike in the total complement of genes (identical twins excepted). Man has at least 25,000 genes (and probably more), and with random matings the odds against two individuals obtaining the same set are astronomical: For all practical purposes such an event can be regarded as an impossibility. Even with selective matings, as is usual in humans, the odds against identity or even close similarity in *total* gene complement are very great—again large enough to be considered virtually impossible. Even incestuous matings will produce genetically different offspring. A child *has* to be different from one of the parents, who must be of opposite sex. This reality immediately introduces an important series of genetic differences.

To say, of course, that the total gene complements of offspring are invariably different from that of either parent is not to say that there are no similarities at all. Indeed about half the genes do come from each parent, but some of each half-set of genes may produce a phenotypic difference from one (or both) of the parents. Thus a blue-eyed child with a blue-eyed mother and a brown-eyed father differs from his father but must have received the determinant gene from him. Similarly a blue-eyed child with two heterozygous brown-eyed parents has received a recessive gene from each of the parents and thus, in this particular trait, is different from both of them.

The observation that a child has inherited few (or none) of the traits of his parents does not mean that he has inherited nothing from anywhere, though some of the more environmental theorists seem to imply this. (It would be equally valid, in fact, to argue that he had learned nothing either.) The child may have inherited much from the grandparents or from even more remote ancestors. Because by far the greater number of studies have involved either parent-child similarities or sibling similarities, the extent to which psychological characteristics appear in more distant forebears has not been studied in detail. There are, of course, some studies of mental illness, and more or less anecdotal accounts of some special talents such as musical abilities running in families for several generations. The extent to which other traits run is difficult to discover. The studies of the inheritance of intelligence mentioned earlier had to rely on crude estimates such as the education or occupation of forebears, which may frequently underestimate a person's potential and may sometimes overestimate it.

It is not only the method of formation of the sex cells that tends to "shuffle" the genes. Special happenings such as crossing-over are also involved. Thus the father does not pass on a duplicate of his genes in which those inherited from *his* father and mother are equally represented but rather transmits a somewhat haphazard selection of them. On the average, over numbers of gametes, one half of the genes will come from each grandparent (and backward in reducing ratios down the two contributing lines), but a particular sperm or a particular ovum may contain a disproportionate number from one or the other.

Another genetic mechanism that tends to increase diversity is heterozygosity. It has been estimated that, for the fruit fly, between 10 and 15 percent of the genes are heterozygous (Lewontin and Hubby, 1966). Dobzhansky (1967) has noted that if we can accept this as a likely percentage for humans, a sizable proportion of the genes handed on are ones that have not contributed to the phenotype of one of the parents. Some genes have contributed to neither.

One of the major contributions of genetics has been evidence showing that two individuals of apparently similar phenotype may be different genotypically and may react differently even when treated alike (Fuller and Thompson, 1960). This point is still baffling to a great many behavioral scientists (J. Hirsch, 1967), who continue to think in terms of types of "standard" individuals.

In our present state of knowledge this raises some difficult questions, and behavioral scientists who decide to ignore these difficulties are not without an excuse. For one thing we commonly lack the information necessary to determine genotype. Even in the simple case of a brown-eyed person we have problems in knowing what his genotype is. We know it must be Bb or BB, but we need extensive knowledge of his family tree to infer for certain which it is. Or alternatively, we would need to cause him to breed somewhat extensively to settle the question, and there are extrascientific difficulties to such experimentation. If we mate him with a blue-eyed female and he has a blue-eyed child, we know he must have been heterozygous, but if he has a brown-eyed child, we still do not know; even after he has produced two dozen brown-eyed children and no blue-eyed ones, we could only say he is *very probably* homozygous.

Some of our difficulties in distinguishing behavioral phenotypes may arise from the crudity of our measures. Two children may have phenotypically the same intelligence— for example, 125 IQ as measured by some standard test—but actually operate intellec-

tually in highly distinct manners. More sophisticated intelligence tests would give not merely the "height" of an individual's performance but its "shape" as well. Now what the origins of these differences are is another question again. It is suggested elsewhere in this chapter that similar overall levels may be achieved by different patterns of the polygenetic determinant of intelligence, and it is argued elsewhere in this book (particularly in Chapter 16) that there are many dimensions to intellectual functioning and wide individual differences in the particular constellation of abilities.

There have been numerous objections to genetic explanations of individual differences in humans, though only (it is significant to note) with respect to psychological variables. That certain physical differences are genetically determined is freely enough admitted. As McClearn (1962) has remarked, much of the nature-nurture controversy has involved ideological rather than scientific considerations. Pastore (1949) has reviewed the history of this aspect of psychology. The democratic ideal that all men are created equal, and with the proper environment would be equal, was reinforced by a reaction against the Nazi concept of the genetically endowed master race. The influence of J. B. Watson and behaviorism has also been strong, especially in North American psychology, in denying or minimizing the role of genetics as a source of human differences.

There are certain arguments of a genuinely scientific nature that caution against too uncritical an acceptance of genetic claims. For example, it is undoubtedly true that parents of superior intelligence will tend to provide a superior environment for their children, and the better-than-average intelligence of their offspring *may* be solely a result of this. Similarly the personality likenesses that are found between parents and children may be due only to learning. On the other hand, if learning is so strong, why are not children *more* like their parents? If two bright parents provide such a stimulating environment, why on the average are their children less bright than themselves? Some explanatory dimension is lacking in a purely environmental account.

The separated identical twin studies that are the *pièce de résistance* of the geneticists are open to objection. Some such pairs do show rather wide discrepancy. Furthermore, it can be claimed that it is not uncommon for separated twins to be reared in different branches of the same family, or at least in families similar in background, and hence have similar learning experiences. Adopted children with genes unrelated to the adoptive parents tend to show *some* similarities to these parents in intelligence, and this may be attributable to the environment. The geneticist may counter that adoption agencies tend to match children in socioeconomic background with the placement families and hence to make at least a crude matching of genetic potentials. And in any case the adoptive child is (on the average) much less like the parents than are the children that the parents bear. (Burks, 1928; Freeman et al., 1928). The argument has gone on for a long time. The final proof has not yet been produced, nor the final word given.

We must reject J. B. Watson's claim that genetics is irrelevant: "There is no such thing as an inheritance of capacity, talent, temperament, mental constitution and characteristics" (Watson, 1925, p. 82). But we must also disclaim the polar opposite: "Heredity and not environment is the chief maker of men. . . . Nearly all the misery and nearly all the happiness in the world are due *not* to environment. . . . The differences among men are due to differences in the germ cells with which they are born" (Wiggam, 1923, p. 42).

In the 1960's one would have to search hard for anybody who would actually repeat Watson's famed challenge (". . . give me a dozen healthy infants . . ."), but one can find many who act as if they believe it. It is true that many texts on child development have at least a section or even a chapter early in the book on genetics, apparently as a gesture toward biology; but having genuflected, the authors make no further reference to the matter. It is certainly not usual to discuss inherited mechanisms as an integral part of the developmental process.

The influence of behaviorism on North American psychology has been discussed by J. Hirsch (1963), among others. He remarks on the belief traditional among behavioral scientists that individuals start life alike and differences that are later observable are all due to variations in experience. He outlines the fallacy of this assumption, but emphasizes that to admit this fallacy is not to reduce the importance of the role of experience, though it is to recognize that the effects of experience are conditioned by the genotype. The genotype must have an environment in which to develop its phenotype.

Another source of inhibition on genetic discussions among developmental psychologists is that such discussion seems to many to introduce a variable that we cannot control. At a practical level it appears fruitless to discuss the matter. The environment is something that one can believe he can control. However, when one comes to consider what is involved in any large-scale manipulations of the environment, the problem is no less massive.

Moreover, the pursuit of science is the search for truth, not for comfortable myths. If human development is in fact controlled (wholly or in part) by innate factors, then we have to know this even if the knowledge is discomforting. Biologists are already talking with some confidence about manipulation of the genes and the control of heredity. It is by no means inconceivable that these processes may be practicable in the not-too-distant future, and the developmental psychologist has an obligation to be informed of their implications to child rearing. He needs to know what psychological characteristics may be subject to this kind of manipulation. If it is to be adopted as social policy, he should be in a position to offer intelligent comment on the problem.

GENETICS AND DEVELOPMENTAL EFFICIENCY

The inheritance of handedness might be taken to illustrate an important developmental concept. Trankell (1955) has produced, on the basis of a number of population studies, a theory of the inheritance of this trait: It involves a dominant gene for right-handedness. The supposed recessive for left-handedness is of incomplete penetrance, so that even among homozygous recessives there are differences in the degree to which left-handedness is manifest.

There are social pressures toward right-handedness. Even where parents and teachers are permissive of sinistrality, many gadgets of modern living are designed for right-handers, and it is less convenient to be odd. Left-handers can learn to use the right hand and commonly do because of these social pressures. Thus some homozygous recessives are phenotypically indistinguishable from those with the dominant gene.

We might take this idea further and suppose that although the genetic left-hander can often learn to use the right hand, he would use the left hand more easily (just as the right-hander will use his right more easily and will have difficulty in learning to use the left). In other words, it requires less effort and is more efficient for him to use the left hand, and a greater expenditure of energy is necessary in acquiring skill with the right hand. This in turn means less energy to invest in other kinds of learning, so that the loss of efficiency is general rather than specific to manual skills. For some left-handers with high expression of sinistrality the task of learning to use the nonpreferred hand is very arduous indeed, and only moderate proficiency may be acquired even after great effort.

It might be assumed that similar mechanisms may apply in other dimensions of development, in which there may be genetically determined tendencies that can be overridden, but only at a cost. For the moderate left-hander (i.e., one with low expression of the genetic influence) the advantages of being right-handed might justify the extra effort required to achieve this condition. The more extreme left-hander might require disproportionate effort and still not be a satisfactory performer with his right.

Each case needs to be considered separately. There may be genetically determined behavioral traits that are socially undesirable and that, in the interests of society, require "training out" if this is possible, even at considerable cost to the individual. Others may be socially desirable and worthy of encouragement. It will, for example, be suggested in later chapters that creativity is a genetically determined trait that tends to be socially undervalued. Many teachers and some parents tend to prefer conformity and "adjustment" and to exert at least mild efforts to train-out creativeness when it appears. On the other hand, there are some teachers and parents who do value creativity and attempt to foster it in all children—perhaps in some who may not be genetically endowed for this kind of cognitive activity. Whether or not *all* children can be creative is an open question; some educationalists assume they can and design curricula accordingly. Whether this is true or not, it seems likely that this trait will be expressed more easily by some than by others. Possibly for some no amount of environmental encouragement will produce good creative performance, whereas others will show such performance whether the environment actively encourages it or not.

The principle of developmental efficiency states that individuals have differing genetic potentials and that, in general, the optimum development for the individual will capitalize on this potential; it will not insist on high performance in functions for which the individual is less well endowed. This supposes, of course, a culture that permits diversity in personality among individuals and that can employ a wide diversity of special skills, aptitudes, and interests.

Four

Innate
Shapers
of
Development

It is possible to discuss much of the behavior of adult organisms without becoming involved in the question of the origins of this behavior. Such a discussion would, of course, be incomplete, but for certain purposes this fact may not be of practical importance. We may study perceptual processes at maturity without considering the developmental changes that have preceded mature perception. Similarly one might investigate learning or memory without consideration of the changes in these functions before maturity. In certain contexts we might discuss social or parental behavior without being concerned about its origins. But a study of development necessarily focuses attention on the origins of behaviors observed at any given stage as well as on the changes, if any, occurring between the first appearance and the mature form of that behavior. The question of how behavior begins leads one to consider the question of the part that innate elements may play in the process, and this brings one face to face with the problem of instincts. In going back in the life history of the individual, do we come to a point in development in which behaviors (or their precursors) emerge unlearned?

The theory of instincts has had many ups and downs, but it persists. Moltz (1965) has commented on the fact that there have been many attempts to exorcise it from the body of science, yet it remains viable. Evidently it must fulfill a need, for others as well as developmentalists.

The recent work of certain biologists, Tinbergen in particular, has led to a reappraisal of the concept of instinct, and the new science of ethology has stimulated considerable interest among psychologists, although the ethologists are primarily zoologists concerned with animal behavior, and some of them, notably Lorenz, have commented on human behavior in ethological terms.

REPRODUCTION IN THE STICKLEBACK

Tinbergen (1951) has made a study of the mating behavior of the stickleback. Already a classic, his study illustrates a number of features of instinctive behaviors in animals. The stickleback is a small fish common in freshwater ponds and streams in England.

FIGURE 4–1. *Male stickleback in nuptial colors. Drawn from photograph by N. Tinbergen. 1952. The curious behavior of the stickleback. Sci. Amer., 187: 24, by permission of the author.*

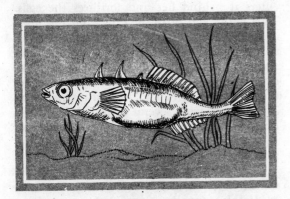

FIGURE 4–2. *Female stickleback, swollen with eggs. Adapted from photograph in N. Tinbergen. 1952. The curious behavior of the stickleback. Sci. Amer., 187: 24, by permission of the author and W. H. Freeman and Company.*

There the "tiddler" is eagerly hunted by small children with nets and jam jars. If it eludes the juvenile fishermen long enough, it grows to about four inches in length. This fish has dorsal and ventral spines—hence its name (see Figures 4–1 and 4–2).

A fundamental requisite of genesis in most animals (and certainly in all higher animals) is the union of the two separate cells; this act of union involves cooperation between the partners, and the pattern of sexual behavior on the part of the two parents facilitates this coordination. The mating behavior of the three-spined stickleback illustrates the manner in which this is secured. During most of the year sticklebacks live in shoals or schools. When the breeding season starts, there is a different system of activity from that found during the rest of the year. First, the males isolate themselves from the shoal and select territories. If another male enters a selected territory, he is attacked. Normally this attack takes the form of the defending male adopting the threat posture (see Figure 4–3); this is often sufficient because the trespassing male usually flees. Actual fighting is somewhat uncommon.

This threat behavior of the male stickleback is interesting. The defending fish darts toward the trespasser with his dorsal spines raised and his mouth open as if to bite. If the

FIGURE 4–3. *Threat posture of male stickleback. Adapted from photograph in N. Tinbergen. 1952. The curious behavior of the stickleback. Sci. Amer., 187: 24, by permission of the author and W. H. Freeman and Company.*

opponent does not flee at once, the owner of the territory does not bite him but points his head down and stands vertically in the water, making jerky movements as if trying to burrow his snout into the sand; often the ventral spines are also erected. This rather strange activity apparently has some sort of signal value to the trespassing male, which almost always flees, so that further aggressive activity on the part of the defender is usually unnecessary.

Having chosen a territory, the male then commences to build a nest by taking out mouthfuls of sand and dumping them a few inches away to make a shallow pit. Then he gathers threads of algae and presses them into the pit and from time to time creeps over the material, secreting from the kidneys a glue that pastes the plant together. When he has accumulated a cluster of this material, he bores a tunnel by wriggling his way through the mass.

By the time the nest is finished, the male has changed to the nuptial colors. The red underside becomes brighter, and the black pigment in the cells of the back contracts to minute dots, taking on a glittering bluish-green appearance; a bright blue circle surrounds the eye. With the green back, the dark red underside, and the brilliant eye, the male is conspicuous at this stage and in this attractive dress parades up and down his territory.

The females have taken no part in the nest building. They have all developed a silvery gloss and their bodies are heavily swollen by the eggs that have developed in the ovaries. They swim around in shoals and repeatedly pass backward and forward through the territories occupied by the males. When the male is ready to receive a female, it makes a dance around the shoal of females. Those females who are not ready to spawn are frightened away by this dancing of the male, but the ripe female acts differently. Instead of fleeing she turns toward the male and adopts a more or less vertical attitude (see Figure 4–4a). The differential reactions of ready and unready females are of obvious value in preventing the male from attempting to mate the unready female. When the female has signaled readiness, the male immediately turns around and swims toward his nest; the female follows. Upon arriving at the nest, the male thrusts its snout into the entrance and turns onto its side with its back toward the female, who now also wriggles into the nest (see Figure 4–4b). When she is completely in, with her head poking out one end and her tail out the other, the male begins, with his snout, to prod her near the tail, giving a series of quick thrusts at her (see Figure 4–4c). This action stimulates the female to spawn: Having done this, she swims through the nest. The male enters it behind her and fertilizes the eggs. This is the end of the mating, and the male chases the female away. He then repairs the nest if it has been torn by preceding activity and ensures that all the eggs are safely concealed within it. He may behave in this way toward two or three females and the nest may contain eggs from several. The female has no further interest in the reproductive process. After this brief encounter with the male she returns to the shoal of fish.

The male continues to occupy his territory, warding off intruders whether they are males or females or other species. His sex drive rapidly wanes and he begins to show other forms of behavior. Important in this phase is fanning. "Standing" in front of the nest entrance with his head pointing obliquely down, the male, with alternate forward movements of the pectoral fins, sends a water current onto the nest, at the same time making forward swimming movements with his tail (see Figure 4–5). In this way the thrust of the pectoral fins are counteracted and he remains in the same spot. The activity keeps the nest well ventilated with fresh water. It occupies more and more of the male's time as the eggs develop and require more oxygen.

The young hatch from the eggs in seven or eight days but remain an additional day

a. In the first stage of courtship the male stickleback (left) zigzags toward the female (right). The female then swims toward him with her head up. The abdomen of the female bulges with from 50 to 100 eggs.

b. In the second stage, seen from above, the male stickleback swims toward the nest he has built and makes a series of thrusts into it with his snout. He also turns on his side and raises his dorsal spines toward the female.

c. In the third stage, also seen from above, the female swims into the nest. The male then prods the base of her tail and causes her to lay her eggs. When the female leaves the nest, the male enters and fertilizes the eggs.

FIGURE 4–4. Courtship in the stickleback. Adapted from photographs in N. Tinbergen. 1952. The curious behavior of the stickleback. Sci. Amer., **187**: 25, by permission of the author and W. H. Freeman and Company. Copyright 1952 by Scientific American, Inc. All rights reserved.

in the nest. When they leave the nest, the male stops fanning and commences to guard the young. As soon as one of them attempts to swim away from the school, the male snaps it up in his mouth and spits it back into the swarm. At this stage the young are usually too slow to escape, but after two weeks they become more active and the parental behavior of the male wanes. The young now swarm together on their own account. The male loses his brilliant colors and shortly leaves his territory and his offspring to rejoin his age mates in the school.

The limitations of our language require that these behaviors be described as if they were purposive. It should be emphasized that in the foregoing description no consciousness of purpose is implied. As will be seen later, the merit of Tinbergen's formulation is that it shows how these seemingly purposive behaviors can be explained in terms of neurophysiological mechanisms in which no assumption of purpose is necessary. With animals at this level we can, in such terms, adequately account for the whole of the behaviors observed during the life span. Whether or not we do so with man is another question. Our language has evolved in a historical climate that has assumed that man behaves purposively, and hence it becomes difficult to write in an acceptable style without appearing to imply purpose even when describing animal behaviors.

Directive behaviors are of a more complex order than those explicable in deterministic terms; the principle of scientific economy demands that the latter sort of explanation be used wherever it is adequate, and that directive explanations be reserved for situations where deterministic ones are inadequate. Purely mechanistic concepts are probably (as they appear to be) unsatisfactory as a convincing explanation of this sort of directive but not purposive behaviors.

The ethological approach to behavior has been criticized by a number of authors (Hebb, 1953; Lehrman, 1953; Schneirla, 1957). Hebb's objections are that it creates a false division into innate and acquired patterns; he claims that the term *instinct* is misleading because it implies processes that are independent of environmental factors and differ from those in which learning is involved. However, in discussing a paper by Eibl-Eibesfeldt (1961) at a symposium on brain mechanisms and learning, he clears up a misunderstanding on this point. He recognizes that, among the ethologists, Eibl-Eibesfeldt, at least, is not denying that learning has any role in instinctive patterns of behavior. He realizes that the experiments of Eibl-Eibesfeldt (on nest building in rats) show quite clearly how learning and the constitutional structure of the animal collaborate in producing behavior, and that there are not different and unrelated kinds of processes. Hebb goes on to say that if the instincts are concerned with laid-down patterns that are modified by learning, then man's behavior is instinctive.

The concepts of the ethologists bring the possibility of understanding the mechanisms underlying instincts and of reconciling them with genetics. As we shall see, the evidence available at the present time suggests that the concept may be readmitted to respectable consideration by psychologists.

The word *instinct* is derived from the Latin, where *instinctus* means "incite"; the Latin was itself derived from the word meaning "prick." It is defined by the Oxford dictionary as an "innate propensity, especially in lower animals, to certain seemingly rational acts performed without conscious design; innate impulse."

In common usage it is often given the sense of intuition ("with a woman's instinct she saw Harry's need for tenderness") or is applied to acquired skills ("the instinctive hands of the potter . . ."; "grammar must become instinctive to the child . . .").

In everyday speech the term *instinct* has come to lack the precision desired in scientific terminology. Originally it was applied, in the manner stated by the Oxford dictionary, to the behavior of animals, which were supposed to be without reason. This was at a time when it was believed that man was always rational in his intellectual processes and when a clear distinction was held between the irrational animals ruled by instinct and rational man guided in his behavior by reason. The instincts of animals were regarded as inherited, though this was before the work of Mendel had become known and before the mechanism underlying genetic transmission had been discovered. The science of genetics later appeared to reduce the value of the concept of instinct, because although it showed how structures could be transmitted by genes, it did not appear to be able to explain the transmission of behaviors.

In fact, to say that the animals (or humans) behave as they do because they have instincts really appeared to say little, when nothing was known of the mechanisms involved. As an explanatory concept, instinct appeared valueless. For this reason the term fell into disrepute with students of behavior, though biologists have continued to use the term descriptively for certain observed actions that appear to be innate or that apparently require no learning. There are, however, a number of recent developments that invite a reappraisal of the theory; among these is the discovery of the nucleic acids, substances that promise an understanding of how complex behavioral sequences can be programmed and transmitted genetically.

FIXED ACTION PATTERNS

The core concept of the new instinct theory is the fixed action pattern (FAP). Moltz (1965) has presented a detailed exposition and critique of this concept. The FAP's are based on neurological entities, which are discussed elsewhere, especially in Chapters 6 and 8.

FAP's are not the kinds of behaviors that are commonly called instinctive—global ones such as the "maternal instinct," "migratory behavior," and so on. The latter kinds of behavior are not innate in the sense of being completely programmed as a continuous sequence controlled by a neurological center, whereas a FAP is presumed to be so programmed. FAP's are presumed to be encoded in the genetic material of the organism; they are in fact only units of which instincts are composed and are hence shorter and more discrete than continuous, controlled sequences.

FAP's are, however, not to be confused with reflexes, for they are more temporally integrated and sustained than reflexes. As Moltz points out, neither the laws governing reflexive actions nor those of learning apply to FAP's, which therefore at a theoretical level form a separate class of phenomena.

There is a distinction to be drawn between *appetitive behaviors* and *consummatory acts*. The former term refers to the initial components of a behavior sequence, and these components are often variable. The consummatory acts (Thorpe, 1956) are the terminal components of a behavioral sequence and, being terminal, must often be rigid and stereotyped. Moltz (1962) refers to the hunting of the falcon, which starts with loose exploratory flights over the territory and ends with the relatively stereotyped actions involved in the kill and the eating of the prey. FAP's are described by Thorpe as commonly constituting these end-point or climactic sequences. It does not, however, seem that they are necessarily end-point phenomena.

There are four properties of FAP's that may be used to distinguish them from other entities. These are described by Moltz as stereotypy, independence from immediate external control, spontaneity, and independence from individual learning.

Stereotypy results from FAPs' usual function as consummatory behaviors, for the external constraints impose a rigidity on the pattern, which will fail in its function if at all variable. As an example, the fanning behavior of the male stickleback has by its very nature to be stereotyped.

The movement pattern of a FAP is independent of afferent regulation. It will often continue to completion even though the external cues are lacking. In this it differs from taxes, which require constant direction by external events. Moltz illustrates the pattern with the egg-retrieving behavior of the graylag goose. To get an egg back into the nest, the goose moves out and extends the neck until the underside of the bill is against the far side of the egg. It then propels the egg back to the nest by two distinct movements, one that keeps the egg rolling toward the breast of the bird and one a side-to-side tapping movement that corrects the egg's tendency to roll away to right or left. The latter movement is a taxis, because it is constantly dependent on the movement of the egg and does not appear unless the egg (or an experimentally substituted object like a cylinder) deviates from its

course; it also ceases as soon as the object is back. The egg-rolling movement is a FAP, so designated because once started, it may continue even if the egg rolls out of reach and the bird appears to be rolling an imaginary egg up to its breast. The actual *in toto* egg-rolling behavior is, of course, a combination of the two kinds of activity. The FAP component cannot be broken down into more simple links. It is a unitary behavior triggered by a definite stimulus pattern (in this case, the sight of the egg away from the nest), and it is not divided into subunits each with its own adequate stimulus.

The third characteristic of FAP is spontaneity, by which Moltz means that the intensity of the behavior varies inversely with the time elapsed since the last evocation. Thus if the male stickleback is restrained from fanning behavior, it fans more vigorously on release. This can be shown experimentally to be independent of external stimuli, such as the waste-product concentration in the water. Similarly, periodic waning is not explicable by fatigue. The most notable example of this spontaneity is *vacuum activity,* where the behavior appears following a long period of non-performance and in the complete absence of any adequate external stimulus at all.

The last criterion of a FAP given by Moltz is that it appears under conditions in which there is no possibility of learning. For example, it is reported that the zigzag dance of the stickleback appears full-blown in males reared in isolation the first time they are exposed to the stimulus of a gravid female (Cullen, 1960). Some FAP's, for example, the side-to-side head movement of the human neonate (Prechtl, 1958), appear so early that learning is virtually excluded. Also, some FAP's may be seen before they are functionally useful. Lorenz (1956) has described how the young gosling's fighting actions are exactly like those of the adult, despite the fact that its wings are not long enough to hit an opponent.

The FAP's are conceived as forming the

nucleus of an animal's response repertoire. More complex sequences of behavior, including instincts, are built up from them. But perhaps more importantly for psychology, FAP's form the basic elements, the innate substructure on which learning is built. Moltz follows Lorenz and Tinbergen when he insists that learning cannot be understood without understanding this fact. Elsewhere in this book this idea is also pursued; learning, especially in early life, consists of uniting basic and innate units such as the FAP's into varying higher-order patterns.

In this view the genetically encoded units of behavior are invariant and not subject to modification by the environment. One research task is to investigate the properties of these "parts" of behavior. What is variable is the manner in which these parts are linked together into higher-order functional patterns, and it is here that learning becomes effective. One difference between lower and higher animals is that in the former, higher-order behavioral sequences are also relatively invariant, being made up of the units of a preformed and inflexible pattern; whereas in the latter there is much greater flexibility in the combination of units. It may be presumed that higher animals not only have greater combinatory possibilities for the basic units but also a greater number of these units. The research task here concerns the rules of combination, from which perhaps we come to Hullian notions of learning.

There is an important aspect of Moltz's formulation that should be emphasized. In discussing instinct he rejects the *template* notion that is at least implicit in most of the instinct theories. This template idea supposes that FAP's arise by a process of passive translation from the genetic encoding. The environment is merely supportive.

Moltz proposes instead an *epigenetic* theory, which states that all (sic) response systems are synthesized during individual development as a result of environmental interaction. Hence the environment is more than supportive and is actively involved in the organization of each response system.

It is not altogether clear whether Moltz intends the use of the adjective *all*, because one of the characteristics of FAP, by his definition, is independence of learning; hence *some* response systems are apparently independent of the *psychological* environment. The physiological environment may, of course, be involved, though it is not clear that Moltz means this. However, even if some of the details of his concept are not entirely explicit, it certainly is important to emphasize the idea that the environment is actively involved in the unfolding of many aspects of behavior that depend also on a genetically encoded substratum.

One dissatisfaction with the formulation proposed by Moltz is that it seems to stop short of an explicit statement of what relation FAP's actually have to instincts. To take one example, he uses the egg-retrieving behavior of the graylag goose; this is presumably an instinct. It is made up of at least two components, a taxis (egg tapping) and a FAP (egg rolling). From this example it would seem legitimate to conclude that instincts are made up, as suggested earlier, of FAP's as one kind of "part." This fairly simple and short-duration instinctive behavior apparently contains just one FAP, but also one taxis as well.

The idea suggested here is that instincts, together with other ingredients of which the taxes are one kind, are compounded from FAP's. Further, it might be supposed that lower species have a fairly limited repertoire of FAP's and taxes that are combinable in only a restricted number of ways. Higher animals (we might suppose) have, as already suggested, a greater range of possibilities for the combination of FAP's and taxes into wider varieties of behaviors. They also, possibly, have a greater number of these basic units. Learning is the mechanism by which this combination of subunits is achieved. Following Hebb, we might further suppose that the lower organisms can learn only a very limited number of combinations (what might be called biological learning), and this limited learning is generally fast. Learning that does *not* involve the combination of FAP's and taxes is, on the contrary, very slow. (Much of the unnatural laboratory learning is of this kind.) Higher organisms, on the other hand, have a much greater range of possibilities for learning, involving a greater number of units in most instances. Hence on the whole the process takes longer. But the possibilities of nonbiological learning are also much greater: That is, higher organisms may also learn in ways that do not involve the simple combination of biologically given subunits. How much of the learning in higher organisms (and in man) is of this kind is problematical.

The empirical significances of FAP are outlined by Moltz. While some of these are of considerable interest to ethologists, they do not seem to have much relevance to the developmentalist as yet. He shows how FAP's can form a basis for classification of behavior; although some classifications (into neurotic behaviors, imitative ones, and so on) are of value, the categories used in the ethological approach do not immediately strike one as helpful to our interests: They are altogether too far removed. Similarly, FAP's have theoretical implications to evolutionary analysis and behavioral genetics—but again at a level somewhat remote from issues in the present discussion.

In other theoretical realms their potential importance is more obvious. If FAP's are conceived as constituting the nucleus of the organism's response repertoire, then they form a basis for the analysis of behavior. The understanding of learning, Moltz points out, will be impossible without considering FAP's if they form the innate bases on which it rests. Among other theoretical issues discussed in his review is the important one to psychology of the FAP as a separate class of behavior that differs from the reflex on the one hand and learned behaviors on the other and that is governed by unique laws not applicable to either. Associated with the FAP's are the innately determined perceptual mechanisms [innate releasing mechanisms (IRM's) and their sign gestalts] that release FAP's.

In critically evaluating the FAP, Moltz points out that the anti-instinct theorists do not deny the existence of FAP's, but rather deny the assumptions that the instinct theories derive from them. Certain of the assumptions cannot be contradicted: For example, he says there is no evidence to show that FAP's cannot be genetically encoded (but this is not a proof that they are).

One possible criticism is that there may be other ways than the encoded blueprint route to the stereotypy that is thought to be a salient feature of the FAP. For instance, the environment rather than endogenous factors might provide the common ground that produces common behaviors in a species.

Another criticism is that FAP's are considered at present to be unlearned because they cannot be explained in terms of any known learning principle. (This proof by default is, of course, one commonly used in science and is heuristically justified—but it has limitations.) However, in many of the examples of such behaviors the importance of experiential factors can be seen. For instance, the fear response to unfamiliar stimuli, which is typical of many vertebrates, implies experience of familiar ones. The fact that male sticklebacks reared in isolation perform the zigzag courtship dance in response to a model of a pregnant female the first time this is presented certainly shows that the social presence of other fish is not necessary to the emergence of the behavior, but this says nothing about other nonsocial environmental effects that may be involved in its organization. The assumption that it all comes from the blueprint unaffected by the environment is unwarranted, Moltz says. However, the principle of Occam's razor, the simplest adequate explanation, might be invoked to support the assumption that this behavior is organized solely by genetic endowment.

FAP's in Children

A detailed study of head-turning movements that are FAP's in the human baby has been made by Prechtl (1958). One of them is the action familiar to anyone who has watched an infant at the breast: When the nipple touches anywhere on the cheek near the mouth, the head turns so that the nipple is against the lips, and it is then taken into the mouth. A similar reaction can be elicited by a finger or a blunt object. This action is commonly preceded by a grosser side-to-side movement of the head, which, if the infant is in the nursing position, brushes the nipple against the cheeks and orients the head to the breast (see Figure 4–6a). When the nipple is touching near the mouth, the finer movements, described above, that actually orient the mouth to the nipple take over (see Figure 4–6b), and once in the mouth, FAP's involved in sucking are evoked.

As might be expected, these FAP's are not readily elicited when the baby is satiated and drowsy, but they become more intense and faster when he is hungry. The adequate stimuli are tactile, and a relatively firm object evokes the response more strongly than a soft object like a pad of cotton wool. These FAP's may also be observed at times in the absence of external stimulation (vacuum activity). Prechtl provides a detailed analysis of these FAP's and speculates about the underlying neurophysiology.

An attempt to apply the technique of ethological observation to young children has been made by Blurton Jones (1967). He seeks to show that FAP's are detectable in the behavior of nursery school children; for example, stereotyped agonistic gestures, facial expressions that appear in specific contexts, a number of approach or avoidance behaviors when confronted by friends or strangers, and so on. Blurton Jones points out the similarities of some of these FAP's to those observable in other primates. He also notes sex differences in certain of these action patterns, for instance, in one best described as "rough-and-tumble" play, which is more typical of the boy.

This study does not report any behavior that is not already familiar, and one might regard it a trifle naive to describe such commonplace action in these terms. Nevertheless, a new look at the familiar is often revealing, and further studies of this kind may well show new facets of behaviors that are almost too familiar to be considered worthy of inspection.

EARLY THEORIES OF INSTINCT

Because the theory of instincts has a long history, it is useful to look briefly at the development of thought in this area.

Fletcher, in his book *Instinct in Man* (1957), reviews the writings of a number of early workers on the concept of instinct, notably Lloyd Morgan (1894, 1896, 1905), Hobhouse (1896, et seq.), Drever (1917), and McDougall (1948), and points out that there is an essential similarity between all their points of view. He shows that these men attempted to deal with two main problems, that of innate behaviors in animals and the place of innate factors in human psychology.

From his review of the major criticisms leveled against the theory of instincts as put forward by the earlier writers, Fletcher concludes that they caused no serious damage to the theory, though they did have the unnecessary effect of making it unfashionable.

Innate Behavior Patterns in Animals

It is a matter of common observation that among lower animals we find patterns of behaviors that seem to be innate. The web-building of spiders is but one of innumerable examples, where the intricate pattern of the web is spun perfectly at the first attempt.

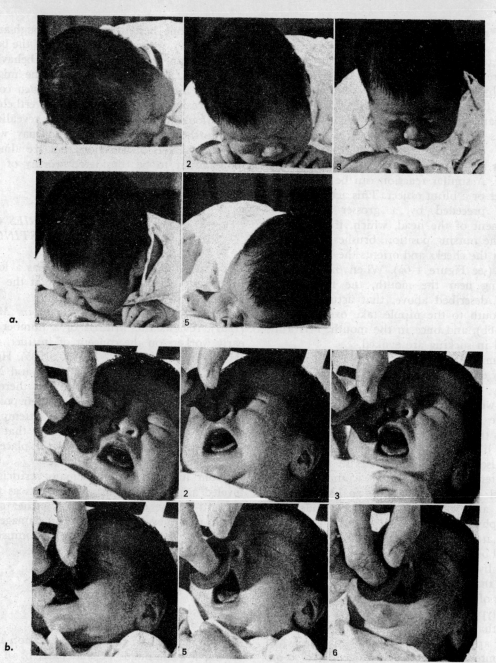

FIGURE 4–6. FAP's in the human infant: head turning and the rooting response. In nature these two actions are related to feeding and are appropriate at the breast, but are difficult to illustrate thus. Here they are artificially separated. (a) The side-to-side movement grossly locates the nipple; (b) the rooting response brings the mouth over the nipple. Photographs taken from film courtesy Montreal Children's Hospital.

There is no possibility of teaching in many species, where the young spiders hatch without any parental contact. Even where there is parental contact, the idea of instruction seems no more parsimonious than genetic transmission as an explanation of the emergence of such complex behavior generation after generation.

Even higher up the scale, at the level of the primates, one can find these innate behavioral patterns. Sackett (1966) has shown how infant rhesus monkeys reared in isolation so that learning is proscribed, still show the typical reaction to threat behavior by another monkey at about two to four months of age. The behavior is typical of normally reared monkeys: We can only assume this to be an inborn fear response. (This study is described in detail on pp. 215-216.)

Such behaviors adapt the animal very satisfactorily to the circumstances of their normal ecology; they seem to be directed toward the attainment of a certain end state. These behaviors appear to be unlearned and are most evident in those species in which the capacity for learning is at a minimum. The particular acts comprising such behaviors are very similar or even identical in all members of the same species (though in some a distinctive pattern for the two sexes is found). These behaviors, which may be protracted over long periods of time and which involve complicated movements, are commonly performed almost to perfection by an individual member of the species the first time they are attempted. They appear to be little dependent upon experience, though in some instances they may be modified to some extent by it. The theory of instincts attempted to account for such behaviors and accepted them as being, in fact, inborn.

The theory of evolution claims that the structural characteristics of a species, as well as certain other characteristics, are the result of hereditary processes. These processes have been continued over long spans of time and their existence in a species at the present depends on mutations and the effects of natural selection.

The inherited characteristics are several and are summarized by Fletcher as follows:

1. The structural or anatomical features of the species
2. The internal physiological processes of the organism
3. The reflexes, which are uniform, automatic behavior mechanisms
4. Certain sensory-motor actions more complex than the reflexes that adapt the species to its ecology
5. Certain cravings, or needs or impulses that are persistent and recurring, that arise from complex internal processes, and that provide the motivation for characteristic 4
6. Certain features of experience, or emotions, that arise from the frustration of the impulses mentioned in characteristics 4 and 5
7. Certain modes of perception that appear to have the function of relating relevant objects in the environment to the impulses mentioned above
8. The cognitive aspects, which are conceived as an experience or feeling of the whole relation between the impulse, appropriate object, and the behavioral reactions involved
9. Certain capacities for modifiability or intelligent control

The sequences of unlearned behavior found among animals are regarded as manifestations of these inherited characteristics of structure and physiological processes, and of the activities and experiences correlated with them and resulting from an interplay between the animal and its environment. Because these features are inherited, we can account for them without the necessity of considering learning or individual experiences.

The instinct, therefore, comprises internal physiological features, experiential features, and manifest behaviors. In the lower animals the coordination of these features is closely determined by genetic factors, so that the instincts in these species are stereotyped and rigid. They adapt the animal very well to its "ecological niche" but do not permit great variability if the environment changes. In these lower species the emotional aspects of instinctive experience and behavior are minimal. As we ascend the phylogenetic scale to more complex animal species, we find less rigidity and stereotypy, both the motor responses and the perceptions being more variable and the emotional elements of the associated experience becoming more prominent. These emotional aspects have an important function in maintaining the animal's motivation and in making the attainment of the end state less dependent on a close relationship with stimuli from the environment.

It is the emotional or conative-affective element that may be regarded as the most distinctive feature of instinct because it gives unity and persistence to the behavior. This is true whether the behavior is rigidly determined by heredity or has elements of variability. It is particularly important in the latter case.

Instinct is not regarded as excluding intelligence, for the capacity for intelligent control is an inherited feature. There are considerable differences between species in the inheritance of this capacity. Generally the lower species inherit such capacities to a negligible extent, and for them only the most minor modifications of behavior by intelligent control are possible; whereas the higher animals become more and more capable of such controls. The highest animals are capable of grasping the relationship among the internal impulses, the perceptions, the ends, and the behavioral means. In man these relationships reach the conceptual and ideational levels. Instinct and intelligence are not regarded as mutually exclusive, for both are inherited and each modifies the other. In addition to modification by intelligent control, instinctive behaviors, and the experiences that go with them, may also be conditioned by habit-formation or learning processes.

Although inherited, the instincts are not necessarily manifest or mature at birth and may emerge at various stages during the growth and maturation of the individual. Some may persist throughout life and others may be effective during certain periods of development or during certain recurring intervals in the life span of the individual.

The theory of instincts, while it holds the instincts of the animal to be specific to its species and to certain situations, does not regard the individual as merely an aggregation of instincts. The individual is a unity, a concept implying some central integration, which is more evident where the capacity for intelligent control is greater. There are pervading features of the experience and behavior of an individual that tend to persist, whether a given instinct is being manifest or not at a given instant. These lead to such concepts as temperament, which may be regarded as the tendency to arousal of certain types of behavior and experiences.

Innate Factors in Man

The hypothesis of evolution regards human behavior, and also human experience, as being continuous with that of the animals, and the theory of instincts is concerned with this continuity: It holds that instinctual experiences and behaviors are discernible in man and play an important part in his nature. Fletcher's review (1957) also covers the development of thought on this topic.

In man, that modifiability of instinctive behavior noted even among the animals reaches a high degree: Factors of experience in learning and intelligent control play a much greater part in changing the innate pattern. Nevertheless, the theory of instinct claims that learning cannot account for the whole pattern, with its behavioral sequences and affective correlates.

In man neither the perceptual features of instinctive activity nor the motor responses are so rigidly established by heredity as they are in many of the lower animals, and neither are the impulses and the emotional aspects of instinctive behavior so closely connected with them. However, the theory holds that there are found in man at least some simple instincts that involve well-defined motor responses; and even in the more complex behaviors that are largely the outcome of learning and experience, at least some responses that are related specifically to innate impulses not entirely learned are involved.

The theory of instinct recognizes that the capacity for adaptation can aid survival in a competitive environment and that modifiability requires a long period of infancy, with dependency and opportunity for learning. These prolonged infancies are found among many of the higher animals, but reach their ultimate in man: It is this long infancy and protracted immaturity that makes possible the plasticity of man.

In applying the concepts of instinct to man, it is the conative-affective features that are of most interest. Because there is a lack of the automatic, highly adaptive, but rigid behaviors found in the lower animals, emotion plays an important part in man's instinctive behavior. It directs and maintains it in the vicissitudes of a changing environment and ensures the continuity of effort that in the lower animals is given by a rigid and blind sequence of activities.

In many of man's instincts it is the emotional aspect that is the most evident because of the nonspecific relationship between the impulses, the perceptions, and the motor responses. In man the instincts involve multiple responses and the necessity for choice; this results from the lack of stereotyped response in any particular situation. In the immature individual, emotion provides a motivating force for learning, and in the mature it maintains the behavior over the time required for the choice or over any period of delay that environmental circumstances may introduce. As in the animals, emotion arises in man when instinctive activities are obstructed.

Because of their greater variation and the overlay of learning, it is not easy to point to clear instances of instincts in man, despite the confidence with which McDougall attempted to do so. In later chapters some human instincts are discussed. For example, in Chapter 9 the evidence that some elements of sexual behaviors are innate in man is presented. What is particularly pertinent in this example is that it is the experiential or conative elements rather than the overt actions that are most marked. This is consistent with the idea being developed here that the emotional component is an essential part of an instinct, and that this aspect of instinctual patterns is increasingly more important as one comes up the phylogenetic scale. Instincts in man are largely feeling: The motor components are highly variable. Another example of human instincts is seen in the smiling response (Chapter 8), an instinct that is manifest in both the infant and the parents. The motor component here is perhaps more marked and stereotyped in the infant than is the affective component (though we have no real certainty of this), whereas the response of the parent is largely affective and much less rigidly motor.

Most of the earlier theories viewed the ends of human behavior as rooted in mechanisms that are innate, so that all human activities, however complex, are ultimately related to instincts. Intelligence may be used to direct behavior toward the achievement of these ends. Certain of the earlier writers, such as Hobhouse and Ginsberg, did concede that some further ends (such as the desire for truth), which cannot be entirely explained in terms of instinct, might be found.

Man is essentially a social animal, and any individual lives in a particular social context. Because of man's modifiability and his capacity for intelligent control, social tradition or culture may be an important factor in molding the behavioral responses. While his instinctual endowment is common to all members of his species and directs the major ends of human activity, the details of this behavior in any individual may be modified by his culture: It will differ from society to society and within societies from group to group. The complexities of both individual and social life modify the basic innate tendencies.

Fletcher's review selects these as the major tenets common to the early theories of instinct in man. They aimed to give an account of the unlearned behaviors and experiences that can be observed through the range of animal species. They endeavored to be consistent with the theory of evolution and in the light of this theory found the same features of instinctive behaviors in man and the animals.

CONTEMPORARY STATUS OF THE THEORY OF INSTINCTS

In outlining the contemporary position with the theory of instincts, Fletcher takes the view that an up-to-date formulation does not require any radical alteration of the general contentions of the earlier theories, only certain amendments and additions as a result of greater knowledge. For example, as mentioned earlier, the older theories regarded the internal physiological processes of the organism as among the inherited characteristics. We now have rather more knowledge about the mode of their inheritance, some more detailed understanding of the hormonal mechanisms at work, and some insight into factors in the central nervous system. Similarly, the earlier theories maintained that some if not all species inherited capacities for modifiability, and they recognized that in man social or cultural forces were among those that exert a modifying influence. We now know somewhat more about the nature of these social influences.

Fletcher maintains that many of the criticisms of the doctrine of instincts were particular to McDougall's formulation, which contained some loose statements; cogent objections were raised to his opinion that *all* human drives derived from the instincts, even

in adulthood. Allport's concept (1937) of "functional autonomy of motives" is one of several views that have insisted that not all behaviors can be explained in terms of instincts, at least at the level of the human adult. Other writers on instinct took these criticisms into consideration in their formulations and the main objections should be regarded as specific to McDougall's thesis and not as destructive to the theory of instincts as a whole.

Hebb (1949) has suggested that much of what is commonly attributed to instinct may in fact be caused by learning that is very rapidly accomplished—so quickly, in fact, that it appears to emerge full-fledged without being learned. He points out the manner in which learning becomes more rapid (even though more limited) in creatures lower on the phylogenetic scale, so that at invertebrate levels it could be that only a matter of seconds is necessary to achieve all the possibilities for learning. Even if we regard the nervous system of simpler animals as permitting the learning of only certain associations that are an inherited property of the nervous system of the species, learning is nonetheless (in this view) essential to the emergence of the behavior dependent on these associations. In the event of failure of opportunity for this learning, the behavior does not appear. It could be that such a notion only elaborates the details of the *modus operandi* of instincts and does not invalidate the concept. The modern point of view does not seek to deny learning and readily admits the possibility that learning plays an essential part in the emergence of innate behavior patterns.

In this view, then, instinct would become an inherited tendency to learn certain behaviors: It would emphasize the often repeated statement that a distinction between innate and learned is a false one. In many instances, particularly in lower animals, it may be difficult to apprehend, in the light of present knowledge, the nature of this learning, and the same applies to the higher animals in infancy. Nonetheless, we might bear in mind the possibility of its importance. The situation is further complicated by the possibility that, as Tinbergen (1951) has suggested, some learning processes occur so early in the development of the individual that they precede the completion of innate patterns.

Concepts of Konrad Lorenz

Some fascinating insights into animal (and particularly avian) behavior have been provided by Lorenz. More recently, in his book *On Aggression* (1966), he has speculated about the implications of instinct theory to human psychology. He has defined instinct as having the following properties (Lorenz, 1950). First, an instinct is an inherited, specific, and stereotyped pattern of behavior. Unlike some other stereotyped and inborn behaviors, like taxes and kineses, it is released complete by the environment rather than guided by it. The most important point for purposes of Lorenz's ideas is that the instincts accumulate what he calls "action specific energy," which gradually lowers the threshold for release and eventually leads to "vacuum activity."

By "action specific energy" Lorenz means that each instinct involves the building up of a specific tension in the central nervous system, and, if the animal is not in a situation appropriate for the release of the instinct, this energy accumulates. This accumulation of the specific energy results in a lowering of the threshold of sensitivity to those stimuli that are appropriate to the release of the instinct. The greater the specific tension, the less strong is the stimulus needed to trigger the instinct. By a "tendency to vacuum activity" Lorenz means that if the energy is allowed to accumulate without being triggered by the appropriate stimulus, the threshold will ultimately become lowered to the point at which it will "fire" in the complete absence of the usually appropriate stimulus. For example, Lorenz noted such vacuum activity in a starling that was hand-reared and fed artificially

and that would go through the entire behavior pattern of insect hunting, including swallowing actions, even when there were no insects around at all. After being fed, a hand-reared tawny owl would go through all the motions of pouncing on a prey, even though it had never experienced the hunting of a living mouse. Lorenz describes the behavior of a budgerigar that appeared to derive substitute gratification from displaying to a ping-pong ball, and Thorpe (1956) also notes that in the prolonged absence of mates birds may often be seen to display toward inanimate objects and even attempt copulation with them.

Tinbergen on Instinct

Tinbergen (1951) has claimed that behavior is a reaction to external stimuli but is also spontaneous insofar as it is dependent on internal causal factors, or motivational factors. He dismisses the old controversy as to whether behavior is spontaneous or reactive on the grounds that it is both.

He further points out that each animal has its own perceptual world (the Ümwelt of von Uexküll) and, when investigating the external stimuli involved with a particular species, it is necessary to know the potential capacities of the sense organs of the animal under consideration. We need to know not only what stimuli the sense organs *can* receive, but also what in fact they customarily *do*.

Although animals are often capable of very acute sensory discriminations on their environment, they actually react to only certain of the possible range of stimuli to which they are potentially sensitive. Thus the water beetle has well-developed compound eyes and can be trained to respond to visual stimuli but does not use vision in catching its prey. What it does respond to is chemical stimulation. A little meat extract added to the water stimulates it to intensive behavior in which it bites at any solid object that it touches. On the

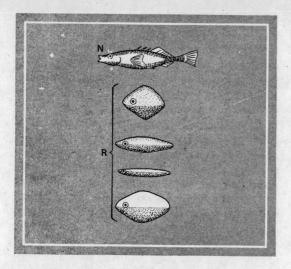

Fighting in the stickleback fish was elicited by the lower four models which did not have the shape of the stickleback, but did have the red underside. The faithful model at the top, lacking the red belly, did not elicit fighting.

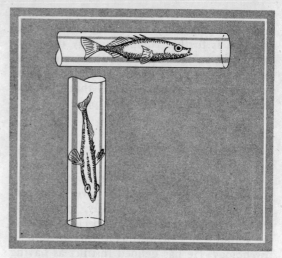

When the three-spined stickleback is prevented from assuming its natural "threat-posture" (top diagram), it elicits far less fighting from other fish than the lower fish which is placed in the "threatening" posture.

FIGURE 4–7.   Models to which the male stickleback responds by fighting. The female responds to these by mating behavior. Adapted from N. Tinbergen. 1951. The study of instinct. Oxford: Clarendon Press, pp. 28 and 38, by permission of the author and the publisher.

other hand a tadpole, presented in a glass tube so that the beetle can see and not smell (or taste) it, excites no reaction. Tactile stimulation alone does not excite the attacking behavior either, unless it is accompanied by the appropriate chemical sensation.

In the same way the male stickleback does not, in his territory, react with the normal threat behavior when presented with a perfect model of a male stickleback that lacks the nuptial red color. It will, however, react to an extremely crude model that has the red underbelly, particularly if it has a blue eye (see Figure 4–7). The fish apparently reacts mainly to the red and neglects other characteristics, even though this species probably has receptors acute enough to distinguish them. Similarly, with the English robin, a male in his territory will not react to a perfect stuffed model robin if it has a dull brown breast,

though it will react vigorously in attacking a mere bundle of red feathers. Such behaviors have been reported in numerous species of animals, and these have been reviewed by Russell (1938). He first used the term *sign stimuli* for these behaviors, and this is the term that Tinbergen has adopted.

Sign Stimuli

We find that animals do not react to all the changes in the environment that their sense organs are capable of receiving, but only to particular features of them. Because of this particularity of the animal's perceptual world, Tinbergen (1951) attaches much importance to the concept of the sign stimulus. He says, "As a rule, an instinctive reaction responds to only a very few stimuli, and the greater part of the environment has little or no influence, even though the animal may have the sensory equipment for receiving numerous details" (p. 27). A domestic hen comes to the rescue of one of her chicks on hearing its distress call but not on seeing it in distress (Tinbergen, 1951). Thus if a chick is placed behind a screen, the hen will go to its rescue when it hears the call, but if it is placed under a glass dome so the mother can see its struggling movements but cannot hear its call, she will ignore it. This is, of course, an artificial situation unlikely to occur in nature where there are no glass domes and where the auditory sign stimulus will be perfectly adequate in any probable contingency.

Another example is the manner in which the female stickleback reacts only to certain elements of the male stickleback at mating,

and ignores others. Tinbergen also points out that the animal's perceptual world is not always the same but changes as different instincts are activated. Although the water beetle may not use vision in detecting its prey, it does use it in other activities.

It would appear that some of the instances of sign stimuli given by the ethologists might require confirmation. Thus Hirsch et al. (1955) failed to duplicate an alleged sign stimulus in the chicken. This does not, of course, invalidate the concept itself; it merely throws into question the particular instance.

Lorenz (1943) has suggested that sign stimuli play a role in human behaviors, the parental instinct, for example, being responsive to the "kewpie-doll" releaser (Figure 4–8), which consists of the following sign stimuli: (1) short face in relation to a large forehead, (2) protruding cheeks, and (3) uncoordinated

FIGURE 4–8. The "kewpie doll" releaser: the features of the human infant head which release parental behaviors are exaggerated in some dolls, but make them particularly "cute." Photographs courtesy Montreal Children's Hospital.

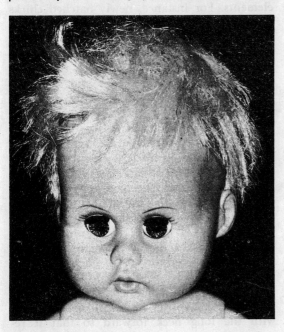
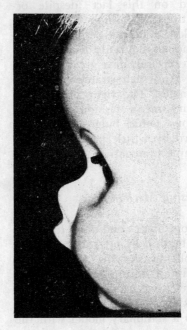

limb movements. This concept will be discussed more fully elsewhere.

A comparative study of sign stimuli for both social and sexual behaviors in primates has been made by Wickler (1967). He considers that much social behavior is influenced by sexual drives; that, for instance, the attraction between male and female forms a basis for social coherence and is a factor in binding social groups. In many species the presentation of the penis in erection is an important sign stimulus in establishing dominance between males and of males over females. Wickler discusses the ethology of human social-sexual behaviors, pointing out that there are indications of similar factors in operation. The wearing of clothes and other social conventions in most advanced societies does, of course, conceal many of the sign stimuli, so their action is not readily observed. But even clothing (as is well known) is frequently used to display and even enhance such stimuli. Thus for males, breasts and buttocks form a salient part of the sign gestalt presented by the female, and feminine fashions generally have capitalized on this fact (despite occasional aberrations of fashion that dictate "breastless" styles). Buttocks perhaps receive less attention, though the bustle of nineteenth-century fashions certainly gave great emphasis to this feature. And such strategies are not confined to females. The tight breeches of eighteenth-century men's fashion showed a quite conspicuous pubic bulge, which was often exaggerated by a little padding. Falsies are not a feminine prerogative.

Innate Releasing Mechanisms

Usually the optimum conditions for a reaction are not obtained by presenting a single sign stimulus but by showing some combination of sign stimuli. This may be illustrated in the case of defensive behavior on the part of the male stickleback in his territory. While he may react to a stationary model with the features mentioned earlier, he reacts much more certainly when the model is in the threat position, vertical in the water, with the head down. Although the behavior *may* be triggered by one sign stimulus alone, it is much more certainly aroused by the combination of the two. Similarly the female's reaction to the courting male is more surely released by two sign stimuli together, the red belly and the male's zigzag dance.

The combination of sign stimuli suggests that there must be some coordinating device in the nervous system: This leads Tinbergen to the concept of the *innate releasing mechanism* (IRM), which is equivalent to what Lorenz called the "receptory correlate." The IRM is the "special neurosensory mechanism that releases the reaction and is responsible for its selective susceptibility to special combinations of sign stimuli" (1951, p. 41). It could possibly be argued that a red belly in zigzag dance is a unitary stimulus, but there is good reason for not regarding it so.

The combination of sign stimuli forms a simple gestalt organization of two (or more) elements. For instance, newly hatched chicks of the herring gull beg for food by pecking at the tip of the parent's bill; the bill is yellow and has a red spot at the end of the lower mandible. On being so stimulated, the parent regurgitates food onto the ground, picks up a little in its beak, and presents it to the young. By experimenting with dummy bills, it can be shown that the chicks react particularly to the red spot. (See Figure 4–9.) However, by presenting models with the red spot irregularly placed, it can be shown that the reaction is not merely to a red patch, but to a red spot at the tip of the lower mandible, that is, to a combination of stimuli (Tinbergen, 1951). Similarly, young birds of other species react differently to models in motion. A model was prepared that had a short protuberance on one side of the wings and a long one on the other. When the model was sailed above the young in one direction with the long neck forward so that it re-

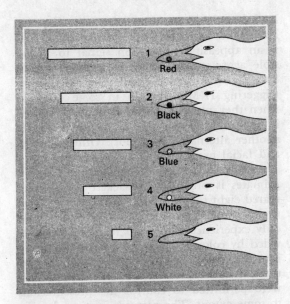

FIGURE 4–9. *Experiment with herring gull models shows that the begging response of the young depended on a spot on the beak, especially on a dark spot and on a red one. Adapted from N. Tinbergen. 1951. The study of instinct. Oxford: Clarendon Press, p. 30, by permission of the author and the publisher.*

sembled a harmless duck, no effect was produced. When sailed the other way with the short part forward, it produced escape responses, for then it resembled a hawk. Not only certain elements of shape but also direction is important in the gestalt of this stimulus configuration. (It should be noted that McNiven [1960] failed to replicate this finding, so reservation is necessary in accepting Tinbergen's contentions in this particular case.) There is also a phenomenon of heterogeneous summation. For instance, the male grayling butterfly shows mating behavior that is released by the following sign stimuli in combination: (1) the fluttering flight movement that is typical of the female of this species, (2) the darkness of coloring of the female, and (3) the closeness of the female. Using models, it can be shown that dark-toned models of the female butterfly have a higher

releasing value to the male than do the light ones. However, a white model can produce as much reaction as the dark one if it is closer; or again, if the dark model is moving smoothly, whereas the white one is fluttering vigorously, the white will produce as much reaction as the dark. There is a kind of quantitative relationship in the elements of the sign stimuli, which are, as it were, "added up" by the central nervous system (Tinbergen, 1951).

Tinbergen maintains that motor responses are also organized in a hierarchical manner, so that there is a configurational character in both the afferent and the efferent aspects of instinctive behavior. He regards these facts as being highly significant because the additive phenomena in connection with sign stimuli suggest that the afferent impulses are collected into a single neurophysiological "integrative center," and transmitted from there to a motor center, which then redispatches the stimuli, distributing them according to the configurational principles.

On the question as to whether this idea of integration is necessary, certain facts may be pointed out. For instance, with the hawk figure, can the stationary figure be regarded as one unitary stimulus and the same shape moving as another but also *unitary* stimulus? Behaviorally, the moving shape is certainly a much more effective stimulus than the stationary one, but is it necessary to regard the moving figure as "shape plus movement," implying synthesis and an integrating center in the nervous system?

Two considerations, without being conclusive, do suggest that the idea of synthesis and an integrative mechanism is valid. First, it fits what we know about the action of the nervous system and is illustrated by clinical conditions such as asteriognosis, in which there appears to be a failure of some integrative process. Second, some sign stimuli involve different sense modalities; thus Lorenz (1952) reports that in mallard ducklings the stimuli involved in imprinting are the visual shape *and* the call of the duck. It is difficult to conceive such a sign gestalt without an integrative mechanism.

Tinbergen also points out that there are both "releasing" and "directing" stimuli; not only do certain stimuli release reactions, but others direct them. Thus it has been shown that in some species of butterflies the flight toward flowers is released by the flowers' odor but is directed by the color. (Sometimes the same sign stimulus may have the effects of both releasing and directing.)

As we have already seen, in the case of many oriented movements two components can be seen. First, there is the FAP, which is mainly dependent on *internal* factors; it is triggered by an external stimulus but then runs its full course under the control of internal mechanisms only. Second, there are the taxes, which are comprised of a series of reactions to external stimuli and result in the guiding or directing of movement. Thus in the egg-retrieving response of the graylag goose the FAP is only *triggered* by stimulation, whereas the taxis constantly depends on stimulation throughout its course.

Eibl-Eibesfeldt (1961) has shown experimentally that IRM does correspond to a real functional unit, and that both it and the fixed motor pattern have value in the analysis of the processes by which unlearned and learned behaviors become integrated into functional unity.

Innate Releaser Mechanisms in Primates

Most of the ethological work on IRM's has been with birds, and some with other non-mammalian vertebrates and with invertebrates. However, there is also a little information on mammals. Eibl-Eibesfeldt (1961) has described fighting in a number of mammalian species in which various innate "signals" in the behavior of the antagonists serve to make fighting for the most part a ritual, in which blood is rarely shed. He has also described how stylized be-haviors enter into forms of mammalian behavior. For instance, in the monkeys, a "grin" is an appeasing submission signal to a possible aggressor and tends to forestall attack. Such signals may be regarded as sign stimuli triggering IRM's (though in some cases, as when they prevent attack, it might be asked if they inhibit IRM's, or perhaps trigger another alternative behavior). Other gestures and facial expressions are threatening.

Some experimental evidence on IRM's in primates is provided by Sackett (1966), who reared eight rhesus monkeys (four of each sex) under conditions of isolation in which their only experience with other monkeys was provided by colored slides projected periodically into the cage. They also saw nonmonkey pictures. After approximately three weeks they were permitted to control the presentations to some extent. The pictures continued to be shown randomly, but following the period of unchosen presentation the monkey could revive a fifteen-second showing of the same picture by pressing a lever and could do this repeatedly for a fixed period of time. During the first month there was for all pictures an equal number of chosen presentations by lever touching. In the second and third months a preference for the monkey pictures emerged. In the third month there was also a marked reduction in calling for pictures of monkeys in threatening postures and also behavioral signs of distress when these pictures were shown unchosen. There was, however, some increase in calling for these threatening pictures in the fifth and sixth months: Maybe it gave a thrill. For all months from the second on the most popular pictures were those of infant monkeys. No such marked preference was found for other monkey pictures.

Sackett concludes that reactions to threat signals depend on unlearned, prepotent activating properties of the stimulus. Similarly the social reaction to the infants is based on unlearned mechanisms. It is interesting that no particular visual reactions were obtained to pictures of adult monkeys. This reinforces

Harlow's conclusions that attachments to adults are mediated largely by tactile stimulation. Evidently visual stimuli do not play a major part. Sackett points out that the maintaining of responses to social stimuli may depend on learning but that initial avocation depends on species-specific structures.

Innate Release Mechanisms in Humans

Most of the innate factors in human psychology are buried—often deeply buried—beneath the learning each individual acquires. For this reason they are difficult to detect, but a number of writers are convinced that IRM's exist in humans and that the appropriate sign stimuli do have an influence on behavior.

Lorenz (quoted by Andrew, 1965) believes there is a very definite IRM in humans, and that it is present in about half the population: It is an IRM to snakes. He claims that the same IRM is also responsible for the horror of mice, because mice share the apparently legless movement that is typical of the snake. Lorenz suggests that there are two components to the stimulus presented by the snake: first, the legless movement; and second, the winding motion. People differ selectively in their response to these two components, and he says that women who fear mice are those that are most responsive to the legless element. He does not say whether there is a sex difference involved here.

According to Lorenz, the characters imputed to certain animals depend on similarities to postures and expressions in humans. He implies that these characters have innate signaling properties, and this is in line with what Darwin suggests about the origins of expressions (see Andrew, 1965) though this is not proved, because the role of learning has not been eliminated. However, according to the theory, the eagle has an undeserved place as symbol of strength and courage (Lorenz says he is less courageous than a raven), which arises solely because the bone covering about the eye and the form and angle of the beak, together with the big eye looking forward, gives it something of the "hero" face of the human fighting male. Similarly, the camel looks stupidly supercilious because the head is held slightly above the horizontal so that the nostrils are higher than the eye; furthermore, the lid of the eye comes down slightly and the nostrils are narrow slits (a protection against desert sand). All these morphological features give the unmistakable impression of human superciliousness. He goes on to say that the same is true of ugliness in humans. The artist usually portrays ugliness not by bizarre distortions, but merely by rendering a body that is too short and fat and bowlegged. Certain other distortions, such as an exaggeration of the broadness of the shoulders or the length of the legs, are not aesthetically offensive.

Lorenz also describes other animal features that may have IRM qualities for humans. The corpus adiposum buccae in the cheeks of the human infant are an important element in the "kewpie-doll" sign gestalt, and some species of infant monkeys in which this is absent fail to look cute. Another appealing quality of the human baby is the rounded buttocks, and again some primate species (such as the chimpanzee) that lack this feature are less cute as infants than others (such as gorillas) that have it. Lorenz points out how much Walt Disney has capitalized on features of this sort in his portrayal of the cuter animals. He goes on to state that among the few instinctive movements left in man, those of expression are prominent. He points out how the male brought into a fighting situation (even if it is only a symbolic fight for an idea) has certain accompanying physical reactions. There is a prickle down the back, tautness of the musculature, the arms are slightly abducted and go forward, and the "hero" face is made. He claims that the person who does not have these reactions is an emotional cripple.

In Chapter 13 it is speculated that a preference found in infants for a bull's-eye pattern might represent a visual sign stimulus by which it locates the breast (it would be interesting to observe what part of the bull's-eye is mainly fixated). Whether or not this sign stimulus really operates, once the breast is located, the sign stimulus for sucking responses in the infant seems to be tactile, provided by the nipple and its protractile tissues when in the mouth (Gunther, 1955). Presumably the anticipatory sucking movements, often seen in infants before the nipple is inserted, are conditioned.

Another possible IRM in humans is suggested by Hutt and Ounsted (1966), who claim that gaze behavior is used in man (as in many other species) as a signaling device for social interaction. The steady gaze can in certain contexts be threatening (Andrew, 1965) (see Figure 4–10).

Hutt and Ounsted observed the behavior of autistic children in whom interpersonal relationships are abnormal. These children consistently avoided eye-to-eye contacts with adults (though in filmed observations of contacts with other children brief eye-to-eye contacts were observed). In an experiment involving models of a happy and a sad human face, a monkey's face and a dog's face, and a blank outline of a face, they observed these children's reactions to the faces when they were placed in an otherwise empty room. The autistic children spent most time investigating the blank face and avoided contact with the human faces, especially the smiling one. This was quite the opposite of the behavior of normal control children, who also coordinated manual and visual inspection, whereas the autistic ones frequently inspected manually without close visual contact.

In an attempt to discover what parts of the face were most aversive to the autistic children, faces were presented lacking mouths or eyes. The latter were avoided more than the former.

The unusual reaction of autistic children

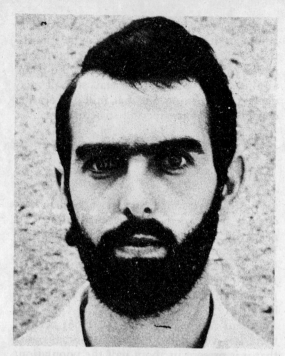

FIGURE 4–10. *Gaze aversion: many people find this photograph disconcerting.*

to the gaze is interpreted by Hutt and Ounsted as an attempt to reduce input. That is, the gaze is threatening or intimidating; this is its natural sign-stimulus property, and as such makes the gaze arousing. These authors assume that autistic children are already in a high state of arousal, and gaze aversion is a device to avoid raising further this chronically high level.

Although the steady gaze may generally have aversive qualities (especially, according to Andrew, if it is in a visual context that includes lowered brows), in certain circumstances it also has the opposite valence. It can, for example, be a signal of attentive interest (E. H. Hess, 1965), and pupil size enters into this sign stimulus. Lovers gazing into one another's eyes are following a fundamental pattern of behavior. The question does not appear to have been studied in humans,

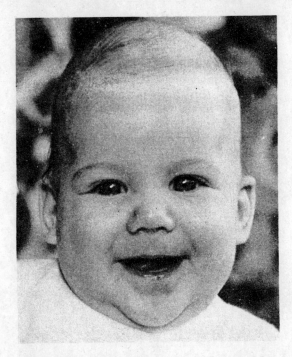

FIGURE 4–11. *Gaze attraction: few people find this photograph aversive.*

but if what is observed in animals is any guide, then it may be that the aversive tendencies must first be allayed. To be stared at by a stranger is disconcerting, even threatening, whereas steady eye-to-eye contact between friends is quite different. Indeed, the amount of such contact might be a sensitive measure of the degree of mutual attraction between persons.

Eye-to-eye contacts may, according to P. Wolff (1963), be sign stimuli influencing maternal (and paternal?) behavior. He noted that there was a change in the attitude of mothers when their babies commenced eye-to-eye contacts at about four to six weeks of age; whereas they had previously been attentive mainly to the material needs of the baby, they changed markedly at this time to a more playful, interested social interaction with the baby. It may be that eye-to-eye contact is

the releaser of this response (see Figure 4–11).

It would seem from Wolff's observations that ontogenetically the attractive eye-to-eye contact appears first. Presumably, the gaze aversion reaction appears with the fear response to unfamiliar stimuli (discussed more fully in Chapter 8), which ends the period of imprinting and the indiscriminant smile response of the infant.

A review of the literature on eye-to-eye contact is given in Robson (1967). In his own observations he noted considerable individual variation in the nature of eye contact in the first six months. Some infants seemed actively to seek and engage this contact, and others merely make it, apparently uninterestedly. Some were noted to avoid contact. Robson discusses the implications of eye contact, noting among other things that parents are commonly delighted when it occurs and respond to it, whereas they are frustrated if the infant avoids it. This contact (or lack of it) may have important developmental sequelae.

It should be noted that in most IRM's so far reported for humans, and in most of the behaviors that could be called instinctive, there is no universality. Some individuals do not show them. This is to be expected in a population in which the normal processes of natural selection are less binding. The wild duckling that fails to imprint does not survive; if its failure is based on a genetic irregularity, then it does not transmit this. Humans, especially in civilized communities, can survive and reproduce despite errors that would be fatal under more competitive conditions. To what extent they are handicapping is another question. For instance, the mother who has not received (or responded to) eye-to-eye stimulation by her infant may continue to nurture it physically but may fail to do so psychologically; she may also find motherhood an unrewarding experience. Among the animals, abandoned babies may result from such failure in sign stimulation on either side. In humans it is both psychologically and practically less easy to abandon offspring, but in some respects the results of failure of sign stimulation may be much the same.

The extent to which IRM failures may underlie developmental abnormalities—or the converse, the extent to which IRM's enter into normal development—cannot be stated at the present time. Part of the thesis of this book is that they may prove to play a more important part than is realized at present.

As suggested in a number of contexts in this book, relationships between people may be directed or modified by innate factors. In particular, parent-child interactions may be subject to this kind of influence. For instance, in many animals a confident approach of one to another can allay attack, whereas withdrawal may provoke. Even a small dog can safely approach a snarling one if it does so with head and tail up; it is the cringing dog that gets bitten. Similarly even a small man, by standing his ground confidently, can resist a threatening bully, whereas backing away invites blows.

In both animal and human young a similar influence can be observed. Some children are rarely put upon either by their peers or by their adults, whereas some cringing children are constantly being ill-used. The environmentalist explanation is that such children become cringing because of these experiences, but one might suspect that these children have started out by providing the sign stimuli for attack (or, perhaps more accurately, by failing to provide those that allay attack behavior in others). It is true, of course, that repeated experiences will make one child more confident and attack-resistant and another more furtive and attack-prone, but it is competent to suggest that in many life histories (not necessarily all) an innately determined factor sets the first reactions to aggression in others and starts the pattern of subsequent interchanges. In this way one can explain how similar experiences produce different effects. This is not to deny the influence of learning: A host of factors will modify the initial responses. Even the child who is in-

nately programmed for the highest degree of attack resistance may be beaten down by a savage environment, presumably. And the attack-resistant child in one milieu may develop into the confident leader and in another into the cocky, bristling person ever quick to assert his rights. The innately attack-prone child may in a kindly environment be lucky enough rarely to invite it and may even learn the techniques of aggression by conscious effort when he reaches a stage of maturity where this is possible. The attack-prone child who has experienced attack may have greater difficulty with the learning of counterbehaviors. A whole range of both peer and parent-child interactions may start with such basic events evoking innate responses on both sides—responses that develop into habitual modes of exchange.

Social Releasers

Many of the sign stimuli important to animal behavior are provided by a member of the same species, and Tinbergen calls these stimuli "social releasers." Thus when a flock of birds is on the ground and one takes alarm, the rest follow, often not by perceiving directly what has alarmed the first, but because his flight forms a sign stimulus to flight in each other bird that perceives it. Crowd behavior in humans may have similar roots, and it is notorious that mobs tend to revert to more primitive levels of behavior from which the veneer of culture is lost. The place of social releasers in early human behavior has not been systematically explored.

Internal Causal Factors in Behavior

Tinbergen endeavors to demonstrate that behavior may be the result of both external and internal forces. A number of pieces of evidence point to the existence of internal factors. For instance, it is noted that under constant conditions there are variations in the intensity or the frequency of the manner in which the animal behaves. For instance, the fanning behavior of the male stickleback does not appear until two or three clutches of eggs have been fertilized and the male's sex drive is waning. The time per day that the male spends in fanning the eggs increases steadily until the eggs hatch, at which time it ceases. It can be demonstrated that this increase in fanning response is partly caused by an external factor, the increased consumption of oxygen by the eggs (Tinbergen, 1951). The more developed the eggs, the greater is their demand for oxygen; and as the oxygen content of the water in the nest is lowered, the fanning behavior increases. But if the partly developed eggs are removed from the nest and younger eggs with a smaller oxygen consumption are put in their place, the fanning behavior continues with little reduction; it does not drop to a level consistent with the oxygen demands of the younger batch (Tinbergen, 1953). Thus, although the fanning behavior is partly caused by the external factor of oxygen concentration of the water in the nest, it also must be affected by some internal mechanism.

Another observation supporting the presence of internal factors is that the minimum stimulus required for the release of a given reaction may vary considerably from time to time. Furthermore, a correlation exists between the threshold intensity of the stimulus and the length of time since the previous performance of the behavior. Indeed, with continued lack of satisfaction, a drive may become so strong that the reaction "fires off" in the absence of the usually necessary stimulus. Lorenz also mentions this point in his concept of vacuum activity. Here the internal factor may become so strong that the external factor is not necessary at all.

As another example, the singing of male birds is part of the reproductive activity. It can be inhibited by low temperatures. Tin-bergen quotes an experiment by Nice in which she measured the temperature at which singing was inhibited during the early spring, and demonstrated that as the season progressed this temperature was no longer effective and that progressively lower temperatures were necessary to inhibit singing. This discovery strongly suggests the influence of growing internal motivational factors.

These examples give somewhat indirect indications of the workings of internal factors. More direct evidence is obtained by hormonal studies. Thus male chicks injected with testosterone show the complete sexual pattern of behavior of the adult cock, including crowing and copulation. There exist numerous similar examples of a quite direct relationship between hormonal factors and behavior among animals (see Ford and Beach, 1951, for others).

Internal Sensory Stimuli

It is well known that certain behaviors are affected by internal sensory stimuli, such as the stimulation provided by contractions of the muscles of the stomach wall in hunger, but these behaviors do not have immediate relevance to the present discussion.

Intrinsic Central Nervous Factors

Tinbergen maintains there are certain forms of spontaneous behavior that cannot be adequately explained, at least so far as present knowledge goes, by hormonal or internal sensory stimuli. For instance, the hunting behavior of dogs is not always suppressed when they are well fed. Further, the waning of specific reactions after satiation suggests that there is associated with each a specific energy that takes time for restoration after being dissipated.

There are a number of studies that suggest an intrinsic activity of the CNS in relation to locomotion. Tinbergen quotes studies by von Holst that suggest that in fish the rhythmic movements of locomotion require only very slight and unspecific external stimuli. In experiments with fish where all but two of the afferent dorsal roots were severed, there were still complete locomotory movements. Tinbergen suggests that there is an intrinsic activity of the spinal cord by which this structure can carry out automatic activities. It appears, however, to require at least a slight external stimulus to set it off, and he suggests that this external stimulus has a function of "removal of a block" that is inhibiting the automatic movements.

Evidence that, in the lower animals at least, the spinal cord is capable of maintaining rhythmic movements is provided by the axolotl. In an experiment by Weiss (1941) a piece of embryonic spinal cord was implanted into the connective tissue of the dorsal trunk muscles of an intact axolotl. A forelimb was also implanted. The implanted spinal cord did not grow a connection with the CNS of the host but did grow both motor and sensory fibers toward the grafted limb. The motor neurones established connection with the limb muscles some time before the sensory fibers came into contact with the receptors, but as soon as the motor neurone connection was made, the limb began to carry out rhythmic movements, even though sensory impulses were not yet being received. Thus the implanted spinal cord was apparently responsible for impulses that were independent of external stimulation. Hamburger (1963) has discussed in some detail this question of the central origin of instructive behaviors.

Tinbergen claims that there are close similarities between the mechanisms underlying locomotion and those basic to an instinctive act: They are both subject to internal factors and external stimuli and both show the characteristic tendency to fire off if they are long without the usual releasing stimuli. Tinbergen and Lorenz formulate essentially the same hypotheses, which the latter has put into the following words:

[I]nstinctive responses too are controlled by automatic centres that send out a continuous flow of impulses to central nervous motor mechanisms. Some kind of block prevents discharge into muscle action, which would lead to chaos. Discharge is brought about by adequate stimuli, namely, a combination of sign stimuli typical of each instinctive response. These sign stimuli act upon the reflex mechanism, which is known to be able to remove the block, thus allowing the accumulated impulses to discharge themselves in muscle actions constituting the motor response [Lorenz, 1950].

The importance that Tinbergen attaches to such observations is that they show that we cannot explain manifest behavior in terms of pure reaction alone but must consider internal causation as well. If this is true, it reveals a need for modification of the stimulus-response approach to psychology.

Coordination of Internal and External Factors

The internal and external causal factors can be seen to exert an additive influence on the motor response, with the result that in spite of the qualitative difference between the internal and external components these combine quantitatively in influencing the motor response.

Tinbergen attempts to explain the manner in which internal and external causal factors are coordinated in instinctive behavior. He concludes that hormones probably act on the CNS and increase the excitability of the sensory-motor mechanism specifically involved in any given instinctive activity. This hormonal influence must be specific and cannot act by increasing a general excitatory state because in many instances the same muscles are used in several instinctive reactions; therefore, in specific reactions it is not special muscles that are used in specific patterns of muscular activity. As can readily be demonstrated, hormones may activate specific reactions, and they must do this by acting on the excitability of specific motor centers in the nervous system.

Thus during the rutting season the male deer becomes sexually excited on perceiving a female, although at other times he is indifferent and not aroused by such perceptions. Many of his responses—as he runs toward the female, for instance—are similar to and involve the same muscles as running in other contexts. The probable explanation of this periodicity is that at this time the blood stream (and hence the whole body) is permeated by a flood of hormones that are absent outside the rutting season. The center controlling copulatory behavior is stimulated by these hormones, and when the other complementary stimulation—perception of a female—is received, the instinct is triggered. Perception of a female at other seasons does not produce this behavior because the appropriate center is not primed by hormones. In the male stickleback, selection of a territory and the appropriate behavior accompanying this action is apparently caused both by internal and external stimuli; among the latter, the temperature of the water is important.

Neurophysiological Factors in Instinctive Behavior

In connection with the hierarchy of mechanisms that Tinbergen proposes as underlying instinctive behavior, there is also proposed a hierarchy of neurophysiological centers. E. H. Hess (1957) has shown that by implanting tiny electrodes in the hypothalamic region of the brain of cats he could induce on stimulation of different regions the behavior patterns of fighting, eating, and sleeping, which were performed complete and with coordination. Thus the animal would seek a place to rest, curl up, and show the physiological signs of normal sleep. In the same manner a center that controls the act of defecation has been found. Electrical stimulation of this center did not merely result in a disorderly opening of the bowels, but it stimulated the normal pattern of such behavior in the cat, including the assumption of the characteristic body

posture. An excellent study of this hierarchical functional organization has been written by von Holst and Saint Paul (1963).

These experiments appear to point to definite anatomical centers controlling instinctive patterns as a whole. Further, although the spinal cord and the medulla oblongata do control certain components of behavior patterns, higher centers of control are contained in the diencephalon (or, more specifically, the hypothalamus). Tinbergen suggests that intermediate centers may also exist between the hypothalamus and the medulla.

In mammals extirpation of the forebrain may result in a loss of certain instinctive behaviors. Hence the ultimate controlling centers for instinctive patterns are probably not situated in the diencephalon. For example, the female in which the forebrain has been removed may no longer care for her young and may even manifest hostility toward them, refusing to suckle and so on. Because removal of the forebrain disrupts instinctive behavior, it would seem that the diencephalic centers for this behavior are not the highest involved but that the forebrain is also concerned.

Instinct Defined

Much of the preceding discussion has implicitly defined instinct, but perhaps it is time for a formal definition. Tinbergen discusses the problem of nomenclature: What is to be called an instinctive act? Lorenz has suggested that this term should be applied to the consummatory act, but Tinbergen prefers to apply the term *instinct* to all levels. Thus, in the case of the reproductive activity of the stickleback, he would call the whole organized pattern of activities the instinct, including such activities as fighting and nest building as kinds of *subinstincts;* the consummatory acts would also be included as part of the instinct (see Figure 4–12).

Tinbergen, on the basis of the material presented, defines an instinct as

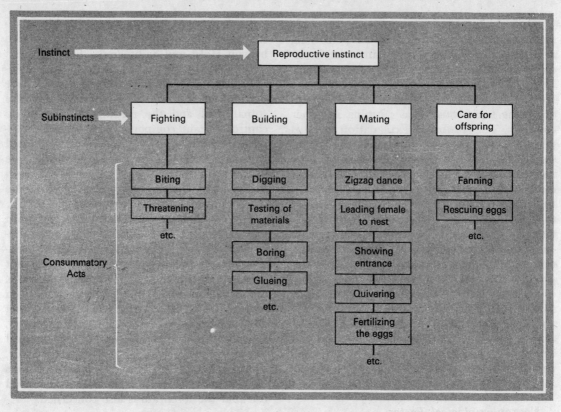

FIGURE 4–12. *The principles of hierarchical organization illustrated by the reproductive instincts of the male three-spined stickleback. Adapted from N. Tinbergen. 1951. The study of instinct. Oxford: Clarendon Press, p. 124, by permission of the author and the publisher.*

a hierarchical organized nervous mechanism which is susceptible to certain priming, releasing and directing impulses of internal as well as of external origin, and which responds to these impulses by co-ordinated movements that contribute to the maintenance of the individual and the species [1951, p. 112].

Tinbergen is careful to point out, and to emphasize repeatedly, that his formulations are tentative and lack sufficient proof for unqualified acceptance. A modified form of Tinbergen's model for representing an "instinctive center" is shown in Figure 4–13.

He suggests that the function of IRM is to "remove a block" placed in the neural con-

ductive system as shown. The intermediate center is under more or less constant stimulation by internal and external stimuli (e.g., hormones may be in the blood stream all the time), and is consequently in a constant state of priming for activity. However, this activity is prevented by the block, until this block is "removed" by IRM. That is, perception of the adequate sign stimuli sets up some kind of neutral mechanism that releases the action of the center, allowing it to "fire" lower centers. These in turn may require other IRM's to release more detailed consummatory acts.

Exception might be taken to the idea of

"removal of a block" on the grounds that many of the known neurological "removal of inhibitions" occur in abnormal states rather than in the mediation of normal behaviors. For example, Parkinsonian tremors and reappearing Babinski reflexes are associated with a breakdown of higher inhibitory centers; here "blocks are removed" and the result is disruptive rather than adaptive behavior. It could be suggested as an alternative that IRM "switches" a neural circuit that bridges a gap between higher and lower centers.

However, it would be pedantic in the present stage of our ignorance to argue closely on this point, and in any case Tinbergen is quite tentative in his proposal of this mechanism.

It will be seen that the preceding formulations are not in any way inconsistent with the original theory of instinct. They do introduce some rather clearly defined (though still hypothetical) factors into the concept, and these have the merit of suggesting lines of research into the mechanisms underlying instincts. They also give an indication of the complexity of the causal factors in behavior and should serve as a warning against oversimplification.

Instincts cannot be considered as if independent of one another, and in many behaviors their interrelationships can be seen. A feature of the courtship behavior of many animals is that fear patterns of behavior, which are commonly very strong, must be overcome before a male and female can copulate. Verwey (Tinbergen, 1953, p. 106) has described how in herons the first reactions of male and female to one another in the spring

FIGURE 4–13. *Modified version of Tinbergen's representation of an instinctive center. Adapted from N. Tinbergen. 1951. The study of instinct. Oxford: Clarendon Press, p. 125, by permission of the author and the publisher.*

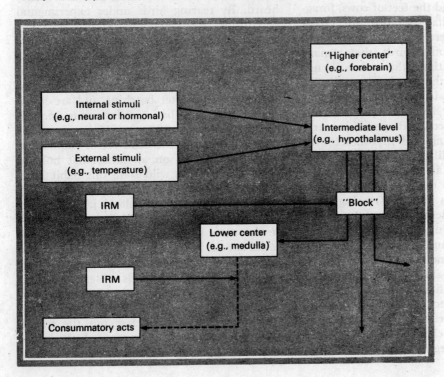

is an approach-avoidance one, in which the song of the male attracts the female to him, but her approach arouses aggressive reactions in him, and he drives her off, then resuming the song. This oscillation between fear and mating behavior is repeated, and as the sex drive increases, it overrides the fear responses of both. Learning is possibly also involved here. Eventually the fear response is suppressed to the extent that mating is possible.

HEREDITY AND BEHAVIOR

In certain situations modifiability of behavior may be a handicap rather than an asset to survival as a species. For example, some birds, like the cowbird in America and the cuckoo in Europe, are regularly reared with other species. The cowbird is a member of the blackbird family, though in its behavior it shows notable differences from most other members of this family. The adult birds pick up insects around the feet of cows, foraging in the ground that they turn up. Often they may be seen perching on the backs of cattle. Unlike most other birds, they remain in flocks at mating time; the males do not select territories and the females do not build nests. The eggs are laid in the nests of other species and are not hatched by their own parents. The young cowbird spends its early days among the young and in contact with the adults of some different species. In spite of this, as an adult it joins other cowbirds in a flock and shows the typical behavior of that bird. With this unusual rearing in a foster nest, it is undesirable that the young cowbird should pick up characteristics of the foster species—for example, the song or other habits. To do this, and to imitate the habits of the foster parents in adult life, would result in the rapid extinction of the cowbird as a species. Resistance to learning has survival value in this particular circumstance.

The European cuckoo has a similar life history and is to a degree unmodified by the habits of the foster parents. It has an additional innate habit, shown during the nestling period, of making vigorous movements of the head, movements that result in the foster parents' own young being ejected from the nest.

It should be mentioned that not even the cuckoo is entirely resistant to learning. The eggs of different strains of cuckoos differ, and these variations tend to resemble those of the preferred host. The female, at least, apparently learns enough to select the nest of this host, and to lay her eggs in it in due course (Lack, 1968). We cannot, even in these species, propose blind instinct entirely untainted by learning.

Most other species of birds, which are normally reared by their own kind, can be shown by laboratory experiments to be capable of modification of their behavior with the change in environment. Many birds, for example, will acquire, if reared with another species, a song not typical of their own; the influence of the hosts' song may be clearly heard. By rearing birds under experimental conditions, we find that certain behaviors appear notwithstanding the environment, whereas others are modified by it. Thus Lorenz has reared jackdaws in captivity and has found that when these birds are taken from their nest soon after hatching and are hand-reared, they show both similarities to and differences from the behavior of the normally reared jackdaws. One behavior of the normal jackdaw is attack on anything that holds a black object. In a wild state this habit is related to the adult jackdaw's attacking any animal that holds a young (black) jackdaw in its mouth. The analogue of this behavior appears in the tame jackdaw if a piece of black material is held in the hand and waved before it; the bird then attacks the hand. This tendency to "attack that which holds a black object" is apparently an innate piece of behavior. Lorenz notes that repeating this two or three times may permanently lose one the friendship of a tame bird; when aroused, the innate behaviors preempt learned ones.

Fleeing from a predatory animal such as a cat is apparently not innate. Lorenz's tame jackdaws showed very little fear of cats and for this reason had reduced chances of survival. Under natural conditions the adult birds make loud warning cries whenever a predator approaches a young one, which apparently reacts with alarm to the cries and hence escapes. It later flees from the predator itself (the conditioned stimulus). The young bird thus learns to escape, but the tame jackdaw not reared with older birds has not been given this learning experience.

Other animals also show a mixture of "natural" and "unnatural" behaviors when reared by humans or under experimental conditions. For example, young fawns raised by hand show certain typical deer behaviors, and if attacked, a tame deer will rear on its hind legs and strike out with its forefeet just as the wild deer does. On the other hand, the tame deer are quite unlike wild ones in that they lack timidity in the face of predators, noises, or people, stimuli which normally frighten the wild deer. It appears that the basic fear reactions (rearing on the hind legs and the like) are inherited, but what is actually feared is something that is learned from generation to generation. There is evident biological usefulness in such an organization for it enables changing conditions that bring in new objects to be feared (such as the man with the gun) to be taken into account and new fear-provoking stimuli to be acquired. It has obvious survival value.

The bighorn sheep of the mountains of western North America originally descended each winter to the lowlands, but agriculture and the fencing off of the lowlands makes the descent impossible today, and these animals no longer migrate. Because the sheep was capable of modification as conditions changed it is evident that this migration was a learned social behavior rather than a rigidly innate one. The modified social behavior was transmitted to subsequent generations by learning.

Other modified social behavior may not be transmitted from generation to generation by learning within the species even though each individual is separately capable of learning it during immaturity. For instance, Scott and his associates (1950) have shown that friendliness toward strangers is an acquired behavior of the domestic dog that is not passed on from parent to offspring. They isolated domesticated adult dogs under conditions in which they no longer had contact with humans, though they could be observed. These dogs behaved toward one another in much the same way as they behaved toward humans, in the manner of domesticated dogs. Their puppies, however, acquired none of these characteristics and showed a fear of strangers that was persistent even when attempts were made to remove it by later training. Evidently suspicion toward strangers is an innate reaction in dogs, though they are capable of learning to override it and acquire friendly behavior. But it also appears that this is not a pattern of behavior that adult dogs can teach their young. They can acquire this only by contact with humans, and as later experiments by Scott showed, most breeds can be successfully domesticated only if they are reared by humans alone, out of contact with their own parent dogs. Friendliness to humans is a modified social behavior of dogs; what is normally transmitted from one generation to the next is friendliness to the *same* species.

Observations of this kind, many other instances of which could be quoted, lead to three general conclusions.

1. The sensory-motor equipment of the animal remains the same, and regardless of the environment the animal must continue to use it; obviously no amount of association with man will enable a dog to use its paws like fingers. It retains essential innate dog behaviors, which, even if it is under domestic conditions, are inappropriate for such activity. Thus the domestic dog continues to make a circular movement before lying down, carrying out a behavior that was useful in flattening out the grass of his natural habitat but that is

useless on the hearthrug. Man's behaviors are also limited by his sensory-motor equipment, even if he does operate within wider limits in some respects.

2. In many species of animals, and particularly in the social species, behavior may be affected by learning. In such animals there is some degree of cultural inheritance. Thus, in accordance with observation 1, the dog's pattern of cocking the leg when it urinates remains the same as in the wild state, though the dog can learn to control elimination and do it only in places its master considers appropriate. Tame animals usually have a poor chance of survival under wild conditions. This is because they have not learned certain behaviors that are appropriate in the wild or may have learned inappropriate behaviors. (A tame cat that has learned to lie down with a tame dog may find too late that this is inappropriate toward a wild dog.) In man, of course, the amount of cultural inheritance is very great.

3. In certain species, and perhaps in all species in certain circumstances, innate behaviors may have advantages over learned ones. This is the case in the cuckoo and cowbird, where learning may actually be inimical to the survival of the species.

The relationship between innate and acquired behaviors is illustrated by the circus animal in which some innately characteristic behavior forms the basis of the "act." For example, the seal has a natural tendency to raise itself on the fore flippers and wave its nose into the air; the addition of a ball to the nose makes a spectacle. The young monkey has an innate tendency to cling firmly to the back of the mother; substituting a dog for the mother but invoking the same reflexes makes a comic jockey of the monkey.

Training an animal for show purposes consists in the main of taking some part of its usual repertoire of behaviors and embellishing it with some additional learning; in many the learned modification is rather minor. The trainer has to start with an innate pattern, and his artistry consists in giving this characteristic pattern some unusual twist. This fact is of interest in discussing the early learning of infants, both animal and human, in which the emergence and modification of innate behaviors forms the basis for the acquisition of learned ones.

Genes and Instincts

One of the difficulties faced by the older (and simpler) ideas of instincts was that of reconciling them with factors of genetics. The pre-Mendelian concept involved some direct relationship between an "inherent factor" and behavior. When the nature of inherent factors became known, it was difficult to see how the direct relationship could occur.

A more feasible, though necessarily less simple, scheme can be given diagrammatically (Figure 4–14). The genes determine both structure and physiology, which interact in behavior; however, the interaction is not direct, except perhaps in the most simple organisms. Rather, a nervous system that has coordinative functions is involved, and this controls behavior. It also incorporates external factors into the behavioral pattern.

To take an instance, the genes in a bird determine the structural features of the individual that makes possible bird-like behavior; they give the structural requisites for flight. The physiological characteristics of the bird, also genetically determined, serve flight; the high metabolic rate provides the great energy output necessary to this behavior. The intervening processes of the nervous system control flight in various ways, such as giving the bird stability in changing air currents, and coordinating the input into the total pattern of behavior, as when flight is directed toward a prey (visually perceived). In certain circumstances, as when prolactin inhibits flight so that the bird sits solidly on the eggs until they hatch, other physiological processes may affect the behaviors.

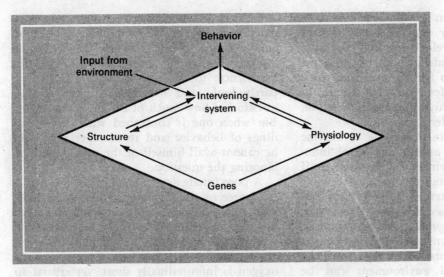

FIGURE 4–14. *Schematic representation of relationship between genes and instinct, avoiding the oversimplification of the idea of a direct relationship between genes and behavior.*

In higher species the nervous system becomes a complex brain. It has certain properties of modifiability (probably inherited) that enlarge the possibilities of behavior and make it more diverse. This system may influence physiology, and hence the double arrows between the two in Figure 4–14.

The various relationships are not so simple as the model suggests. The intervening processes are themselves not independent of structure (the forebrain or the hypothalamus, for example, is a structural entity). In many cases the structure of the nervous system may predetermine behavior, as in the innate behavior patterns. In other cases there may be greater modifiability.

The relationship between the "intervening system" and physiology is two-way: Physiological processes, such as hormones, may "prime" this system to certain activities, but physiological processes may also be affected via the intervening system, as they are when a perceived danger excites adrenaline secretion.

Similarly, structure modifies the intervening processes, determining, for instance, the

sorts of behaviors that are possible for an organism. Structures may also be affected in the reverse direction, as when nervous impulses excite muscles to contraction.

EPILOGUE

Many psychologists in recent times have preferred to use the concept of *drive* rather than *instinct,* the term *drive* (or its synonym *motivation*) standing for the complex causal conditions of behavior, without implying the innateness or the like of these conditions (e.g., Nissen, 1954). It might be said that this merely circumvents argument by a verbal device—by substitution of a term that is neutral in its implications on this point. For many purposes such a stratagem is legitimate and indeed justified if it enables discussion to go forward without semantic arguments that are really irrelevant to the issue.

It is appropriate to mention that both sides of the nature-nurture argument have greatly underestimated the complexity of the causation of behavior. Even at a physical level it is questionable whether one can really talk of a "purely" innate development. It is becoming evident that the Mendelian idea of one gene-one character is even further from the truth than was realized a few years ago. Genes, in fact, operate in highly complex interaction, as suggested in Chapter 3.

The complex route from gene to enzyme to character implies an environmental influence even if this environment is internal. If one takes (as an instance) mental deficiency in PKU as a character resulting from a certain genetic state, this condition creates a particular internal environment in the organism, an accumulation of unexcreted phenylalanine (which comes, of course, externally from the diet). This internal environment can be changed (or at least circumvented) by an *external* manipulation, the provision of a phenylalanine-free diet. As another example, there is evidence of a genetically determined susceptibility to tuberculosis, but even with low resistance the organism will not become diseased unless the environment provides the bacilli. In the psychological sphere, intellectual capacity may be subject to genetically determined limits, but it is also markedly influenced by the environment.

On the other hand, the more extreme environmentalists have spoken as if the physical organism were entirely passive, imposing nothing of itself upon the modifications brought about by the environment. No doubt today one would have difficulty in finding a reincarnated J. B. Watson, but one can find a large number of psychologists—perhaps a majority—who when pressed will admit that the organism modifies the input but tacitly ignores the fact in their formulations. They concentrate their attentions almost exclusively on the modification of the organism by the input and regard the modification of input by the organism as a negligible factor. Another facet of the question that is commonly ignored is selectivity among the input, the idea that certain stimulus patterns are more readily perceived than others.

Even if the possibility that some behaviors may be innate is admitted, there sooner or later comes a point at which the purity of this pristine state becomes contaminated by experience; the observed behavior is in fact partly both, and for many discussions the question of how much of each is unnecessary. But when one is concerned with the beginnings of behavior and its changes with age, he cannot avail himself of the convenience of ignoring the question.

A pure innate act, unmodified in the slightest degree by the previous history of the individual organism showing that act, might have so brief an existence as to be imperceptible but yet be important nevertheless. For example, the fleeting "free" existence of nascent oxygen is infinitesimally short, yet crucial to certain reactions of the element. Moreover, even though the elemental purity of an innate behavior may soon be lost, it may not be totally lost in that instant, and a period of modification having a time span of some significance might conceivably follow. The developmental psychologist must concern himself with these periods in the life history of the organism.

The opponents of instinct theory have not, in fact, demonstrated that there are no such entities: All they have shown in effect is that for many theoretical issues the question is unnecessary and can be ignored. For developmental psychology the concept is a useful one, and its usefulness is considered justification for using it. The objection that the proposing of instincts stultifies the investigation of the development of behavior by implying that it is inborn, and therefore need not be examined further, is based on the misconception that instincts are necessarily present at birth and explode full-blown into action. The unjust criticism leveled against McDougall was based on the mistaken notion that he believed this. Even if some instincts are present at birth, it is not clear why this must prevent one from investigating them. As was seen in the arguments of Chapter 3, there is no reason for believing that instincts are *all* manifest at birth, that they are perpetually active, or that they are immutable properties of the organism. Within species they may become apparent at varying times, and they most certainly are subject to individual variation.

The earlier in its development that one studies an individual from a species, the less opportunity there has been for learning; further, in the case of man in particular, the early maturity of the nervous system and the relative inefficiency of learning in infancy makes the acquisition of behavior difficult (Chapter 12). At this stage it is reasonable to suppose that many, if not all, of the behaviors observed are innate rather than learned.

The points raised in this chapter will be raised again. The main purpose of the chapter is to review the "New Look in Instincts" and to insist that whatever the objections to the theory in other contexts it is a useful concept to the developmentalist. Because the greater part of the work on this topic in recent years has been done by the ethologists, who are primarily zoologists concerned with animal rather than human behavior, the data on the latter concept are scanty. However, there are many points at which the concepts the ethologists are producing are useful to developmental psychology, and the somewhat lengthy discussion of these ideas is a preparation for the later arguments.

As we grow older, we find that the "Old Man" was not so perverse as we found him in adolescence, and it may be time to admit that our professional fathers—Hobhouse, the elder Drever, McDougall, and the others—were not without some useful insights after all. When one gets away from philosophical discussions about the meanings of words, or from ideal concepts of the content of psychology, or from artificial experiments, to the study of how real people really behave and how real children grow up, then the practical value of the frame of reference provided by the neoinstinctual theory becomes apparent.

Part of the thesis of this book is that humans also have the kinds of preset behaviors described by the ethologists. The main theoretical support for this notion comes from evolutionary concepts and the assumption that man is continuous with the animals. When one looks for signs of these innate behaviors in man, a number are apparent and will be discussed. The evidence that they are indeed innate may not be ironclad, but it is at least persuasive.

Another assumption that can be made is that learning is most effective when it follows the lines of force of innate behaviors. This is not to say that lines cannot be overridden, and indeed we may at times need to make a value judgment about the innate direction of some behaviors and decide to override them. But at least we should know where the lines of force are, or where the directiveness is taking us.

What is being suggested is that some human behaviors are the result not of "pure" learning (as the environmentalists imply) but of the emergence of innate patterns of response. The child is not a *tabula rasa,* an empty organism waiting to be filled. He comes already equipped with certain biases—biases to respond to particular stimuli with particular patterns of response.

In their simpler forms these patterns are illustrated by the kinds of tendencies described by the gestaltists—closure or certain of the illusions. In the grouping tendencies they describe, it is easier to perceive the pattern of Figure 4–15a as two groups of dots: one of two, the other of three. One *can* see that it is five dots, or can even view it as a three-dot unit followed closely by two dots, as in Figure 4–15b, but this is less readily done and imposes, as it were, a strain. It requires less effort to perceive according to the gestalt laws, which are expressions of a fundamental biological principle. We do not *learn* to see in these ways, but our sight is somehow determined by the innate nature of the nervous system.

It is suggested that this situation may apply to more complex situations. We could, for example, arbitrarily divide the written line into units of three letters, thus

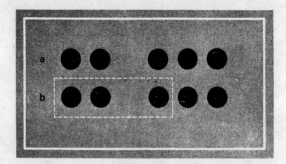

FIGURE 4–15. *Gestalt principles of organization.*

Isa llt his tal kab out ins tin cts non sen se?

And we could no doubt teach children to read this way, but to do so would introduce an unnecessary difficulty by ignoring a fundamental organizational property of the nervous system.

Largely by a system of trial and error we have probably evolved systems and procedures of teaching that avoid at least the more blatant errors of this kind, but it may well be that in ignorance of more subtle factors we are introducing unnecessary obstacles into learning.

Similarly, much social learning may be influenced by factors of this kind. Thus the

learning of prejudices may be based on a fundamental reaction, dislike of the strange. For this reason it might be easier to learn prejudices than to learn nonprejudice. Prejudice is a highly generalizable state, whereas a nonprejudiced attitude is more specific and must be acquired toward particular groups. Of course, having learned to ignore the basic negative reaction toward one group of strangers, it may become easier to do so toward another, but this negative attitude to the strange has response primacy.

In the same way, we may propose that the human male is programmed to react in certain positive but emotionally tinged manners to a sign stimulus that is approximately like that in Figure 4–16a. By learning, males may acquire a preference for a particular modification of this basic pattern, as in Figure 4–16b or c. In some societies, anthropologists assure us, Figure 4–16c is the preferred variation. Some males even acquire a preference for the variant in Figure 4–17, but it is presumably harder to do this than to learn the variants in Figures 4–16b or c.

It is necessary to observe that the whole question here is complex. For instance, al-

FIGURE 4–16. *Sign stimuli to which the human male responds: (a) well-endowed type; (b) underdeveloped type; (c) buxom type.*

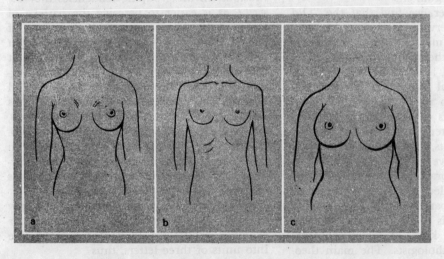

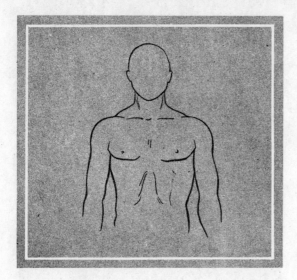

FIGURE 4–17. *Aberrant variation of male sign stimulus.*

than adults (see Chapter 9). However, this does make it rather easy for males to make this kind of reaction to immature boys and even to learn a preference for this stimulus rather than the total one represented in Figure 4–16 (though this is a tendency severely suppressed in our own and many other societies). The growth of hair on the chest and elsewhere very definitely detracts from this sign stimulus for most males.

It is not being implied here that *all* learning is built up around a core of innate tendencies or that it develops from a kind of seed that is present in the CNS. The idea that we cannot learn anything that is not already provided for in some embryonic form would be as false, probably, as the opposite assertion that everything is learned and no tendencies to specific behaviors are present in the naive organism. However, the point of view that will be presented in the following chapters is that more is programmed to the organism (including the human one) than is currently recognized by psychologists. One of the tasks for the developmentalist is to try to tease out the tangled interaction of learning upon the innate basis and to discover how best to use the innate to facilitate learning. It is also important to emphasize that the capacity for modification and intelligent control is part of the innate equipment of the organism.

though the sign stimulus depicted in Figure 4–16 represents one element of a sign gestalt that is erotically arousing to males, it is almost certainly not the full account. A smooth, hairless skin is a feature that enhances the effect of the simple sign stimulus. Young boys share this particular element of the total sign gestalt, and they are frequently erotically arousing, especially to adolescent males who tend to have a wider range of arousal stimuli

Five | Constitutional Psychology

Since earliest times it has been supposed that there is a relationship between the personality and the body that is its vehicle. Empedocles in 450 B.C. proposed that the cosmos is made up of four "elements"—air, earth, fire, and water—and Hippocrates adopted this concept into a "humoral psychology" that related air to blood and to the "sanguine' temperament. In a similar manner each of the other elements was related to a temperamental type, the "melancholic," "choleric," and "phlegmatic," respectively.

PHYSIOGNOMY

From Greek times onward numerous attempts have been made to type men according to certain characteristics of their bodies, and particularly according to their facial appearance. One such typology attempted to use animal models—the man who looks like a fox is sly, the man who looks like a donkey is slow and stupid—a characterology by no means dead today. Another Greek author suggested

that the man who was excessively pale or dark should be judged a coward, for are not Ethiopians dark and women pale and both alike cowardly?

These somewhat unsophisticated notions lay dormant in the Dark Ages. In thirteenth-century Europe there was a great revival in interest in the Greek culture, and with this the Greek typologies were again discussed and even practiced. Indeed, so much charlatanism arose from this exploitation that in the sixteenth century, during the reign of Queen Elizabeth, an act was passed whereby any person pretending skill in physiognomy was to be declared a vagabond, publicly whipped, and sent to a house of correction. In the eighteenth century, a similar enactment was made in the reign of George II. In spite of these legal sanctions, character reading has been such profitable business to its practitioners that it has flourished even up to today. The most recent example of such practice is seen in the computer, set up in many shopping centers to give for a fee a personality assessment based on one's signature. Such assessments are made possible by the salesmanship of the practitioners and the gullibility of the public in their uncritical acceptance. Another approach to this art is the cult of phrenology, which attempts to measure character and aptitude from the bumps on the cranium, and the lines on the palm of the hand have led to the old practice of palmistry. Because body typing with its offshoots has, as a means of understanding human behavior, been for centuries the province of charlatans, it has fallen into disrepute, but this should not stand in the way of a properly scientific approach to the question of relationships between body and personality.

KRETSCHMER'S "PHYSIQUE AND CHARACTER"

In Germany in 1921, Kretschmer produced an influential book that opened the field to the scientific study of human typology (published in English in 1925). He noted that in mental hospitals the dementia praecox patients were more often of a frail, somewhat thin body type, which he called asthenic. Manic depressive patients, on the other hand, were most often of a short and rounded body type that he called pyknic. Based upon these observations, he proposed a theory of the relationship between physique and normal personality. This gave him the following scheme:

1. Schizothyme—tall, slender physiques: introversion, idealism, romanticism
   a. Athletic, a subtype
   b. Dyplastic, a subtype
2. Cyclothyme—rounded, heavy physiques: moody but often jovial, extraverted, realistic

Although Kretschmer's contentions proved to be overoptimistic and not entirely coincident with the facts when they were carefully studied, they have stimulated research that has led to somewhat more satisfactory somatotyping, and in particular they have led to the system proposed by Sheldon.

SHELDON'S "VARIETIES OF HUMAN PHYSIQUE"

In 1940, Sheldon and his collaborators produced a book that has stimulated some profitable research in the field of human typology and has advanced from the concepts of Kretschmer in a manner more likely to lead to productive results. It was followed in 1942 by a work on the varieties of temperament.

Individuals could not be meaningfully fitted into the few categories of Kretschmer's scheme. Sheldon attempted a system of typology that is more in keeping with the wide variations in the human form. Instead of Kretschmer's categories, Sheldon proposed three "body types" that are related to the three germ layers of the embryo, and to each of these body types he assigned a temperament:

Endoderm—endomorph—viscerotonia
Mesoderm—mesomorph—somatotonia
Ectoderm—ectomorph—cerebronia

The refinement of the system lies in the assumption that every individual has elements of all three components, though in differing degrees. According to defined criteria, the body is assessed on each component and rated on a scale from 1 to 7. This scale permits a considerable number of distinct categories and hence more realistic dealing with the variety of human forms than is possible with a simple system like Kretschmer's.

In this system the extreme endomorph is rated 711, the extreme mesomorph 171, and the extreme ectomorph 117. In fact, most people fall in the middle ranges, as one would expect, with the hypothetical "average man" being a 444. A high rating on any one dimension implies lower ratings on the others, so the combinability of the three scores is necessarily limited. Though in theory there are 343 possible types based on the threefold seven-point scale, Sheldon noted that the sum of the three numbers in practice falls between 9 and 12, giving fewer than eighty types, and some of them are uncommon. By adopting an increased scale, for instance, a fifteen-point one using half-points (e.g., $5:2\frac{1}{2}:3\frac{1}{2}$), the number of categories can be increased, though, of course, more refined measuring techniques are required.

The greater part of Sheldon's efforts before his death went into the development of the anthropometric methods. However, the aim was to relate these precisely to psychological characters, and Sheldon was preparing for a constitutional psychology. This to him was the study of the psychological aspects of behavior in relation to the morphology and physiology of the body. He insisted that one cannot study the mind in separation from the body or ignore the body and its processes in formulating psychological principles. Sheldon's definition of personality is similar to that of Allport (1939) and emphasizes the dynamic organization of the cognitive, affective, physiological, and morphological aspects of the individual.

To expand somewhat on his primary physical and psychological categories, *endomorphy* refers descriptively to a relative roundness and softness in the various regions of the body. The digestive viscera are massive and dominate the bodily economy. These elements are derived from the endodermal embryonic layer —hence the name. The psychological characteristics of *viscerotonia* are love of comfort, relaxation, sociability, and sometimes gluttony. The motivational organization of the person is dominated by the gut and the processes of anabolism.

Mesomorphy involves a relative predominance of muscle and bone derived from the mesoderm. The body form is hard and rectangular. Psychologically, *somatotonia* implies a motivational system dominated by the will to exertion and vigorous self-expression.

The *ectomorph* is linear and fragile in form, and the brain, nervous system, and skin (of ectodermal origin) dominate the economy. There is relatively greater sensory exposure to the environment in this type. The psychological correlates emphasize the attentional and inhibitory aspects of temperament, the

cerebrotonic being tense and inhibited and tending to symbolic expression more than direct action.

The characteristics defining body type differ, of course, for the two sexes, though the general features of the types are similar.

One can represent Sheldon's scheme diagrammatically as in Figure 5–1, which makes it clear that he is *not* proposing that a given personality results from having a particular body type. Rather, he is proposing that body type and temperament are both related to common factors at a more basic level. (Thus one will expect a less than perfect correlation between them.) Physiological processes have an influence on body form, though a less direct one than the "anatomy" or structural route. Similarly, anatomy (for example, body size) has an influence on temperament, though perhaps a less potent one, in the "body image." The actual *behavior* of the individual is the outcome of environmental influences on his temperamental reactivity, and personality is, of course, the sum of his consistent patterns of behaving.

There are, in Sheldon's system, a number of subindices, one of which is what he calls *gynandromorphy* (represented by the *g* index), which recognizes the existence of opposite-sex characteristics in the body from the fact that individuals of one sex display to greater or lesser extent characteristics of the other. A high *g* index implies a marked degree of opposite-sex somatic characters.

Another factor is *dysplasia*, which refers to the fact that some individuals show somatotype differences in various regions of the body. The legs and trunk, for example, may be disharmonious with the head and neck.

Arguing within a system of typology, one could regard the human male and female as physically differing types with "masculine" and "feminine" psychological correlates. Though in fact there has been no considerable amount of attention to this question within constitutional psychology, both body form and temperament are regarded as sex-specific.

Sheldon's technique of somatotyping con-

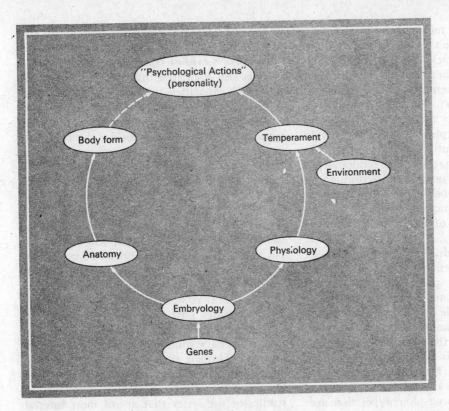

FIGURE 5–1. Constitutional psychology as a model.

sisted in the main of visual examination and measurement of photographs, supplemented by certain other data, notably weight. The subjects were photographed nude—front, side, and back—under standard conditions against a grid; the necessary measurements were taken from the photographs. With careful training a high degree of reliability between raters can be achieved, but critics have complained that somatotyping under these conditions is an art, not a science, and that it is not fully objective. The method also carries disadvantages in cost and time, in addition to which many subjects are reluctant to pose so indelicately before the camera.

An alternative method of somatotyping based on Sheldon has been developed by Parnell (1958); this method uses direct measures from the body. It is quicker than Sheldon's method and avoids the delay of film processing. It is also claimed that it is more objective and more readily replicated.

The essence of constitutional psychology is as follows: Because of their basic differences in total psychophysiological economy, endomorphs, mesomorphs, and ectomorphs tend to view the world differently and to react distinctively to environmental forces. Given the same environment, the three types are differently influenced by it. The easygoing endomorphic adolescent, receiving a bawling out from a teacher, will tend to accept it passively but without long-lasting disturbance (or perhaps effect); he will laugh it off. The ectomorph, on the other hand, is more likely to take it seriously to heart, to brood over it, perhaps to weep silently in some corner; the incident remains with him a long time. The mesomorph is much more likely than either of the others to blame the teacher rather than himself, to answer back or even impulsively strike out at the teacher; in the latter case he gets called a delinquent. Given an unhappy home, the mesomorph, because he is subject to acting out, is likely to become delinquent. The solitary ectomorph, on the other hand, is more prone to neurosis as a result of adverse family circumstances. The endomorph is less prone either to neurosis or delinquency, though because he tends to be a follower, he may join with a delinquent gang; he is not, however, an initiator of action, delinquent or otherwise.

A point that needs consideration is one raised in discussing genetics (Chapter 3)—that individuals who are phenotypically similar may in fact belong to different genotypes. Whether it is possible for a genotypic ectomorph to look like a mesomorph is not known. If we are to believe the advertisers of body-building courses, it *is* possible, moreover in twelve easy lessons. Presumably the more subtle are one's measures of body type, the less the risk of confusing phenotypes that are genotypically different. However, we cannot on present information say whether appearance can be deceptive or what *behavioral* phenotype we shall find in a mesomorph-mimicking ectomorph.

The implications of constitutional psychology to child rearing and education have been discussed at some length by Sheldon. He suggests that our educational system, with its emphasis on competitiveness, on self-assertion, and on physical prowess in organized sports, is geared to the mesomorph rather than the endomorph or the ectomorph. The last, in particular, is poorly provided for in this philistine system. His plea is for greater diversity in education and a recognition that different types have differing needs. Forcing everyone into the same mold is damaging to many.

The somatotonic child, Sheldon suggests, may need rather rigid discipline for best development and may find "reasoning" techniques of treatment quite frustrating, at least

in the earlier years. The cerebrotonic, on the other hand, is best suited to a flexible and "discussive" style of rearing.

It is also suggested that the exercise of intellectual capacities may differ in the three types, but Sheldon points out that many of the attempts to relate intelligence to physical types have neglected to consider the complexity of the situation. Endomorphy of itself is rather meaningless. The endomorphic body type 514 is a long-legged, round-shouldered, soft, and somewhat effeminate boy; whereas the 541 is a powerful, active boy, full of energy and likely to become the president of something. The expression of intellectual capacities is quite distinct in the two cases. Perhaps Sheldon might have tempered some of his other suggestions with this consideration, but the point is well taken.

The greater part of Sheldon's research efforts were with young adult males, and, in fact, university students are numerous in his samples. Though the question has not been entirely neglected, women and children have been less extensively studied. It is, of course, studies of the latter that are of most interest to the present context.

SOMATOTYPING WITH CHILDREN

One of the few studies of children is by Walker (1962), who uses nursery school children (in the Gesell Institute), aged two to four years. This study applied Sheldon's photographic somatotyping technique and compared body build with teachers' ratings of personality. Walker found that in this age group important correlations do exist between physique and behavior, and in general the correlations are consistent with Sheldon's assertions, though the associations found were somewhat lower than Sheldon reported for adult males. Walker points out that the relationships are multidetermined, coming from bodily characteristics such as strength, energy level, sensory thresholds, and from the learning of modes of behavior and adjustive techniques, as well as from less direct factors such as expectations and value systems and the kinds of opportunity for learning the environment has provided.

Sex differences were already noticeable in Walker's study: the mesomorphic girls, for example, channeled energies to social activities, and the mesomorphic boys adapted them to physical and gross motor activity.

The endomorphic children showed few clusters of behavior with body build, and in this sample the relationships were apparently low. Mesomorphs did show significant relationships, especially for boys. Both sexes tended to be assertive and dominating, with high energy levels, fearlessness, and openness of expression. The girls were sociable, cheerful, and warm in these traits, whereas boys tended more to hostile traits like quarrelsomeness and inconsideration and to impulsive, noisy activity.

The ectomorphic boys showed a higher relation between build and personality than such girls did, but for this body type both sexes showed aloofness, nonsociability, daydreaming, and emotional restraint. Overall, the ectomorphic boys tended to low energy, quietness, unassertiveness, and to looking to adults rather than peers for approval. The ectomorphic girls tended to a somber unfriendliness and irritability.

An interesting sidelight was noted in the photography. More girls than boys were discomforted by the nudity, and, contrary to expectations from Sheldon's observations, it was the endomorphs rather than the ectomorphs who tended to be most resistant. As he predicted, the mesomorphs were compliant, but so were the ectomorphs.

In England, Parnell and his associates have undertaken more extensive studies of children (Davidson et al., 1957; Parnell, 1958). It is noted that signs of adult somatotype characteristics begin to appear at about age five, which means, of course, that only then can one commence to type children according to the adult standards. The longitudinal studies

necessary to knowing whether at this age we can predict the individual's future adult status have not yet been undertaken.

In a study in Oxford of 100 children, age seven, a discernible association between body type and personality factors was found (Davidson et al., 1957). The authors demonstrate that somatic components are definitely measurable at this age.

There is a moderate correlation between somatic *phenotype* at ages seven and eleven (Parnell, 1958), though how this is related to the somatic genotype, which presumably determines adult somatotype, is not known. Parnell suggests that because of the prepubertal fluctuations of growth earlier measures might in fact be a better predictor of adult status than ones at age eleven.

A longitudinal study over the adolescent period, from the tenth to the seventeenth year in boys, was reported by Hunt and Barton (1959), using Sheldon's photographic technique. They typed at six-month intervals and found rather low consistency. This they attributed principally to the method, though it may (as perhaps is likely) have been related to adolescent fluctuations in physique. Broverman et al. (1964) have reported that growth during adolescence is variable, whereas the preadolescent bodily dimensions correspond to the postadolescent ones. In older age groups, Cortés and Gatti (1965) have shown in late adolescent boys and young adult girls highly significant correlations between self-descriptions of temperament and body type.

There is an interesting finding in Parnell's study (1958), though just what it means is problematical. He noted that mothers with a high degree of a bodily trait he calls "muscle dominance" tend to have markedly more male children than would be predicted by chance. Nash and Hayes (1965), in studying a population of male homosexuals, noted that there is a highly significant excess of brothers in their families, a finding common to a number of studies. Unfortunately Parnell gives little data on the psychological correlates of muscularity, and one is led to ask if there could not be a connection. If "muscular" women tend to the child-rearing practices conducive to homosexual development (Nash, 1965, 1969) and at the same time have more boys, this excess of brothers could be explained. It illustrates a possible interplay of diverse influences that might bring together apparently quite unrelated factors.

There is a whole range of possibilities opened up here. Presumably parents of the various body types will tend to adopt differing child-rearing practices and to provide different milieus for their children. Is there a tendency for similar types to marry, thereby increasing the probability of having children like themselves? What are the effects of dissimilarities in body type between parents and offspring?

One of the questions raised by the idea of body typing is whether the rates and course of development of the various types are strictly parallel. Such evidence as there is is conflicting. A number of studies have reported slower growth and later maturing in linear individuals of ectomorphic build (Bayley, 1943; Dupertuis and Michael, 1953; Richey, 1937; Tanner, 1962) as compared with those of mesomorphic build. However, Livson and McNeill (1962) have reported no differences, and Reynolds and Winer (1951) have reported *earlier* sexual maturation in ectomorphs. Broverman et al. (1964) have suggested that these discrepant results may come from failure to control for the irregular course of development during adolescence, a failure which causes it to be more reliable to relate prepubertal body type to adult type than it is to attempt to predict the latter during adolescence. One would certainly expect that if the hypothesized differences in bodily economy between the types are real, then developmental patterns will differ.

Related to the question of type differences in developmental schedules is the concept of biological age. Bouterline Young (1963) has pointed out how the chronological age is a poor guide to biological age, especially in childhood. He has proposed the notion of "puberal age," based on a number of measur-

able criteria, and shows how greatly the time of adolescence can vary using such measures.

BODY TYPE AND DELINQUENCY

The relationship between body type and delinquency has aroused particular interest. It has been investigated by Sheldon et al. (1949), and an extensive study was made by Glueck and Glueck (1950). The latter study covered an intensive investigation of 500 adolescent delinquents drawn from two industrial schools in Massachusetts. They were matched with 500 nondelinquents in terms of age, IQ, ethnico-racial derivation, and residence from economically and socioculturally underprivileged areas of greater Boston.

A feature of this investigation was that the inquiry was divided into segments, which included the somatic, intellectual, characterial (Rorschach test), temperamental emotional (psychiatric), and sociocultural: These separate segments were explored independently by different teams of workers. While this method did involve numerous difficulties, it was felt to have very strong advantages in the reliability of the data gathered. Thus specialists in the psychiatric, anthropological, psychological, and other fields did not taint one another, as they worked in ignorance of the others' findings; for this reason any concurrence is the more reliable. The Gluecks themselves coordinated the material and had the overview.

The study found the delinquent group to be distinguishable from the controls in a number of ways. Physically, they tended to be solid and muscular, essentially mesomorphic in constitution. They also showed the temperamental characteristics Sheldon would associate with this, being energetic, impulsive, extroverted, socially assertive, and adventurous; they were also aggressive, destructive, and sometimes sadistic, showing traits not necessarily found in socialized somatotypes, though obviously related to their basic characteristics. In attitude they were hostile, defiant, and suspicious. Intellectually, they tended to be concrete and direct rather than symbolic.

There were also sociocultural differences in that the delinquents were more often reared in homes where there was little understanding and affection, and often poor example. The Gluecks suggest that although these environmental conditions might be considered of themselves adequate to explain their delinquency, in fact they are probably only one area of influence, delinquency being generally the outcome of the interplay of internal and external forces.

In their conclusions the Gluecks suggest that the excess among delinquents of mesomorphs as compared with other body types may be because boys of this physique are endowed with constitutional traits that predispose them to the delinquent role when sociocultural conditions are unfavorable. In particular, the impulsive, unreflective, and energetic nature of the mesomorph would incline him to delinquent behavior more than it would the indolent, easygoing endomorph or the tense, introverted, and reflective ectomorph.

Body typing has been used as one factor of significance in attempts to predict juvenile delinquency, that is, to identify delinquency-prone children before they become a social problem and to take preventative measures. Efforts in this area are praiseworthy. Such measures depend on the assumption that given certain environmental conditions, particularly in family relationships, the mesomorphic boy is the one most likely to react antisocially.

MATURATIONAL FACTORS AND PSYCHOLOGICAL DEVELOPMENT

Though they are not strictly within the context of constitutional psychology as conceived by Sheldon, there have been a few studies relating physical to psychological maturation. Like the constitutional psychologists, authors of these studies have assumed a rela-tionship between bodily and psychic development.

The influence of hormonal factors on psychological maturity is shown in a study by Sollenberger (1940), who found a positive relationship between androgenic urinary excretions in pubertal boys and the maturity of their interests and attitudes. The correlation between maturity and hormones was higher than with chronological age.

There has been a series of longitudinal studies using the Oakland Growth Study sample (Jones and Bayley, 1950), reviewed by Eichorn (1963). They showed a consistent relationship between certain broad psychological characteristics and rate of maturation as indicated by skeletal age. Another study was commenced in the 1930's by H. E. Jones (1938), who used age of adolescence as a variable. A series of studies have followed up these subjects until they were in their forties (M. C. Jones, 1965).

Such investigations show that there are plain concordances between measures of somatic growth and personality and that the concordances are persistent. In general the early maturer tends to be at a social advantage in the peer culture, and as an adult is a conforming achiever, poised and responsible, but conventional in thought and attitudes. The late maturer, on the other hand, uses compensatory mechanisms in the teens and tends to be active and exploratory. As an adult he is independent, insightful, and impulsive. As M. C. Jones points out, there are individual differences, which are due to the complexity of the interaction between somatic and cultural influences on development.

The idea of biological age is also brought up in a study by Simon (1959). Using a body-typing method for children proposed in Germany by Zeller (1936), she showed how school readiness can be predicted from an assessment of bodily status. In Zeller's system there are three stages of childhood, as identified by the bodily configuration. The infantile figure of early childhood is "top heavy," with the head and trunk disproportionately large; the abdomen protrudes, the shoulders slope, and the other well-known characteristics of the infant body are still present. This form passes through an intermediate stage to the body form of middle childhood, which is well-definably different. Only the child who has entered this third stage is ready for school, Zeller claimed, and Simon demonstrated a relationship between success or failure in grade one and the state of maturity assessed by this method.

Over the past several decades there has been a steady acceleration in our culture in the rate of physical maturation as measured by age of puberty, height, and weight. Tanner (1968) has taken figures from various parts of the world and notes that in the past 100 years the age of puberty has decreased generally by about 3 years, and in some regions by as much as 5 years. The age at which a given height or weight is reached also occurs earlier, but the age of cessation of growth is advanced, and whereas growth once continued into the early twenties, it now virtually ceases at nineteen. In the United States he finds that the trend toward earlier maturing is leveling off, though this is not apparent elsewhere.

The leveling off in the United States suggests that the age of maturation there is approaching its earliest limit. Also consistent with the idea of an ultimate limit to human body size is the finding that although adults are bigger than in the past, the increase in size in the fully grown is less than one might expect from the increase in children at younger ages. Though there are some regional differences, the increases are generally present at birth and all subsequent ages.

The increases are linked with economic well-being, as one might expect, and are greatest in the economically most advantaged populations. There is a fluctuation with the general economic state of the community and with other variables—wartime shortages, for instance. Boys are more susceptible to these effects than girls, and this greater susceptibility of the male to environmental influences is noticeable in a number of contexts.

These observations raise the question of whether the phenomena are confined to the aspects of physical maturation noted or whether they are indicators of a speeding up of *all* aspects of physical maturation. The latter is most likely; indeed, it would seem somewhat improbable that these particular aspects of growth should be affected and others not. This leads to the further question of whether the psychological processes that depend on these biological bases are also advanced. Again, this would seem likely, though it is as yet unproved.

One of the most interesting matters arising from these observations is that there is apparently an optimal environment (which so far as physical growth is concerned, the United States is fortunate enough to be near) and that no improvement beyond this point has further effects on growth. Given this environment, the rate of growth is determined entirely by the innate constitution of the organism. This discovery raises the further question of whether psychological processes are also limited in the effects of environmental enrichment and like growth can be accelerated by maximum "feeding," though only up to a ceiling determined by the innate properties of the organism. When this point is reached, the environment may no longer be effective as a source of variation.

A further point is that under optimal environmental conditions, individual differences become more entirely influenced by genetic factors. For instance, in a well-nourished society individual variation in the age of menarche in girls is related almost entirely to genetics (Tanner, 1968).

CONSTITUTIONAL IRREGULARITIES OF DEVELOPMENT

This book is mainly concerned with normal developmental processes, and abnormal ones are discussed mainly for the light they throw on the normal. The line between the normal and the strange is an indefinite one, and there is a range of what might be called normal-abnormal effects in prenatal and perinatal life. These are not the grosser intrauterine effects, such as those of maternal rubella or syphilitic infections, that can produce marked abnormalities of development or things such as serious anoxia at birth with attendant gross brain damage. Rather what is referred to here is the slighter (and often undetectable) irregularity of development that leads to "misprogramming" in the CNS or that leads to the subtle effects often called minimal brain damage, but which are perhaps better described as minimal brain *dysfunction*. Damage implies a previously "correct" organ that is now mechanically altered, whereas what may occur is a slight developmental abnormality—the nervous system gets (metaphorically speaking) wired up a little incorrectly, a few wrong connections are made, or some minor element fails to grow. There is no detectable scar, but one can see that the organism does not function quite like others of his species, and there is some dysfunction in the organization of the nervous system. The so-called "perceptual-motor" difficulties found in some children with school learning problems may be of this kind. Similar effects may be produced by faulty learning following birth, but some (if not all) of these effects may be intrinsic to the structure of the nervous system of these children. The origins of some of these effects may be genetic and are often mutative.

Some such effects are probably rather common—frequent enough, perhaps, to be considered "normal" in the statistical sense; others are more rare. They produce an individual with rather subtle deficiences or variations of behavior or functioning.

EPILOGUE

In appraising constitutional psychology, it is proposed that the theoretical premises that emphasize the interdependence of somatic factors and psychological processes are sound.

This is true whether the particular relationships proposed by Sheldon among embryological structures, body type, and temperament are valid or not. The important thing is that the theory represents an attempt to examine a relationship that must exist, even if not in precisely this form.

From the technical point of view there are many objections to typology, at least as Sheldon presented it. Parnell has gone some way toward meeting these objections and permitting objective and more sophisticated classifications of body type. However, it may be that there are essential weaknesses in any system that relies only on observations of external body form, and perhaps a really sophisticated system should not merely involve gross morphological features but use measures reflecting internal processes in a more direct manner. For example, measures of neural reactivity—perseveration or reaction time—together with biochemical measures such as androgen level or characteristic levels of adrenaline secretion might be included, though we are perhaps not yet in a position to say just which are pertinent. (Nor perhaps do we yet have the technical resources to make such assays on any large scale.) The attempts, by Klaiber et al. (1965), to relate cognitive styles to biochemical factors might be incorporated into this context and form one element in a more advanced typology (this study is discussed in Chapter 16).

Another source of difficulty for typology arises from the fact (discussed in Chapter 3) that similar phenotypes may not necessarily have the same genotype. Errors from this source may be particularly common when the somewhat superficial estimates of type common to the current systems are used. Again, more refined techniques may distinguish more subtle variations and reduce errors from this source.

It is common observation that there is wide individual variation in reactions to child-rearing or other environmental influences, and one of the bugbears in the prediction of the psychological outcome of any particular event or system is that we have little knowledge of the factors that underlie these differing reactions. One of the major theoretical merits of constitutional psychology is that it offers an explanation of an important source of individual variation in reaction to the environment. It also offers a means of improving the predictability of the outcome of particular developmental regimes or events.

There is a further criticism of typologies, whether of physique or of psychological characteristics, that should be mentioned. In this chapter (and in the works cited) expressions such as "the ectomorph" are freely used. In so doing, one masks the individual variations that were highlighted in Chapter 2. In other places in this book I object to concepts of "standard organisms," and the same objection applies here. All that can be claimed is that "ectomorphs" tend to be more like one another than they are like "mesomorphs" or "endomorphs."

I do not wish to insist that Sheldon's particular designations are necessarily the only or the best ones. It could be that some other clusters of physical characteristics, and possibly ones involving other measures, such as autonomic reactivity, might relate more accurately to personality and its development.

In other words, it is suggested that the basic ideas underlying constitutional psychology are sound, though we may not yet have hit upon the right techniques to exploit the potential value of this approach.

Six Development of the Nervous System

In the past many psychologists have not felt it necessary to consider the functioning of the nervous system in proposing psychological theories. Thus in the field of intelligence neither Thorndike nor Spearman tied their theories to neurological facts; they made only rather vague and passing references to what might be called the neurology of intelligence, and then in terms that most neurologists would find unacceptable. Spearman spoke of "nervous energy" as if the brain has a reservoir of it that differs in size for different individuals. This is a concept the neurologists find meaningless. The "behavioristic" school of psychology deliberately excluded from consideration the mysterious happenings within the organism and concentrated only on the outwardly observable, the stimulus and the response to it.

More recently, such writers as Hebb have endeavored to suggest psychological theories that are consistent with both neurological and physiological facts—by no means an easy task because these facts are most scanty at the points most pertinent to psychology. Psychologists working with neurologists are also concerned in a practical way with the same problem.

Most of the literature on the nervous system is concerned with its mature form. Relatively few studies of the developing CNS have been made and fewer still relate structural growth to the changes in behavior of the developing organism. For this reason a certain amount of speculation is involved, and at few points can wholly decisive and validated statements be made about the relationship between the physical changes in the nervous system and behavioral changes over the span of development.

Even in its simplest forms in lowly creatures, the nervous system displays some amazing properties. In higher organisms, and most of all in man, it is a system of incredible complexity, capable of the most astonishing functions and possessed of enormous properties of plasticity. Although it is usual to discuss these things in the matter-of-fact language of prosaic science, superlatives are necessary to describe the true nature of this structure.

The available evidence, which is considerable, suggests that the nerve cells of the brain are the same for man as for other animal species: Human abilities depend not on some special nerve tissue, but on the fact that there are in the human brain more neurons and more complex interconnection between them (Russell, 1959).

As might be expected, the total number of neurons affects functioning. Bressler and Bitterman (1969) have shown that fish given "superbrains" by adding transplanted brain tissue during embryonic development can acquire reversal learning, which is normally atypical of fishes, though typical of rats.

Although the general principles underlying neurological functions may be the same throughout the animal kingdom, there are important differences in organization, at least between orders. For instance, Stettner and Matyniak (1968) have shown that intelligent behavior in birds is mediated without the dependence on the cerebral cortex found in mammals. For certain kinds of intelligent behavior, such as solving oddity problems and counting, some species of birds are clearly superior to some primates. These matters would have to be considered in any detailed comparative consideration of neurological function and could not be ignored in any extensive discussion of neurological phylogeny; but for the purposes of the present discussion they need only be noted.

MYELINATION

A feature of the CNS that is of special interest in the present context is the myelin sheath on the axons of many nerve cells. In the early stages of embryological growth nerve fibers are without this sheath; many acquire it before birth, but others do so postnatally, and for several years after birth this change in nervous tissue continues. Not all fibers are myelinated, even in maturity.

Flechsig's observations (1927) led him to formulate the "myelinogenetic law," which states that myelination of fibers in the brain follows a definite chronological sequence that is constant for all members of a given species. It also states that the fibers forming a particular functional system all become myelinated together. Langworthy (1933) has remarked that the orders of myelination in three widely separated mammals (opposum, cat, and man) are very similar and in general tracts become myelinated in the order of their phylogenetic development, which is also the order of their importance in controlling fundamental activities, those more basic to life developing first.

Myelination of the pyramidal tracts (those from spinal cord to cortex concerned with motor control, particularly of the extremities) is relatively late in fetal growth, and in man myelination of the fibers of some parts of the cortex is not complete at birth. Some areas probably continue the process of myelination until puberty (Tanner, 1961); the areas most likely to be late are the association areas and the so-called "silent areas" of the frontal and parietal lobes.

However, nerve fibers can conduct before they are myelinated; for instance, the neonate rat has a CNS almost completely lacking in myelinated fibers but is yet capable of motor activity (Angulo and Gonzalez, 1929). According to Le Gros Clark (1958), the myelin sheath has important effects on the transmission of impulses along the axon. An essential basis of transmission is increased permeability along the plasma membranes at the surface of the axon. Because the myelin sheath insulates the axon membrane (except at the nodes of Ranvier),[1] the rate of internodal conduction is accelerated, giving a saltatory conduction from node to node. The thicker the myelin sheath, the more rapid the conduction. The sheath also makes for economy of energy expenditure by restricting electrical activity to the nodal region and insulating against dispersion to surrounding tissue. Recent work

[1] Nodes of Ranvier are "joints" where the cells making up the myelin sheath around certain nerve cells meet. This sheath is made up of a series of single cells wrapped (as it were) around the axon.

by Davison (1969) advances our understanding of the process of myelinogenesis.

It may be assumed that full efficiency of conduction is achieved with myelination. Le Gros Clark points out that because myelin affects the rate of conduction and nervous activity depends on very precise timing of arrival and departure of impulses to brain and spinal centers, it is reasonable to suppose that efficiency of functioning is markedly influenced by myelination.

The idea that there is some connection between function and myelination is strengthened by the observation that influences that accelerate or retard the onset of a functional activity also affect the time of myelination. Thus, when a child is born prematurely, the process of myelination is speeded. Or, if in a newborn animal light is excluded from one eye, then myelination of the optic nerve of that eye is retarded compared with the functioning one (Le Gros Clark, 1951).

Layers of the Cerebral Cortex

In most parts of the cerebral cortex, six distinct layers of cells can be identified:

1. The outer or molecular layer (small cells)
2. The outer granular layer (granular cells)
3. The pyramidal layer (dense pyramidal cells)
4. The inner granular layer (granular cells)
5. The ganglionic layer (large pyramidal cells)
6. The fusiform cell layer (spindle-shaped cells)

These layers are all made up of gray matter (unmyelinated), and below them comes the white matter consisting of myelinated nerve fibers.

Conel has studied certain aspects of the development of cortical tissue and finds that closely correlated with the degree of myelination of this tissue are changes in the width of the entire cortex and each of its horizontal layers. The number and size of nerve cells, the condition of the chromophil (Nissl) sub-stance,[2] the state of the fibrils, and the size, structure, and length of the axonic and dendritic processes all change together with the changes of myelinization. The amount of myelin formed is readily seen by staining techniques and thus forms a convenient index of the state of maturation of the cells (Conel, 1939). This maturation includes changes in the chemical composition of the nerve cells (Folch-Pi, 1955).

POSTNATAL DEVELOPMENT OF THE NERVOUS SYSTEM

By the time of birth the human nervous system is in one sense complete in that the total number of neurons that make up the nervous system are present, so that no new nerve cells will develop. The individual has the complement of neurons that must last throughout life. Many of these cells, of course, must grow with the general increase in body size, but this growth is in size and maturation only and is not a result of the addition of any new cells.

Insofar as the peripheral nervous system is concerned, development is fairly well complete, and those fibers that are myelinated have their sheath by the time of birth. Much of the CNS is also complete, but in the so-called "higher parts" of the brain there is evidence of much immaturity. At birth, the most advanced parts of the cortex are the primary motor cortex, and the corresponding primary sensory projection areas are in a late stage of myelination. The primary sensory projection areas for vision, touch, and hearing are also developmentally well advanced at birth. However, other parts of the cortex are notably undeveloped when the infant is born, and these include considerable proportions

[2] These are bodies within certain regions of most nerve cells. Their nature differs in different cells and they are involved in the neurophysiology of nerve function.

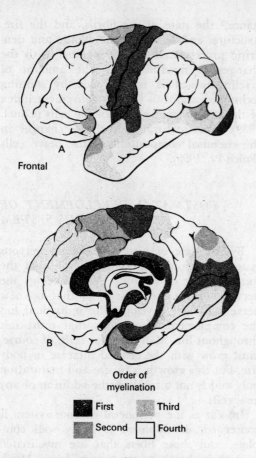

A

Frontal

B

Order of
myelination

- ■ First
- ■ Second
- ▨ Third
- □ Fourth

FIGURE 6–1. Order of myelination of the human
cortex. Part (a) shows the left hemisphere. Part (b) is a
section in the median place showing the right hemisphere. The white areas are the last to myelinate.
Adapted from P. Flechsig. 1927. Meine Myelogenetische
Hirnlehre mit Biographischer Einleitung. Berlin:
Springer.

of the parietal, occipital, and frontal lobes
(Figure 6–1).

In a series of histological studies, Conel
(1939, 1941, 1947, 1955, 1959) has traced an
approximate sequence of early maturation in
the cerebral cortex. He used a number of
criteria of maturation: In addition to the extent of myelination he took into account eight
other indices of developmental status from the
various layers.

Any inference about function from such
histological studies depends on an assumption
about the localization of function in the various areas.

At birth the neonate is essentially a pre-
cortical organism (Conel, 1939) and at one
month has developed only a little beyond this
stage (Conel, 1941). This may be seen as
consistent with the fact that in these early
weeks the main functional changes are in the
reflexive mechanisms of adaptation (G. Bronson, 1963).

In the second and third months there is
rapid development and by the third differential rates of development in various areas
are detectable (Conel, 1947). The motor primary area is more advanced than the sensory
primary area, but both are ahead of the corresponding association areas.[3] In the sensory
areas the somaesthetic is the most developed,
followed somewhat later (and roughly together) by the visual and auditory areas. At
this stage the prefrontal lobes are still further
behind in maturation. One of the results of
this may be that tactile stimulation at first
plays a leading role as a source of sensory
input; this is consistent with the findings of
Harlow and others (see Chapter 11). Because
maturation almost certainly depends in part
on "feeding" by sensory input, this early tactile stimulation plays a crucial role in development.

It would appear from Conel's data (1959)
that the association areas develop more slowly
than the primary ones for at least the first
two years. Such a factor must influence learning and cognition.

Another point arising from Conel's data
is that at first the visual and auditory primary
areas are approximately together in maturation (from the evidence of auditory primacy
discussed in Chapter 13, the auditory area
may be *functionally* in advance), but the
striate cortex (visual) develops more rapidly
after about six months. In his fifteen-month

3 See p. 115.

data (1955) it is the most advanced of the primary sensory areas.

There are not many data on the final course of development of the prefrontal lobes. They are still immature when Conel's data (1959) leaves us at twenty-four months. In view of their probable importance to "higher" mental functions involving such matters as delay of response and more advanced motivations, the immaturity of this part of the cortex can be expected to have a marked influence on behavior.

There is now some data on the development of particular neuronal connections, a topic reviewed by Jacobson (1969). He believes (on the basis of the evidence) that some neurons are highly specific and are fully predetermined in their ultimate connections. Others are incompletely specified and are capable of forming a variety of connections. It is apparently the short axon neurons that have this potential plurality of connections. As development proceeds, the capacity for forming new neuronal connections is reduced, though the short axon neurons do maintain plasticity fairly late in development, enabling the nervous system to be modified by varied experiences. It is those neurons which are latest in ontogenetic maturation that retain the greatest degree of plasticity, and, as shown in Figure 6–1, these comprise much of the frontal lobe and other regions concerned with "higher" intellectual processes.

EEG AND ITS DEVELOPMENTAL CHANGES

There are changes in ionic balances, associated with the activation of nerve cells, that result in electrical phenomena and that are detectable by electroencephalogram (EEG) techniques. There are differences between the EEG patterns when asleep and awake and under a variety of other states of the organism, including maturation. There is a range of differences between species in the EEG characteristics in a given state, but within a species there is a fair measure of consistency of the pattern characteristic of a particular state.

The changes with age of EEG have been studied in a number of animals, and the rate of maturation appears to be related closely to that of more general development. Thus in guinea pigs, which are well developed at birth, a mature form of EEG is found prenatally, in the seventh week of gestation (Jasper et al., 1937). In rats the mature EEG is developed in about eight to eleven days after birth (Schadé, 1957). With rabbits there is a rather sudden maturation of the EEG pattern between ten and fifteen days after birth, at which time it becomes indistinguishable from the adult (Schadé, 1959). In dogs the mature EEG is obtained by about four to five weeks of age (Charles and Fuller, 1956), whereas for monkeys (Macaca mulatta) the time is more prolonged (Kennard and Nims, 1942). From investigations with rabbits, it appears that the changing EEG pattern is related to dendritic developments that are incomplete in the immature animal (Schadé, 1959).

Human EEG

A number of characteristic types of EEG activity have been described for humans under various conditions. The four most common are the following:

1. Slow waves, known as *delta waves,* which occur at speeds varying from one-half per second to about three per second
2. Intermediate slow waves, *theta waves,* which occur at a speed about four to seven per second
3. The *alpha waves,* which have an average frequency of about ten per second, varying from eight to thirteen
4. Fast waves, *beta waves,* with frequencies of eighteen to thirty per second.

There are individual differences in EEG characteristics, and other wave frequencies sometimes found are intermediate fast waves of about fourteen to seventeen per second and very fast waves, about thirty per second; the latter are unusual.

The waves also vary in amplitude, but it is technically difficult to measure these variations at all accurately. They range between about 5 and 1000 microvolts.

In the normal adult, most of the frequencies found are in the alpha and beta bands; other frequencies are less commonly detected. The alpha rhythm is most clearly seen in the occipital and parietal regions when the eyes are closed; it disappears when the eyes are open. Its wave patterns are fairly symmetrical on both sides of the head The beta band is usually more irregular than the alpha and is found mostly over the frontal and temporal areas.

With normal adults the EEG record does not show any marked change under a mild physiological stress, such as that caused by certain drugs or by hyperventilation. Organic patients, such as epileptics, do, under these conditions, show changes in EEG, which can be used diagnostically.

EEG in Children

Changes are noted in EEG from birth to maturity, and these changes have been summarized by Fois (1961). At birth EEG is irregular, asymmetrical, and formless. Often no rhythm is detectable in these pulsations, and if any is present, it is usually in the slow delta band. No change is found between eyes-open and eyes-closed pulsations.

During the first year the activity becomes more regular, begins to show rhythm of delta frequency, and becomes symmetrical on the two sides. The waves from the occipital region do not yet have a regular alpha rhythm, but by one year there is a change in the occipital rhythm when the eyes are open, as compared with the eyes-closed frequency. The dominant rhythm, very slow at first, gradually increases until the alpha frequency is found at about ten years of age. At this stage the

voltage of the alpha rhythm is high and gradually declines until it reaches the normal adult level of about 50 microvolts by about fourteen years of age. The slow waves over the frontal and temporal regions, which are characteristic of childhood, are gradually replaced by beta rhythms, which are established by about the age of sixteen.

Under mild physiological stress, such as is occasioned by hyperventilation, children show considerable fluctuation of rhythm, but with the normal child the fluctuations are fairly symmetrical bilaterally.

Adolescent EEG

As already mentioned, the maturer alpha rhythm is established by about fourteen years of age, and the beta rhythm by about sixteen. From this time the record is essentially similar to that of adults, though during adolescence it is more liable to fluctuation under mild physiological stress than is the normal adult EEG.

EEG in Sleep

The characteristic EEG pattern for the adult in light sleep is the alpha rhythm. In deep sleep this alpha rhythm is replaced by very slow and irregular pulsations at about three per second. These rather rhythmless pulsations are also characteristic of the infant, whether he is asleep or awake, and give support to the statement, made from myelination studies, that the neonate is precorticate, or in functional terms "unconscious."

It must be assumed that these changes in EEG are a reflection of the changing nature of brain functioning as maturation proceeds. That EEG does reflect function is assumed in many contexts, for example, when it is used as an index of dreaming in sleep studies, or in EEG changes accompanying learning and extinction. On this evidence it would seem that the human brain requires some fifteen or sixteen years before reaching an adult level of functioning. It is worth noting that this is the time at which intellectual functioning, as measured by tests such as the Stanford-Binet, tapers off its growth.

It has been known for some time that EEG changes accompany psychological functioning. For example, Rowland (1959), has demonstrated changes accompanying both learning and extinction of learning in cats, a finding which supports the idea that the EEG does correspond in some real manner to the functioning of the brain. The literature on this topic is reviewed by Morrell (1961). N. E. Miller (1969) has reported experiments (with cats) in which *learned* changes in brain waves have been induced, a technique that he claims may be useful in elucidating the functions of specific parts of the brain.

NEUROCHEMISTRY OF DEVELOPMENT

An older view of learning took the telephone switchboard as its model but required an unusual kind of switchboard in that the most used connections alone become easier to make. In this scheme the developing child acquired an increasing number of facile connections despite the loss of some by disuse. This model persisted for a long time, in spite of being absurd, perhaps because it seemed clear and easy to discuss. It came nowhere close to a satisfactory analogy for brain functioning, nor could it explain learning and memory or even adequately provide a working model for them.

It has long been evident that no theory in terms of neural connections alone could be satisfactory. For one thing, although there is an astronomical number of synapses in the human brain, there still does not seem to be enough to account for the incredible amount of information that is acquired in childhood and continues to be stored and added to over a lifetime (Gerard, 1953). Moreover, there are such facts as short- and long-term memory to

be accounted for. Explanations in terms of reverberating circuits seemed quite inadequate, at least to explain long-term memory. More recently the fascinating discovery of the nucleic acids has opened new possibilities of explanation that seem more likely to be sufficient. Their role in the transmission of genetic information seems reasonably well established, and the possibility that ribonucleic acid (RNA) is involved in memory storage has been seriously proposed by a number of authors (e.g., Gaito, 1961; Gaito and Zavala, 1964; Landauer, 1964). There have been attempts to show the role of nucleic acid synthesis in short- and long-term memory (Agranoff, 1967).

There is now a considerable amount of evidence, which has been reviewed by Gurowitz (1968), on the chemical basis of memory. A number of studies confirm the role of RNA in memory transfer and even the possibility of transfer from one donor to another by the donation of RNA from "educated" to naive organisms (e.g., Faiszt and György, 1968).

In spite of all the exciting possibilities of this most interesting work, there is at present little of specifically developmental import. However, research in developmental neurochemistry has been started in Britain. Balazs (1969) has used labelled nucleic acids to study protein synthesis in specific brain loci. Gaitonde (1969) has found complex changes with age in the protein composition of the developing brain. Other work has related dietary deficiencies to abnormal brain development. We should soon be able to clarify the role of the biochemistry of the brain in intellectual development.

FUNCTIONAL ORGANIZATION IN THE BRAIN

Historically there have been two views about the organization of the brain (Penfield and Roberts, 1959). Scientists at the beginning of the nineteenth century regarded the brain quite simply as the organ of the mind. They conceived of it as working like other organs of the body—as a whole. Another view was that espoused by the phrenologist, who regarded the brain as being made up of a considerable number of suborgans, each responsible for a given trait or intellectual faculty, such as benevolence, sexual passion, acquisitiveness, language, and so on; the list in some instances became very long. They further claimed that there were lumps in the skull corresponding to these organs, so that by examining the bump on the head, one could determine the state of development of the trait or faculty supposed to lie beneath it. Thus an individual with a large bump of benevolence was supposed to exhibit this trait markedly in his daily life.

These authors go on to say that present-day neurologists are largely under the influence of a point of view that does not differ radically from that of the phrenologists. They tend to speak of the representation in the cortex of movement here and a sensation there as though they were independent.

There is a good deal of evidence that encourages this point of view and this evidence has been accumulated since Broca demonstrated at an autopsy that a patient who had lost the power of speech without any other noticeable defect had a restricted lesion in the left hemisphere of the brain; this was in 1861. In 1870, Fritch and Hitzig applied an electric current to the cortex of a dog that had been lightly anesthetized. They found the limbs on the opposite side of the body to move, thus giving experimental support to Hughlings Jackson's conclusions, based on clinical observations, about brain functioning. These and many other examples added since that time have tended to encourage the thinking of a strict localization of functions within the brain.

Penfield, in pointing out the fallacy of the preceding, draws the analogy of a clock. One might ascribe a unitary function to the clock —telling time. Examination of the works, however, shows that it is possible to break down somewhat this functional unity. Thus the minute, hour, and second hands have separate mechanisms, and it is possible to remove one of these without necessarily interfering with the others, so that in a fashion the function can continue in the absence of one of the submechanisms. Other mechanisms, such as chimes, might be incorporated in the whole but not be essential to the telling of time.

From this analogy we get some idea of the modern view of the localization of function in the brain, a view which in a sense is a combination of the two historical ones. The brain is conceived as working as a whole—but with certain specific functions having a locus in a particular part of the brain. Thus a patient with a lesion in the speech area would continue most of the essential functions of the brain—writing, reading, listening, thinking, and many forms of voluntary activity— yet be disabled in one particular activity, that of speech.

Russel Brain, in discussing this general question of the function of the brain, says that it is naive to propose a direct anatomical-to-psychological relationship, as many earlier students have done. The case is rather that there are certain anatomical regions of physiological activities, and it is on physiological processes that psychological ones depend. The connection between neuroanatomy and psychology is thus somewhat remote, neurophysiological processes intervening in the study of each (Brain, 1961). Some of the subtleties of this holistic-localized working of the brain are revealed by a long series of experiments on monkeys performed by Pribram and his colleagues (Pribram, 1969). These experiments show the immense reserve capacity of the brain for the "switching" of activities to new regions when some area suffers damage, and that strict localization of function is not a necessary condition (even if there normally is localization). Pribram uses a hologram model to account for some aspects of memory. (This model may explain the activation of memory with RNA being the recording medium.)

A number of localities of function in humans (some well documented, others based on one or two observations) have been reported by various workers. As with Penfield's conclusions, most have been derived from studies of patients suffering from head injuries in wounds or accidents or suffering brain damage from tumors, vascular accidents, and similar internal causes.

Pribram's techniques of multiple implanted electrodes might reveal some highly interesting data on the development of neurophysiological processes, but the technical problems of the actual surgery of newly born animals may present considerable handicaps to work in this field.

In general, we find that many incoming nerve fibers are routed (usually via "lower" brain structures) to a specific part of the cortex. For example, those of the optic nerves from the retinas come via the midbrain to the cortex in the occipital region, and visual functions are chiefly mediated there. The visual areas of the occipital lobe thus become a focus of visual functioning but are not the only part involved in this process. Ablations in parts of the temporal lobe may destroy visual recognition, so that an object can still be seen perfectly, but recognition of its use or its significance to the animal may be lost. In man, the creative or intellectual use of visual information may be impaired by frontal damage.

Although a given function may have a focus in a particular location, so that there is a kind of concentration of that function in that region of the brain, the function is not usually exclusive to that part. The brain works as an integrated "mechanism," and, except in the simplest of behaviors, more than one region is involved in any activity of the organism.

Because different parts of the brain mature at different times, the brain is probably not fully capable of some of its part-functions during childhood, and not until adulthood does it become capable of fully integrated activity. This unevenness and incompleteness of function has important implications to the understanding of the psychology of the immature organism.

An understanding of the organization of the brain, correlated with its developmental progress, will obviously throw much light on the psychological changes over infancy and childhood and into maturity. There is the beginnings of such knowledge but by no means any detailed information. Some interesting data on the functioning of the brain come from Penfield and Roberts (1959), who made observations during the course of brain surgery. As part of the operative procedure, in conscious patients under local anesthesia the exposed cortex is stimulated by the touch of a fine electrode carrying a mild current. The patient is asked to report his experience as this is done. (The object of this treatment is in the first place practical—to determine the function, in that particular brain, of the area surrounding diseased tissue, as to aid in deciding the permissible extent of excision.) Although individual brains are unique in detail, similar effects generally arise from comparable regions of different brains. Depending on the region stimulated, the effects may be behavioral—for example, vocalization or limb movements—or private and experiential—such as flashes of light on the revival of memories. Certain areas producing consistent effects have been delineated by this method.

While there are many areas of the brain that form a "focus" of influence for specific functions, it is important to avoid a phrenological view of the brain's workings. Even in localization there is a totality of function so that even the highest areas, such as the prefrontal association area, have intimate connections with the lower and phylogenetically older parts of the brain. Thus certain of the cell layers of the frontal cortex have direct thalamic and hypothalamic connections and give it an intimate relationship to primitive emotions. The modern view on localization of function is as follows: Although there are areas of the brain that are particularly influential in certain functions, they are not autonomous; their intimate connection with other areas and the complex intertwining of pathways between all regions and all levels of the brain ensure that no region works uninfluenced by the others.

SPEECH AND BRAIN FUNCTIONS

Speech is probably among the most complex of human activities and is one that most requires the full functioning of a mature and intact brain. Much of our knowledge on brain mechanisms and speech comes from the study of patients who have suffered impairment of the brain, either through injury or because of tumors, bursting blood vessels, and the like. In many cases the effects of impairment are

subtle and difficult to detect. When speech is affected, the results are often more clearly observable and perhaps for this reason have been widely studied. These studies have thrown some interesting light not only on speech itself but on the general working of the brain.

There are two main types of speech disorders, each involving distinct cortical mechanisms: the aphasias, which involve the ideational aspects of speech, and the dysarthrias, which involve the motor aspects of speaking. Aphasia (or dysphasia) is defined by Penfield as

a difficulty in the ideation or elaboration of speech as distinguished from defective verbal articulation. Aphasia is characterized by the following defects in varying proportions: Ideational defect in speaking, reading, writing, naming, and defective comprehension of speech.

Dysarthria (or anarthria) is defined as a difficulty in the articulation of words. This diffi-

FIGURE 6–2. *Areas of dominant hemisphere involved in ideational speech.*
Adapted in part from W. Penfield and L. Roberts. 1959. Speech and brain mechanisms.
Princeton, N.J.: Princeton Univ. Press, Figs. X–1, X–3, and X–4, pp. 195, 200, and
201, by permission of the authors and the publisher.

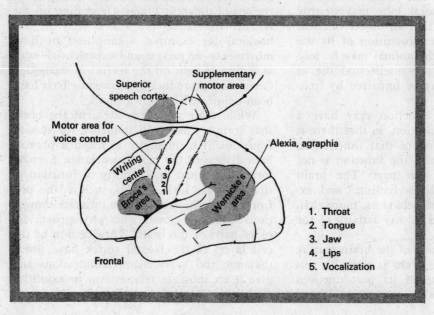

culty may include the use of the muscles of respiration and vocalization as well as of the lips, tongue, and throat, and involve the cerebellum and lower motor neurones.

Speech Centers

Using the stimulation technique, Penfield has produced experimental aphasia, or what he calls "aphasic arrest." The speech difficulty lasts as long as the stimulation is continued. There are three distinct areas in which this effect can be produced: (1) the posterior temporal and posterior inferior parietal areas, also known as Wernicke's area; (2) a small area in the posterior part of the third frontal convolution, known as the anterior speech area or Broca's area; and (3) an area just anterior to the supplementary motor area in the longitudinal fissure, shown in Figure 6–2 as the superior speech cortex. Some speech functions are located in the nondominant hemisphere (see Figure 6–3).

Penfield's observations lead him to suppose that the superior speech cortex is dispensable, and ablations of this region in the dominant hemisphere lead only to temporary aphasia. In cases in which Penfield has removed this area, the aphasia has lasted only a few weeks. Broca's area is apparently less easily dispensed with, though Penfield claims that a number of cases have shown eventual, though somewhat delayed, clearing of the resultant aphasia when this area has been destroyed. In other cases the aphasia has been permanent. Lenneberg (1967), however, claims that there is no clear evidence implicating this area in speech.

According to Penfield, it is destruction in the posterior speech area of the dominant hemisphere, or Wernicke's area, that leads to the most severe aphasia, particularly if the under-

FIGURE 6–3. *Location of speech motor mechanisms in nondominant hemisphere. Reproduced from W. Penfield and L. Roberts. 1959. Speech and brain mechanisms. Princeton, N.J.: Princeton Univ. Press, Fig. X–13, p. 214, by permission of the authors and the publisher.*

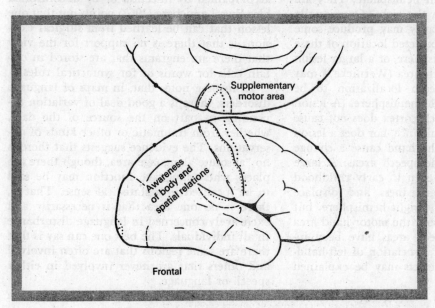

lying projection areas of the thalamus are involved. (In the nondominant hemisphere, ablations or destructions in the corresponding area have led to an impairment of the awareness of the body schema and of spatial relationships.)

The mechanism for ideational speech is thus unilateral, and damage to any of these areas results in aphasia. As mentioned, this aphasia is short-lived if the damage is in the superior speech area, normal speech being regained in a matter of weeks. Damage in the anterior speech area results in a longer-lasting aphasia, but, according to Penfield, there is still a possibility of return to normal function. It is important to emphasize that normal speech involves all three speech areas. The fact that speech functions can recover after damage to these areas is an illustration of the plasticity of the brain.

As Penfield points out, the human cerebral hemispheres are never twice the same in form or in the patterning of the convolutions and fissures. In a vast majority of individuals the three cortical speech areas—the superior speech cortex, Broca's area, and Wernicke's area— are situated in the left hemisphere. They are more rarely found in the right. Occasionally a small lesion in infancy may produce some displacement of the expected location of these areas within the hemisphere, or a larger lesion in the posterior speech area (Wernicke's) may cause the whole speech localization to be transferred to the right hemisphere. (A lesion restricted to the speech cortex does not cause a change of hand dominance, nor does a lesion in the area serving the hand cause a change in the position of the speech areas. A large lesion in infancy or even in early childhood may produce left-handedness and displace speech function to the right hemisphere, but it does this because both the motor hand area and the cortical speech areas have been involved. The frequent association of left-handedness and speech defects may be explained by this.)

It is of interest to note that the effects of the removal of cortical tissue in the treatment of epileptic seizures are different from those of removal caused by sudden traumatic head injuries. While ablations of cortical tissue for this purpose are reported by Penfield and Roberts (1959) for almost all parts of the cortex, there are very few cases in which the excision of cortical tissue to remove epileptic foci have resulted in any long-lasting dysphasia; language is usually restored within days or at the most weeks. Not infrequently excisions, even within the critical language areas, have produced no disturbance of language. Penfield and Roberts believe that the actual site of the lesion does not form the epileptogenic focus, which is adjacent to it. A lesion is an irritant that induces irregular functioning in the healthy tissue that surrounds it; in many cases the site of the lesion itself has been nonfunctional for many years, and the functions of that area have shifted to adjacent ones. Therefore, the removal of this lesion causes little disruption. Traumatic removal of tissue, on the other hand, affects healthy functional tissue. Surgical lesions are by their nature different, being usually shallow and not accompanied by infection or by uncontrolled bleeding. Lenneberg (1967) points out that one lesson that can be learned from surgical excisions is that there is no support for the view that there are engrams that are stored in certain cells for words or for syntactical rules.

Lenneberg notes that, in maps of language disorders, there is a good deal of variation depending in part on the source of the data, whether from traumatic or other kinds of observations. The evidence suggests that there is no "absolute" language area, though there are places where language function may be said to be localized in a statistical sense. That is, there is no one area that is necessarily and exclusively concerned in language disturbance in all individuals. The best one can say is that there are some regions that are often involved and others that are never involved in either speech or language.

Of the areas most often implicated in

speech, lesions around the left Rolandic fissure [4] often interfere with the production of speech. Lesions in the left parietal and temporal lobe (Wernicke's area) frequently interfere with the comprehension of language. Lenneberg states that there is no clear evidence implicating Broca's area in speech functions. He also points out that there is nothing of a cytoarchitectural nature to distinguish the cortical areas involved in language.

The workings of the brain are vastly more complex than one can imagine at first, and we have to move far from the simpleminded ideas of earlier psychologists—perhaps even of some neurologists. For instance, there is some evidence suggesting that the visual cortex might mediate certain nonvisual functions also. Lubar et al. (1967) have demonstrated deficits in an active-avoidance response depending on auditory cues in cats following lesions in the visual cortex. Evidently there is interaction between areas, and one may not be able to think of functions as restricted, rigidly specific areas. More sophisticated ideas than the current ones about the nature of functional localization might be called for.

Subcortical Speech Functions

Speech is not merely a cortical function, and Lenneberg (1967) has drawn attention to certain facts that have been known for some time but that have generally been overlooked in discussing this topic. Penfield and Roberts (1959) have proposed a hypothetical "centrencephalic center" as a subcortical entity essential to higher mental processes (it might now be identified with the reticular activating system) and have spoken of a thalamic system

that coordinates the functions of the three cortical speech areas.

The evidence supporting such a view is varied, and some of it is comparative. Bailey and Davis (1942) and Kelly et al. (1946) showed that vocalization in cats was affected by electrolytic lesions in the periaqueduct gray matter.[5] Skultety (1961) has reported comparable findings for dogs, producing mutism. The evidence on humans comes from clinical observation. Tumors in the region of the posterior fossa [6] produces dysarthria in children (Bailey et al., 1939). Penfield and Roberts (1959) have commented on the fact that cortical ablations usually produce no lasting aphasias, whereas deep damage to brain tissue usually does. Lenneberg (1967) also mentions more recent evidence, from his own observations and from those of others, on this point. However, these difficulties may result from damage to cerebellar pathways in deep wounds rather than from involvement of some thalamic or other subcortical center (Blundell, 1967).

Motor Mechanisms of Speech

Penfield has produced information on the motor mechanisms of speech, largely from the technique of electrical stimulation of conscious patients. Vocalization has been produced by stimulation, in both hemispheres, of that part of the motor cortex numbered 5 in Figure 6–2. Vocalization can also be produced by stimulation of the supplementary motor area on either side. When any of these four areas is stimulated, the patient makes a drawn-out vowel sound, which he continues so long as the stimulation is applied. If the stimulation is maintained, the patient may pause for breath, but apart from such involuntary pauses is unable to stop the vocalization.

---

[4] Rolandic fissure (or central sulcus) is a well-marked crevice that forms the boundary between the frontal and parietal lobes. There are numerous other fissures (sulci), with raised areas (or gyrii) between them. On either side of the Rolandic fissure are the pre- and postcentral gyrii.

[5] The aqueduct is a narrow canal connecting the third and fourth ventricles.
[6] A depression in the frontal bone region of the cranium.

Voice control, which involves the fine coordination of the lips, jaw, tongue, and throat and the capacity for vocalization already mentioned, is mediated by the lower part of the motor cortex, that is, by the regions numbered 1 to 5 in Figure 6–2. It appears that only one of these areas (which are bilaterally represented) is essential to speech: Excision of this area on one side gives only a temporary dysarthria, which gradually clears spontaneously. The supplementary motor areas are similarly expendable; either one can be removed without producing permanent paralysis of the mouth or limbs. Its removal from the speech-dominant hemisphere produces an aphasis of several weeks' duration, which clears up completely, though some motor difficulty elsewhere may be noted, particularly in rapid alternating movements of either the hand or foot.

Using the technique of electrical stimulation, Penfield has marked out, roughly at least, an area of the cortex that he calls the "interpretive cortex." It is located in each temporal lobe, partly on the lateral surface, and extending into the Sylvian fissure, as illustrated in Figures 6–4 and 6–5. Its exact location, especially in those areas less accessible within the Sylvian fissure, has not been clearly delineated. Stimulation in this general area gives rise to psychical experiences, which Penfield has described under two headings, experiential and interpretive illusions.

By experiential physical experiences he means those instances in which patients respond to stimulation by a kind of "flashback," where they relive some previous period of their lifetime and again become aware of

FIGURE 6–4. *Left hemisphere, showing the approximate positions of the motor, sensory, and "interpretive" areas of the cortex. Reproduced from W. Penfield and L. Roberts. 1959. Speech and brain mechanisms. Princeton, N.J.: Princeton Univ. Press, Fig. III–2, p. 41, by permission of the authors and the publisher.*

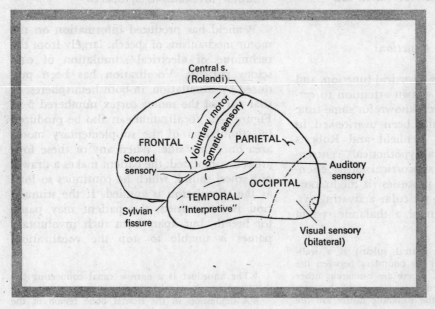

things of which they were conscious then. Patients report a kind of double consciousness. They are aware that they are in the present and that they are looking back on the past, but yet simultaneously they have a feeling that they are reexperiencing that past: The experience apparently has more to it than mere remembrance. Many epileptic patients have reported similar experiences in the aura of epileptic seizures. This topic is extensively discussed in Penfield and Perot (1963).

The interpretive illusions described by Penfield are apparently very similar to the "déjà vu" phenomenon in which there is a sense of familiarity with the present, as if the present had previously been experienced. On stimulation of this area, some patients report such phenomena and others report a kind of reverse feeling in which everything seems strange and unfamiliar. In both cases there is an alteration in the perception of the present. Emotional experiences, sometimes fearful, may accompany these feelings.

Penfield regards both kinds of phenomena as evidence of interpretive functions corresponding to the judgments that the normal individual is constantly making as he compares the present with past experience. The judgment is made as to whether this present experience is familiar, appropriate, menacing, or what have you, and this judgment implies a record of past experience against which the present can be interpreted.

Penfield claims that these responses to electrical stimulation suggest the existence of a permanent ganglionic recording of the stream of consciousness. Because no comparable responses have been elicited by the stimulation of other parts of the cerebrum, Penfield assumes that this function is localized here. It

FIGURE 6–5. *The inner or medial surface of the left hemisphere and the corresponding representations there. Reproduced from W. Penfield and L. Roberts. 1959. Speech and brain mechanisms. Princeton, N.J.: Princeton Univ. Press, Fig. III–2, p. 41, by permission of the authors and the publisher.*

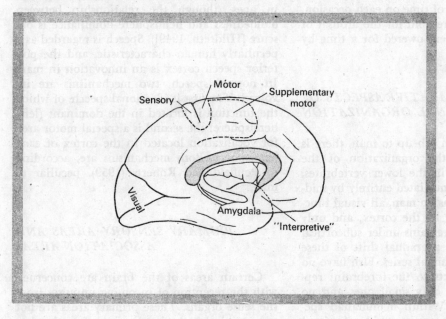

seems as if in stimulating a part of this area one sets going a portion of the recording of "consciousness past." Patients speak of the reality and vividness of these experiences, which have something of the character of hallucinations. However, the patients have not reacted like psychotic hallucinating patients in that they have had no difficulty in recognizing the "hallucinations" as revived bits of past experience and have not attempted to react to them as if they were present reality.

Penfield states that this experience is dynamic and is not a still picture. It moves forward and has visual and auditory components, and sometimes also involves a sense of position. No patients have reported pain, taste, or smell during these experiential responses (his number of cases is not large). He also notes that the "strip" always runs forward, never backward. The pace also appears unchanged; the experience seems to happen at the speed of the original one. The experience continues so long as the electrode is held in place and ceases abruptly as soon as it is removed. Restimulation of the same point can lead to repetition of the same experience, which always starts at the same moment of time on each occasion. It seems as if the threshold for the arousal of that response has been lowered for a time by the first stimulation.

COMPARATIVE ASPECTS OF FUNCTIONAL ORGANIZATION

In evolution, from fish up to man, there is radical change in the organization of the CNS. For example, in the lower vertebrates, visual functions are mediated entirely by midbrain centers, whereas, in man, all visual functions are taken over by the cortex, and only the pupillary reflex remains under subcortical mediation. There is a gradual shift of these functions over the animal series. Fish have no optic projection tracts to the forebrain; reptiles and birds have only small ones and no true striate cortex. Within mammalian species, there is a progressive shift of visual

functions from the superior colliculus to the striate cortex. Discriminative spatial functions are the first functions assumed by the cortex. The progressive importance of the cortex is illustrated by the removal of the visual area. In the lowest vertebrates, the fish, such removal results in no impairment of visual behavior; birds show some loss of detail vision but grosser vision is unimpaired; rats can no longer discriminate visual patterns but can distinguish brightness, position, and distance. Cats and dogs can still detect brightness differences, but all other visual functions are destroyed. In the monkey there remains some ability to detect *change* in illumination. In man, total blindness results from destruction of the striate area, and the pupillary reflex is the only remaining reaction to light (Marquis, 1935).

There is not a great deal of information available on other comparative aspects of functional organization in the brain. According to Penfield and Roberts (1959), the localization of function to one hemisphere is new in mammalian evolution. It is not, however, unique to man, for right-handedness has been reported in apes (though the relationship between handedness and hemisphere dominance is obscure [Hildreth, 1949]). Speech is regarded as a peculiarly human characteristic, and the posterior speech cortex is an innovation in man. In normal speech, two mechanisms are involved: The first is ideational speech, of which the function is located in the dominant (left) hemisphere; the second is a special motor area for vocalization located in the cortex of each hemisphere. Both mechanisms are, according to Penfield and Roberts (1959), peculiar to man.

PRIMARY SENSORY AREAS AND ASSOCIATION AREAS

Certain areas of the brain are concerned with the reception of incoming impulses from the sense organs. These primary areas are not responsible for the localization of a stimulus, that is, for actual *conscious* awareness of what part of the body is being stimulated or what sensory pattern is received. Nor is recall, or memory of a sensation, one of their functions. Further, they are not concerned in the accurate differentiation of intensity of stimuli. All these functions are functions of other areas of the brain, the association areas. Impulses are relayed to the association areas from the primary areas.

Association Areas

Just in front of and more or less surrounding the visual cortex is an area sometimes called the visual association area, or the prestriate area. Just behind the somaesthetic sensory area and occupying the principal part of the parietal lobe is the parietal association area, which is concerned in somaesthetic discrimination. Near the primary auditory area of the temporal lobe is an auditory association area. Each sense, therefore, has a region, related to its primary cortical area, that functions as an associated area.

The function of these association areas is not fully understood, but there are two general facts that are known about them. They sometimes have an equivalence of function with primary areas, though in a limited fashion. For instance, in an experiment, monkeys were taught to make visual discriminations in size, color, and form. The prestriate areas were removed on both sides. After allowing time for surgical recovery, the animals were retested on the discrimination habits and a complete amnesia for them was found. On retraining it was found that they could relearn the habits about as quickly as they had learned them preoperatively. Thus it appears that the prestriate association areas were important in the original learning of the habit, but that the remainder of the visual system could, in their absence, take over this function. Similar results concerning the respective discriminations that depend on them have been obtained for other association areas (Ades, 1946).

The second general fact known about the sensory association areas is that they are involved in a more complex sensory discrimination. For example, a chimpanzee was taught to discriminate a cone from a pyramid by touch alone, being unable to see the objects and permitted only to handle them. The animal was also taught the more difficult discrimination between a wedge and a pyramid. The posterior parietal association area was then removed, and after the operation, the animal lost both habits. On retraining it was able to learn again the simpler discrimination between the pyramid and cone, but extensive retraining failed to teach the animal the more difficult discrimination between the wedge and the pyramid. It would thus appear that the association areas are necessary for learning the more difficult discriminations (Ruch et al., 1938).

We see a similar phenomenon in humans when there are lesions in the sensory association area of the parietal cortex. These lead to the condition, known as *astereognosis,* in which patients are still capable of estimating properties such as size, weight, shape, texture, and temperature, all of which are mediated by the primary sensory area. If, however, a blindfolded patient with a lesion in the parietal association area is handed a common object, he may be unable to identify it because although he is able separately to receive sensations of these types in the primary area, the disruption of function in the association area prevents his amalgamating and interpreting all these clues and thereby identifying the object. This synthesizing of discrete sensations into a unitary perception and the matching of this perception with past experience is the function of the association area.

Frontal Association Areas

There are relatively large areas of the frontal lobe that are not concerned with specific functions (they are sometimes called the "silent" areas because their stimulation does not produce memories or sensations as does stimulation of some others) but are nevertheless important in intellectual processes. They are the prefrontal parts of the frontal association areas. Important changes follow their removal in both man and animals.

Destruction of these prefrontal areas impairs the ability to attend to a task, and distractibility is one of the symptoms of lesions here. Delayed behaviors, which require sustained attention, are also affected, as has been shown in experiments with monkeys that have been taught a delayed reaction. In a typical experiment a monkey is shown that food is under one of two cans; a screen is lowered between him and the cans, in such a way that he cannot "hold" the correct can by staring at it fixedly. After an interval the screen is removed, and the monkey is allowed to select the correct can. Normal animals can do this after delays of several minutes, but monkeys with prefrontal destruction usually cannot perform this task if the delay is more than a few seconds. With these animals it is possible to increase the delay by reducing distractions during the interval—by having them spend the interval in darkness, for instance. The fact that it is, under suitable conditions, possible for these behaviors to be elicited without the frontal lobes, shows that the prefrontal association area is not absolutely essential to them, but we can conclude from this evidence that prefrontal animals have an increased difficulty in attending and in many situations would be seriously impaired (Jacobsen, 1935; Harlow and Johnson, 1943).

Humans with prefrontal destruction show similar symptoms, relative to their normal level of functioning. They are still able to carry out tasks that are relatively simple by human standards but in more complex situations have a difficulty similar to the monkeys. Following prefrontal damage, personality changes, as well as difficulty in attending to a task for any sustained length of time, have been described. Patients with such damage are frequently unmindful about the future (they were not so before damage), and are likely to shun responsibility and be inconsiderate and impulsive (Russell, 1959). For these reasons some writers describe the function of the prefrontal areas as concerned in planning and organization for the future, activities which may often involve inhibition of present desires that are contrary to a long-term welfare.

At the time of normal birth the eyes and ears are functional, that is, there is evidence of responsiveness to light and sounds. Pain sensations may be absent but other somaesthetic sensations are probably developed, at least in a crude form. The primary sensory areas of the cortex corresponding to these sense organs can be seen, by comparison with Figure 6–1, to be myelinated at birth and hence presumably functional. The association areas are as yet relatively undeveloped. This fact of some discrepancy in development between the primary and association areas has important implications for learning in the immature organism.

Taking the comparative approach, it seems that there is a correspondence between the size of a motor area in the brain and the amount of skill with which the movement represented in that area can be used (Gerard, 1959). Thus the spider monkey with a highly manipulable prehensile tail has a considerable area of the motor cortex devoted to it. Gerard suggests that a chimpanzee can never learn to talk simply because the motor areas for the tongue and larynx are too small to permit such complex motor activity. In humans the motor area for the tongue is much larger than that for the whole leg. Presumably a similar relationship exists for other areas of the brain. In the dog, for instance, the olfactory cortex is large. Thus different species have different distributions of available cortical tissue and the distribution is reflected in function.

Within a species, there is some evidence that differences between individuals in early experience may influence the development of cortical areas. Krech et al. (1963) and Bennett et al. (1964) have reported that rats that were reared in darkness, or that were enucleated, but that were given an enriched though sightless environment, showed an increase in weight of the somaesthetic cortex as compared with seeing controls reared in a similar but lighted environment. It was assumed that the increased reliance of the experimental animals on somaesthetic information led to greater development in the brain area concerned. A decrease in the weight of the rest of the cortex was also found.

These results were not replicated entirely in an experiment by MacNeill and Zubek (1967). In this experiment a nonsignificant decrease in visual and auditory cortical weight was found but no somaesthetic increase was reported (these results might be due to differences either in the strain used or in experimental procedure). However, there was a difference in the total sensory cortex between animals reared in impoverished environments and those reared in enriched ones and this difference is consistent with results reported by Bennett et al. (1964). Gyllensten et al. (1966) have reported growth increase in the auditory cortex of mice reared in darkness, and they interpret this as the result of increased dependence on auditory cues.

Thus for certain rodents (and frequently for other species) the nature of the early environment has an influence on cortical development; an enriched environment increases total growth, and it is possibly the case that deficiencies in specific input lead to compensatory growth of alternative sensory areas. This additional growth is presumably not in the number of cells, which seemingly is fixed at earlier stages and possibly genetically, but in the nature of the cells already existing. Other experiments by the Berkeley group (Krech et al., 1960) show effects of early enrichment on brain chemistry.

As will be seen in later sections of this book, psychological functions of any degree of complexity involve the interaction of numerous factors. One weakness of much current experimentation is that it oversimplifies function. Thus, most perceptual experiments involve one modality (usually vision), whereas most real-life behaviors involve multimodality func-

tions. Pribram (1966) suggests that there may be parts of the brain concerned with supra-modality organization and on the evidence of Brenda Milner (1958) and Teuber et al. (1960) places one of these in the "silent" association area of the temperoparietal cortex. This area might be concerned with visuo-somatic-spatial organization and is thus not modality-specific. There may also be a location for verbal behavior, irrespective of mode. Another modality-unspecific region might involve the fronto-limbic formation already referred to, an area which is involved in retention and in delay of response. Ablations in this area lead to defects in tasks involving delayed response or delayed alternation. The evidence on any of these areas is sketchy at present, but when one considers what behavior really is (as distinct from what it is in experimental situations), then coordinating, organizing functions of this sort must occur. The regions in which they occur may not be clearly localized, but presumably they are not in any of those areas having rather highly specific functions connected with motor actions, sensation, and so on. That is, the (silent) areas of the frontal and parietal lobes would seem by elimination to be their location.

Another point in connection with the localization and development of function is that the brain is highly flexible in its operations, especially in early life, and there is some scope for transfer of function from one area to another. This is apparently more true of the "higher" functions than the phylogenetically older ones. The primary motor and sensory areas are seemingly quite fixed, whereas there is some evidence that other areas can wander to some extent, even to another hemisphere.

CEREBRAL DOMINANCE AND FUNCTION

A developmentally significant event in the CNS may be the establishment of cerebral dominance, but it is a little difficult to state specifically what its special importance might be. The idea that dominance of hand and eye is significant of something has been present for a long time. Galton was much interested in the question and in 1884 collected at a health exhibition a mass of data which was not analyzed until forty years later (Woo and Pearson, 1927). The analysis revealed no correspondence between eye and hand dominance, thus suggesting that both these traits cannot be related in any simple way to cerebral dominance. Zangwill (1960) has also shown that the correspondence between handedness and cerebral dominance is less clearcut than many of the earlier investigators had thought. Hence although lateral dominance or "handedness" may be found even at the level of the rat (Peterson and Barnett, 1961) and is reported in other mammals, it does not necessarily follow that such a discovery represents dominance of one cerebral hemisphere.

Indeed, Penfield and Roberts (1959) state that the localization of function in one hemisphere is a recent evolutionary innovation and that its relation to speech is peculiar to the human brain. It would seem, therefore, that no simple relationship connecting eyedness, handedness, and speech functions is likely to be found. However, there has in the past been a good deal of speculation about mixed dominance (where hand and eye are opposedly dominant) as a causal factor in difficulties of speech (e.g., Wile, 1942; Berner and Berner, 1953).

In general terms, the dominance of one hemisphere of the human brain is well established, and in about 95 percent of the population the dominant hemisphere is the left one if handedness is taken as a criterion. It may be questioned, of course, whether handedness is sufficient for the definition of dominance and whether leg dominance (and perhaps other areas of dominance) should not be included. Dominance is probably a complex pattern of functioning. Laterality appears to be generalized throughout the hemisphere, or at least there is some evidence that it affects the occipital lobes. Eason et al. (1967) have reported, in the contralateral occipital lobe, a greater amplitude of evoked cortical potentials when a stimulus appeared in the visual field on the side of the dominant hand than when it appeared on the other side.

Gooddy and McKissock (1951) have emphasized the fact that no two brains are the same in their organization or in the precise pattern of localization of function. There is no standard brain. Early trauma may account for shifts of function, but even in cases where there is none of this, localization is individual.

The idea that speech and communicative functions are generally located in the dominant hemisphere is widely accepted and is supported by a good deal of evidence (Penfield and Roberts, 1959), but it seems that early bilateral damage is more disruptive to speech than is unilateral damage, even if the latter is grosser. (This is true for other functions, too.) From a study of four patients in whom speech development was delayed, Dreifuss (1963) found them to give signs of bilateral brain disease, without strong neurological stigmata. Compared with cases having unilateral damage of early onset, in which even severe damage may produce little effect (Gooddy and McKissock, 1951), the relatively mild bilateral deficits in these cases markedly affected speech and the acquisition of handedness. This may be because bilateral damage, even if slight, may, as there is no intact hemisphere to take them over, hinder the transfer of speech functions.

Evidence of critical changes in the organization of cerebral functions in the first year is contained in two papers by McFie (1961a, b). Both from his own observations of children in whom one hemisphere is removed because of disease and from other sources, he finds that hemispherectomy in the first year results in a fairly complete transfer of function to the remaining hemisphere. This is particularly the case with total removal, and partial removal makes functioning comparatively less adequate. After the end of the first year the results of hemispherectomy begin to approximate those found in adults. That is, both hemispheres have taken on functions that become progressively irreplaceable. (It should be mentioned that the operation performed by McFie was not strictly hemispherectomy, but hemicortisectomy: Subcortical structures are left, and the residual function *could* be there and not in the other hemisphere [Blundell, 1967].)

It is noteworthy that even though there was usually a rise in IQ following hemispherectomy almost all children showed verbal deficiencies of varying degrees of severity—no matter which hemisphere remained. Thus it would seem that a highly complex function such as speech requires an intact brain.

Other points that should be mentioned are that speech seems more firmly located in the left hemisphere of right-handed persons than it is in the right hemisphere of sinistrals, and that there seems to be greater variation in the localization of function in the brains of sinistrals (Zangwill, 1960). While there is not the absolute relationship between handedness, eyedness, and speech functions that is claimed by some of the earlier investigations, some relationship does exist. But as Zangwill says, cerebral dominance is probably a graded characteristic varying widely between individuals and having a relation to handedness (and other functions) yet to be ascertained. It may be that other factors, such as auditory localization (Kimura, 1963), have to be taken into account in considering speech in this context.

There is some evidence that specific defects in speech, reading, spelling, and so on are not isolated but part of a complex developmental syndrome and that indeterminate cerebral dominance may be associated with sensitivity to stress and temperamental instability (Zangwill, 1960).

Concerning the origins of handedness, it seems to be a familial trait in many instances (Burt, 1946; Zangwill, 1960), though as already mentioned, some "sinistrals" are actually dextrals shifted because of early brain dysfunction. Presumably cerebral laterality is also an inherited trait.

When one makes a comparison of the order of maturation of the brain with the function of the various areas, it is evident that at least a rough correspondence can be seen. At birth the infant is capable of sensation (see Chapter 13), and the primary sensory areas are relatively well on in development. He cannot yet perceive (i.e., interpret sensations), and this lack of function is correlated with the immaturity of the association areas for each modality. The neonate is capable of a considerable amount of motor activity, and the motor cortex is relatively advanced in maturation. Although he can vocalize (a motor activity), he cannot yet control the sounds (such control is a *skilled* motor activity involving the less developed sensory area) nor speak, for speech is a highly skilled activity requiring not only complicated motor control but also high-order intellectual functions involving late-maturing regions of the brain.

Thus many of the differences in psychological functioning between children and adults may be explained in terms of differences in the nervous system. In certain respects the child is a different organism from the adult: The organization of the CNS is different because the immature system does not function in the same way as the mature one.

In an earlier chapter on the neoinstinctual theories it was suggested that even in man a considerable amount of behavior depends on factors that are genetically transmitted and become an inherent part of the organism's repertoire. The nervous system is, as it were, preprogrammed to function in certain ways. Just how the information contained in the deoxyribonucleic acid (DNA) becomes translated into behavior is a mystery, but there is a good deal of evidence (some of which will be discussed in later chapters) that certain functions have a locus in the CNS (not necessarily in a single place) and that this locus is "wired-up" to mediate certain kinds of actions. These actions often—indeed usually—depend on the existence of certain conditions, for instance, a certain hormonal stimulation as well as extrinsic stimulation. In the higher animals certain prior experiences are frequently a condition for activation of the program.

PREPROGRAMMED BEHAVIORS

The idea of functional localization implies definite systems of connections between parts of the brain and between peripheral and central organs. The existence of the latter connections has, of course, been common knowledge for a long time, but recent work is showing that these connections are not gross but highly specific and intricately organized. Sperry (1963) has revived in different form the older notions of psychologists about strict connections being established between anatomical loci. Rather than being the result of learning, as the earlier behaviorists claimed, they seem to be innate. For instance, Attardi and Sperry (1963) and Gaze et al. (1965) have shown evidence that there is a structurally fixed and orderly relationship in the fiber connections between end-organ cells and internuncial and central neurons. If, in immature vertebrates, these cells are surgically rearranged, then the original connections reestablish themselves by regenerative processes. The regeneration does not occur in mature organisms, where such rearrangements result in permanent dysfunction. It seems that in embryological development highly specific connections are set, some chemical "marker" causing a particular nerve fiber to connect to its destined end organ (Sperry, 1963). It has also been noted that no evidence can be found for neuroanatomical restructuring as a result of learning.

Just what the relationship between these facts and behavior may be has not been proved, but it is difficult to avoid the assumption that the precision with which the organism seems to be wired-up has strong influences on behavior. This does not of necessity mean that behavior is irrevocably determined by the nature of the wiring, that is, by the interconnections laid down. In higher organisms, at least, it would seem that there are numerous alternative connections and behavior can be flexible. In these higher organisms it seems frequently to be the case that environmental factors (i.e., learning) are necessary to making functional these "prewired" incipient patterns. But presumably such "ready-to-go" behavioral patterns are more easily elicited than those for which no neural patterns of interconnections exist. This idea will be referred to at various points in this book.

It will be noted that if the idea of neural interconnections underlying learning must be rejected, then it would seem that there are two kinds of phenomena having the appearance of learning. One is the kind where a neural preprogramming exists and merely requires certain stimuli in the environment to make the program operative. Imprinting is probably such a case. The other phenomenon is "true" learning, the acquisition of some "behavior" (using this term very broadly) for which *no* preprogramming exists. Memories are learning of this type. They involve neural changes of a kind, but probably in the nucleic acids of nerve cells rather than in fibers or synapses. (There may be a difference here between short- and long-term memories, or between temporary and permanent behavioral acquisitions: This statement refers to the long-term memories and permanent behavioral acquisitions.) How these biochemical changes are made, or how they are translated via the nervous system into behavior, is as yet a complete mystery.

Individuals of species of higher organisms in particular gain over the life span a considerable number of these nonpreprogrammed changes and these are translated into unprogrammed or noninnate behaviors. However, one thesis of this book is that even in man there is a considerable range of preprogrammed behaviors that are an integral property of the nervous system, and that these are easier to elicit and more economical in function than are unprogrammed ones.

HIERARCHICAL ORGANIZATION

Any discussion of the function of the brain must take cognizance of the fact that it is hierarchically organized, and that the highly involved brain of the primates functions at levels of various evolutionary ages. One major difference between the higher animals and lower ones is the increased importance of the cortex, which takes over more and more of the functions of older parts of the brain; in man these more ancient parts mediate only vegetative (though vital) functions. One of the reasons for man's long childhood is that the cortex of the brain takes so long to mature.

Incidentally, it is reported that the age of puberty is arriving earlier in the well-nourished nations. It would be interesting and significant to know if this is merely a matter of maturation of the reproductive system or whether the cortex shares in this acceleration.

Another aspect of brain functioning to be taken into account is the crucial interaction between the cortex and the reticular activating systems of the midbrain and brain stem. A model of brain function that takes into account both aspects and their developmental relevance is given by G. Bronson (1965). In this model there are three levels, the first and lowest being the brain stem, which includes the brain stem reticular system.[7] Level 2 consists of the subcortical brain stem, including the thalamus, hypothalamus, and limbic system. Level 3 is the neocortex. Within each of these levels there is a network of short axon neurons with multiple interconnections and also long axon neurons that interconnect regions within the level. Other long axon neurons connect the levels both upward and downward. There are in addition the peripheral afferents and efferents that connect the sense organs with the CNS at the various levels, allowing increasingly refined, and successively more differentiating, sensory and motor discriminations to be made by the networks. The long axon neurons for vertical integrations between the levels permit the more primitive systems to exercise an upward control on the programming of patterns of cerebral activation. Those projecting downward from the higher levels impose tonic inhibition, and more selective phasic excitations and inhibitions, on the lower level systems, thus differentiating overall functions. There is an interesting diversity of neural interconnections within the higher levels in more advanced species, and this diversity allows for an increasing development of specialized functions in the short axon networks.

Bronson goes on to point out that activity in the lower two levels is influenced by changes in the internal chemical environment, and that, from the interplay of these factors at level 1 upward, projections affect the general or tonic level of sensory alertness and motor responsiveness of the organism. Networks within level 2 integrate input from various exterioceptive and proprioceptive sources and project up to level 3, thereby modulating the more varied or phasic activation patterns in

---

[7] Certain brain structures are defined loosely by anatomists and even more loosely by neuropsychologists. The latter tend to define regions by their function rather than by their more obvious anatomical boundaries, and this is one source of confusion in terminology. The following definitions are therefore only approximate.

1. *Reticular formation* (RF): The RF is a complex of nerve centers. There are two main divisions, the lower or brain stem RF, and the upper or midbrain RF, which includes parts situated in the hypothalamus and thalamus.

2. *Reticular activating system* (RAS): The RAS is a *functional* entity and ramifies throughout the brain. The RF is an anatomical region and is an essential element in the RAS, but the functions of the RAS are widespread and not confined to the RF.

3. *Limbic system:* The limbic system includes lower cortical and midbrain structures. It has connections with the viscera and is sometimes called the "visceral brain." In lower animals it is largely concerned with the sense of smell, but in higher ones it has much more diverse implications for behavior and is strongly involved in fear, anger, and motivation generally. The septum, tegmentum and other structures referred to in Chapter 9 are part of this system.

4. *Amygdala:* The amygdala is part of the limbic system, q.v.

5. *Pyriform lobe:* The pyriform lobe is part of the limbic system, q.v.

the association area of the neocortex and giving a focus of attention on particular stimulus patterns. It is through the particular sensitivities of levels 1 and 2 that the neocortex is adaptive to the physiological state of the organism.

Having outlined this general model for CNS organization, Bronson goes on to discuss in greater detail the functions of these levels. He does this by reviewing a good deal of the relevant literature and, as must be the case in any discussion on this topic, he draws upon Samuels' comprehensive review (1959) of work on the reticular activating system.

Level-1 Networks

Level 1 is phylogenetically ancient and mediates gross motor functions. The brain stem reticular activating system, together with the motor nuclei of this level, are involved in the coordination of gross bodily movement. For instance, innate mechanisms that are involved in bilateral coordination of the head, eyes, and trunk and that produce orienting responses to tactile visual or motor stimuli are mediated at level 1. Certain stimulus response systems like the sucking, rooting, and pupillary reflexes are also present here. In the more primitive vertebrates, such reflexes represent the total behavioral repertoire. In man they form a background pattern from which evolve more differentiated motor responses controlled by higher neural systems. Some of these reflexes disappear shortly after birth, for they are soon inhibited by neocortical systems.

An important function mediated at this level is the *orientation reaction,* a readiness to respond to external stimuli. It involves orienting responses of receptor organs (e.g., turning of the head, eyes, and ears), increase of muscular tonus, and autonomic reactions preparative to activity—all reflected in EEG arousal. There is also a *defensive reaction,* which has much in common with the orienting reaction

but is a response to intense stimulation or to pain. In later childhood perceptual patterns mediated by the neocortex, as well as learned stimulus patterns, can mediate the orienting and defensive reactions

In its vertical functions, the reticular system of level 1 is a neocortical activating system. It has gross effects on sensory and motor responsiveness. It has priority over the more focal activation of the neocortex controlled by the thalamic activating system in level 2, and thus brings the organism out of a narrower attentional focus to more generalized alertness in response to danger.

The reticular system at this level is responsive to a number of internal chemical conditions, such as blood sugar level, the sex hormones, and adrenaline. The brain-stem reticular system also receives input from all the sensory modalities but has limited capacity for discriminations within them. While there is downward control of the reticular activating system from many areas of the neocortex, controls from the areas involved in memory and emotion (superior, temporal, cingulate, and hippocampal gyrii) are most important. The relevance of this control to motivation needs no emphasis. Maturation can, by selective excitation and inhibition of the reticular networks after recognition of significant stimuli, lead to control of reticular function by neocortical centers.

There are probably two kinds of orientations produced by level-1 activation of the higher CNS, and each depends on the intensity of reticular excitation. If the excitation is moderate in response to a novel object or environment, it initially produces the orientation reaction and leads to exploration, which is terminated by familiarity with the novel stimulus or habituation. The waning of this generalized alerting response leads to a narrowing of attention as level-2 mechanisms resume control of neocortical activations. More intense reticular activation produces the defense reaction, which is followed by either innate or acquired fear reactions and is ended either by escape from the arousing stimuli or by habituation; in the latter case arousal may eventually subside to a level inducing exploration rather than fear.

Bronson points out that in humans the individual may not be aware of the stimuli that produce intense activation of the brain-stem reticular networks, for example, the stimuli that are chemical factors in the blood or repressed ideational factors, and in this case innocent objects may become the focus of escape or attack behavior. If the environment does not supply an object upon which to focus the defensive reaction, the reaction may lead to general irritability or diffuse anxiety and be basic to some neurotic syndrome.

Level-2 Networks

Bronson points out that the networks interconnecting the subcortical areas within the mammalian brain are highly complex and not well understood. However, some general statements can be made about them. First, they provide more refined sensory discrimination and motor coordination than do ones of the lower level. Second, they are concerned in specific motivational and emotional arousal and support ongoing purposive behavioral sequences. Third, they provide mechanisms for control of attention.

In man the first of these networks functions as an integrating mechanism within the extrapyramidal system; especially under high motivation, even with loss of sensory or motor areas of the neocortex, these subcortical areas can provide some gross motor control of the limbs and facial expressions. However, in man, visual and auditory experiences depend on level-3 functions.

It is not the motor aspects, but the motivational aspects of this level, that are of most interest in man. Bronson points out that the motivational networks within level 2, which both initiate and maintain purposive behaviors, are responsive to certain chemical changes within the organism and probably also to input from pain and genital afferents in mature organisms. They are also influenced by auditory and visual perceptions that are mediated via the neocortical systems.

The limbic system has a central role in the mediation of emotional behavior. Those studies using artificial stimulation by implanted electrodes make it clear that both pleasant and unpleasant sensations are mediated here. The verbal reports of human subjects tell us that these pleasurable sensations are often sexual in nature (some of this material is reviewed in Chapter 9).

There are vertical interconnections between the thalamic reticular system and certain areas of the neocortex, and these mediate the attentional functions of the level-2 system. The reaction here is different from the global arousing function of the brain-stem reticular system. The thalamic RAS produces a more focalized and rapidly changing learning mechanism that makes for a focus of attention on specific sensory modes, and such a mechanism is probably selective within the mode. The projections from these thalamic nuclei go mainly to the primary sensory reception areas in the parietal, occipital, and temporal areas of the neocortex. It is probably by way of the descending pathways from these areas that the neocortex exerts a control over the thalamic RAS and thus holds at least partial control over its own excitation; it can be selective to a significant part of the input (Samuels, 1959). It is likely that when no specific motivational system (such as hunger or thirst) has dominance, perceptual novelty is one important factor directing attention. In this situation exploratory behavior appears.

Level-3 Networks

The third of Bronson's levels is the neocortex. The relevant aspects of cortical functions are discussed elsewhere in this chapter, and need no repetition here. Welker (1961) states that those species with fewer inborn responses to specific patterns of stimuli show most exploratory behavior and also notes that among species there is a relation between the preferred mode for exploration and the state of development of the various sensory areas of the cortex. These facts suggest that in the higher species the neocortex plays a major role in the instigation and direction of exploratory behaviors.

A further suggestion made by Bronson is that the more enduring exploratory and fear orientations that appear in maturer organisms develop from the transient orientation and defensive reactions mentioned earlier. These later exploratory and fear responses result from perceptions mediated at a cortical level, for this level maintains RAS activity by descending pathways. The RAS is responsive only to change in stimulation, either in the mode or in the intensity of input into level 1, and therefore habituation is rapid; in a stable environment the orientation reaction will be brief. However, the downward activation from the cortical perceptual systems is sufficiently varied in most environments to provide the changes necessary to maintain level-1 RAS activation and thus an alert awareness of the environment; in these climates habituation will not set in. Where the environment has a sufficient degree of novelty, exploratory behavior is shown.

In more mature organisms, Bronson says, there is a fear orientation in response to complex stimulus patterns of greater novelty. He believes that this arises from the defensive reaction, which is mediated at level 1, to intense stimulation or to pain. There are many species that show an innate fearfulness to perceptual novelty, and this reaction develops later than the capacity for complex pattern discrimination. This matter is discussed in the chapter on imprinting and is a factor that allows time for the development of primary attachments. The onset of the fear reaction ends the critical period for attachments. It would seem, therefore, that fearfulness in response to novelty either requires more extended visual experience than is needed for object recognition, or is dependent on further maturation in the CNS. Bronson interprets Riesen's data (1958) on the later development of chimpanzees reared for the first seven months in diffused light as showing the influence of maturation. In these animals the fear of strange objects appears either before or at about the same time as visual recognition. This Bronson takes as an indication that maturation initiates the fear of strangeness; normally reared animals have already developed cortically mediated object recognition by this time. It may be assumed (though proof is lacking) that this maturation is within the limbic system, in which case developments, in infancy, from the brief defensive reaction to the longer-lasting fear orientation depends on maturational processes in level 2 and level 3.

It would seem from Conel's work on the maturation of the human cerebral cortex that the neocortical systems are probably nonfunctional in the first month after birth and that therefore behavior during this first month is limited to functions appropriate to level-1 mediation. This is supported by observations of anencephalic infants whose adaptive motor patterns are reflexive and similar in form to that of normal neonates (Jung and Hassler, 1960). In the first month, sensitivity to stimulation is limited to changes in intensity of input and to pain; there is no evidence of pattern discrimination. Bronson interprets Fantz's data (1958) on differential fixation in the first week of life as the product of intensity discrimination mediated at a retinal level. In this he follows Sackett (1963). Visual following, which is a response to spatiotemporal intensity changes, is seen in anencephalic infants and is therefore presumably a subcortically mediated reflex.

Thus Bronson suggests that the sensory and motor capabilities of the neonate are limited to the capacities of level-1 systems. Similarly the emotional capacities of the neonate are also within the range that can be mediated by changes in level-1 RAS activity. The stimuli effective at this level are certain internal biochemical changes, sudden intense stimulation, and pain. As noted elsewhere (Chapter 14), the resulting behavior is the same whatever the precipitating stimulus.

Again following Conel's data (1947), it would seem that there is rapid neocortical maturation commencing in the second and third month. During this period there are behavioral developments that involve neocortical mediation, thus showing that level-3 systems have matured to a level of some function.

Bronson believes that the appearance of the smiling response in the second month is evidence of pattern discrimination and recognition. According to Jersild (1946), there is a consensus of opinion that in the second month the undifferentiated emotional responses of the newborn begin to become more varied. Bronson assumes that this increasing repertoire of emotional behaviors reflects increased motivational differentiation as well as greater cognitive capabilities. He notes again the importance of level-2 networks in this change.

Another change at about three months is the development of the transient orienting reaction of the neonate into the more persistent exploratory behavior of the older infant. Bühler (1930) and Piaget (1952) have noted the beginning of active visual interest in the environment in the second month, and of overt exploratory behavior in the third month. Sleep patterns also show this development. In the first month the infant awakes only for short periods; unless aroused by nutritional deficiencies, sudden intense stimulation, or pain, all of which stimuli are mediated by level-1 systems. By about three months, however, there are longer periods of quiet daytime wakefulness (nighttime sleep showing little change), which is presumably maintained by an interest in novelty in the environment. Another change at this time is seen with respect to fear reactions; the neonatal defensive reaction to intense stimuli comes to include the possibility of fear reactions to pattern stimuli. There is now, in addition to the innate fear of perceptual strangeness already noted, the capacity for acquiring fears.

Adaptive Mechanisms Hierarchically Organized

One point that is evident in the consideration of evolutionary development of the nervous system is that there is a repetition in the higher species of various adaptive mechanisms at different levels of the CNS. With each repetition there is elaboration and refinement. Bronson points out that this is of interest to understanding human development because there is in this development a sequential appearance of successively more refined adaptive mechanisms, and in later functioning there is a complex interaction between systems which are of different levels, having analogous functions but different degrees of complexity.

This effect can be seen in a number of contexts, but notably in those of learning and motivation. The applications of this model to learning are discussed in Chapter 12.

The "motivational hierarchy" has at its base the vegetative needs, ones that affect the internal environment—food, drink, sex, and so on. These needs produce cyclical periods of increased activity (Dell, 1958) and appear to be like exploratory behaviors; however, unlike exploratory behaviors, they are stimulated by perceptual novelty and are directed toward specific stimulus patterns related to the necessary consummatory activity. The apparently exploratory aspects of this behavior tend to lessen as the animal acquires the information necessary to consummation.

Centers sensitive to the internal environment are present both in level 1 and in the hypothalamus of level 2. The latter is more differentiated anatomically in that it has nuclei specifically responsive to certain biochemical states and directs behavior toward specific goals. The lower level, on the other hand, affects only general alertness and motor activity.

It is altogether likely that Bronson's speculations about the role of the cortical mechanisms in "higher motives" are appropriate. He points out that one of the features of higher organisms (especially humans) is the capacity for complex behaviors involving flexible goal-oriented actions (discussed in Chapter 14) that are not dependent on close environmental stimulation and that are not related directly to physiological needs. Developmentally, functional autonomy and other sophisticated motivations must depend on maturation of the cortex.

AUTONOMIC NERVOUS SYSTEM

Most of this chapter has concerned itself with the so-called "higher" part of the nervous system. This is perhaps a reflection of the preoccupation of psychologists with intellectual and other "higher functions." Elsewhere in this book it is suggested that emotional functions merit greater prestige than generally accorded them by psychologists (at least of the nonclinical variety). N. E. Miller (1969) has made a plea for the autonomic nervous system (ANS), which he thinks is unjustly regarded as "inferior." Its role in psychosomatic and homeostatic functions is well recognized, but he has for some years been conducting experiments which he believes to indicate deep implications of the ANS for theories of learning. He believes that the ANS is not only involved in "automatic" homeostatic responses such as temperature regulation, but that it is also capable of *learning* homeostatic responses. It is also possible that learning in the ANS may underlie the development of individual differences in reactions to stress, and that a new approach to psychotherapy might involve visceral learning, unlearning, or relearning. It is too early to say what the real significance of these findings is, but they certainly open up an area for consideration.

In summary, it is evident from the material reviewed in this chapter that the infant is an organism neurologically different from the adult and that he remains different for some years. As yet the precise nature of these neurological differences have not been spelled out, but some of the general indications are discernible. The time relationships are at present only rather vaguely known, but again there are fairly clear indications that a temporal sequence of development takes place and that these changes extend into adolescence and perhaps later life.

In this sequence of changes, the older and more primitive parts of the brain (called level 1 by Bronson) mature first and are functional at birth, or at some time before. In the early months there is maturation of middle levels of function and also concurrent development of certain cortical functions. However, the latter continue their development for some years.

From what is known of functional localization in the brain, it is possible to say with some certainty that these developments influence somewhat specific functions. That about which most is known at present is language, which has been used as an instance of the correlation between regional maturation and function, though no doubt in the course of time we shall learn more about the developmental changes in the neurology of other cognitive functions also. Because cognition is a highly complex matter (markedly influenced, for instance, by language), there must be a considerable interplay of developmental forces involved.

Because the brain operates as a functional unity of great complexity, it is obvious that these changes must bring about shifts in the whole organization of the brain. In the early years the CNS is highly plastic, and under certain circumstances, as in early brain damage, marked modifications of normal organization can occur. However, it is altogether possible that there is, quite apart from traumatic reorganization, a fairly wide range of individual differences in functional organization of the brain.

As the brain matures, the growing organization tends to become self-perpetuating and increasingly to inhibit reorganization. Insofar as language is concerned, there is, according to Lenneberg (1967), a rapid decline after puberty in the capacity of the brain for self-organization with respect to most aspects of verbal behavior: The brain becomes, as it were, set in its ways of operating. The same may well be true of other aspects of cognitive function.

The factors that determine this self-organization of the brain are highly varied. Some, no doubt, are innate. The experiences of the organism, and especially the early ones, must also have a marked influence on this organization. Some of these modifying conditions are dealt with in other chapters.

Seven

Critical Periods in Development

The concept of the critical period is illustrated in embryology; it is well known that in the early embryological stages of tissue growth tissue is unspecific and development is determined by location. For example, tissue from the presumptive neural groove, which will shortly become the primitive nervous system and ultimately the CNS, can, in early stages, be transplanted to another part of the embryo, where it will develop in a manner consistent with its new location but in a form unlike the form it would have taken had it remained where it originally was. Thus what was originally destined to become nerve tissue may, after transplant, become skin tissue. There is, however, in this development, a critical point when the tissue does become determined in its nature, and after this point it will retain its own identity if transplanted (Speman, 1938).

Later in embryological growth we find that the development of the embryo may be affected by extraneous factors that modify it at particular times but not at others. J. P. Scott (1937) has shown, in experiments with genetic, physical, and chemical agents applied in early embryological development, that the injuries that result from interferences with growth are not the same at all times but depend on the developmental process going on at any particular time. There are in the embryological development of any organ critical periods that usually coincide with periods of rapid growth. In humans, maternal rubella during pregnancy which coincides with the earlier stages of fetal development—stages in which the basic organs are commencing their differentiation—may affect this development, causing defects such as cardiac abnormalities; the same disease in the mother later in pregnancy may have no such effect. Thalidomide babies provide a dramatic example of the influence of the presence in the maternal bloodstream during the same critical period of a substance toxic to the fetus.

Thus from embryology we gain the idea that, during its course of development, the organism passes through phases during which it is sensitive to particular influences, whereas at other stages of development it may be less sensitive, or even insensitive, to the same influences.

In postnatal physical development as well there are instances of critical events having differential effects according to the time of occurrence. For example, larval female bees fed throughout development on the so-called "royal jelly" (which is richer in protein than the usual diet) become queens; those fed, after about the middle of the third day, on a plebeian diet of honey and pollen become workers; intermediates result if royal jelly is resumed in the later stages of larval growth (Wigglesworth, 1953). Even within more limited physical processes there may be critical periods. Selye (1955) has demonstrated that in rats there is a normal pattern of skin reaction to an irritant and that if a stress is applied at different times during the course of this reaction, the pattern is modified in varying ways.

The idea of a critical period is not a new one in psychology. In the 1890's William James discussed what he called the "transitoriness of instincts" and in doing this he put forward the notion that the organism has enhanced susceptibility to a given experience at certain stages of development. While he speaks in the psychological language of the time and does not use the term itself, the idea of the critical period is quite clearly presented. The idea is also implicit in Freud's discussion of the phases of development. Although the notion of a period of heightened susceptibility is thus to be found in psychological writings before the beginning of the twentieth century, it has only been comparatively recently that it has been amplified or that the term *critical period* as such has appeared in the literature. Following James, it seems that the critical period involves some constitutional basis, probably genetically determined, and is part of the normal maturation of the species.

A question arises as to whether the critical period must be considered a maturational phenomenon or not. That is, does there necessarily have to be a *physical* change of some kind underlying the emergence and ending of the period? It is feasible that some events may be critical in that prior learning affects later learning, there being a facilitatory or an inhibitory effect of what is learned before on what comes later. This effect is a well-established phenomenon. Similarly, cognitive habits that influence all subsequent cognition may be acquired. Styles of action may be acquired (characteristic reactions to frustration, for example) that have a persistent effect on later responses of the same class. To take another case, and a trite one, the concept of number must be acquired before addition and all other arithmetical concepts can be understood. In each case one could describe the period of initial acquisition as critical to later performance.

How one uses a term is a matter of definition. It seems here that one has two distinct phenomena. One of them involves some ongoing maturational process that results in a particular sensitivity of the biological substratum to certain psychological events, and is taken as the definition of *critical period*.

Some other term is required for the case in which one psychological event influences later psychological events without depending on a *maturational* change in the biological substratum. (One might argue that any psychological event results in a biological change in the organism—a modification of RNA or the laying down of a new cell assembly. Hence the term *maturational* is a key one.) In this class of phenomenon the timing is not so important, because it does not have to coincide with a maturational event; hence the word *period* with its time connotation would be rather misleading. In many cases, of course, there will be a rough time element imposed by various factors—the fact that the event is earlier rather than later or the fact that most children in our society tend to acquire certain psychological modifications according to an imposed chronology, or the grade-one curriculum, or so on. But here the timing is not inexorable.

The term *salient event* is suggested for this

class of phenomenon. A salient event is one that determines or modifies later psychological responses. In a sense most psychological events have a determinant effect. Each cigarette smoked tends to predetermine the smoking of another. (This is perhaps not a good example because the addictive properties of nicotine introduce a physiological element.) But the original first step that made a smoker out of a nonsmoker was a salient event. (This may not have been the actual lighting of the first cigarette but rather the early training that created a favorable or unfavorable attitude to smoking.) A salient event is thus one that sets in sequence one chain of action rather than another or one kind of response rather than another—for example, refusing cigarettes rather than accepting them. The salient event may not be punctate in time.

Distinguishing critical periods from salient events may not always be easy. To be certain of the former, one must demonstrate a maturational correlate, and there is at present no instance in which we can do this: We can infer it in a number of cases, but that is not the same thing. For the present, however, we must be content with inferences.

A feature of the critical period is that it has a fairly rigid timing with which the critical event must coincide, whereas, in principle at least, a salient event can take place at any time. However, missed salient events may often seem to be missed critical events in that they may be difficult to impose later. The person who somehow misses out on geography at school is rather likely to remain permanently lacking here—but simply because he then moves in circles in which the acquisition of this knowledge is unlikely. An extra effort is needed to obtain the facilities for studying such a subject after school is left. Our social system does not make provision for the dropout.

Another factor that may give a spurious appearance of a critical period is that some events may have different effects according to the stage of psychological development of the organism. Thus Barry (1956) has described

what he calls a critical period for the development of a psychoneurosis, the critical event being the death of the mother and the time period being the first five years. Now it could be that the event is crucial at this time not because of some basic maturational state of the child's nervous system but because he has not yet developed psychological mechanisms to cope with this situation. However, there is the counterargument that the reason psychological coping mechanisms are undeveloped is that the child is neurally immature. There are no data to appeal to in settling this argument; one can only protest that this neurological factor is probably an indirect rather than a direct one.

To take another instance where there may be ambiguity, Stendler (1952) has discussed the development of independency–dependency socialization in children in terms of critical periods. Independency is built upon from an initial dependency relationship with the parents. The first critical period (Stendler suggests) comes at about twelve months, when the child's awareness of the relationship between himself and the parent as a socializing agent is in a state of flux. The child tests his dependency on the parents by increased demands, and if these testing demands are not met, overdependency may result.

Between two and three years of age there is a second "critical period," which Stendler relates to society's imposition of pressure toward culturally approved independence behaviors. The manner in which this process is handled (in particular if traumatic events such as the loss of a parent coincide) may cause overdependent behavior. It will be noted that this second period, as described by Stendler, differs from the use of the critical period concept as suggested here. In this example the changes underlying the acquisition of behavior are supposed to lie not in the child but externally, in a change in society's demands. These changes may constitute a salient event, but they cannot, the way Stendler puts it, be considered dependent on a critical period.

However, just to show how difficult the matter is, it might be argued that the negativism of the three-year-old is the result of a maturational event, and is not, as Stendler suggests, an imposed expectation. Hence it is a critical period in the true sense.

These reservations may seem to make the distinction between critical periods and salient events one that is not especially useful, and one must admit to the merit of this argument at the present time. However, it would seem of value to keep the possibility of a difference in mind; hopefully, being aware of the distinction may aid the interpretation of any data that may come forward and may direct research in the future. Some of the phenomena, in the discussion that follows, that are presumed to be examples of critical period happenings may prove to be salient events, that is, ones not dependent on a maturational change. But it is being presumed that not all of them fall in this class and that, in the course of time, with some at least, the maturational basis will be demonstrated rather than inferred as at present.

It is evident that the critical period phenomenon has two distinct but inseparable components. One is the change in the maturational substratum that is presumed to underlie the periodicity of the phenomenon. The period really refers to the time of this physical development. The other component is the experiential event that must occur during this time; this is the critical event. Thus critical periods have both intrinsic and extrinsic aspects. (It might be pedantic to ask if both the base and the event could be internal. This might well occur in physiological critical periods, where, for example, a maturational neural change may be coincident with a hormonal event, but a psychological critical period would seem necessarily to involve an external perceptual event. Or must it? Could a cognitive event—a fantasy, for instance—take the place of an external one? There is scope for avant-garde theorizing here.)

In nature the experiential events essential to development are probably so common as to be virtually inevitable. In the rare cases where they fail, the organism will perish; but it is only in the unnatural conditions of laboratories or civilizations that any significant number of growing organisms will miss critical events.

It will be noted that two distinct situations apply in what might be called *critical period abnormality:* One is the case where an individual fails to experience a critical event that is part of the normal developmental history of his species, and the other occurs when he experiences a critical event that is not a usual one. The first, or deprivation, situation would include such things as failure of a perceptual event (e.g., lack of imprinting or, at a more global level, such events as parental bereavement, in which the main effect on the child stems from deprivation of an affectional relationship). The other situation arises when some extraneous event that is not a normal one, in the sense of being shared by all members of the species, occurs at a critical period in a particular individual's history. It would include such examples as training in the herding of sheep by dogs, or traumatic events and other unusual experiences in human childhood.

The fact that a given piece of behavior may be instinctive, which implies that it is innate, does not preclude the possibility that learning plays an important part in the full emergence of that behavior. For example, while young birds may go through all the motions of drinking behavior (placing the head down in a scooping movement and throwing it upward and backward), and while this behavior emerges as an apparently innate and unlearned sequence, the bird must still learn that water is the proper thing to drink (Craig, 1912). Similarly, pecking behavior appears innately; but for certain species at least, the young bird must learn what to peck at—that is, what is good as food (Moseley, 1925; Padilla, 1930). Thus, although there are inborn patterns of motor behaviors, the animal must learn the appropriate object toward which these behaviors must be directed.

There are behaviors that do appear to be entirely innate and show little if any change with experience. In many others, particularly among the higher animals, there may be observed an improvement with practice, even in those that are partly innate. Thus with many birds the nest-building behavior is largely innate; but there is a clumsiness and lack of skill demonstrated in the building of the first nest, while subsequent ones are more neatly and expeditiously executed, with improvement in the selection of appropriate materials (Thorpe, 1956). Instinctive behaviors are often subject to modification by learning.

In those instinctive behaviors which are entirely innate and in which learning takes no place (assuming there are such), there would be no critical event involved, at least not one of a psychological nature; however, there may still be a physiological one. Also, forms of behavior that are largely innate (such as the pecking of birds, nest building, and a host of others at various animal levels) but that do involve learning as well may involve critical periods. Under natural conditions the critical event is unlikely to fail; for instance, in the case of the hatching gosling in the wild, the first large, moving object it perceives is almost certain to be one of the parent birds, to which it becomes imprinted.

In some cases the ending of a critical period is quite clearly related to the emergence of a new pattern of behavior that is antagonistic to that involved in an earlier phase. For instance, Spalding noted that fearfulness as a behavioral pattern appeared in chicks at about the fourth day; chicks unimprinted at this time could no longer be imprinted because they fled instead of following. James has also commented on the same phenomenon, with calves as well as with chicks. The study of Freedman et al. (1961) observes the same thing with cocker spaniels. In such instances as these the effect of imprinting is the exclusion of the object to which the young is imprinted from the more general flight reac-

tion toward a larger class of objects, and particularly toward unfamiliar ones. Usually, of course, the effect is to exclude the parents, and, by generalization the animal's own species, from the flight reaction.

In other cases the exclusion might be from other forms of behavior. We see such exclusion in Kuo's findings that kittens reared with rats excluded rats from the killing pattern of behavior. Cats and rats brought together after the emergence of killing behavior in the former will obviously not form a friendly relationship.

There is some evidence, in a study by Jaynes (1957), for latent imprinting, that is to say, imprinting that is not manifested in overt behavior while it is occurring but that appears later. Some of the birds did not follow the cube to which imprinting was being attempted in the neonate period but quite suddenly did so at a later stage. Although we cannot accept latent imprinting as an established fact, Jaynes' observation does arouse the thought that some early experiences may result in no observable change in behavior but may nevertheless "prime" the organism and make it more receptive to later events. Some of the rather mysterious aspects of development may be explained in this way, which accounts both for the fact that experiences that might be expected to result in modifications of behavior sometimes apparently fail to do so and also for the sudden and seemingly unprepared emergence of behaviors that is often a feature of development.

It will be noted that in cases where the same species has been studied by different authors there is no close agreement as to the time of the critical period with which they are concerned. Most of the studies have involved small numbers, and because of individual differences, rather wide variations are to be expected even when a valid reference point can be fixed. However, in many cases a valid datum point has not been defined and errors have become multivariate.

Gottlieb (1961), in discussing imprinting

in ducks, has commented on the variations in the age at which the critical period is found by different authors studying the same species. He supposes that this is due to the convention of taking posthatching age as the criterion; because of individual differences in developmental rates, and also because entirely extraneous factors such as heat and humidity may affect the shell and influence the time at which it can be broken by the young bird, hatching is not a reliable criterion. He suggests that "developmental age" based upon the time of the onset of incubation should be used instead and gives a method by which this may be calculated. With mammals, in particular, the definition of precise developmental age presents many difficulties, and fairly wide variation in the limits of critical periods is to be expected from study to study.

TIMING OF CRITICAL PERIODS

Because it is assumed that critical periods have a maturational basis, it is logical to look for such periods at times of physical change. There are probably five major periods of postnatal physical change in the human individual: (1) infancy and early childhood, from birth until about the end of the fifth year; (2) middle childhood, from about the end of the fifth year until about the ninth year; (3) prepuberty; (4) adolescence; and (5) maturity. We cannot, of course, suppose that obvious physical changes of this kind will accompany every critical period, for in many cases these changes will not be at all open to inspection but will take place in the fastness of the central nervous system. The first, third, and fourth phases have been fairly widely studied (though not specifically as critical periods), but, as Simon (1959) has pointed out, the second period has been neglected in the literature. The second period coincides with school entry. Simon has produced some evidence to show that there are subtle but fairly well-defined physical changes between the first and second

period and that "readiness for school" is correlated fairly highly with maturation into the second period. In other words, the child who at the legal age of school entry is not yet maturationally in middle childhood is likely to be unready for school. The mere observation that this is a time of change does not, of course, prove that it is critical in the sense given here, but this is the kind of developmental phase in which it might be most profitable to begin a search for the critical periods in human development.

An essential feature of the critical period is that it has both a beginning and an end. William James, in his discussion of transitory instincts, uses the familiar expression "strike while the iron is hot," with the implication that the iron is cold both before and after this period of malleability; the organism, in some respects at least, does not remain indefinitely plastic. The critical period is thus a special case among maturational processes, a case in which there is a rise in susceptibility to a given influence, a plateau of definite duration, and following this, a decline in susceptibility. We need not suppose that susceptibility returns to zero in all cases, but in both the precritical and postcritical periods the efficiency of acquisition is low as compared with the maximum reached during the period.

Presumably the acquisition of any behavior pattern depends on maturational readiness (that is, the organism must have achieved at least the minimum state of development that permits that pattern to be performed and retained), but those patterns involving a critical period are to be distinguished from the ones in which there is reduced efficiency of acquisition before maturational readiness, but which may efficiently be acquired at any time following this. One of the features, then, of the critical period is that it coincides with some maturational change in the organism. The critical event must occur during this critical period, when the maturational substratum is in an optimal state of change. Before this, the substratum has not reached readiness and afterward it may have moved on to other states of change in which the critical event cannot so effectively "take."

NEUROLOGICAL BASIS OF CRITICAL PERIODS

We have seen, in discussing the development of the nervous system, that the cortex matures slowly and that different regions of it mature at different times. This "bit-by-bit" process of maturation continues at least until puberty and perhaps longer. It is logical to relate psychological development to this maturation of the nervous system: In other words, the maturational basis for psychological readiness is presumably to be found here (though perhaps not exclusively here). The critical period for a given psychological development commences when that part of the CNS concerned with it has reached a minimum state of maturation and begins to become functional. Before this time, the critical event is ineffectual because the cortex is not ready to "receive" it.

It has been demonstrated that if a given cortical area is not employed in its usual fashion, then it does not degenerate but probably is used instead in the service of some other modality. For example, if rats are blinded before the eyes open, then degeneration can be detected later in the peripheral parts of the optic nerves, up to the geniculate body, but not in the visual cortex, which shows no histological changes. It can be shown that this part of the cortex is functioning in these blinded rats—but evidently in the service of some function other than vision (see Lashley, 1950; and Tsang, 1934).

Using Hebb's concept of "cell assemblies" being filled out in the cortex, we can make a guess at what is happening; it may even be a reasonable guess. In the normal organism the parts of the cortex concerned in vision become "filled out" with "assemblies" related to visual experiences. In the case of the animal denied these visual experiences, this ma-

turing cortex does not remain idle but becomes filled out with some other experiences, possibly the increased tactual or auditory ones on which it must rely more heavily.

This may be the explanation of Tsang's finding that in rats blind from birth maze-running behavior learned as adults was lost with destruction of the visual cortex, just as it was with sighted ones. He was interested in the idea that visual space concepts are integrated in the visual cortex of normal rats. Blinded rats, having no such concepts, should then show no loss on visual cortical destruction. The fact that they *did* show loss suggests that this part of the brain might have become involved in the additional tactile (or other) sensory cues that replaced visual ones used by the normal rats. (However, this suggestion still leaves unexplained his finding that there was *equal* loss; the idea put forward here would lead one to expect only partial loss.)

Thus, if the critical event does not occur during the optimal time, when the appropriate cortical area is ready, the cortical area may be preempted by some other function and the input from the tardy critical event may be "crowded out"—the cortex is less receptive or even unreceptive. The function may, of course, be able to find some other location in the cortex, but if we assume that these cell assemblies are mostly in association areas with some structural relationship to a primary area of the cortex, then any other location may be less accessible (less efficient) in relation to the primary area. Further, if the event is long delayed, more and more of the cortex will have been taken over and will be less available.

G. Bronson (1965) attempted to relate the state of organization of the developing nervous system to critical periods. As noted in Chapter 6, he identifies three levels of CNS functioning. To recapitulate these briefly, the first is a brain-stem level, including the brain-stem reticular system. Gross motor functions are mediated at this level, and the reticular system coordinates gross bodily movements and such action as orienting responses (e.g., postural reflexes and auditory locating reflexes). In cats, brain-stem preparations are responsive to gross changes such as in the intensity of stimuli, but sensory discrimination is limited. The reticular system at this level receives afferents from the sensory structures and is also well supplied with afferents from the genitalia, but pain and proprioceptive stimuli are especially salient here (Samuels, 1959).

The second level is in the subcortical forebrain, which includes the hypothalamus, thalamus, and limbic system. The functions of this level are several, including the mediation of more refined sensory discrimination and finer motor coordination than is carried out at level 1. More important to the present discussion is its role in the emotional and motivational elements in behavior and in the control of attention.

The third level is the neocortical one, which mediates highly developed motor activities as well as perceptual and cognitive functions. It plays a crucial role in exploratory behavior and thus is most important in those species with fewer inborn responses to specific stimuli. In higher animals the neocortex is essential to exploratory activities.

Maturationally, the three levels develop in the order 1 to 3, though there is not much data on the rates within level 2.

Bronson goes on to say that the data on critical periods can be described under three categories: first, the nature of the stimuli to which the organism is sensitive during the period; second, the nature of the behavior patterns that are later affected; and third, the developmental stage during which these stimuli have their maximum effect on later behavior.

On the basis of the preceding categories the data from critical period studies can be ordered under three additional headings. The first is a critical period when the animal is grossly sensitive to unpatterned stimulation, which affects its later emotionality; the time is immediately after birth. The second is a period that depends on pattern discrimination and affects primary socialization; it occurs some time after birth in most species. The third period requires a complex or rich perceptual and behavioral environment involving fine pattern discriminations and motor coordinations and influences the development of learning abilities; it begins later than either of the others, but its upper limit is as yet ill-defined.

Bronson states that the first of these periods will probably be found only in those species born with a relatively immature nervous system and in particular in those species in which the neocortical auditory and visual systems are not yet fully functional and do not exert the controlling influence on lower centers that they eventually do. This is consistent with the fact that unpatterned somaesthetic stimuli are the effective ones—for example, tactile stimuli (disturbances, such as shaking, electric shock, and cooling). Most of the evidence on these long-term effects is from rats and mice but, presumably, the effects hold for higher mammals with neonatal immaturity. Bronson refers to the work of Levine (reviewed in Chapter 11) and to the autonomic responses to stress that are influenced by early stimulation; the stress responses are markedly (and permanently) affected by experiences in this early critical period. It will be noted that suckling apparently does not supply the stimulation required for this effect, whereas brief amounts of stressful stimulation do.

One of the most obvious aspects of critical period phenomena is the delay in the emergence of behavioral effects of early response. Bronson relates this to the hierarchical organization of the developing nervous system. The late-maturing networks are affected by the amount of stimulation of the first-level systems, the early experiences making this level less generally emotionally reactive and hence influencing its effect on higher levels. The other levels, when mature, determine the objects of emotional significance.

The second class of critical phenomena is related to primary socialization; its period appears when the level of pattern discrimination permitted by the second level (the subcortical forebrain) has developed. The animal becomes attached to an object (in nature, the parents) toward which certain kinds of responses are made during the critical period. Just what these responses are differs a good deal from species to species. In chicks it is following; in monkeys, and presumably in human infants too, it is clinging to a warm, soft object. Bronson suggests that this formation of early attachments is a type of instrumental learning, but his tentative and inconclusive formulation should be considered in the light of the discussion in Chapter 8 as to whether or not imprinting should be regarded as a form of learning. Although in some species visual and auditory discrimination mediated by the neocortical level may be involved, Bronson suggests that such discrimination is not primary; this may be especially true of the mammals.

It will be noted that in the human infant the critical stimulus is anything resembling a human face. At this stage the child smiles indiscriminantly at any such stimulus, even at a mask. There is thus *some* pattern discrimination, but it is gross. Finer discriminations in which masks and faces can be separated, and in which familiar and unfamiliar faces can be distinguished, come later.

As Bronson says, several theorists have mentioned the onset of fearfulness as the factor that brings this second critical period to an end. He notes the role of level-2 mechanisms, and especially of the limbic system, in fear behaviors. However, any connection between these two facts is speculative at present because little is known about the maturation of these parts of the brain.

The third kind of critical period phenomena depends on complex perceptual and motor experiences. These have their effect on later learning abilities. Bronson interprets the results of the Melzack and Scott studies (1957) of isolation-reared puppies in terms of a deficiency in the perceptual organization of the sensory environment, though because one of the most marked effects—the reaction to pain—involves the first level rather than the third,

one might question this aspect of the matter. The difficulty possibly arises from the fact that the puppies in this experiment might have suffered deprivation of experience affecting level 2, and perhaps level 1 also, so that a "pure" effect on level 3 was not obtained (and would be technically difficult to arrange, because, for one thing, we do not know the timing precisely enough).

Bronson states that there is as yet no clear upper limit discernible for this stage but suggests that it is not likely that it is ended by inhibitory effects caused by the maturation of the systems. Rather, it involves a gradual "loss of plasticity" (Riesen, 1958), and Jacobson's work (see Chapter 6) shows how there is a steady reduction, with age, of undetermined neurons (Jacobson, 1969).

The third period, Bronson states, differs from the others in being mediated by systems that have no superior levels to inhibit them or supplant their activities. For this reason the systems are less sharply delineated, are more reversible (the evidence for this is not clear), and have later effects that appear in behavioral features more similar to those in which the critical experiences occur, rather than being modified, as lower systems are, by upper ones.

Bronson points to the fact that learning in this stage appears to resemble latent learning; the stage could be called a critical period of especially rapid learning of this kind. This is particularly interesting in view of the observed deficiencies in latent learning of institutionalized children.

MUTABILITY OF CRITICAL PERIODS

A question that arises, but that cannot at this stage be definitely answered, is whether the biological substratum underlying critical periods follows its inexorable course of growth uninfluenced by anything happening outside the nervous system or external to the organism. One can infer that this is improbable. We know, for example, that function influences the development of the perceptual systems (Chapters 6 and 13) and that there are a number of factors that alter the timing of imprinting (Chapter 8). In the latter, some of these factors are external (e.g., perceptual stimuli such as sounds or shocks) and some are internal (such as drugs). It is impossible to say whether these influences act directly on the presumed biological substratum of the critical period or whether they act in some indirect manner (such as affecting the general level of arousal). One would hesitate to claim that the *effective* timing of critical periods is immutable, whatever the mechanism operating in these changes.

One might suggest, however, that no radical alterations in timing are likely. Time is an essential (but little regarded) element in biological processes. In psychobiological processes it may be that speed of nerve conduction is one crucial factor influencing the time relationships of neuropsychological events. Another time-bound effect is seen in the conversion of short-term memories to long-term storage. In developmental processes, physical growth can be accelerated or retarded within limits, but only within somewhat narrow ones. Biological time is inevitable both in the short and transient processes of life and in the long-span processes from conception to death.

CRITICAL PERIOD SCHEDULE

Inherent within the critical period hypothesis is the notion that the periods impose on development a timetable in which pace is determined by the waxing and waning of progressive phases. Though subject to influence, the maturational substratum moves on. Successive periods may be inimical to earlier ones, and a missed early period may leave the organism unprepared for a later one. In higher animals especially, the timetable imposed by critical periods may not be completely rigid

but it will almost certainly be significant.

A question quite apart from whether acceleration or retardation is possible is whether either is desirable. In our hasty age, of course, retardation is regarded out-of-hand as undesirable, but even this assumption might be worth examining. In a number of quarters there have been attempts to accelerate educational procedures, but, granting that such is feasible, the long-term effects are unexamined. It is notorious that quick cramming for exams is possible—every student knows this—but many professors suspect that this quickly gained material is as quickly lost and that the long-term effects are unhappy if one supposes that an education should have lasting properties. (It is not suggested that the kinds of acceleration being experimented with, such as the early teaching of concepts [discussed in Chapter 16], are necessarily analogous to cramming, though one wonders if the effects may not be similar.)

Another point is that development is a vast and interlocking complex of events. Accelerating one of the events might be feasible, but what is the influence of this acceleration on the total pattern of development? By selecting some one element for acceleration, do we thereby accelerate all the dependent relationships and consequent effects or do we disrupt a pattern so that the overall results are a disjunction of development?

It might be appropriate to ask why we need to change the time schedule of development. Piaget talks of the "American Question." When he comes to North America to discuss the acquisition of concepts, the first question always asked is, "Can they be speeded up?" To which his reply is, "What is the hurry? Why not let the child develop at his own pace?"

Acceleration may, of course, be a practical necessity, if the education for life in a highly complex technological society demands that an increasing volume of knowledge be acquired. Is a leisured childhood a luxury that must be denied future generations?

CRITICAL PERIODS IN THE BEHAVIORAL DEVELOPMENT OF ANIMALS

One of the earliest experiments in the area of animal development and critical periods was by Spalding (1873), who segregated newly hatched chicks. He noted that the chicks that had been separated for only a day or two after hatching responded on release to the call of the hen by running to her. If this separation continued for nine or ten days, the behavior could not be elicited, and he found that the period of "ripeness" seemed to be over. He also performed experiments on the flight of swallows and found that if young birds were restrained from making any flight movements they showed, in learning to fly, a difficulty that was proportional to the length of restraint. Dennis (1941) repeated this experiment with young buzzards, caging two of them at the time when they were beginning to feather and would normally be starting to acquire flight behavior. They were restrained for ten weeks, and at the end of this time they merely ran along the ground, from which they could lift themselves only a foot or so. They had poor balance and when placed on a perch they would tend to fall rather than fly to the ground. Control birds of the same age but which were left unrestrained were flying proficiently at this time.

It should be emphasized that the existence of a critical period in the development of a given behavior in one species does not justify the assumption that a similar critical period occurs at the corresponding point in the development of other species. For instance, Grohmann (1938), using a technique (similar to Spalding's) for restraint of young pigeons during the preflight period of development, found that there was no noticeable effect, as evidenced by comparison with a control group, of this restraint on the acquisition of flight. Evidently in this species flight is a purely maturational development and does not necessitate experience or environmental facilitation for its appearance.

Another early experiment was by Yerkes and Bloomfield (1910), who studied the mouse-killing behavior of kittens. They noted that there is a sudden marked change in the proficiency of this behavior and that this suggests a maturational rather than a learned development. They also noted that the older the animal was when it was first given the opportunity to hunt and kill a mouse, the harder it became to evoke this behavior, a result which suggests that a period of readiness was over.

Lorenz (1935) spoke of the critical period for imprinting in birds, and Tinbergen (1951) gives as an example of a critical period in learning the territory-defending behavior of the Eskimo dogs of eastern Greenland. He observes that the dogs live in packs of five to ten and that they collectively defend their territory against all others. The adult dogs of an Eskimo settlement have a precise knowledge of the boundaries of their own territories and of the bordering territories of other packs; they appear to have a good knowledge of where trespassing attackers are likely to enter their territory, and they defend such territory vigorously. The immature dogs do not defend the territory but roam indiscriminately into other territories, apparently having not yet learned the boundaries. During these excursions they may be severely maltreated by the defending dogs, but Tinbergen remarks that the observer is amazed at their apparent stupidity and failure to benefit from these experiences. However, at the time they are maturing sexually, they quite suddenly begin to defend their own territory and avoid foreign territories; in two instances he observed that these new behaviors occurred within a week of the first copulation.

From the evidence that he presents, Tinbergen is justified in the assumption that the dogs' susceptibility to learning this behavior is low during the juvenile period and suddenly increases as it matures to puberty. But if we are to define a critical period as one having both a beginning and an end to the phase of heightened susceptibility, then he has not demonstrated such a period. To do so, it would be necessary to show that animals denied this experience during their pubertal period, which is apparently the critical one in this particular learning, fail to acquire the behavior afterward. We must, therefore, be reserved about accepting this report as an established instance of a critical period, though certainly Tinbergen's observation is of interest.

Melzack and Scott (1957) have shown that dogs reared in isolation show abnormal reactions to pain during maturity. The dogs in their experiment had evidently been deprived of some early perceptual experience that determines the usual emergence of overt responses to pain, responses such as their actual capacity to perceive pain. The authors were not investigating the critical period specifically, so their study does not delineate one, but it seems evident that a critical period involving a definite end point had occurred sometime during the isolation, because these dogs' reactions to pain remained abnormal in spite of their experiences after the isolation was ended. Probably the sheltered conditions that accompanied the isolation had prevented their experiencing pain and learning avoidance behaviors; they had not experienced the rough-and-tumble of normal puppy life.

Another study that suggests a critical period is one by Thompson and Melzack (1956). In this experiment Scottish Terrier puppies were kept in isolation for the first seven to ten months, during which they saw neither their keepers nor other dogs. After weaning, litter mates separated as controls were, over the same period, reared in families as pets. The experimental animals showed materially different behaviors from the control groups, the behaviors persisting for several years and presumably being permanent. The differences were found both in emotional behavior and in problem-solving tests to which both groups of dogs were subjected. The authors conclude that the restriction of experience during the crucial period (of the first ten months of the dog's life) can result in enduring retardation of the animal in various psychological traits. Again, this study does not give us a precise delineation of the critical period; it merely indicates that the critical period apparently occurs at some time during this ten-month period.

Levine and Otis (1958) have presented evidence suggestive of a critical period in the pre-weaning stage of development of the rat, a stage during which tactile stimulation by handling results in greater resistance to severe physiological stress (starvation). In contrast to McClelland's view (1956) that the *amount* of infantile handling is the important variable, these authors suggest that the *age* at which it occurs is more crucial.

There have been a number of experiments with various mammalian species that show the important effects of stimulation in infancy on both physical and psychological development (these are reviewed in Chapter 11). In most of these experiments stimulation takes the form of handling or "gentling." In general, unstimulated animals are slower in growth and maturation and show marked behavioral differences from ones stimulated in infancy; exploratory behavior is at a minimum, for example. Levine (1960) has found in the rat evidence of a critical period for the maximum effects of stimulation. The period apparently occurs early after birth. Animals not stimulated until sometime following the sixth day showed markedly reduced effects of this stimulation as compared with those stimulated between the second and fifth days.

Other experiments have also indicated the positive effects of preweaning gentling on the development of rats, both in growth and emotional characteristics. Thus Weininger (1956) and Ruegemar and Silverman (1956) found large increases in body weight; Mogenson et al. (1957) found smaller increases. However, for other such experiments, negative results are also reported: J. H. Scott (1955) found no increase in weight of rats with handling. Mogenson and Ehrlich (1958) have proposed an explanation of these contradictory results and suggest that they may illustrate the existence of critical periods that come at different times for different individuals and groups, depending on variations in such factors as intrauterine conditions, early experience with the mother, general routines of the animal colony, and strain differences. There are extrinsic factors that influence the time at which the critical period for imprinting occurs (Chapter 8). For the rat there appears to be a later postweaning critical period in about the fourth week (between twenty-one and twenty-seven days in the strain used in this experiment). This is the period when critical experience has an effect on later "intelligent" behavior (Hymovitch, 1952). The results of early impoverishment cannot be reversed by an enriched environment in adult life. The effects of specifically developed motor abilities or motivational systems were ruled out. The experiment is also of interest in showing that not all kinds of learning are affected—rote learning was not, whereas the enriched rats were superior in tasks utilizing a "wider sensory environment" or "broader cognitive maps."

Bingham and Griffiths (1952) reared rats from twenty-one days onward in an enriched environment and also found a superiority in adult maze learning but not in discriminatory behavior. Forgays and Forgays (1952) reared rats in a variety of environments from twenty-six days on and found a rough proportionality between the degree of complexity of early environment and adult problem-solving ability.

It should be noted, however, that the irreversibility of lack of early experience has been questioned by Fuller (1966). He supposed that general emotional disturbance, rather than faulty perceptual organization in a critical period, might account for the effects in late performance. He found that learning in a "benign environment" was quite effective for beagle puppies, even after early restriction. However, he was using a form of reversal learning, and in view of some evidence reviewed elsewhere (Chapter 11) that the effects of early stimulation (or lack of it) are different for different kinds of learning, one perhaps needs to know more about the detailed influ-

ences of stimulation before making a general statement.

Hess (1961) has mentioned the possibility of a critical period of neurosensory maturation that permits the learning of "foreign" perceptual tendencies. He derives this from the experiments in which chicks, when reared in top- or bottom-lit environments, learned a preference for top- or bottom-lighted grains (this is discussed in Chapter 12). For the chick this learning occurs at about seven weeks after hatching.

CRITICAL PERIODS IN SOCIAL BEHAVIOR

Jaynes (1957) has made an experimental study of the imprinting phenomenon in the chick and found that susceptibility to permanent imprinting (to a moving object) is low in the first day of life, reaches a peak between about thirty-six and forty hours, and is apparently ended at about fifty-four hours. The animals were imprinted to a green cube moved slowly in a ten-foot alley by a mechanical device that ensured constant rates of motion with irregularly placed but standard pauses. Imprinting was assessed by the birds' tendency to follow the cube as it moved. A higher proportion of chicks followed the cube on the first day than on other days, but retention in these animals was found to be poor when they were retested ten days later; whereas animals imprinted later, up to the peak mentioned, tended to show increasingly better retention. It is interesting to note that although a smaller proportion of the birds were successfully imprinted when the first experience came later (that is, between forty and fifty-four hours), the animals that *were* imprinted then showed an increasing vigor in the following response.

Hess (1959) found, for imprinting of the mallard duckling, a critical period that ranged from five to twenty-four hours from hatching, the susceptibility to imprinting having a peak at thirteen to sixteen hours. He also showed some evidence that the critical period may be artificially prolonged by the use of drugs that reduce metabolism (meprobamate and chlorpromazine).

According to J. P. Scott (1958), there is in mammals an early period when the primary social relationships are formed. Compared with lower animals, this period is relatively long in the primates: This is in contrast to the few hours usually taken in birds and the few weeks taken in the dog. Infant chimpanzees can be socialized to human beings quite readily if socialization is done in the first few years; it becomes increasingly difficult to do it after this period.

On the basis of his observations with animals, Scott regards the process of socialization as being in two stages, primary and secondary. Primary socialization usually takes place early in life, often soon after birth, though not necessarily so. This primary socialization determines the group of animals to which the infant will become attached. Normally in nature this attachment is to the same species, though experiments have demonstrated that transfer to other species is possible with many animals. Later in development, the secondary socialization to other animals or groups occurs, sex relationships are included in this process. The primary socialization often imposes a limitation on the kind of secondary socialization that can take place, and most species, according to Scott, appear to have behavioral mechanisms that make it unlikely that the animal will form attachments to members of other species after the primary socialization has occurred.

It is also known by dog trainers that for many breeds an attachment between dog and master must be formed early in life and that some dogs are incapable of transferring their affection. (According to Lorenz [1952], the Chow in particular is a "one-man dog.") It is probably the fact that there is a critical period involved and that this period gives the dog the faithfulness that makes it such an en-dearing companion to humans. After a dog has established such a relationship to others of its own kind or to one master, it cannot transfer readily to another. Lorenz believes that imprinting cannot be reversed, and that it cannot be transferred to another object: The original imprinting is final and lifelong. Some writers have questioned this contention (e.g., Steven, 1955), but the evidence of reversibility is inconclusive; it could be that species differences are found here, and in dogs the degree of wildness of the older animal may be a crucial factor.

Scott and Marston (1950) have studied critical periods in the development of social behavior in dogs and from their experiments have concluded that the social behavior in the puppy shows several natural periods in its development. During certain of these periods the puppy is much more responsive to "social learning" and appears to gain a more lasting effect from experiences. The experiment consisted of both tests and observations made on a total of seventy-three dogs belonging to six different species observed from birth up to sixteen weeks of age. On the basis of these observations, the authors divided development into periods, as follows:

Period I, neonate: from birth until the eyes open

Period II, transition: from opening of the eyes until leaving the nest

Period III, socialization: from leaving the nest until weaning

Period IV, juvenile: from weaning until sexual maturity

As its name suggests, it is the third period that is the critical one in the development of social behavior. Scott and Marston also observed a differential reaction in one litter in which the mother died at the beginning of this period (which usually lasted from about four weeks to ten weeks, by the end of which time puppies are normally weaned). In this litter the puppies showed obvious signs of distress at the absence of the mother; these signs are not observed in other dogs when they are separated from the bitch at the end of this period, that is, at about ten weeks.

Elliot and Scott (1961) have shown that, in puppies, the severest emotional reactions to separation in a strange place occur at six to seven weeks, that is, during the critical period for primary socialization, and are presumably related to this period. The reactions may serve to strengthen the social bond (J. P. Scott, 1962).

Freedman et al. (1961) have confirmed Scott and Marston's results with cocker spaniels. Dogs isolated from human contacts until fourteen weeks of age were not susceptible to taming or socialization to humans; they persistently fled on a man's approach. The authors found this period of receptivity to human socialization to lie between two and one-half weeks and nine to thirteen weeks of age, with the seventh week being the time of maximum receptivity. They point out the balance of factors that appears to be important: First, motor and perceptual development are rapid in this time, and second, the pattern of flight behavior from strangers is not yet strong.

In rhesus monkeys the effects of total social isolation and perceptual impoverishment during the first three months are not apparently permanent (Griffin, 1965), but if these processes are continued beyond this period permanent effects do occur (Sackett, 1965). Thus, in this species, the critical period would seem to be within three months, though the precise time has not been delineated.

It will be noted that in this discussion of socialization it is being assumed that a critical period, rather than a salient event, is involved. That is, it is assumed that a maturational change underlies the time during which the critical event is effective. It will be recognized that there is at present no certainty that this is the case, but the assumption is put forward with the confidence that in the future the maturational factor will be demonstrated.

It seems that in rhesus monkeys the period of play is a critical one in the development of various behaviors, including sexual ones (Harlow, quoted in J. P. Scott, 1962). Monkeys denied the opportunity of play with other young monkeys before the natural period of juvenile play wanes are socially inept as adults, and their lack of skill extends to the particular social behaviors involved in mating.

Denenberg (1964) has extended that part of J. P. Scott's formulation (1962) about critical period that concerns the effects of early stimulation. In a series of experiments (with rats) he has shown that the *amount* of early stimulation is a crucial variable. He proposes that early stimulation tends to lower adult emotionality, thus reducing the interference with learning and other behavior that would result from too high a level of emotionality induced by novelty or by other "threats" incidental to these behaviors. He suggests (on the basis of his evidence) that there is a monotonic relationship between stimulus intensity in infancy and adequacy of consummatory behavior.

Denenberg does not regard his formulation as a refutation of the critical period hypothesis but rather as an elaboration of it. He agrees with Levine (1962) that any theory of infantile stimulation must take account of both stimulus input and age of stimulation.

BEGINNING AND ENDING OF CRITICAL PERIODS

An important question is what starts a critical period and what brings it to an end. Behaviorally, there are some signs of changes that coincide with the beginnings of the period of primary socialization. Fuller et al. (1960) have shown that in puppies there is an initial period when conditioned responses (to noxious stimuli) cannot readily be elicited but that stable conditioned responses can be established at about eighteen to twenty-one days of age. They note that this corresponds with the beginning of the critical period for socialization mentioned by Scott. This suggests that, in puppies at least, the onset of susceptibility to conditioning may be a prerequisite for imprinting, and a reflection of maturational changes making this period possible.

Reference has already been made to fear of strangers as a feature of the end of the period of primary socialization in puppies. There have been numerous studies, reviewed by Sluckin (1965), that indicate that the fear response in birds ends the period of imprinting. Obviously a fleeing response is antagonistic to a following one, and if it has expressive priority, it will inhibit following, thus preventing imprinting if it has not already occurred.

There is obviously some selectivity in this fear response. The study by Elliot and Scott (1961) has already been mentioned: It showed a fear of *strange places* as a strong response in puppies during the height of the critical period for primary socialization: indeed, the authors interpret this as a factor aiding imprinting. On the other hand, the response ending the imprinting period is a fear of *strange objects*. This is perhaps a subtle distinction. The precise relationship between familiar/unfamiliar objects in familiar/unfamiliar environments has not been explored. The Elliot and Scott study might suggest that familiar objects in an unfamiliar setting may be more salient than the same object in a familiar milieu. Presumably, too, an unfamiliar object in an unfamiliar setting is in the later period more fear-provoking than one in a familiar setting. From the beginning young birds apparently react fearfully (as indicated by cheeping) to a strange setting, and perhaps there is an "imprinting" to an environment that precedes that to the parent.

Hebb (1946) has suggested an "incongruity" hypothesis in which fear is aroused when a perceived object has sufficient similarity to previously seen ones to arouse habitual processes of perception, yet is sufficiently different to arouse incompatible processes and hence disrupt neural patterns established by earlier stimulation. Thus the fear response is not a purely maturational phenomenon but depends on experience also: The infant must be able to discriminate the strange as different.

This hypothesis has been criticized by Schaffer (1966), who finds it in need of extension. For one thing, he points out that in human development, at least, there is no sharp transition from positive to negative reactions to strangers but rather an intervening period of some two or three months in which the infant shows the ability to discriminate between familiar and unfamiliar persons, but does so without the fear response to the latter: This response comes later. Thus the ability to distinguish may be a necessary condition for the fear response but it is not a sufficient one.

The fear response, Schaffer suggests, goes through another transition from stimulus orientation to object orientation. There is a period when it is not a stranger per se who excites a fear response; but some stimulus attribute, such as a loud voice or sudden movement, is responsible for the reaction. Even a familiar person may on occasion cause fear by presenting such stimuli.

It may be observed that generally the mere presence of a stranger is not sufficient to excite fear. The stranger must more actively impinge on the infant. (This could, however, be seen as a separate matter, the fear response to certain stimuli being independent of familiarity.)

A third modification by Schaffer of the incongruity hypothesis arises from the observations that there are cross-cultural similarities in the mean time of emergence of the fear response, and that these occur despite marked differences in child-rearing practices. There are also individual variations in the time of onset and these are suggestive of genetic factors (D. G. Freedman, 1965).

Thus the fear of strangers is probably a multidimensioned effect. The perception of unfamiliarity does not of itself bring about fear; intraorganismic effects, as well as certain properties of the stimulus, are involved (Schaffer, 1966). The same is no doubt true of other critical periods, in which there may be, in the organism, no single or simple change that brings about the beginning or the ending of the period of heightened sensitivity to certain stimuli or susceptibility to certain experiences. Rather, there is probably in most instances a complex change in a balance of factors.

The evidence on the development of fear responses in primates (including man) and certain other mammals has been reviewed by G. Bronson (1968). As he says, a potential to fear the strange must be regarded as inherent in many species. The idea that fear is acquired only after painful experiences is no longer tenable in the light of this evidence.

The development of the fear of novelty passes through three stages. The first is manifest in a "distress reaction" to a diversity of unpatterned stimuli—sudden noises and the like. In humans, and in some other species, *visual* novelty does not arouse this reaction until later. "Mothering" activities reduce the intensity of these reactions. The second stage in humans and some other species is a fear of visual novelty, and this fear also is reduced by the visual presence of the mother (or her surrogate). The consensus of a number of studies is that in humans this second stage appears around the seventh to ninth month. Stage 3 is represented by an increasing ability to deal with novelty in the absence of the mother.

Whether or not these stages of development of fear responses are to be regarded as critical periods is a further question. Bronson reviews evidence that shows that a proper transition through each of these stages is necessary to the emergence of normal fear reactions in later life, and that this is true of subhuman as well as human species. Failure of appropriate experiences concordant with the stage (e.g., lack of "maternal" reassurance in stage 1) results in abnormal reactions, such as exaggerated responses to novelty, in adulthood. This evidence for criticality in these stages is circumstantial and definitive experiments remain to be performed.

CRITICAL PERIODS IN HUMAN DEVELOPMENT

Bowlby (1953) was among the writers who revived interest in the idea of critical periods in the development of the human child. Scott and Marston (1950) have also discussed the periods in man that correspond to those in other mammals. While both the absolute and relative lengths of these periods appear to differ from species to species, Scott and Marston claim that similar phases appear to be found at all mammalian levels. They point out that human social development may involve stages comparable to those found in the dog.

The study of critical periods at the human level is by no means easy. Bearing in mind the animal models that we have for it, one has difficulty in thinking of features of human development that show clearly the hallmarks of the critical period as found in animals. In many cases, after one knows what to observe, these periods in animals are plain to see. Although it is certainly reasonable to suppose that there are critical periods in human development, it is probable that these periods are less clear-cut than many seen in animals, having, it is likely, a slower rise to maximum and a slower decline at the end of the period. This theory is in accordance with the generally slower pace of human development and with its greater complexity. These factors would tend to make critical periods in humans much more difficult to detect. Furthermore, ethical considerations prevent one from subjecting children to the kinds of procedures that would be necessary to determine the limits of such periods.

Some of the questions aroused by a consideration of critical periods in childhood in their relation to educational procedures are illustrated in a study by Oakden and Sturt (1922). They documented the observation, familiar to teachers, that children in the early grades have a very poor conception of historical time. For example, told that Robin Hood was alive in 1187, many grade 1 and 2 children will blithely reveal that they think their mothers might have met him. Even "last week" is a very confusing notion. However, between eight and eleven years, there is an acquisition of more accurate notions of time spans.

Supposing that we can accept this observed change as, in this particular instance and perhaps in others like it, having the characteristics of a critical period, the question remains as to the influence of school instruction. Do children between the eighth and eleventh years show a change in time concepts because the schools are teaching them in these grades? Do schools teach them then because experience has shown this period to be most favorable? (Most teachers can testify to the difficulties of teaching seven-year-olds to tell time, and most parents know too well their curious notions of time spans.) Is there a maturational basis to the acquisition of such concepts, or is the basis purely educational? A knowledge of numbers is involved in reading a clock, and therefore acquaintance with them is a necessary prerequisite for this activity: Is such previous learning the only essential precursor, or are there more basic maturational processes involved? In other words, is this genuinely a critical period phenomenon, or is it one involving a salient event? To separate the two sorts of processes that may underlie development, either together or exclusively, is a research problem in this area.

It is evident from the work of Piaget that many aspects of development go through definite and sequential stages (this topic is discussed in some detail in Chapter 16). The development of concepts of time, for example, go through phases (Piaget, 1946). The child

at first is unable to apprehend the fact that if two cars move different distances, but start and stop simultaneously, the time interval is the same for both. Time, movement, and velocity are closely interwoven concepts that the child at first has difficulties in sorting out.

If Piaget is correct in his insistence on the sequential nature of the development of the child's knowledge of the world (see Chapter 16), then each period must be critical in the sense that no later stage can be reached until the previous stages on which it is dependent have been passed through. Whether these stages form critical periods in the special sense of the term adopted here is as yet an open question, and whether or not a *maturational* substratum underlies them remains to be demonstrated. Such a demonstration will be difficult (and perhaps immoral), because it will involve denying children the opportunity of acquisition at the appropriate stage and testing whether acquisition is hindered after this time of maturational readiness. We shall need data to decide whether Piaget's stages represent *periods of salience* (with corresponding salient events in the environment) or whether they are *critical periods* as defined here.

The well-known experiments by McGraw (1935) showed that there are times in the development of motor skills when practice has little effect (or even a negative effect), whereas at other times similar practice produces rapid acquisition. In 1946 she suggested that in each kind of motor skill involving coordinated muscular activity there is a period when the ability to learn is at an optimum.

In connection with speech development, Stinchfield and Young (1938) have spoken of a period of "readiness to speak" at about twelve to eighteen months. Speech acquisition delayed outside this period is more likely to be defective. Another possible period of critical import to speech development is a period of "readiness to listen," described by Fry and Whetnall (1954). From observation of hard-of-hearing children and from efforts at training them to speak, Fry and Whetnall conclude that this time lasts from the first to third years, during which time the ability to recognize sounds is developed. After the third year there is a decline in the ability to recognize new speech sounds. If a hard-of-hearing child has not been taught speech (using hearing aids and other devices), by five years of age it is difficult to teach it to him, and by seven it is almost impossible.

Tinbergen's account of the behavior of the immature Eskimo dog must have a ring of familiarity to many parents and teachers who have witnessed, in children, a similar imperviousness to admonishment or experience. Children will persistently fail to learn desirable habits, even when it seems to their advantage to do so, and often-repeated lessons will fail to "take." Yet suddenly the situation will change and at last they will learn. Presumably both the children and their preceptors could be spared much frustration by a knowledge of the critical period in which to supply a critical event.

CRITICAL PERIODS IN HUMAN SOCIAL DEVELOPMENT

In the discussion of imprinting (Chapter 8), it is suggested that the smiling response is involved in human imprinting. Spitz and Wolf (1946b) have spoken of the period of indiscriminate smiling (to any human face or to similar sign stimuli) as the critical period in what Scott has called primary socialization. Gray (1958) believes the beginning of this critical period to be the onset of conditionability and the fear response to strangers to be its end.

Bowlby (1946) has reviewed the literature on children deprived of normal parental relationships by being hospitalized or placed in orphanages during the early years of life. From his review it seems reasonable to suppose that, in the human infant, the period between about six months and three years of age is a critical one in the formation of social relationships. Children separated from their families and deprived of parental affection during this time often show very intense emotional reactions, following which they tend to organize their social relations so that they do not include a particular human being as the object of their affection. If this deprivation is prolonged, it tends to become permanent. It may well be the origin of the psychopathic type of personality, a type in which the individual is incapable of normal affectional relationships with others and social behavior is abnormal. Delinquency and other behavioral disorders are also related to infantile deprivation.

It will be noticed that there are two critical periods suggested for human social development. The first is an imprinting one, lasting from about six weeks to six months (Gray); the second one, in which more extensive affectional and social relationships are formed, lasts from about three months to three years (Bowlby). The periods overlap in their ranges for groups but do not necessarily do so in individual cases. This is analogous to the findings, in animal studies, that imprinting determines the class of objects to which social relations are directed, and that a later period determines more detailed learning with and from that class. Thus the lamb first imprints to its own mother and subsequently to this, and consequently upon it, extends the imprinting to social behavior toward sheep in general.

Money et al. (1957), from a study of hermaphroditic children reared at first in one sex and then changed to another, suggest that about two and one-half years of age is a critical period for the development of sex-role identity. Before this age sex-role changes can be accomplished without much difficulty; after it, they are hazardous. Two developmental events (both presumably maturationally based) coincide with this age: One is the emergence of language as a usable aid to understanding, and the other is the emergence of true play involving peers.

A number of psychoanalytically oriented writers have spoken of critical periods, following Freud's interest in the topic. Bowlby (1960) has spoken of the second half of the first year as a critical period in mother-child relationships, with profound implications for later development.

Erikson (1959) has spoken of a period, during the second and third years, that is critical to the acquisition of a sense of autonomy, which he defines as self-confidence, independence, and self-approval rather than approval derived from others. R. W. White (1960) has also spoken of the importance of this period of curiosity and independence in the development of an attitude of mastery toward the environment.

G. Bronson (1962) has analyzed data from the Berkeley growth study (Jones and Bayley, 1941), which gives some support, based on normal children, to the notion of a critical period in the second half of the first year. There was a positive relationship between ratings in "responsiveness to persons" at one and one-half years of age and ratings of "involvement with people" at nine to ten and one-half years of age. This would be expected from the existence of a critical period in interpersonal relationships at the younger age.

Bronson also found corroboration of the Erikson hypothesis of a critical period for acquisition of a sense of autonomy at two to three years of age in that there was again a positive correlation between ratings of intensity of involvement in the handling of new play material at two to three years of age and competence orientation in the approach to intellectual problems at nine to ten and one-half years. Interestingly, neither relationship held with girls.

These results might, of course, be seen merely as an instance of the consistency of personality traits, but it is interesting to view them as illustrative of critical periods. Certainly longitudinal studies of this kind are needed if critical period phenomena are to be revealed.

Werner (1957) devotes a few paragraphs to the discussion of critical periods and states that such periods are involved in the development of what he calls the "ego-world relation." This relation is the increasing distance between the ego and the world or the growing differentiation between the person and society as interdependent but discrete organisms. There are, he states, at least three such periods in the development of the child's personality: first, the period when the infant is weaned; second, the "resistance period" of the young child (or the so-called "age of negativism"); and third, the period of pubescence.

Earlier in this chapter we discussed G. Bronson's article (1968) on the fear response. This response might be related to the development of the social attitudes involved in prejudice. In Chapter 4 it was suggested that "prejudice" has its origins in this innate fear response to the unfamiliar. It would be interesting to relate bigotry to early childhood experiences, using the hypothesis that early "mothering" is a factor in the degree to which "aversion to the novel" is shown. This aversion is common to all but is exaggerated in the bigot.

The investigation of these critical periods appears to be a matter of considerable practical importance as well as of scientific interest. It could be that some educational experiences are being given to children at an uneconomic time when the ability to learn that particular matter is low: To be able to strike the critical time for such an experience would obviously be more efficient.

The question of critical periods also has relevance to psychotherapy. We have seen that the efficiency of learning is much reduced, or even impossible, outside the critical period. This fact may account for the well-known difficulty in the treatment of the psychopath: Any attempts at psychotherapy consist in giving these individuals a relationship experience, but they have missed the initial experience on which all later ones depend and for which the critical period is long past. Similar situations may apply in many neurotic conditions. While this consideration might cast doubt on the feasibility of psychotherapeutic techniques for such conditions, it might encourage us to redouble efforts in preventive measures.

There is an interesting suggestion, contained in a discussion by E. H. Hess (1964), that behaviors normally acquired during a critical period by one process may be acquired outside it by a different mechanism. Hess is referring specifically to following in birds, in which situation imprinted birds can be trained to make a following response by association learning processes that superficially appear to be like those formed in imprinting. Whether the other social responses that generalize from imprinting are the same is another question. From all the work done on critical periods it would seem that such alternative routes, even if possible, are more difficult, and that even if the results are phenotypically similar, they are virtually different. Thus the sociopath may learn the "proper" social responses or the neurotic the "normal" behaviors and yet both may remain basically unchanged. This may account for the common (but apparently unsubstantiated) clinical statement that sociopaths appear normal by about forty. They are slow learners, but by then they have been able to erect a facade of socially approved responsiveness. Presumably, their more basic responses reemerge under stress.

EPILOGUE

The notion of critical periods is a most important one for developmental psychology, and it is regrettable that our information is not more specific, especially for humans. There is at least enough evidence to show that these periods are real phenomena in animals, and even if the data are not without controversy as applied to man, it is at least reasonable to suppose that these periods do influence the course of human development.

The main elements of this idea of critical periods are summarized in Figure 7–1. The biological substratum (a global term covering a multiplicity of factors, including neurological and endocrinological ones) is in constant flux during development. First one and then another facet of this complex stream of maturational happenings emerges, more or less briefly, as a dominant state of faster moving change.

A host of events presenting environmental stimuli are constantly impinging on the organism. In Figure 7–1 these events are represented by a, b, and c. At first none of them "takes"; the organism is apparently indifferent to them. Then it may be noted that a begins to have an effect—susceptibility to this stimulus (or complex of stimuli) rises, as represented by the change in slope of A; and then change is correlated with the maturational event 1. There is, in fact, a causal relationship between 1 and A. The decline of A may be related to one or both of at least two factors; the "hardening" of the biological substratum as the flux of this particular change dies away, and the competition of the now-emerging responsiveness to stimulus b. This responsiveness to b may involve a conflict of attention that swamps out attending to stimulus a, or it may involve a response that is incompatible with the response to a (or it may involve both). In due course c assumes primacy, and so on. Some later maturational event 6 underlies selective attention to stimulus f and ushers in the critical period F. However, the ability to respond to f may depend on the establishment of responses to c, so that the emergence of the behavioral change related to period F is contingent not only on the maturational event 6 but also on the prior establishment of behaviors related to C. Thus failure of appropriate development during C may bring a further series of failures in later development.

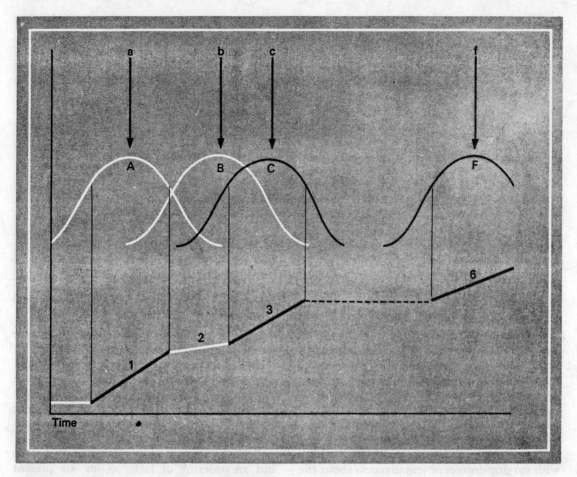

FIGURE 7–1. *The waxing and waning of critical periods.*

It is not suggested, of course, that critical periods are necessarily sequential; that is, more than one period may arise simultaneously, but only, presumably, for unrelated phases of development. Many aspects of development are sequential, however. This is one of the main points of Piaget's thesis, to be reviewed in later chapters. For such kinds of developmental progressions sequencing is crucial. In this scheme, interference with one critical period can have wide effects on later development.

The imposition of the critical event at the peak of the critical period is, developmentally, most efficient, but this does not of necessity mean that a similar-appearing effect cannot be achieved at other times. An organism can learn, possibly, to mimic the effects of critical period acquisition. This may be what happens in a Dale Carnegie course, which teaches non-friendly and uninfluential men and women to "win friends and influence people" by mimicking the actions of "naturals" in this skill. But this method is almost certainly much less efficient than is the teaching of these social skills in childhood.

Eight | Imprinting

Imprinting is a topic with the promise of considerable theoretical implication to human development but without much sign of realization of that promise at the present time. That is, empirical data to support the plausible notion that imprinting is significant in human psychological growth are not easy to find.

However, a number of authors in psychology, psychiatry, and other fields are talking with varying degrees of tentativeness about the matter. Dr. Spock, for example, makes mention of the possibility that babies imprint to the mother (Spock, 1963). The question of human imprinting was also discussed by the Fourth Tavistock Study Group (Foss, 1969). A number of psychiatric writers use the concept in explaining the etiology of mental illness (e.g., Weiland and Rudnik, 1961).

The evidence on the question is, unfortunately, very sparse indeed. Most of what there is is discussed by Gray in a paper published in 1958; there appears to have been little fresh data added since then, though a good deal more speculation has been made.

The reality of the imprinting phenomenon in animal behavioral development can hardly be denied, as there is a considerable literature on the topic giving experimental evidence of it in a wide range of species. On the assumption of evolutionary continuity between the animals and man, it is considered reasonable to believe that this phenomenon might not entirely disappear as a factor in the early development of the human infant.

Science is not, however, a system of beliefs but an ordering of facts, so for the present the matter is in the realm of hypothesis, though this after all is the scientific equivalent of a belief.

Lorenz's original account of imprinting described it as a specifically avian phenomenon, but the term is no longer restricted to birds and is commonly used to describe similar phenomena in the social development of other animals. It has been reported for fish (Baerends and Baerends-van Roon, 1950); and Thorpe (1956) has discussed imprinting in insects, but his use of the term extends beyond the more common one: Most authors restrict the term to the following behavior of the young, whereas Thorpe uses it in connection with such things as the acquisition of song in grasshoppers and the learning of locality in bees. A number of other authors have also used the term more broadly than Lorenz used it. Burghardt and Hess (1965) have spoken of food imprinting in the turtle, in which feeding behavior is determined by early food supplies. This is not, apparently, the absolute attachment determined by classical imprinting but rather a preference for a particular diet when a choice is available.

Thorpe (1965) has suggested "environmental imprinting" by which the young animal becomes attached to its early habitat, but his suggestion has not been followed up by experimental studies. The idea has some merit and the strong patriotic behavior of some animals, a behavior in which they remain near the birthplace though quite capable of wider roaming, is well known. Even man could be said to show distinct signs of such behavior, but it would be a debate without factual data to discuss whether or not these signs are evidence of imprinting.

The application of the term *imprinting* to behaviors of this kind seems to have semantic dangers, because there is almost no end to the situations in which it might be used; it might be made so general as to be meaningless. It would seem preferable to restrict *imprinting* to the mechanism whereby infants become attached to their parents (or in experimental situations to objects standing in the place of the parents).

Several investigators have found imprinting in mammals. Seward (1940) has noted strong attachments of infant guinea pigs to the mothers, and J. Allen (1904) had earlier noted that this behavior could not be elicited until the early hours of the third day of life. Gray (1958) also reported imprinting to himself of hand-reared guinea pigs, and he found the latter part of the second day to be the time at which this imprinting happened. The imprinting was permanent, and the animals did not mix with their own kind at maturity. In some preliminary studies Hess (1959) has placed the time of best imprinting in guinea

pigs rather earlier than in the other two studies—toward the end of the first day. Shipley (1963), too, has demonstrated imprinting in guinea pigs. The phenomenon has also been observed in deer (Darling, 1938) and buffalo (Hediger, 1938). Many farms have a pet sheep, usually a bottle-fed orphan lamb, that later fails to show the normal social behavior of its species and ignores the flock in preference to human companions. Scott and his associates (1951) have shown that this behavior is a misplaced imprinting phenomenon. The usual imprinting to the mother occurs in the first ten days of the lamb's life: If separated from the ewe during this critical period, the lamb may imprint to humans instead and after this period will not imprint to its mother —nor in later life will it generalize following behavior to the flock. A review of imprinting in birds has been given by Gray (1963), and a comprehensive treatment of the topic, including the phenomenon in nonavian species, has been given by Sluckin (1965).

IMPRINTING AS LEARNING

One of the theoretical issues in the matter of imprinting is whether or not it should be regarded as a form of learning, and this is a question of considerable speculative interest to the present discussion. Lorenz at first regarded it as something different from learning (1935) but later (1960) moved to the view that it is a type of conditioning. E. H. Hess (1959a, b) has reviewed some of the literature on this question and has shown that a number of authors now accept the phenomenon as simple association learning. Hess gives reasons why it cannot be so regarded. One of these is the existence of critical periods. Such periods, he says, are not applicable to associative learning, yet imprinting does not occur outside the critical stage: If it is associative learning, it should take place at any time. Hinde (1962) has criticized Hess's contentions; he says, for example, that the critical period phenomenon is not peculiar to imprinting but appears in many situations in which learning occurs.

One of the strong points of Lorenz's original statement on imprinting was its irreversibility. He was convinced that after the bird is imprinted to one object it cannot shift to any other. Hinde (1962) believes Lorenz's view to be an overstatement but apparently bases this belief upon only two studies, those of Craig (1912, 1914) and Steven (1955), who also state that it is now generally agreed that imprinting is not invariably irreversible. Because death is about the only invariable event in nature, it would be surprising if imprinting were not sometimes reversible. However, the evidence in support of reversal is not extensive. Steven's article involved observations of a single case, a white-fronted goose that transferred from an initial imprinting to its own species, from which it was separated accidentally, to an imprinting to ornithologists. Its age at separation is not stated but was evidently past normal imprinting time. Steven discusses this reimprinting in terms of habituation; the initial fear reactions to man had to abate before reimprinting could occur. Steven is properly cautious in his conclusions and admits he is assuming that he was not dealing with an abnormal specimen with defective initial imprinting to its own species. The fact that it *did* become separated makes one ask whether it was properly imprinted in the first place. When later housed in the Edinburgh Zoo with other geese, it is reported to have shown little interest in them, and its imprinting to man appears to have been final.

Whether or not imprinting is absolutely unchangeable, it appears certainly to be very stable, and in a high proportion of individuals in a species the originally imprinted object remains an important influence on behavior throughout life. An amusing account is given by Lorenz of a male bittern raised by a man and later placed in the Amsterdam Zoo. The bittern was caged with a female and at first refused to be sociable but eventually accepted her, mated, and reared several broods. But whenever the fosterfather appeared, he had precedence, and the male would chase the female off the nest and by nest-relief display invite the man to sit on the eggs.

Another argument put forward by Hess arises from what he has called the law of effort. Association learning is most effective when practice trials are spaced rather than massed. Hess produces evidence to show that the efficacy of imprinting is proportional to the amount of effort the animal must expend in following the imprinted object; placing hurdles in the way or making the animal walk uphill, for instance, increases the strength of the response. Hess implies that this mechanism is equivalent to that in a massed-trial situation and hence atypical of optimal association learning.

Hinde has found the relevance of this argument unclear and quotes Moltz (1960) and Sluckin and Salzen (1962) as presenting evidence that shows Hess's results to be less general than Hess claims they are. Imprinting to stationary objects is possible in birds (Gray, 1960; Abercrombie and Abercrombie, 1961) but only under special conditions unlikely to obtain in a natural environment. Collins (1965) has found both contact and following of a model to be unnecessary to imprinting; all that is required with chicks, under his experimental conditions, is opportunity to observe the model. He concludes that Hess's law of effort is not upheld. Klopfer and Hailman (1964) have reached a similar conclusion. Fische (1966), in studying the effects of distribution of practice, concludes that imprinting and association learning are similar.

On the other hand, Thompson and Dubanoski (1964) have, with chicks, results that they regard as agreeing with Hess's law, but they cannot be taken as conclusive confirmation because the relative importance of efferent and afferent variables is not taken into account. That is, the study still does not clarify whether learning can take place in the absence of a detectable response. The matter of acquisition without performance is a controversial one in both association learning and imprinting. MacDonald and Solandt (1966) immobilized chicks with drugs, unsuccessfully attempted imprinting, and concluded that some form of response is necessary.

The law of effort certainly introduces a difficulty for human imprinting because at the time imprinting is assumed to occur, locomotor following is not possible; the most that is possible is ocular or head movements involving only small expeditures of energy. This fact does not, perhaps, rule out entirely the application of the law but does render it somewhat implausible. However, the evidence leaves the present status of the law of effort somewhat uncertain, and in any case its relevance to human imprinting is left untouched by these studies of birds. If one chooses to give more weight to those that deny the law, then human imprinting seems more feasible.

Hess goes on to point out that in ordinary discrimination learning recency of experience makes for maximum effectiveness, but claims experimental evidence to show that for imprinting primacy is the most effective variable. For instance, a duckling presented in an imprinting runway with a male model duck then with a female model, or vice versa, showed preference for the first model presented rather than for the second as the law of recency would predict. Hinde objects to accepting this evidence on several grounds. One is that Hess does not mention the time relations involved, and the second presentation might have been at a time when the critical period was waning. Even if this is not so and primacy is more important than recency, extraneous, rather than intrinsic, factors might account for the phenomenon. But this does not seem to answer the apparently strong influence of primacy in imprinting, and Hinde's objections on this point seem no more puissant than Hess's statement. However, Kaye (1965) has concluded from his experiments that there is little support in the primacy-recency dimension for the idea that imprinting differs from other forms of conditioning.

These experiments have concerned avian imprinting. It is worth noting the study by Fuller et al. (1950), who found that in puppies the beginning of the critical period for primary socialization (imprinting) coincided with the onset of conditionability. This does not, of course, prove that the ability to form conditioned responses is necessary to imprinting, but it is suggestive of such a relationship.

Kovach et al. (1966) have discussed imprinting in terms of perceptual learning. They suggest that it is the fact that the "very first sensory impression is provided by the imprinting stimulus" and the fact that the stimulus is the first to impinge on an "experientially uncluttered system" that give imprinting its special qualities. They criticize Sluckin and Salzen (1961), who have also discussed imprinting in terms of perceptual learning, for failing to appreciate this point. They believe it is this, rather than the formation of an irreversible bond as Lorenz would suggest or the setting up of social bonds as Scott (1962) would argue, that accounts for the phenomenon. Whatever the merits of these arguments when considering imprinting of birds, their cogency with other species may be less clear. For the human infant in our own society the first visual experience is often an upside-down view of a masked obstetrician, and any theory that can be generated from this truth is alarming.

A further difference between imprinting and association learning is that in association learning a punishing stimulation causes aversion to the negative stimulus. Hess claims that, in imprinting, a painful stimulus in temporal contiguity with the presentation of the imprinting object enhances the process. Hinde admits that other evidence does support this notion—for example, fear-provoking stimuli may facilitate imprinting. Moltz (1963) also found that shocks administered during following increased the strength of the response.

Fisher (1955) found that fox terrier puppies whose early social contacts with humans were punishing ones showed stronger following responses as compared with petted controls. Kovach and Hess (1963), in an imprinting runway, shocked chicks of various ages by means of electrodes attached to the wings. They found that the following response was enhanced in the youngest chicks but reduced in older ones. Hinde regards (and probably rightly) such studies as showing an effect on the situation in which following occurs rather than on the initial imprinting: This may seem like hair-splitting.

There is also, according to experiments by Hess, a difference between the effects of certain drugs on ordinary learning and on imprinting. A depressant drug such as meprobamate does not adversely affect discrimination learning, whereas it does affect imprinting, making it almost impossible. Hinde's objection to this finding is that there is no indication whether the effect is peripheral or central, and its relevance to the question is obscure.

Hess's argument is that the ordinary laws of association learning do not apply to imprinting; he is not denying that imprinting is a form of learning but is saying only that it is some special form governed by different principles. Hinde's argument is that there are no grounds for this assumption and that imprinting should not be regarded as a special form of learning obeying laws that differ from those governing "ordinary" associative learning. The principle of parsimony may support Hinde's argument, but the argument contains the gratuitous notion that we really understand learning well enough to dismiss the idea that imprinting might be some distinct variety of it.

In a later article, E. H. Hess (1964) reiterates his contention that imprinting is a type of learning different from association learning; he, adds further experimental data to support this but makes no reference to Hinde's criticisms. On the face of it, imprinting would seem to be sufficiently clearly different from "ordinary" learning to throw the burden of proof on those who would argue otherwise. As we have seen, there are those who would claim to have produced this proof; perhaps we are not yet clear enough about association learning to really tell whether or not imprinting is identical with it. This point is, however, one of the finer ones and does not greatly concern the main issues of this book, in which the aftereffects of imprinting are of more concern than its mechanisms.

The theoretical point at issue here is whether imprinting represents an innately programmed tendency to certain learning or whether it merely represents learning. Learning, as usually conceived, does not involve special characteristics in the stimuli beyond their necessity to be within the perceptual capacities of the organism (that is, to discriminate from similar but nonidentical ones). In this view any discriminable stimulus can be attached by learning to any response that is within the behavioral repertoire of the organism. All equally discriminable stimuli are equally available for this purpose. Imprinting, on the other hand, seems to represent a special case in which certain stimuli (or stimulus patterns) have a special susceptibility (which is probably innate) to attachment to certain behavioral responses. The latter are usually fairly specific (in fact, they give identity to imprinting), whereas the stimuli are usually simple and are to be found in a number of circumstances; they do not seem as highly specific as the responses.

In the conditions of the natural life of the species this generality may not, however, show; under natural conditions the relevant stimulus may be highly specific. The graylag gosling, for example, is imprintable to any stimulus pattern having the simple properties of being large and having movement. In nature, however, the first object bearing these properties is highly likely to be one of the parent birds, and wastage by imprinting to other objects is insignificant. In other words, imprinting as an innately programmed form of learning produces a workable level of probability that the young will be attached to the parents and to no other object. Furthermore, even if imprinting is not completely irreversible, it is apparently sufficiently permanent to assure that most of the young will remain attached to the parents. It is highly desirable to survival that an infant should become attached to the parents and to no other individuals, and imprinting provides a mechanism by which this attachment is achieved. As J. A. Deutsch (1960) says, other learning needs to be more flexible. For instance, it would not do for an animal to become determined in its food choices by the first object it happens to taste, unless the environment is such that this object will invariably be a nutritious and readily available food source.

One manner in which imprinting certainly is a special case among learning is that it is first acquired without reinforcement and remains stable without it. Latent learning does not seem to cover this situation, because latently learned stimuli usually become attractive only when they become subgoals, that is, rewarding (J. A. Deutsch, 1960). Unless one is to argue that reinforcement is indispensable to any definition of learning, this evidence does not disqualify imprinting from being a form of learning, but makes it evidently some special form.

One possible way of looking at imprinting is that a particular set of responses has an unusually low threshold for reaction to a particular predetermined set of stimuli, and thus facilitate an especially easy form of learning. It is primed and ready to go. Moreover, it is highly resistant to extinction. The theoretical question this raises is whether there are not other events at other times in the life history of the individual that are in the same class. Or put another way, imprinting represents a class of learning in which there are ready-made "sets" that exert a strong (if not inevitable) influence on the forms it takes. Possibly the actual learning process itself is no different; what is different about imprinting is the existence of a "preset."

Just what a *preset* is in physiological terms, or what evidence can be produced for its existence, is difficult to say. Valentine (1930) has suggested that a fear response to long wiggly objects may be innate; possibly this could be rephrased as meaning not that such objects are invariably and unlearnedly feared but that a fear response to such objects is more easily learned (because of some inherent property of the nervous system) than one to other objects. This thesis is easily testable.

OTHER FACTORS IN IMPRINTING

In discussing imprinting, Moltz has rejected the traditional division into maturational or environmental effects and, instead, taken the interactionist view. That is, imprinting is determined neither wholly genetically nor wholly environmentally; the total pattern of emerging behavior is the result of an interaction between intrinsic and extrinsic factors (Moltz, 1963). He calls his outlook the epigenetic approach. One experiment, for example, shows that deprivation of patterned light in ducklings lengthens the critical period for imprinting, suggesting that structured visual experience prior to imprinting has an influence on the time at which imprinting will occur (Moltz and Stettner, 1961).

In the discussion, in Chapter 11, of early stimulation it will be seen that early stress, which coud be termed early emotional arousal, has a marked influence on later psychological functioning, including learning. It is of interest to note that emotional arousal during imprinting facilitates its later maintenance (Moltz, 1963). This may be taken as an instance of the manner in which extrinsic factors enter into the development and organization of the imprinting response, and Moltz uses it to illustrate his epigenetic approach to the topic. Pitz and Ross (1961) have shown that arousal by intense auditory stimulation as the chick approaches the object enhances the imprinting response, and Thompson and Dubanoski (1964) have reported that prior arousal outside the test situation facilitates imprinting.

Another extrinsic factor that influences imprinting is socialization. E. H. Hess (1964) has reported a series of studies on chicks and ducks that show that socializing with peers affects the course of imprinting but that the nature of the differences produced varies with the species. In chicks, socialization with siblings prior to imprinting enhances the effect; in ducklings, it detracts from it. Polt and Hess (1964, 1966) have also shown prior social experiences to have this effect on imprinting—in chicks, facilitating the efficacy of imprinting to a blue ball (they did not test with a hen). Whether these effects are social per se or the result of extra stimulation provided by noisy, moving peers, is impossible to say; maybe the distinction is meaningless anyway, but its value could be tested by providing an environment with similar but inanimate complexity. Haywood and Zimmerman (1964) have done this and found that complexity of environment does indeed enhance imprinting and also accelerates the onset of the critical period. This may be a special instance of the effect of an enriched early environment. The study by Fisher (1955) in which a punishing social contact enhanced imprinting (or, at least, the following response) in dogs is of interest. Possibly it illustrates the effects of social contact plus arousal, though this assumes that punishmment is more arousing than the petting received by the controls. Such studies may illustrate an important point: Perhaps there is no such thing as a purely maturational critical period but only an interaction between some physiological substratum and experiential factors, the onset and ending of the period being determined not solely by the former but also by the latter.

Salk (1966) has produced a theory that involves imprinting *in utero* to the sound of the maternal heartbeat. He gives evidence that neonates exposed to a lub-dub sound seventy-two times per minute showed behavioral differences from controls. They were more relaxed, fell asleep more quickly, and gained weight more rapidly on the same food intake. This alleged uterine imprinting was assumed to lend comforting qualities to similar sound patterns perceived postnatally. Even adults, according to Salk, find comfort from rhythms, in music or elsewhere, that occur at about this frequency. There are only two relevant animal studies; one was reported by E. H. Hess (1950), who failed in attempts at imprinting unhatched mallard ducklings to the call of a female to her young. After continuous exposure of the eggs to this taped sound for forty-eight hours preceding hatching, the ducklings showed, after hatching, no preference for this over the "gock" sound used in Hess's regular imprinting experiments. Gottlieb (1963), on the other hand, has reported from naturalistic observations auditory imprinting in certain species of ducks in which the hen "calls" to the eggs for up to thirty-six hours before hatching and in which the hatched ducklings do show signs of imprinting to this call. He regards, in fact, this auditory response as an important reinforcer of visual imprinting. Fische (1966) also claims that in chicks auditory stimuli give a basis for recognition of the parent and also increase arousal, thus facilitating imprinting; here she is referring to posthatching auditory cues.

Salk's theory is a rather intriguing one but lacks verification. It would be interesting to study, in relation to their responses to recorded heartbeats, premature infants who had been untimely ripped from the comfortable womb and its rhythmic sound.

IMPRINTING AND THE CRITICAL PERIOD

Imprinting provides one of the best examples of the critical period phenomenon, and this aspect of its significance is discussed in Chapter 7. The appearance of an antagonistic response, that of fear to strangers or unfamiliar objects, brings to an end the period of relative fearlessness that is obviously necessary if the animal is to follow rather than flee from what moves across its gaze.

HUMAN IMPRINTING

There has been some interest in the question of human infantile smiling since Darwin (1877) noted the first smile to appear at about forty-five days—not, of course, that Darwin was the first to observe that babies smile; he was merely early in wondering about its scientific significance. Gray (1958) has proposed that the smiling response is the human analogue of the following response in birds. J. P. Scott (1963) has suggested that in canine puppies tail wagging is the corresponding action and that each species makes a behavioral response that is within its repertoire at the time imprinting occurs. This may be the answer to the earlier argument about the necessity for active following.

Spitz and Wolf (1946b) followed Kaila in studying the smiling response and showed that at first it could be brought about by anything rudimentarily resembling a human face but that later only a familiar face would be effective in producing it. In an orphanage population they found little smiling before two months of age and nearly 100 percent response between about three and five months. By the sixth month the smile would show only to a familiar adult face and was not given to strangers. Evidently by this age discrimination is possible; the findings also suggest attachment to specific persons. Ambrose (1963) has reported a study that is consistent with the results of Spitz and Wolf, but he found both the beginning and the end of the indiscriminate smiling period to be earlier in home-reared infants than in those in orphanages. His results, however, are based upon small numbers (four in each group). Both Gray (1958) and J. P. Scott (1963) regard this period of indiscriminate smiling as one in which the child is establishing social contacts. Before about five or six weeks these contacts are impossible, or at least difficult, and from the data on deprivation (reviewed in Chapter 11) produced by Bowlby and others, it is concluded that the end of indiscriminate smiling also represents the end of the period of imprinting or of establishing social relations. If no social relationships are formed by this age, then all subsequent ones, especially those more intense and permanent ones we call "attachments," are rendered more difficult.

Apparently the smile is not in the early days a response specific to the face or its representation. Salzen (1963) has reported that it can be elicited by a change in brightness.

From studies of a large number of Russian children, Kistyakovskaya (1965) has concluded that smiling in infants is a response not only to people but to a range of prolonged visual or auditory stimuli as well. Other "positive emotional responses" also accompany these stimuli, and both these responses and smiling are independent of the satisfaction of organic needs. She does not, however, regard smiling as an innate response.

Babies may be observed smiling to themselves, without any obvious stimulus being apparent and when the observer is hidden. Some naturalistic observations of this phenomenon might modify theorizing in this area. The fact that infants might smile spontaneously or in response to a broad range of stimuli would not necessarily invalidate the idea that smiling is primarily a social response; it could be, for example, that the human face is the commonest or most potent arouser, but this suggestion needs to be checked.

This emphasis on visual stimuli in the imprinting of the human infant arouses questions about blind children. There is no evidence to suggest that their socialization as adults is adversely affected, at least beyond what one could attribute directly to their handicap. It seems that some alternative method of imprinting is available. A number of studies show that the efficacy of imprinting in animals can be improved by adding auditory stimuli to the visual ones (Gottlieb, 1963). Also, auditory stimuli alone can elicit following in birds (Collias, 1952; Collias and Collias,

1956). It may be that in some species born blind, such as the cat, imprinting is essentially a nonvisual procedure. The role of auditory or other sensations in human imprinting has not been explored, but it is suggested that the literature that treats it as a specifically visual phenomenon may be oversimplifying the matter.

An important point about imprinting, for developmental theory, is that it appears to provide an explanation for the beginnings of socialization. J. P. Scott (1963) has spoken of primary socialization during the "smiling" period, when the infant becomes attached to the parents. This attachment is the first social relationship to be formed. From it the infant generalizes (by what Scott calls secondary socialization) attachments to the species to which the parents (and the infant itself) belong. That is, by way of this initial imprinting the young animal becomes a socialized member of its species.

Animals misimprinted to other species show a variety of abnormal social behaviors as adults. In many cases they will ignore their own kind and direct their attentions to those they had known in infancy. Sluckin (1965) has reviewed in a variety of species a number of cases of courtship behaviors that are directed toward an inappropriate object; for example, he talks of birds making their courtship display to men or even to inanimate objects, when imprinted to these things. Despite tall stories and ancient myths about infants reared by wolves, we have no reliable accounts of humans misimprinted in this way, though Harlow gives good accounts of rhesus monkeys imprinted to cloth mother surrogates (see Chapter 11). What we might have in humans is nonimprinted infants. Bowlby and others have spoken of the origins of psychopathy (better perhaps called sociopathy) in adults who as children were separated from their parents over the critical imprinting period (the smiling one) and who thus lack the initial primary socialization from which all later social relationships are assumed to derive.

Under natural conditions an animal misimprinted or not imprinted at all would have little chance of survival. This might be also true in many primitive human communities and the sociopath might be an artificial product of civilized societies. Not only is imprinting fairly permanent, but the results of nonimprinting are also long-lasting; the difficulties of producing normal social responses from sociopaths are notorious to clinicians.

From the summed data of a number of studies of children deprived of normal parental care at various times in the first three years it appears that the first three months are not critical to imprinting, that the period from three to six months is the critical one, and that susceptibility to imprinting may wane after six months. Schaffer and Emerson (1964), in a study of sixty infants, found an initial period of indiscriminate attachments to people, followed in the sixth to ninth months by specific attachments to those most consistently around them.

One question about imprinting is whether or not it is an all-or-none phenomenon. Many of the experimenters refer to the strength of the following response; it is evident that there are variations in this behavior that are correlated with environmental differences (and perhaps, too, though this seems unexplored, with genetic differences between individuals and strains). If, however, we regard imprinting not merely in the context of this specific behavior but also as the precursor of more varied social behaviors, then the question arises as to the relationship between early strength of following and later social responses. Are the weaker followers less responsive in their social interactions, or is there an all-or-none relationship so that there are no effective differences in imprinting? In this case any strength of imprinting above threshold would be effective, and in later life these early differences would be lost. There does seem to be an experimental answer to this question. Clinical observations do suggest degrees of imprinting.

Most of the literature treats imprinting as

a one-way phenomenon, with offspring imprinting to their parents. A few writers speak of the reverse, parents imprinting to their young, and there is enough evidence to suggest that this is a real phenomenon, at least in some species.

In cats, according to Schneirla and Rosenblatt (1961), the odor of birth fluids plays an important role in forming the tie between the mother and her kittens. Blauvelt (1955) found that in goats the period immediately following birth is a critical one in the development of mother-young relationships. As soon as the kid leaves the mother's body, she licks it, and she keeps her head close to the kid lying on the ground until it can stand up and walk to her. If the mother is restrained from this licking after birth and is removed for a short time, she does not lick on return, and it may take a long time for the mother-kid relationship to be established. Even after only a few minutes of separation, the mother may be quite disturbed when the kid is reintroduced. If the mother is allowed to feed the kid before this separation, the reunion is much quicker afterward. It would seem that the effects of severance are permanent; Hersher et al. (1958) separated newborn kids from their mothers at times ranging from five to ten minutes after birth and kept them separated between thirty minutes and one hour. After the separation, the kids were helped to suckle from their own mother (apparently they could not do so successfully without help), after which there was no further interference for two to three months. At the end of this time the animals were tested by placing the mother in an experimental chamber with three kids, one of which was her own. Control mothers were highly selective in suckling their own kids, but the experimental ones spent significantly more time suckling others.

Collias (1956) has given experimental confirmation of what shepherds have long known, that the ewe is attracted to the newborn by odor. Normally a ewe will accept a young lamb in place of her own, but an orphan lamb can be transferred to a bereaved ewe only if the lamb is covered with the skin of her dead lamb for a time. If newborn lambs are separated from the mother for two to four hours following birth, the mother will reject them.

There is no information on this point over a wide range of species, but such data as there are suggest that lower down the scale these immediate postpartum experiences may be less vital. Labriola (1953) compared primiparous female rats whose young were born by Cesarean section with those having normal births. The Cesarean mothers did not have the opportunity of postpartum licking of the young, but on retrieving tests carried out at twenty-four hours after birth there was no difference between the two groups. The rat mother, who will quite readily adopt other young, is, however, able to recognize her own (Beach and Jaynes, 1956a, b).

Mother chimpanzees have been observed to show signs of recognition of their own offspring, even one year after separation from them, provided they had reared the young for the first year. Several of the domesticated species, such as fowls, will adopt birds of other species if they incubate the eggs of these birds themselves. In such cases they may be observed to peck at and chase away young that are different from the adopted ones, even though these "strangers" are of their own species (Ramsey, 1951). Tinbergen (1939) noted that parent herring gulls do not apparently discriminate between young gulls until their own brood is about five days old, after which time they recognize their own and chase off others.

The idea that human parents may imprint to their offspring has been suggested by Lorenz (1943). He points to the fact that infants of many species have features distinctive from those of the adult and that a protuberous forehead is common to many infants; he claims that this has sign-stimulus properties to adults and elicits parental behavior. The particular features of the human infant are the prominent forehead and the billowing cheeks (visible result of the sucking pads), which he calls the "kewpie-doll" configuration.

It is a common observation that an unwed mother often has great difficulty in giving up her baby for adoption after she has been exposed to it. If Lorenz's suggestion about the "kewpie-doll" sign stimulus is valid, it may be one perceptual cue that mediates the imprinting of human parents to their offspring. Reference has been made (p. 216) to individual differences in cuddling in babies: This may well be another crucial variable in the formation of an attachment, the "noncuddling" being less stimulating to the parent and hence less imprinted to.

Another feature of early parent-child interaction is related to eye-to-eye contact. A review of the literature on this topic has been given in Robson (1967). In his own observations he noted considerable individual variation in the nature of eye contact in the first six months. Some infants seemed actively to seek and engage this contact, whereas others merely made it, apparently uninterestedly. Some were noted to avoid contact. Robson discusses the implications of eye contact, noting among other things that parents are commonly delighted when it occurs and respond to it, whereas they are frustrated if the infant avoids it. This contact (or lack of it) may have important developmental sequelae, which one may regard as an element in the imprinting of parents. A marked change in parental behavior, from "caretaker" role to affectionate attachment, is said to accompany imprinting.

Whether one should define such social attachments in the parent-offspring direction as imprinting is perhaps a matter of choice. If a strict definition is to imply a following response by offspring to movements in their parents (or a surrogate) that have some kind of innate basis, then parent-offspring attachments are excluded. If, on the other hand, imprinting is taken to imply the formation of a social attachment between two individuals, one of whom is an infant, and in which there is some kind of inbuilt readiness to respond to certain perceptual cues, then the term can apply to both directions.

If the existence of a critical period is to be considered an essential part of the definition of imprinting, clear evidence on whether or not such periods exist in parent-offspring imprinting in primates is needed. Such evidence is not at present forthcoming. Certainly the females of many nonprimate species will only suckle young, or accept them as offspring, while in specific hormonal states; in this sense critical periods do exist for these species. Assuming that the "kewpie-doll" sign gestalt already mentioned does operate, there is a significant time during which the human infant bears these features, which he loses in due course. This time would not, however, qualify as a critical period because it involves a change external to the parent, not within him. However, there could still be within the parent, conditions specifically postpartum and limited in time, that coincide with the existence of a specific sign gestalt in the offspring in such a way that the parent is particularly sensitive to some perceptual cues at this time. The argument will apply especially to the mother, but in those species in which both parents are involved in care of the offspring, the supposed sensitivity might be part of the species-specific equipment and present in both sexes. Although this analysis is highly speculative when applied to humans, it is worth bearing in mind in observations of human parental behaviors.

A point of psychoanalytic theory has been the importance of the feeding process in attaching the infant to the mother, in such a way feeding plays a crucial role in socialization. Harlow (1958) has thrown doubt on this theory by his well-known experiments with rhesus monkeys, in which he showed that infants "fed" by a wire surrogate mother spent only enough time with "her" to feed and passed the greater part of their time with a cloth surrogate that was never associated with feeding. In a series of experiments he has convincingly demonstrated the strong and permanent affective tie that the infant monkey will form with the cloth surrogate mother, even though it is never fed by it, and the weakness of the link formed with the feeding wire surrogate. When frightened, the young monkey would seek comfort from the cloth surrogate and thus comforted would face a frightening object or explore an open field, whereas it could get no such assurance or support from the feeding wire surrogate. The feeding relationship is apparently irrelevant to the forming of these ties between infant and mother. Harlow suggests that tactile creature comfort derived from the soft and cuddly cloth surrogate is, in this tie, the crucial element and evidently one having considerable implications for development.

A couple of other studies with dogs also show the feeding relationship to be irrelevant to socialization. Brodbeck (1954) raised puppies during the critical period of socialization under two conditions: Half were fed by hand and the other half by machine, but all had the same amount of human contact. There was no difference between the groups in their attachment to people. Fisher (1955) reared fox terriers in isolation boxes throughout the period of socialization and fed them mechanically. They were released for regular intervals of contact with the experimenter and again their socialization to him was unaffected by their being divorced from feeding experience.

In discussing early social development, Bowlby (1951) and others have emphasized the importance of a consistent relationship with a single mother figure. These authors believe, in fact, that the child needs to be imprinted to a single mother. It certainly seems to be the case with some species that the infant does imprint to a specific individual; this is particularly true of the sheep, in which each lamb follows its mother and continues to do so into adulthood. This following is, in fact, the basis of the flocking behavior of the sheep, in which each follows the mother, who follows her mother, and so on up to the matriarch. However, in the early stages this seems to be not because the lamb is discriminating but because the mother is.

As mentioned earlier, the mother will accept only her own offspring, which she recognizes on the basis of smell, and will chase off a stranger. The literature does not say for how long the lamb remains indiscriminate in this matter. It seems that in many other species, too, it is the parents who reject young to which they are not themselves imprinted (even if these are of her own species, as when a hen rears ducklings and rejects chicks). As already mentioned, the human infant is in the beginning quite indiscriminate so far as the smiling response is concerned, but even when he begins to distinguish strangers from familiar faces, he still continues to smile to each of the familiar faces, and there is no suggestion in the literature of any favoritism among the equally familiar ones. Now it may be that in the matricentric style of child rearing of our society there is one face in particular that is more constantly around than others, but in some other communities where infant care is shared, there must be a greater range of equally familiar faces, and it would be interesting to study the smiling response in relation to each of these. Imprinting, in social species at least, is essentially the attachment of an infant to his species, and it may be that we should not overemphasize the imprinting relationship between the infant and the mother specifically.

EPILOGUE

Imprinting is a well-established phenomenon found in many species, and there is some evidence of its existence in the primates. On the basis that a feature of behavioral development apparently widespread across species would not be likely suddenly to disappear in humans, it is assumed that imprinting is a factor in human development also. This is admittedly not a strong argument, but it does have some supporting evidence to give it plausibility.

The discussion of the nature of imprinting, whether it is simply a form of association learning or some special kind of learning, is inconclusive on present evidence, which encourages one to make his own decision. It would seem reasonable to assume, with Hess, that imprinting is a special form of learning in which there is a genetically given present readiness to attach certain behavioral responses to certain stimulus patterns. There is genuine learning involved in that, to establish the bond, the environment must bring the responses and stimuli together during the critical period of maturation readiness; but because the organism is ready-primed, the learning proceeds swiftly. Once established, this learned response becomes a firm part of the organism's repertoire and is difficult (if not impossible) to alter.

To put it another way, the assumption is being made that imprinting is a biological predisposition to certain forms of learning. That is, the learning involved is of a special nature in that it has a lower threshold than some other forms. Most learning theories seem to imply an empty organism, a *tabula rasa,* at least for early learning, whereas with imprinting it would seem as if the organism comes with the learning already half-done. Whether this makes the learning process itself any different is an open question, and perhaps we do not have to assume that it does, in which case we can possibly reconcile Hess and Hinde. Maybe Hess is right in assuming some special readiness to learn in imprinting and Hinde correct in assuming that when the learning occurs it is associative.

The idea of special predispositions to certain learnings is an important one that will be referred to in other contexts. Imprinting may not be a unique phenomenon but one instance of a more general class of developmental events in which there is an innate predilection to particular learning. Because of this prepriming, some behaviors are easier to learn than others. Those who claim that all behavior is learned may be right, or largely so, but perhaps some behaviors are more learned than others. The others are those that are primed and that require less learning than those for which there is no constitutional precedent.

Whatever the nature of imprinting, it has marked consequences for the infants' subsequent relations with his parents and, by generalization, for all his later social interactions with his fellows. It is assumed that in humans the adult face provides the essential sign gestalt for triggering the imprinting response, which is smiling, though probably other stimuli are also effective. This mechanism occurs during a critical period between about three to six months of age. The possibility exists of imprinting (or some process similar to it) of parents to their offspring, and this possibility also has developmental implications.

The consequences of failure of imprinting are probably fatal to survival under natural conditions for most species, but the human infant can survive, physically. The psychological consequences to him may be extensive. If there is merely failure of imprinting without other perceptual deprivation, an individual of normal cognitive development, but with the deficiencies in social interactions that make up the sociopathic personality, may result. If, as is probably more often the case, conditions leading to failure of imprinting also reduce total stimulation, a sociopath of stunted cognitive development may be produced.

It is perhaps necessary to conclude with a cautious note to temper the somewhat enthusiastic account of imprinting given in this chapter. As Clarke (1968) has warned us, there are some qualifiers that need consideration. It could be that the influence and permanence of imprinting is, in fact, different from what is at present assumed by those who read much into it. Nevertheless, some important research is suggested by the work on imprinting, and even if the results of this research prove in the long run not quite what some of us could expect, the results may still advance our knowledge of human development.

Nine Biology of Human Sex Behaviors

One of the topics with which the developmentalist must concern himself is the relationship between biological and environmental factors in the emergence of various sorts of behavior. There have been times in the recent history of thought about human behavior when biological factors were overemphasized. Not so long ago there was a great deal of talk about the "glands of destiny," and the belief was strong that the endocrine glands and their secretions exercised the ultimate control on human behavior. This is one extreme. There is also the opposite extreme, in which physiological factors are ignored and human behavior is explained entirely in terms of environmental forces. The eclectic approach predisposes one to believe that the truth lies somewhere between any extreme positions, though not necessarily midway, of course. On this assumption, both biological and environmental factors play a part in the development of behavior, and the task is to define the relative contributions of both. In attempting to define this balance between physiological and environmental factors in the emergence of psychological activities, it is proposed to take the development of sex behaviors as an example, even though psychosexual development is also in its own right an important aspect of the development of personality. The general principles involved in the interplay between biological and experiential factors in the development of mature sexual behaviors are presumed to hold in other dimensions also.

The development of sex behaviors is complex, and as with most other matters, the more we discover, the more complex we find it to be. For instance, the pineal gland exerts an influence on the development of the genital system in mammals (Kitay and Altschule, 1954; Kitay, 1967), and Baum (1968) has shown that early dark rearing and pinealectomy later increases the rate of copulation in the adult rat. This effect is possibly caused by the removal of some inhibitory influence on androgen level in the infant rat, but there is evidently some complex optic-pineal interaction involved. This chapter deals only with some aspects of the development of sex behaviors and should be recognized as a simplification of the actual (and little understood) process.

There is also a range of exteroceptive stimuli that affect the course of both reproductive development and sexual behavior. Some of these are discussed in this chapter, but the interested reader will find a more extensive survey in Clegg and Doyle (1967).

HOW IS SEX DEFINED?

There are several ways in which sex can be designated. Hampson and Hampson (1961) have distinguished seven designations. Perhaps first should be put *sex of assignment and rearing*, as this seems to provide one definition of sex for a psychologist. Other definitions of sex are physical.

Ontogenetically, of course, *chromosomal sex* comes first. Normally assigned sex is consistent with this classification, but is not necessarily so. Moreover, in a small proportion of cases, chromosomal sex is ambiguous. Developmentally, *gonadal sex* comes next and is usually determined by the sex chromosomes, but it may be discrepant with both assigned and chromosomal sex. *Hormonal sex* normally corresponds to the gonads, but the testes do not always secrete effective androgens; nor the ovaries, estrogens. Moreover, in some females a hyperadrenocorticism may flood the bloodstream with androgens and produce virilism of the body. Inguinal testes in simulant females may produce estrogens that feminize the body. There is also the *sex of internal accessory organs*, principally the uterus and the prostate and seminal vesicles. The *sex of external genitalia* usually determines the sex of assignment, but as we shall see, in hermaphrodites and pseudohermaphrodites it may not correspond with all the other sexual categories. Finally (and again important to the psychologist) there is *psychological sex* or *gender role*, which does not necessarily correspond with all the physical defining marks. It may also differ from assigned sex, as is the case when some individuals who are socially designated as one sex and are ostensibly reared in that sex are psychologically inclined to be of the other one.

The embryological development of the reproductive system is illustrated in Figures 9–1 through 9–4, which show how initially bipotential structures develop into a male or a female system. It will be evident that abnormal

FIGURE 9–1. *Embryological origins of the reproductive systems. The primitive mammalian embryonic structures which become the reproductive system may be represented by a Y-shaped diagram. Very early in fetal life the precursors of both the female and male organs are present. The ovotestis has the potentiality of becoming either an ovary or a testis. Both the primitive precursors of the female ovary duct (the Müllerian duct) and the male duct (the Wolffian duct) are present. The Müllerian duct will become the Fallopian tubes and the uterus if a female is to develop; or if a male, then the Wolffian duct forms into the vas deferens and the structures that connect the testis to the penis.*

The lower limb of the Y is the primitive genital, which can become either the labia and vagina of a female, or the urethra of a male, and its associated structures like the prostate. Included in the primitive genital is the tubercle, which becomes either the clitoris or the penis.

A variety of errors of development can occur, but normally, of course, the whole system develops harmoniously, and such errors are in fact rare. When they do occur, they produce the conditions of hermaphroditism (where one side of the upper part of the Y develops male, the other side female) or pseudohermaphroditism (where the lower part of the Y develops discordantly with the upper parts).

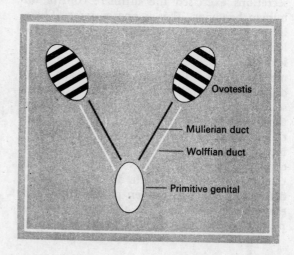

development of these structures *can* lead to mixed male-female structures, though this in fact rarely happens.

THE GLANDS AND SEXUAL BEHAVIOR

Taking up again the old notion of "glands of destiny," it is worthwhile to review the evidence on the actual place of the endocrines in sex behaviors. During what might be called the "endocrine era" in psychology, it was believed by many that these glands exert a controlling influence on both normal and deviant sex activities. Homosexuality was thought to be the result of some irregularity in the balance of hormones and in particular in the overproduction of opposite-sex hormones.

Disturbances of hormonal secretions often cause irregular development of the reproductive system. While they certainly result in modifications of the anatomical sex structures, whether they also cause any shift in sex behaviors is another question. On the basis of any close one-to-one relationship between the functioning of the reproductive system and sex behavior, one might expect these abnormalities of anatomy to be accompanied by psychological aberrations: Whether these in fact occur is another matter. The commonest cause of abnormality in the reproductive system lies in the cortex of the adrenal glands (Soffer et al., 1961). The more dramatic abnormalities result from oversecretion of the

FIGURE 9–2. *Schematic representation of the sexually undifferentiated urogenital system. Adapted from B. M. Patten. 1953. Human embryology, 2nd ed. New York: McGraw-Hill, Fig. 358, p. 575, by permission of the author and the publisher.*

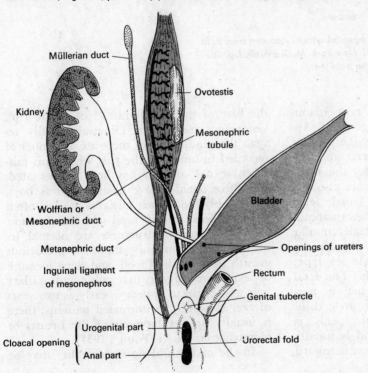

Müllerian duct

Kidney

Ovotestis

Mesonephric tubule

Wolffian or Mesonephric duct

Bladder

Metanephric duct

Openings of ureters

Inguinal ligament of mesonephros

Rectum

Genital tubercle

Urogenital part

Cloacal opening

Anal part

Urorectal fold

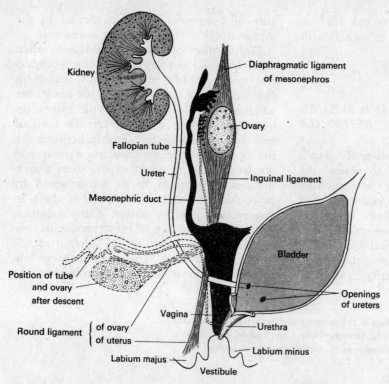

Kidney

Diaphragmatic ligament
of mesonephros

Ovary

Fallopian tube

Ureter

Inguinal ligament

Mesonephric duct

Bladder

Position of tube
and ovary
after descent

Openings
of ureters

Round ligament { of ovary
of uterus

Vagina

Urethra

Labium minus

Labium majus

Vestibule

FIGURE 9–3. The developing female urogenital system. Adapted from B. M. Patten. 1953. Human embryology, 2nd ed. New York: McGraw-Hill, Fig. 361, p. 578, by permission of the author and the publisher.

fetal adrenal cortex, a somewhat rare circumstance that may have an inherited basis. Apparently for different individuals the time of onset of this oversecretion differs, and the earlier it occurs in prenatal life, the more gross are the results. The effects are also different for the two sexes. In the female fetus the condition results in pseudohermaphroditism, producing an apparent male (insofar as external structures go), even though the chromosomal makeup is of female sex type; the internal structures are female. The fetal phallus is enlarged and at birth may be mistaken for a penis, the birth of a male child being mistakenly announced. This "penis" is in reality an enlarged clitoris and is usually hypospadic (that is, the ureter opens toward

the base of the organ instead of at the tip). Competent medical examination readily reveals the condition, but there are a number of recorded instances in the past where this mistaken sexual identity has been perpetuated, and these females have been reared as boys. Presumably today such mistakes are less often made, at least in advanced societies. In most cases the internal structures are normal female ones. Commonly there is precocious growth in early childhood, and some measure of sexual precocity in that pubic and axillary hair may begin to appear as early as two years of age. However, in untreated patients, there is usually no development of the breasts or menstruation (H. H. Young, 1937).

In the male child no abnormality may be

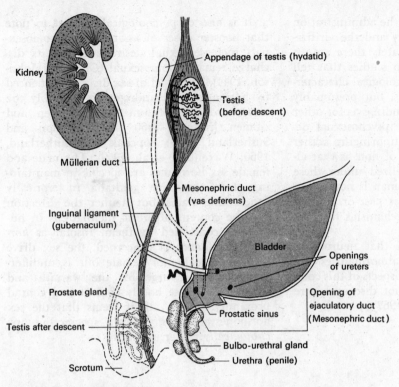

Kidney

Appendage of testis (hydatid)

Testis
(before descent)

Müllerian duct

Mesonephric duct
(vas deferens)

Inguinal ligament
(gubernaculum)

Bladder

Openings
of ureters

Opening of
ejaculatory duct
(Mesonephric duct)

Prostate gland

Prostatic sinus

Testis after descent

Bulbo-urethral gland

Urethra (penile)

Scrotum

FIGURE 9–4. The developing male urogenital system. Adapted from B. M.
Patten. 1953. Human embryology, 2nd ed. New York: McGraw-Hill, Fig. 362,
p. 579, by permission of the author and the publisher.

evident at birth, but at two or three years of age an "infant Hercules" develops. Growth of bone is rapid but ceases prematurely, so that the stature is short; muscle is well developed and adolescent in type. The penis may grow to adult size and pubic hair develops, but the testes are immature (and in this the condition differs from certain other forms of sexual precocity).

Not uncommonly, prenatal adrenal over-secretion is accompanied by gross disturbances in salt metabolism, which result in serious chronic illness or early death if left untreated. However, a small proportion of these rare individuals have escaped both the more disabling medical effects of their condition and also the detection for many years of their

strange sexual state. These people will be referred to later in discussing the psychological aspects of the matter, because there are some points of considerable developmental interest to be gained from such a study.

Another source of reproductive maldevelopment that should be mentioned for the sake of completeness is the administration of androgens to women during pregnancy (testosterone has been used to arrest carcinoma of the breasts). This affects female fetuses only. Diamond and Young (1963) have listed a number of cases, cited in the literature, in which such administration has resulted in the birth of female pseudohermaphrodites. They also give the results of their own experiments with guinea pigs, which show that there is a direct relationship between the administration of testosterone in pregnancy and the virilization of the fetus. Unfortunately there are, in the literature, no follow-up studies that tell us anything about the psychological characteristics of these virilized girls, but presumably we could expect the same findings as for other pseudohermaphrodites—that psychosexual development corresponds to upbringing rather than to structures. A point of note is that although the fetuses are virilized under these conditions the pregnant woman is not, either because the critical period is past or because she has other hormonal mechanisms that are protective.

It should be mentioned that neuroendocrine functions, and their abnormalities, are complex. A review of many aspects of this complex interaction that are not discussed here is given by Oppenheimer (1967).

Nonspecificity of Sex Hormones

A considerable number of experiments have been performed since Steinach (1912) demonstrated that "feminine" behaviors can be seen in castrated male rats and guinea pigs after implantation of ovaries. The literature has been reviewed by W. C. Young (1961), who shows that both androgens *and* estrogens can produce male and female behaviors in both males and females. That is, the sex hormones are not highly specific.

However, the hormones are not completely unspecific either, because although they can elicit opposite sex patterns, estrogens typically produce only weakly "feminine" behaviors in males, and that only with relatively high doses. Thus males are comparatively unresponsive to estrogens. Females are more responsive to androgens but tend to show feminine rather than masculine behaviors under their influence (though some "masculine" behaviors are reported).

It is also of psychological interest to note that booster doses of androgens in homosexuals increase sexual desire but that its discharge remains homosexual (Glass and Johnson, 1944). The level of sex drive is influenced by hormones, and androgen is probably the erotic arousal hormone in both men and women (Money, 1960, 1961b; Schon and Sutherland, 1960; Sopchak and Sutherland, 1960; Waxenberg et al., 1959). The male and female sex hormones are specific in maintaining their respective genitalia in erotically functioning states, but neither the direction nor the content of erotic inclinations in humans is controlled by them. Insofar as *hormonal* influence is concerned, the sex drive is neither male nor female but is undifferentiated as an urge for the warmth and sensation of close bodily contact and genital proximity. All in all, it seems that the sex hormones are *physiologically* specific but *psychologically* rather unspecific.

BIOLOGY OF HUMAN PSYCHOSEXUALITY

The foregoing review of some of the research on hormones in relation to psychosexual development might lead to the conclusion that they have no significant role at all. This would be a too-hasty decision, and the evidence requires more careful consideration.

Those theories of psychosexual development that emphasize experiential factors and take no account of physiological ones would seem to imply that the latter are irrelevant. On the other hand, there are theories that have placed considerable stress on hormonal factors in the development of normal sex behaviors, and even though such theories are not much in fashion today, they do contain some points that need to be examined if one is to obtain a full and complete picture of all the various factors that enter into the development of psychosexual orientation.

HORMONES AND SEX IN LOWER AND HIGHER ANIMALS

Postpubertal Castration

A source of misunderstanding about the relationship between physiological and psychological sex in humans has been those animal studies that have shown a close relationship between hormones and behavior, and in the lower animals this relationship is sometimes very close. The mating of rats, for example, can be eliminated by removal of the sex glands. The castrated male will show no interest in a female in heat, and a female without ovaries does not come into heat and will not respond to the advances of a male. On the other hand, the mating behavior of the castrated rat can be readily revived by the injection of the appropriate hormone and will continue as long as the injections are maintained, ceasing again when they are discontinued.

In these animals, learning plays little part in the emergence of mating behavior at maturity. Thus male rats reared in isolation, with no opportunity for learning, copulate quite expertly when first given access to a female in heat. There are, in lower animals, many instances of inborn or unlearned patterns of sex behavior that are closely under hormonal control, and this has led in the past to the assumption that a similar state of affairs exists higher up the scale. In the higher animals, however, the picture is different. The castration of adult higher animals does not consistently lead to a complete loss of sexual behavior, as it does in the lower ones. For instance, dogs from which the testes have been removed after puberty have continued to show excitement toward a bitch in heat and have copulated almost as frequently as before the operation (Beach, 1947).

A sex difference is seen here, because bitches from which the ovaries have been removed permanently and promptly cease to show sexual behavior; they also become completely unattractive to the male. In the higher primates, castration after puberty usually has no very marked effect on sexual activity. Although some reduction, as well as a slow decline in potency with time, may be found, some sexuality is continued indefinitely. In the higher primates the sex difference noted above is also less marked: Female chimpanzees following ovarectomy are less responsive to the advances of a male but will still respond to a particularly aggressive one (Yerkes and Elder, 1936).

It is also true that at the human level sexuality can survive removal of the gonads, and cases are on record of an apparently normal sex life being continued for thirty years or more following castration. Readers of *The Arabian Nights* (but not the nursery copy) will find it reported that at least some eunuchs could be accomplished performers and that some women preferred intercourse with them because the act was enjoyably prolonged, as the men did not ejaculate and become quiescent. Similarly, there are reports of women who have continued a normal sex life following the removal of the ovaries, and some of these have even reported an increase in the frequency and enjoyment of conjugal activity because the fear of pregnancy was removed. (It should be mentioned that the results of human castration are highly variable and some castrates do show a loss of eroticism. Whether these differences are related to physiological or psychological factors is unknown.)

The results of postpubertal castration have been reviewed by Money (1961c), who cites Bremer's study (1959) showing how variable the results can be. The results range from total loss of sexual function to reports of no change. (There is, of course, difficulty in assessing these subjective reports.) In general, it seems that the older a subject is at the time of castration, the less marked the psychological effects are. In other words, the more experienced and practiced the individual is, the less dependent he is on the gonads. The physiological effects of postpubertal castration also appear to be highly variable; in some cases there is loss of potency to the degree that erections cannot be maintained, and in others this disability is apparently less severe.

From all the evidence reviewed up to this point, it would appear that, especially in higher animals, hormones are less specific than was once believed, and that their influence on sex behavior is less direct; moreover, sexual activity may continue in their absence. In humans at least, it might seem possible to conclude that the hormones do not provide either a necessary or a sufficient basis for sexual behavior, but this would be too hasty a conclusion.

Prepubertal Castration

While postpubertal castration in higher mammals and humans may not lead to any loss of psychosexuality, it may lead to impotence because the ability to get an erection is impaired (Vest and Howard, 1939); however, the desire commonly remains. The situation with prepubertal absence of gonadal function is different. In hypogonadism, or in early loss of gonadal function by disease or accident, there is no obvious effect until the time at which puberty should occur but does not. The secondary sex characteristics fail to appear, the voice remains high-pitched, and there are growth abnormalities. The condition is commonly distressing to the individual; the psychosexual accompaniments are typically an absence of erotic interest and mediocre sexual performance, if any at all. The effects of hormone-replacement therapy are often dramatic and by contrast emphasize the deficiencies in the untreated state. Vest and Howard (1939) have reported on six cases of hypogonadism in which there was little or no erotic interest prior to treatment but in which interest was aroused by the treatment. J. P. Pratt (1942) has described the case of a physician and endocrinologist who suffered hypogonadism (his choice of specialty is not surprising). As a youth and young man he was shy about dating and was particularly self-conscious about his high-pitched voice. His sexual urges were weak. Following treatment, his whole sense of well-being improved, and he became erotically interested in women and also more dominant in social relationships. Heller and Nelson (1945) have described fifteen cases of eunuchoidism treated with testosterone, and again following treatment the previous low level of sex interest was markedly elevated and dominance-aggressive behavior also increased. Muscular strength and resistance to fatigue improved markedly. C. Allen (1962) has reported the case of a handsome but hypogonadal man who was much sought after by the ladies but who could not avail himself of the opportunities thus presented until treated with hormones. S. L. Simpson (1948) gave one of the best sources of data on the topic. He shows how the untreated eunuch tends to be placid, unassertive, and without much erotic force until provided artificially with hormones. In the untreated condition erections are infrequent and never long sustained, but they become normal with therapy. H. H. Young (1937) made some graphic contrasts between the treated and untreated state.

From the experimental point of view there are objections to the data. The absence of untreated controls is perhaps not an unshakable criticism, because the effects of no treatment are well known. More pertinent is the absence of studies using placebo controls, but the manner in which the patient usually relapses if treatment is discontinued and improves again on resumption suggests that the effect is genuinely hormonal. In other words, the *prepubertal* castrate does seem to illustrate a close relationship between hormones and psychological functioning.

None of this tells very much about the mode of action of hormones. One manner in which they might act would be in altering the level of sensory input (Harris et al., 1958). It may be that the prepubertal castrate has, rather, than no response at all, a very high threshold to erotic arousal.

The effects of the hormones are not only specifically sexual but also influence a wide range of behaviors. Money (1960, 1961a) has pointed out that the sex hormones have an indirect influence on social maturity through their effect in maturing the body, and Sollenberger (1940) has shown a relationship between the urinary excretion of androgens in boys and their social interests and attitudes. There was a closer correlation between hormone output and maturity than between chronological age and maturity. The prepubertal castrate represents an extreme form of the effect of hormone lack, but late maturity has, at least temporarily, some of the same effects.

Nongonadal Hormones and Sex Behaviors

The discussion so far has implied that it is only the specific sex hormones that are involved in sex behaviors. This might be an oversimplification of the matter, and the secretions of the pituitary, adrenal cortex, and thyroid in particular may have some role. The evidence on the question, however, is not altogether clear. Judging from a review by W. C. Young (1961), there is most evidence on the role of the thyroid in mating behavior. He states that although this gland has received much attention, well-designed studies are not numerous. After reviewing a number of studies, some of them giving conflicting results, Young remarks,

It is apparent that reproductive processes, including the display of mating behavior in the male and female, often require a functioning thyroid gland, that a level of thyroid activity exists which is optimal for reproduction, and that deviations in either direction may be followed by changes in, if not the elimination of, mating behavior [p. 1211].

He goes on to point out that it is apparently possible for there to be quite marked deviations from normal levels of thyroid secretion without any noticeable effect on mating behaviors. Another fact that emerges is that there seems to be a great deal of difference between species as to the influence of the thyroid and also considerable variation among individuals within a species. Thus in a species or an individual for which a high level of thyroid secretion is necessary to reproductive behavior, the effects of a reduction of thyroid secretion may be marked. Conversely, the species or individual normally requiring a low level of thyroid secretion might have sexual activity enhanced by even a small degree of oversecretion (Young and Peterson, 1952).

As this relates to the present context, there seems to be no evidence whatever to suggest that the thyroid can have any influence on the *direction* of erotic activity (causing homosexuality, for instance), but there are indications that the level of thyroid activity may well influence the amount of sexual arousal that is customary in the individual. In Young's review there is no comment as to whether man is one of the species to be typified as high, medium, or low in the level of thyroid activity necessary to optimal reproductive activity.

Insofar as the other endocrine glands are concerned, there seem to be both less data and even less possibility of drawing a consistent conclusion from what data there are. For the adrenal cortex, Young concludes that the weight of evidence is against any direct participation of adrenocortical hormones in the stimulation of mating behavior (see also Cooper and Aronson, 1958). This may be a surprising conclusion, but there it is. Money (1961a), on the contrary, has claimed that excess androgens of adrenal origin lower the threshold for erotic arousal in women and also cause clitoral tumescence. One manner in which the adrenal cortex may be important is in influencing the general level of activity. In some studies, the amount of running during estrus of rats and other species has been taken as an indication of a level of sexual arousal or excitement. Because, however, gonadectomy does not greatly affect the running activity of either male or female wild Norway rats (Richter and Uhlenhtuh, 1945), it is concluded that it is steroids from the adrenals that contribute to this level of activity. It might be postulated, therefore, that the adrenals affect activity level in general; when sexually stimulated an animal with a high level of general activity is likely to show a high level of sexual activity. Waxenberg et al. (1959) produced clinical evidence on fourteen female patients from which the adrenals were removed in the course of treatment of metastatic breast cancers, and in twelve of these women there was a postoperative decline in sexual functioning. These authors also present evidence that removal of the ovaries has little effect on sexual behavior and conclude that the adrenals are as important as the ovaries in the hormonal basis of human sexuality. However, it could be that knowing what the *general* level of activity of these patients was following the operation would reconcile these apparently conflicting results.

W. C. Young (1961) quotes a number of studies that seem to exclude any direct action by the pituitary on mating behavior. Any effects of removal of the pituitary, such as general reduction of all activity or widespread metabolic effects, are indirect.

THE BRAIN AND SEXUAL BEHAVIOR

So far the discussion has proceeded as if sex behaviors somehow emanated from the hormones directly. These behaviors are, in fact, complex and involve highly coordinated reactions to stimuli by complicated sequences of motor activity.

Obviously all levels of the brain are implicated in such complex patterns of activity. However, hypothalamic centers, being sensitive to the presence of sex hormones in the bloodstream (Harris et al., 1958), have a key role in the neural control of these behaviors.

Numerous experiments on the effects of the implantation of sex hormones in the brain have been reviewed by Pfaff (1965), who shows that behaviors can be elicited by this technique. Lehrman (1962) has spoken of some of the difficulties in the interpretation of such data, pointing out that they do not necessarily mean that behavior is organized within or "emitted" from these centers, because peripheral contributions to the total pattern may also be present. External stimulation added to this internal one is an example of such a case.

In lower animals, the sequence of events' would appear to be as follows: Hormones present in the bloodstream affect the arousal center in the hypothalamus, which in turn influences the limbic system and "primes" the organism for sexual activity; the hypothalamus also coordinates this activity when it occurs. The cortex facilitates action, making it smoother and better performed, but in lower animals is not essential. Nerve networks (presumably innate) mediate the basic patterns of activity that are involved. These are the emotional experiences (which we infer to be present), responses to appropriate stimuli and the motor action necessary to consummation. The first and essential link in this process is the triggering of the hypothalamic center by the hormone, and in the absence of this hormone there is no behavior. In these lower animals the behavior is determined from below upward, and the cortex, as it were, merely polishes and refines patterns of activity that can take place in its absence. Somewhat higher up the animal scale, the cortex takes on the integrative role that is performed by the limbic system in lower species. Without the cortex the performance in these species is clumsy and may not be well enough organized for successful completion of the act. Still higher up the scale, the cortex becomes vital, because without it the animal cannot function optimally. It cannot, for one thing, readily sense the presence of a mate or coordinate movement toward it. In the decorticate state, the highest animals are completely comatose and are incapable of any purposive behavior at all. In the higher animals the direction of influence can be downward as well as upward, the cortex being capable of initiating sexual behavior in the absence of hormonal stimulation of the hypothalamus (as in the case, for instance, of the castrated dog). In these higher species, while the basic innate tendencies to behavior still exist, learning and experience are necessary to their successful performance (as will be discussed later). In humans the cortex can initiate fantasied sexual stimulation without the necessity for any adequate external stimulus. We may presume that the tendency toward fantasies of this kind may be greater in certain hormonal states than in others, but we lack any information about the precise relationship between these factors. We have no means of knowing whether such fantasied stimulation is possible among the animals. In man, the intervention of the cortex can lead to very extensive modification of patterns of sexual behavior and makes possible the enormous variety in psychosexuality that is found. Because of his highly evolved cortex, man is able to apprehend abstract concepts such as chastity and to modify his activities in concordance with them.

In the males of many mammalian species, and this is true of all the primates, sex hormones are constantly in the blood stream. In females of these species, however, there are periodic fluctuations in the level of hormones present. This difference is one source of the behavioral differences that are found between males and females, but is less marked at the human level than it is among the animals. However, even in humans there is a periodicity in coitus (Udry and Morris, 1968), coitus and orgasm being more frequent by a considerable margin at the time of ovulation than at other times in the cycle.

A review of studies of nervous system-hormonal interactions in lower mammals has been provided by Lisk (1967). In Chapter 10 the evidence that males and females actually have different nervous systems is discussed. This, together with other matters dealt with in this section, leads one to question the current notion that males and females have the potentiality at birth for the behaviors of both sexes and that it is the hormones that determine which behaviors appear. One effect of the male hormones, in this view, is the masking or blocking of the expression of female behaviors, and vice versa. If it is true that males and females have different nervous systems, then bipotentiality for behavior seems unlikely. This is not to say that the capacity for the expression of *any* opposite sex behavior is entirely lost, but presumably this expression will be affected, at least to the extent of raising the threshold for other-sex behaviors, and probably qualitative effects will also be found. This might explain the relative nonspecificity of the hormones already spoken of in another section.

VARIETY IN SEXUAL BEHAVIOR

Another feature of the behavior of lower animals is that it is "stimulus-bound"; that is, the behavior can be triggered only by a definite stimulus and usually a highly specific one. Thus the red breast of the robin is an essential stimulus to courtship behavior (as well as to fighting), and it is possible to play an unkind practical joke on the robin by dyeing the breast brown, in which case it fails to excite many of the normal mating responses from another (Lack, 1953).

Further up the scale, the range of variation of sexual behaviors becomes more extensive, and among the primates "perverted" behaviors are quite common. The term "unnatural vice" has been commonly used for behaviors of these kinds—homosexuality, masturbation, fetishism, and heterosexual activities that are not those prescribed by some code—but the expression is an unfortunate one. If it is intended to mean "not found in the natural state," it is a singularly ill-informed term, because in fact such behaviors are common among the higher animals. The licking of the female genitalia by the male (cunnilingus) is a regular part of the sex behavior of the dog and is observed in apes. Homosexual activities are also observed in many species, and masturbation by friction against inanimate objects has been observed in a number of mammals. All these behaviors are regularly seen in the primates. While such behaviors might be called unaesthetic, they can hardly be called unnatural, if by this we mean not found in nature.

BRAIN LOCI FOR SPECIFIC BEHAVIORS

The brain contains a considerable number of specific centers that control the inbuilt neural patterns that mediate particular behavioral sequences. The existence of these innate neural patterns is demonstrated by numerous animal experiments in which electrodes have been implanted in various regions of the brain and a wide variety of behaviors elicited by electrical stimulation via them. The technique and its results have been extensively reviewed by several authors in Sheer (1961).

A more popular account has been given by V. Holst (1962), who has described how, by implantations in the brain stem of the domestic fowl, he could elicit such behaviors as sitting from the standing position or rising when the animal was sitting. The behaviors aroused by stimulation of these regions appear to be perfectly natural; the standing hen, for example, will select a place to sit and settle and fluff the feathers in the manner typical of the species. By the simultaneous stimulation of antagonistic centers (those for standing and sitting, for instance) the animal can be thrown into a state of behavioral indecision in which the conflict between the two patterns is quite evident.

Other centers have been discovered, in subcortical regions, that do not produce such highly specific behavioral patterns as these but instead produce unspecific sensations that may be either pleasurable or aversive (Olds and Milner, 1954; Olds and Olds, 1962). (Or rather, one should say that the animal behaves as if it was receiving pleasant or unpleasant stimulation, because we really do not know what its sensations are like, though human experiments do suggest their nature.)

The elicitation, by electrical stimulation of the brain, of parts of the pattern of sexual behavior has been described by O. J. Miller (1961). For example, there seems to be a center mediating penile erection (MacLean, 1962) and another that controls ejaculation. Miller suggests that sexual behavior may be made up of a number of components, which are integrated in normal behavior but which may be activated separately by such artificial means as electrical stimulation. Thus there may be involved in such a complex pattern of behavior as is found in reproduction, a network of nuclei rather than any single center controlling this function as a whole. In total, there are a considerable number of experiments involving electrical stimulation in the brain in a wide variety of species, including some of the higher primates, and these studies suggest that there are ready-programmed behavioral patterns that extend over appreciable lengths of time and that can be stimulated by brief excitation artificially. On the assumption that man is continuous with the lower animals and is endowed with the same kinds of physiological mechanisms, we can assume that similar inbuilt neural pathways are to be found in him also. Technically, the task of proving this to be the case is simple, but ethically it raises obvious and serious problems. In spite of these difficulties there are now a number of instances in the literature of the application to human subjects of the brain-stimulation techniques widely used in animal experiment. Heath (1964) has reported findings on fifty-four subjects, nearly all patients suffering from either severe psychosis, epilepsy, or intractable pain in cancer. These experiments involve both electrical and chemical stimulation of various brain regions. The psychotic patients were studied in the hope of finding a technique of motivation that might be useful in therapy, and the experiments on the patients in pain were an attempt to find a method of alleviation by producing a state of euphoria by septal stimulation. Such a technique, it was felt, might circumvent the addictive properties of the drugs used for this purpose.

One of the most interesting aspects of these experiments is that it was often possible to obtain the subjective report of the patient on his experiences during self-actuated stimulation of the brain, a source of data that is completely lacking in animal studies. It is true that Heath's subjects were not normal, but there really does not seem to be any reason for supposing that the result would have been any different had normal subjects been used. When both a normal rat and a psychotic man signify that septal self-stimulation is pleasurable by repeatedly giving it to themselves, it would not seem improbable that a normal man would do the same, especially when the psychotic reports that he does it because "it feels good." This supposition is heightened when we find that there are corresponding areas, in both the rat and the psychotic human, in which self-stimulation is *not* repeated and for which the psychotic reports an unpleasurable sensation. (The types of aversive reactions reported in these experiments were sometimes a general discomfort and at other times feelings of intense nausea related to the visceral system.)

Not all the psychotic subjects actually reported pleasurable sensations, some being too severely deteriorated to communicate, but all showed behavioral signs of pleasure. With septal stimulation, even the seriously deteriorated patients brightened, became more alert, and appeared more attentive to the environment for at least a few minutes afterward. The less deteriorated patients became more verbal and were more productive in their thinking, and those prone to depressive content in their speech became more optimistic and genial.

Heath claims that his findings suggest that, within the human brain, the distribution of sites that are positive or preferred for self-stimulation are very similar to those found in animals. These reward sites are found through the septal region, and this region's main outflow pathway (the medial forebrain bundle) is into the interpeduncular nuclei of the mesencephalic tegmentum. The aversive sites were close to the reward ones and in a similar manner were scattered through deep cerebral regions, particularly through the midline diencephalon and the mesencephalon.

There is a sexual element in septal stimulation that had largely passed unnoticed, although MacLean (1959) had discussed the relation between septal stimulation and sexual behavior in the monkey. Heath describes how one patient, given passive (non-self-administered) stimulation in the septal area while he was in the course of a very depressed conversation and almost in tears, suddenly grinned and switched the topic to plans to date and seduce a girl friend. He was unable to account for the sudden change of topic, but merely said that the thought of the girl had suddenly come to his mind. This switch from depression to gaiety was repeated several times with this subject. Another patient with a two-year history of severe agitated depression also switched on a sudden smile after stimulation and recounted a youthful sexual experience. In another instance a male patient was given three buttons for intercranial self-stimulation (ICSS)—one connected to the septal region, another to the hippocampus, and a third to the mesencephalic tegmentum. He found stimulation of the last region extremely unpleasant, and wedged a hairpin under the button to prevent its being pressed. Hippocampal stimulation was mildly aversive, whereas the septal one was pleasurable and often repeated. This patient's problem was narcolepsy, but by use of a portable stimulator he was able to keep awake by giving himself a jog each time he felt sleep coming on and to continue his employment as an entertainer in a night club. If he did inadvertently fall asleep, his friends would wake him with the button. His subjective report was that the feeling he got from ICSS was "good," and that it made him feel he was building up to a sexual orgasm. This, however, never reached a climax, which matter he sometimes found frustrating. While these "sexual" feelings were commonly reported by Heath's subjects, there were only three instances of penile erection accompanying them (other brain centers are apparently concerned in erection).

It would be noted that the results of ICSS in the septal region are not always entirely rewarding. As already noted, some of the subjects were frustrated by the noncompletion of the sexual arousal. Other patients reported fleeting memories or déjà-vu experiences that were also annoying by being incomplete: They set the subject the bothersome task of trying to revive more thoroughly the half-aroused memory. In an attempt to aid the process, the patient, hoping to replace the frustration by a sense of euphoria, often followed the original stimulation with repeated self-stimulation. In other words, in trying to assess the results of ICSS, it is necessary to know what motivational state is induced in the subject by this stimulation, and it is only in human experiments that we have the possibility of doing so.

The sexual element in Heath's findings is of particular interest in the present context, because it supports the idea that certain of the psychic or experiential aspects accompanying sex behaviors are inbuilt—in other words, that the conative aspects of instinctual behaviors are, as suggested in Chapter 4, indeed part of man's innate biological equipment.

These artificial-stimulation experiments need to be brought into perspective. This question is discussed in Chapter 6, and, as Moltz (1965) has pointed out, the fact that an extrinsic stimulus, either electrical or chemical, can produce an integrated response

does not tell us much about the neural events that normally precede it. It is quite evident that earlier events (including previous learning) influenced the responses of Heath's patients. They did not, for instance, go into an automatic performance of the sexual act, and in spite of being psychotics they remained remarkably constrained. What in fact seems to have been predominantly aroused was fantasy or other cognitive events. These events were correlated with the "storage" of information of the individual, for instance, fantasies related to a particular girl. No doubt in appropriate circumstances these cognitive events could lead to overt actions, which would also involve other patterns of neural events (those, for example, mediating the bodily changes associated with sexual behaviors), giving a total complex of coordinated internal and external events.

We have no means of knowing what cognitive events take place in the laboratory animals under septal stimulation, but we can perhaps hazard a guess. It is evident that the animals get some kind of fun out of ICSS in the septal region, and if we can extrapolate from man to the rat, maybe this pleasure is sexual in nature.

Experiments by N. E. Miller (1958, 1960) show how previous experiences can be elicited by hypothalamic stimulation. Rats earlier taught bar-pressing for a food reward would bar-press on ventromedial nucleic stimulation even though satiated. This is just an extension of other work that has shown feeding in satiate animals in response to similar stimulation. Even in the rat, what is triggered by the excitement of the brain center is not a rigid bit of automatism but a coordinated pattern of behavior adapted to the immediate circumstances and invoking relevant experience.

It seems evident that septal stimulation is not a local effect but one that irradiates to other brain centers, upward as well as downward; and that the behavior that emerges is the resultant of a complex of interactions aroused by this one stimulus. It may be that a stimulus at any point in the complex can arouse the whole, but evidence on this theory is incomplete.

The theoretical importance of all this is that it shows the human brain, as well as the brain of lower animals, to be "prewired" or programmed for certain aspects of sexual behavior. In lower animals it may be that this innate "programming" is fairly complete, so that given the appropriate internal conditions and external stimuli the behavior proceeds to consummation without much need for learning to piece the program sequences together. In higher primates and humans, and especially in males, the programming is less complete in the sense that it needs sequencing, but it is still present. For instance, the mechanisms for bodily changes such as erection of the penis or clitoris as well as for other bodily changes, exist. There is also the tendency to certain qualities of emotional experience and possibly innate sign gestalts that relate to these. A considerable amount of learning is necessary to bring these elements into a skilled sequence of behaviors, but the fact that learning is important does not mean it is all-important. The part taken by the biological substratum should not be denied or overlooked. The task for the developmentalist is to show how these biological and experiential factors are coordinated in achieving the patterns of behavior found in maturity.

EARLY HUMAN SEX BEHAVIORS

A suggestion from the discussion so far is that the human organism comes biologically equipped for at least some aspects of sex behaviors, and the question arises as to the early manifestations of these behaviors. There is a fairly extensive literature on childhood sex behaviors and numerous articles by Kinsey et al. (1953). However, much of this is anecdotal, or consists of theoretical discussions of the question within a psychoanalytic framework, or of case discussion. These writings make it clear that there *is* preadolescent sex behavior (notwithstanding Valentine [1942] to the contrary) but give little indication as to whether it is universal, merely common, or rare or whether it is confined in any way.

About the only attempts at a normative survey of early sex behaviors are those in the Kinsey Reports (1948, 1953), though Schofield (1965) has surveyed such behaviors in adolescents in England. It is a little difficult to assess the reliability of the Kinsey data: Some of it was apparently derived from reports of pedophiles describing the sexual reactions of their young partners. Other observers are mentioned, but without any indication of the conditions under which the observations were made. This is obviously an area in which we are going to remain without any data of a thorough, scientific nature; studies of the kind carried out by Masters and Johnson (1966) on adults are not likely to be countenanced in this area and rightly so.

One distinction made by Kinsey et al. is that between orgasm as a physiological event and as a psychological one. Physiological orgasms have been witnessed in prepubertal boys from a few months of age onward. Kinsey et al. remark that such events in young girls are much less common. Apart from the actual ejection of seminal fluid, these orgasms appear to be very similar to that of the adult, at least insofar as the physical aspects go. There is seen the tenseness of the body, the spasmodic motions, increased respiration and flushing, sometimes a cry, with the sudden letdown and quiescence typical of the adult climax. These authors state that erections and orgasms are easily aroused in preadolescent and early adolescent boys—markedly more readily than in maturity. The capacity for frequent orgasms at short intervals is also greater in immature males than in mature ones.

Just what the psychological concomitants of these physiological orgasms are is not known for any truly representative sample. Kinsey et al. quote reports of preadolescents who have had repeated contacts with adults as stating that these orgasms were erotically pleasurable. One infers that these boys were promiscuous and willingly had relationships of this kind; in what manners they might differ from their more inhibited peers is not known.

If the Kinsey data are to be relied on, then it seems that in preadolescence there is a considerably wide range of psychologically erotic stimuli for the male, this actually being narrowed down by adolescent experiences. Numerous physical sources of erotic response are quoted from statements of respondents. Friction with clothing, sitting on warm sand, wrestling, and fast bicycle riding are examples of such sources. A longer list of emotional stimulants, such as fear, watching fires, punishments, and entering an empty house, are also sources of erotic response. Even the national anthem is reported as an erotic stimulus. There are also quoted a number of more specifically sexual sources of erotic response, ranging from seeing and thinking about females as the most numerous to such things as pictures and seeing one's own nude body in a mirror, down to burlesque shows and dancing as the least numerous (possibly as a result of lack of opportunity). On the basis of their data, Kinsey et al. suggest that at first *any* emotional arousal may be the basis for the sexual response. By late adolescence this is narrowed down to direct physical stimulation of the genitalia or to psychic arousal of a specifically sexual nature. In the older individual, even genital and other physically erotic stimulation may be ineffectual unless the psychological concomitants are appropriate.

While admitting that their data are incomplete and may be based on a biased sample, Kinsey et al. claim that preadolescent sex play, involving contacts with either boys or girls of a similar age, is very common. They suggest that much of this may be for-

gotten and hence not reported later. They also claim that this sex play is markedly less common among girls (hence most of the boys' experience must be with other boys). Play of this nature reaches a peak in boys between the ages of about eight and thirteen, but it is found at all ages up to puberty. The first experiences of sex play are usually with a somewhat older child. As already mentioned, some of the children in the Kinsey sample had been involved in sex activities with adults, but presumably this is unusual and only a minority of the general population are initiated in this manner.

Homosexual contacts of one sort or another (mostly with peers) form a considerable proportion of preadolescent sex activities, though according to the Kinsey data actual coital play is not all that common, involving only about 13 percent at age thirteen and rather less at ages fourteen and fifteen. According to the Kinsey figures, by far the greater part of heterosexual preadolescent sex play does not involve actual coitus, though it may involve mutual manipulation of the genitalia, and Kinsey et al. believe that this is because, in our culture at least, children at this age are not aware of the possibilities of coitus. ("Coital" sex play in other societies is reported by anthropologists.)

Early sexuality has also been discussed by Money (1961c), who speaks of childhood rehearsals and their role in the development of sexual behaviors. He points out that, although hormonally immature, children do have thoughts and fantasies that are reflected in their play and that are cognitional rehearsals of erotic behavior. Kindergarten romances are common and sometimes long sustained. In our society in particular, genital or copulatory imagery is not necessarily a part of these rehearsals, but such imagery is by no means alien to the play repertoire of young children in other cultures (Mead, 1961).

Money (1961c) reviews the cognitional rehearsals of fourteen children who had matured in their physical sex before the age of eight and who were examined between the ages of five and twelve. The occurrence of sexual dreams and daydreams was variable. Five of the twelve girls said that they had daydreams of a romantic nature, but the dreams were stereotyped and without any genital element; dreams while asleep were of the same character. None of these girls produced any evidence of orgasm dreams, and there was no evidence of an orgasm in any of them, either asleep or awake. One of the two boys reported nocturnal emissions but no dreams or daydreams. The other boy was seen periodically between ages five and eleven; at age six and again at age nine, he reported sexual dreams and daydreams of a florid nature involving naked women and kissing, and these occurred before he gave any evidence of ejaculation. There are also data on eight cases of boys with hyperadrenocortical syndrome leading to testicular precocity that continued after the original cause was corrected, so that the boys were well advanced in puberty before the age of eight. Two of the eight boys had erotic daydreams and at night wet dreams involving erotic imagery. Two of the remaining boys spoke of daydreams involving kissing and petting girls and accompanied by erection. Another reported erections accompanying noncrotic, adventurous fantasies. Overall, Money concludes that the erotic play of these precocious children was typical of their social age rather than their hormonal age and that the thematic content of their fantasies was also in the main consistent with their social age. Rafferty and Stein (1958) and Karnaby (1945) have reported similar observations.

The social age of the children in these studies seemed to have been determined by their life experiences and did not necessarily correspond closely to chronological age. Although precocious puberty had not made any marked difference in the content of the erotic imagery or of the erotic play of these children, it had some influence on the frequency of occurrence of both.

LEARNING AND THE ACQUISITION OF SEX BEHAVIORS

The importance of learning in the initiation and continuing of sex behaviors parallels, as it does for all other forms of behavior, the development of the cortex of the brain. Lower mammals, such as the rat, have a small cortex and a limited capacity for learning, and in such species a considerable proportion of the cortex can be removed without marked effect on behavior. In female rats the entire cortex can be removed, and they will still display periodic mating behavior as they come into heat. In male rats complete removal of the cortex destroys mating activity, but fairly extensive removal of cortical tissue can be made before sex behavior disappears. Because cortical removal is known to affect learned behaviors (for instance, an animal that has learned a specific task loses this learning on removal of cortical tissue and may have difficulty in relearning it), it would seem legitimate to assume that behaviors that do remain after cortical removal are unlearned and are part of the animal's innate repertoire. On this basis we may assume that the sexual behavior of the male rat is to some extent dependent on learning but that of the female little if at all. (This is not a necessary conclusion, merely a possible and reasonable one: The results could mean only that the innate behaviors of the male rat involve the cortex and that those of the female do not. At least, it seems that male and female brains are differently organized with respect to certain behaviors.)

Ascending the phylogenetic scale, removal of relatively smaller amounts of cortex results in loss of many forms of behavior, including sexual ones. This may be taken as an indication of the importance of learning in the behaviors in these species. Cortical organization presumably plays a large role in the responses of this kind, and this cortical organization is achieved by learning. As Ford and Beach (1951) have pointed out, the disturbance of the pattern on cortical ablation is, in all species studied, greater for males than for females; this may be taken to suggest that learning is more important for the males than for the females. Information of this kind becomes somewhat ambiguous, however, at the primate level, because cortical ablation so much disrupts all kinds of behaviors that any specific effects on sexual ones are impossible to see.

There can be no reasonable doubt that the role of learning is very considerable in the development of human sex behaviors and that it may be said to be relatively much greater than the role of hormonal influences, though it is, of course, impossible to give any sort of quantitative estimate. Ford and Beach also suggest that even in humans the relatively greater importance of learning in males as compared with females still holds. There is no conclusive evidence on this point and evidence will be difficult to obtain, but the hypothesis does seem to be consistent with the fact that sex behaviors in men are apparently more variable than in women. According to the Kinsey studies, the heterosexual patterns of males tend to cover a wider range than those of the females, the former liking variety in their sexual activities and the latter being content with less range of sexual pleasures. Furthermore, it seems to be the case that the human male is more prone than the female to acquire unusual and surrogate modes of sexual expression, as in fetishes, in voyeurisms and exhibitionism, and in the variety of homosexual patterns.

When humans are experimentally injected with same-sex hormones, they report a feeling of sexual tension, but this is handled in the manner that has been learned. In most experiments this means that they do nothing, because even in laboratories the conventions still hold, and massive doses of hormones do not lead to unrestrained sexual activity; release is delayed. The injection of opposite-sex hormones usually has little effect in small amounts, though in large doses it also may arouse sexual tension—but with the same feel-ing tone as is characteristic of the individual and no different. The experiment of injecting homosexuals with androgens has been tried, and they have reported, as others have, an increase of tension—but this they discharge in the homosexual manner they have preferred (Glass and Johnson, 1944).

Not only are sex behaviors different for each sex (as it is hardly necessary to point out), but there are also a wide range of behavioral patterns, that are not specifically sexual, in which there are differences. These include maternal and paternal patterns of activity toward the young and territorial behaviors, which often are specific to the male and include aggressive behaviors toward intruders; in many species there is a dominance-submission pattern that is specific to each sex, the female commonly deferring to the male. In the lower animals there would not be argument that these pattern differences are based upon innate factors, and such differences also extend up the scale to the primates; one can hardly doubt that they exist in humans also. Underlying these sex differences are the differences between males and females in hormonal balance, in the organization of the nervous system, and in many aspects of bodily functioning. As already stated, the mating behavior of the adults of lower species does not in general depend to any great extent on learning, but as we come up the scale there is a tendency for learning during the juvenile period of development to take a more and more important place in the emergence of adult behaviors of all kinds, including those concerned in reproduction. This is especially true of the primates, and what might be called "juvenile sex play" is evidently essential to the learning of reproductive activities.

Harlow and Harlow (1962, 1965) have described experiments in which rhesus monkeys have been reared in isolation, having neither adult care nor infant companions. These animals as adults are abnormal in their sex behaviors. Many of the males were never able to make a successful coitus, even with a normally reared and experienced female. The isolated females were somewhat less inept than the males, but their responsiveness to males was impaired. Apparently the play that is part of the juvenile experience of a normally reared monkey is essential in some way to the learning of the behavior pattern of the adult, and this is especially true in the male.

In the chimpanzees, even after normal juvenile play, the young adult male requires experience before becoming competent in mating, whereas females more readily perform their part of the sexual act untutored. If an inexperienced young male and female are placed together, the female shows the greater skill and may actually attempt to assist and "instruct" the male (Yerkes and Elder, 1936). It would seem that the social play of ape childhood supplies the female with the necessary feminine responses, whereas the male requires more direct experience and a further amount of training before reaching efficiency in his part of the coital pattern. It is not known just what the elements of these lessons are, but rudiments of adult activities are to be seen in the play of young apes, and these activities evidently contain the experiences necessary to the learning that precedes natural performance.

In animals, and probably in man too, dominance-submission behaviors have important bearings on sexual aptitude (without being specifically sexual in content, because they also appear in other activities, such as competition for food). The "peck order" of the domestic fowl is a well-known phenomenon, and in a short time a flock of hens will establish themselves in a strict hierarchy, which is particularly evident at feeding time. There is one hen that pecks at all the others and drives them away from any tidbit she fancies. She is rarely pecked herself. Next is the number two hen, who pecks at all but the first and is rarely pecked at except by the first. This order continues down the line to the last wretched bird, pecked by every other,

never pecking in retaliation, able to secure only the leftovers of food unnoticed by the others. After an initial period of competition, each bird knows her station and defers to those above her so that open conflict becomes uncommon. An inferior bird passively moves away from a superior one. In this class-conscious society of the barnyard, the cock usually (but not invariably) tops the order and is rarely required to exert his authority, though the occasional henpecked cock has become a byword. After the administration of androgens, a lowly bird becomes rebellious and promotes herself in the hierarchy (Allee, 1936, 1942), but because early experiences also affect order, it has to be questioned whether hormones are the only factor involved even at this level.

Dominance hierarchies of a similar kind have been observed in many species of animals. In baboons, the more dominant male secures the favors of the female, and the highest ranking ones have not only the most attractive females but a harem as well. Consequently, the lesser males who can secure only casual sexual gratification from a female do so, at some risk, when the more dominant males are not around. They may be reduced to homosexual outlets when their superiors are vigilant (Zuckerman, 1932).

Money (1961a) has pointed out that there is a close relationship between the morphological development of the body and social sex behavior in adolescents. Boys and girls who are late in sexual maturation tend to show less dating and similar behaviors than their age-mates, and conversely, those that are advanced in maturation tend to show more (though this, as we have already seen, does not go to the extent of leading to dating behavior in sexually precocious young children). In the latter case, the absence of age-mates who are at this stage of social development might be a factor. We have noted also that males low in androgen tend to show passive behavior patterns and would rank low in dominance hierarchies.

RELATION BETWEEN
CONSTITUTION AND LEARNING

Some insights into the relationship between physical and experiential factors have been provided by Hampson and Hampson (1961), who note that in hermaphrodites and pseudo-hermaphrodites psychological sex generally corresponds to upbringing even if this is inconsistent with the physical aspects of sex. This fact leads them to state that the theory of bisexuality must be discarded. Gender role, they insist, is the result of upbringing, and at birth psychological sex is undifferentiated or neutral: It has no instinctive basis. The individual becomes masculine or feminine, psychologically, as a result of experiences after birth. To the evidence of the hermaphrodites one may add that of homosexuality, where psychosexuality appears to transgress biology.

However, this may oversimplify the situation. In discussing sex differences in a later section (Chapter 10) it is suggested that there are biological differences between males and females. At birth the individual is *not* neutral but is either female or male, not merely anatomically but in certain aspects of organization that have important bearings on later psychological development. At birth there is already a commitment one way or the other. True, this may be modified by experiences, sometimes radically, but an initial bias is present and effective.

It is a misunderstanding to suppose that a homosexual male is necessarily "feminine." I would insist from clinical observation that most homosexuals are in fact quite definitely masculine: They think like men and respond like men to stimulation. They regard themselves as men and often perform successfully in male occupations. The only difference from other males is that they are erotically interested in males to an extent most males are not. Often, though not invariably, they are not interested in females. But, in responding to males, they are transposing fundamentally male processes of perception and reaction

that are normally directed toward females (this is discussed rather more fully in Chapter 10). The dominance hierarchy requires less dominant homosexuals to take the "passive" role in sexual activities (Nash and Hayes, 1965); this passive role is sometimes and misleadingly called the female role, but there is really nothing very feminine about it.

The majority of homosexuals are different from the minority that would like to regard themselves as women and adopt feminine mannerisms and sometimes female dress. It is perhaps unfortunate to use the same term to cover both kinds of men. Though I must admit to having no evidence beyond the valuable mysticism of clinical insight, I would affirm that the former or masculine group of homosexuals are fundamentally male, even in most aspects of gender role and psychosexuality. They have (I suspect) male-type nervous systems. It is merely that they are like misimprinted birds (Chapter 8) who direct their responses to the wrong object. As is the case with misimprinted birds, it is experience that determines the phenomenon.

Again offering no more support than my observations, I claim that some of the "feminine" group of homosexuals are also male-type in neural organization. They achieve only a sad parody of femininity and on introduction one knows at once that they are men in drag. One can only regret their tragic urge to be something unattainable to them. A few are more successful, and even in groups where one is alerted to wondering who is what, one may be deceived. It may be speculated whether these men have unmasculinized nervous systems. For both types, certain life experiences (discussed more fully in Chapter 19) are crucial to the development of their state.

Having had no opportunity to observe many of the hermaphrodites reviewed by Hampson and Hampson, I can only speculate about them, but I would inquire about the specific quality of their femininity and masculinity and how well gender role really is established in them.

The purpose here is not to dispute the important point which the Hampsons are making that experiences play a crucial part in gender role determination and the development of psychosexuality. This is undeniable in the light of the evidence, and later sections of this book will elaborate on the critical influence of experience. What is intended here is to question the statement that these experiences are superimposed on a neutral, undifferentiated basis.

As already mentioned, the sexuality of paraplegic patients has been reviewed by Money (1961a), who found that genital arousal may be reflexively mediated by local stimulation of the tactile receptors of the genital area and can go right through to ejaculation in spite of the loss of cerebral and cognitional involvement. On the other hand, in spite of loss of large areas of erotic sensory tissue in the case of extensive surgical repair to the genitalia, there may still be erotic arousal that goes through to orgasm. In prostatic resection, orgasm can occur without the emission of seminal fluid. In postpriapism impotence, orgasm can occur without erection. In eunuchism and hypogonadism, there may be erotic arousal and climax despite the deficiencies in hormones. Money concludes therefore that there are three dimensions of sexual function. They involve the genitopelvic anatomy, the hormones, and the brain. Any one of these dimensions can be lacking without the total loss of orgastic experience. Fertility is, of course, dependent on the proper action of the gonads and their hormones. Money points out that although none of these three coordinates of sexual functioning can be said to be indispensable, the loss of any of them is a great handicap to effective sexual activity.

From the evidence presented by sexuality in castrates, hermaphrodites, precociously pubertal children, and a variety of other abnormal conditions, Money (1961c) concludes that the sex hormones have no one-to-one relationship with either the direction or the content of erotic inclination in humans. He assumes that both these aspects are experientially determined. In the case, for instance, of hermaphrodites, who have hormonal supplies inconsistent with the sex of rearing, there is nevertheless a general tendency to establish eroticism consistently with the sex of upbringing. Money assumes that they have accumulated sequences of cognitional rehearsals that are in accord with their experiences in the sex of assignment. These experiences have their formative influence independently of chromosomal sex, gonadal sex, hormonal sex, or morphological sex. He points out that where this general rule is not followed, there have been experiential factors to account for the diversion; for instance, there may have been uncertainty as to which physical sex the child really belongs to and hence ambivalence in rearing. He regards homosexuality as fundamentally a disorder of cognitional eroticism, having at most only peripheral relationship to other variables of sex.

Money regards cognitional eroticism as an imprinting phenomenon and disorders of cognitional eroticism as some kind of misprint. There seems to be a critical period, between about eight months and three years, for this "imprinting," because after this age it becomes very difficult for a hermaphrodite to be reassigned to the other sex. It is also pointed out that this critical period corresponds to one for the establishment of native language, which makes good sense, even if no causal relationship is proved. The individual imprinted (or misprinted) to homosexual cognitional patterns at this stage is extremely difficult to shift, whereas homosexual experiences after this age have little effect. Similarly the individual correctly imprinted, during this critical period, to a cognitional eroticism consistent with physical sex is extremely difficult to move from such imprinting. Psychological sex is thus an autonomous phenomenon and may or may not be concordant with the various physical aspects of sex.

One question that arises is whether psychological stimuli are all-sufficient for eroticism in men or whether genital sources have some influence. If the latter is the case, then man cannot be claimed to be fully emancipated from hormonal control, because the hormones do have a direct relationship on genital eroticism. Everyone can supply introspective evidence of genital eroticism, but whether this is cognitional first and then related to the genitalia, or vice versa, is an open question. It is certainly the case (Money, 1961a) that paraplegic patients, who are no longer capable of any genital sexuality, still have erotic dreams, which presumably are not triggered by any actual physical stimuli. Evidently the brain records and stores erotic signals that exert a constant and ineradicable influence on the individual's mental life.

A SYNTHESIS

To recapitulate the arguments so far, it seems that genetics have no direct bearing on sexual behaviors but that they do have an indirect one in determining a number of the mechanisms, including hormonal ones, that are influential. In humans at least, the hormones are not essential to eroticism in the adult (though they may influence potency and other matters involved in effective reproductive behaviors). This statement requires modification, however, in that erotic interest (and potency) is generally low in adults who have not had hormones during the prepubertal and pubertal period. This factor gives a clue to a possible relationship between hormones and sex behaviors: Once established, sex behaviors may become autonomous and not dependent on endocrine secretions, but the latter may be important during the time of organization of these behaviors. This statement implies, of course, that learning, as well as physiological mechanisms, plays a part in the final form of sexual behavior.

This idea receives some experimental support. The cat is among the mammals in which experience is important to the full emergence of adult sexual behavior. In one study (Rosenblatt and Aronson, 1958) male kittens were castrated before puberty (at about four months), and their sexual behavior when fully grown was observed: They were quite unresponsive to a female in heat and showed little sexual activity.

They were divided into two groups. The first had testosterone given to them and were also permitted sexual experience during the time the hormone was being administered. The other groups also had testosterone treatment but were denied any sexual experience during this time. The administration of hormone was then discontinued, and they were given access to a female in heat. This time most of the animals that had the opportunity of sex learning concurrently with hormone treatment showed a complete and normal pattern of sexual behavior. The group that had hormone only, and no learning, mostly showed no advance in sexual proficiency over their first test, though a few did, after prolonged attempts, show incomplete sexual responsiveness to the female. It may be concluded from this study that the presence of androgens at *the time of learning* is important to the effectiveness of this learning. If this is so, then a further point arises. As already stated, normal males differ among themselves in what might be called their sexual aptitude —the general level of erotic interest, the strength of the sex drive, and the mode of performance. No doubt experiential factors are important here, but perhaps differences in levels of androgen secretion, or some other basic mechanism, might have an influence also.

The differences noted between individuals losing the gonadal hormones after experience of sexual behavior in their presence and those who never had them or lost them early would support the idea that in humans the presence of hormones during the learning phase is important. The experienced person can often continue to function psychosexually without hormones, whereas the inexperienced one is closely dependent on them. However, the accounts of postpubertal treatment of prepubertal castrates or hypogonadals (pp. 165-167) commonly state that following treatment the interests and performance of the individual are markedly improved. Unfortunately nearly all these accounts are by endocrinologists and provide only meager information about the psychological factors. The usual criterion for improvement is coitus, which makes the individuals reproductively functional; they can perform the sex act, that is, maintain an erection, penetrate, and ejaculate into the vagina. But there is not usually any assessment of the psychological effectiveness of the act—whether, for instance, it is a fully satisfying experience to both or either of the parties.

Another thing of interest to the present discussion is the childhood experiences of these people, but reports on this matter are lacking. On the face of it, there is no particular reason for supposing that their childhoods would have been any different from others, especially if one assumes that the gonadal influences become significant only at puberty. But on the other hand, the reported placidity and unaggressiveness of prepubertal eunuchs suggest that there may have been personality differences (relatable to their condition) even in childhood. One also wonders what their childhood rehearsals were like.

The idea that individual differences in sexual aptitude of young males is related to differences in androgen secretion runs into difficulties from two sources. First, the output of androgens in the early stages of life, when learning is apparently very important, is low, but it is not entirely absent (Kinsey et al., 1953). There may still be effective differences in the amounts of these small secretions. However, experiments by Grunt and Young (1952, 1953) suggest that the role of testicular hormones in male sexual behavior may be more complicated than it appears at first sight. In guinea pigs, under normal conditions, there are marked individual differences in the sexual performance of males. In their experi-

ments, these authors rated the males in a colony into those low, medium, and high in their sexual proficiency. They were then castrated, and when their sexual activity had declined to a common base line, they were all injected with the *same* amount of testosterone relative to their body weight. They then each returned to the previous level of sexual performance. Furthermore, even massive doses of testosterone did not increase the rank of the low-performance males. These results are interpreted as supporting a hypothesis that a somatic or constitutional factor limits the action of the hormone and accounts for the differences that were displayed during the precastrational period (W. C. Young, 1961). Grunt and Young (1953) suggest that there is a minimum amount of androgen that will trigger sexual behavior but that beyond this level the amount is immaterial and the frequency and nature of sexual activity is dependent on some other factors. In other words, there is a limit to the responsiveness of the tissues to testosterone, but each individual has his own level of responsiveness. This conclusion might, however, be valid only with certain species, including the guinea pig but not including other species, such as the rat, in which some proportionality of behavior to dosage has been demonstrated. For example, Kagan and Beach (1953) have shown that supplementary doses of androgen in normal male rats does increase their sexual behavior. Similarly, Beach and Holz-Tucker (1946) have shown that in castrated rats doses of testosterone proportionately greater than that needed to bring behavior back to the precastration level increased behavior beyond this level.

The Grunt and Young study tells us nothing about the precastration factors that might have underlain the differences in the groups noted. These may have been inherited, and hence mainly physiological, or the result of early experiences, or perhaps they may have resulted from a combination of both factors. Further experimentation is needed to elucidate these points, and experiments will have to be carefully devised if we are to be sure whether or not what look like learned differences depend on physiological differences. For instance, high androgen output (relatively speaking) in the prepubertal period may sensitize the organism to environmental influences, making learning more effective (or put another way, the same learning may occur with less exposure to the relevant cues). The low-androgen individual requires, in this view, greater opportunities for learning to reach the same degree of proficiency. Whether or not androgen level *is* the crucial variable is unknown; it might be safer to speak more vaguely at present of differences in some unspecified constitutional factor.

In Chapter 17 the kinds of learning underlying psychosexual orientation are discussed. Certain environmental conditions make for heterosexuality, and others, for homosexuality. One fact that requires an explanation is that one individual brought up in those conditions that appear to be conducive to homosexuality becomes a homosexual, whereas another in apparently comparable circumstances does not. This raises the question of whether there may not be in some individuals a proneness to homosexuality. Or to put it another way, and perhaps more accurately, whether there are not individual differences in the potency of those constitutional factors that make for heterosexuality. In this view the individual low in heterosexual potential more readily becomes homosexual if conditions are favorable to such development; conversely the heterosexual-high one can more easily resist such environmental influences. In neurophysiological terms, some individuals are better programmed than others for heterosexual behaviors. Stated this way, there is no physiological tendency to homosexual behaviors but instead varying degrees to the ease with which innate heterosexual patterns can be elicited. What might be called heterosexual potentiality may be zero but never a negative amount.

There is, in fact, not much evidence at present to give direct support to the idea of individual differences in heterosexual potential, but at the same time there is none to contradict it. We know that in adults—in human ones at least—the sex hormones have little influence on the direction or the quality of sex behaviors, *once learned,* but we really have little information beyond what is reviewed here about constitutional (including hormonal) factors that may be operative in the learning period.

Further discussion will have to be deferred until sex differences have been enlarged upon (Chapter 10), but to anticipate this section of the argument, early (mainly fetal) hormonal influences may lead to differences in the brain, the brain being potentially female in type but becoming male in type under the influence of fetal androgens. Such differences are unlikely to be all-or-none but instead may range in degree, leaving open the possibility that some male brains are more male than others or that some female ones are less feminine in the sense of being partially influenced by masculinizing factors.

It will be noted that there is implied a directionality in this constitutional factor. If androgen level alone (for example) were to prove to be the critical factor, then one would expect those individuals low in prepubertal androgens to be low in sexual learning altogether, whereas those high in this factor would learn either homosexual or heterosexual patterns equally facilely. There is no evidence to appeal to, but the clinical impressions are that some individuals are high in heterosexual and low in homosexual potential; the converse is probably not true. The idea that early androgen levels might determine the "maleness" of the nervous system would accommodate this possibility.

Another point that complicates the matter is that of dominance ranking in relation to sexual behaviors. It is suggested that dominance-submission behaviors have some bearing on sexual ones and that ranking on this continuum might be influenced by androgen levels. Contrary to popular beliefs, homosexuals are not necessarily low-dominance individuals. Elsewhere (Nash and Hayes, 1965) it is suggested that homosexual males, when compared with males in general, range all the way from high to low in dominance rank, this variation influencing the preferred type of sexual role, but that factors other than dominance decide whether eroticism is homosexually or heterosexually directed.

If early androgens both determine the "maleness" of the brain and underlie early dominance learning, then the high-dominance homosexual is rather difficult to explain. However, it is prenatal androgens that determine (so it is believed) the "maleness" of the brain, whereas it is presumably postnatal androgens that underlie dominance learnings. A shift in balance postnatally toward more androgen might account for the matter. Maybe the relationship between androgens and dominance is less direct than that between early sex behavior and testosterone.

To describe the relationship between learning and constitution in the acquisition of sex behaviors, one might use the analogy of a sailing vessel moving over a tidal stream. The course-made-good is the resultant of two forces, the wind and the tide. The tide represents the constitutional forces and the wind the culture and all the learning it provides. In different individuals the strength of the undercurrent may vary, and for different individuals the winds of culture may blow relatively more or less strongly.

Just as it is possible for a sailing vessel to move against the tide, so the individual can stem the biological undercurrent to acquire learning that is discordant with it, but only when the wind is stronger than the tide. Thus, in spite of innate tendencies to masculine kinds of behaviors, the male can override these to acquire "feminine" ones. (What is meant by "masculine" and "feminine" behaviors is discussed more fully in Chapter 10.) But the best passages are made when the wind and

tide are together; the vessel stemming a current makes tardy progress.

As always with analogies, this one can be misleading if pressed too far. For one thing, the human individual is differently influenced by the undercurrent at different times in life. He does what vessels do not, that is, he responds variably to the tide. However, he probably does this only at some cost. We have defined one of the aims of developmental psychology as a search for those conditions that maximize the individual's realization of his full potentialities. It has also been suggested that a fully developed sex life is one facet of this complete flowering. In this view, because of their complementarity, the zenith of sexual delight is achieved between man and woman, and any other sexual union is less than perfect. This joy spreads out to what is the most satisfying of human relationships in the social as well as in the more limited sexual sense. In discussing this topic, one needs to go beyond what might be called the Playboy approach. Its insistence that society must rethink its attitudes to sex is well taken; but the Playboy Philosophy seems to emphasize the sensuous and physical aspects of sex without showing how we can break through the loneliness of the individuals involved. There may be greater sexual freedom today, and more perhaps to come, but such freedom may be a permissiveness in mutual masturbation rather than an approach to a true communion of two persons. Maybe it is a first step toward achieving this poetic condition, but the next step must be examined before we can be sure the sexual revolution is won.

This is not to deny the right of those who prefer some other form of sexual life to follow their preference (provided they do so without harm to anyone else, especially those with different preferences). In the ideal human society homosexuality would be accepted, but one of the arguments of this book is that because an ideal society would provide for the optimal rearing of its children, male and female, homosexuality would not exist.

Another variable in sex behaviors is the strength of the erotic impulse. We have no eroticometer—no measure of the energy that a human individual customarily invests in the saitsfaction of erotic needs or the amount of frustration he will overcome to secure gratification. (In animal work there are such measures, for example, the level of shock that the animal will tolerate in crossing a grid to get to a mate.) Because of this lack, we have no experimental data on individual differences in the strength of the urge, but it is a matter of common observation that these differences do exist. Some individuals can tolerate abstinence quite happily, and others must go to great pains to secure gratification.

The view of the development of sex behaviors being advocated here is that the biological basis of such behaviors must include theree major components:

1. Femaleness-maleness of the brain
2. Dominance-submission
3. Strength of eroticism

These components do not of themselves lead to the adequate expression of sociosexual behaviors (though they might to solitary expressions); they are merely the constitutional basis on which such behaviors rest. Learning and experience are necessary before sexuality can be expressed.

The optimally heterosexual male adult has the male-type brain, at least moderate ranking on the dominance scale, and at least a modicum of erotic impulse strength; but in addition to these qualities he must have certain rearing conditions (which are the subject of another chapter). An individual with a low-masculine brain (or even perhaps a female-type brain) might become homosexual if his early life experiences are conducive to this; so might a masculine-brained individual if the environmental conditions are strong, but he would do so less readily than the former. In either case, his dominance ranking and strength of eroticism will influence the type and amount of activity indulged in.

This chapter has reviewed current knowledge on the manner in which physiological, and in particular biochemical, factors enter into the determination of behavior. The discussion has centered around sex behaviors, partly because rather more is known about these than about some other forms of behavior to which similar mechanisms may be important and partly because various aspects of male- and female-specific behaviors are major areas of concern to later sections of the book.

The main point emerging from this extensive review of the contrasting arguments relating to the relevance or irrelevance of biological factors in human psychology is the comfortable one that *both* sides are correct. In man, as the environmentalists insist, learning is important to the acquisition of both normal and deviant sexual behaviors. However, this learning is not poured (as it were) into an empty vessel but is imposed on an organism that is innately selective of the stimuli that impinge on it and that already has certain propensities to behavior. It can learn to select other stimuli and to make other responses, but the "programmed" stimulus-response patterns have a lower threshold and are easier to elicit.

Certain of these stimulus-response patterns are sex-linked. This applies especially to sex behaviors proper but also to a range of behaviors with varying degrees of influence on sex behaviors. These innate tendencies to behaviors are not so strong in humans as to be imperative, though in general there are certain behaviors that come more readily to males, and others more commonly seen in females. Furthermore, it is supposed that in humans the elements of these sex behaviors are initially uncoordinated and require experience and practice to be coordinated into a smooth and efficient total pattern of behavior. This is especially the case with the male. The priming and impetus of the biological substratum are of considerable importance during this initial period of acquisition and practice, but after the behaviors are learned and consolidated, the importance of the biological factors declines, and they may become unessential. It is also suggested that there are individual differences among males in the potency of the innate tendencies to masculine behaviors. These differences determine the threshold to relevant stimuli and the ease of learning of male-type behaviors. Those low in biological masculinity are most susceptible to the learning of other stimuli and inappropriate responses, if the environment is conducive to these. Similarly females are predisposed to learning feminine-type behaviors, and in fact this biological predisposition may be relatively stronger than in males. The peer culture provides experiences important to psychosexual development, but parental relationships are paramount because they influence peer-culture relationships (Chapters 17 and 18).

Although the major debate of this chapter has centered around sex behaviors, it is supposed that similar biological factors may underlie the acquisition of other kinds of behaviors, for instance, the customary modes of response called *temperament*. Thus the individual's characteristic speed of response may be related to biochemical factors, with the thyroid hormone as a key one. The infant low in thyroid hormone will tend to be slow in response. Such a child can, presumably, learn to react more quickly but will do so less easily than one with the necessary biochemical "priming" to quick response. Further, in later life the habitual speed of response may tend to persist even if the thyroid varies. The child who has acquired habits of slow movement because of temporarily low thyroid secretion during the learning period may persist in these even though higher levels of secretion are present later, or the fast-moving child may

continue to move in this way despite lowered secretions (unless, of course, these variations are gross, as in myxoedema, where there is a marked slowing of function).

There are a number of other topics in which a detailed account of the interaction of influences may one day be made. For example, Pitts (1969) has reported on the manner in which anxiety neurosis in adults may be related to a high concentration of lactate in the blood. Non-neurotic adults will show anxiety symptoms on administration of lactates, and the symptoms of anxiety in neurotics can be relieved by the giving of a drug. This drug (propranolol) apparently blocks the metabolism of adrenaline, excessive levels of adrenaline being precursors of high lactate production. Studies have not been made of children, but presumably high-lactate children may be more prone to learning anxiety neurotic modes of response to their environment. A related finding is presented by Weiss et al. (1969), from an experiment in which hypophysectomised rats that lacked adrenocorticotrophic hormone (ACTH) showed *less* fear in a standard passive avoidance situation than normal rats. Apparently the ACTH normally present increases arousal or emotionality. On the other hand, adrenalectromised rats showed *more* fear, because they lack certain of the adrenal steroids that inhibit fear responses when present in normal animals. Again, we can see how a balance between these endogenous factors may influence the characteristic response to fearful situations in children.

Early behaviors tend to be highly persistent, and these early behaviors are, to a greater extent than later ones, determined by biological factors. Thus the biological influences may have an enduring effect on psychological functioning, even after they themselves have disappeared.

Ten | Sex Differences and Their Origins

The whole question of sex differences is in an untidy state. For one thing, there is a mass of studies that are random observations and difficult to relate to one another or to any more general principle. To take just one, Himmelstein (1964) has reported that a significantly greater proportion of female college students locate the self in the chest and body areas than do males. This no doubt reflects some difference in self-concept, but it is not easy to say what the origins or the consequences of this fact might be. It is not suggested that observations of this kind are either useless or meaningless but merely that their meaning (and hence their value) eludes us at present.

For the present it would seem more economical of effort to direct questions to some of the areas that have more obvious theoretical relevance. Some of the studies to be mentioned in the following review are unreplicated, and even where there are related studies, strict comparison of results is commonly lacking. But one thing that does become apparent is that males and females differ in a surprising variety of ways. There is even a re-

port of a highly significant sex difference in extrasensory perception between high school boys and girls (Freeman, 1966), but no basis for the difference can be suggested at present.

Some clues as to the bases of some of the reported differences are emerging, but we are not yet in a position to be dogmatic about these matters. As Anastasi (1958) has said, the greater part of the literature on sex differences is descriptive in nature. There is, in fact, an enormous number of studies describing differences between males and females in a great range of behaviors, but little is known about the origins of such behaviors. There are several comprehensive reviews of the studies reporting sex differences, and the aim of this chapter is not to undertake an exhaustive examination of these reports but to attempt to elucidate the still inconclusive question of origin, or at least to discuss a point of view.

Another feature of the question is its academic nature. That is, although sex differences are known to exist extensively, the fact has had surprisingly little influence on practice in child rearing or in education, for boys and girls are in general treated as if no difference existed between them. That is, they are taught the same curriculum over the greater part of their school careers, they are treated as if boys and girls of the same chronological age are equal in maturation, and in general little more than lip service is paid to the distinctiveness that exists in a variety of dimensions.

There are perhaps two reasons that may account for these facts. The first is that although in many physiological and psychological measures there are indisputable differences in the *means* for males and females, the dispersions are usually wide, so that the overlap is considerable. This has made it easy to overlook the differences and even to regard them logically as of little significance. The other reason is ideological: One gets the impression that for many people the notion of sex difference is inconsistent with belief in the ethical equality of the sexes, and that acknowledgment of distinctions is somehow betraying this ideal. Really, of course, such differences are as irrelevant to the question of ethical parity as the fact that some people have red hair and others none at all.

Havelock Ellis apparently received opprobrium for suggesting in his book *Man and Woman* (1898) that there are intrinsic differences between the sexes and in a preface to the sixth edition (1926) addressed himself to the "enthusiastic young feminists" who had misconstrued his arguments. Freud (1950) also found himself under fire for suggesting that there are important psychological differences between men and women; he writes, "We must not allow ourselves to be deflected from such conclusions by the denials of feminists, who are anxious to force us to regard the two sexes as completely equal in position and worth. . . ." The tone of Freud's assertions in this essay [1] could not fail to be provocative, and it is hardly surprising that exception should be taken to them, leaving aside any

[1] *Some Psychological Consequences of the Anatomical Distinction between the Sexes.*

question of their scientific validity: It might be instructive for some historian of psychology to trace the influence of such statements on the later discussion of the topic of sex differences.

As Tyler (1956) has pointed out, much of the research up until about 1935 was undertaken with the desire to prove that females are not inferior to males; there was a marked tendency to minimize the differences and to explain them as imposed by culture rather than caused by differences in the biological substratum. Today one is no longer abused for discussing the topic; he is merely out of fashion. However, a number of writers are again discussing sex differences, and there are signs of a reappraisal of the question.

The scientific procedure is to examine the question with the highest attainable degree of impartiality, for today conclusions cannot be dictated by irrelevant considerations. Even in the past, powerful theological arguments backed up by the stake could not deter scientific inquiry about man and the universe. We must in this tradition examine the question of sex differences bravely, and if the facts tell us that women are to inherit the earth, then men must accept the evidence.

SEX DIFFERENCES AS BIOLOGICALLY BASED

Sex Differences in Subhuman Species

Sex differences in behavior are a widespread phenomenon in the animal kingdom and insofar as reproductive activities are concerned are necessarily universal among those organisms reproducing sexually. In the invertebrates we frequently find not only different forms of behavior among males and females but also, in some species, grossly different anatomical forms. The situation among the invertebrates is, of course, complicated by the fact that some species are hermaphroditic and both male and female patterns of reproductive behavior can be seen in the same organism. However, in most of the more advanced invertebrate species, behavioral sex differences are to be found, and these are not always specific to reproduction. The differentiation of roles in social insects such as bees and ants is an example of such differences. (There are, of course, some species in which reproduction is the sole function of the short-lived adult form.)

It is in the vertebrates that widespread differences that are not merely specific to reproduction but general to many forms of behavior are to be found. Familiar examples of these differences are those between the cock and the hen or between the bull and the cow. In these particular species (as in many others), the whole personality of the male is different from that of the female. These differences extend up into the primates (e.g., Zuckermann, 1932), and Harlow (1962) has noted that sex differences are quite evident in rhesus monkeys from the second month of life. These differences are not only in social behaviors but also in the precursors of sexual behaviors. Males, he observed, showed earlier manifestations of sex behavior than did females and did so more frequently. The males were more aggressive, showing "threatening" behavior, whereas contact play and its initiation was mainly observed among the females. Sex differences in peer interactions are also noted in Harlow and Harlow (1965).

Sex differences in behaviors directed toward infants by both young and adult animals have been noted in several primate species. Bolwig (1959) and De Vore (1963) have noted it in baboons, Itani (1959) in the macaque, Jay (1963) in the langur, and Schaller (1963) in the gorilla. Natural observations of chimpanzees in the wild show that immature females take an active interest in infants, and sometimes form a strong attachment and become second "mothers" (Lawick-Goodall, 1965).

Further evidence along these lines has been discussed by Chamove et al. (1967), who found that preadolescent female rhesus monkeys showed significantly more positive social behavior and less hostility toward an infant monkey than did males of the same age group. These authors point out that this behavior precedes the hormonal changes of puberty and speculate that it might depend on neural mechanisms. They do regard their experiment as giving unequivocal (sic) evidence that biological factors in these young monkeys influence maternal-type behaviors. Certainly one would have to be firmly wedded to the idea of cultural determinants to equivocate. Though one *might* argue for cultural transmission in the early peer and maternal social contacts (none had paternal contacts), the argument would seem unconvincing. Incidentally, males are not hostile to the young in every species; Itani (1959) has noted paternal behavior in the macaque.

Sex differences in immature langur monkeys have been described by Jay (1965). These differences are well marked between young males and females in play, particularly in the amount of playful fighting and general level of activity. Differences in size, age for age, also appear early. An especially interesting juvenile feature in this species is a period of close social interaction between juvenile and adult males. At about ten months the male infant starts to approach adult males without touching, later touching the adult's hindquarters, and later still mounting adult males in a behavior reminiscent of the mounting of a female by a male, or a male by another male in dominance behavior. Jay says, however, that this behavior in the juvenile is neither sexual nor dominant. Later a front-to-front embracing pattern between juvenile and adult males is seen, and this is initiated by the juvenile. These behaviors are observed up to about the fourth year. None of these behaviors toward a male were observed in juvenile females (nor apparently were such behaviors toward a female found in them). From an early age young langurs take part in mutual grooming, but young males spend, in this activity, markedly less time with females than with males. Another male-type activity emerging in adolescence is a dominance-assertive behavior toward adult females.

Physiological Sex Differences in Humans

The notion of sex differences as based on biology has a fairly long history. Geddes and Thomson (1897) were among the earlier writers who took this standpoint. They argued that differences in constitution are reducible to metabolic differences, women being more anabolic and men more katabolic in their biochemical functions. The physical and mental traits characteristic of males and females stem from this difference. Burt and Moore (1912) also spoke of biological differences that pervade the whole organism, and they pointed out that the sexes are complementary to each other in many areas of functioning.

There are certain physiological differences between men and women that are widely known and quoted in all the discussions of this topic. In all human societies, insofar as is known, men are bigger and stronger than women. On the average the male is about 6 percent taller and 20 percent heavier, with larger bones and with greater bulk and strength of muscle.

In keeping with the latter differences is a sex difference in potassium concentrations that has been noted by Anderson and Langham (1959) and that is related to changes in muscular development. There are, during life, characteristic changes in the curve of K concentrations for each sex. In the first eight or nine years there is an increase, followed by a decline in both sexes. There is at first no marked sex differentiation, but at puberty a wide difference appears. This is maintained throughout life, males being higher.

Williams (1956) has spoken of the fact that the basic musculatures of men and of women are different, which is the reason the *average* woman cannot throw a ball as a man can or run as fast as he. The muscular difference is apparent even at birth, despite the more advanced maturation of the female. Bell and Darling (1965) found in the prone head reaction that male neonates raise the head higher and for longer periods than females do. The differences in the musculature and CNS of males and females are reflected in the typical manners of throwing seen in young boys and girls. No doubt with training these patterns can be modified, but left to perform these actions spontaneously, girls throw a ball overhand by holding the ball at the back of the shoulder and throwing with a forward and downward movement, the weight of the body being mainly on the right foot. Boys, on the other hand, spontaneously tend to throw with a horizontal motion at shoulder level; they draw the hand up at the side and rotate and twist the body to place the weight on the left foot, and the whole body, especially the shoulders, enters into the actual throwing movement. Such differences are perhaps also basic to the characteristics of gesture in males and females. Innate differences such as these have probably been important in the past when the throwing of stones and spears were useful skills. Today in advanced technological societies they may only show in less utilitarian activities but may still be fundamental to the development of certain interests and the acquisition of some physical skills in which sex differences are apparent.

Men have a higher metabolic rate, produce more physical energy, and hence require more food. Correlatively, the male heart beats more strongly and male blood is richer in red corpuscles to the extent of some 300,000 more per cubic millimeter. These differences have an obvious relationship to the higher oxygen supply necessitated by the activity of the male. The greater physical potential for activity of males also has its correlates in psychological characteristics, which will be discussed later.

The greater activity of boys is reflected in

a study by Goldberg and Lewis (1969), who studied year-old children in a standard play situation and found the boys to be more exploratory and more active in overcoming obstacles, girls more often passively accepting a barrier that kept them from a desired part of the play area, or more often crying in passive frustration.

It is also commonly pointed out that although males are bigger and more muscular than females, they are biologically weaker, and this difference is apparent from the moment of conception. There are more than 120 male conceptions to every 100 female ones, but prenatal mortality is higher among male fetuses so that by the end of term the ratio is reduced to about 105 male live births to every 100 female ones. The greater mortality of males continues beyond this time, and during the first year of life there are about 25 percent more deaths among male babies; this seems to be independent of culture. The higher male mortality continues, and at present in the United States the life expectancy for a female is about 73 years, and that for a male, 67. (Studies of life spans of nuns and monks sheltered in cloisters from the usual rush of life show approximately the same figures, and this suggests that the stresses and strains of modern life are not the critical factor in the higher male mortality.)

It is sometimes pointed out that males and females differ in every cell of their bodies, in that the nucleus of every cell in normal individuals contains either the XX or XY chromosome pair, according to whether the individual is female or male. In addition, the nuclei of cells in female bodies contain the sex chromatin substance that is absent from the cells of males, though precisely what functional significance this difference has is not known at the present time. It is certainly the case that a great range of physical characteristics depends on the type of chromosome makeup, whether XX or XY in type. However, the psychological significance of this difference is rather unclear at the present time;

but unless we are to believe that mind and body are entirely independent realms, it is difficult to see how the range of physical differences between males and females can fail to result in psychological differences also.

Sex Differences in the Nervous System

A number of writers in the past have put forward the notion that males may have differences in the nervous system that result in a distinctive mode of functioning. This idea has arisen from observations such as the well-established fact that women do markedly and consistently better than men in tasks that require quick response and rapid perception of detail. Vocational aptitude tests, such as the Minnesota Clerical, are instances of the kind of situation in which this sex difference is demonstrated. Males are superior to females in rapid movements made under conditions in which the attention remains relatively fixed, whereas females are superior in rapid movements in activities in which the direction of attention is shifting and rapid adaptation to changing stimuli is required (Woolley, 1910, 1914).

Book (1932) has argued that sex differences like these might be caused by differences in the basic neurophysiology, specifically those that influence the rate of conductivity of nerve tissue. She claims that because longer refractory periods are characteristic of males, statistically more of rapidly repeated stimuli fall into the refractory period of previous ones, and the adaptations of men are therefore slower. Women, on the other hand, have a shorter refractory period and a greater number of nerve impulses per unit time and therefore are able to respond quickly to more details and to adapt more quickly to changing test situations. She takes Adrian's idea (1928) of "postural" and "phasic" receptors. The postural type is slow to adapt, with a longer excitatory process; they produce a series of impulses, such as are characteristic of sustained response to stimulation. Book suggests that this is the male type. In the phasic type of receptor there is quick adaptation and shorter excitation, with many rapid discrete responses producing quickly fluctuating movements. These Book regards as the feminine type. She also notes that many of the sex differences that have been described are in relation to simple activities, but that as activities become more complex, the sex differences tend to disappear. She explains this by the fact that the more complex activities will require more persistent effort and therefore involve the postural type of activity. Under these conditions the women would tend to lose the advantage of having phasic-type receptors. Book also points out the manner in which women tend to do better in tasks that are fractional, or divided into discrete parts, whereas men have the advantage if the task is continuous. Women are the quick, perceptual type, and men, the slow-moving explorers.

On this basis she explains the observed fact in her study that men did better on tasks, like mazes or block counting, that required a more sustained, logical, and analytic approach but did not require attention to detail or to quick change of stimuli. Women, on the other hand, were better on tasks, like number checking, that required attention to detail and quick adaptation to changing stimuli.

Such differences would have their influence on a wide range of skills and are perhaps responsible, in part at least, for the fact that girls are consistently more rapid readers than boys, up to college entry (J. E. Moore, 1939, 1940).

Whether or not Book is correct in her characterizations of male and female nervous systems is difficult to say. It probably oversimplifies. For one thing, the jump from functions like speed of response to logical, analytical modes of thinking seems rather a far one. But her theory does contain the idea that there are two kinds of nervous systems with differing modes of functioning, and this

theory is receiving support from recent findings. The differences Book speaks of may be but one of several dimensions of distinction.

More recently this idea has been taken up by Harris (1964a, b), who also claimed that males and females have different types of nervous systems, the female type being the more basic or elemental. In the fetus or the early neonate of mammals (depending on the species) the CNS is at first sexually undifferentiated but in the absence of hormonal intervention develops into a female-type nervous system. There is, however, in this development, a critical period when the presence of male hormones influences the development of a male-type CNS. The growth of a female-type CNS is apparently dependent only on the absence of the male hormone and not on the presence of female hormones, because the female-type CNS develops if testosterone is absent whether estrogens are present or not.

It will be noted that there is a spiraling action here: The early presence of androgens modifies the course of CNS development, and this modified CNS in turn influences further hormonal secretions. Most of the work to date in this area has been done on lower levels, such as the rat and guinea pig, and, though similar mechanisms apparently operate, little information is available on the primates.

In this sense, the female-type nervous system may be said to be more basic, and it is in this sense that Ford and Beach (1951) have described the male as more highly evolved. There could be anatomical differences consistent with this. For instance, Morel and Weissfeiler (1931) have called the gray commissure a regressing feature of the brain, pointing out that as one ascends the phylogenetic scale this structure becomes less complex and prominent, though it is present in all mammals below man. Only in human brains is it sometimes absent altogether, and presumably it is in the course of evolutionary disappearance. However, it is markedly more often absent from male brains than from female ones.

Harris is not specific as to the nature of the male CNS and the female CNS but deduces the existence of a difference from the effects. He has shown how hormonal secretions are influenced and controlled by the hypothalamus, which is itself under the control of higher centers. In particular, the CNS of male animals maintains a steady state of gonadotropic secretions, and this in turn results in the steady pattern of sexual activity seen in the male; whereas in females the hypothalamus induces a rhythmic state of gonadotropic secretion, with its behavioral correlates. Transplants of ovarian tissues into males show how the rhythm of follicular activity is dependent on the gonadotropic pattern.

Phoenix et al. (1959) have suggested that the sex hormones may affect the organization of the nervous system and thereby ultimately lead to sex differences in behavior. By injecting the pregnant mother with androgens, they produced hermaphroditic female guinea pigs. In subsequent tests of mating behavior, they showed patterns of behavior typical to the male, which (though not entirely absent in normal female guinea pigs) were now shown with a frequency approaching that of normal males. It was not so much the behavior itself that was sex-specific but its threshold and frequency. They interpreted this as evidence of the masculinization of the nervous system in these hermaphrodites.

These differences are to be found not only in the CNS but also in the autonomic system. Weller and Bell (1965) used skin conductance as an autonomic measure in neonates between 60 and 110 hours of age and found a positive correlation between activity and conductance. Females were significantly higher in conductance than males. A number of studies report sex differences in skin conductance and GSR (for example, Goldstein and Rosenblüt, 1965; Kimmel and Kimmel, 1965; Coules and Avery, 1966; Purohit, 1966).

Levine (1966) has followed up Harris' suggestion and has experimentally demonstrated the validity of Harris' contentions that male and female brains differ in some important respects. For instance, the normal male rat in mating behavior goes through, from the initial mounting to ejaculation, a characteristic pattern that is quite distinct from that of the female. Obviously these patterns are controlled by the CNS. In the rat the critical period for differentiation of the brain occurs shortly after birth. (In longer-gestating animals it takes place before birth, making them less convenient for study.) Levine has shown that female rats injected with testosterone soon after birth and before this critical period lose the normal female pattern of response and do not (as in the case with later-ovarectomized animals) regain it on injection of estrogen and progesterone. But more than this, on injection of testosterone as adults they show a remarkably masculinized pattern of behavior, even down to movements, normally accompanying ejaculation in the male, which go far beyond the incomplete parodies of male behavior often observed in the merely ovarectomized female on testosterone injection (and even on occasion in normal females). Evidently this early injection of testosterone had determined the development of a male-type brain in these females. Further evidence that the nervous system of females may be masculinized by early administration of testosterone has been provided by Edwards (1969). Female mice so treated showed, as adults, the fighting behaviors typical of males, suggesting that the early androgenic stimulation had organized the neural structures mediating aggression, structures usually organized only in the male.

When male rats are castrated before the critical period so that there is no testosterone to produce the male-type brain, then, as adults, even small doses of estrogen and progesterone could induce them to a fairly precise display of female sexual behavior (Levine, 1966). This effect has also been reported by Hart (1968), who notes that the neonatal testicular hormones of male rats appear to have an organizational influence at the spinal level on neural tissue mediating sexual reflexes. Castration in the neonatal period resulted in an incomplete copulatory response when the rats were injected with testosterone as adults.

As Harris had suggested, in the absence of testosterone the brain develops female characteristics. It is the brain itself that is sensitive to the presence of hormones. Harris and Michael (1958) have demonstrated this by implanting stilbestrol (synthetic estrogen) into the hypothalamus of female cats and evoking the full pattern of female sexual behavior even though the cats were not in estrus. Davidson (1966) has similarly shown male behavior to be aroused in castrated male cats on implantation of testosterone in the brain.

The behaviors controlled by the male- or female-type brain go beyond the reproductive. The full extent of the influence of brain type has not been explored, but Levine (1966) quotes some experiments showing differences in nonsexual behaviors. In the activity wheel C. P. Richter (1927) found, in females, a cyclical pattern with a peak in running at the height of estrus. The same pattern can be found in male rats castrated at birth and later implanted with ovaries (Harris, 1964a). Levine also reports sex differences in the open-field apparatus. Female rats normally are more exploratory and defecate less often, but the masculinized female rats show male characteristics of behavior (i.e., less exploration and more defecation).

Levine reports for other species, such as the guinea pig and the monkey, similar findings which show that these species also develop male-type brains in response to testosterone, but here the critical period is prenatal. In man the critical period is probably quite early; we have seen (Chapter 9) that the differentiation of the male reproductive system comes under hormonal influence very early in fetal growth, and that the differentiation of the brain likely has its critical period at about the same time.

An untimely birth apparently has greater effects on male fetuses. Braine et al. (1966) have reported a highly significant difference between male and female prematures on the Cattell Scale at thirteen and a half months. The effect takes some time to become manifest, for, although a difference in the same direction was in evidence at seven and a half months, it did not reach significance. The differences in a control group of term infants at both ages were insignificant. This suggests that the developmental effects of prematurity are more severe for males than for females, having greater effects on the nervous system of males, but that there is some delay in these effects becoming evident. This might be taken as an indication that prenatally the nervous system of the male is in some different state of organization from that of females—a state that makes it more vulnerable to the adverse conditions of premature birth. The most likely difference is that it is maturationally less advanced, and most embryological organ systems seem more susceptible to maldevelopment in earlier than in later stages. A different speed of maturation would also suggest some basic difference in the way the CNS grows. A slower rate of development would be consistent with the idea that male brains are more highly evolved.

There are other suggestions of cerebral nervous system differences between the sexes. As Connolly (1950) has pointed out, a number of neuroanatomists have commented on a sex difference in the surface anatomy of the brains of primates (including man) in which there is more simplicity and regularity of convolution in the female brain; while this is not an invariable characteristic, it is a fairly consistent one. Weil (1943, 1944) has reported a sex difference in phospholipid content in male and female brains, but because Sperry et al. (1949) failed to replicate the finding, it must be viewed with reserve. It is, however, because choline is essential to phospholipid metabolism, interesting to note the finding by Williams (1956) that female rats have markedly lower choline requirements in the diet and can survive on a lower minimum intake than males. We have no knowledge at present of what these differences mean in terms of function, but it is reasonable to suppose that they do mean something. Michael (1962) has obtained evidence (the behavioral correlates of which are more obvious) in female cats of the existence of neurons possessing a selective biochemical affinity for estrogen. He postulates that these cells form part of a neuronal apparatus specifically sensitive to the hormone and mediate the expression of sexuality.

A difference between the sexes in reaction to lesions of the brain (of rats) is reported by Cox et al. (1969). Similar lesions in the ventromedial hypothalamus (VMH) produced marked overeating and weight gain in females, but a significantly lesser effect in males. It appears that the endocrine-metabolic reaction to the lesion is different for the two sexes, which seems to indicate that the VMH-biochemical relationship acts differently in males and females.

In an animal study with chickens, Zielinski (1960) found in using an inhibitory conditioned reaction that there was no sex difference on a first trial, but that on the second trial the latency period was shorter in cockerels than in pullets; these differences were not caused by differing alimentary excitability. This could be taken as suggestive of a difference in neural organization. There are other data that could also be interpreted in terms of differentiated male and female nervous systems. For example, the fact that men recover from intense glare quicker than women (Torkelson et al., 1941) could be taken as implying a different nervous system; it is, in fact, difficult to see how else to interpret it, because it is unconvincing to propose that it is a learned difference.

Lansdell (1964) has observed that if one examines Conel's data on the myelination of the brain of four-year-old children, some suggestive sex differences are apparent. In four out of the five female brains investigated, the amount of myelination was greater in the left-hand area of the motor cortex than in the corresponding area on the right, while in the three male brains this difference was reversed. At the same time, the number of exogenous fibers in layer 1 of this area was greater on the right in the four female brains but greater on the left in two of the three male brains. Although neither of these differences would, because the numbers are so small, satisfy a statistical test of significance, Lansdell does speculate as to whether they might be related to such findings as the sex differences in the tactual thresholds of the thumbs of young children (Ghent, 1961) or to differences in speech lateralization (Kimura, 1963).

When different spoken digits are given simultaneously to the two ears of adults, those arriving at the ear having direct pathways to the dominant hemisphere (i.e., the right ear for most subjects) predominate and are more efficiently recognized (Kimura, 1961). In a later paper Kimura (1963) showed that this effect is to be found in four-year-old children, and thus that the right-ear predominance is established by this age. However, there was a sex difference in overall efficiency at ages four, five, and six, that disappeared sharply at seven. She points out that a sex difference might be found at earlier ages, but that the technique was unsuccessful with younger children. This is in line with the idea that girls go through the developmental cycle more rapidly than boys but that the latter arrive eventually at the same level of maturity (McCarthy, 1930). There was also an indication of a sex difference in the left-handed children. Of eleven left-handed girls, ten were more efficient on the right ear (i.e., showed the normal effect) and the other one showed no difference between ears. Among the fourteen left-handed boys, however, five were more efficient on the left ear, as is typical of subjects with speech located in the right hemisphere (Kimura, 1961). L. B. Taylor (1962), using the same technique with children with reading disorders, found atypical speech lateralization in boys but not in girls.

A study of disruptive states that reveals different effects on the two sexes and that may be the result of a differing fundamental organization is one by Lansdell (1962) of the results of temporal lobectomy, using the Graves' Design Test of Artistic Appreciation. Following temporal operation on the nondominant hemisphere, women showed a rise in mean score, whereas males showed a drop (the change being significant). On the other hand, when the operation was on the dominant hemisphere, the opposite effect was obtained. Lansdell concludes that this may be interpreted as an indication that in the female brain physiological mechanisms underlying artistic judgments and verbal ability may overlap, whereas in the male brain they are located in different hemispheres. He relates this to the observation that girls show a correspondence between level of artistic interest and competence in verbal reasoning, whereas in boys these factors are unrelated (O. K. Bennett et al., 1952).

Such findings cannot as yet be regarded as by any means fully established, but they do suggest that at certain stages of development male and female brains function differently in some respects and also that there might be a sex difference in children with abnormal cerebral organization. A speculation that arises from hints of this kind is that transitory physiological differences may influence psychological developments, the psychological results persisting after the biological substratum differences have become undetectable. Hence investigation of such phenomena would involve subtle longitudinal studies, and the differences are unlikely to be revealed by the sorts of physiological or psychological experiments currently being undertaken.

Because there have not been wide or systematic investigations of psychophysiological sex differences, we have only snippets of information, such as the foregoing, upon which to base theorizing, but findings like them, relating to rather specific (and in some cases rather unimpressive) phenomena, might be taken as indications of other differences that may become apparent as more is known. Similar small differences over a number of systems may add up to significant differences in total organization.

There are many other well-established sex differences that are rather more controversial as to the role that learning might play but that could be taken as evidence of the influence of a different CNS. Thus in tests involving color sorting, naming, or manipulation, girls show an awareness and use of color that, as compared with such qualities in boys, steadily increases with age (Dubois, 1939). These increases could be regarded as arising from cultural artifacts but for the finding that this difference in color reactivity is detectable at the fifth month of life, when culture has hardly had an opportunity to exert itself. Similar results are also reported in India (Agrawel, 1966). These findings are more readily explicable if we assume that the female nervous system is in its nature more reactive to color and has greater powers of color discrimination. Because of this basic advantage, girls more readily learn to manipulate color and show an interest in it earlier. In other words, the cultural differences between males and females in relation to color are not arbitrary but are based upon the biology of males and females.

There is evidence of the sex hormones having differential threshold effects in the CNS. Women in general have greater acuity for smell than men, and this characteristic appears to be, for some compounds at least, influenced by estrogen levels. Le Magnen (1952) has shown that the acuity of women is reduced after ovarectomy but is restored by giving estrogen. Hypophysectomy has been shown to bring about a loss of the sense of smell, perhaps because it suppresses ovarian functions (Schon, 1958). According to Schneider and Woolf (1955), there is a periodic fluctuation in the acuity of women, it being at its lowest when they are menstruating or in the progesterone part of the menstrual cycle.

It is commonly stated that women are more tolerant of pain than men are, and this too receives experimental confirmation in a study by Josey and Miller (1932). Women are also superior to men in tactile sensitivity (H. B. Thompson, 1903), and this may be basic to the fact, discussed elsewhere, that sexual arousal in women depends to a greater extent on tactile stimulation than it does in men. According to a study by Bell and Costello (1964), who found evidence of greater tactile sensitivity in female neonates, this sex difference is present at birth.

A sex difference in preference for complexity (of polygons of varying degrees) has been reported by Eisenman (1967), who found females to prefer greater complexity in these stimuli than males do.

Differences in ideational fluency have been reported for adolescents by Riers et al. (1960), girls being more fluent than boys. Bereiter (1960) has reported that the factors for ideational fluency differ between the sexes. However, in what is presumably a related function, another difference was found. In comparing high-achieving gifted high school children on cognitive thinking and expressiveness, the boys were found to be significantly more expressive than the girls (Gallagher, 1966). Findings of this sort are not necessarily conflicting, as they may arise from viewing a complex pattern of functioning from a shifted vantage point.

Marked sex differences in the perception of complex figures in the embedded figures test (EFT) have been reported for adults by Witkin (1950) and Witkin et al. (1954). Bieri et al. (1958) designed an experiment to investigate more fully the bases underlying these differences, and they concluded that the observed sex differences in performance on the EFT stem from the tendency of men to combine, more effectively than women do, mathematical aptitude and a conceptual approach to stimuli.

The developmental history of this difference is not known. According to Goodenough

and Eagle (1963), it has not emerged by the eighth year, but this may be because young children of either sex have great difficulty in extracting a figure from an embedded context, although there is improvement in this capacity between five and eight (the ages they tested).

Another area in which Witkin reports marked sex differences is in what he calls field dependence (Witkin et al., 1954, 1962), a trait measured by such tests as perception of the vertical within a tilted frame. Females are markedly more prone to have their judgment influenced by the perceptual context. Males from the age of about eight onward are markedly less influenced by the perceptual context and are, in his terms, field-independent. These findings have been confirmed in a large number of studies in various cultures (D. R. Goodenough, 1963).

This work has also received confirmation by Gross (1959), who found highly significant sex differences in the perception of the upright, though, in this particular experimental setup, a somewhat narrower range of judgments with lower mean deviation scores was found. Gross discusses Witkin's theory that it is the greater field dependency of females that underlies this difference and also the idea that this dependency is to be explained by cultural factors (that is, the assumption that our culture encourages independence and an active analytical approach in males) and says that while this explanation might be valid, its acceptance at this stage might have an inhibiting effect on further investigation. Gross suggests that there may, in fact, be greater psychological differences in perception between males and females than is generally acknowledged.

Another area of extensively documented sex differences is in space perception; the literature on this topic has been reviewed by Sherman (1967). She proposes a causal explanation of this difference in spatial perception that is based in part upon differential practice. Boys tend to engage in all kinds of activities that practice spatial skills—tinkering with cars and so on—to a much greater extent than girls do. But Sherman also discusses the idea that this aspect of intellectual functioning, and probably other aspects too, may be based upon some more fundamental factor that is sex-biased, though she tends to place most emphasis on the learned component.

Sex Differences in Critical Periods

One study makes the interesting suggestion that certain critical periods may be more critical for boys than for girls. G. Bronson (1962) investigated two periods he believes to be of this kind. One occurs in the first year of life and is determinant of the basic orientation toward others. The second is crucial to what he called a sense of autonomy and confidence in one's ability to cope independently without constant need for approval or guidance. He proposes that this sense of autonomy is developed during the critical period in the second and third years.

He found that with boys it was possible to predict at an early age (nine to ten and a half) the later manifestations of these traits, whereas with girls it was not. He notes that either a cultural or biological explanation is possible. The cultural explanation involves society's expectations of boys and girls, but, as we argue elsewhere in this chapter, these expectations may be a result of society's experience with boys and girls; that is, they are the product of the nature of the two kinds of child and not the determinant of the two varieties. Thus the biological explanation, that the course and manner of development differs radically on a constitutional basis, is to be preferred.

In view of the considerable differences in the rate and manner of maturation between males and females, it would be altogether reasonable to expect that critical periods may appear at different times for the two sexes;

but further than that, it is quite possible that some of these periods may be distinct in their effects. This is a question that might reward further study.

Sex Differences in Reactions to the Environment

A point that is implicit in much of the discussion of this chapter is that ostensibly similar environmental events may produce different reactions from each sex. There are animal studies showing these effects. For example, Sawrey and Long (1962) subjected rats to a conflict situation in which a shock was received each time the animal attempted to approach food or water. An analysis of covariance was performed on the number of gastric ulcers produced, with weight held constant. Males generally had more ulcers than females. Ader (1962) placed rats in a conflict situation in adulthood after receiving one of three early treatments: removal from the mother at the usual age of twenty-one days, removal at fifteen days, or removal at twenty-one days without having been permitted to suckle since the fifteenth day. In opposition to the suggestion that dietary effect underlies the effect of early separation, more ulcers were found in the fifteenth day removal groups than in either of the other groups. This difference was found only in males. Ader concludes that the basic interaction between a mother rat and her offspring may be different for males than for females. An interaction between sex and environmental factors is illustrated in the rat by the exploratory drive. Male rats leave a home cage sooner to explore a novel environment when they are food-deprived than when they are satiated. The reverse is true of females. Apparently the fear response to a novel environment is handled differently by each sex under the two conditions (Lester, 1967a, b).

At the human level, the idea that boys and girls react differently to environmental situations is illustrated in a study by Schaefer and Bayley (1963), who noted that maternal child-rearing practices had distinct effects for sons and daughters. Maternal early behavior on a hostility-love dimension was positively correlated with daughters' behavior for a limited time after, whereas it persisted through to adolescence with boys. The authors also report, at adolescence, rapid social and emotional changes that begin earlier for the girls.

There is evidence that infant boys and infant girls react differently to the nursing situation. Heinstein (1963) found for boys that no advantage of breast over bottle feeding could be shown, whether the maternal relationship was favorable or unfavorable (i.e., warm or rejecting). For girls breast-feeding by a warm mother was markedly preferable to bottle feeding by her, but if the mother was cold, it was less disturbing if she bottle fed. For boys, short nursing was preferable with a cold mother, and long nursing with a warm one. For girls the opposite was true; short nursing produced fewer problems when the mother was favorable, and long nursing, less maladjustment if the mother was unstable. In other words, girls seemed more affected by the feeding relationship than boys were. Anticipating some remarks on tactile stimulation in Chapter 11, one is tempted to ask if boys are more dependent on it than girls are. The fact, mentioned elsewhere, that females are more reactive to tactile stimulation might mean that they can achieve the same developmental effect with less of it.

An instance of the manner in which the two sexes *take* differently *from* the environment is provided by Sears et al. (1946), who found that preschool boys whose fathers were absent on war service were less aggressive than those with fathers present, whereas no difference was found in girls with such father relationships. Allowing that the boy is biologically predisposed to showing more aggression than the girl, he still needs certain environmental cues (normally provided by the father) for the emergence of this trait. The girl does not require this particular kind of stimulus feeding and shows little effect if it is lacking.

The parent child relationship is a most important aspect of the child's social environment and Goldin (1969) has reviewed the literature on children's reports of parental behavior—reports which reflect both children's perceptions of their parents and the social significance of parents to them. Sex differences in the perception of both father and mother are documented. Goldberg and Lewis (1969) also report a study of mother-child interactions with 13-month-old children in a play situation; girls were more dependent upon the mother than boys. These authors note that parents behave differently toward girls and boys, thus reinforcing sex-appropriate behavior. They do acknowledge, however, that differential behavior by the mother may also be a response to differential behavior in the infant. Thus the statement that parents reinforce sex-appropriate behaviors is only partly true. What happens (at least in part) is that parents have different behaviors *elicited from them* by boys and by girls, and these differential responses tend further to augment sex-appropriate behaviors. Thus sex-appropriate behaviors develop not only because parents reinforce them, but because parents are led by the children themselves to act toward boys and girls in these distinctive manners.

Infants show a variety of fixation patterns; in particular, intrinsically interesting visual arrays, such as human faces, tend to show few but long fixations, whereas others may elicit numerous short ones (Lewis et al., 1966). In a detailed analysis of fixation patterns these authors found marked sex differences in infants at twenty-four weeks. In general, girls to a significantly greater extent than boys showed "interest fixations" to pictures of human faces and also different patterns of fixations to designs. It is difficult to believe that this is a cultural difference, but it may represent an innate predisposition on the part of females to attend to different aspects of the environment. This greater "interest" in faces by infant girls might be the developmental precursor of the greater interest in persons shown by them later (E. W. Goodenough, 1957). It is of interest in this context to view sociometric studies of school-age children. For example, girls who scored high on a sociometric measure of "need for approval" were most popular with other girls, whereas the reverse relationship existed for boys, the high need-for-approval boys being least popular with their peers (Tulkin et al., 1969). These authors interpret the data in the light of sex-role theory, assuming that it is more important (in America) for girls to appear socially acceptable than for boys, and this may be true, though not an explanation of the real origins of the difference. It might also be argued that effects like these are the sequel of more fundamental differences, like those shown in infancy before cultural differences are effective.

Another aspect of differing reactivity to events is shown in a study by E. T. Fitzgerald (1966), revealing sex differences in what Schachter (1959) has called "openness to experience," the capacity to loosen fixed anticipations or sets and not to be bound by rigid rules or preconceptions. This trait differs between the sexes, according to Freedman's data, which showed that males who were high on "openness" were responsive to *inner* experience, and the high females, to *outer*. In being open to experience (a prerequisite to creativity) the male is, of course, contravening male norms in that he tends to a rich inner life, or is introversive. The female who is high on openness tends to an extraversive, expressive reaction to outer experience.

Differential reactions to sensory deprivation have been reported by Walters et al. (1962), though it is a little difficult to say just what these differences mean. Based on the field-dependence hypothesis of Witkins et al. (1954), they predicted that under conditions of sensory isolation (immersion in water at neutral temperature in darkness and sound insulation) women would become more stimulus-bound than men, but they actually found the opposite. There were also marked differences in the postexperimental report of the experience and in reaction to sex of experimenter. It was evident that the same experience had different effects and valences for the two sexes.

It would be of interest to study any differences that might appear in the pattern of change in cognitive functions under isolation. Such changes have been noted (T. H. Scott, 1954), usually in the direction of apathy and reduced effectiveness, but sex differences have not been investigated. Whether early social deprivation has different effects on the development of boys and girls has not been studied either.

One factor (no doubt of many) underlying differing reactions to the environment may be language. In a longitudinal study of children between six months and eight years, T. Moore (1967) found that language is a more important factor in mental development in girls than it is in boys. The latter are more responsive to the properties of objects, whereas girls are more communicative. This difference could have far-reaching consequences and is one deserving full investigation.

Sex Differences in Intelligence

Brown and Bryan (1957) have pointed out that although the commonly used tests of intelligence are supposed to show no differences between the sexes in test performance, such differences have in fact been demonstrated in a number of studies. They point out that there are three logical ways to account for these observations: First, that the tests are unbiased and one sex is actually superior to the other in performance on the test; second, that the sexes are equal in mental ability but that there are biases in the chosen items that favor one sex, and third, that general ability is un-differentiated as to sex but that in the particular study the sampling of one of the sexes was somehow biased. The first of these conclusions is almost always avoided, and recourse to the second or third logical alternative is commonly taken to explain the findings. These authors also remark that the possibility of sex differences in intelligence test performance seems to have been an unacceptable hypothesis, because of a general conviction that sex differences could not exist, as this would imply that one sex is superior to the other. Rather, they say, it might be better to accept the possibility that qualitative differences may exist and intelligence as it is measured is therefore not necessarily equal for the sexes.

While it might be said that it is generally agreed today, probably on democratic rather than scientific grounds, that no difference in general intelligence exists between males and females, this is in fact a very difficult question to approach, because we do not know which performances are the best indices of general intelligence. Because many of the tasks that might be used in tests of general intelligence are known to involve a sex difference, we can readily prove that either males or females are superior by appropriate selection of these tests. The established measures of general intelligence have, in fact, attempted to avoid those tasks that do show a sex bias, and even where small sex biases have remained on certain subtests, these have been carefully balanced by opposite biases in other units, so that the widely used tests, such as the Binet and the Wechsler, are claimed to be undifferentiated as to sex.

As a generality it would therefore seem to be valid to say that neither males nor females are superior in *overall* intellectual ability. However, since the time of Binet one of the fundamental principles of testing intellectual functions has been to avoid reliance on any one type of cognitive process and to devise tests tapping as many different ones as is practically possible. While such tests may show no differences between males and females on the gross final score, there may well be differences in the pattern of performance that make up these scores. For instance, Strange and Palmer (1953) have found significant sex differences in Wechsler-Bellevue subtests, and they suggest that Wechsler's claims that there are no important sex differences might need to be reexamined. Wechsler has indeed noted the question, because in the fourth edition (1958) of his well-known book he has remarked that women seem to use different resources in the exercise of intelligence (or perhaps use the same resources to differing degrees). He notes that these findings confirm the folklore that men and women both act and think differently. Kostick (1954) studied the abilities of boys and girls (300 of each) of ages fifteen to seventeen to apply acquired knowledge in science and home economics to new situations. Deductive items were given that required the transfer of knowledge to this new situation, and the areas were chosen to cater to both boys' and girls' interests. However, the boys proved to be superior in transfer, not only in the science section but also in the home economics section of the test. When one examines specific mental abilities, other such differences are to be observed. Thus, Book (1932), in a careful experiment involving 475 men and an equal number of women and using a test battery of four subtests, showed a superiority for the men in mazes and in block counting, whereas the women were significantly superior in a cross-out pattern test and in a number-checking test.

Book (1932) also examined the idea that the sex differences might be caused by the greater variability of one sex or the other, but in these particular measures she found negligible differences in the variability of the scores for either sex on any of the tests. This idea of greater variability has been aroused in several contexts. There are differences in variability of a number of physiological measures, and in some respects the male may be considered as working with narrower limits; Terman and Tyler (1954) have reviewed some studies showing this. But it is also suggested that males are more variable in intelligence. Terman et al. (1925) point out that the greater number of boys in the group of gifted children might be in part caused by this factor. However, Tyler (1956), after reviewing a number of studies, concludes that the consensus does not support this notion of greater male variability.

Sigel (1963) has pointed out that while many studies of cognitive processes show no descriptive differences between males and females, the possibility still exists that numerically similar scores are derived from functionally different procedures. This idea that boys and girls may arrive at similar end results by differing routes is supported by the study by Strange and Palmer, which shows differences in subtest pattern on the Wechsler test.

Broadly, it would seem that in most tests that involve verbal skills, and also in some types of situations involving memory, girls are consistently better than boys. On the other hand, boys do better than girls in most tests involving arithmetical or numerical manipulations and also in tests involving spatial relationships. This has been shown by Anastasi and Foley (1953), who have reviewed the literature on sex differences in intellectual functions and found that in the commonly used tests sex differences in scores are slight, but that verbal tests do tend to favor girls, whereas numerical and spatial relations tests tend to favor boys. Again, the existence of such differences might be taken as an indication of a differently organized CNS.

Oetsel (1962) has reviewed sex differences in a number of studies relating to cognitive development. Dividing these into four major areas—language development, vocabulary, numerical reasoning, and spatial abilities—some fairly marked trends were evident in the twenty-six studies cited. In language development, twenty-three of the studies show girls to be significantly higher than boys in their development and in verbal fluency, whereas only one study showed the reverse. In vocabulary, the difference was less dramatic, but still markedly in favor of the girls. On the other hand, in reasoning, numerical reasoning, and spatial abilities the boys were markedly superior to the girls.

A study by Amthauer (1963) also shows differences in test performance. Three groups of high school boys and girls were tested on a battery of twenty-three psychological tests selected for their geometrical, space, and reasoning factor content. There were 113 boys and 151 girls from a coeducational school, and 189 boys from a boys' school. The results were factor-analyzed separately for the three groups, using Thurston's complete centroid method. Further analyses were carried out, and the results of the three centroid solutions and of extracted factors are discussed in detail. Extensive discussion is devoted to the sex difference observed.

An analysis of performance into specific (S) and compensatory (C) factors reveals sex differences in performance that are generally denied by intelligence tests. C factors will be high in tasks where specific abilities are lacking. Correlation between C factors and verbal, mathematical, and practical technical performances indicated specific abilities for girls in the verbal area, while boys showed stronger abilities in the other two areas. It is concluded from these results that sex differences in performance cannot be overlooked any longer because the constant use of compensatory performances increases the stress in a person and leads to exhaustion.

There are indications of fundamental differences in the manner in which the sexes approach a cognitive task. For example, Hoffman and Maier (1961) found differences in performance in the horse-trading problem (which, incidentally, is solved markedly more often by men than women when the individual is working alone; about half the men and one quarter of the women solved it themselves). However, in the group situation, males were significantly more successful than females in using discussion to reach a solution. Women did better in mixed groups than in all-female ones. Burke (1965) modified this problem by requiring the subjects not to solve the problem outright but only to recognize the correct method and its answer. The sex difference still persisted (significant at the .01 level) despite this change. In a further study (Maier and Burke, 1967) the factors entering the difficulty for women in a problem of this sort were studied, and it was concluded that women are more prone to certain distractors. These authors discuss the possible antecedents of these sex differences but admit that whether they are cultural or genetic is unanswered. Whichever it is, the behavioral repertoire differs for males and females. If one is skeptical about extrasensory perception, he might explain Freeman's results (mentioned earlier) on the basis of a different approach to the task by the boys and girls.

One dimension along which sex differences may operate has been suggested by Tyler (1965), who notes that females are usually less apt than men in solving problems that require active restructuring of stimulus elements. In one phase of their study Gall and Mendelsohn (1967) used a technique that facilitated restructuring, and this again may be a useful problem-solving strategy to emphasize for women; men habitually use it and have less need of this kind of facilitation. One should hasten to point out that not all the advantages go to the men. Using strategies of commonality and a conservative method of solution, girls were superior to boys on another concept-attainment problem (Togatz, 1967).

Differences in Developmental Schedules

The well-known fact that girls mature faster than boys is reflected in a study by Richards and Ross (1967), who showed girls to produce more mature drawings (the subject being a cat and kittens drawn under test conditions) at an earlier age. The possibility that male and female intellectual development follows different courses, or at least different timetables, is suggested by a study by Honzik (1963). In a representative urban sample of 248 children, years of schooling of both parents showed an increasing relationship to their sons' and daughters' IQ's between twenty-one months and fifteen years. The parent-child correlation was observable and became statistically significant for girls by three years but was not so for boys until five years. Earlier parent-daughter resemblance was also noted when ratings of mothers' intelligence and social status were correlated with the children's scores. Siblings' IQ's yielded comparable sex differences in relation to parents' education. This finding was further confirmed in the correlations of the IQ's of a second-generation sample with the IQ's of the parent in the original group at age fifteen years. Sex difference in rate of mental growth is suggested as the major determinant of these results.

An interesting and suggestive finding has been reported by Anastasiow (1965), who reports that the more masculine boys (as measured by a toy-preference test) of ages five to six years showed higher scores on achievement tests and were rated by their teachers as more successful in school. The explanation given was that sex-role adoption facilitates learning in school.

Several lines of speculation follow from this observation. One is that a global effect operates: The boys who are established in sex-role learning have more energy to invest in school learning than those who are still working on this important aspect of development. Another might be that the more masculine boys have a more masculine-type CNS and are more efficiently organized. (The possibility that teachers may rate more masculine boys differently is presumably answered by the objective tests, although it is still possible that they treat them differently in school.)

A longitudinal study involving (among other things) age changes in certain aspects of sex differences has been provided by Wanda Bronson (1966). The subjects were part of the Berkeley Growth Study and were followed from shortly after birth until the early 1930's; forty-five subjects were males, and forty, females. Three broad areas that comprised central patterns of attitude emerged: withdrawal-expressiveness, reactivity-placidity, and passivity-dominance. Analyzing the age changes in these areas for the two sexes, the author concludes that the timing and the nature of both environmental and internal pressures differ for males and females, thereby producing different developmental patterns.

There are very marked sex differences in the statistics of children showing learning and behavior disorders. Educational clinics dealing with children who are having reading or other curriculum difficulties universally report a heavy preponderance of males among their clients (Money, 1962). There is a tendency to explain these figures in cultural terms, for example, by the idea that parents are more concerned about the failure of boys than that of girls and hence more usually seek a remedy. It is also said that boys are simply expected to have more problems, though if this expectation is not based in some way upon the nature of the boy, then it is difficult to see how it would arise as a purely cultural artifact. Bentzen (1963) has criticized such assumptions of cultural determination. Reviewing statistics on the matter, she concludes that learning and behavior disorders occur from three to ten times more frequently among boys than among girls. She points out that it is an established fact that the human male matures more slowly than the female; before adult status is reached, the male is less mature at any given chronological age than the female. She advances the hypothesis that some, at least, of the greater number of disorders to be found among boys are a stress response to the demands of a society that fails to make proper provision for this biological age differential.

Sex Differences in Creativity

Reference has already been made to the observation that males are more frequently recognized for creativity in the arts and other fields than women are. The idea that this is a real difference and not a culturally imposed one is provided by a few studies of creativity or nonconventional thinking that show it to appear in children. Torrance (1962b) has reported that elementary schoolboys are consistently superior to girls in the ability to produce inventive or creative ideas. Smith (1962) found that preadolescent boys of high IQ show more divergent thinking on a battery of Guilford-type tests than girls of similar intelligence do. Mendel (1965) has reported young boys to prefer novelty (in a toy array experimental situation) markedly more often than girls do. This question is discussed more fully in Chapter 16. The cultural theory can, of course, be applied, but the same counterarguments are also apposite.

One study (Rivlin, 1959) has reported large differences in IQ between high school boys rated as creative by teachers and those rated as able but noncreative. Little difference in scores was found for girls. Whether this tells us something about boys and girls or about teachers is an open question.

Sex differences in creative problem solving were found, by Gall and Mendelsohn (1967), in a study of the effects of facilitating techniques (notably incubation) and subject-experimenter interaction on the process. Females to a marked extent were influenced by social factors (i.e., experimenter participation), whereas for males this influence was negligible, and we may have here a clue to one measure that might improve the creative output of women. This pointer would be worth following up and might have important educational implications.

Cultural Drift in Interests

Terman and Tyler (1954) noted a shift in the preceding twenty years or so in the interests of girls; they were becoming more like those of boys. Rosenberg and Sutton-Smith (1960) have produced evidence that the trend toward the masculinization of the interest of girls continues. In a checklist experiment involving traditionally male and female play activities, these authors found evidence of the increasing masculinity of the feminine self-concept. In a more comprehensive survey, the same authors have confirmed these results (Rosenberg and Sutton-Smith, 1964b).

These results do, of course, represent a cultural shift: Presumably the basic biological aspects of sex differences are unchanged. One function of the psychologist as scientist is to record such changes, but he also has the obligation to comment on them and to judge them. This will be done in Chapter 20.

Measures of Masculinity-Femininity

It is evident from all the foregoing that masculinity or femininity is a highly complex phenomenon ramifying into almost every aspect of psychological functioning. There are a number of measures of masculinity-femininity (mf), some of which have been subjected to analysis.

An early study of mf scales was by de Cillis and Orbison (1950), who found that although the mf scales of the MMPI and of the Terman-Miles test both differentiated clearly between the sexes, they showed low correlations with one another. They concluded that these tests are measuring some dimensions related to psychological sex but that each is tapping a different one.

Shepler (1951) compared four measures of mf (the Strong VIB, the mf scale of the MMPI, the Terman-Miles, and the Franck) and found that three of these correlated moderately highly with one another but that the

Franck Completion Test did not correlate significantly with any of the others, in spite of the fact that it (as well as the others) reliably discriminated males from females. He suggests that this may be because the Franck test measures some quite different aspect of mf from the others. It could also be said that because none of the other correlations were high (they were of the order .5 to .6) all the tests are measuring something rather different (though the difference might, of course, be caused by contamination). Aaronson (1959) showed that the mf scale of the MMPI and an index based on the Hs, Hy, Pa, and Pt scales both distinguish males and females but have only a low relationship with one another. He suggests that these results and those of Shepler would seem to indicate that differences are on more than one dimension, though he disagrees with Reed (1957), who compared perceptual-motor tests and the mf scale and explained the differences he found by postulating that the one measures id functions, and the other, superego. These studies confirm the obvious fact that masculinity and femininity are highly variegated phenomena that cannot be tapped by any simple or single measure. If we are to use tests of mf, they must be specific to the aspect of this multidimensional entity that is under consideration.

DIFFERENCES IN SOCIAL EFFECTS ON COGNITIVE PROCESSES

It is well known that in a variety of experimental situations the sex of the examiner and that of the subjects have been found to be variables influencing results, and while no explanation has been given, it is generally assumed that this is a social effect. McNeil (1964) has claimed that in school the differential development of reading ability in boys and girls is influenced by a similar factor, interactions between female teachers and boys being less conducive to learning in the latter. A study of teacher-pupil interactions did in fact show that the women teachers tended to give less reading practice to boys, to be harsher in reprimanding errors by boys, and in general to create different classroom climates for the boys and for the girls, which was less favorable to the former. In an experiment in which learning was from a teaching machine, and in which the interpersonal element was removed, boys did as well as girls.

An interesting aspect of sex in relation to social problem solving is contained in a study by Gurnee (1937) in which a maze problem situation was set up for group solution. The groups consisted of about ten individuals, and each move was decided by vote. In the main, this "committee" method of procedure was highly efficient and the correct solution was obtained significantly quicker than by individual action, because in the collective situation each was able to profit by the learning of his fellows. However, this increased efficiency was least when the groups consisted of the two sexes in approximately equal numbers and was greatest when the groups consisted principally of either males or females.

South (1927) made a similar observation with respect to committee work in an experimental situation. There seems to be rather fundamental differences in the way in which the two sexes approach a task. This is reflected in several manners, such as that in which imposing a time limit increases the efficiency of male discussion but reduces that of females. Why the sex composition of the groups should be a variable is not altogether clear; whether it is a purely social effect or whether the admixture of male and female learning processes is the crucial factor is impossible to say.

An interesting difference in what might be called the cognitive-social area is revealed by Rapport and Chammah (1965). This study uses the "prisoners' dilemma game," one form of which involves the following anecdote: Two prisoners are accused of the same crime and are held separately without communication. Each has a choice of confessing to the crime or not doing so. If both confess, then both are convicted; but if neither confesses, both must be acquitted. If only one prisoner confesses, he not only goes free but gets a reward for turning state's witness; the prisoner who refuses to confess gets a more severe sentence than if he had confessed. The dilemma arises from the fact that it is to each prisoner's individual advantage to confess, but at the same time it is better for both of them not to confess than for both to confess.

The subjects in this experiment were in pairs; they could see one another but could not communicate. They each made 300 responses in a two-hour session in which they either gained or lost one cent according to whether they were acquitted or convicted. The subjects were in three groups, 70 male pairs, 70 female pairs, and 70 mixed pairs. There were thus four conditions of play, men against men, men against women, women against men, and women against women. There were large differences between male pairs and female pairs, the principal one being that there was a considerably greater frequency of cooperative choices by men. However, when men and women played against each other, these differences disappeared, the men becoming more like women and the women more like men. A particularly interesting observation is that no differences in the frequency of cooperative choices were seen in the early plays of the sequence. This suggests that the overall differences arise from interaction patterns in men and women rather than from different initial tendencies to cooperate. These authors suggest that this arises from the greater tendency for the men to give tit for tat in situations of this sort, in other words, to imitate or respond in kind. These findings can be explained in social terms but also raise the question of fundamental differences in the approach to a task of this kind.

Social effects in children are shown by Saltzstein and Diamond (1967), who found girls to show a markedly greater transfer of social influence in a number-judging task when paired with boys than when paired with other girls.

SEX DIFFERENCES
AS CULTURALLY DETERMINED

The debate as to whether sex differences are the result of nature or nurture goes back to at least the beginning of the twentieth century and no doubt much farther than that. Woolley (1910) argued that the observed differences were due to environmental factors and the methods of upbringing for the two sexes. H. E. Jones (1913) also supported this point of view. More recently other writers have emphasized the importance of culture and of social expectation on the development of personality and in determining differences between males and females. Among these are Erikson (1950), Honigmann (1954), Maslow (1954), Merrill and Eldredge (1952), and Whiting and Child (1953). While it is not universal, it would probably be true to say that the general tenor of opinion in North American psychology in the 1960's favors the idea that sex differences are mainly determined by upbringing.

Some writers in the past have gone so far as to deny strongly that any factors other than cultural ones enter into the question of sex differences. Mead (1935, 1947), for instance, has taken the extreme view that sex differences are unrelated to temperamental factors in personality and are entirely the result of cultural determinants. In her well-known book (1935), she has described three cultures that she uses to illustrate this point. Among the Arapesh she found both men and women to be cooperative, gentle, unaggressive, and solicitous of the well-being of others, so that she saw both men and women in this society as displaying traits that (she claims) our society would regard as feminine. Conversely, the Mundugumor seemed to her uniformly violent, aggressive, competitive, and suspicious—the women equally with the men—and sex differences were minimal. In the Tchambuli, Mead saw the sex roles as reversed, the women showing characteristics that we would regard as masculine—being the more aggressive, doing the fishing, and making the most

important items of trade; the men, on the other hand, engaged in artistic and nonutilitarian pursuits. Here it was the women who were practical and efficient, and they were condescending toward the men, whom Mead described as timid, sensitive, dependent, and graceful. An aggressive or dominant man would be considered a sexual deviate. On the basis of her field work among these three peoples, Mead concluded that the characteristics of males and females in any society are solely the product of the expectations of that society and are not dependent on any biological basis. She has more recently again emphasized the part played by cultural factors in the determination of sexual behaviors (Mead, 1961).

Mead's writings are persuasive and have enjoyed wide popularity and influence. However, Piddington (1957) has pointed out that Mead's fieldwork in these societies is poorly documented and states that biased conclusions were based on insufficient facts, so that her data cannot really be considered as evidence sufficient to support her opinions.

The existence of matriarchal societies has also been taken as evidence for the cultural nature of sex differences, especially in matters of dominance and leadership. The fact is that matriarchal societies are both unusual (and hence atypical) and also involve an apparent rather than a real dominance by women (Piddington, 1950). The Iroquois is often cited as an example of a matriarchal society; it was an amalgamation of five tribes (with a sixth added later) living in the territory that is now included mainly in the State of New York, around the Hudson River. This union was arranged by the male chiefs, according to tradition led by Hiawatha, in order to facilitate the conquest of neighboring tribes. This union was so successful in war that it subdued all the tribes for hundreds of miles around. In the course of these extended war-like expeditions, almost every active man was away for many weeks at a time, and only the infirm men and the women and children were left at home. Because many men died young and active in battle, there was reduced survival of wise old men to run the affairs of the tribe at home, and of necessity a great deal of authority was delegated to the women. However, the important business of this society was making war, and this remained firmly in the hands of the men (Piddington, 1950). Similar instances can be seen today in various parts of Europe, as in Scottish fishing communities. Here also there is what could be described as a matriarchy and for somewhat the same reason. Each year the men spend several months away from home as they follow the shoals of herring around the coast, and the women remain at home in charge of affairs there. They administer the finances, and frequently order the gear and supplies that are needed for the boats. One might interpret this as a feminine control, but again the central activity of the community is held by the men, who maintain the boats and take them to sea.

Whether or not true matriarchy has ever existed in human societies is debatable, but it does seem fairly certain that it is very uncommon, and it would seem that the great majority of societies in the past and at present are patriarchal in their organization. This is probably true even of those that are matrilineal in descent (which usually means only that title, property, or authority pass from *man* to *man* via the female line).

All in all, the evidence for the existence of any human society, either now or in the past, that could truly be said to be feminine-oriented and -controlled is not very convincing. Whether or not this *should* be the case, or whether it *has* to be, are other questions, but the fact seems to be that the male-dominated human society is a universal phenomenon.

Turning from the place of men and women in the broad structure of human society, there are a number of social statistics in which differences appear. For example, there is a very marked sex difference with relation to crime (Cressey, 1963) and universally among cultures the available statistics show a heavy preponderance of male to female criminals. In the United States male arrests are ten times as frequent, and committals to prisons are twenty times as frequent, as female ones. In juvenile courts, 85 percent of the defendants are boys. This state of affairs is no doubt to some extent cultural, as is shown by the tendency for an inverse relationship between the status and freedom of women and female crime, those cultures being most restrictive on women showing the least incidence (Broom and Selznick, 1957). However, if we assume that the United States has a culture that imposes minimal restrictions on women, then the statistics for that country are perhaps close to rock bottom and least influenced by cultural factors; here the difference is still very great, and it is difficult to believe that if all the cultural factors could be partialed out this difference would disappear. In other words, factors other than cultural ones must surely be at work. This is not to deny an important cultural loading, but while these findings could be accounted for partially by cultural factors (e.g., the fact that boys might tend to more aggressive forms of behavior disorder that are more likely to be troublesome to parents or teachers and to precipitate action), such an explanation still leaves open the question of *why* boys are more aggressive in the first place. Again, this might be answered in terms of cultural expectation —boys learning that they are expected to be noisy, dirty, aggressive, and naughty—but in view of the fact that the male is biologically better equipped for aggression and because of his biological makeup tends to activities that are noisy and messy, and which are not altogether catered for by urban living, such an explanation does not seem entirely convincing. Some other forms of difficulty are even less plausibly accounted for by cultural explanation; for instance, the fact that speech disorders are also markedly more common among boys (Wallin, 1916; West, 1931; Louttit and Halls, 1936; Schuell, 1946) does not lend itself to any explanation in such terms. Just what cultural pressures can be said to encourage the boy to stammer or stutter more than the girl are not easily seen, and it would appear more reasonable to suggest that the biological equipment of the male is such as to render him more prone to this type of disorder.

Women are generally regarded as more liable to neuroticism than men, and Costello and Brachman (1962) have reported evidence from a personality inventory of this difference in children. Whether we are to take this as the result of cultural forces or of a differential reaction to the environment engendered by some basic difference in organization is impossible to say (it may even, of course, be just a reflection of how we define neuroticism), but the possibility that it represents a different reaction to the environment is worth bearing in mind.

The relation of biological to cultural factors may be illustrated by chess. Not even in Russia is there a woman chess player of grandmaster status, and everywhere the game is very much a male preserve. Reider (1959) has given a psychoanalytical explanation of this: The object of chess is to "murder" the king —a father figure. Women lack this hostility to the father and hence lack the motive for the game that men have. This is perhaps one level of explanation, though the assumption that chess involves some basic cognitive process that is relatively less common in women is an alternative and possibly more convincing one. Because ability in chess seems to be a special skill unrelated (so far as has been shown) to any more useful cognitive function, even the ardent femininist may be willing to concede this point.

This is not to say that cultural factors do not operate. The chess community is largely a male one to which women are not particularly attracted and in which they may not be made especially welcome, not because they are women but because they are mostly not very good at chess. (It is not suggested that "chess-men" are necessarily unattracted to women or that away from the chessboard they are uninterested in them, but it seems a fact that in the context of the game they show a single-mindedness that excludes other considerations.)

One can see this as the result and not the cause of women's position in this skill. Because of relatively lesser endowment in whatever factors are involved, women have made little headway in chess clubs, which have tended to become male-dominated, not because women were actually excluded but because few were attracted to join. And the more enthusiastic a population of chess players becomes and the keener the competition, the fewer the women who can make a place for themselves. Thus the "culture" of the chess community has evolved into a masculine one not because of arbitrary exclusion of females but because of a sex linkage in some fundamental property of the cognitive processes involved. There has been a natural selection.

The idea that a trait such as field dependence may be genetic or constitutional and sex-linked does not preclude the possibility of environmental influences also playing a part. For instance, Bieri (1960) found that women who had identified with their fathers tended to be more field-independent than those who had identified with their mothers. The converse effect is reported by Barclay and Cusumano (1967), who found father-absent adolescent boys to be more field-dependent than controls with fathers. Thus there is a tendency for environmental influences to modify this character in both sexes. However, we are not told whether father-identified girls are as field-independent as normal boys or whether father-absent boys are as field-dependent as girls, that is, whether the differences are entirely suppressed. Even if these differences are removed, this would not of necessity prove that field dependence is entirely cultural in origin. It could still be that field dependence is a sex-linked genetic trait that is modifiable (or even removable) by certain environmental influences. The distinction is not purely academic. It raises the question of whether a male-simulating female or a female-simulating male functions at optimal efficiency.

Epilogue

The insistence in this chapter that sex differences are based upon biological influences is not to be taken as a total rejection of the idea that cultural factors operate. For one thing, it is possible that some differences are entirely culturally determined. For instance, Deutsch and Proshansky (1961) interviewed men and women in New York at the time of the Quemoy controversy and found the men to be markedly better informed on the topic than the women. The discrepancy was most marked in the less educated groups, but even among college-educated men and women there was still a rather large difference. Such a finding could be explained fully in terms of culturally determined interests, though even here, if one starts to inquire what lies behind these interests he might move toward more fundamental differences. However, it is not intended to deny the existence of culturally based differences or to claim that *every* difference must have a biological basis.

Broadly, it is suggested that many of the differences in interests and attitudes found between males and females have an ultimate biological base, related to such differences as those in dominance, aggressivity, motility, and the like, differences which radiate out into subtle influences in all manners of ways. Some of these may be related directly or indirectly to the kinds of differences noted in sex behaviors. Further, the distinct possibility that males and females have differently organized CNS may be seen to underlie a considerable range of cognitive activities, and this too will influence in subtle manners most aspects of psychological functioning.

As already mentioned, in almost any dimension in which sex differences are to be found the overlap is considerable, but it can be assumed that these differences compound to a whole organization that is distinctive. It might be said, of course, that these differences could cancel one another out, though what is meant by "canceling out" is not easy to see. If one makes an omnibus mf test, in which the masculine and feminine items are equal in *score,* then the final reckoning may cancel out and show no differences between males and females. But this is an artifact that masks the distinctiveness of the pattern that makes up this score, just as IQ scores on an intelligence test obliterate the vast differences in actual mode of intellectual functioning between individuals.

Returning to the question of culture in relation to sex differences, as repeated several times already, the thesis of this chapter is that human cultures have evolved differential expectancies for males and females because experience over the ages has shown that they *are* different. That is, these expectations are the result of biological factors, and the differences are not always the result of the expectancies.

It is true, of course, that some expectancies might arise that are only indirectly related to fundamentals, or even unrelated at all. But in the main the expectancies will serve to augment and reinforce the basic differences. Much of current research that deals with cultural factors in the development of sex differences are really (though often unawares) showing how culture augments a basic trend.

Margaret Mead notwithstanding, the kinds of broad sex differences outlined in this chapter seem universal to human cultures. This is not to say, however, that societies could not be produced that obliterate these differences in some regards or even reverse some of them. Humans are marvelously plastic and adaptable, but there are probably limits to these qualities. As mentioned elsewhere, homosexual males seem to retain the essential characteristics of their sex, at least insofar as erotic stimulation is concerned. Clever as some of the homosexuals are in initiating feminine gestures and ambiences, there is a phoniness about such gestures. One suspects that their basic cognitive processes remain male. Among the great mysteries for men is how the world really looks to a woman; one might doubt if the feminine homosexuals have really plumbed this mystery. And whether women really fathom men is also a question of doubt.

The point to be made is that males and females have distinctive styles of cognition and of life that give directionality to the development of boys and girls. These directives may be ignored, overridden, or even reversed, but only at a price. Optimal development follows the lines of force and realizes the full potential of the individual; maleness or femaleness is one aspect of this potential.

It has been suggested that field dependence may be a sex-linked genetic trait. Whether it is or not is uncertain, but supposing that it is, does the fact that it is modifiable by environmental factors make its genetic basis entirely irrelevant? Perhaps it does if we think in terms of the status quo. However, part of the argument of this book is that we should be considering the broad effects of child rearing. Evidently we can, if we choose, rear children that are all (or mostly) field-dependent or all field-independent. Or we can rear boys that are field-dependent and girls that are field-independent.

But we may also ask (as I do) whether we should not be rearing boys that are masculine and girls that are feminine and regard field independence as a tiny bit of masculinity (maybe not an important part, but at least a piece in the mosaic). Field independence, we may suppose, comes more naturally, and in terms of the pattern norm is more efficient. Similarly, field dependence is a small part of femininity and something to be preserved in that context. Should we identify all the traits that make up masculinity and femininity in their broadest sense and then foster them? This question will be discussed more fully in Chapter 20. The answer may be, of course, that we should not emphasize sex differences or take pains to develop masculinity and femininity, but at least the matter should be considered and a decision reached on rational grounds.

If one may leap from psychological theory into social philosophy, he would claim that a really just society will not seek to submerge and blur the differences between men and women but will allow them to flower to the full. This means a radical change in the whole structure of our educational and child-rearing systems.

This chapter has not said much about the developmental origins of sex differences in detail. Rather it has attempted to survey the nature and range of these differences and to argue that their general origins may be found in basic biological factors that determine the nature of the interreactions of males and females with the environment. From this differential reactivity to experiences there emerge differing behavioral repertoires. Some of these differences, it appears, are not evident until maturity, whereas others emerge at various times over childhood. Here, as in most other topics, longitudinal studies are urgently needed.

Implications for Education

It is a plain corollary of the argument put forward here that males and females differ in certain important respects and that these differences require them to have distinct child rearings or, at least, to be reared in manners more distinct than is customary in our society. Not only, it is suggested, do boys and girls react differently to the same experience, but they also require some different experiences with differing emphases. In our present state of knowledge it is not possible to spell out in detail what these differences are, but attempts to do this will be made elsewhere in the book. However, it is already appropriate to suggest that we should begin to look seriously at our coeducational system of schooling and our indistinctly differentiated child-rearing practices and to ask if they really meet the developmental needs of girls and boys.

Eleven *Early Stimulation*

There was a time when adolescence was considered to be the crucial stage in development. In Stanley Hall's theory (that during the course of development the individual repeats the history of the species) adolescence was considered to be the period during which the child finally threw off his animal epochs and became human. It was probably Freud more than anyone else who challenged this view and focused attention on the earliest years of life as being the most critical, although the Jesuits are commonly credited with having realized this for a very long time, as expressed in their dictum "Give us a child until he is seven. . . ." Implicit in the Freudian position was the idea that the early relationships with the mother are crucial in these years. Bowlby (himself a practicing psychoanalyst) was one writer strongly influenced by the Freudian point of view. In a clinical study of children referred to a child guidance clinic in which a history of theft was the major presenting complaint, he sought to show that maternal deprivation and abnormal early mother-child relationships were causal to the common personality syndrome shown by

the children, a syndrome which he called "the affectionless personality." These children failed to show normal affectionate relationships with other people and lacked a sense of shame or personal responsibility (Bowlby, 1946).

EFFECTS OF INSTITUTIONAL REARING

Interest in the effects of early "deprived" rearing came from observations of children lacking normal family life. Bowlby (1951) reviewed a number of studies of children brought up in institutions, or suffering long periods of hospitalization, or other forms of separation from the family during early life. Among these he reviewed the important contributions of Goldfarb (1944a, b; 1945a, b; 1947). Goldfarb showed a clear superiority, in various aspects of development, of children reared from infancy in foster homes as compared with matched infants who remained in institutions. Bowlby's review made it clear that a number of dire consequences, including the failure to thrive, known as "anaclitic depression" (Spitz and Wolf, 1946a), are associated with rearing children under institutional or hospital conditions.

Another long-term series of studies showing that institutional treatment does have effects are those of Skodak and her associates (summarized in Skodak, 1966) in which two groups of institutionalized children were followed from early childhood into adult life. One group remained in the orphanage, which was as bleak and barren and understaffed as such institutions commonly were in the 1930's. The other group went from the same institution to foster homes before the third birthday. Improvement in intellectual status followed foster-home placement almost immediately, whereas the institutionalized group showed a decline in such status. These differences were maintained into adult life, the foster-home group enjoying the advantage of paying income tax, whereas a third of the institutionalized group remained a charge to the community and the rest were economically marginal.

Another point that is emphasized by Bowlby and others is the necessity for continuous care by one person during early infancy. This is in keeping with a theoretical bias that emphasizes the sanctity of the mother-child relationship. One of the defects of institutions is said to be that the parent surrogates tend to work in shifts, and children do not get a consistent relationship with any of them. Mead (1953) has questioned the validity of this assumption, pointing out that in many primitive communities the care of young children is distributed over several persons, and not always female ones, without any evidence of ill effects. In view of the anthropological data it may be questioned whether the disadvantages of institutions in this area are as severe as some would claim. But there is one point that needs to be borne in mind: Even if the child in some families does receive care from a miscellaneous collection of siblings, aunts, and uncles, to say nothing of the father,

he still comes to recognize who his *real* parents are. This is true even in those societies where classificatory kinship gives a child several people who are addressed as "father" or "mother," and this must affect social development. The institutionalized child lacks the assurance that this knowledge gives. But insofar as the effects on early cognitive development—the kinds of effects to be reviewed later in this chapter—are concerned, the distribution of stimulation over a number of agents may not be such a disadvantage as some would claim. In other words, the deficiencies may not rest mainly in the distributed nature of their care but more on other factors.

A number of authors have commented on what they consider to be the exaggerated nature of some of the studies quoted by Bowlby, in particular those of Spitz. Bakwin (1942) remarked that in a large institution containing 250 children, of whom more than half were under one year of age, there was not a single infant showing the more extreme symptoms described by Spitz. This was attributed to the fact that in this particular institution the children did receive a large amount of stimulation. Others have commented on this same point, and I, in a large institution containing nearly 200 children under the age of five years, also did not observe any of these more serious manifestations of deprivation, apart from one case of early infantile autism (which is also to be found outside institutions and might anyway have a genetic basis). However, even if these more extreme effects are not found, one only has to spend a little time in such an institution to realize that there are differences. The institution referred to had a large staff of resident tradesmen on the maintenance crews, and their children of school age attended the Home's school along with the children in care. Although in social-class background the tradesmen's children were not much different from the institutionalized children, and were no differently dressed, they still stood out in alertness and general bearing and one had only to watch them at work or at play to pick them from a group. This is a thing that the author has noticed on several occasions where normally reared children mix with institutionalized ones; the differences are quite obvious.

The alarming picture of the effects of institutional care painted by the earlier critics was no doubt the result of engaging not merely in scientific debate but also in active (and entirely laudable) efforts to get institutions improved. However, it seems that results of early institutionalization are not necessarily as severe as those reported by such writers as Spitz. Klackenberg (1956) has reported a study of a total of 121 young children in a Swedish social welfare institution in which, after varying lengths of institutionalization up to twelve months in the first year of life, the range of DQ's on the Bühler-Hetzer scale was distributed around 100 in a more or less normal manner. But this was in an institution with a staff-child ratio of 1:3 *maximum,* compared with a *minimum* of 1:8 in the institution reported by Spitz (1949). However, it is evident from Klackenberg's data that the emotional effects of this kind of care were like those reported elsewhere: These children were disturbed. Rheingold (1956) has reported similar findings.

As a result of an intensive investigation of some eighty-five young children in one home, Flint (1966) is rather more optimistic than many in this area and has shown that even with four years of such experience children can make considerable growth gains when placed in a more stimulating foster home. However, it is not easy to see from her data at what ages the children had entered the home and what effects experiences prior to entry might have had. Taylor (1968) has also studied the question, following up thirty children who had suffered "extreme conditions of maternal deprivation" in an institution up to two and a half years, but had then gone to foster homes with an active program of rehabilitation. She reports that these children showed healthy potential, in contrast to some

of the earlier studies. There were, however individual differences and some of the children were more disturbed than others.

One question that is always unanswered is how much better the apparently healthy "deprived" children might have been with more stimulating experiences. They may still be operating below their inherent potential.

It is evident from the studies reviewed elsewhere that the more serious effects of institutional care follow when it commences early; it is not the length of institutional care, so much as its timing, that is crucial. But even if the revolt against institutions might be based more upon intuition than on scientifically clear evidence, anyone responsible for the care of children would be well advised to follow the former. An absence of valid scientific evidence entitles one to an agnostic intellectual position in the matter, but action should be positive, nevertheless.

One problem in studies that show children under a given regime to develop in a particular way is that one never knows for certain whether these particular children would not have developed similarly under any other regime. For example, studies have been cited that show orphanage children to develop poorly in intellectual skills, to be emotionally flat, and so on. But one might argue that children who get placed in orphanages tend to come from backgrounds that predispose them to these characteristics anyway. For instance, the bulk of children placed early in institutions are illegitimate, and it is said that it is the duller women who fail to take precautions against pregnancy. Control groups to answer such queries are usually impracticable. However, studies of orphanage children placed in foster homes, such as those earlier ones of Goldfarb and Skeels, do give a partial answer to such objections, suggesting that effects are not specific to any particular genetic population.

In any case, it could be that the later studies of institutions show lesser effects on the children because the work of Bowlby, Spitz, and others has had an effect on adults running institutions. Whatever the scientific merits of their writings, their social influence has undoubtedly been commendable, apart from one flaw, that of ignoring paternal factors in child rearing.

MECHANISM OF DEPRIVATION EFFECTS

As we have seen, certain writers have related all the effects of deprivation specifically to the absence of an affectional relationship with the mother. As Nash (1952) pointed out, children reared under institutional conditions lack a father as well as a mother, and Bowlby was going beyond the evidence in relating these effects to the lack of a female parent only. Parental deprivation is thus a more accurate term, though most of the literature speaks only of maternal deprivation.

The now-extensive literature on maternal deprivation has been reviewed by Yarrow (1961), and he shows that there is a general consensus of opinion that disturbances in intellectual and in social-personal functioning tend to follow what he has called "deviating conditions of maternal care in early infancy." A widely known contributor to the maternal deprivation literature is Ribble (1944), who emphasized the infant's need of consistent and intense "mothering," though in the second edition (1965) she acknowledges the importance of "fathering" also. Some writers felt that her contribution, as well as that of others, was not possessed of sufficient scientific caution. Orlansky (1949) and Pinneau (1950) have both criticized the work of Ribble, and in a later article Pinneau (1955) has also attacked the series of articles on hospitalism and anaclitic depression, to which Spitz is a major contributor. However, in the byplay that is an endearing quality of the *Psychological Bulletin,* Pinneau, in replying to Spitz's reply to Pinneau, has made it clear that what he is attacking is the methodology of the studies rather than their conclusions. In effect, he admits that the conclusions may be valid even if the evidence upon which they are based is less than satisfactory to a strict experimentalist.

There are no *experiments* on long-term deprivation in human infants that would satisfy a strict methodologist—and we must hope there never will be any—but there is some corroborative data on primates, largely from the Wisconsin laboratories using rhesus monkeys, though these studies show some interesting differences from what might be expected from the human data. These studies will be reviewed here.

Stimulus Deprivation in Primates

The concept of *maternal deprivation* is highly global, and even *parental deprivation,* which is perhaps more accurate, remains unspecific. The criticisms of Ribble's contribution were in some respects unjust, because she had attempted to make the concept of "mothering" more specific by relating it to three types of sensory experience that she considered essential to the proper development of the infant: These are tactile, auditory, and kinaesthetic stimulation, which are supplied by the mother who handles, fondles, and talks to the child. Her basic idea that the nervous system of the infant needs some kind of "stimulus feeding" is borne out by subsequent animal investigations (W. R. Thompson, 1955). Harlow (1949) has presented convincing evidence of the importance of tactile stimulation, as well as of kinaesthetic stimulation, in the early development of primates. For the latter stimulation he used a rocking mother surrogate. A terry-towel-covered rocker was a little more effective than a stationary terry-towel surrogate, but a wire rocker was like the stationary wire surrogate, ineffectual as a "mother." The interesting idea of tactile primacy is suggested.

An important point of psychoanalytic

theory is the part played in early development by the suckling relationship. Emotional ties are supposed to develop between the child and his mother as a result of the gratification of hunger at the breast. However, there is evidence from Wisconsin that the emotional attachment between mother and child is independent of the feeding relationship. In these well-known experiments infants showed no attachment (outside feeding itself) to the wire-mother surrogate from which they fed but displayed strong attachment to the cloth mother from which they received no food but tactile comfort. The manner in which these monkeys obtained clear succor from the cloth mother when frightened, but failed to get any from the wire one, is convincing evidence that it is some element other than food gratification that is crucial to the forming of an emotional tie between parent and child. It seems rather that tactile sensations play an important role in the formation of this bond (Harlow and Zimmermann, 1958, 1959). The evidence on the topic for humans has been reviewed by Heinstein (1963), who also concludes that for humans the feeding relationship as such does not have the valence imputed to it by psychoanalytic theory, in that no clear superiority for breast-feeding over bottle feeding can be demonstrated. This is not to deny that much stimulation occurs incidentally to feeding, but it does mean that a nonfeeder (the father, for instance) can supply the elements essential to the formation of emotional bonds.

One short-term experiment in this area is by Rheingold (1956), who "mothered" and provided extra nurturance to a group of institutional babies consistently over an eight-week period, while a control group continued to be given their normal institutional care, with routine attention distributed over several women, who gave no special attention. The "nurtured" infants showed greater social responsiveness even after this relatively brief period of heightened stimulation and maintained this effect a month later.

The independence of emotional ties from feeding is also supported in a study by Kistyakovskaya (1965), who from experimental observations of a large number of infants concluded that the adult who merely satisfies organic needs does not obtain positive emotional responses or smiling. Talking, smiling, and other stimulation are also required, and the adult becomes the source of positive response because he satisfied the infant's need for stimulation. The weakness of the Harlow experiments is that they do not tell us whether tactile stimulation is the solely effective one or even the most salient kind of stimulation at this stage. It is difficult to believe it is the only inlet for sensory feeding, but in view of the immaturity of other systems it may well be among the more important inputs. Experiments on this question would be of interest.

Observations of chimpanzees in the wild (Lawick-Goodall, 1965) show that the early contacts between infant and mother are important in this species too. Lawick-Goodall describes behaviors exactly comparable to those found by Harlow in the captive rhesus monkey—the manner, for example, in which the frightened infant will run to the mother, receive comfort, and then explore the cause of its fright. She also notes that throughout life tactile contact between adults as well as young is sought and apparently enjoyed, especially in situations in which reassurance seems necessary. It also appears in complementary "role" tasks such as fur grooming and lice picking. However, this happy contact is only between friends or relatives and is avoided with strangers.

The results of certain other of the Wisconsin experiments have been reviewed by Sackett (1965), who reports that this work shows that rearing infant monkeys under conditions of social isolation and perceptual impoverishment produces animals that are inactive and that display little of the exploratory behaviors that is so marked a feature of normal monkeys. In contrast to the situation in such experiments as those of Fantz (Chapter 13), in which normal human infants prefer stimuli of greater to those of low complexity, these animals preferred visual stimuli and manipulative situations of a simple nature. Perhaps the greatest abnormalities were in social behaviors, these animals being grossly inept in social interactions as adults; these deficiencies were particularly evident in their sexual and parental activities.

The deficiencies as mothers of isolation reared monkeys is also discussed further by Harlow and Harlow (1969), who show that some of these mothers were not merely inept, but actively brutal toward their offspring.

One notable difference from human findings that Sackett mentions is that no intellectual deficits, as measured by the learning of problems or in concept formation, were evident. This is in contrast to the many papers that produce evidence of intellectual retardation in deprived children (for instance, the Goldfarb studies). Whether this is a genuine species difference or an artifact of the methods of assessment (in one or other of the species) is difficult to say.

A question is raised by the common observation that some infants seem rejecting of the kinds of close tactile stimulation that Ribble and others recommend and that Harlow's monkeys seemed to seek. Schaffer and Emerson (1964) have documented this fact in observations of thirty-seven infants as part of a longitudinal study of the formation of social attachments. Out of this sample, nineteen of the babies were "cuddlers," that is, infants who from parental reports appeared to enjoy and solicit close handling, dandling, and other bodily contacts. Nine were "noncuddlers," who characteristically reacted against close contact; and an additional nine were "intermediates" who sometimes rejected contact but would accept it at other times (usually when tired). If this sample is at all representative, contact seeking is by no means a universal phenomenon in human infants; there are no published data on individual differences in other species. Schaffer and Emerson recognize that the differences might arise from the par-

ents—in their manner of handling—but believe that they come from within the child. Certainly many pediatricians know of apparently warm and accepting mothers who complain of cold and rejecting babies, though not many psychologists in this mother-blaming era appear to have noticed the phenomenon. This matter merits further study.

Three theoretical possibilities are suggested by these observations: (1) that this phenomenon arises from a sufficiency of stimulation from other sources in these infants (self-stimulation or kinaesthesis, for instance) so that extra cuddling raises the total above the optimum and tolerable level, (2) that the infants have an exceptionally low optimum, or (3) that they are differently "programmed" in the nervous system. Follow-up data on the subsequent development of such infants to show whether they display the characteristics of unstimulated infants will be of great interest.

A theoretical observation that may be relevant here is one by Hutt and Ounsted (1966), already discussed in Chapter 4. They suggest that eye-to-eye contact is arousing (and is avoided by autistic children because they already have a too-high level of arousal). It would be interesting to know if noncuddling children are high in eye-to-eye contact, which provides an alternative avenue of stimulation, bringing the total input to optimal levels.

A point of debate is whether it is the *quality* or the *quantity* of stimulation that is crucial. It has been suggested by Moltz (1963) that in animal development it is not the *quality* of stimulation that is important, but its intensity; Schaffer (1963) has indicated that the same may be true of human infants.

As already mentioned, Mead (1953) has taken issue with the assumption in our culture of the necessity of one mother/one child. She points out that this is possible in a society with adequate methods of family planning but is not typical of primitive cultures in which child care is often distributed over several persons, with no evident bad effects. Ainsworth (1962) has pointed out that there is a difference between maternal separation and deprivation, the former not necessarily leading to the latter if adequate surrogate care is provided.

It may be that this distinction between quality and quantity is a false one. If one concentrates on some smaller aspect of development (for example, the intellectual), it may be that quantity is the main emphasis. But considering broader issues (for example, the fact that a child is to grow into a particular society in which the nuclear rather than the extended family is the accepted pattern), then no doubt both the quality or nature of the stimulus relationships, as well as their mere quantity, may be important.

Nonprimate Studies of Early Experience

The greater part of the literature on the effects of early experiences, or lack of them, have involved experiments with nonprimate species. Beach and Jaynes (1954) have reviewed much of the literature, from Aristotle to 1953, on the effects of early experiences on the behavior of animals. Many of the studies cited by these authors are discussed in various contexts in this book. It is clear from this review that certain early experiences have marked effects on adult behaviors, even in the lower animals (though it should be noted that there are also many instances of nondependence on early experiences, especially in the lower animals). The keynote of most of these studies is "perceptual deprivation," and experiments for the most part involve rearing under conditions in which the infant animal is denied certain experiences that are normal to the species. For various technical and practical reasons, complete deprivation in any sense modality is not possible if one is to produce an animal capable of later response, so experiments usually involve reduced stimulation rather than its total absence.

Haywood and Zimmerman (1964) have shown that, in chicks, rearing in different environments can influence as basic a matter as imprinting. Groups raised in an enriched environment, with a high level of sensory stimulation from the moment of hatching on, showed an earlier critical period and an increased strength in the following response as compared with those raised in a restricted milieu.

While the perceptual deprivation approach to the delineation of the effects of early experience is a degree more specific than the highly global maternal deprivation concept, it is still far from original causes. There have been a number of attempts at a reductionist attack on the question, that is, toward relating the effects of early experience to basic physiological processes. It has already been noted that there may be gross psychophysical involvement when early deprivation is severe.

There have been two main approaches to the study of psychophysiological effects. One is to rear animals under conditions of enrichment (implying a supernormal effect as contrasted with the subnormal one of deprivation). The other is to impose conditions of stress, stimulation by shocks or other traumata. This relates to the point made earlier, that stimulus *intensity*, rather than the nature of a stimulus, is a critical variable.

MATURATIONAL THEORIES OF EARLY STIMULATION

One approach to explaining the effects of early stimulation has proposed primarily physical effects. A number of studies have reported growth increases as a result of early stimulation in rats and mice (e.g., Weininger, 1956; Denenberg and Karas, 1959, 1961). The idea that early stress may influence human growth has been examined by Landauer and Whiting (1964). They collected data from anthropological reports of cultures in which infants are subjected to such stresses as circumcision, scarification, ear or nose piercing, molding of the head or limbs, extreme cold, and so on. They found adult males in these societies to have an average height of more than two inches greater than those in societies where such practices are not found. This difference is highly significant. They examine some of the possible alternative explanations, such as genetic ones or diet, and show that while these cannot be ruled out entirely, they are improbable. These authors are properly cautious in interpreting these results, but in the light of the animal findings the data is suggestive that similar physiological responses to early stress may occur in humans.

They also examine the question of the critical period for this effect. Again the evidence is not unequivocal but does suggest that the first two years are the crucial ones. Animal experiments suggest that up to weaning is the critical period, and this would roughly correspond to the first two years in primitive cultures, where weaning is generally later than in our own society. It should not be difficult to obtain data on circumcized versus uncircumcized adults in our own society.

Krech et al. (1960) predicted that enriching an animal's experience would lead to a rise in the activity of the enzyme acetylcholinesterase (ChE) in the brain, because the greater the amount of neural transmission the greater is the production of acetylcholine. This transmitter substance is de-activated by acetylcholinesterase, which is present at the synapse immediately following firing, to remove the acetylcholine and prevent continuous firing. The concentration of ChE is thus a measure of synaptic activity. This prediction was not entirely borne out by experiment, in that while there was evidence of significantly more ChE activity per unit of weight in the subcortical brain, there was actually significantly *less* activity per unit weight in the cortex.

In later studies (Rosenzweig et al., 1962a, b; E. L. Bennett et al., 1964) these experiments were replicated and extended, and a total increase in brain weight with early environmental enrichment was also found. This was unexpected since the notion of "cerebral exercise" affecting brain formation had been rejected by a generation of psychologists. Rosenzweig et al. (1962a) suggest that an explanation of the unexpected results in their 1960 study might be that the increase in cortical weight was faster than the increase in total ChE activity, so that the actual increase in ChE, as measured per unit of brain weight, was masked.

These results are discrepant with those from a study by Altman et al. (1968), who found that early handling (from day 2 to 11) led to a *decrease* in brain weight over nonhandled controls. It would seem that the effect is complex and that not all the variables are yet known.

One aspect of this complexity might be time of stimulation, for while the Rosenzweig studies did concern themselves with early experience, it was not *very* early experience, because it was postweaning. Tapp and Markowitz (1963) have produced data on the preweaning effects of stimulation. Their results suggest that preweaning experiences have different effects on brain chemistry from postweaning ones, the preweaning handling affecting the subcortical brain and postweaning environmental enrichment affecting the neocortex. This factor still leaves an unanswered problem raised by the Altman study.

However, experiments like these do suggest that early experiences cause some change in the CNS and presumably a permanent one, though they carry us only one step toward an explanation. We still do not know what physiological mechanisms underlie these changes.

It appears that not only may early experiences affect brain development but that they may involve other systems too. Bovard (1958) has reviewed a number of studies that show that early handling affects the viability of the rat under potentially lethal conditions. For instance, those handled in infancy take longer to starve to death than nonhandled ones, and a number of similarly unkind experiments show early-stimulated animals to have a greater capacity for survival under a variety of stressful conditions. Thus the effects of early experience appear to be total rather than specifically psychological.

Bovard proposes a hypothesis that the increased sensory input from early handling results in effects on the amygdaloid complex and its functioning. This in turn affects the hypothalamus, causing a shift in the excitability of the anterior region as compared with the posterior. He suggests a number of mechanisms that might be affected by this shift, notably increased growth hormone output (early handled animals being bigger) and a decrease in the activity of the pituitary-adrenocortical system and the sympathetico-adrenal medulla system under both normal and stressful conditions.

Thus it seems that the physiological effects of early stimulation are widespread. Levine and Alpert (1959) have demonstrated that myelination of the CNS is quickened by the early manipulation of infant rats, and Levine (1962) has expressed the belief that many aspects of physical development are affected by infantile stimulation. Whether these physiological accelerations have any long-term psychological effects is another matter, but because psychological differences *are* detectable in early stimulated animals, it is not unreasonable to suppose that the two realms of observation are related. These results are extended in a later experiment (Levine, 1968) that shows the pattern of adrenocortical response to differ for handled and nonhandled animals, being higher in the handled ones. For this reason a complex new balance of neuro-endocrine influences on development is established for these animals.

Manipulation has also been shown to affect the maturation of the hypothalamic-pituitary complex (Levine et al., 1958) and of the pituitary-adrenal system (Levine and Lewis, 1959), and it may well be that Levine is correct in believing that the stimulated infant is a physiologically different adult. The nature of the psychological differences ensuing depends on whether these changes (and in particular the earlier maturation of systems) enable the or-

ganism to reach higher levels of psychological functioning. For instance, does earlier maturation of the CNS permit a longer effective learning period and hence a greater amount of learning? Or do these physiological changes merely bring earlier a state that is ultimately reached anyway, so that the final product is no different; does it merely mean that the organism reaches at n days a ceiling that it would anyway have reached by $n + x$ days, and no more?

Another line of inquiry is into the effects of early stimulation on visual processes. Some investigations of this are mentioned in Chapter 13. Riesen (1958) has reviewed some studies of the effects of early visual stimulation on later perception, and he follows Hebb (1949) in supposing that sensory-sensory (S-S) modifications may be a special characteristic of early mammalian development. The speed with which particular constellations of sensory inputs can be influential on behavior depends on previous experience with them. He points out that learning theorists have fragmented stimuli into clicks and flashes and then lumped these together with complex spatiotemporal patterns of stimuli, thereby causing confusion in dealing with neurophysiological matters. Riesen believes that even the notion of S-S combinations and sequences may be oversimplified. Any stimulus complex that has been discriminated by the organism tends to arouse orienting and recognition behaviors that then supply fresh sensory input. The central events that go with these must surely lose identity as either stimulus or response units, and this loss leads to psychological speculations about these events in terms of cell assemblies and phase sequences that are intermittently under sensory control. This question has particular significance as the animal progresses from infancy to maturity.

The ability to recognize new faces is an instance of these S-S integrations; memories of familiar faces give a basis from which discriminations are made between as yet unfamiliar ones. Thus from a basis of established "units of sensory patterns" a widening array of such units are built up, permitting finer and finer discriminations. One's first efforts to distinguish histological preparations under a microscope are almost hopeless, and finding the cues that distinguish one tissue from another is difficult. It is only after considerable exposure to a large number of preparations that seeing these differences becomes easy. Similarly the experienced radiologist sees in an X ray things that are undetectable to the novice.

From his own studies (Riesen et al., 1951) Riesen shows that the effects of extensive restriction of vision in early life are physiological; that is, there is optic nerve atrophy. This is reversible if not too long continued (beyond about seven months in the chimpanzee) but is irreversible if continued much beyond this time even when there has been a period of normal light experience for eight months preceding it. Riesen reviews studies in other species giving comparable results and also describing other physiological effects of total deprivation.

Psychologists are more interested in "pure" effects where the physiological substratum is normal, but this demands a perhaps unwarrantable division between the two realms. Apparently normal physiological systems can develop when the only visual experience is diffuse, unpatterned light. This form of deprivation avoids at least the grosser physiological effects of total deprivation.

However, it may be asked whether these seemingly normal systems are indeed so. Riesen (1958) is inclined toward a basically physiological explanation of the effects of early perceptual experience, or lack of it, though evidence on this is admittedly still very meager. He points to such biochemical changes as that in pentrose nucleoprotein (PNP) in retinal ganglion cells on stimulation. These effects are transitory ones to recent stimulation and hence do not of themselves form a basis for long-term memory; they might, however, underlie neurological changes that serve short-time memory and that are precursors of long-term storage and more permanent change.

Similarly chimpanzees (Chow and Nissen, 1955) and kittens (Riesen et al., 1953) reared early with one eye receiving only unpatterned stimulation, the other being allowed pattern vision, showed great difficulty with interocular transfer later. Control animals readily transferred learning in one eye to the other, whereas the monocularly reared ones showed considerable difficulty when required to learn with the "unpatterned eye" discrimination that had previously been learned with the "pattern-stimulated" one.

There is a related phenomenon in binocular fusion under certain conditions of flicker-phasing (G. J. Thomas, 1954), in which some individuals find fusion very difficult, and their binocular CFF thresholds are similar to monocular ones. Sherrington (according to Riesen) favored a psychic explanation of such phenomena, whereas Riesen believes them to have a physiological explanation in terms of neural integration that is developed by patterned stimulation. (The problem, of course, is to explain why some children have a "lazy" eye; possibly a developmental lag or some subtle one-sided defect in the system causes the other to be strongly preferred.)

In Riesen's view, then, the effects of early perceptual stimulation are psychophysiological: the early-stimulated and the early-unstimulated organisms are physiologically, as well as psychologically, different. One or both of these components is relatively permanently determined by early experiences. Such evidence as there is suggests it might be the physiological part (if such a division is valid).

These contentions have been supported by Fox et al. (1968), who have shown how in the dog visual deprivation in the first five weeks has effects that are different from deprivation after this period. During this time the CNS is particularly sensitive to stimulation, and deprivation leads to marked anatomical, electrophysiological, and biochemical changes. After this period such effects are minimal.

PSYCHOLOGICAL EXPLANATIONS OF STIMULATION EFFECTS

Early experiential influences are emphasized by Denenberg and his associates (Whimbey and Denenberg, 1966; Denenberg et al., 1968), who have shown how differing "programs" of early rearing can produce differing life histories in rats. Such studies may show that certain early experiences can mimic genetic influences in their effects. This does not, of course, imply a contradiction but merely says that similar effects can (in certain circumstances) be produced either by genetic mechanisms or by learning. (Presumably an effect will be most marked when genetic and environmental influences are consistent.)

There is no sharp dividing line, as indeed there cannot be, between explanations of the effects of early stimulation that propose growth changes or altered physiological processes and those that offer explanations on a more psychic level.

An example commonly quoted here of the effects of early experience on perception is the study by Nissen et al. (1935) of the performance of West African natives compared with that of Europeans. On form boards, the comparison is highly unfavorable to the Africans, but on tracking in the bush it is just as unfavorable to the white men. An important point is that their differences are presumably not permanent. The speed with which Africans (and others) can become familiar with foreign notions (in technology, for example) shows that they are not permanently restricted to fine discriminations within the bush setting. Similarly histologists and radiologists are not usually exposed to slides or X-ray plates until a fairly advanced age, and these items are certainly not a common part of their childhood experiences. Yet they are able to make necessary discriminations after a suitable exposure to such objects. One expects that the European could learn to follow a track as skillfully as the native if he would set himself to studying as assiduously as he might study histology. And the African can learn histology too.

In naturalistic observations of institution-reared children I have often wondered what their perceptual world can be. I have the impression that it is much less rich in detail than that of normally reared ones. Sent to tidy the yard, such a child will just not see a newspaper that litters it. Some will prefer to explain this in motivational terms, oppositioned tendencies leading to motivated "blindness," and this may occur. But from observation and questioning, I am convinced that this is not the only explanation and that such children actually see less. The child is, of course, perfectly capable of seeing the paper when it is pointed out to him, or even of noticing it for himself if he happens to glance directly at it. But in scanning a scene, he actually seems to pick up less detail. It is as if there were large blind areas, so even though by closure he perceives a completed scene, much detail is lost. (It would be interesting to study closure in such children. One would predict that bigger "gaps" are closed in simple patterns, though recognition of more complex ones by closure might be inferior.)

Every parent knows that their own uninstitutionalized children can be equally unheeding of detail—toys not put away are unnoticed. But these children are capable of finer perception when motivated, whereas the institutionalized child seems incapable even when motivated (he is often, of course, also more difficult to motivate, and the defect is multidimensional).

It is as if the institution-reared child has a restricted range of effective vision. He sees only what is directly fixated and what is specifically attended to. Hence, incidental or latent learning is restricted. Moreover, the range of relevance is reduced too because he tends to perceive only what is immediately relevant. Visual acuity as such is not impaired (or if it is, it has never been reported). It is not simple visual discrimination such as distinguishing fine lines, but more complex visual exercises that require interpretation rather than merely sensing that is lacking.

The institutionalized child also differs in that he may be more or less permanently incapacitated in making these kinds of perceptual integration; the effects of this early deprivation may be difficult if not impossible to change. The stimulated nervous system, on the other hand, retains, at least for a long time, the capacity for acquiring fine discriminations and integrations in new realms of perceptual activity, as it does when the African or European medical student learns histology. Riesen is no doubt right in talking of the early plasticity of the nervous system, but another of the effects of early perceptual experience may be greatly to extend this period of plasticity. While early stimulation may play a crucial role in raising plasticity to higher levels, it would seem (from naturalistic observation rather than from experimental evidence) that continued stimulation is necessary to maintain the early acquired high level. Continuously stimulated individuals (such as professors) may retain this plasticity until an advanced age.

A problem is that the effects noted are not exclusive to institutionalized children. One does find individuals reared in families under apparently optimal conditions who show phenotypically similar effects. While the proportion of institutionalized children showing the defect seems to be relatively high and its presence in the general population low, there is some overlap. This is not explained by the cultural deprivation of the underprivileged home, because some of those apparently understimulated children that one sees in clinical practice come from privileged homes, homes in which, insofar as can be detected, there were no special circumstances at the

time of the children's infancy that would have prevented stimulation. Of course, such undetected environmental factors might exist, but a more plausible explanation is that these individuals have some inborn physiological difference that has made the nervous system less susceptible to the effects of early experience; these individuals are less able to profit from stimulation.

Another fact requiring explanation is that some institutionalized children do not show these effects (e.g., Maas, 1963). Possibly these are individuals with especially reactive physiological processes, so that they can produce normal effects with less than normal amounts of stimulation. Again, of course, an environmental explanation, such as being favored by someone on the institutional staff, is possible, but there is often no sign of such an explanation. These are questions that merit systematic exploration.

Coordinating Functions. An important area of functioning is visual-motor coordination, in which eye and hand work together, a highly skilled maneuver normally taken for granted. Deficiencies in this functioning may underlie certain of the difficulties some children encounter in school learning, though precisely how they do this is not adequately explained. Held and Bauer (1967) have shown that rearing infant monkeys under conditions in which eye-hand coordination practice is denied results in impairment in the ability to make smooth visually guided reaching movements toward objects. The animals were reared from birth in an apparatus with a ruff, around the neck, that prevented any sight of the hands even though there was free movement of them. Thus neither vision nor grasping and manipulation was denied —only the conjunction of the two. These authors suppose that the earliest experiences of watching the moving limb provide the information by which the eye and head movements necessary to fixate the target visually are integrated with the actual movements of the limb in reaching; the information gained is essential to integration of the two control systems. Insofar as the species they used (female macaques) is concerned, these effects are seemingly not permanent; and even after restriction of experience for eight months, the effects were no longer detectable at one year of age.

In thinking about the alleged human visuomotor disturbances, this study would lead one to ask about their possible origins. The conditions producing the effects were highly artificial, and it is difficult to think of any that would remotely resemble them in Western child rearing, even under the most deprived conditions. One situation in which they might be found to some extent is in cradle-board rearing, but even here the infants do gain occasional sight of the hands when periodically off the board. Nobody has reported any deficiency in the later visuomotor performance of these children (but maybe nobody has looked). However, on the basis of this slender evidence, one might suppose that visuomotor incoordination in children may be more a question of nervous system organization than of early experience. Almost any environment whatever provides enough of the necessary experience to integrate the control systems where the nervous system is normal.

Because there is no great amount of data on the question of intersensory integration and its development, any further thoughts must also be speculative. However, the data such as they are do tempt one to ask if the integration of sensory modalities is not a function that can occur at any time; it evidently depends on experience rather than maturation. Held and Bauer's subjects required time to become proficient, but eventually they did become so. They had relatively unrestricted use of both vision and manipulation separately and hence avoided the effects of restriction in these two modalities. Thus these two systems developed normally, and given this development, the integration of

their control systems could take place at any time (though it should be noted that the longer-treated animals took progressively longer to acquire smooth integration).

There is obviously a whole area for research here, in which the various combinations of intersensory integrations would be investigated, and refined studies to discover if more subtle effects than Held and Bauer examined result from intermodality restrictions would be undertaken.

Emotionality Hypothesis of Early Stimulation

Levine (1956) has suggested the hypothesis that early stimulation reduces the emotional response of the adult when faced with a novel situation, thereby improving psychological functioning under the potential stress of novelty.

Denenberg (1964) has proposed an inverse relationship between amount of early stimulation and adult emotionality. In a series of investigations this theory was applied to the learning situation, and it was found that handled infants became adults who were significantly better learners than nonhandled controls.

With mice, however, the results are apparently contradictory, though differences in experimental method confuse the issue. Lindzey et al. (1963) subjected several strains of mice to intense auditory stimulation in the first week and found them to be more emotionally reactive than controls. Winston (1963) has reported them to be less adept at maze learning.

For cats the effects are in general similar to those with rats (Wilson et al., 1965), though there are again experimental differences that are confusing when compared. Kittens handled for five minutes daily for the first forty-five days were less emotional (i.e., approached strange situations more readily) than controls, were more active in open-field testing, and also made fewer errors in the Hebb-Williams maze.

The relationship between the amount of early handling and emotionality is not, however, a simple one, because rats with ten days of infantile handling were better than those with twenty days (Denenberg and Karas, 1960a, b). This is explained by supposing that the twenty-day animals were too unemotional to function optimally. These results were confirmed in further experiments (Karas and Denenberg, 1961). Similar results were found by Griffiths and Stringer (1952), who reported no difference between stimulated and control rats when intense stimulation was given from birth until fifty-seven days of age.

Levine et al. (1967) have related the effects of early stress to a marked effect on the adrenocortical response to novel stimuli. While all the subjects (rats at time of weaning) showed an increase in adrenocortical steroids in the blood plasma following exposure to novel stimuli, the increase was significantly less for those handled in infancy. This study points up the fact that the maturational and emotionality hypotheses are not really distinct but merely refer to different aspects of the same thing. However, the maturational effects are more fundamental, the changes in emotionality being one consequence of them.

It does not of necessity follow that the effect on emotionality of too much stimulation arises merely from some kind of overreached maturation. Possibly a certain level of early stimulation produces maturational changes of which reduced emotionality is one result. But stimulation beyond this produces no further maturational change, and some fresh mechanism, such as psychic satiation, takes over. Since none of the studies have plotted the effects of early stimulation to a maximum, this speculation is unanswered.

It is not surprising that there is no evidence to show whether the same kind of relationship exists at the human level, because amounts of early stimulation cannot be controlled and measured as they can in rats. The idea that too much early stimulation can be as undesirable as too little is an intriguing one, but there are little data either to refute or support it. Certainly in clinical practice one sees children with apparently normal infancies, and a proper complement of loving parents, who are low in motivation; they are commonly referred to clinics as school failures. One can be reasonably certain that these children did not have too little infantile handling; whether they had too much has never been explored.

One notable feature of the animal experiments is how little manipulation is necessary to produce the effect: A minute or two of picking up once a day for about ten days is, in the rat, all that is required to produce a marked change from the unhandled state. Incidentally, this "gentling" may not be all that gentle, as Gulliver could attest from his experiences in Brobdingnag, and may be a most stressful event for a rat or mouse pup. Indeed some experiments use shocks to produce the same effect (e.g., A. M. Smith, 1967). It is not difficult to believe that too much stimulation can overreach itself, at least in a simple nervous system like that of the rodent. Whether the same is true of the human nervous system may be another matter.

The behavior of autistic children has been interpreted by Hutt and Ounsted (1966) in terms of arousal. They were specifically concerned with gaze aversion, a typical feature of the behavior of these children. These authors point out that fairly universally among animals the sight of another's eye is a highly arousing stimulus and that the same is probably true of humans. The eye conveys much information and gaze fixation is intimidating; it therefore increases arousal, and gaze aversion is a built-in biological response reducing this arousal.

Autistic children, they suggest, have a chronically high level of arousal, and their customary gaze aversion is an adaptation toward its reduction. As they say, the origin of this high arousal level is unknown, but the

RAS is no doubt involved at some point in the chain of events. Biochemical factors may possibly stimulate the RAS, but what causes them is not known. Since the familial antecedent of autism is said to be the cold, unstimulating "refrigerator mother" (Kanner, 1949), one might ask whether these children are not somehow like the unstimulated animals with their excessive arousal level. However, this does not seem to be a wholly adequate explanation. For one thing the refrigerator mother concept is a suspect one (Rimland, 1964) and not apparently an invariable correlate of the condition. There may well be some other factor, and possibly a genetic one; these children may be improperly programmed to deal with even a normal level of sensory input.

In the discussion on imprinting (Chapter 9) it was seen that there is some evidence to suggest that painful or punishing stimulation may be as effective as any other kind (or even more effective) in producing the following response. It is early to make any theoretical capital out of these somewhat tentative experiments, but they do raise the question of whether "tender loving care" is all that is claimed for it. One might be unduly hasty to recommend any relaxation of the TLC approach to child rearing on the basis of these results, but the results do warn us to keep a critical watch on theorizing in the area. While the gap between theory and practice is so large, it would be wise to stick to TLC for the latter.

Filter Hypothesis

Melzack (1965) has discussed the possible mechanisms that might underlie the effects of early restriction of experience. First, he says, it is possible that sensory restriction leads to a degeneration of either peripheral fibers or central afferent neurons. Riesen (1958), for example, has demonstrated structural differences, in comparison with controls, in the macula and

in the chemistry of the optic fibers in dark-reared animals. Similarly Hubel and Wiesel (personal communication to Melzack) reported degeneration of geniculate cells and cortical cells involved in selective response to pattern stimulation when one eye of a cat is sutured so that pattern vision is prevented. Melzack regards this as an unlikely explanation in the case of the dogs in his experiment, for although they were reared in a restricted environment, they had received considerable visual, auditory, and somaesthetic input.

A second possibility discussed by Melzack is that reduction of patterned sensory stimulation may be sufficient to produce a deficit in perceptual processes. He does not feel, however, that this adequately accounts for the observed behavior of the restricted dogs, which seem to reflect a disruption of behavior rather than some simple perceptual deficit. Similarly, although they frequently failed to respond to noxious stimuli at normal intensities, the dogs did respond to high intensities.

Melzack's third proposal involves a double process in which there is primarily an inadequate filtering of inputs because memories of significant stimuli are not acquired in early experiences. As a consequence, there is a barrage of this unfiltered input that excessively arouses the CNS.

However, as Melzack points out, this model does not seem to be applicable to the human situation, where early rearing in a restricted environment (institutionalization) leads not to the excited overreaction to all and sundry stimuli, as in the dog, but rather to apathy and apparently an inhibition of most of the incoming stimuli. Effects similar to those in the dog, a general overexcitement, are reported in cats by Riesen (1961a), whereas effects similar to those in humans are reported by Harlow and Harlow (1962) for rhesus monkeys. On this somewhat slender evidence one is tempted to propose a change with phylogenetic level, inhibition rather than lack of it being a primate characteristic.

Melzack has suggested, however (private

communication), that the discrepancy between primates and carnivores may be more apparent than real. Both in isolated monkeys and in deprived children a persistent rocking behavior is commonly observed, and this may be a substitute for the excitable overactivity reported in the lower orders.

Not only do institutionalized children differ from Melzack's dogs and Riesen's cats in showing apathy rather than overenthusiasm, as I can confirm from personal experience with them, but they also differ in their response to painful stimuli. Nothing in the literature reports a lack of response to noxious stimuli by institutionalized children, and in a nine-month period of intensive observation of such children I did not note anything to suggest that their responses to pain were abnormal; if anything, they were rather less stoical than normally reared children.

Melzack's model assumes that the immature system admits all the input; as it matures, it matches the input with the "record" being built up and rejects the "nonmatches." In other words, what develops is a rejection mechanism. An alternative would be to assume that the system natively tends to reject, and what it has to develop is an admission mechanism based on "recognition." This would seem better to explain the apathy and "depression" of deprived children, supposing their undeveloped filters to reject too much of the input.

The trouble with such a model is explaining how stimuli ever get in to start building up the "record" that will permit matching and admission of an optimal proportion of the input. However, it is not being proposed that the immature filter is an absolute barrier but rather that it is one in the statistical sense. It at first randomly filters out a high proportion of the input, but some does get in haphazardly, and it is this portion that starts the record going. This is consistent with the slowness and inefficiency of early learning (Chapter 12). As the filter matures, it admits a greater proportion of the input and, moreover, does this selectively and not randomly. It may be that there is no absolute increase in the amount admitted through the filter and that the admission simply becomes less and less random. Thus an increasing proportion of pertinent information is admitted, but the proportion of irrelevant material is decreased. For this reason there might even be a decrease in total input with age.

Melzack bases his proposal upon the fact that sensory stimulation of the skin evokes nerve impulse patterns that travel to the CNS along fibers having different speeds of conduction (Melzack and Wall, 1962). Stimuli along the fastest conducting fibers are transmitted (via various lower centers) to the cortex, not to elicit sensations but to initiate a step in the process of information selection; they give, as it were, advance warning that facilitates the process of detection and categorization of patterns necessary to perception and response. He suggests it is reasonable to suppose that these fast inputs to the cortex activate "phase sequences" that correspond to earlier experiences and that these exert control over the patterns ascending behind them in the slower fibers that are carrying information on a variety of stimulus properties. Thus past experience can favorably influence the selection of certain patterns and inhibit that of others.

This model is competent whether the filter system is primarily an unselective one that becomes "rejective," as Melzack suggests, or whether it is natively a "rejective" one, later becoming selective as suggested here.

SYNTHESIS OF THEORETICAL APPROACHES TO STIMULATION EFFECTS

We have three approaches to an explanation of the effects *on animals* of early experience: that of Levine, Rosenzweig, Riesen, and others in terms of an influence on maturation; that of Denenberg, which proposes motivational changes; and that of Melzack, which suggests that early experience "programs" the attentional or filter mechanisms.

In human deprivation studies there are (according to Schaffer, 1965) three main theoretical approaches to causation. Spitz (1945) uses an explanation of the effects in terms of emotional changes following separation from the mother. Dennis and Najarian (1957) explain them in terms of restricted learning opportunities, leading to cognitive deficiencies. Provence and Lipton (1962) give what is essentially a motivational explanation, a "decrease of investment" that leads to incomplete use of the potentialities still available to the child. Schaffer (1965b) also favors a motivational explanation and assumes no basic developmental change, and thus the effects are reversible.

An attempt at a synthesis of the various theories of the effects of stimulation, or their converse, an absence of stimulation, is not easy. The human-based theories are not readily matched with the three theories of animal stimulation effects. For one thing, maturational effects are ignored in the human approaches. Also, the motivational effects proposed by Provence and Lipton and by Schaffer are dissimilar from those spoken of by Denenberg. They say, in effect, that the unstimulated institutionalized child is too unemotional (or undermotivated) to perform adequately, whereas Denenberg claims the effect to be too much emotion. The approach of Dennis and Najarian perhaps has something in common with Riesen's formulations, but the similarities are not striking.

There is, however, one thing about these heterogeneous approaches: They are not mutually exclusive. It could well be that all these factors are involved and that the effects of early experience are highly complex; that is, that these are each facets of pervasive changes in total functioning.

One observation of interest is that Harlow has reported in the seriously deprived wiremother monkeys a kind of masochistic behavior in which they seemed deliberately to hurt themselves, apparently to gain stimulation. This differs from Melzack's observation, in which the dogs, although they did not avoid potentially painful situations, did not actively seek them. It is a well-known clinical fact that institutionalized humans are not infrequently observed in head banging and other pain-producing acts. In the Curtis Report (1946) and other documents, references are made to deprived children who seek physical punishment and seem to derive gratification from it. A possible interpretation of these observations at both infrahuman and human levels is that they serve to increase the sensory input under conditions where this is intolerably low. It is evident from various human experiments on reduced sensory input that too low a level is intolerable. There is no suggestion that these pain-seeking children were hypoesthetic: indeed, if one is to interpret their behavior as stimulus-seeking, it would fail in this if not painful. (In other contexts it might, of course, be interpreted as attention-seeking.)

One question here is whether tolerance to perceptual deprivation is always related to previous levels of stimulation or whether there is in all organisms a minimum threshold that is independent of levels actually experienced. The Harlow work suggests that the latter might be the case; that is, there might be an optimal level of stimulation and that levels below this are "painful" even if the animal has never experienced the optimum. Possibly in enriched environments this basic level is raised and a new threshold for tolerance is established.

One result of early stimulation will be that there are greater areas of the environment that are familiar. As we have already seen in the previous chapter, novelty-seeking is a feature of perception. The seeking of novelty, or the "curiosity drive," is discussed more fully in the next chapter. It is incorporated into the theorizing of Piaget (1951), who has noted how the child's spontaneous interest in the new is a factor in the beginning of differentiation between the subjective and objective. Berlyne (1960) has also theorized on this point (see Chapter 14). J. McV. Hunt (1961) attempts to integrate the notion of novelty-seeking with optimal arousal theories.

If the early-stimulated child has a greater scope of familiarity, he must range more widely to seek novelty and in so doing will be exposed to greater stimulation and higher levels of arousal. A raising of the tolerance level will be a necessary adaptation, but presumably there remains a limit to the level attainable.

One problem that needs to be accounted for is the apparent key position of tactile stimulation in early experiences. Harlow's monkeys reared on the wire surrogate mother showed much more markedly the effects of isolation than those reared on the cloth mother, yet apart from this difference the two environments were equally barren. Both groups must have had equivalent amounts of visual and auditory and nontactile somaesthetic stimulation. It might be that the amount of extra stimulation provided tactually to the cloth-mother animals was sufficient to raise the *total* amount of stimulation above a threshold (a point that could be checked by providing extra stimulation in other modalities to wire-mother animals), but Harlow is insistent that it is tactile stimulation per se that makes the difference. It is as if early tactile stimulation in some manner influences the whole development of perceptual processes.

Moreover, this effect may be more general: The cloth-mother animals were emotionally as well as perceptually different. It could be that early tactile experience affects in some manner the development of motivational systems in the young animal and that the perceptual effects are related to this effect. G. Bronson (1965) has offered an explanation in terms of maturation of the CNS, perceptual effects being mediated by a level that is mature before finer visual or auditory discriminations become possible (see pp. 249-250).

Another noticeable difference between the cloth- and wire-mother monkeys was in the lack of curiosity of the latter. The former, as is vividly shown in Harlow's films, gained sufficient reassurance from clinging to the tactually satisfying cloth mother to explore even a frightening environment, whereas the wire-mother animals merely froze. Again this difference is typical of institution-reared children, who show a singular lack of interest in the environment. The writer made repeated attempts by field trips and other "enriching" experiences, to expose a group of these children to interesting possibilities. Granted this *may* tell more about the writer than about the children, but he also knows colleagues with good records as inspiring teachers of normal children who were completely frustrated in attempts to strike a spark out of institutional ones.

Another striking feature of institution-reared children is their imperviousness to incidental learning; from my clinical observations I believe this merits investigation, though insofar as I am aware there are no published studies.

One point that needs to be clarified is whether "subnormal" and "supernormal" environments have equal but opposite effects as compared with a "normal" environment (assuming this can be adequately defined). Many of the experiments in the area have reared animals (or observed children) under conditions of presumably reduced stimulation, though often without any clear statement of the baseline from which this reduction is taken. Other experiments have gone the other way and used what are described as enriched levels—but again without making specific what this really means. In animal experiments *reduced* or *enriched* are usually used with reference to the conditions of housing and care of laboratory-bred and reared animals, but this tells us little about changes from the natural state of the animal.

In some contexts this may be unimportant, but one of the questions of practical importance to the developmentalist is the extent to which what might be called the natural equipment of the organism can be exploited. It might be argued that all "normally" reared laboratory animals are raised under restricted conditions as compared with the feral state and that so-called "enriched" laboratory environments merely approximate the natural one in complexity. That is, by these conditions we do not produce a "supernormal" animal but merely one that makes full use of its potential.

In the human situation reference is made to the "culturally deprived" environment of the underprivileged home or the institution. In terms of organ potential is the "normal" home merely that producing function at an average but not a maximal (or even necessarily optimal) level? How much beyond this level can we effectively enrich the environment to produce "supernormal" individuals? In some contexts perhaps the question is a meaningless one, but when we ask "What is the potential of the human organism and how closely do we approach it," the question does take on interest.

Although there may be no direct proof of this, it would seem likely that a law of diminishing returns holds, increasing complexity in the environment producing smaller and smaller increments in performance until this levels out at a point where further increase produces no changes. Indeed, further increase beyond this point may (and probably does) produce a decrement in functioning, the environment becoming too complicated to be dealt with at all. The task is then to define the point of maximal functioning and to avoid going beyond it.

Another aspect of the question is the relationship between "complexity" and "stimulation." Can *complexity* be defined in terms of number of discrete stimuli per unit time? If it can, then a number of additional questions follow. One factor that is doubtless important is stimulus change (e.g., switching a stimulus pattern on and off being more effective than a static presentation of the pattern), which raises questions of number of changes per unit time. Another aspect is the repetition of the same versus different stimuli in this time. Can complexity be defined only in terms of rate of change or must the dimension of stimulus variety also be considered? One suspects that it must; that is, that repeating the same stimulus at the optimal rate is not equivalent to repeating different stimuli at the same rate; in the long run the latter is probably more effective. If this is true, then a complex environment is one in which there is not merely repetitive presentation of the same stimulus pattern but also an alteration of a variety of such patterns, and one thing that requires definition is the optimal characteristic of change (e.g., alternation of the different stimuli one at a time regularly, in blocks, or randomly). What is the influence of alternation of modality? A whole range of experiments that will serve to define environmental complexity and that will perhaps ultimately lead to statements about the optimal nature of environmental enrichment that will make for maximal organism functioning, suggest themselves.

One point that this review makes clear is the inseparability of psychological and physiological factors in dealing with early development. At this stage it seems that we cannot deal with the psychological but only with the psychophysical. How long this remains the case is a moot point. It does not of necessity mean that there is no place for a discussion of development on a purely psychological level. It may well be that "psychological" stimulation in the early stages at first mediates physiological changes but that these reach a plateau on which continued stimulation produces no further physiological developmental change, and at this point it becomes permissible to talk in purely psychological terms. (The quotes around psychological in this sentence are there because it may be debated whether sensory stimulations of the young sense organs should be regarded as physiological or psychological events. It might be argued that they become the latter only when they acquire meanings, but this is not the place to pursue such a philosophical question.) One point that should not be lost sight of is that these early psychophysical events may have considerable influence on the direction that later psychological development may take.

Another matter that requires notice is that the effects of early stimulation, or lack of it, have wide individual differences, at least in humans. Much of the animal work tends to give the impression that the effects of either enrichment or impoverishment of early stimulation lead to consistent effects in all individuals. Whether this is because the lower species are more consistent, or whether it is because psychologists working with animals do not generally interest themselves in individual differences, is an open question.

One possible factor of significance may be innate intelligence. If we assume that an aspect of high intelligence is greater awareness of the environment, or in other words more susceptibility to stimulation, it could be argued that intelligent individuals will be able to "extract" a greater variety of stimuli from a barren environment than less intelligent ones and hence will be less affected. On the other hand, it could be argued that the more intelligent individual has a greater demand for "stimulus feeding" and hence is more adversely affected by an impoverished environment. These are interesting alternative speculations with no data to aid a decision between them.

But even Bowlby has admitted that not all children exposed to early institutional experiences show the more severe effects and that, in fact, only a small minority display the most serious disabilities of personality (Bowlby et al., 1956). This is not, of course, to say that the majority of relatively unaffected ones are not to some degree handicapped by these experiences, and it is sound mental hygiene to adopt the view that institutionalization is always undesirable even if this view is scientifically inaccurate. This is particularly the case when we have no means of predicting which children will suffer the

most; it is good social policy to protect all.

However, in this context we are interested in the scientific evidence and the theoretical considerations that stem from it, and this leads us to ask why some children escape and others succumb. The most probable explanation is that there are individual differences in the constitutional susceptibility to the effects of stimulation, though what the nature of these differences may be we have no clue. These presumed constitutional bases for reaction to environmental complexity would seem to operate both ways. Some individuals do not develop superbly in spite of enriched environments, and others develop adequately in poor ones (though there is always the possibility that they might have developed *more* adequately in better ones). But it seems tenable to suppose that for each individual there is an optimal level of environmental stimulation that will make for fullest development and that this level varies widely in the population. This is, of course, a purely academic point until we can identify an individual's needs for stimulation, but perhaps one day we shall know them.

This chapter has emphasized the influence of early experience on later development. It is necessary, because neither early experience nor genetic factors that precede them are the only influences on development, to introduce a qualifier into the discussion. Clarke (1968) has been critical of the current assumption in the literature that the first five years are of paramount importance. Much of the literature ignores genetic or biological influences but also ignores influences in the years following the fifth. One important affect of middle-childhood learning, Clarke points out, is the reinforcement, or lack of it, given to early learning. In this period some of what is acquired in the preschool period is confirmed, and some drops out because of nonreinforcement. Also, we might add, some new learning that *may* not have any direct preceding conditions established in the first five years possibly occurs.

Twelve | Development of the Capacity for Learning

This chapter and Chapter 13 on perception have presented me with a considerable, and perhaps insoluble, problem of didactic strategy. Perception and learning are so intimately connected that one cannot really discuss them in isolation. On the other hand, to make a discussion possible, some breakdown of the material is essential, and this has to be largely arbitrary. Whether one should discuss learning before perception, or the other way about, is also debatable, though the order adopted here is not quite arbitrary because I have fallen into the habit of teaching this way, under the impression that it is didactically preferable.

As Tighe and Tighe (1966a) have shown, there are two historical approaches to the important field of psychology known as "discrimination learning," or the acquisition of different responses to different stimuli. One of the approaches to discrimination learning involves a "mediation theory," which really emphasizes the *learning* component of the term. This, they say, is at present the dominant approach. The other is a "differentiation theory," which emphasizes the perceptual component of the term. A complete understanding of the question presumably will involve both approaches.

Discrimination learning is obviously of great interest to the developmentalist, because much of his work can be described as an attempt to explain how the child acquires an increasingly greater range of responses to more diverse and complex stimuli.

LEARNED AND NONLEARNED BEHAVIORS

A universal characteristic of animals from the protozoa up is a capacity for modification of behavior by experience—the ability to learn. This capacity may be limited in the lower animals, but it is there. Hebb (1966) has given one example in the fact that ants discriminate strangers from members of their own colony by odor; fellow members given the odor of another colony are attacked. If, however, normally antagonistic species are intermingled in the first twelve hours after hatching, they coexist peacefully thereafter, and evidently the "friendly" odor is learned.

Imprinting (Chapter 8) is another instance in which the bird's early experience determines the class of objects to which it will direct its social behavior throughout life. It normally and in nature almost inevitably involves a parent bird, but dramatic modification is possible during a brief critical period. This is what happens when the bird is imprinted to a man or to a cube. Marler and Tamura (1964) have shown how the song of the male white-crowned sparrow has regional "dialects" and the way in which these dialects are learned by young males from older ones during the first 100 days of life. Once learned, this behavior is unaffected by further exposure to other dialects. Interestingly, this species learns only dialect variations of its own species-song. It does not acquire the "foreign" song of other species of sparrows, and learning operates only within narrow limits set by the innate basis. One might view learning of this kind as involving the linking of a limited range of FAP's, such as was discussed in Chapter 4.

In mammals, similar changes from "natural" behaviors are possible. Since times unknown dogs have shared a social life with man, but only because each new generation has becomes socialized to him by its early experiences. Chimpanzees reared with man show much the same kinds of adaptation, which are in some respects, as in the use of eating utensils, more marked.

The Scottish terrier experiments by Melzack and Thompson (1956), which were reviewed earlier, demonstrate convincingly the relation between early experiences and adult behavior. Comparable results were obtained in experiments by Nissen et al. (1951) in which a chimpanzee was reared under conditions of somaesthetic restriction. The lower arms and legs were encased in cardboard tubes that permitted movements of joints but prevented tactual exploration of the body or the environment. These cuffs were constantly worn until thirty months of age. The ape was abnormal in activities involving somaesthesis, being, for instance, inaccurate in localizing and removing irritating stimuli. Like the dogs, it also showed unusual reaction to normally painful stimuli like pinpricks. Learning a left-right discrimination that was fairly easy for control animals was extremely difficult for this one.

A number of human studies that show the influence of early experience on later learning (together with a more detailed discussion of animal data) were covered in Chapter 11. As these data show, there is good reason to suppose that at the human level also—perhaps more especially at the human level—early experiences have profound effects on later functioning in learning as well as in other matters. However, we find in many of the lower organisms behaviors that are difficult to explain on the basis of learning and that we can assume to be innate. For instance, in many species of spiders the eggs are left to hatch for themselves. The young have no contact with the parent, and yet the young spider's first attempt at web building is perfect or very nearly so, in spite of having had no opportunity to learn, or indeed any previous experience with a web. Numerous such instances can be quoted among the invertebrates, but higher up the animal scale we find behaviors that are also difficult to explain by learning.

The young cuckoo, for example, is reared by a foster parent of a different species, and because the eggs are laid singly in the unwitting foster parents' nest, the young bird never has any contact with either immature or mature members of its own kind. In spite of this, it develops the behaviors typical of the cuckoo; it develops the cuckoo song and not that of the foster parents, and its other habits are those of its own kind, uninfluenced by those of its hosts. The most reasonable explanation for the development of cuckoo behavior is that it is innate.

Whether such unlearned behaviors exist at the human level is uncertain, even though many psychologists today would claim with no uncertainty that they do not, except only in the case of such simple behaviors as the reflexes. However, even though no complex human behaviors are unlearned, it may still be the case that innate factors underlie and influence some behaviors in which learning is necessary to the full emergence of these activities. These nonlearned presets may influence such learning in two ways: by facilitating certain kinds of acquisitions or by constraining others.

One of the problems for developmental psychology is the determination of the limits on human behavior imposed by innate factors and of those acquired by learning. This is not, as some would claim, a merely pedantic question; it has practical implications. If there is (as evidence suggests) some "learning how to learn," then a precise knowledge of whether or not this has limits has obvious educational implications. If the ability to learn is innately determined and limited, we should know this. Do we seek the early educational experiences that will draw out almost limitless improvements in the learning capacities of children, or do we have to reconcile ourselves to accepting biological limits and set ourselves the task of enabling the child to make best use of this predetermined potential?

A number of writers take the view that intelligence (learning capacity) is acquirable. Hunt (1961, 1966), for instance, has stated that the idea of an innately fixed IQ needs revision and claims that given appropriate early stimulation large advances in intelligence (thirty points or so of IQ) might be possible and considerable improvement might be attained in the child's ability to learn. (But why only thirty points? Does some extraneous factor set this limit?) Bruner (1960) has claimed that any subject can be taught effectively to any child and moreover that this can be done at any stage of development. This would seem to be a bold claim. For one thing, there is a limiting factor imposed by time alone that it is difficult to see how one can

circumvent. It is evident from much current research that there are fairly severe limits to the amount of information that can be handled by the input systems of the organism, overloading of the input channels tending to disruption and a closing off of all of them. Even on a twenty-four-hour schedule, using sleep-learning techniques (assuming them to be effective) would still permit only limited input. Possibly the split-brain technique of Sperry (1961) might double the capacity (if the disadvantages it brings do not outweigh the advantages), but even here, and with highly radical procedures, the amount of input is strictly finite. Moreover, Linda Siegal (1968) has given experimental evidence that the ability to process information does in fact change with age in children.

We cannot at this stage anticipate such revolutionary changes in man's abilities to learn. A profitable line of research would be to investigate more fully the limiting factors in handling multiple inputs, with a view to finding means of maximizing the effective encoding of the greatest range of input. It could also be that learning can become more flexible in some directions but not in others, the possibilities for modification depending on what learning is under consideration.

As we have seen (Chapter 4), earlier generations of psychologists, such as William McDougall and his contemporaries, were inclined to explain human behavior largely in terms of innate patterns. According to this view, where learning did occur, it was mainly in the recombination of innate elements of behavior into new patterns. More recent opinions have tended to support a view that comparatively little of human behavior is innate, and indeed learning has been demonstrated to be important in the acquisition of behaviors that even recently were considered to be undoubtedly inborn.

The thesis being developed in this book is that even in humans there are innate factors that give directionality to learning, though learning may not be—indeed, certainly is not

—rigidly controlled by these innate factors. One of the features of the human organism is its capacity to free itself of biological determinants, to counter innate trends, but only at a price, for development is presumably easiest in the direction of flow given by the biological substratum. Whether or not this current should be followed or stemmed is a value judgment that must be examined in another context.

From this preamble, the discussion turns to reviewing the thesis that the early learning of humans has much in common with the kinds of learning observed in animals and that mature human learning is qualitatively different from this early learning.

Phylogenetic Differences in Initial Learning

Lashley (1942) has stated that although simple habits do not seem to be learned at differential rates along the phylogenetic scale, evolution does bring with it a consistent broadening of both the capacity to learn and the acquisition of complex skills. He bases this in part on a study by Pechstein (1921) in which rats and human subjects learned mazes with similar patterns that showed that there were no essential differences between the rats and college students; in fact, in one respect the rats scored better. Lashley also points out that, with simple habits, lower species, feeble-minded men, and normal men all learn at about the same speed. Further, even extensive brain damage may not affect the rates of acquisition of such habits.

Many animals can establish lifelong memories on the basis of one experience, as, for instance, the chimpanzee Bimba did. In the Yerkes Laboratory, she showed a lasting avoidance of a lancet after being pricked once, but she did not avoid other objects of similar size and proportions. Other instances of "one-trial" learning are not uncommon in animals. Hebb (1949) has summarized the phyloge-

netic changes in learning capacity as follows: (1) more complex relationships can be learned by higher species at maturity; (2) simple relationships are learned about as promptly by lower as by higher species; and (3) the first learning is slower in higher than in lower species. It is this third point that is of importance at this stage of the argument. Lashley's remarks referred to mature organisms, but there appears to be a phylogenetic progression in the length of the first stages of slow learning.

Hebb (1937) has shown that training in pattern vision of rats reared in total darkness is slower than that of rats reared normally but that compared with chimpanzees this retardation is relatively slight. The rat reared in darkness is capable of a selective visual discrimination after a total visual experience of less than fifteen minutes. On the average, the dark-reared rats required six times as many trials as normal controls to learn a discrimination of horizontal from vertical stripes and twice as many trials for erect versus inverted triangles, but within an hour or so the behavior of such rats could not be distinguished from that of normally reared animals. This is in sharp contrast to the weeks or months required by primates for this learning after dark rearing.

There is little comparative data on other vertebrates, but as already noted, many forms of invertebrate behavior appear so promptly as to suggest that they are innate. We cannot, of course, be sure that no learning is involved, but if it is, then it would seem that in the insects learning commences at a mature level of efficiency and does not require any prolonged period of development. It could be that the learning involved requires only a few seconds, and that the associations that are formed are only those certain ones to which the nervous system of the particular species is adapted.

Ascending the phylogenic scale, we find an increasing ability to learn complex relationships in the mature animal but also a slower and slower rate of learning in infancy. Apes have a relatively long childhood compared with lower animals, and man has a much more protracted period of immaturity even than that of apes. The rat is adult in about three months, the dog in about six months, the chimpanzee in ten years, and a man in about twenty years.

Even among the vertebrates we do, however, still find instances of behaviors that are "one-trial learned" and are then unmodifiable, being apparently similar to those of invertebrates—the imprinting phenomena in birds, for example. These behaviors have been discussed more fully in connection with critical periods, where it was suggested that some behaviors at mammalian, and even at human, levels may be established by rapid means similar in principle to these one-trial modes. This does not vitiate the general statement that higher organisms are also capable of more flexible but less readily established types of learning, leading to more variable behaviors.

One characteristic, then, of the first learning of primates is that it is extremely slow, and this is one difference it has from learning at maturity. The learning processes of the infant are difficult to study, but Hebb assumes that the visual learning of the adult reared avisually because of congenital cataract is similar to that of the newborn infant. He draws several conclusions from Senden's study (1932) of the early visual experiences of patients who have had cataracts removed. (Some of the queries and reservations that accompany this source of evidence are discussed in Chapter 13.)

There is, of course, an important difference between Senden's subjects and the infant in that the former had physically mature nervous systems, whereas the infant has an immature one. It is uncertain at present to what extent the lack of visual experience had affected the maturation of the relevant parts of the nervous system in these subjects, so we cannot be certain that even though other parts of the nervous system may have been fully mature

those concerned with vision were necessarily so. Whether or not critical period phenomena are involved is also open to question. Further, these people had motor and speech developments at an advanced stage when vision was first given, and this would likely have given them an advantage over the infant. In spite of these possible reservations in the interpretation of this evidence, it does seem reasonable to draw the conclusion from Senden's observations that the first learning is extremely inefficient, and perhaps the fact that it is so in otherwise mature individuals serves to emphasize the role of learning. This inefficiency is not due merely to poor motivation, because these cataract patients had long looked forward with eagerness to receiving sight. Certainly the subjects did tend at some stage of learning to show disturbances of motivation when the expectations of seeing were not immediately realized, but this came at a later stage, for the patients were at first delighted with the new experience, particularly with that of color. The crisis in motivation occurred when the patient became discouraged at the difficulty he had in the effective use of patterns in vision. Many subjects reverted during this stage to their old blind habits, but provided they kept the eyes open, there was evidently learning taking place even during this plateau.

Riesen's experiments (1947) with chimpanzees also demonstrated that motivation is not the decisive factor in the efficiency of early visual learning, because his apes were inept even when strongly motivated by hunger to find food visually. Moreover, they did not learn visually to avoid a distinctive object that gave a strong electric shock, even though normally reared animals will do so in a single trial. After some forty or fifty hours of visual experience, these apes had still not learned to discriminate the white-clad attendant from any other part of the visual environment, even though they were strongly motivated to cling to him whenever they were out of the cage. Such observations suggest that it is not defective motivation that is the cause of the inefficiency of early visual learning but that the ineffectiveness is due to some other fundamental property in the learning process of primates.

Conditioning in Childhood

Another aspect of the changes referred to here is illustrated by those in simple conditioning in infants. The earlier literature on this has been reviewed by Munn (1954) and shows that while conditioning is reported in young infants, it is not easily established. Rendle-Short (1961), using the eyeblink as the conditioned reflex and an air puff as UCS, found that infants under six months of age could not be conditioned but that after that age there was a linear progression with age in the ease with which conditioning was established, until at four years the response was established as easily as in adults (i.e., in two puffs, on the average). It seems, however, that the ease or lack of ease of infant conditioning may depend on the reflex involved. Brackbill et al. (1967) established temporal conditioning of the pupillary responses in infants of twenty-six to eighty-six days of age with greater ease than in adults. (This involved flashing a light into the eyes at twenty-second intervals until the pupillary contraction occurred without the stimulus and, conversely, conditioning dilation by a period of darkness every twenty seconds.) Conditioning of pupillary reflexes to sound was not achieved in these same infants.

Part of the difficulty in conditioning neonates may be due to the use of responses unsuitable to subjects of this age. Siqueland (1968) has demonstrated both conditioning and extinction in new-born infants using the head-turning response, which is a well-established part of the behavioral repertoire at this age (see Chapter 4).

Other recent studies have also chosen their responses carefully. Sheppard (1969) reports the establishement of an operant discrimina-

tive response in an infant in the first three months of life. He chose another two responses within the baby's repertoire, the leg kick and vocalization. The leg kick activated a switch which recorded the response, and was reinforced by a flashing light together with a record of the mother's voice. Vocalization was reinforced by a vibrator taped to the hand: vocalization was monitored by a voice-switch. A red light was the discriminative stimulus, on or off (on for kicking, off for vocalization). Training started at ten days, and was continued until these operant behaviors were clearly established. At first the two behaviors were trained separately, but in the latter part of the experiment they were elicited consecutively within training sessions. Within three months these discriminative operant behaviors were clearly established.

Operant discrimination techniques have been used to establish stimulus control in young children in a number of studies, one of which is by Weisberg (1969). He used eight babies of 15 to 25 months. Four children were trained to press a lever for a reward (a small piece of cookie) in response to a steady light, but were unreinforced to a flashing light. For another four children the procedure was reversed. Although all the infants acquired this operant learning, there were rather marked individual differences in the learning curves and in the patterns of responding.

It is also noteworthy that, despite a late start, susceptibility to conditioning in general reaches a peak at about six years of age, then declines again (Razran, 1933). Thus the lesser conditionability of adults noted above is consistent with other findings.

"Visceral" Learning

In Chapter 6, brief mention was made of the suggestion by N. E. Miller (1969) that the ANS plays a role in behavior which should be considered more nearly allied to that of the CNS that psychologists have traditionally believed. He has discussed experiments which he maintains show that visceral learning and glandular learning are both possible and significant. Moreover, this learning is not merely of the classical conditioning kind: It is more than salivation in response to conditioned stimuli. The ANS, Miller insists, is capable of instrumental learning also. This is in contradiction to orthodoxy, as expressed, for example, by Kimble (1961), who categorically denies the possibility of modification of autonomic responses by instrumental training methods.

The principles of Yoga may take on a new interest to psychologists in the light of some of the data reported by Miller. For instance, one experiment involved the learned control of the blood supply to specific organs. DiCara and Miller (1968a) rewarded, by electrical stimulation of the "pleasure centers" of the brain, changes in the blood supply to the tails of rats, and these animals *learned* vasodilation and vasoconstriction in the tail to secure reward. In another experiment (DiCara and Miller, 1968b) they produced learned control of the blood supply to one ear. Carmona (quoted by N. E. Miller, 1969) produced by instrumental learning both increases and decreases in stomach contraction. Other experiments have produced learned changes in heart rate, and DiCara and Weiss (1969) have produced changes in emotionality in rats by this technique. In an avoidance learning situation rats that had previously learned a decrease in heart-rate learned better than those that had learned an increase, presumably because the latter were more emotional and hence learned less well. Even the EEG is susceptible to learned modification (N. E. Miller, 1966).

A number of interesting speculations based on this work suggest themselves. On the theoretical side, it would seem that we might have to revise our ideas on the neurology of learning, and cease to regard it as an exclusively CNS phenomenon. On the practical side, there are exciting possibilities for extending the method of psychotherapy known as

Behavior Modification to new areas. For instance, Engel and Melmon (quoted by N. E. Miller, 1969) have attempted to apply the technique to the treatment of organic cardiac arrhythmia, and Miller also reports with epileptic patients some initial successes in suppressing paroxysmal spikes in the EEG.

For developmental psychology, the experiments provide a new dimension of explanation of how children may learn differing reactions to stress. Thus Miller gives a hypothetical example of a child who on a specific occasion fears going to school and feigns sickness. His mother expresses concern over what she conceives as cardiovascular symptoms, and the child learns cardiac responses: another child might learn gastric responses in the same way. Elsewhere in this book it is suggested that individual differences in temperament (which is related to autonomic function in part) are largely inherited, but this is not to deny that some phenotypically similar characteristics may be learned. Even here, of course, some individual may be genetically prone to the learning of one particular response rather than another.

It is too early to pursue in detail the speculations and practical implications of findings of these kinds, but here is an opening field of inquiry that might produce interesting results.

LEARNING OF TWO KINDS

The evidence is not extensive, but the matters reviewed above seem to suggest that, whereas an adult level of learning is quickly established in the rat, it requires an increasingly longer time, even when viewed relative to the life span, in higher animals and longest of all in humans.

It is also important to emphasize that in the development of learning, phylogenetically, we may find the emergence of new kinds of learning. Even if adult rats and humans learn mazes at similar rates and (it is implied) in similar manners, it can be asked whether humans are also capable of kinds of learning that rats are not. That is, differences may not, in the degree of complexity that can be attained, be merely quantitative, but qualitative also.

Hebb on Two Learnings

Hebb believes that of the two main schools of thought concerning the nature of learning, both are correct, one being typical of learning in infancy and the other of mature learning. Essential to this formulation is the idea that learning in children does not merely change in degree, but in kind. One may see here a parallel to the ideas put forward by Bitterman (1965), that phylogenetically one finds *qualitative* differences in intelligence (as manifest in learning) between lower and higher species. This may seem to revive the old idea of Stanley Hall of ontogeny repeating phylogeny, though one would not wish to press this point too far. Nonetheless, there is some merit to the notion that the learning of humans in its early stage is akin to that of lower species, with the more complex styles found in higher species appearing later. The kind of investigations carried out by Bitterman and his associates has not been applied to the growth of learning in humans, but his experiments do suggest a line of inquiry.

To make this suggestion is not to insist that young children learn just like mature specimens of lower orders, because some marked differences (e.g., in speed of learning) will be described. Rather, it is suggested that the limits of learning at various human stages *may* show parallels with phylogenetic stages. The point of this differentiation is that in applying knowledge of learning derived from animal experiments one must consider not only what species the results are derived from but also the stage of human development to which they are being applied. The greater part of our information on learning has been derived from one rather lowly mammalian species and Bitterman's plea for a comparative

study of learning should be heard with sympathy by the developmental psychologist.

Hebb (1949) has pointed out that the nature of the learning process changes markedly during the course of development. Early learning is in his terms "non-set-influenced"; such learning is a kind that once established is not affected by set and does not apparently require reinforcement. The eye blink of the mature animal is an example of such behavior, and Hebb claims that this probably comes the closest to an S-R learning that the mammal ever approaches.

The second type of learning is "set-influenced" and is typical of learning during later childhood and also in maturity. The behaviors so acquired are subject to extinction, and even when overlearned, they remain a function of set and drive. We can explain the non-set-influenced behaviors in terms of sensory-motor connections, whereas the set-influenced behaviors cannot possibly be explained in any such terms but involve the organization of the cortex, which controls the behavior. Another way of distinguishing non-set-influenced from set-influenced learning is to contrast those theories that have stressed steady increments in acquisition, such as those of the behaviorists with gestalt or configurationist theories that emphasize insight.

The behavioristic theories state that learning is graded in the sense of being steadily built up by small increments and usually independent of any special factor such as insight. This slow-increment type of learning in which there is no evidence of insight is typical of infancy. Hebb maintains it is also found in other special instances, for example, in the visual learning of the mature animal that has been reared in darkness.

The configurationists, on the other hand, have stressed a type of learning in which insight is important; this kind of learning typically occurs suddenly, though there may be discrete steps preceding the flash of insight. This type of learning, Hebb claims, is found only in the more mature animal. The first type of learning may also occur in the mature animal but only in situations in which there is nothing familiar, so that no past experience can be drawn upon. In fact, such situations are probably uncommon, so that the animal is rarely presented with an entirely novel situation, with no transfer effects and no insight, except in some laboratory situations.

If insight depends on early experiences, the question arises as to how these early experiences originate. From the material that will be reviewed in Chapter 13, it is obvious that certain kinds of perceptual organization are innate. We may deduce from Riesen's experiment and from Senden's observations that the earliest experiences serve to elaborate these elements of perception. From these, more complex perceptions are made up, and the organization of these elements form the basis for all later responses to the environment. At a somewhat later stage there is the establishment of simple association and conceptual sequences. It is during this period that meaning first begins to appear. The two stages lead to the types of learning characteristic of the mature animal. According to Hebb, even with the rat this later learning is essentially conceptual.

However, taking up a matter discussed in Chapter 4, it might be suggested that there is a broad range of non-set-influenced learning that involves the linking up of taxes and FAP's. One might go even further and suggest that most if not all learning in the early stages of life is of this kind. Because as yet we have only fragmentary knowledge of these FAP's in humans, it is not yet possible to make many concrete statements about them. It seems fairly clear that not all are manifest at birth, and it may well be that for some time after birth a relatively small number of them have appeared in the human infant. Hence the range available for combination and recombination is restricted.

In this view early learning consists (as it were) in the linking together of ready-made components of behavior, whereas later learning may consist in the *making* of components and the linking of them (it does not follow of

necessity that *all* later learning is of this kind; some may consist of more complex patterning of constellations of ready-made parts).

According to this idea, there is a third category of origin of behavior. There are three classes of behavioral phenomena: those that emerge unlearned, those that are entirely learned, and those that are part-learned. The last refers to the class of (hypothetical) behaviors for which there are presets. That is, for these behaviors the "wiring" of the organism disposes it to attend to certain stimuli under certain conditions (e.g., of hunger or of hormonal influence) and to make certain responses to these stimuli. Learning is necessary to connect stimulus and response, but because the "pathways" are already laid down in the nervous system, this learning is relatively rapid and also resistant to extinction.

It might be questioned, in the sense that one could argue that no behavior is entirely learned, whether part-learned and fully learned behaviors are really distinct. That is, in any acquired action there will be involved some elements that are unlearned. Thus in learning to respond to a particular stimulus by a particular behavior, such as lever pressing, an organism uses actions already in its response repertoire; these actions may be unlearned, as some almost certainly are. The stimuli to which the organism is responsive are those perceptible to its receptor systems. It becomes, therefore, a matter for philosophical debate whether "partly learned" and "learned" can really be separated in the final analysis. Nonetheless, it may be convenient to use such a distinction even if it is not logically defensible, just as we find it convenient to talk of "learned" and "unlearned" over the protests of logicians.

NEUROLOGICAL CHANGES AND LEARNING

The development of the nervous system must obviously have a critical influence on changes in learning. In an earlier chapter we discussed Penfield's suggestion that the "interpretative cortex" of the temporal lobe is the part of the brain concerned in the storage of past experience. It would appear that it is here that previous learning is stored, or at least is made a recording of the stream of consciousness. It is here, it would seem, that the "sets" important to set-influenced learning may be stored. We have seen that this is a late-maturing part of the cortex. We are not certain as to precisely what functions are present in this temporal area of the brain at birth, but we may presume from the fact that at this time it is yet incompletely developed that it is incomplete in function also. It may be that the infant is yet incapable of starting to make a record of his stream of consciousness; further, in a sense we may speak of the newly born child of being unconscious even when awake and hence having no stream of consciousness to record anyway. Even if we are not correct in assuming that this part of the cortex is nonfunctional at this stage, it is almost certainly the case that it is inefficient and records events only poorly. The transfer effects so important to later learning cannot be influential until they can be recorded, and the neural development of this part of the cortex is one of the factors concerned in the development of mature types of learning; its immaturity at birth is one of the causes of the slowness and inefficiency of early learning. In addition, the association areas for each sensory mode are immature and presumably ill-functioning.

The EEG characteristics of the infant, as Hebb (1949) has remarked, give further indication of the neurological factors influencing learning. The slow and relatively large waves typical of the early months suggest that very large masses of cells are in synchronous excitation; that is, large populations of cells are firing rhythmically. More complex cerebral activities demand, we may presume, not the synchronous firing of large masses of nerve cells but more differentiated and localized firings of smaller units. This condition is probably represented by the fast low-voltage waves of the active brain in adulthood.

This massive synchrony of the infant cortex presumably means that whole areas, or even the whole cortex itself, are periodically in a refractory phase, so that no incoming impulses can excite them. Thus visual impulses coming into area 18 may do so at a time when the whole of area 17, the visual association area, is refractory, and the association impulses from 18 to 17 are blocked. Statistically, therefore, a large proportion of the incoming impulses may be abortive, and this may be another of the reasons learning at this stage is so slow. The more mature brain with greater differentiation of function does not fire in such massive synchrony, and whole areas are not made refractory at one time.

Hebb speaks of the "intrinsic organization" of cortical activity that appears at birth and is represented by the large slow waves of the infant EEG. It is also found with older individuals in sleep or coma. The behavior correlated with this condition of intrinsic organization is vegetative, with an absence of voluntary and purposeful behavior and a high threshold for sensory stimulation. This intrinsic organization is, as it were, the basic state of the living brain. A considerable amount of activity of an autonomic, vegetative nature is carried out by the brain when it is in this condition. The mature brain in this state has the possibility of arousal into other states of activity, but the infant's brain at first lacks this capacity. This infantile state of the cortex represents the extreme from the active brain in the awake adult. It also represents the extreme in the possibilities for learning, and in this condition learning is elementary, very slow, and highly inefficient.

In his formulation Hebb (1949) is concerned with perceptual learning. No doubt much of early learning is concerned with perception, but presumably similar processes enter learning in other dimensions. When a stimulus is received by a sense organ, corresponding impulses are transmitted inward to the primary sensory area concerned (e.g., if the eye receives stimulation by light, the impulses are conducted to the visual area of the occipital lobe). These primary sensory areas are developed at birth, and in the main (this is somewhat an oversimplification) one might say that they receive raw sensations, which have to be evaluated and compared with past experience before being refined into perceptions.

This process of refinement is the function of the association area, which at birth is undeveloped, or at least is relatively less developed than the primary area. For learning to take place, these association areas must be functional; because of their undeveloped state, they may not be so at birth and are probably only partially functional for some time afterward. For this reason such learning may not then be possible, but may be increasingly possible with the further development of the cortex.

Hebb explains the first learning (probably occurring sometime after birth) in the following terms: When a stimulus is received, a corresponding afferent activity impinges on the association areas of the brain. The repetition of this stimulus has a cumulative effect and builds up an "assembly" of cells that constitute the first learning. In other words, these cells begin to store up a record of previous sensations, which can later be organized into perceptions. This first learning in human infants is very slow and very inefficient, and only small gains are made over long periods of time.

This idea perhaps explains the difference between lower and higher species. The process of perceptual learning can be conceived of as establishing a control of association area activity by sensory events; that is, a store of memories of previous sensations is built up, with the possibility of comparison of the sensation of a given instant with those that have previously impinged on the organism and of the recognition of similarities and discrimination of differences. We may presume that the larger the association areas relative to the size

of the sensory projection areas, the slower is the establishment of this control, and also the less rigid and more complex is the final form of possible control. The lower down the phylogenetic scale, the less important are the association areas, and the lower organisms are anatomically provided with them in very meager proportions. It does not take long to fill out the cell assemblies of these simple association areas, which are very small relative to the sensory projection areas. For this reason perceptual learning in the lower animals is quick but also is lacking in plasticity and complexity.

Hebb suggests that with a cortex of a given size, the length of the primary learning period is roughly proportional to the ratio between the total association cortex and the total sensory cortex. In lower animals the sensory cortex is considerably larger than the association cortex, and perceptual learning is swift. As we ascend the phylogenetic scale, the association cortex for each modality becomes larger and larger relative to the sensory cortex, and at the human level the association cortex is large and the sensory projection area for each sensation is relatively small, so the period of "primary learning" is very long.

A larger brain also implies a larger number of transmission units in the association areas, and this permits much greater variability in the activity of these areas and a very much greater number of synaptic connections. This enormously increases the possibilities of flexible and complex activity but also further increases the length of the period of learning.

During this process of learning, connections are being established, as it were, inward between the association areas and the environment (we are not yet concerned with sensory-motor connections). With the neonate the environment "gets into" the brain only as far as the sensory projection areas. As the retina, for example, is stimulated, certain changes take place in the neurons of the visual projection area in the occipital lobe. These changes are, however, merely neural changes, and they have no meaning or interpretive significance to the infant. Only as corresponding events in the association areas are gradually built up, and there is a background of experience stored there, do these crude sensations become meaningful, that is, become perceptions. Speaking somewhat metaphorically, we may say that the environment "gets into" the organism further than the sensory projection areas, getting into the association areas as well in the course of development.

Implied in the assumption that perceptual learning involves the laying down of cell assemblies in the association areas that are correlated with the stimuli coming into the sensory areas is the idea that the stimulus activates the same cell assembly each time it is repeated. This raises a problem owing to the fact of spontaneous central activity. Nerve cells left unstimulated will eventually fire spontaneously, and this spontaneous firing could interfere with the incoming impulses. Such spontaneous firing cannot happen in the cell that is being constantly stimulated; so as long as the receptor surfaces are being stimulated, the sensory projection areas of the cortex must remain under environmental control. Spontaneous activity cannot occur.

This means that the fibers that lead from the sensory areas to the association areas are also under this environmental control. Hebb's idea is that this control is extended gradually, synapse by synapse. If the association areas are made up of a population of transmission units, there are two factors that affect the length of time needed to bring all these units under control: the number of controlling fibers leading from the sensory areas into the association areas, and the number of transmission units in the association areas themselves.

The idea that maturational factors, such as those reviewed in this section, play a role in development has been questioned by Gagné (1968), who suggests that intellectual development can be explained adequately in terms of an accretion of learnings, building up more and more complex patterns of intellectual competence. To me such a notion seems quite inconsistent with the biological evidence, which makes it impossible to dispense with maturation as a developmental concept.

RELATION OF EARLY TO LATER LEARNING

Hebb, in addition to proposing that the characteristics of learning undergo changes as the animal grows, particularly in the higher mammals, also accepts Mowrer's proposal (1941) that all learning tends to influence and build on any earlier learning, instead of replacing it. As Tinbergen (1942) has shown, this tendency gives a permanence to much of the early learning. Further, while the learning of the mature animal is relatively efficient, it is dependent on the slow and less efficient learning that has preceded it and may be limited by this learning.

The fact that learning is often influenced by earlier learning is a well-known experimental fact, as numerous studies of transfer of training have shown, and learning in one situation may be facilitated, retarded, or otherwise changed by preceding learning. Most of these experiments have concerned themselves with the effect of one specific piece of learning on some other and (it is pertinent to remark here) have usually been performed with mature organisms.

McGeoch (1942) has also stated that all learning, after a certain point in early life, is influenced by transfer. We are dependent on it in acquiring complex or abstract notions, as well as in demonstrating insight or creativity in problem solving. All levels of perception, indeed every complex psychological event, he believes, are inevitably functions of transfer.

If the learning of the mature animal is so markedly influenced by transfer effects, then the properties of the original learning from which these effects came is obviously of considerable importance. It is also implied that a theory of learning cannot be constructed on data derived from mature animals only but must also consider the developmental aspects of learning. As already pointed out, most of the experiments on the transfer of training have been performed with mature subjects, and very little is known about this transfer from immaturity to maturity.

Hebb quotes one of his students as pointing out that James' experiment of memorization begged the question, because it was performed on mature subjects. James wanted to see if practice in memorization would increase the ability to memorize, but because he performed his experiments on adults who had already had long practice in memorization, it may be presumed that any transfer of effects must have been complete before the experiment began and therefore could not be demonstrated by this method. The conclusion that practice has little or no transfer value in memorization may be valid with mature subjects, and particularly with highly educated subjects such as James used, but it is not necessarily a valid assumption with less mature subjects.

Perception and learning have important interrelationships, and perception is influenced by past experience. Koffka (1935) has proposed that patterns may be seen and remembered by the arousal of what he calls "older trace system." Woodworth (1938) has described all perceiving as "schema with correction," by which he means that all perceiving is in terms of earlier perceptual habits. These views raise the question as to the origins of these older trace systems or of the original "schema" that is corrected. What is the nature of the earliest learning, when there are no earlier learned habits upon which it can be based?

As we have seen, Hebb speaks only of two stages of learning, the primary learning and learning in maturity. Primary learning is, he says, non-set-influenced, whereas that of maturity may be set-influenced (though it is by no means invariably so; the infant is incapable of the latter type of learning, whereas the adult can use both). This raises the question, however, of the manner in which the transition is achieved from the primary type to the secondary type. There seems to be a logical difficulty in that it is claimed that *all* learning of this second type depends on transfer from previous learning, but at first the organism has no previous learning. The obvious explanation is that primary learning provides the sets on which the newly emerging type of learning can rest, but the obvious is not necessarily the true explanation. The eye blink is given as an instance of non-set-influenced learning, and if this is a typical example, it is a rather unconvincing basis for the complexity of the sets underlying more advanced learning. Sets themselves presumably involve learning, but again, how does such learning get started unless it is assumed that the first sets at least can be acquired by non-set-influenced processes?

There seems to be no evidence one can call in to adjudicate the matter, but a possible explanation that can be put forward is that the organism has a ready-made repertoire of sets, the innate releaser mechanisms (IRM's) of the ethologists. Imprinting is another instance of such preprimed learning. These mechanisms will be discussed in greater detail in a later section, so it is sufficient here to mention that they may provide an explanation of the emergence of set-influenced learning. If this is accepted, then one need not regard the second type of learning as emergent from the first; they could be independent forms.

Harlow (1949) might make an alternative suggestion, that the transformation from trial-and-error adapting to the environment to adaptation by insight is achieved by learning how to learn—by the formation of learning sets. This concept, that organisms can learn to learn, is an important one, and a useful illustration of a developmental fact, but it falls short as an explanation because it still leaves unanswered the question of how they learn-how-to-learn how-to-learn or whether they have to do this.

CONCEPTUAL DEVELOPMENT AS THE BASIS OF LEARNING

The importance of concepts in learning is illustrated by Hebb (1949) by the development of language. There have been some attempts to explain language as a collection of conditioned reflexes in which specific stimulations directly control specific motor responses. The fact that this cannot be the case is suggested by such features in the development of language in small children as the confusion of opposites. Between about two and four years of age many children have difficulty with opposites such as up-down, back-front, or left-right. The interesting thing is that "up" is confused only with its opposite and never with "back" or "right." The conditioned reflex view of language would suggest that if there is confusion, there is no reason it should be confined in this manner. The fact that this rarely happens, whereas confusion between opposites is common, suggests that conceptual processes are also involved. A word first acquires an association with a definite and limited set of conceptual coordinates, and unconnected concepts are not confused because they do not lie on these coordinates. Further, during this time the word has a clear-cut association with its conceptual coordinate (the word *up*, for instance, with the vertical dimension) but has no association with any particular motor act such as raising the hands or looking at the ceiling.

Hebb illustrates the development of adult learning with the instance of the discrimination of right and left. The three-year-old can quite readily learn that left and right refer to sides of the body but has great difficulty in learning which is which. He thus places them on a conceptual coordinate ("sidedness") but is still unclear as to their position on this coordinate. The words *left* and *right* readily arouse this concept of sidedness to the child but do not arouse any specific motor response. According to the association theory of language, we might expect the stimulus word *right* to be readily associated with a definite motor act, such as turning to the right. The difficulty that all children (and many adults too) have in turning correctly at a word of command belies this theory. Definite responses to the conceptual organization set up in childhood are late in development. It is interesting to note that left and right is a much more difficult discrimination to make than up and down, and this in turn is harder than black and white. (It might be objected that Hebb underestimates the roles of motor acts in the learning of such opposites as left and right. Even adults often show incipient motor acts in deciding which is left or right, and children frequently show overt motor actions. However, this does not destroy the argument that conceptual coordinates are built up, even if motor acts are important in the acquisition and as references in placement on that coordinate.)

Hebb then, and others since, suggest that the learning capacity changes with growth as a result of conceptual development, including with this term both the percept and the concept, which are intimately related. There is not merely an elaboration in the number of specific motor responses.

As an illustration of the way in which early experiences, by giving a conceptual frame, can facilitate the formation of new habits involving a new but similar stimulus and a new but similar response, Hebb cites learning to recognize chimpanzee faces. Those exposed to primates report difficulties in distinguishing chimpanzees by their faces. Presumably chimps have similar difficulties with men. However, seeing a number of individuals sets up a conceptual frame of reference in which individual deviations become quite noticeable and recognition of differences more easy. Thus, having learned to recognize four apes, learning to recognize a fifth becomes much quicker. Facilitation in learning of this kind appears to be a general phenomenon, particularly in intelligent learning, as distinct from rote learning, with meaningful material. (The role of verbal mediation in learning will be discussed in another section.)

Perception involves much learning, and, as with other forms of learning, the transfer of training can be generalized readily enough to similar situations but becomes less and less effective as situations become less similar. Thus the facilitation of learning is determined by the extent of early experiences and has limited generalization to performances not covered by these experiences. It has been shown that West African natives score poorly on form boards used as an intelligence test because they have had no early experience of this kind of material (Nissen et al., 1935). Analysis of their difficulty showed that the low scores were not caused by slowness of movement but by slowness in identifying geometrical shapes, an experience that their early perceptual learning had not included; almost all their early learning was limited to nongeometrical objects. We apparently learn to "see" not generally but rather specifically.

The fact is emphasized when the Western-born man attempts to see things in the bush that are quite readily apparent to the West African natives. Fitting shapes in a form board or following signs on a trail are apparently more a function of early learning than of the inherited properties of the brain or nervous system.

In many instances the experiences acquired early may have permanent effects on attitudes, interests, and abilities. This has been demonstrated in animals, as in Hunt's experiments (1941) in which he showed that rats kept hungry when young hoarded more as adults even though plentifully fed.

In the Hebbian view that the learning of young children and that of adults are of qualitatively different kinds, there is the necessity for some transition from one kind to the other. Kendler and Kendler (1962a) propose an S-R explanation of learning in which there is a single-unit S-R to account for the behavior of rats, while a mediational S-R theory (of the S-r-s-R type) is required for the concept learn-

ing of articulate humans. There is then, in their view, discontinuity between the behavior of rats and college students, and as they point out, somewhere on a hypothetical evolutionary dimension between the rat and the college student there should be a point where the transition is made from a single unit to mediational control. It is obvious that however one views the learning of young children and of adults, whether in Spencian terms like the Kendlers or otherwise, if he conceives that they are different, then this transition period must exist.

Verbal mediation plays a crucial role in the Kendlers' account, but it may be questioned whether verbalization is the only factor involved, because other studies fail to show a verbalization effect and some even show a *negative* one (J. L. Wolff, 1967). However, for children at least it seems that verbal mechanisms are an important factor, if not a sole mechanism, in certain kinds of learning (Kendler and Kendler, 1966).

In the Kendlers' term, a single-unit S-R is an assumption of a direct association between a physical stimulus and an overt response. This idea predicts that an organism that has to learn a response opposite to one that it has previously learned (that is, a reversal shift) will learn more slowly than when it has to learn some irrelevant new response. These authors make this formulation specific to inarticulate organisms, but it might be objected that inarticulate organisms may be able to mediate.

The *reversal shift* forms an important element in the Kendlers' experimental approach to testing their hypotheses. The experimental paradigm is to provide a stimulus that varies in two dimensions, for example, black/white, large/small. One of these stimulus properties is irrelevant and is reinforced randomly (that is, 50 percent of the time in total, but irregularly). A *shift* in these experiments means moving to a different response to the same or similar stimuli. A reversal shift requires the subject to respond to the same stimulus but in an opposite manner; if he was previously rewarded for responding to white rather than to black, large or small being irrelevant, he now has to respond to black. A nonreversal shift would involve new learning; he would now be required with the same material to respond to size and ignore brightness. In the Kendlers' experiment for the nonreversal shift, responses to large and small had been reinforced randomly, that is, each 50 percent of the time. In the case of a reversal shift, responses to the stimulus to be attended to had been unrewarded.

Kendler and Kendler go on to say that human beings learn to make verbal or symbolic responses to physical stimuli and in so doing produce mediating stimuli that stand between the external stimulus and the overt response and make learning different from the simpler, single-unit S-R type. Kendler and D'Amato (1955) proposed a mediational theory of S-r-s-R type: The subjects' behavior consists of two successive S-R associations; the first is between the stimulus items and the symbolic implicit responses made to them (implicit verbal or symbolic responses), while the second is between the implicit response-produced cues and the overt response (in this experiment card sorting).

It was predicted that in college students the learning of a response that reversed a first-learned concept in the *same* stimulus dimension would occur more readily than the learning of an unrelated task with similar material (that is, learning shifting from one concept to another using a *different* stimulus dimension, or a nonreversal shift). This would be true because at the completion of the learning of the first task the symbolic or mediational cues appropriate to the second one were already available to the subjects who had learned the nonreversal shift. They are, it is true, attached to what are now the wrong sorting response, but the mediational cues that have been acquired more than offset this disadvantage. That is, the verbal mediating response does more than provide mediating stimuli; it organizes the possible cue values into dimensions each with other characteristics (e.g., large/small-black/white) and thus it should make learning easier. In the experiment of Kendler and D'Amato this prediction was confirmed.

Kendler and Kendler (1959) carried out a similar experiment with kindergarten children, aged four years, ten months to six years, six months. Taking the groups overall there was no difference between the reversal and nonreversal shifts. But when the group was divided into fast and slow learners on the basis of their performance in the initial training series, interesting differences were shown. The fast initial learners responded in a way consistent with the mediational S-R theory; that is, reversal was faster than nonreversal. On the other hand, the slow initial learners responded in a manner consistent with the single-unit S-R theory, reversal being slower than nonreversal. These authors interpret the results as showing that the group of children as a whole were in a process of developing mediating responses, the faster-learning children being those who have progressed the farthest in this development. If the children were divided roughly half-and-half between those still in single-unit S-R stages and those in the mediational S-R stage, then the halves would tend to cancel out and no significant differences between the groups would be found. This experiment suggests that the supposed transition phase is in the fourth, fifth, and sixth years (possibly with considerable individual differences as to its timing). Kendler et al. (1960) found that between three and four years less than 50 percent of the children mediated. Obviously, replication experiments with both younger and older children, as well as with children of this age, are required. The experiment as it stands does not demonstrate that the faster learners were ones that had shifted from some more primitive stage of learning to a more advanced one. These may have been children who all along were learning faster. No mention is made of the intelligence of these children, and the authors seem to have assumed that they were all of equal intelligence. As has been mentioned elsewhere, differences of intelligence may not be particularly relevant to the very simplest of tasks, whereas it may be relevant to tasks of a mediational nature. It would not, of course, necessarily invalidate the Kendlers' arguments if the faster learners were the more intelligent children; it might merely mean that they were maturationally ahead and were entering the stage of mediational learning sooner. However, this is a matter that would seem to require further investigation by longitudinal studies. A considerable amount of research in this area has been performed since this early Kendler work, and much is reviewed by S. H. White (1965). Greater difficulty for three-year-old children in reversal shift as compared with non-reversal is reported by Saravo and Kolodny (1969). They relate this to an early tendency to cue perseveration. These authors also point to an interesting interaction effect in which change in procedure—for instance, from reversal to non-reversal or from one dimension to another—acted as a "disinhibitor" and improved performance. This is similar to the effect of a novel stimulus.

Zeiler (1964), also using an S-R frame of reference, has substantiated the hypothesis that learning processes differ with developmental level. After training three-, five-, and seven-year-old children on a two-situational discrimination task, in which components were presented in only one of the two possible spatial arrangements, half of the subjects at each age level were then tested on a component problem with the same stimulus elements correct in both training and test, while the other half, the configuration groups, had to respond to the same spatial positions as they did during training. The youngest children were found to have learned on a configurational basis, and the importance of component learning increased with age. It is suggested that there are at least two processes accounting for the differences between three- and seven-year-old children's learning and that

these do not necessarily develop simultaneously.

Other phenomena, such as interference, also show age changes and may be explicable in similar manners. Koppenaal et al. (1964) found that in preschool children who were naive to laboratory learning there was very little interference effect between the learning of two lists of paired pictures; this is, of course, in contrast to well-established findings with older subjects. Cutout pictures were presented in pairs, a pair at a time, in lists of four pairs; the lists were in an a-b, a-c relationship. While it is difficult to know just how to interpret these results, the authors point out that if interference operates at the level of mediation, then the age differences in mediation noted in other studies could also be responsible for the age effect on interference.

It is evident from these developmental studies of conceptual mediating processes in learning that the child's ability to form concepts does undergo change with age. Thus Hebb's contentions are being confirmed; higher-order forms of learning (in his terms, set-influenced; for others, mediated learning; and so on) do appear over childhood.

VERBAL INFLUENCES ON LEARNING

Hebb's suggestions point to the importance of the use of language in learning. In view of the amount of work on verbal learning with adults (mostly, of course, college students), the output on this topic in children is not very extensive, judging from a survey by Keppel (1964). As he says, more replication of studies done on adults using child subjects will not be particularly rewarding. There is, however, the Piaget-Vygotsky work on language and thought and also that of Bruner. These authors are reviewed in Chapter 15.

To be of value to the learning theorist, studies must be tied to theory, and this may account for the somewhat slight interest so far, because few learning theories permit developmental predictions—or, at least, not many such predictions have been made. Similarly, the developmentalist does not find much to help him in the formulations of the main theories of learning and has not therefore drawn much inspiration from them or from the experiments they have generated.

Russian psychology acknowledges the part played by language as a mediator in learning:

[A] complete examination of the role of language, as a stimulus in the analytic-synthetic activity of the brain, is the pre-requisite for significant advances in the theory of higher nervous activity, and in a study of the mechanism of psychic activity [Luria, 1957, p. 115].

As the author so rightly points out, language is itself learned and is a form of learning that has profound influences on other learning. (Pavlov, of course, regarded the acquisition of language as a process of conditioning, but whether this is true is another matter.)

Reference has already been made to the use of mediating processes in children's learning. Language is important to these mediating processes. It is not apparently essential, however, because rats can acquire reversal shifts, though less easily than they do nonreversal shifts (Kelleher, 1956). Kendler et al. (1962) have studied, in a concept-formation task, the changes with age in the verbal mediating responses of children. In this study they found that there was an increase in the frequency of reversal shift with age. Moreover, there was a correlation between the verbalizing of a dimension and responses involving a reversal shift. This suggests verbal mediation, but the mere possession of the appropriate words in the vocabulary was not apparently sufficient to ensure verbal mediation. The dimensions involved in this experiment were quite elementary—black and white and large and small, and even the youngest children were quite familiar with them. Although the youngest children knew of black and white as discrete properties, they behaved as if they were not placing them on a black/white dimension.

As further experiments showed, even though the young children were not making spontaneous use of verbal mediation, they could be trained to use verbal labels successfully. Gollin and Liss (1962) also produced evidence that preschool children who could verbalize a principle still tended not to make use of this ability in a learning situation.

Reese (1962) has made a review of studies of verbal mediation as a function of age. He concludes that within a number of experimental paradigms there is revealed a deficiency in mediation processes in young children when they are compared with older ones. Though many studies do show evidence of change in role of verbal mediation, there is no great consistency in the actual period at which this takes place. Experiments involving different concepts produce different ages of change. One factor that does appear to be relevant is that inadequately learned stimulus names used for rehearsal in learning situations can produce interference (Spiker, 1961). Reese (1960) also obtained evidence consistent with this position. Apparently language has to be quite fluent before it becomes useful as a mediator. This is quite consistent with everyday experience. An imperfectly acquired foreign language or a half-learned technical argot is a poor vehicle for thinking about a problem.

LEARNING TO LEARN

Montessori (1912) long ago claimed that young children have to learn how to learn, and her educational system consisted of exercises to foster this process. This idea apparently lay dormant as a psychological concept. James' experiment on memorization in adults has already been mentioned; it seemed to show that practice in memorization produced no improvement, but, as has been pointed out, it may merely show that there is a ceiling to improvement by practice and that these subjects had reached it. Gates and

Taylor (1925) did find that with children, aged four to five and two-thirds years, training in digit-span memorization over three months produced an effect, and Drees (1941), also using three months of practice, showed a training effect in associating objects with two-digit numbers. Spiker (1960a) showed that training of fifth- and sixth-grade children in mnemonic devices for the learning of a list of words produced improvement in the learning of another list. Such studies suggest that in children simple associative learning can be improved with training, at least up to the age of eleven or so (evidence on where the ceiling is reached is lacking).

More recently Montessori's concepts in relation to more complex forms of learning have been revived and given experimental support. Harlow (1949) has shown that both mature rhesus monkeys and young children between two and five years of age can *learn* insight. They can learn-how-to-learn a kind of problem (in other words, to acquire learning sets), and they can transfer this learning from problem to problem. Thus they can improve their efficiency of learning new solutions to fresh problems. Kendler and Kendler (1962a) suggest that the learning-how-to-learn phenomenon probably involves the organism's learning to mediate.

Unfortunately, Harlow's conclusions are based upon a small number of children, seventeen in all, and these were of above average IQ (109 to 151, mean not stated). It is not possible to tell from the data given how the younger children compared with the older. It is not doubted that this is a genuine phenomenon, but much more experimentation is called for in what is a most important developmental concept.

EPILOGUE

The material reviewed in this chapter does show that further experiments support the idea, put forward by Hebb, that there is a change in the form that learning takes as the organism develops. The evidence is not yet extensive enough for one to map out the course of this development from the early infantile form to that of maturity in any detail. We cannot at this stage say whether all forms of learning follow a similar pattern of growth. Nor can we say what processes underlie the change from early to later forms. Maturation no doubt plays an important part in this; the changes in the nervous system can hardly fail to influence learning.

In his conceptual model of the CNS as hierarchically organized, G. Bronson (1965) suggests that the different levels (and areas within them) have differing inputs to which they are responsive. The input results in structural changes (Bronson does not attempt to say just what these changes are, and we should not expect him to do so). Moreover, he assumes that the integrative functions of these levels and areas themselves also produce structural changes that affect subsequent activation patterns.

Thus there is not only a maturational influence as the levels themselves develop sequentially; there are also ongoing changes derived from the continuing input as the organism increases its interaction with the environment. These changes constitute learning as it is broadly defined.

Bronson distinguishes various types of learning: habituation (as the simplest), classical conditioning, instrumental learning (including trial-and-error learning and operant conditioning), and latent learning. He proposes two characteristics that distinguish the quality of learning mediated by different levels of the CNS. One is the degree of sensory and motor differentiation involved; the greater capacity of the higher levels for more complex perceptual discrimination and integration, together with the increased ability for motor control, permit more complex learning. Thus, for example, habituation in the cat shows three progressive levels of changes. Level 1 can respond only to changes in intensity; level 2 responds to change of frequency; pattern variations involve the cortex and require level 3 (Sharpless and Jasper, 1956). In some mammals there is a loss of pattern recognition with neocortical damage but retention of intensity discrimination (C. T. Morgan, 1951). In man, however, almost all responsiveness to light is lost with extensive damage to the visual cortex. The only response left is the pupillary reflex, which is a response to intensity and presumably a level-1 function.

Unfortunately for Bronson's developmental scheme, there is no clear evidence of progression through the three stages. The experiments by Fantz (1963), reviewed in Chapter 13, show that infants are capable of much more than intensity discriminations; on the contrary, they show a preference for complexity of stimulation at an early age and seem then to be making pattern discriminations of a sort. Level-3 and level-1 functions seem to be present together. However, the fact that the infant can make discriminations at the three levels does not necessarily mean that he can base learning upon these discriminations.

Instrumental learning is related by Bronson to level-2 functions. In most instances of this form, the rewards are stimuli associated with consummation (copulation, eating, and so on), and he notes that these never appear in the absence of level-2 networks. Moreover, implanted electrode stimulation as reward is effective only at this level.

Latent learning depends on an alert cortex excited by variation in the sensory input and hence is a level-3 phenomenon. It is essential, Bronson points out, to the sensori-sensory learning that Hebb regards as fundamental to perceptual development. The neocortex is apparently necessary to exploratory behavior in mammals, and latent learning is not found in those deprived of the cortex.

Bronson also points out that in mature and intact animals different forms of learning may appear concurrently, as when incidental learning of goal-irrelevant cues occurs during in-

strumental learning. Such facts suggest that mediational processes are occurring at more than one level.

Another feature of the levels is the time element involved. Classical conditioning, mediated at level 1, requires temporal overlap between the UCS and the CS. Instrumental learning that involves level 2 can be effective with greater delay between the events to be learned and the reinforcement. In level-3 functions the kinds of perceptual organization occurring during the exploratory behaviors with their excitatory effects may be relatively long.

Bronson may not be correct in his ages, especially in attributing classical conditioning to the neonate, but his sequences no doubt are right. That is, conditioning is the first-appearing form of learning, and is followed by instrumental learning and latent learning as the neural networks involved in these mature.

The suggestion that latent learning is a particularly advanced form is of interest in view of the observation that children deprived of early stimulation seem to show a deficiency in this kind of learning (this was discussed more fully in Chapter 11). While the more elementary forms of learning, such as conditioning, may be little influenced by early experiences, advanced forms of learning may be more dependent on them.

A. W. Siegel (1968) has suggested that the increase in incidental learning with age depends on an increased tendency to attend to incidental stimuli rather than on any change in the actual ability to learn. Experimentally he found rise in incidental learning up to about the middle of the eleventh year, followed by a decrease. This decrease is attributed to a newly emerging tendency to select and to inhibit perception of irrelevant stimuli. Further experiments partially support this idea that changes in the inhibition of irrelevance underlie the changes in learning. They are not apparently the sole factors involved.

The observation, mentioned earlier, that adults are less readily conditioned than children at about the sixth year makes one ask whether the development of more advanced forms of learning do in fact inhibit the simpler forms. If this is the case, it would be of interest to compare the conditionability of adults with deprived childhoods with that of those with normal childhood stimulation. One would predict less decline in conditionability for the former.

A highly important developmental event is the change from the more elementary forms of learning characteristic of the young child to the more advanced forms of the adult. More specific information on the age at which this transition, from what might be called "animal" to "human" learning, takes place has been given by S. H. White (1965). Based upon a number of experiments by other authors whom he reviews and also on his own investigations, he shows that the period from about five to seven years is an important one in this regard. A number of changes in learning processes are reported during this time—for instance, the peak in conditionability already mentioned, a peak in simple discrimination learning (Kendler and Kendler, 1962b), and other changes reviewed by White.

There are also at this stage perceptual changes (which are discussed in Chapter 13) and transitions in such things as left/right knowledge (Piaget, 1959), spatial orientation (Emerson, 1931), and the face-hand test (younger children being unable to discriminate a touch to the hand or arm if it is simultaneous with one to the face) (Cohn, 1951; Fink and Bender, 1953.)

Changes at this period are discernible in measures of intellectual functioning. F. L. Goodenough (1954), after reviewing numerous studies of the predictive accuracy of intelligence tests, has noted that all the evidence shows only a low correlation between the early IQ and standing in maturity, whereas by about age six a reasonably high correlation with adult IQ is found. Bayley (1955) has

reported similar findings from the Berkeley Growth Study.

White's review shows that a range of functions have a transition in this five-to-seven-year period. For example, young children are little affected in speech by delayed auditory feedback (DAF), whereas by about six the disruptive effects of DAF appear (Chase et al., 1961). Such changes suggest that some kind of reorganization of function is taking place, and this is presumably bound to have an effect on a broad range of interactions with the environment and to influence learning, among other things.

In reviewing the needs for further research, it seems that the relationship between experience and maturation requires fuller exploration. As is protested in other contexts, this is not an idle question. There is considerable interest among educators in children who fail to learn, and many of these children have high intelligence as measured by the usual tests. For a long time poor motivation was assumed to account for these failures, but recently it has become recognized that one cannot always account for failure to learn on this basis, and the existence of some deficiency in the learning process itself has been suggested. However, the question arises as to whether the deficiency is in the basic equipment of the child, that is, in some error in the innate programming of the nervous system, or whether the child has missed some essential experience and the imposed program is consequently defective. Much reeducational endeavor is being invested in this latter assumption—on very slender and purely circumstantial evidence. It is also pertinent to ask whether, even if the latter explanation is valid, the maturational substratum may not show critical periods, so that out-of-season learning is ineffectual.

To anticipate matters to be discussed in detail in later chapters, it would seem that the five-to-seven-year period is an important one in development. There is a maturation of the level-3 functions spoken of by Bronson and concurrently (and presumably relatedly) the development of effective language and verbal mediation. There is also the development of selective voluntary attention, conservation, the ability to form abstract learning sets, incidental learning, and so on. It may prove to be the case that Bronson's suggestions provide an understanding of the maturational basis on which all these developments depend. On the other hand, we must not assume maturation to be the only factor involved. Tighe and Tighe (1966b) have shown overtraining to influence reversal shift in three- to four-year-old children and point to the fact that the previous experience of the organism is a factor also.

It is important to again draw attention to the controversy between the nativists and the learning theorists and to point out that pheno-

typically similar behaviors may be acquired by the two routes. The fact that stable and complex individual differences of a kind often thought to be genetically determined can be produced by manipulation of early experience (Whimbey and Denenberg, 1966; Denenberg et al., 1968) does not mean that such effects cannot be genetic. It may well be that we can at least mimic some of the genetic effects by environmental means (i.e., by learning), but the question must be asked whether it is developmentally efficient to do so. The idea that learning and genetic effects may be to some extent interchangeable will be referred to again in other contexts.

It is evident that this review of learning processes in childhood opens up many more questions than it answers.

Thirteen

Development of Perception

It might be debated whether a discussion of learning should follow or precede a discussion of perception. Perception may be thought of as primary in the sense that only that which comes into the organism via the sensory receptors can be learned and this might be taken as a logical reason for dealing with perception first. However, this logic is weakened by the fact that much learning goes into the maturer forms of perception; there is a reciprocal relationship, and it is only for convenience of discourse that one discusses the two processes separately at all. In both learning and perception, the developmentally earlier features are largely dictated by the immaturity of the CNS compounded by the organism's lack of experience. It is didactic strategy rather than any logical necessity that has directed the sequence of these two chapters.

There are some points that might be raised about the statement that learning depends on the sensory receptors. For instance, direct stimulation of certain brain centers can produce learning, but it is evident from some of the experiments cited in Chapter 9 that sensations do accompany at least some of these intercranial stimuli, though the exteroreceptors are not involved. One must evidently include in the statement interoceptors—brain centers sensitive to blood androgen level, for example. But even here, though a raised androgen level may arouse, via the mediation of these centers, certain feeling tones that predispose particular action patterns, there has to be some external and perceived object toward which to direct these actions (unless one wishes to argue that autoerotic practices are an exception). The learning that is motivated by these intercranial phenomena (whether natural or artificial) usually involves in some way the external environment and hence the sensory receptors. However, beyond noting that the problem exists, it does not seem necessary to discuss it further here.

It is hardly necessary to say that without perception the organism is cut off from all contact with the external world or, indeed in the terms mentioned above, with his own internal world and that hence without perception he would be denied a whole range of influences crucial to his development. The development of perception, or that of the organism's capacity to apprehend the world around him, must therefore play a critical part in the development of the organism as a whole. In spite of this crucial role, as Wohlwill (1960) has pointed out, this has been a neglected field of inquiry, by both perceptionists and developmental psychologists. Perceptual development could, in fact, provide a theoretical framework for child development, and Baldwin (1955) has made an assay in this direction. Werner's book (1957) is also in this idiom.

In a number of contexts it seems that early psychological functioning is dominated by perception. Piaget's theories of intellectual development emphasize the gradual growth toward freedom from perceptual domination of cognitive processes in the young child, to processes that are based upon perceptions (as they must be) but that are not dictated solely by the more obvious perceptual features; the achievement of conservation is one instance of this growth (Chapter 16).

SENSATION AND PERCEPTION

In discussing sensation and perception, it is convenient to draw a distinction between them, even though this division is an artificial one and not entirely defensible. By *sensation,* for the purposes of the present discussion, is meant the raw changes that take place in the CNS following stimulation of a sensory receptor. At least some degree of organization is involved here.

By *perception* is meant the organization and *interpretation* of those changes. We may conveniently think of sensations as being mediated by neural changes that take place in the receptors themselves and in central structures up to and including the primary sensory areas of the cortex (though one should not hold too rigidly the idea that the association areas cannot be involved), whereas perception necessarily involves the association areas also. Sensation may be innate—a native

property of the nervous system—but by this definition perception cannot be entirely native.

It is contrary to current thinking to hold a distinction between sensation and perception. This view is exemplified, for instance, by Gibson (1950), and does not follow the Gestaltists' arguments on this point. It is, on the other hand, the position taken by Hebb (1966). Whatever the logical merits for saying that the perceptions of mature individuals cannot be divided in this way, it is useful to the developmentalist to think of the infant as having sensations only and to attempt to describe the processes by which they become elaborated into perceptions. One point at which this supposition may be weak is that it assumes the neonate has "empty" association areas in the cortex. At the same time it is being assumed that quite complex organizations of neural mechanisms involving sensations are built into the CNS. This is implicit in the notion of sign gestalts (to be discussed), and we do not know that they do not involve the associative cortex. If they do, then the distinction becomes one between these sign gestalts and perceptions that involve not *prior* organization but *imposed* organization. This distinction may seem to be splitting hairs and meaningless to those whose interest is mature perception, but it is a useful distinction for the developmentalist to bear in mind. This chapter first discusses the evidence on sensation, that is, the original sensory functions, and then proceeds to discuss the modifications of these functions that constitute perceptions.

Again there is a debate that could arise from the statements made. An adult must have a sensation in order to have a perception; that is, there must be receptor activity parallel with associative cortical activity. What may be questioned is whether an adult can have a raw sensation, that is, receptor activity with no associative attachments. Present an adult with a pure red stimulus, and immediately the sensation is accompanied by associations—traffic lights, blood, communism, frenzy, even musical tones—most of which are the result of learning. It might be asked, of course, how long the infant remains with entirely unattached sensations. In view of the relative inefficiency of early learning, it is possible that some naiveté may persist for a while, and this is the assumption made here. Organization continues to be *imposed* for some time in development, in some cases modifying prior organization and in others imposing an organization on sensations that would otherwise remain unorganized, that is, that would never become perceptions without this organization. The relationship between imposed and prior organizations must, however, remain an intimate one. For instance, in learning to recognize histological specimens under the microscope, the student must impose an organization on the strange sensory field he sees, but his ability to do this depends on existing organizations, some of which may be "prior" organizations, that is, innate sensations. The ability for figure-ground organization is one of these prior organizations.

A question that may be asked in this connection is whether such things as the illusions and the constancies are to be regarded as sensory or perceptual phenomena. The answer is by no means clear-cut, but insofar as they are the result of *experience,* they are perceptual in terms of the definition given here. However, there is evidence that at least some of these phenomena may be a function of the manner of organization of the nervous system and be independent of experience; that is, they may be sensory.

What are termed *sensations* here may include not merely elementary changes accompanying stimulation of receptors but also quite a high level of organization of these patterns of change. In any case, the term *elementary* is relative. The neural activities that produce a sensation of green to one mixture of wavelengths of light are probably by no means simple, and the activities that produce varying neural correlates of unitary changes in wavelengths are not simple either.

We have very little information about how the child actually perceives the world about him. One may have early memory of rooms in which there are forests of legs of tables, chairs, and people—of tables that are roofs to walk under rather than surfaces to place things down on, staircases that reach to the sky, and cupboards that are caverns. The shrinkage of childhood homes and places visited after a long absence is a familiar experience.

All these changes are related obviously enough to the size of the child and the space scale this size engenders. But how do colors look to the child? Odors have a peculiar capacity to evoke old memories: Does this suggest that smells formed a larger part of the perceptual world of the child than of that of the adult?

An example of the experimental evidence that the child does perceive differently is given by a study by Olum (1956), who uses the Michotte disc with seven-year-old children (see Figure 13–1). In this technique, thick curved lines—one red, one black—on a disc are varying distances apart and touch at one point only. As the disc is rotated behind a screen with a narrow slit, the effect is that of two rectangles (black and red) that move in relation to one another and at one point come together; at another point in the cycle they disappear. The phenomenal effect varies with speed of rotation. (In the original experiment, Michotte varied the actual speed of rotation of the discs. Olum produced the same effect by having three discs on which the distance between the lines changes and hence the apparent speed of the relative movement varied.) At faster speeds there is a strong causal effect of one of the rectangles pushing or banging the other away. At lower speeds the effect is noncausal, the two appearing to move independently. At intermediate speeds there is a phenomenon in which one of the rectangles

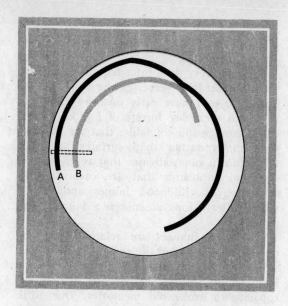

FIGURE 13–1. The Olum disk for testing differences in perception. Adapted from Vivian Olum. 1956. Developmental differences in the perception of causality. Amer. J. Psych., **69**: Fig. 1, p. 418, by permission of The American Journal of Psychology and the University of Illinois Press.

by touching the other seems to release it, but without the impression of an actual transfer of energy such as exists at faster speeds.

Olum tested six- and seven-year-olds and adults and found a class of response in the former never elicited from the latter. Responses were categorized as

1. Lancement (L), or the causal response, in which one rectangle was said to hit or push the other.
2. Nonlancement (NL), or noncausal response, in which the two movements were seen as independent, or as one releasing the other but without dynamic import of lancement.
3. Mutual approach (M), in which both rectangles are described as hitting or pushing at each other (e.g., "red hits black, then black hits red"; "they push each other").
4. Passing (P), in which one rectangle is said to pass the other ("the black goes in front of the red"; "the red passes over the black").

Adult responses were almost exclusively of the L and NL type (according to the speed). M responses were uncommon and P responses were not given by any adults. On the other hand, both M and P responses were common in the children, but L and NL were the more numerous.

Olum has suggested possible explanations of these findings, which may give examples of the manners in which immature perceiving differs from the more developed kind. The P phenomenon showed mostly at the slower speeds, where the relative speeds of the two rectangles are more nearly equal. Before a causal effect can be perceived, there must be a differentiation of the cause and the effect. When the speeds are nearly equal, color is the only striking difference between the two stimuli, and this alone is insufficient to produce a causal perception in young children; the breakdown into two separate movements is beyond the perceptual powers of the child.

The M phenomenon, Olum says, may be caused by a difference in the perception of stroboscopic movement. According to Gautenbein (1952), children still perceive induced movements at slower speeds where adults report successive events. Most of the M responses were for the slowest disc (i.e., the one in which the relative speed of apparent movement was least). However, this alone would not account for the disappearance of M responses on the faster discs in children, nor does it really explain why adults do not report the M phenomenon on the faster discs where stroboscopic effects are presumably possible for them. But whatever the explanation, children apparently do perceive differently, if we can use their verbal reports as a fair indication of what they are perceiving.

Much of Piaget's work also documents ways in which children's perceptions differ from those of maturity. Some of these examples describe how they differ: The conservation experiments show how the young child can perceive one element (height or surface area) but cannot combine elements into the higher-order concept (of volume). The explanation of such phenomena lies as much within cognitive as within perceptual development, and for convenience (rather than for more logical necessity) these matters will be discussed in another chapter.

SENSORY DEVELOPMENT

In the consideration of certain aspects of human development the phylogenetic approach is often of value. This is especially the case where there is a steady progression as one ascends the scale, and where some information can be obtained by extrapolation from lower levels to ones above. In general the sensory processes are so highly developed in the lower vertebrates as to leave virtually no room for improvement between them and those of man. Man can claim no superiority in the detection of stimuli; his advantage is in the use he makes of what is detected.

There are in the invertebrates a wide range of form of receptors sensitive to light, but in the vertebrates the range is somewhat more restricted and the general structure involving a lens is similar for all species. There are variations, such as the accommodative device in fish, some amphibia, and some reptiles, in which the lens is moved rather than deformed as it is in higher vertebrates. If visual acuity is to be taken as a criterion of excellence, the eyes of most mammals (including those of man) are inferior to those of birds. Also, some animals have visual experiences denied to man —such as detection of the polarization of light or the perception of ultraviolet. An interesting sidelight is the fact that while cats have the retinal structures for color sensitivity, they apparently lack the central mechanism for dealing with the sensations (Waters et al., 1960), and insofar as can be determined, they perceive in monochrome. This may be taken as a warning against too hasty deductions from anatomy to behavior.

In audition the human ear is almost as sensitive as is practically possible, because with much further increase of acuity it would pick up the noise of Brownian movements of air molecules and be subjected to a constant interference from this source. A similar degree of sensitivity is common to many other creatures, however, including some insects.

Taste and smell are said to be less acute in man than in animals, but smell at least is incredibly sensitive in man, some substances being detectable in minute concentration. It may be that man tends to make less use of the potentiality of the chemical senses, which can be developed by training, as tea-tasters and eonophils can bear witness.

Growth Changes in
Visual Sensation

It need hardly be said that the development of the sensory organs themselves must have an important place in the development of sensation. The embryological origins of the various sensory organs have been summarized elsewhere. A detailed discussion of sensory development in late fetal and neonatal life in humans is to be found in the White House Conference Report (1933).

Man is in many respects a visual animal. Some responsiveness to light, in evidence of an ability to distinguish light from dark, is manifest in fetuses several weeks before normal birth. The peripheral parts of the retina, where rods are most abundant, are fully developed by the seventh fetal month. The pupillary reflex is also present in the latter part of fetal life. However, vision is relatively undeveloped at birth, and it is not until this time that the visual cortex of the occipital lobe begins to differentiate. Also, it is not until about sixteen weeks after birth that the macula and fovea are structurally differentiated. About this time, or a little before, the visual fibers complete their myelinization. The development of the macula continues and the ability to fixate accurately and hence to see details is correlated with this development, though it is plain from the Fantz studies (p. 267) that fixation is possible quite early. Further development of the macula continues up to about six years of age.

The eye of the infant is small and therefore generally hyperopic; this condition is said to lead to poor visual acuity. 20/20 vision is not achieved until about seven years, but some studies of infantile visual acuity will be discussed below.

It is commonly stated in the textbooks of ophthalmology (for example, Walsh, 1957) that fusion of the visual images from the two eyes is not achieved until about the sixth year because central mechanisms for fusion are not yet matured. The authority for this statement is not specified. It seems to imply that up until this time children are seeing double. This may be somewhat surprising to those who are accustomed to observing the behavior of young children, who do not typically seem to show any evidence of such a disability. The only experimental study known to me is one by Johnson and Beck (1941), whose findings are contradictory to this statement; they found stereoscopic vision in children at the age of two years.

Changes in Electrical Activity Associated with Visual Sensation

The electroretinographic (ERG) technique, developed by Zetterström (1951), has been used to study the retinal activity of infants. The neonate shows no sign of ERG activity, and Zetterström has interpreted this result as suggesting that the visual purple or other chemical substances in the receptors are not yet formed or functional. In adult ERG's there are two characteristic wave forms, a negative one known as the A wave and a large positive or B wave. Minimal traces of a B wave become apparent in the infant ERG three or four days after birth, and gradually a more definite B wave develops, but it is not until the twelfth month that an A wave makes its appearance. Just what this means in perceptual terms is difficult to say, but it does seem to indicate that the retinal processes of the young child are different from those of older ones.

In the cat (as with several other species studied) there are marked developmental changes in the responses in the visual cortex evoked by a flash of light, these evoked responses being measured by implanted electrodes. The earliest responses (which occur sometime after birth in kittens) are highly variable in wave form, show long latency, and are more "fatiguable" (that is, longer intervals between flashes are necessary for full response to be shown) when compared with adult responses. Development is rapid at first, slowing later, and reaching adult form in a few weeks. The range of individual differences is very wide among the younger animals at the same age, this range tending to decrease among the older ones (Ellingson and Wilcott, 1960). Compared with the cat, the human visual system is more mature at birth, but the developmental changes are similar. Dustman and Beck (1966) studied the potentials evoked by flashes of light in subjects between one month of age and eighty-one years. The responses recorded from the occipital lobe showed marked age changes over the first sixteen years of life, with no significant changes after that. There was a rapid increase in amplitude up to the five to six year group, a rapid decline from seven years to about fourteen, and a smaller but abrupt increase again at this age. At sixteen, the amplitude stabilized and changed little from then on. Dustman and Beck note that these changes are similar to those reported for brain wave frequency and amplitude in other studies, and are probably of cerebral origin. These changes are presumably related to some maturational event, though just what is quite mysterious. One might also expect some perceptual changes to correspond with these stages, but what these might be is not obvious.

A review of the literature on the ERG and EEG in infants is provided by Lodge et al. (1969), who discuss the correlation of this evidence with other studies of vision in early infancy. In a study of the ERG responses of human newborns to white and orange light, they found the electrophysiological activity of the neonate to be well differentiated in response to differing stimuli, and to be generally similar in wave form to the ERG and visual evoked potentials of adults. The electrophysiological data thus supports the behavioral indications (reviewed later in this chapter) that certain visual-sensory capacities are present at birth.

Perceptual Organization

Some kinds of organization take place more peripherally and are presumably innate. Granit (1955) some time ago pointed to the existence of a gating mechanism in vision whereby pupillary changes apparently cause changes in the pattern of firing of the retinal cells; the muscular changes are related backward to more central areas and then outward again to the retina. There is also an outward-working gating, as shown when the less dominant eye during binocular rivalry shows a less acute pupillary reflex compared with the dominant one. Here again, nothing is known of the developmental antecedents of these peripheral organizations.

Elemental Facets of Sensation

Such studies as follow are an interesting start on relatively simple elements of seeing, but Teuber (1960) has insisted that we can understand perception only when we begin to consider all the complexity of its interactions. Investigations restricted to such unnatural stimuli as points of lights, clicks, and pure tones can never tell us how organisms perceive. His conclusions on a survey of neurophysiological correlates may be disheartening

in that he shows how far we are from an understanding of perception, but yet it points to what must be done if we are to know. The developmental perceptionist, perhaps even more than those concerned with the organism at maturity, must take his admonition to heart.

Color Vision

It is difficult to draw any conclusions from comparative studies about the evolutionary primacy of either achromatic or chromatic vision. The most primitive light receptors are apparently indiscriminant of color, but whether or not we should regard these as the forerunners of rods and hence regard rod vision as the more elementary human receptor is a point that need not concern us. Certainly color vision is well developed in many invertebrate species, as demonstrated, for example, by the bees. Von Frisch (1955) and Walls (1934a, b) regarded cones as the more elementary, and rods as a phylogenetically later development. Among mammals generally, because so many species are nocturnal, color vision is rather poorly developed (Waters et al. 1960); primates are unusual among the mammals in having highly developed chromatic vision.

Color vision is a topic that has long intrigued psychologists, and it is not surprising that a number of attempts have been made to discover whether or not infants can perceive color. The obvious methodological difficulties of studying the matter in young children have made any results somewhat uncertain. The studies of newly sighted cataract patients (to be discussed in more detail elsewhere) do suggest that color vision is an elemental and basic phenomenon.

A major source of difficulty in investigations of color vision is in ensuring that the subject is genuinely discriminating differences of color and not merely those of brightness. None of the studies of color vision in young children have been able unequivocally to meet this difficulty. Mann (1928) has reviewed a number of the studies; most of them have assumed that brightness values of different hues are the same for infants and adults, but this may not be a legitimate assumption. However, Peiper (1925), in an ingenious study of the Purkinje shift, did obtain results that suggest that brightness values for infants and adults may be closely the same. He used the fact that in young infants there is an eye-neck reflexive response to strong light (a light on the retina causes the infant to throw back the head), but there is a threshold below which this reflex is not elicited.

Peiper used red, green, yellow, and blue lights, starting at high intensities and gradually reducing the intensity of each until the eye-neck reflex disappeared. He reasoned that the intensity values at which the response failed to occur would be an indicator of the brightness threshold of the color. He found that when infants were adapted to daylight vision they showed yellow to have the highest brightness value (i.e., the lowest threshold), whereas under conditions of twilight vision, blue was the brightest. These findings are the same as for adults. Peiper concluded that the presence of a Purkinje shift indicated the presence of color sensitivity in infants, and it might also be concluded that the brightness values are similar to those in adults. However, Peiper's results have been strongly criticized on a number of technical grounds, but only one replication has been attempted, that by J. M. Smith (1936), who found similar results but did not avoid criticism either.

One study that did attempt to control for brightness difference was by Chase (1937), who moved a spot of color over a background of a different hue, both these colors being equated for brightness (for the adult eye). As a control, a colorless (white) spot was moved over a colorless background and also over a colored background that was at least 25 percent lighter than the spot. In neither case were pursuit movements found, whereas pursuit move-

ments for the colored spot were reported for all the colors used; in some cases they were reported as early as fifteen days after birth. Chase concluded that the infants were in fact responding to color and not to brightness or other differences. In another experiment, Staples (1932) presented infants with two discs of the same size—one gray, the other colored —and of equal brightness to the adult eye. The time spent fixating each of these discs was noted, and by the age of three months it was found that the children spent almost double the time fixating the colored disc that they spent on the gray one. This was taken as evidence for color vision.

If we can assume that the brightness values for colors are the same for infants and adults, then it might be legitimate to conclude that young infants do indeed sense color, but the crux of the matter would seem to be establishing that brightness values are in fact the same. With this reservation, it might be further concluded that color is an innate sensation, awaiting only the requisite development of the cones. In this connection it is interesting to note that some of the patients reported by von Senden (1932) quoted color as one of the immediate and striking aspects of their first visual experience.

Some relevant data are provided by Doris et al. (1967), who studied brightness reactions in infants between 1 and 113 days of age and found that the differential brightness threshold develops rapidly in the first months of life. At first the Weber fraction is large—that is, a big difference in brightness is necessary before a difference is detected in the response of the infant—but this fraction rapidly decreases. (These authors used the optokinetic nystagmus to a moving field of alternate light and darker stripes in which the contrast between the light and dark stripes could be varied. Obviously when there were no brightness differences detected, there would be no nystagmic pursuit movements of the eye.) This study in some ways confuses the issue, because it shows that detection of brightness *differential* is not acute in the infant, but it does not tell us about absolute thresholds as compared with adults about *colored* stimuli. However, it does provide an ingenious technique for further investigation.

One question is whether color dominates form or vice versa. Spears (1964), using fixation time as criterion, compared color and shape preferences and found that shape dominated color. Among the shapes he used, the bull's-eye was the most preferred, whatever its color, but a blue bull's-eye was preferred to a gray one.

Movement as Stimulus

A particularly salient sensory stimulus is provided by movement. The frog will ignore an insect within striking range so long as it is still, but as soon as the insect moves, it strikes with the tongue. "Freezing" is an essential part of this camouflage of many species. It is well known that the attention of the human infant is early arrested by movement. Wilcox and Clayton (1968) found a marked preference, in five-month-old infants, for a motion picture of a woman's face as compared with fixations of the same face in still. This preference for movement is predictable from the fact that infants also show it for moving as against still checkerboard patterns (Silfen and Ames, 1964).

Development of Gestalts

A point of theoretical interest is the extent to which the (presumably) innate gestalt principles of perceptual organization operate in infants. In birds—or at least in the herring gull—young animals operate on the principle of summation and mature ones on gestalts (Weidman and Weidman, 1958).

An interesting line of investigation has been opened up by Bower (1966b). He suggests that early perception is summatory, but

that later gestalt principles, in which the whole becomes more than the sum of its parts, emerge. He demonstrates a developmental shift in preference for wholes between eight and twenty weeks in the human infant. The younger infants responded in a conditioning situation to "parts" as much as a "whole" (Figure 13–2), but by twenty weeks they were responding in a highly significantly preferential manner to the whole. The change apparently occurred somewhere after the twelfth week.

In a study of one infant, Bower (1967) found certain of the gestalt principles, notably *good continuation,* to operate at thirty-six days, whereas another, *proximity,* was not effective at this age.

Illusions as Sensory Phenomena

Because we are considering the innately organized aspects of perceptual phenomena as sensations, the question of whether at least some of the illusions should not be discussed as sensory rather than perceptual phenomena is aroused. Katz and Révész (1921) have shown that domestic fowls, as well as man, are sub

FIGURE 13–2. *The part-whole stimuli.*

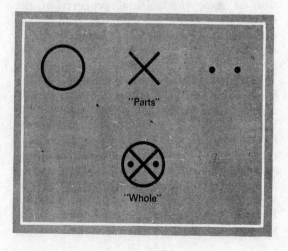

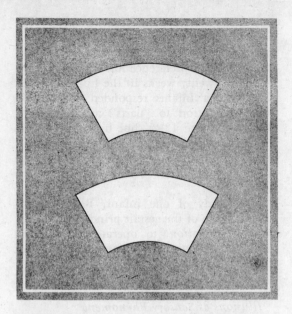

FIGURE 13–3. The Jastrow ring segment illusion.

ject to certain of the illusions, such as the Jastrow ring segment (Figure 13–3). The fact that many of the illusions are so persistent is suggestive; not even the most sophisticated of perceptionists becomes entirely immune to the Muller-Lyer illusion. This, together with their presence in lower species, does lead one to suppose that illusions might be a reflection of some fundamental property of the organization of the nervous system. There is only one study known to me bearing on this question. Neonates presented with moving stripes show an optokinetic nystagmus in which there is a slow movement of the eyes in the direction of motion of the stripe followed by a rapid return to the middle position (Dayton et al., 1964). Tauber and Koffler (1966) have reported that newborn infants (between ten hours and four and a half days) showed this optokinetic reflex when placed in a striped stationary cylinder lighted stroboscopically to produce the illusion of rotation. Because there was no difference between the younger and older neonates, neither learning

nor maturation would seem to be involved; this particular illusion is a phenomenon present very early in life and is apparently innate. The extent to which other illusions are part of basic equipment has not been investigated in neonates. In a later section some age changes which may reflect experience in certain illusions are reviewed.

Perceptual Constancies

An important feature of visual perception is the constancy of size, shape, and color, which is remarkable in adults. Since the formulations of Helmholtz some theories have held that the constancies are the result of experience and that shape constancy, for example, becomes possible only after the organism has become familiar with the object in a variety of orientations.

The alternative idea that constancy is part of the intrinsic organization of the nervous system would seem to be making heavy demands on it, yet it may still be within the capacity of this amazing system. It could be that it is part of the capacity for generalization that is so remarkable a feature of the brain. On the other hand, learning seems at first sight to be a more parsimonious means to achieving constancy, but when one considers what this possibility involves, it may be debated. If learning requires separate experience for each possible angle of sight for each object, then this supposes an enormous amount of learning. Again the problem is simplified by invoking the power of generalization, but in so doing this explanation becomes less distinct from the other. A satisfactory developmental study of perceptual constancy has great theoretical interest.

It has long been part of the folklore of child psychologists that young children recognize pictures equally well in any orientation, that is, show a high degree of constancy. This no doubt stems from the observation that in their early use of books they seem quite as happy with an upside-down picture as a right-side-up one. Brooks and Goldstein (1963) have reviewed some of the literature on this topic; while numerous early studies supported the belief, they were mostly anecdotal or experimentally weak. In their own experiment, using photographs of classmates presented right-way-up and inverted, there was an increase with age in the recognition of the inverted photograph, but even the youngest children (three years old) showed almost 70 percent correct identification of the inverted face, and this was not greatly different from the correct responses to the upright (79 percent). Perhaps more pertinent is the wide range among individuals of correct responses in the three-year-old group (17–100 percent), compared with the fourteen-year-old group (73–100 percent). Brooks and Goldstein find their results consistent with those of Ghent (1960, 1961) and Ghent and Bernstein (1961) and use their explanation in terms of visual scanning, derived from Hebb (1949). Ghent assumes that figures have focal parts that draw the eye and are particularly involved in recognition. In faces these are probably the eyes; moreover, she assumes a top-to-bottom progression of scanning, so that in an upright photograph the eyes are scanned sooner than in an inverted one, and recognition is delayed in the latter. This is somewhat dubious because the eyes are not far from the midpoint, but it is at least a testable hypothesis.

As Gibson (1950) has pointed out, birds show evidence of size constancy at least, and this without any apparent need for learning. Other studies of constancy in animals have been mentioned by Teuber (1960). Koffka (1935) has stated the Gestaltist view that the constancies are an integral part of perceptual organization. However, the question of whether the constancies are innate in man or the result of experience with objects is not readily determined. Locke (1938) has argued that constancy is a feature of lower organisms, including children, and that as intelligence grows, the constancies are lessened.

It is well known that familiar objects are more readily estimated for size at a variety of distances than unfamiliar ones, and familiar objects in unusual sizes can upset distance estimates. The apparent size of known objects is one cue to distance estimation. Common objects can sometimes be quite effectively disguised by presentation in unusual angles; a parlor game consists of photographs of toothbrushes, bottles, and similar household objects taken from angles at which they are not often seen. The objects then become difficult to recognize. Color constancy can readily be demonstrated when there is some reference point—for example, when it is known that the light is variable—but may be lost under conditions where no reference clues are given. These and similar observations have led to the view that the constancies are the result of learning and experience. This idea was early proposed by Helmholtz, and was more recently put forward by Brunswick (1956). Attempts to plot the course of constancy development in children have not elucidated the question, because the results are too diverse. If Locke is correct, then the growth trend will be toward lessened constancy, at least for constancies that depend on the person's normative expectations of familiar properties.

Gibson and Olum (1960) have reviewed many of the studies of constancy in children and conclude in effect that there is insufficient consistency in experimental method to make any valid comparison between studies or to reach any general statement about the trends; some studies report constancy, and others do not. Teuber (1960) also finds the evidence conflicting.

Bower (1966b) has reformulated the problem by pointing out that there are undoubted changes in perceptual capacities with age, yet some functions make their appearance very early in life (so early, in fact, as to strongly suggest innateness). In effect he insists what has been insisted in other contexts, too, that the problem is not the development of specific local functions (such as simple constancies) but the development of general capacities to deal simultaneously with multiple variables and invariants.

Bower (1965) has, based upon motion parallax cues (which also permit distance estimation, as shown by Gibson and Walk (1960) in other experiments), demonstrated size constancy in infants between forty and seventy days of age.

It is probable that both nature and nurture play their part, and the conflicting results obtained might arise from some constancies being part of the constitutional organization of the nervous system and others being acquired. It is likely, too, that even innate constancies may be modified by experience.

Shape constancy in infants between fifty and sixty days of age was studied by Bower (1966a), who found that at this age there is some capacity for constancy. Bower suggests that his results indicate that young humans possess the capacity for shape constancy and the ability to detect the invariants of shape under rotational transformation in the third dimension. Results of his experiments suggest further that the infant has a capacity-limited perceptual machinery that is set to respond to high-order invariants, such as projective shape, and to ignore low-order ones, such as orientation. When both high- and low-order invariants are present, it may be difficult for the infant to respond to the low-order ones; there is a competition for central access within the perceptual system. Bower's experiments shift emphasis from an attempt to understand how infants learn to compute "real shape" from projective shape and orientation to an attempt to comprehend how the ability to register simultaneously orientation and real shape develops. This helps to resolve the fact that perceptual constancies do change with age. Development toward a general capacity to handle simultaneously multiple variables and invariants is proposed. This seems to suggest that shape constancy is a complex function built into the nervous system, because it is difficult to give a convincing account of the acquisition of constancy at this age by learning.

A number of studies (reviewed by Richman et al., 1968) have shown closer approximation to perfect size constancy in organic retardates as compared with familial retardates and normals, the last showing least constancy. This suggests that constancy is a "primitive" function and that higher-order conceptual functioning actually reduces constancy because there is greater flexibility in the interpretation of perceptual data.

Sensing of Form and Space

There is now a fair body of evidence that suggests that the ability to sense certain aspects of form and visual space is present very early in life and that it is probably innate. This ability is usually referred to as form and space perception, but in keeping with the distinction being drawn here, it is better to refer to it as sensory rather than perceptual. However, because some of the phenomena under consideration *do* involve learning, and hence are perceptual as the term is used here, it is appropriate to use the term *perception* in connection with them. The following sections are mainly about the elemental aspects of space and form, but at points the term *perception* must be used.

Line-Detecting Mechanisms. Among the more elementary aspects of the seeing of form is the detection of line, or the contours that produce shape. Sutherland (1957, 1958, 1960) has shown that the octopus can readily discriminate horizontal from vertical rectangles, but is confused by rectangles in opposite-oblique presentations, such as:

We do not know, of course, whether the octopus sees a rectangle as rectangular—that is, with *straight* edges. Nor do we know whether the human infant can natively detect a straight edge, though we do know that straight-edge detecting cells are present in amphibia (Sackett, 1963). The retinal image is always curved, and what underlies the discrimination of the difference between the curved image of a straight line and the image of a curved line is unknown. Presumably the curved projection of a straight line is the simplest possible retinal curve. It would be interesting to take a naive infant (say one born in a primitive community in which straight edges are very unusual) and test its first reaction to a straight line as a novel stimulus. If it does react to it as novel, it would suggest that detection of straight edges is innately programmed.

The difficulty the octopus has with obliques is similar to the difficulty which troubles humans for some time, for Rudel and Teuber (1963a) found similar results in young children aged three and a half to eight and a half years. In their experiment the children learned simultaneous discriminations between vertical and horizontal lines, between oblique lines, and between rightsideup and upsidedown figures:

⌐ vs. ⌐

and opposite directions:

⌐ vs. ⌐

Almost all the children (even the youngest) mastered the first and third discriminations, whereas no three-year-old and only one four-year-old mastered the oblique discrimination:

∨ vs. ∨

The opposite directions items were difficult, and only one three-year-old and two four-year-olds mastered it. Even the oldest subjects found the horizontal and up-and-down discriminations easiest.

In a second experiment five-year-old chil-

dren were trained successively to discriminate a vertical from an oblique and a horizontal from an oblique and were tested for transfer to other forms. Here, too, there was confusion between the obliques; discriminating a horizontal from an oblique was markedly easier than discriminating a vertical from an oblique. There was no transfer from obliques to diamonds.

The detection and recognition of obliques by children aged four and six were also studied by Over and Over (1967). They have results that suggest that at these ages the difficulties children have with obliques are not due to the sensory coding of them but to difficulties in remembering which shape is which. That is, under experimental conditions requiring recognition, children show the effects of their lack of categorizing ability. This illustrates a point to be made later—that perceptual and intellectual development are interwoven.

Lashley (1938) claimed that levels of difficulty in visual discrimination learning were much the same for rats and men. The Rudel and Teuber experiment (1963a) also (when compared with Sutherland's results [1958]) suggests that young children and octopuses are also not markedly different in some aspects of perception.

Sutherland has suggested a shape-analyzing mechanism in the octopus in which visual stimulation is fed into a two-dimensional cell array. A counting of excitation along rows and columns leads to discrimination of the horizontal and the vertical. Further, this mechanism is such as to be more efficient in the analysis of horizontal extents than of vertical ones. This is consistent with the experimental findings, including the greater ease of discrimination of up-down mirror images (in which the distinguishing feature is in the horizontal plane) and the prevalence of left-right confusion (in which the critical stimuli are in the vertical plane). In this experiment, the difficulty of discriminating

⌐ vs. ⌐

is consistent with the common left-right confusion in children. It is of interest to relate these findings to the fact that young children draw horizontal lines before they draw vertical ones; motor development and perceptual development are closely interwoven.

Not only may some aspects of shape be sensed by mechanisms built into the nervous system, but other perceptual dimensions may also have their systems. There is evidence of spatial filters that provide a presumably innate size-detecting mechanism in humans (Pantle and Sekular, 1968). They may contribute to the size constancy phenomenon.

It is evident from the work of Hubel and Wiesel (1963) that the innate mechanisms detecting slope of line depend upon stimulation for their continued functioning. Newborn kittens reared for the first two months with a translucent covering of the eyes no longer showed excitation of the specialized cells involved when the covers were removed. The innate mechanisms had been lost during this disuse. How much minimum stimulation is necessary to maintain the mechanism is not known, but it would be of interest to find out. Presumably any normal environment provides more than enough stimulation for maintenance, but what level of stimulation greater than that provided by diffuse, unpatterned light is required would be worth knowing. It would have relevance to understanding some perceptual anomalies in children.

Form Sensitivity

We have seen that as far as available evidence goes, one of the givens of visual sensation is color. William James characterized the world of the infant as a "booming, buzzing confusion," but it does seem likely that this confusion is at least a surrealistic painting. There is also evidence that movement might be another of the fundamental properties of perception, so that this surrealistic phantasm of color would also be in motion. The question is whether this is the whole of the story or whether this phantasmagoria is not further ordered to some extent by sensing of form. The environmentalist's view that all perception has to be learned needs to be modified to the extent at least of admitting that the perception of color and movement do not need to be; but does the child have to learn all else, to perceive shape, pattern, size, and solidity? Infants can and do discriminate configurational differences at least by the second month, and the development of selective visual attention to configurational variables may represent an early stage of basic perceptual-cognitive development (Fantz and Nevis, 1967).

Taking the phylogenetic approach, we do know that some species of birds, such as the domestic fowl, can perceive form as soon as they hatch from their eggs. Fantz (1957) has shown that newly hatched chicks presented with a variety of stimuli to peck at show a definite and consistent preference for objects with certain properties. They prefer rounded objects and will peck at circular forms rather than angular ones; they also have a size preference, pecking more frequently at circular objects of about one-eighth inch in diameter rather than at those smaller or larger than this size. Further, they consistently prefer a spherical object to a flat disc. These predilections show that the chick can discriminate shape, size, and three-dimensionality or solidity, apparently without the need for any learning. Under the experimental conditions that Fantz set up, the chicks did not get any reward for their pecking behavior, and in some views of learning, without reward there is no learning. Whether this is true or not, these chicks seemingly required no learning for these discriminations. Differing kinds of form discrimination are to be seen in other birds. One example is the pecking behavior of a newly hatched herring gull toward the shape of the parental bill, but colors also are involved in this particular response (Tinbergen and Perdeck, 1950).

In the case of the chick, the special constellation of properties to which it innately reacts would (in nature) give a high probability that objects pecked at would be seeds and edible. (As can be demonstrated, further learning does take place to modify the pecking response in that nonedible objects of similar appearance become rejected.) In the case of the gull, the particular response cited is also related to feeding, as the pecking at the bill of the parent is a signal to it to regurgitate food that the young gull can then eat. Before discussing the question of whether there are any biologically useful innate perceptions in the human infant that are important in feeding behavior, the question of the amount of the innate form sensation must be decided. An experimental technique that makes possible an approach to the very difficult question of deciding what infants can perceive has been developed by Fantz (1958b).

Because the motor behavior of the young chick is so much further developed, it can

readily make a response that enables us clearly to deduce what its perceptions are. The human infant is capable of very little response, but he can move the eyes and to some degree fixate an object, and Fantz has used this behavior as the basis of his technique. He set up a "looking chamber" (Figure 13–4) in which the infant was flat on its back in a crib and could gaze at objects placed above the eyes; simultaneously an observer peeping through holes in the low "ceiling" of the apparatus could observe the direction of the infant's gaze by seeing images of the fixated object reflected in the baby's eyes. When this image is over the pupil of the eye, it is assumed that an image of the object can be projected onto the retina. If the infant is, however, seeing nothing in particular, then one would expect random movements of the eyes in which no object was at the pupil for any length of time or consistently. Fantz discovered that there were, in fact, consistent fixations in

FIGURE 13–4. The Fantz "looking chamber." Adapted from Robert L. Fantz. 1964–65. Studying Visual Perception and the Effects of Visual Exposure in Early Infancy. Rassegna di Psicologia Generale e Clinica, 7: Fig. 5, p. 7, by permission of the author.

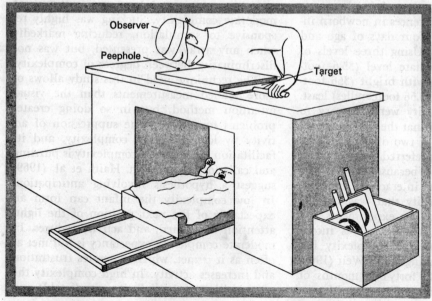

young children even as early as one week after birth. In these fixations certain objects would be at the pupil for significantly longer times and more often than other objects. The existence of these clear "preferences" may be taken as evidence that the object is "seen." It is at least sensed, if not perceived. (The use of the word *preference* should not be taken as implying a conscious mental process.)

By means of this technique, Fantz has been able to demonstrate that form sensitivity is present in the human infant from an early age and that it is presumably unlearned. He ran series of experiments in which infants' reactions to a variety of patterns were tested. Unlike the response in the chick, there was no clear preference for rounded as against angular shapes, although in one pairing a square card with a bull's-eye pattern of concentric circles was markedly preferred to one with horizontal stripes, and one might like to equate the circular design with the maternal breast and nipple. Spears (1964) also found a preference for the bull's-eye pattern.

Fantz (1961a) reported a clear preference for complex patterns as against simpler ones, but Hershenson (1964), using a technique similar to that of Fantz tested brightness as well as complexity preferences in newborn infants between two and four days of age and questions these results. Using three levels of brightness, the intermediate level (35.6 foot-candles) was preferred, with bright (356 foot-candles) next, and dim (3.56 footcandles) least. His results on complexity were contrary to those of Fantz (1963) in that the *least* complex (a four-square pattern of two diagonal blocks and two whites) was preferred. However (as Hershenson points out), because there is also the possibility of an interaction between brightness and complexity that was not accounted for in either of the experiments, the results of both must be regarded as inconclusive. The preference for complexity has been confirmed by Munsinger and Weir (1967) for children of nine to forty-one months of age who found it to increase linearly with age.

The matter of response to complexity has been studied with different parameters by Haith et al. (1969), using infants between two and four months of age. Instead of giving different amounts of geometrical complexity, they varied *sequential* complexity of the visual stimulation. Their apparatus included a three-by-three array of nine lights. A simple sequential pattern would be one in which the outside lights come on consecutively to produce a "square" pattern of apparent movement. A variety of more and more complex sequences, in which only one light is on at any given moment, can be devised. (They did not go into the added complexity of simultaneous lights). Instead of using eye movements or fixations as a measure, they filmed the infant and scored movements of the hands and feet, or sucking, as measures of response. It has been found, in the case of limb movement, that there is a change in ongoing activity with stimulation (Haith 1966a,b). Moreover, sucking tends to be inhibited by stimulation (Sameroff, 1965).

In the latter experiment there was a decrease in movement with stimulus patterns of both simple and complex nature; and an increase in movement in response to stimuli of moderate complexity. Sucking was highly responsive to stimulation, reducing markedly when any array was presented, but was not discriminative between degrees of complexity.

The technique used in this study allows of more refined measurements than the visual attention method, but in so doing creates problems for theory. The suppression of activity by low and high complexity, and its facilitation by moderate complexity is puzzling and calls for explanation. Haith et al. (1969) suggest a hypothesis involving anticipation. In low complexity the infant can form an expectancy of the next position of the light, attention is arrested, and activity reduces. In moderate complexity expectancy is *not* met as often as it *is* met, which generates frustration and increases activity. In high complexity the next position of the light is unpredictable and the infant soon extinguishes any expectancy: The stimulus is interesting rather than frustrating, and as with the low complexity situation, activity reduces. As the authors point out, this is one of several possible explanations, but has the merit of being testable.

The suggestion that infants prefer novelty and fixate less familiar stimuli rather than ones with which they are familiar is also questioned by Meyers and Cantor (1966, 1967). While this might be true in some circumstances, it is not, they say, valid as a generalization. The decrements in observation time apply particularly when the stimuli are relatively simple—there are long exposure intervals—and probably also when there is the simultaneous presentation such as was used in the Fantz experiment (Fantz, 1964).

Using decrease in heart rate as a measure of autonomic response decrement (Kagan and Lewis, 1965), Meyers and Cantor (1966) found no evidence of response decrement on repeated presentation of a stimulus when using sixteen-month-old infants as subjects. The stimuli used were a photograph of a multicolored ball and a photograph of a doll clown. These were presented singly. In another phase of the experiment in which the stimuli were presented paired with another and novel stimulus, there was an affect, but it was sex-dependent. Males showed significant decreases in heart rate in response to the nonfamiliar picture, whereas *no decrease was found in females.*

Another article that questions the "complexity" notion is by McCall and Kagan (1967). Its opposition rests on the grounds that complexity of random shapes or checkerboards may not be adequately described in such terms as number of turns or of squares and also that some dimension other than complexity may be involved in fixation preferences. Although obviously some tighter definition of stimulus properties are called for as a methodological refinement, it might be argued that it is unnecessary to abandon the provisional findings based upon a somewhat intuitive estimate of complexity. It certainly seems that some patterns are more "interesting" than others, and McCall and Kagan confirm the finding that faces are preferred to random shapes.

In another series of experiments in which solid and flat spherical objects were presented, Fantz demonstrated depth sensitivity in infants (Fantz, 1961a). The tests were made under both binocular and monocular conditions. Overall the results showed a significant preference for the sphere over a flat disc. Using both textured and smooth objects, it was found that all cues, texture as well as shadow, are necessary to maximum distinction. He also obtained some interesting evidence that suggests that in the early months of life binocular vision is actually something of a handicap to visual perception and that monocular discriminations are better. This is presumably because at this time binocular coordination is poor. In older infants, binocular conditions markedly aided differentiation. Fantz discusses the question of whether in this situation the infant was actually responding to "depth" as such or whether it was responding to the more complex pattern presented by a spherical object, particularly when textured, as against a flat one. We have already seen that pattern complexity tends to be preferred. He points out that even if the infant's selective interest in the solid object is based upon patterned stimulation it is still relevant to understanding depth perception, because such patterning is an integral part of the perception of depth.

In further experiments, Fantz and his collaborators (Fantz, 1961a; Fantz et al., 1962) used a modification of the technique to investigate visual acuity in infants and their ability to resolve fine patterns. They had discovered that infants prefer a patterned stimulus to a plain colored one and prefer a pattern of black stripes to a plain gray stimulus card. Black lines on a white background drawn so fine and so close together that the eye is unable to resolve them give, of course, the impression of a plain gray. Using this fact and varying the width of the stripes and distance apart, it is possible to test the infant's ability to distinguish the striped pattern from a plain gray and to indicate this ability by his fixation preferences. Using cards with black stripes, $\frac{1}{8}$, $\frac{1}{16}$, $\frac{1}{32}$, and $\frac{1}{64}$ inch in width, separated by equal distances of white, and presenting them together with a plain gray card, it was demonstrated that in the first month of life infants can distinguish the $\frac{1}{8}$-inch stripe from plain gray and by six months can visually resolve the $\frac{1}{64}$-inch stripes.

As we have already seen, it is commonly stated that young children are hyperopic and cannot accommodate for close vision. Using these visual acuity tests at varying distances from five to twenty inches, Fantz and his collaborators discovered no difference in visual acuity between these limits; this suggests that the ability to accommodate for close vision is developed (to some degree at least) in early infancy. They also found that the infants tended to maintain a central fixation of a pattern rather than to use peripheral vision, as is sometimes suggested on the grounds that in maturation the periphery of the retina is more advanced than the macula.

In Fantz et al. (1962), it is concluded that while there is a marked increase in the precision of patterned vision during the first six months of life, some patterned vision is present even in the neonate, and these authors take this as implying that all parts of the visual mechanism, including the cortex, are functional to some degree at birth. (Hebb would object that the presence of such stereotyped and stimulus-bound responses could be handled by subcortical structures and that there is no need to suppose cortical involvement.) This is not to ignore the extensive maturation of the visual system that still must occur after birth; among the changes they point out are the increased density of the macula receptors, the completion of myelinization of nerve fibers, further maturation of the visual cortex, and increased skill in foveal fixation. They insist, however, that response

to a patterned stimulus is possible (when the stimulus is intrinsically interesting) without learning and without the need for postnatal maturation. This is not, of course, to deny that both learning and maturation are important in the refinement of vision.

One question of considerable interest is the young infant's ability to distinguish the human face. Fantz (1961a) has commented experimentally on this question also. Flat objects, the size and shape of the head, were presented to the infant with three different patterns painted in black on them (see Figure 13–5). One of them had a stylized face in black on a pink background; another had the same stylized features (hair, eyebrows, nose, mouth, and so on) but was painted on the pink background in a scrambled fashion. The third consisted of black at one end and pink at the other, the area of black being equivalent to the area in the other objects. This last stimulus was almost ignored by the infants, who (as might be predicted from previous statements) preferred the more complex stimuli. However, although the other two stimuli were equivalent in complexity, there was a marked preference for the one that gave a recognizable representation of a face.

FIGURE 13–5. Stylized and scrambled faces as used in infant perception experiments: a and b are equivalent in complexity; in c the dark area is equal to that of a and b so that it is equal in contrast. Adapted from R. L. Fantz. 1961. The origin of form perception. Sci. Amer., 204 (5): 72, by permission of the author and W. H. Freeman and Company. © 1961 by Scientific American, Inc. All rights reserved.

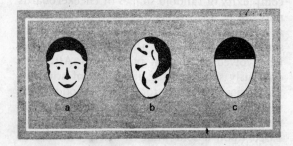

In other series of experiments presenting discs bearing patterns of varying colors and degrees of complexity, there was again a marked preference in infants over two months old for a disc bearing a stylized face, even though it was not the most complex stimulus presented. It was also preferred to the bull's-eye pattern of concentric circles used in a previous series.

In a later experiment, Fantz (1963) obtained similar results on infants in the first five days of life. Again, there were selective visual responses, with a preference for the face pattern. As Fantz points out, it would be unwarranted to assume that this implies "instinctive recognition" of a human face. That is, it does not imply a pattern with some unique significance. What it does suggest, Fantz states, is that a pattern with certain similarities to social objects has stimulus properties to the infant. It should facilitate the development of social responsiveness, because what is responded to must first be attended to.

Using the pupillary reflex as a measure, H. E. Fitzgerald (1968) has reported greater change in pupil size—even at one month of age—when the infant is presented with social stimuli (faces) than when he is presented with non-social ones (checkerboards and triangles). At four months the mother's face produced greater change than a strange female face did. These observations are of interest to the question of sign gestalts which is discussed in Chapter 4.

Wilcox and Clayton (1968), using fixation as the measure of interest, found in five-month-old infants no preferences between various facial expressions presented either as stills or as motion pictures. In a later article it is pointed out that the data on preference for "regular" face are inconsistent, preference at a statistically significant level appearing at only isolated ages (Wilcox, 1969). The various studies are also inconsistent as to nature of the stimuli. In her own study Wilcox measured preferences for "scrambled" faces, a face outline with schematic eyes only, one with schematic mouth and nose only, a realistic drawing of face, and a photograph. She found a moderate preference for *complexity* rather than "faceness" in infants four, ten, and sixteen weeks of age. The oldest group did show a tendency to prefer the photograph (though one might object that the photo was a head and shoulders, whereas the other pictures were of a face only). Wilcox notes that contrast, rather than other factors, might have been involved in determining the preference. On the whole, it would seem that the evidence for the reputed preferences for the "real" face in human infants is ambiguous.

Fixations in young children show definite and rather complex patterns, depending on the nature of the visual stimulus. Lewis et al. (1966) have distinguished five patterns of visual fixation in children at twenty-four weeks. One might be called an "interest pattern" and occurs in response to certain visual gestalts that are apparently intrinsically interesting. It consists of few but prolonged fixations. As already noted, the human face is one of these fixations. There is a sex difference, female infants showing this response to faces more consistently than males do. Less "interesting" visual arrays show repeated short fixations. The total time may be similar to that in interest patterns but is differently distributed. Evidently the study of fixations requires subtle measurement in which the characteristics of the stimulus, the sex of the child, and the particular measure used are all relevant factors.

Some of these findings are extended in a study by Kagan et al. (1966), who also noted cardiac deceleration and smiling in addition to fixation measurements. Four-month infants showed equivalent fixation times to regular faces and to irregularly rearranged ones, but in response to the former they also smiled and had large decreases in heart rate. For the present this study has perhaps more methodological than theoretical import, though as the authors point out, it does suggest that each response has a plurality of meanings, and a sensitive combination of response patterns is needed in studying the relation between stimulus, schema, and act.

Russian studies of the development of visual perception of forms of objects have been reviewed by Zaporozhets and Zinchenko (1966). In particular, they studied the behavior of the eye in the process of visual perception of objects. Children of different ages from three to six examined a filmed presentation of a figure, and eye movements were measured. The three-year-olds made relatively few eye movements compared with the other children; these children were unable to pick out the features that may help them to recognize the figure in a later presentation. The authors conclude that in the three-year-old perceptual activity with regard to the given sensory content is just beginning to form.

Four-year-olds also moved their eyes mainly inside the figure. They tried to orient themselves with size and area. However, there were still few attempts to study contour. This came later, at the five-year level. Only in the six-year-old children were there fully formed methods of perceptual activity. These children determined the most informative characteristics of the object that had to be examined.

The authors therefore concluded that the development of perceptual activity proceeds along the line of isolating a specific sensory content that is increasingly more commensurate with the material presented. A further study using pictures of familiar content (i.e., fairy tales) indicated that the level of development of perceptual activity is not an absolute characteristic of age. It must always be correlated with the material presented as the object of this activity.

Further Russian studies examine the development of the sense of touch in children. They found that in learning to identify shapes tactually there were again different stages. In keeping with Marxist orthodoxy, the experimental data are interpreted as suggesting that perceptual activity is not inborn but that it

forms and develops in the course of childhood. However, the authors do suggest that the development of perception takes place spontaneously without specially organized sensory training, and this perhaps belies the argument of nonnativity. They suppose that, with specially organized training, the rates of development of children's perception may be quickened.

Some of the Russian researchers have suggested that the stages of development of visual perception in children are well defined, turning from abortive eye movements to a purely visual orientation, gradually following the contour of the figure and modeling its characteristics in every detail, concentrating on the most informative characteristics of the object. Final stages of visual perception include the ability to perceive the object without extensive explorations. One glance should enable instant discernment of the properties of the object.

Origins of Space Sensation

A review of recent work in this area has been made by Epstein (1964), who concludes that no universal statement can be made about the genetic basis of space sensation. He cites Carr, who as far back as 1935 reached the same conclusion on the basis of evidence then available. Some aspects of space sensation are apparently innate; in others learning plays an essential role. It should also be noted that in many instances where the capacity is almost certainly genetically originated, learning may modify it.

It is not necessary to repeat a discussion of all the studies reviewed by Epstein. He distinguishes three main kinds of investigation. One has examined the first visual reactions of organisms reared from birth without normal visual experience. In most animal experiments this has involved rearing in darkness, though there are some accounts of human deprivation involving patients suffering from congenital cataracts, whose early experiences on first receiving sight on removal of the cataracts have been described. Epstein discusses the methodological objections that made some of the earlier investigations in this area inconclusive, though more sophisticated experiments tend to support the results of the earlier ones. Among these recent studies are those by Fantz (1958a), who reared chicks in darkness, and the test constituted their first visual experience. We have seen already that chicks prefer three-dimensional to flat figures. These dark-reared chicks were presented with pairs of hemispherical stimuli, one with the curved surface outmost and the other so that only the flat segment was visible. Under both direct

and diffuse lighting (in which shading was minimized) there was a significant preference for the curved surface, which implies perception of space or three-dimensionality, apparently without the need for learning. However, in another experiment (Fantz, 1957), results suggest that with visual experience shading cues are learned and enhance the preference.

The visual cliff procedure devised by Walk and Gibson (1961) produces similar results. They simulated a cliff by laying a board across a sheet of plate glass supported above the floor (see Figure 13–6). On one side of this board material (usually a checkerboard pattern) was placed flush with the undersurface

FIGURE 13–6. *Child's depth perception is tested on the visual cliff. The apparatus consists of a board laid across a sheet of heavy glass, with a patterned material directly beneath the glass on one side and several feet below it on the other. Placed on the center board, the child crawls to its mother across the "shallow" side. However, called from the "deep" side, he pats the glass, but despite this tactic evidence that the "cliff" is in fact a solid surface he refuses to cross over to the mother. Adapted from Eleanor T. Gibson and Richard D. Walk. 1960. The visual cliff. Sci. Amer., 202: 65, by permission of the authors and W. H. Freeman and Company. © 1960 by Scientific American, Inc. All rights reserved.*

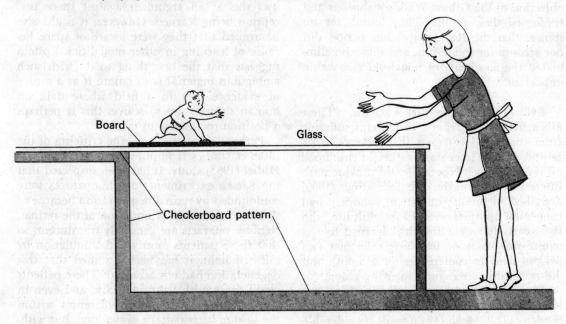

Board

Glass

Checkerboard pattern

of the glass, giving the appearance of solidity, whereas at the other side of the board it fell steeply to the floor, producing a cliff. Animals that cannot discriminate depth may be expected to leave the board on either side; in neither case will they fall because of the glass (though this is virtually invisible, or at least phenomenally nonexistent, as the behavior of the animals shows). Rats reared in darkness until ninety days showed the same preference for the shallow side as ninety-day-old rats reared in the light. Other experiments revealed that motion parallax was the vital cue to detecting depth in naive animals. Further cues to spatial perception, such as textual density, are apparently learned. These authors (Gibson and Walk, 1960), on the evidence of experiments with other species, have suggested that seeing animals are able to discriminate depth at the same time they can move around, even when locomotion begins at birth. However, some experiments by Held and Hein (1963) may cause modification of this statement (they will be reviewed in a later section). Nealey and Edwards (1960) examined some of the methodological points that might cause objection to the Gibson-Walk conclusions and confirmed their results. They found, for instance, that the light adaptation period did not account for the results, and they also eliminated the possibility of nonvisual cues being important.

Evidence from Cataract Patients. There are a number of reports of humans suffering from congenital cataracts that have been removed at some later stage, either in childhood or as adults. Such reports should provide most interesting data on the question. Miner (1905) described an intelligent patient, who had had congenital cataracts removed in adult life, who two years after operation had learned to recognize only four or five faces. She met two persons daily in conferences for a month and did not learn to recognize them by vision.

The most extensive reports are those collected in a review of the literature by von Senden (1932). Hebb (1949) made considerable

theoretical capital out of this material and has reaffirmed his conclusions based on this work (Hebb, 1963). However, others have questioned the validity of any conclusions drawn from this material, because few of the studies were experimentally adequate; most were anecdotal and often very sketchy in detail. Epstein (1964) is among these sceptics. Long-standing cataracts are now so rare in any civilized society (being removed in early infancy) that no new cases for careful study seem to have presented themselves. London (1960) gave a summary of a Russian report by Pokrovskii, but the details are no clearer than in von Senden's reports. In relation to perception in general, the consensus of these sources seems to be that vision is not the same for these people as for normals and that a good deal of learning is necessary before they can cope satisfactorily with the visual world. On the matter of space perception specifically, the information is meager. They showed difficulty in judging distance, being unable to distinguish between close and far objects. Epstein points out that they do reach out, attempting to grasp objects, and are aware of space; he uses this as an argument against space perception being learned. However, it could also be argued that they were aware of space because of learning in other modalities. Epstein suggests that the best thing to do with such ambiguous material is to ignore it as a source of evidence, but in a field where data on human subjects are so scarce, this is perhaps a position too ascetic to take.

Perhaps the more damaging criticism of the cataract studies is implicit in the Wiesel and Hubel (1963) study. It has been suspected that the Riesen experiments on chimpanzees were confounded by retinal degeneration because of the total absence of stimulation of the retinas. Because cataracts are generally translucent, so that these patients mostly had stimulation by diffused light, it has been assumed that this degeneration had not occurred. These patients could distinguish light and dark, and even in some cases broad intensity differences within the field (a fuzzy pattern of shading), but without more discrete pattern vision. The Wiesel and Hubel study of kittens, where translucent coverings were as disrupting to vision as was suturing the eyes, casts doubt on the assumption that such vision is enough to prevent actual neurological changes. On the other hand, Riesen (1961b) has contended that although light stimulation is necessary to the growth and function of the visual system, the relationship between visual deficit and behavior is not clear-cut. And Walk (1965) points out that optic system damages are found that cannot be related to behavioral deficiencies, and that visual functioning may be apparently normal despite known systematic damage.

Hebb (1966) has discussed the Hubel and Weisel findings in relation to the Riesen and Senden material and says that even though dark-reared animals and those without pattern vision may have defective visual mechanisms it is difficult to account for *all* the observations on this basis. Degenerated nerve cells do not regenerate, yet pattern vision does ultimately develop, and it would seem that some learning process is superimposed on this, albeit defective, visual system.

Drever (1955) has reversed the procedure of deprivation studies by testing the degree of normality in the perception of later-blind subjects and has produced evidence on the spatial perception of early- and later-blinded subjects that he regards as somewhat ambiguous in relation to Hebb's position but that on the whole may be taken as supporting it. The ambiguity arises from the fact that while this study did show a relation between early and later learning, it did not prove to Drever's satisfaction a necessary *causal* relation between them. He found associated with early blindness a generalized defect of space perception that is consistent with the studies already mentioned. Relative to the question of learning, he notes that perception of objects in space seems to require an initial apprenticeship early in life that length of later experience does little to modify.

Hunter (1954) has demonstrated that blind subjects tend to be more objective than the sighted in the use of tactile-kinesthetic cues in perceiving space and that the later blinded, who had some visual experience to aid them, tended to be most superior. This difference between blind and seeing people is no doubt related to greater importance of nonvisual cues to the former and hence the greater concentration by them on the development of the skill.

A second line of approach is to study visually naive subjects, which in most species means newborn ones. The Gibson and Walk study already mentioned did not test subjects right at birth, though chicks, lambs, and goats, which can walk in the first day of life, all showed avoidance of the visual cliff within a few hours of birth. Tallarico (1961) found a 91 percent preference for the shallow side in three-hour-old chicks, and Fishman and Tallarico (1961a,b) found evidence of visual depth sensitivity in three-hour-old chicks in their avoidance reaction to an approaching object. A study by Schiff et al. (1962) using infant rhesus monkeys discovered an avoidance reaction to an expanding contour, as if the contour were perceived as approaching. However, Riesen (1947) reported that dark-reared chimpanzees did not respond to an approaching object with the eye blink which is usual. (The fact that his apes had oculomotor disturbances may account for this rather than prove that the response is absent in normal naive animals.)

The experiments by Fantz (1961a) already described in connection with form sensation have given evidence of an ability in young infants (of about fifteen weeks) to discriminate solidity, using textural and brightness cues. However, these data could be interpreted as a response to complexity rather than to space. Wertheimer (1961) studied the motor coordination of visual and auditory space in a girl between three and ten minutes after delivery, showing eye movement responses to clicks sounded in the left or right ear.

The third type of experimental approach described in Epstein's review is that of variation of stimulation. The Stratton (1896) experiments on vision with noninverted retinal images is a classical example of this approach. From the developmental point of view it involves the somewhat dubious supposition that in relearning to interpret the visual world that at first appears inverted the older subject is recapitulating the original infantile learning to perceive; the idea that learning is involved is implicit. Drever (1955) has commented on the validity of these assumptions, but the fact that essentially similar results were obtained (in experiments by Held [1965]) for kitten's first learning and for human relearning encourage one to make this assumption. These experiments are discussed in connection with sensory-motor factors in perceptual change. A nice approach to the question could be obtained only by disrupting the images of naive subjects. The only attempt at this is a study by Hess in which hoods containing prismatic lenses were fitted to chicks so that the visual field was displaced seven degrees either to the right or to the left. Control animals had hoods with no lenses. The chicks were tested at one day by pecking at a brass nail embedded in modeling clay; this permitted a record of the pecks (or at least of those that did not hit the nail on the head). If spatial localization is learned, then one would expect the early pecks to be randomly distributed around the target, gradually converging closer and closer to it; the displacing prisms should make no difference, being compensated for; this possibility was not confirmed. If spatial localization is innate, the pecks of the experimental chicks would cluster seven degrees off target, whereas those of the controls would center on it, and this was the outcome that was found.

After this test on the first day, the groups were divided. Half the experimentals and half the controls were housed in a cage with grain scattered on the floor; the others were in cages containing bowls of mash. At three to four days they were retested on pecking. The two halves of the control group were more accurate in pecking and in good health. The two halves of the experimental group also showed improved pecking in that there was tighter clustering of pecks, but these were still seven degrees off target (the improved consistency being perhaps the result of better motor control). Moreover, the group fed on mash (where accuracy was not important) were in good health, whereas those fed on grain were in poor condition and were evidently not eating enough. It would seem that spatial localization in chicks is not only innate but unmodifiable.

The only other relevant experiments in the area that have involved changing the stimulus are also by E. H. Hess (1950, 1961), and these, too, used chicks as subjects. Hess found that chicks would peck at photographs of grains of wheat. Normally reared chicks showed a marked preference for top-lighted grains, that is, photographs with shadows below, rather than for identical pictures inverted so that the shadow was above as if lit from below.

Hess reared two groups of chicks, a control group with normal lighting from above and an experimental group in similar enclosures but with the lighting from below. Both groups fed on grain from glass dishes. At seven weeks the birds were tested in an enclosure containing the two photographs of grain side by side in the vertical plane (these were evenly illuminated from the sides). Not all chicks responded to the photos, but of those that did, the first pecks were in almost complete agreement with experience—that is, the control chicks pecked at top-lighted grains and the experimental ones at bottom-lighted ones. Both groups showed a strong preference in all their subsequent pecking for the grains apparently lit in the way to which they had become accustomed.

Further experiments were designed to test the development of these preferences; at first there were none at all, and in the first three weeks there were no clear trends in preference irrespective of lighting. From the third week, preferences in line with the lighting experience began to emerge, and by five weeks the control group had a clearly marked choice for top-lighted grains. It was not until the seventh week that so marked a preference was established for the experimental animals; when it came, it was rapid.

This difference is interesting. Hess suggests that there might be an innate tendency to favor top lighting (which is more consistent with the universal experience of the species; bottom lighting is highly unnatural) but that this can be overriden by learning. The sudden emergence of this learning at seven weeks might be the consequence of a critical period of maturation of neurosensory organization that permits this kind of acquisition.

This suggestion that some perceptual learning may have to override innate proclivities is an important one and will be referred to again in connection with other forms of learning.

Changes in Auditory Sensation

Whether or not hearing may be considered secondary to vision as a source of information, and hence as a developmental agent in humans, is a purely pedantic question. The tremendous importance of auditory language to development makes any such comparison of vision and hearing somewhat hazardous and perhaps pointless. It is said that the deaf are more cut off from social interchange than are the blind.

The structural differentiation of the ear is complete before birth, at about eight months after conception. However, the fact that the middle ear is filled with a gelatinous fluid until some hours after birth renders its functional status before this time somewhat uncertain. Before birth there would seem to be no possibility of fetal stimulation of the eyes, but in the case of hearing there is at least the possibility of aural stimulation prenatally. Indeed, with maternal intestinal rumblings, respiratory rustlings, and heart beat, to say nothing of the possibilities of loud external

sounds, the womb must be a somewhat noisy place. Salk (1962) has indeed based a psychological theory upon prenatal auditory conditioning.

A number of studies have attempted to discover whether the unborn child can hear, and one of the earliest of these was by Peiper (1925). He claimed that about a third of the fetuses in his study responded to a loud, shrill automobile horn by movement, and, with adequate preparation of the mother for the noise, he believed that these responses were genuinely fetal rather than maternal ones. There is also the well-known observation by Forbes and Forbes (1927) in which an eight-month-pregnant woman was lying in a bath tub of water that was accidentally struck by a hard object, and she observed a responsive movement to the sound by the fetus. Experimental repetitions on subsequent occasions also produced a response of the fetus to the striking of the bath tub below the water line, and these were thought to be responses to noise rather than to vibrations set up by the impact. Later studies (e.g., Bernard and Sontag, 1947) using rather more sophisticated methods tend to support this conclusion, and it may be that the fetus is capable of sound sensation.

In the case of vision we have seen that some considerable structural changes are still to occur in the visual apparatus after birth. For hearing, the draining away of the amniotic fluid from the middle ear, which occurs during the first week postnatally, is about the only major structural change that has to occur. Until this fluid has drained away, sounds may be dulled, as they are when infection causes fluid to collect in the inner ear.

The work of Hernandez-Péon et al. (1956) and Galambos et al. (1956) have shown adaptation effects in the more peripheral nuclei of the auditory nerve, indicating that adaptation is not entirely a central phenomenon. Because nothing has been described as yet of the developmental history of such effects, it is not possible to say whether the speculation about these being part of the intrinsic organization of the nervous system, rather than imposed, will be borne out with further research.

As already commented on, audition has received very much less attention than vision. Gibson and Olum (1960), in their extensive review entitled *Experimental Methods of Studying Perception in Children* (which has been of great help to me), have quoted a considerable number of studies in various aspects of visual perception but very few in any of the other modalities. This does, of course, parallel the neglect of audition by perceptionists in general; in view of the importance of hearing (and its corollary, language) to development, this neglect is much to be regretted.

There is to auditory perception a temporal element that is of fundamental importance and that makes such perception different from most (though not all) other perceptual phenomena. That is, an auditory pattern is essentially a pattern in time; while a visual pattern may be temporal, as in stroboscopic effects and the cinema, it is not necessarily so. (It might be argued that the scanning movements by which a complex visual pattern is inspected involve a time element—a pattern is certainly not perceived instantaneously and simultaneously in all its parts, but the precise sequencing of these scanning movements is unimportant, and except in special circumstances such as tachistoscopic presentation, their timing may not matter.) As another instance of this temporal element, the acute perception of minute differences in time of arrival at the two ears is fundamental to the apprehension of auditory space. Not much is said in the literature about this aspect of audition and nothing at all is said about its developmental significance, if any. The fact that young infants can localize a sound and turn the head in its direction (Wertheimer, 1961) suggests that the detection of these phase differences in the two ears is possible very early in human life and may be innate.

J. Hirsh (1967) has stated that sequence and temporal pattern must play the same role in auditory perception as form or shape

has in the gestalts of visual perceptions. One of the few studies of auditory sequencing is by Warren et al. (1969), who found that listeners (students) exposed to patterns of three or four sounds could clearly identify the sounds, but could not report the *order* in which they occurred. This was despite the fact that the duration of sounds (200 msec) was far longer than the average of 75 msec per speech sound involved in normal speech and the 50 msec required for the perceiving of successive musical tones. This raises some speculations as to how children even at an early age become able to recognize different words which involve speech sounds in varying orders at approximately the adult level of speed of presentation. The learning of morse code may be an analogous situation, in which the beginner can distinguish sequences (e.g., · – – · from · · – – or – – · ·) only when presented at slow speeds, later advancing to the incredibly high rate of recognition of the skilled morse operator. Recognition is perhaps the key word. At high speeds there is not time for rehearsal and the placing into memory storage of the pattern, whereas there is time for the recall or recognition of patterns already in storage. Presumably the subjects in Warren's study had not enough previous learning to bring the "nonsense" patterns of sounds presented to them to the same level of recognition facility as words.

A study of the developmental aspects of this question will be of great interest to understanding certain aspects of the development of language, and a fruitful line of investigation is suggested.

In the 1920's in England it was the custom to contribute to National Savings Certificates by buying sixpenny stamps. To encourage school children in habits of thrift, they were sold in the schools, and presumably to give the greatest publicity to the virtuous, they were sold weekly at an assembly of the whole school, after morning prayers. Among my early memories of schooldays is being alarmed each week by the headmistress shouting "nash!"—this being the only part of the announcement calling us to buy our National Savings stamps that impinged itself on my startled perception. To what extent this anecdote is peculiar to one dreamy (and evidently guilty-conscienced) five-year-old is difficult to say, but it may illustrate the fact that only the more familiar sections of an auditory time sequence are apprehended and that recognition of the whole of complex sequences presupposes experience with all its parts. This is not different from other perceptions, except that an auditory pattern disappears, whereas the visual pattern NATIONAL SAVINGS CERTIFICATE can be inspected at leisure and spelled out piecemeal without involving memory. Immediate memory must play a crucial role in auditory perception, whereas it may be less important to visual processes.

It has long been observed that a moderate level of auditory stimulation is soothing to infants, inducing low activity, drowsiness, and sleep. The age-old lullabies are the outcome of this observation. Brackbill et al. (1966) have demonstrated this phenomenon experimentally, using heart rate and other measures. They found lullabies to be no more effective than other sounds but did find the infants to be significantly calmer with *any* moderate sound as compared with no sound. They also found Salk's heart-beat sound to be no more effective than others in bringing contentment.

Insofar as available evidence goes (and insofar as comparison is valid), the auditory mechanisms are more advanced at birth than are the visual. This is reflected in a study by Eisenberg et al. (1964), who found systematic relations between signal input and behavioral output in infants between 3 and 200 hours of age. They regard this as indicative of a complex sort of neuronal organization that is present at birth and probably not much different from that of later life. These authors also found systematic age changes in those aspects of auditory behavior that bear on time relations in the CNS. Latent responses (characterized by a longer-than-average interval between stimulus and response) were found only in the first 72 hours. Sequential responses (in

which there is increased response time because there are several behavioral components in consecutive order) varied linearly with age and may be taken as a measure of maturation. These changes refer to the response to auditory stimulation rather than to the temporal features of the stimulation itself and are not the same matters as those discussed above.

Changes in Temperature Sensitivity

As with pain, rather little is known about the neurological bases of temperature sensitivity and particularly about their structural origins in the fetus. For this reason it is again difficult to correlate structural and functional changes. However, fairly clear temperature sensitivity has been noted in fetuses (K. C. Pratt, 1946), cold stimulation evoking respiratory and circulatory changes; these are well marked in neonates. Warm stimuli do not produce such clear-cut responses but do lead to a rather vague approach movement.

While there has been a certain amount of interest in temperature sensitivity as a psychological phenomenon, nothing is known of its development, though there is no reason to regard this as a serious lack in our knowledge.

Growth of the Chemical Senses

Taste buds first appear during the third fetal month and are widely distributed throughout the mouth as well as on the tongue itself in the early fetal period (Parker, 1922). In later fetal life they recede from the nontongue areas, and in the neonate and early childhood they are concentrated mainly around the tip of the tongue, and only a few remain at the back of the mouth. In later childhood they recede from the front of the tongue toward the back, and in maturity the majority are concentrated on the hind third of the tongue and around the larynx (Arey et al., 1935).

The fact that taste buds are apparently well developed prenatally has led to speculations as to whether the fetus can taste the amniotic fluid. Because the composition, and hence presumably the taste of this fluid, remains fairly constant throughout pregnancy, it would seem probable that even if taste sensations are possible, the fetus would be thoroughly habituated to them. It is only after birth that stimulation, which implies change, is possible.

Phylogenetically, olfaction is one of the most primitive of senses, being highly developed in the fish. In man, the sense of smell is by comparison rather poor but is still surprisingly acute, certain substances being readily detectable even in infinitesimally small concentrations. Like the organs of taste, those of smell are well developed early in fetal life, and may lead to speculation as to whether the fetus can "smell" in the manner that fish detect chemical substances in their watery medium. However, the constancy of the amniotic fluid would seem to rule out the change that is necessary to stimulation, and in any case, for the vertebrates, smell implies an airborne rather than a waterborne chemical stimulant (even though it probably has to pass into solution before becoming effective).

As mentioned, the structural aspects of olfaction are well developed by birth, but according to C. G. Smith (1942), from birth onward there is a steady loss of fibers in the olfactory nerve, at the rate of approximately 1 percent per year on the average. There are, however, very wide individual differences in the rates of this loss, and it may well be that disease, rather than natural processes, are causal.

Changes in Cutaneous Sensitivity

Relatively little is known about the embryological development of the various cutaneous perceptors. It is not, therefore, easy to relate structure and function in the fetus. The studies of fetal sensitivity to pressure or touch have been reviewed by Carmichael (1954), and such studies show that the human fetus can respond to a light touch by the third month if this stimulus is in the region of the lips or nose, and that from this zone sensitivity later spreads downward in the usual cephalocaudal manner. Furthermore, the data show that with increasing age the fetus is able to make more specific motor responses to localized stimulation, though it is impossible to say whether the earlier gross movements mask greater sensitivity. By birth the sensitivity to pressure or touch is widely distributed, although it is most evident on the face, hands, and soles of the feet, whereas the shoulders, abdomen, and torso generally are relatively insensitive. Histological examination of Meissner's corpuscles at various ages shows a steady reduction from the age of ten onward in the number of these pressure-sensitive organs in the finger tips (Ronge, 1943).

Kinesthetic Sensitivity Changes

The kinesthetic receptors are present at about the end of the first trimester of the fetal period and may be functional as soon as movements are possible. According to Carmichael (1954), the kinesthetic mechanisms are highly developed by the time of birth. Much of the initiation and control of behavior at this time is no doubt mediated by kinesthesis, but because the obvious methodological difficulties are not readily solved, there has been little study of kinesthetic sensitivity in very young children.

Pain Sensitivity

Pain is a special case among the sensations in that it is usually unpleasant. (There are certain special instances that make it impossible to say it is *always* unpleasant; it should also be noted that intense stimulation of other receptors is unpleasant.) The neurological bases of pain reception are still something of a mystery, and little can be said in this section about the structural and neurological changes underlying pain sensation in fetuses or in young children. It is generally agreed that the fetus, and the neonate for some hours, has a very high pain threshold (Pratt, 1946).

Another special thing about pain is that it is very difficult to say what its sensory and perceptual elements are. Some of the evidence seems to suggest that there is no pain sensation but only pain perception, that is, that pain interpretation is entirely learned. Or put another way, it indicates that there are certain sensory qualities that are of themselves neutral and become affectively toned in a negative manner only as the result of experience. This would seem too extreme a circumstance to be credible, yet it has not readily been disproved by any present knowledge.

Sensory Discrimination

The available studies show an increasing ability with age to make finer discriminations in all sense modalities, that is, not merely to detect stimulation but to distinguish varying degrees of intensity. It is impossible to say how much is due to refinement of the neural equipment and how much is due to learning. Staples (1932) and Chase (1937) both report in infants gross hue discriminations when colors are far enough apart in the spectrum. With older children, where matching techniques can be used, there is a steady increase with age in the accuracy with which hues can be selected and matched (Gilbert, 1894; Cook, 1931; Heider and Heider, 1940). Accuracy of color naming also increases with age (Cook, 1931), but this is another matter. Visual acuity is closely related to discrimination and increases with age, though a degree of acuity is present from an early age (Fantz, 1958b).

Pitch discrimination shows the same age trend (W. Peters, 1927). Insofar as pitch is concerned, training has some influence on the improvement (Wyatt, 1945), but what relative

effects learning and maturation have, or even the mere ability to comprehend the task has, is not known. While there are threshold studies in the chemical senses, and in temperature, touch, and pressure sensitivity, there is no satisfactory information on the development of discriminations between stimuli of differing intensities in these modalities.

Sensory Laterality

There is an increasing amount of evidence, reviewed by Turkewitz et al. (1966), showing that the human neonate is asymmetrical in the response to both tactile and auditory stimulation, being more responsive to right-sided than to left-sided stimuli. There are two possible explanations of this: one being that the infant is intrinsically organized in such a manner as to produce this effect, and the other that the effect is a postnatal consequence of sensory input. Turkewitz et al. favor the second alternative, pointing out that the typical head-prone posture of the infant, with the head turned to the right (or downward), shields the right ear and makes the left one more accessible to auditory stimuli. The right ear is thus less adapted to auditory stimuli and hence is more sensitive, having a lower threshold. They tested this hypothesis by holding the head in the midline position and noted that the difference in auditory sensitivity disappeared when both ears were continuously and equally stimulated (for eight minutes per session).

On this basis they argue that lateral dominance emerges from the asymmetrical stimulation of the normal head-prone position, generalizing to far-reaching consequences for the organization of later behavior. However, this formulation does not take into account one pertinent question: *why* most infants tend to adopt the right head-prone position in the first place. This fact seems to point to some intrinsic and prior organization that favors this position and leads one to ask if laterality may not be as discussed in Chapter 6, the result of some organizational feature that probably has a fairly long history in mammalian evolution.

Summary of Sensory Development

It is evident from the foregoing review that organisms, including humans, probably start life with a fairly elaborate set of preformed sensory organizations. In some species these may provide all or almost all the information necessary to functioning in the environment. These species operate on sensations. For other species the preformed set provides the rudiments of informational input but requires elaboration before the organism can function optimally. This elaboration is given by the use and experience and is modifiable. It is these modified sensations that constitute perceptions.

It may be that in man the amount of modification is very great and the dependence on learning very considerable. Nevertheless, it is useful for the developmental psychologist to know how much is programmed into the organism and how much is attributable to experience. This has not only theoretical but practical value. For instance, in children with certain forms of school learning difficulties—reading problems and the like—it is being assumed that the child starts with a sensory *tabula rasa* and that there has been some failure of perceptual (or perceptual-motor) *learning* as a causal factor. Remedial endeavors are being based upon these supposed learning lacks by providing certain experiences (the nature of which differ with different schools of thought). However, one weakness of this approach is that most of the children had had apparently normal opportunities for learning, and it is necessary to explain how those exposed to the same environment and range of stimulation as any other child have failed to profit from these experiences. A possible explanation is that the basic equipment is at fault. These children have (as it were)

a programming error. If this should prove to be the case, it would shift the focus of remedial endeavor.

DEVELOPMENT OF PERCEPTION PROPER

In this section it is intended to review material that bears on the modification of sensations by extraneous factors, developing them into perceptions. The word *intended* is mandatory, because with much of this material it in fact becomes a point of debate whether it should be considered as *sensory* or *perceptual*. This will be no surprise to those who would claim that there is no logical basis for the division, but as already stated, it is not logic but descriptive convenience that leads me to make the distinction.

The origins of perception have been a point of debate since before psychology became a formal science. The question of whether perception is innate or the result of experience has occupied the argumentative capacities of psychologists for a long time. Perceptionists today tend to regard the question as not especially worthy of an answer, or as unanswerable, and adopt the middle-of-the-road view that it is in fact both inborn and acquired. This has enabled them to turn attention from interminable, and in some contexts pointless, arguments to more constructive ends. For the inquirer concerned with the organism at some particular point in time, and more particularly (as most are) with the mature organism, this is a legitimate stratagem to simplify the problems with which he must cope. The developmental psychologist is not in the enviable position of being able to ignore this question. Moreover, even among those who are not primarily developmentalists, the argument is not entirely dead. Pastore (1960) argued that the most parsimonious theoretical position to take in considering perception is that its major features are determined by the intrinsic properties of the nervous system and that learning has no determinative influence. Learning factors, he said, should be assigned a secondary role; if they exert influence, it is only when the perception to be modified is already an existent one.

Pastore bases his arguments in part upon phylogenetic considerations, on the similarity of perceptual functioning in man and the lower animals. Sillman (1960), also arguing phylogenetically, has reached the opposite conclusion. He points out that the mammalian process of reproduction allows for slower, more intricate, and exquisite organization of the developing creature. The developing mammal is plastic and motile and founds his modifiability on perceptions that are gained from experience rather than from innate perceptual patternings as in lower animals. He points to the phenomenon of sexualization or erotization of the body surfaces and orifices, so that the body takes on an increased sensory capacity; this eroticism of the mammals has tended to expand the areas of the brain given over to sensation and has played a role in the evolution of its complexities. Thus to Sillman, the evolutionary advantage of the mammals, and particularly of the higher ones, is a relative freedom from innately determined perceptual processes and a greatly increased capacity to benefit from experience.

Sillman goes on to state that in the lower vertebrates vision is the primary sensory modality, whereas in the mammals a radical step forward in perception is reached in the elaboration of two nonvisual sense modalities, olfaction and audition, both of which he claims are very highly developed relative to comparable mechanisms in the lower vertebrates. In the majority of mammals, and certainly in the lower ones, olfaction (he says) has come to dominate the sensory activity of the brain as is shown anatomically by the absorption of visual activity into the telencephalon or small brain. He elaborates the disadvantages of visual perception in an environment that is in darkness half of the time. For this reason the superseding of visual dominance by olfactory dominance represents an evolutionary step forward.

In the case of the highest mammals, and of man in particular, this olfactory domination has in turn been superseded by a further evolutionary advance, auditory domination. He argues that olfactory precedence made possible this second big step forward, allowing the emergence of audition as the dominant sense modality by freeing the organism from visual dependence. This is seen anatomically in the growth of the temporal lobes. Audition has, in man, made language possible, with all its potentialities for communication, not only with others, but also with himself. It has made it possible for man to internalize his experience and the memories that are derived through visual, auditory, olfactory, and tactile modalities.

Consonant with this idea of auditory primacy in man is the suggestion by McGeoch and Irion (1952, p. 482) that in young children auditory presentation of material for learning is more effective than visual, the difference becoming less marked as age increases. These authors state that "the data indicate" this to be the case but do not say what the data are. However, Budoff and Quinlan (1964) found that seven- and eight-year-old children learned word pairs aurally presented more readily than ones presented by visual presentation. An investigation by one of my students has shown young school children to have a memory preference for auditory rather than visual material when the two are presented simultaneously (Silcoff, 1966). This seems to be the total of the evidence to support McGeoch and Irion's suggestion (apart from whatever evidence they had), but change with age is shown by Mondfrans and Travers (1964), who with young adults found the auditory presentation of nonsense syllables to be *less* conducive to learning than either visual or auditory-visual simultaneous presentation was.

The idea that auditory perception is ahead of visual perception in young children is also supported experimentally in a study by Carterette and Jones (1967). They found that first-grade children had greater difficulty in the continuous processing of visual than of auditory information. Both auditory and visual processing improve with age, but the visual rises more steeply; by fifth grade the child has reached the adult level, at least for the kind of task employed in this experiment (recognition of real and nonsense words). These authors suggest that at school entry the auditory skills are superior but that the intensive visual intake involved in learning to read underlies the rapid increase in visual skills. It would be of interest to study the slopes of acquisition of the two modalities in illiterate cultures. From this slender evidence one might propose a developmental sequence in which audition leads but is eventually overtaken by vision. It might even be that because audition is more fundamentally organized, it is less plastic and hence that learning plays a more crucial role in the development of visual than of auditory perception. This is highly speculative, but nonetheless interesting.

Individual Styles of Perception

As is common in psychology, studies of perception mostly make the tacit assumption that all individuals perceive in the same manner. Some recognize that in certain situations males may perceive differently from females, or that children of a certain age perceive differently from those at another age level, but no great amount of attention has been given to individual differences.

Witkin et al. (1954) have suggested that some individuals are "field-dependent" and others "field-independent" in perceptual processes. This is discussed in detail in Chapter 16. Kagan et al. (1963) have made a step toward the study of individual styles of perceptual and conceptual approach by showing that some children are "analytic" and others "nonanalytic." That is, some tend to analyze the stimulus environment, whereas others base

their cognitive processes upon the stimulus as a whole. The idea that people are one or the other, cleanly cut, is probably naive, though this is a naiveté forced on us by the scientific tendency to categorize. Science would be reduced to chaos by the too-debated consideration of individuality. In many clinical situations, perhaps, scientific tidiness must be sacrificed to the consideration of the individual (and not vice versa), but here we are endeavoring to approach the question of perception scientifically, and this section is merely a reminder that certain things are lost by such an approach.

Sensory Interplay

For civilized man the invention of writing has translated these important auditory perceptions—words—into visual patterns, and language in its fullest sense is an auditory-visual-motor complex (if we include the act of writing or speaking, as we must, in this totality).

In the conditions of real life, perception commonly involves more than one sense modality. Even quite elementary forms of perceptual phenomena may involve sensory interplay (or perhaps, more accurately, sensory summation), as when the imprinting of ducklings is facilitated by the addition of the *sound* of a duck to the presentation of a moving object to be imprinted to.

Research so far has concerned itself almost entirely with development in one modality at a time and mainly with development in vision. Research in the other sensory areas is less extensive. The developmental effects of interaction between modalities has been little studied (and when one considers the methodological difficulties, this is understandable).

One investigation of the growth of intersensory functioning in children is by Birch and Lefford (1963), who studied visual-haptic and visual-kinesthetic interactions. They found an increase with age in the ability to make intersensory judgments (in their experiment to recognize similarities or differences in geometric forms), and it would seem that even at ages where recognition in one modality is quite facile, intersensory transfer is still difficult. In earlier stages the modalities are, it seems, isolated from one another.

In discussing the role of differentiation and intersensory integration in the development of voluntary motor control, Birch and Lefford (1967) have assumed that by five years teleorceptor (distance receptor) participation in the control of voluntary directed motor actions, especially of the visual elements of these, is already well established. However, there is still development necessary in the integration of visual information with kinesthetic and proprioceptive information. They show in a series of experiments, interpreted in the light of other data from the literature, that the developing organism has a changing pool of sensory input that contributes to the development of intersensory integrations at new levels and to intrasensory differentiations

of increasing fineness. This learning produces better and better integration of the sensory input and more organized patterns of interrelationships of actions, producing an individual of increasing competence.

Abravanel (1967) studied the developmental changes in intersensory patterning of spatial position for children three to five and six to seven years of age under four conditions. Vision and touch were experimentally separated by means of a "screening device." The subjects made same-different judgments and recognition matches between haptic and visual modalities. The accuracy of intersensory patterning was low at three and four years, improved considerably by age five, and was nearly perfect for three of the four conditions by age six.

In a more extensive report, going up to fourteen years, Abravanel (1968) found an increase in the accuracy of intersensory perception that approximated a typical logarithmic growth curve (Figure 13–7). The greatest increase in accuracy was between three and

FIGURE 13–7. Logarithmic growth curve.

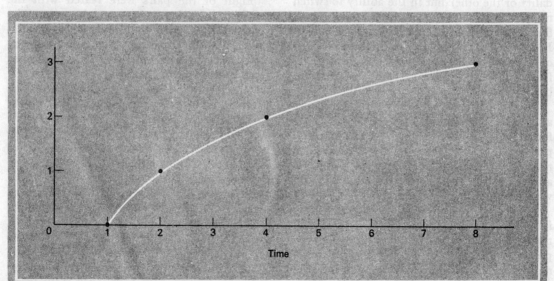

seven years, which he notes corresponds to the period when Piaget says concrete operations are being elaborated. Abravanel discusses this in the light of our understanding of intellectual growth; this is a point that we shall discuss in detail later.

Another study that points to the importance of real-life sensory interplay is one by Katz and Deutsch (1963) on reading achievement. They pointed out that many of the studies of children who have failed to learn to read successfully have assumed some perceptual dysfunctioning or developmental lag in either visual or auditory perception but have not usually considered both factors to be involved. These authors recognize that there may be many cases of reading retardation in which a visual or an auditory difficulty may be found and may be causal in isolation, but they do suggest that in other cases early reading difficulties might be caused by more subtle impairments of perceptual functioning. These authors point out that learning to read involves the use of both auditory and visual skills, and in an experimental study with a group of retarded readers they found that the deficiency was not so much in one sense modality or the other but in the ability to switch rapidly from visual to auditory cues. These findings are also supported in a study by Beery (1967), who noted that retarded readers of normal intelligence were significantly inferior in their ability to make comparisons between visual and auditory stimuli.

The importance of intersensory effects are also noted by Rudnick et al. (1967), who found that as development proceeds visual perceptual abilities become less important to reading, whereas auditory perception and the ability to transpose between audition and vision become more important.

It may be that the case of visual-auditory interaction is inherently more complicated than others. A cross is a cross whether apprehended visually or hapticly, whereas the recognition of the similarity between the seen cat and a heard meow appears to require

greater abstraction (and the similarity between the printed CAT and the spoken word even more).

Birch and Belmont (1965) in a developmental study found a rapid increase in auditory-visual integration during the earlier school years, up to the fifth grade, by which time it was more or less complete. The correlations obtained showed intelligence to be a factor but not the sole one.

Experiments by Held and Hein (1963) and Held (1965) throw light on an important aspect of perceptual development. Riesen (1961a) has suggested that the deficits found in subjects deprived of sensory stimulation in early life are due to the lack of development of sensory-sensory associations. Held and Hein (1963) take this idea further by suggesting that sensory feedback from self-induced movements are an essential ingredient in the development of visual guided behavior. In their experiment, ten pairs of kittens (each pair from a different litter) were reared by the mother cat in darkness, together with their littermates. This method of rearing avoided the social isolation effects of some other sensory deprivation experiments.

Eight of the pairs were reared with the mother in darkness for several weeks. The remaining two pairs were also reared in darkness, but with three hours exposure per day to patterned light (during which time they were not permitted to walk).

One member of each pair was assigned the "active" role, that is, it was allowed to walk in the apparatus shown in Figure 13–8, but was harnessed to the arm which is propelled as it walked. The age at which the active kitten was strong enough to do this varied between eight and twelve weeks, at which time the experiment began. The "passive" assigned kitten was placed in the gondola, which permitted only head movements. It passively moved a similar distance to the active kitten, including side-to-side and some vertical movements, which were translated to it by the mechanism, which could move in all

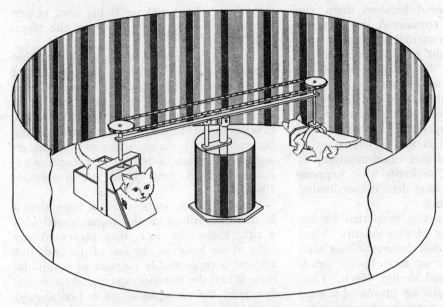

FIGURE 13–8.   *Active and passive viewing. Adapted from R. Held and A. Hein. 1963. Movement-produced stimulation in the development of visually guided behavior. J. Comp. Phys. Psych.,* **56***: Fig. 1, p. 873, by permission of the authors and the American Psychological Association. Copyright © 1963 by the American Psychological Association.*

three dimensions. The passive kitten thus had essentially the same *visual* experience as the active one, but lacked the tactile and kinesthetic experiences of the latter. For both kittens of each pair in the first group, the first visual experience of patterned light was in this apparatus.

Three visual tests were used: (1) visually guided paw placement (a normally reared kitten carried in the hand slowly forward and downward toward a horizontal surface will extend its paws in preparation for "landing"); (2) avoidance of a visual cliff (using the Walk and Gibson [1961] technique); (3) eye blink to an approaching object.

Initially all animals showed abnormal results on the visual tests mentioned; that is, they did not show paw placement, did not show preference for the "safe" side of the visual cliff, and did not show a consistent eye-blink response. (Other tests showed that

visual-cliff recognition does not occur in normally reared animals until paw placement has occurred; one infers from the data that this is after locomotion has commenced, but this inference is not entirely clear.)

After about thirty hours of experience in the apparatus, all the active animals were showing positive results on these tests. At the time that these were showing invariable preference for the "safe" side of the cliff, the passive animals were still responding randomly and were not apparently discriminating the "safe" from the "cliff" side. However, after forty-eight hours of free running in a lighted environment, all the passive group showed normal paw placement and an invariable preference for the shallow side of the cliff.

One point of difficulty with this study is the possibility of retinal change because of dark rearing (see p. 274). However, because both groups had equal deprivation and a difference was still found between them, the question might be considered irrelevant to this particular experimental situation.

These results might modify somewhat the Gibson-Walk stand that recognition of the visual cliff is innate, at least insofar as cats are concerned. Apparently some visual experience is necessary. Moreover, these authors claim that it is visual experience in conjunction with motor movements that is important to the emergence of depth discrimination. It would be intriguing to know what happens to animals that are long denied coordinated visual-motor experience.

These results were also supported by human relearning types of experiments. Adult subjects with prisms that distorted either arm-and-hand movements or total bodily movements in space showed similar effects. Thus subjects wearing displacing prisms who were permited active movements in a large circular "drum" such as that for the kittens more rapidly adjusted to them than subjects in a wheelchair having only passive movements. Apparently sensory-motor feedback plays an important role in perceptual adaptations and may well be a crucial factor in the development of perceptual-motor skills in the immature organism.

One question that is not answered by these authors is that of whether or not factors other than mere locomotion are involved. It could be, for instance, that the kitten restrained in the gondola is frightened by the situation and has too high a level of emotional arousal to benefit from the visual experience. Or the man passively moving inside a drum is too bored —has too low a level of arousal—and is suffering a degree of perceptual deprivation; this deprivation is known to interfere with learning. Maybe the crucial point is having an optimum level of extraneous stimulation (the moving subject getting this from kinesthetic stimuli), irrespective of whether it involves motor activity. It would be interesting to provide the passive partner with, for instance, auditory stimulation (which the active part-

ner is not given) and see if his level of performance is then still inferior on the visual task.

There are, however, some other data that support the idea that the development of sensorily guided behavior and its maintenance do depend on bodily movement in the environment. According to these data, stable functioning of the plastic systems coordinating perceptual and motor activities depend on ordered information derived from the sensory-motor feedback loop (Held and Freedman, 1963).

This feedback loop has also been shown in primates. Infant monkeys were reared with a ruff, about the neck, that prevented any sight of the hands or the rest of the body but allowed a considerable measure of manipulation. When the restraint was ended (at thirty-five days) the young monkeys at first showed prolonged visual inspection of the hands but were poor in visually guided reachings. With practice they showed fairly rapid improvement in eye-hand coordination (Held and Bauer, 1967). The particular attention paid to the hand is interesting and leads one to ask if some innate tendency makes it an especially arresting object of inspection.

White and Castle (1964) studied the interest and visual exploratory behavior of infants following handling during the first five weeks of life, using babies in a creche. They found an increase in visual attentiveness in the handled infants. These infants were, of course, like the passive kittens. The authors distinguish "visual attentiveness" from "informative visual-motor contact with the environment," and the infants showed the former without having the latter, which involves feedback accompanying self-produced movement in the environment. However, visual attentiveness is presumably a prerequisite to this feedback loop, and the stimulation of handling may well play an important part in its development. These authors found no marked difference at three to four months in visually directed reaching and other visual-motor behavior between the handled group and nonhandled controls, but this is not to say that long-term results may not show a difference. The more attentive group might be expected to show better use of equal activity; only a lengthy longitudinal study will explicate this.

Abercrombie (1968) suggests that early deficiencies in feedback because of cerebral palsy may affect the perceptual development of children suffering this disability.

On the question of the further development of sensory feedback, Smith et al. (1963) have produced some data from an ingenious series of experiments involving closed-circuit television by which the infant could control by simple orientative movements, or by voice, the kinds of stimuli he would receive. The infant was thus able to exercise this control at an age when manipulative controls would have been impossible. These authors found evidence that orientative sensory-feedback regulation of the visual environment develops up to about twenty months of age and appears well in advance of even the simplest manual control.

The kinds of sensory feedback involved in drawing tasks under displaced, inverted, and reversed vision conditions apparently develop much later. Smith and Greene (1963) found that subjects under twelve were rarely successful in tasks involving such situations, but that there is sudden shift at about this age after which the task is quite easy. These authors speak of a critical period at this age, but since they do not demonstrate impaired performance in subjects denied whatever experiences are involved at this time, this is not necessarily a critical period in the sense the term is used in this book.

Broadbent (1958) has suggested that when two (or more) sensory modalities are stimulated simultaneously, the information input is controlled so that only one channel at a time is relayed to the higher parts of the CNS. The nonadmitted information is held in storage until the higher centers are free of the other input and then is relayed on. If the delay is too long (more than a few seconds), the information may decay and be lost. On the other hand, simultaneous presentation at a fast rate may result in a jamming of *all* lines of input, so that none of the information can be used. According to this model, ability to shift channels rapidly (as well as an imposed input permitting this) would be necessary as a requisite to intersensory functioning. It has already been suggested (p. 279) that the auditory channel might be preferred in young children, which presumably means, in Broadbent's terms, that this channel more readily secures the upward pathways to the cortex. Since Broadbent's hypotheses still lack extensive experimental support, all this is speculative. Mondfrans and Travers (1964) did not confirm his predictions using adults; what the results would be using immature subjects is not known, apart from the slight evidence of auditory primacy already discussed.

Attentional Factors in Perception

An essential (but often neglected) element in perception is attention. This is especially true if we define *perception* as sensation interpreted. At any given instant an organism is commonly bombarded by stimuli impinging on all sensory receptors. But usually only one of the receptors occupies the attention, and when more than one does, it is often because the several stimuli form a pattern and in this sense are unitary.

At a physiological level the reticular activating system (including the cortical connections) plays an essential role in the process of attending, in selecting the center of attention, and in filtering out irrelevant stimulations (Samuels, 1959). However, we have little information about the developmental status of the RAS during childhood. From its location in the "older" parts of the brain (in the evolutionary sense) it would seem likely that this region of the CNS is anatomically well advanced at birth and that neurophysiological changes with age may be mostly in the cortical component of corticoreticular relationships. The RAS is, as it were, ready, but the cortex is not.

Melzack (1965) has proposed a theory to account for the effects of early sensory deprivation that involves the RAS. He suggests that with normal experience the neural substrates of memories of prior experience exert control over information selection. With severe restriction of early experience, a majority of stimuli in a new environment have no prior associations and hence no basis for the selective filtering of sensory input. For this reason the total input (relevant or not) reaches the cortex and results in overload of the neural systems of sensory and affective arousal. Perceptual discrimination and adaptive responses are therefore disrupted. In other words, normal functioning depends on the filtering mediated by the RAS, and the opportunity for experience and learning plays an essential part in this filtering.

Dallenback (1914) showed that drill in perceiving letters, figures, and geometric figures improved the span of apprehension, and that this effect was apparently permanent. Other experiments have shown that training can improve performance in situations involving tachistoscopic perception (Gates, 1925; Freeburne, 1949). It would seem that the ability to attend appears early (and is perhaps innate) but under some conditions is capable of improvement by learning. This effect has been demonstrated only for simple perceptual situations, and whether the kinds of attentional sets developed by tachistoscopic or other techniques can be generalized to more complex situations is problematical. Goins (1958) has reviewed the findings on this question and has demonstrated that tachistoscopic training does not transfer to reading. If this is the case, it is sad, since much remedial effort is directed toward specific training of this kind. Studies of transfer of training in attention, and of means of maximizing it, are of considerable practical importance.

Visual attention in older children has been studied by Lewis and Goldberg (1969), who used subjects of about three and a half years of age, and found that attention to familiar stimuli reduced and was re-arrested by the presentation of novel stimuli. These authors used hand and eye fixations, heart rate, smiling, and pointing as measures. Like the previous authors, they used expectancy as an explanatory principle, but go further in relating this to theories of emotion. Lewis and Goldberg use Pribram's formulation (1967) that the physiological state underlying emotion should be called "uncertainty" rather than "arousal." Part of the experience of emotion is derived from the attempt to reduce uncertainty by internal adjustments in the CNS. Here we might see a link with N. E. Miller (1969) and his insistence on the importance of the ANS (see Chapter 6), and moreover, the beginnings of a theoretical framework to link perception, cognition, and emotion.

Maturation and Perception

Because many of the developmental changes in perception are related to maturation, it is surprising to find no studies relating such perceptual shifts to measures of physical maturity or developmental age, as distinct from chronological age. There are, however, a few studies that relate perceptual phenomena to intelligence, which is one aspect of maturation. Witkin et al. (1954) found that brighter children more readily extracted embedded figures from test figures (Witkin, 1950). In a study of the ring-segment illusion in which a series was presented so that what was previously an apparently larger stimulus now appeared as apparently smaller, Dixon (1957) found feebleminded children to respond more on the basis of expectation from the previous trial than on present appearance, whereas mentally more mature children of the same chronological age responded in terms of the immediate (though illusionary) perception.

This cannot be taken, however, as indicating a direct relationship between intelligence and susceptibility to illusions, since with some at least, humans and lower animals are equally deceived. Katz and Révész (1921), for instance, have shown chickens and men to be alike in response to the ring-segment illusion when presented alone rather than in a series as in Dixon's experiment, so Dixon's results are evidently a function of some additional factor. The available evidence is not extensive, but it would seem that certain of the illusions are a result of the fundamental organization of the nervous system and that in these, when maturational (and experiential) factors modify them, it is because there is a change in the context within which the illusion is viewed.

It need not be supposed that maturation occurs only within the CNS. Sackett (1963) suggests that certain fixed action patterns (a term he prefers over instinct) depend on perceptual organization at the periphery rather than centrally. The evidence supporting this comes mainly from studies of amphibia, in which there are cells having specific responsiveness—to detection of edge, for example. There are, in fact, cells responsive to straight edges and others responsive to convex ones; others detect changing contrast, dimming and darkness. There is also evidence of similar mechanisms in mammals (e.g., the Hubel and Wiesel data discussed earlier). Sackett suggests that much visual organization takes place at the level of the retinal ganglion cells. This organization may be sufficient to mediate the detection of the simplified sign stimuli involved in imprinting, feeding responses, and others of the innate responses described in Chapter 4. In human infants the apparently inborn perceptions of form and pattern described by Fantz are possibly mediated by such retinal mechanisms. Imprinting and the smiling response (Chapter 8) may also involve them.

(An interesting question arises here: What is the biological usefulness of a straight-edge-detecting mechanism to amphibia or even to man in his natural environment? The natural world contains few straight lines, and it is difficult to think of a single instance of a straight edge which is of adaptive significance to any species. It is, of course, a logical necessity that a mechanism capable of detecting any of the infinite varieties of curve should be able to detect a "zero curve," but this capacity is significant only to man in an artificial environment. It makes one wonder how many other biologically nonutilitarian capacities of the nervous system are usefully exploited by man.)

As Berlyne (1960) has pointed out, the retinal cells may not commence to function until stimulated, and Sackett takes up this point to suggest that there may be an initial period of maturation in the retina of the human infant. These maturational changes may underlie certain perceptual changes found—the increasing interest in complexity, for instance.

Similarly, the time-bound responsiveness to moving objects found in the imprinting phenomenon may depend on such a maturational change; Sackett suggests that cells responsive to brightness, contrast, and contour may mature more rapidly, and it is only when those responsive to movement become functional that the critical period for imprinting can begin. Sackett goes so far as to suggest that peripheral retinal maturation may be more important in perceptual development than central factors are, though because in this book a distinction is being held between perception and sensation, one might prefer to substitute the latter term in his statement. Perceptions (as defined here) necessarily involve cortical functions.

In Chapter 12 it was suggested that the period between five and seven years is an important transitional one in the development of learning. S. H. White (1965) has noted evidence of a similar transition in perceptual processes.

A number of authors speak of a transition at this time from tactual to visual exploration or from reliance on the "near" receptors involved in tactile, kinesthetic, proprioceptive, and visceral sensations to reliance on the "distant" receptors of vision and audition. Bruner (1964) spoke of the young child as "enactive" (see Chapter 16), dealing with motor patterns and developing from this condition to storage of environmental inputs as visual imagery and later as symbolic representations. The studies by Birch and Lefford (1963, 1967) show how children slowly integrate haptic and kinesthetic percepts with visual ones as they mature. White quotes a Russian study by Boguslavskaya (Zaporazhets, 1961) in which three- to four-year-old children were predominately tactual in exploration of objects, whereas by six to seven a majority of the children were visual. He also quotes an unpublished study by Schopler (1964) which showed a progressive increase from three to nine in the amount of time spent playing with visual material in a situation permitting free choice.

These facts do not mean, of course, that young children are avisual but merely that they tend to a nonvisual preference. Within visual processes there is a shift from color to form dominance. This change occurs at about six years (S. H. White, 1965). It may be that language plays a role in this shift. Deaf children are apparently color-dominant well past the age at which hearing children are form-dominant (Doehring, 1960).

As Jackson (1957) has remarked, there is need for more studies of intellectual abilities in relation to mode of perception, and this is especially true in the developmental field. A method that may well prove useful here is a test of perceptual maturity devised by van de Castle (1965). Studies that relate perceptual changes to developmental status rather than chronological age are also needed, though really sophisticated approaches would require measurement of the maturational status of the perceptual system under consideration (rather than some more remote general estimate such as wrist X rays or dentition), and we do not at present have the technique for this.

Motivation and Perceptual Processes

Motivation is discussed in detail in Chapter 14 and it is not proposed in this context to discuss this important question in relation to perception. Solley and Murphy (1960) have reviewed the studies of the manners in which motivation does influence perception, both to facilitate it in some situations and to retard it in others.

In the course of development the child acquires many social motives that influence his behavior, including his perception. But he probably starts with a fundamental motivational system, which Harlow (1953) has called curiosity and Hebb (1958) the need to maintain exteroceptive contact with the environment. The driving force behind much perceptual learning lies here, though hunger and thirst no doubt also play their role (perhaps less so in our well-fed society than in others); the role of sex as a motivation in infancy and in early childhood is problematical.

Language and Perception

Leeper (1935) long ago showed that in adults perceptual organization is facilitated by verbally aroused redintegration and that after it is set other possible organizations are more difficult. The role of prelanguage organization on perceptual processes in children and the impact of the advent of language have not been unraveled. No doubt their effects are considerable, though subtle and difficult to study. This is yet another area requiring research.

Experiential Factors and Perception

Although the human organism may be programmed for at least some measure of constancy, this does not mean that other factors, and notably experience, do not improve this innate capacity. V. Hamilton (1966) re-examined the usually accepted negative correlation between intelligence and size constancy. Size estimates of three standards were obtained from two groups of school children with different IQ's. Four major conclusions were that knowledge of the laws of perspective influences reduction in underconstancy. Though underconstancy as well as overconstancy may occur with low as well as with high IQ's, overconstancy appears to be the more usual and adaptive behavior with higher cognitive development, and significant changes away from underconstancy are associated with higher intellectual levels.

The role of experience in perceptual development is also shown by Eichengreen et al. (1966), who found that rats reared in an enriched environment show the preference for the shallow side of the visual-cliff apparatus at an earlier age than those reared under normal laboratory conditions. The authors recognize that the explanation of this finding may rely on emotional and attentional effects of early rearing, but they believe that the differences probably reflect differences in the perception of depths.

Such findings as these are not contradictory to the notion that such features of perception are innate. They may be interpreted as showing that environmental factors can modify the timing of emergence of innate behaviors and can even, as in the bottom-lighted grain, quite substantially modify the adequate stimulus. Innate does not mean inevitable.

There are a number of developmental studies which show shifts in perceptual processes that are not readily related to any particular factor. All that can really be said is that the longer the child has been perceiving, the greater these shifts appear to be, though whether one should relate them to maturation or experience, or change in motivation or attention, to language, or to what else is really impossible to say. They are called experiential here, but may be misnamed.

Piaget and Morf (1958) take the view that perception is not innately organized but is a developing system becoming more and more adaptive with growth. This is not to deny a given basis, and in Piaget's view early perception is dominated by "best" organizations of the field, or, put another way, is centered on the dominant figure in the visual field. In this he would not seem in disagreement with the Gestaltists. With growth, however, perception becomes active and imposes restructuring on the field so that other possible organizations (as, for example, in ambiguous figures) can be achieved. This is the process Piaget has called the "decentering of perception." Among the results of this are an overestimation by younger children of stimuli in the center of the visual field. Piaget and his team (Piaget et al., 1942–1956) have performed an extensive series of experiments on this question, among them studies of overestimation of apparent size, as in some of the illusions. There are changes with increased experience (Piaget regards these as caused by learning) in which the child is able to shift attention more readily to the less dominant parts of the visual field and hence to gain a more objective picture of the external world —one that incorporates a greater variety of elements. These changes may be illustrated by the "assimilation" and "contrast" phenomena (Wohlwill, 1960), as in the Delboeuf illusion (Figure 13–9). Experimentally, the subject is asked to select a circle that is the same in size as the standard (inner) circle by stating when it matches in size a variable circle presented for comparison.

In situation A, in which the two concentric circles are not greatly different in size, the illusion is one of assimilation. The inner circle is seen as larger than it objectively is (is matched to a too-large variable); that is, it is assimilated in size to the outer one. When the concentric circles are markedly different in size (B), the effect of contrast appears, and the inner circle is now matched to a smaller

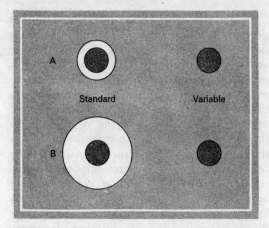

FIGURE 13-9. The Delboeuf illusion.

one. In general, it is claimed, assimilation effects are greatest in young children and tend to decrease with age; whereas contrast effects increase.

Examination of this effect by the usual psychophysical methods is possible only with children mature enough to follow the instructions and to perform the matching required to say when the variable is objectively the same size as the standard. Also (by verbal means), the child's attention must be centered on the inner or standard circle. In so doing, it is focused on the concentric pattern (which, being more complex, might attract a preference anyway, as we see from the Fantz experiments). We thus have a total pattern that is larger than the standard and that, by the centration effect, tends to enlarge this standard. As the child becomes more capable of separating the two circles, judgments become more objective and the assimilation effect decreases.

In situation B, the domination of the standard is established, probably, by the suggestion or set given in the instructions, but for the young child the outer circle is perceptually remote and his responses tend therefore at first to be more objective than in the case of A. However, as the centration effect lessens

with age, the outer circle comes more influentially within the visual field also and exerts its effects on the perception of the standard; the contrast effect therefore emerges.

One point at which this explanation, based upon Piaget, is somewhat unconvincing is that with increasing lability in the direction of attention or increasing ability to shift and focus, greater objectivity of judgment might be expected in both A and B (Piaget does not use the term *objective* in this connection, but his arguments can be fairly interpreted using this term). Against this it could be said that complete objectivity of judgment is hardly to be expected from all that we know of perception but that the developmental trend is toward a fairly consistent and moderate level of deviation from objectivity.

However, in addition to such logical questioning of Piaget's explanation, it may be asked whether the age trends reported are in fact genuine. Santostefano (1963) obtained results that differ from those of earlier investigators, as reviewed by Wohlwill (1960). He points out that because the statistical handling of the data in earlier studies was not altogether appropriate comparison of results is not clear. His data, he thinks, might be consistent for the positive illusion (assimilation effect) but are contradictory for the negative or contrast effect.

Rather than an explanation based upon age trends, Santostefano suggests one using individual differences in cognitive controls of perception. This is based upon Gardner (1961), who suggested individual differences in scanning movements; some persons are extensive scanners, ranging over the visual field, and others are limited scanners (or focusers, in Santostefano's terms). Gardner derived these notions from Piaget and relates extensive scanning to decentration, but he suggests that an explanation of illusions in terms of attention deployment is more economical than Piaget's explanation. It could be, of course, that deployment of attention changes with age too, but the data are not explicit, and individuals may remain consistent in this regard over their histories. This is not necessarily to throw into question the whole of Piaget's centration theory, but to do so only with its applicability to the illusions; many more data are needed here.

In another illusion, that of parallelism, Smith and Smith (1963) found age changes (decrease in the effect) but also evidence of individual variation. Some young children performed like adults. It might be that there are wide differences in the ages at which a given phenomenon appears, and the assumption of uniform and closely age-related progression might be invalid.

The studies of field dependence by Witkin and his associates (1954) also show developmental shifts. They found that children between about eight and ten years of age tend to perceive a given item in terms of its surrounding context (as demonstrated by the rod-and-frame experiments, in which the tilted frame influences the estimate of verticality), whereas between about ten and twelve this effect of the context decreases markedly, with rather slower decrease until about seventeen (when in their studies there was a mild increase in context influence). This is consistent with the decrease of the assimilation effect, but the contrast effect is less readily reconciled with this observation, since it seems to imply increased field dependence rather than lessening influence. However, the apparent inconsistency might be caused by the difference in ages of subjects, and it may be that it is the assimilation effect that is not comparable. The increasing contrast effect of Piaget occurred in five- to seven-year-old children and might be continuous with Witkin's groups of eight-year-olds and over. The assimilation effect might be related to some other process that looks similar. It would be necessary to consider both phenomena in the same children at various ages to elucidate the common properties.

Elkind and Scott (1962) have studied the development of decentering using ambiguous figures (ones with reversing perspectives) and found that the ability to perceive the alternative figures increases with age and also with IQ. The more articulated figures (those with most supporting detail) were the more readily seen by younger children. They explain these results in terms of Piaget's centration theory and regard their experiment as a crucial test between Piaget's position and the satiation theory of Köhler and Wallach (1944).

They point out that Piaget's model is a logical one, whereas that of Köhler and Wallach is neurological. The latter authors suggest that as the "neural excitation" corresponding to the perception of one figure-ground relationship is continued, satiation sets in, raising the resistance in these pathways and hence favoring a shift to an alternative one, permitting another figure-ground organization. According to this theory, reversals should lessen with age because a "permanent satiation" (in both pathways) tends to build up as time passes, slowing down the rate of shift. In the view of these authors the child is perceptually confused by a constant and rapid instability of figure-ground relationships. Elkind and Scott, on the basis of their own and other evidence, reject the Köhler and Wallach model in favor of Piaget's. But however useful a logical model, such as that of Piaget, may be as a guide to fact-gathering, an ultimate explanation of such perceptual phenomena must involve neurological considerations. At this level a purely logical explanation will be insufficient, and the conclusion must not be that neurological models are inadequate but only that this particular one is.

Elkind et al. (1964) have discussed other experimental findings in terms of decentering. They presented children with figures that could be seen in a part-whole manner (e.g., an arrangement of fruits that could be seen holistically as a clown). In their study preschool children tended to see both part and whole, and they explain this in terms of Piaget's concept, in which there is an ability to shift (decenter) from one manner of perception to form a new perception, as when the several fruits become one clown (or when the clown becomes a number of fruits). Differing from Piaget's own experiments, the children here were dealing with meaningful material, and conceptual and verbal factors might play a part. However, a study by Reese (1963b), discussed on pp. 299 and 300, suggests that such mediational influences may not be crucial.

Another perceptual area in which experiential factors are important is the perception of pain. Melzack and Wall (1965) have outlined the controversies that have gone on for a long time about the nature of pain. They divide the current theories into two kinds. On the one hand, there is the specificity theory, which regards pain as a specific sense modality like the others, having receptors and central apparatus, including a pain center in the brain. The other is pattern theory, which maintains that there are no specific receptors but that a pattern of impulses in the CNS is set up by the *intense* stimulation of nonspecific receptors.

These authors show that, among other difficulties, the psychological evidence fails to support the assumption made by the specificity theory of a one-to-one relationship between the intensity of stimulation of specialized pain receptors and the perception of pain. Unlike the situation with other sensory modalities, there appears to be no definite cortical area for the reception of pain impulses. Rather, they say that the amount and quality of perceived pain is determined not merely by the sensory input but also by psychological variables. They point to observations of soldiers suffering wounds in battles, for whom these wounds represented honorable escape from a dangerous situation. Even severe wounds were apparently without pain, and medication was frequently refused (Beecher, 1959). Reports of Cossack soldiers undergoing surgery without anesthetic and without apparent discomfort, and accounts of martyrs, show that an attitude to pain that makes it painless can be acquired culturally or by individuals in certain states, such as religious ecstasy.

Not only can there be no pain in spite of adequate stimulation, there can also be pain in the absence of what might be considered adequate stimulation, as is the case in the phantom limb (Livingston, 1943). In some of Pavlov's experiments, dogs for which electric shocks, burns, or cuts were the conditioned stimulus for salivation eventually gave no sign of pain, which had become for them simply a signal for eating behavior. Moreover, this was not a generally acquired indifference to pain, because they responded normally to painful stimuli other than those involved in the experiment and even to the same stimulus applied to some other part of the body (Pavlov, 1927, 1928).

It is evident from facts such as these that in pain mechanisms there is the possibility of input control, and a theory must take account of this. This input control is the point of major interest to the present discussion.

Another factor that has to be considered is central summation, because evidence (reviewed by Melzack and Wall) suggests that there is a summation of inputs from various levels. This is an aspect of the matter that cannot concern us here, though it may become important to theorizing in the future when more is known about the nature of this summation process and its development. Other questions raised by these authors—such as receptor specialization—are more purely physiological and need not enter into this discussion.

Some evidence of importance to understanding the development of pain perception is contained in a study by Melzack and Scott (1957). They reared Scottish terriers, from weaning at about one month until eight months, under conditions of sensory deprivation in which they were in social isolation in cages that also restricted movement. Littermate controls were reared in a free environment; that is, they were reared as pets, in what are normal conditions for domestic dogs. As young adults (and subsequently) the restricted dogs showed abnormal responsiveness, especially to noxious stimuli. They did not react in a normal manner to pinprick or burns or other painful events and seemed unable to learn to avoid situations involving such stimuli in the manner dogs usually can. These authors interpreted the results as showing that perceiving and responding to pain in the manner considered normal in adults requires early (and prolonged) perceptual experience and that without this experience overt responsiveness to noxious stimulation is abnormal and the capacity to perceive pain is impaired.

In a later article Melzack (1965) has changed the emphasis of the interpretation of reactions of the restricted animals. The abnormal responses were to stimuli of low and moderate intensity, whereas high levels of noxious stimulation did invariably produce the usual responses. The animals also show markedly inferior performance on cognitive tasks, unusual social submissiveness, and excess of such behaviors as licking. He now interprets these reactions to pain as part of a more general pattern. As a result of experience (and normal rearing contains adequate amounts of it) memories or phase sequences (using Hebbian terms) are built up, and on the basis of these the input is filtered as to its relevance. In this way the total input to the CNS is reduced by the elimination of the irrelevant input. Because the restricted animals have not built up these memories, the filtering is inadequate and the CNS is overloaded with excessive input; relevant cues are masked by irrelevant ones, and responsiveness is disorganized.

The biological function of pain is not as clear-cut as it might appear at first sight, and a great deal of philosophical discussion has centered on the problem. It is commonly a signal of disease and in civilized man can often lead to appropriate action, though it does not usually do so in a state of nature. The biological usefulness of toothache to a horse, or even to primitive man, is not easy to know, though in a more general sense the survival value, especially to the integument, of painful stimuli is obvious enough. There are cases reported in the literature (e.g., McMurray, 1950; Cohen et al., 1955) of insensitivity to pain; the condition is apparently congenital. Such individuals suffer constant injuries, which they do not learn to avoid, and are seriously handicapped in a variety of ways even in our society; under primitive conditions one must assume they would soon fall victim to sepsis if not to more violent demise.

Because pain, and its avoidance, occupies a key position in numerous psychological theories of motivation, these cases of insensitivity to it are of particular interest. Some theories of personality also point to pain as a factor in development, though Sternbach (1963) has denied its importance. McMurray (1955), in a review of the literature on insensitivity, concludes that, first, too little is known about the origins of the condition and, second, too little about the behavioral sequelae to draw any useful conclusions from the cases so far described. Longitudinal developmental studies of such cases are needed to answer the outstanding questions. More recently Schneider (1964) has reiterated this warning.

Perceptual Learning

The foregoing has dealt mainly with the question of what is the basic sensory and perceptual equipment of the child. The evidence may not be conclusive beyond any shadow of doubt, and perhaps we never shall know for certain, but it does seem likely that there is a considerable amount of innate sensory organization. In the visual realm, color, movement, space, and form are sensed early and so far as we can determine without the need for learning. There is some evidence, too, that certain patterns are "recognized" innately; that is, that they are sign gestalts. It would seem that Locke was wrong about the *tabula rasa* of the child's mind—a blank waiting to be impressed; the Gestaltists were, in part at least, more correct. Nor, it would seem, is early perception such a vague and undifferentiated thing as Piaget, Vernon, and Werner suggest it is.

However, reference has already been made to the fact that learning modifies these innate sensory organizations. Even the chick, which innately selects grain-like objects to peck at, learns to recognize actual grain and to discriminate it from nonedible objects of similar size and shape. How long the human child retains any entirely naive sensations, unalloyed by learning, is impossible to say. He probably does not do so for long.

Unraveling the part played by learning would involve knowing more about the mechanisms involved. For instance, how does the chick come to discriminate grain from similar objects—must we, or can we, assume that learning is necessary? The current learning models involve some crucial factor, such as contiguity, need satisfaction, or drive reduction. A naive chick busily pecking at pieces of gravel having the visual characteristics of grain (and it is only the *visual* properties that have so far been described) will not reduce its hunger, but how is the crucial link established between what should be pecked at and hunger reduction? As hunger mounts, one would expect even more vigorous pecking impelled by this instinctive mechanism at the unsatisfactory pebbles. Or, in a mixed diet of grain and gravel, what learning process differentiates the grain as "rewarding" from the gravel, which is not? This is unexplained. Obviously some additional factor is at work—taste, maybe. But how does the chick "know" the taste of grain? One explanation would be another sign gestalt, gustatory this time, but this seems to carry the matter away from learning; in this view the chick merely responds to another innate sensory organization, so that a complete description of the sign stimuli necessary to realizing pecking behavior involves taste as well as visual cues.

The purpose of this example is not to argue that learning is not involved in perception; to do so and say it is *all* "instinct" would seem to be arguing way behind the times. The purpose is more to show that to pinpoint the role of learning is not so easy as some would suppose. Perhaps what the learning depends on is the reward of a (presumably) pleasant taste. The chick learns to look more carefully and to discriminate the more subtle visual cues that distinguish the rewarding good-tasting objects from the unrewarding, tasteless gravel. An experiment involving grain-flavored gravel suggests itself. But it can do this only because the taste of grain is *innately* pleasurable. There seems to be no need to suppose that the chick can learn that things which taste thus are hunger-drive-reducing and that those that do not are not. Hunger reduction (as distinct from a full crop) is not immediate; digestive processes probably involve a time span that for the chick is too long; reward must follow more immediately upon action. With higher organisms, and particularly with the human adult, the permissible time lapse is much greater. The human infant, however, is probably not much different from the chick in this regard, and learning (it is proposed) serves to link a series of innate sign stimuli rather than to make greater leaps. This topic is discussed more fully in Chapter 12.

If this view is accepted, it seems contrary to the arguments of Murphy (1947), Piaget (1954), Witkin et al. (1954), and Werner (1957), who all say that the perceptual mechanisms of the child are most plastic in the earlier years. Moreover, this apparent contradiction disappears if we assume that the earliest perceptual learning consists in the linking up of innate sign stimuli in the manner proposed above. To accept this involves the proposal of a considerable number of linkings that can be combined and recombined in a vast number of ways. Any one of these linkings involves only a small learning jump, but they add up (it is supposed) to something extensive.

The paradigm for this notion may be the imprinting phenomenon (discussed more fully in Chapter 8), which may be described as one-shot learning that links certain innate behaviors-in-readiness to certain perceptual cues.

We have, admittedly, very little knowledge at the present time of any such range of innate sign stimuli in humans, but this may be only because no one has looked for them. As is pointed out in Chapter 4, these innate elements of perceptual organization may be so overlaid in adults as to be indiscernible; they are the forgotten, dissipated acorns from which the oaks have arisen. The hypothesis being argued here is that together and in total they are of crucial importance to the foundations on which are laid the elaborate superstructure of later perceptual learning, or (to retain the metaphor just used) the invisible roots which support the visible tree.

The nature-nurture question as it relates to perceptual learning therefore becomes in part that of how these given sign stimuli are interlinked. One might modify the statement (of the authors mentioned above) that earlier perceptual processes are most plastic by saying that the *earliest* ones are rigid and in large measure predetermined, awaiting only the provision by the environment of the appropriate cues. This primary stage is followed by a rapid accumulation of cell assemblies (in Hebbian terms), and this is the phase of greatest plasticity. As the potential for cell-assembly formation becomes limited (as presumably it does) by the properties of those already formed, then this greatest plasticity is lost, and the third stage of lesser pliability is reached. Human adults (and even those of lesser breeds) remain amazingly plastic, but relative to the enormous flexibility of childhood, their plasticity is reduced.

It is not suggested, however, that *all* perceptual learning consists in the interlinking of innate sign stimuli but only that an appreciable proportion of earlier learning does. Experimental data on perceptual learning of any kind treated developmentally are not extensive, so there is no great body of data to appeal to.

Elkind (1964) has used ambiguous figures in a developmental study of what he has called perceptual learning. He did indeed find an increase in perceptual organization in that older children were better able than younger ones to reorganize the stimulus in order to see the hidden figure. There was also a low but positive correlation with intelligence as measured by the Kuhlmann-Anderson group test. Whether or not this undoubted change in perceptual organization can be attributed to learning is another matter.

Elkind et al. (1964) studied part-whole perception in children by using drawings that could be seen either as parts or as a different totality; that is, an apple, a pear, two bunches of grapes, and two bananas were so arranged that they could also be seen together as a mannequin or as a clown. Using groups of children from four to nine years of age, they found an increase with age in the ability to integrate the parts into a whole. Some of the younger children did report seeing wholes, but most saw parts only, and there was a steady increase with age in the ability to see both parts and wholes. Surprisingly perhaps, the more intelligent children tended to perceive parts more readily than wholes.

What place learning, as opposed to other possible forms of perceptual development, such as maturational changes in the organizing capacity of the CNS, might take in this change is problematical. Certainly this study does not demonstrate that learning is the crucial variable, and it is difficult to find any studies that do isolate the part played by learning in this process. Indeed, when one comes to consider the methodological difficulties involved, this is hardly surprising. It would seem unreasonable to suppose that learning plays no part in the development of perceptual processes in children, but demonstrating that it does play a part is less than easy.

In studying perceptual learning in adults, a common device is to establish some particular set and then to measure its influence on perception. Reese (1963a,b) has used this technique with children. He used the Bugelski rat-man figure, an ambiguous one that can be seen either as a rat or as a man's face. Preceding the presentation of the Bugelski figure, he showed a series of either six animals or six human faces. These figures were unambiguous. In preschool children, the presentation of one series or the other did not particularly predispose the children to respond to the ambiguous figure consistently with the particular series shown; in other words, there was no marked tendency to a set effect. However, as Reese points out, there are two possible explanations, other than age correlation, of this: that the series was too short for the learning to take place or that the younger children did not respond conceptually; that is, they did not see the items of the training series as being members of a class. Reese experimentally ruled out these two possibilities and concluded that the tendency to establish conceptual sets in young children is weak but increases with age.

Gibson (1950) and Gibson and Gibson (1955a,b) have argued that perceptual development progresses toward greater psychophysical veridicality. There is a difference between the "assumptive world" of the individual and the "literal world," and the child moves toward a greater correspondence between the two (though, one suspects, never quite reaching it). Taking the Gibsons' idea, the sign gestalts as described by the ethologists are nonveridical indeed, in the sense that only certain simple elements of the complex "real" stimulus gestalt are necessary to efficacy in releasing behavior. The male stickleback responds hostilely to a grossly untrue representation of another male (p. 62), though this parody of a fish does have certain properties of the true one. The human infant and the fish may be alike in this responsiveness to the "untrue" (or, anyway, the barely representational), but the former (unlike the latter) has the potential capacity for the recognition of finer details. (Strictly, of course, we do not know what the fish actually sees in the female; we only know that what he responds to does not seem to be

a very good likeness to us.) But even the human adult may not be so greatly different. The adult male can recognize minute differences between one woman's face and another; the perception of which he is *capable* may be extremely rich in detail, yet he may respond to much more elemental features of curve and form, possibly ones that he could not himself identify. Sex appeal, which some women have in abundance and others have less of, may consist of basic sign gestalts that are really very simple, if we can find them.

Under experimental conditions, this trend toward veridicality can be demonstrated, as it is when the vertical is more truly estimated by older subjects in the tilted-frame situation. As Gibson (1950) put it, we learn to recognize those aspects of visual stimulation that correspond to the real environment, or at least those features of it that are significant to us.

EPILOGUE

In discussing the development of perception, it would be a happy thing to know what development is toward. If we had a neat description of what mature perception consists of, the task of the developmental perceptionist would be greatly simplified. Unfortunately there is no such model available to us, and one is faced with a variety of suggested models of varying degrees of vagueness.

One possible developmental shift in the human child is from perceiving the whole as the sum of its parts to the whole as more than the sum. In other words, the child moves from simple perceptual summations to gestalten. This parallels a phylogenetic progression in which lower organisms operate on this principle of heterogeneous summation but higher ones on Gestalt principles (Klopfer, 1962).

As we have already seen, Bower (1966b) has investigated gestalten in infants. The implications of Bower's experiments for Gestalt theory need to be worked out. They could call into question the notion that Gestalt perception is innate, though they might mean that some maturation is necessary before this innate tendency becomes manifest. Bower discusses the theoretical implications of his studies and suggests some further experiments that might be performed and that may well prove to be a profitable line of inquiry. Bower himself is, according to a statement made at a McGill colloquium (1968), apparently moving toward the idea that these findings may be evidence of rapid early learning, rather than innateness. In view of the general inefficiency of early learning discussed in Chapter 12, it could be argued that only learning that is "preset" could be so rapid at this stage of development. In other words, gestalts are innate and not innate. That is, learning may be involved in the emergence of Gestalt perceptions, but the capacity for this particular kind of learning is innately present, so that the organism is inherently predisposed to this kind of learning, just as it is innately predisposed to the learning involved in imprinting.

Another possible approach is that of Bruner (1957). To him, perception is a process of categorization. Objects acquire a categorical identity, and the process of perceptual development is a movement from cues by inferential mechanisms to these categories. An object or a sensory event is labeled by this process in terms of cues; these cues are more or less reliable according to the environment in which the organism must live. The study by Over and Over (1967) is consistent with this idea.

A difficulty with this model is knowing just how to fit it into the framework of hypothesis that this chapter is attempting to evolve. If by *cues* in his terms we think of *sensations* (in our terms), then questions arise. Many species of birds show an aversion (which may be innate) to insects having black and yellow stripes on the abdomen. This spares them stings, but it also means that certain harmless insects, with protective mimicry of this sort, that could safely form a morsel are also avoided; however, response to these cues (*sign stimuli* is our term) is more or less reliable. This is a process of categorization but one that

can with reasonable confidence be regarded as innate, whereas what Bruner has in mind is a learned system of categorization, though his idea of primitive categorization to include prior-constructed cell assemblies would seem to cover the innate situation. He states that whether or not primitive categorization does involve prior assemblies is a matter that need not concern us; they may not concern him, but us they must. Bruner is, of course, implicitly concerned with human perception and is not taking a comparative approach, whereas we are assuming the perceptual processes of the child to be in essence no different from those of lower animals. We are making certain assumptions, admittedly on somewhat slender evidence at present, like the assumption that fear reactions to snakes and snake-like objects are in both humans and animals innately triggered without the necessity of any learning or experience by these creatures (Jones and Jones, 1928). We are proposing that sign combinations of stimuli (for example, a long, wiggly object) have invested in them these cue properties triggering certain behavioral responses, and although we have knowledge of only a few of these properties, we assume that they are in fact more numerous.

The "primitive categorizations" of Bruner are thus of considerable interest to us, but he does not develop them further. If he means what he is here being taken to mean, then his scheme may be useful to us, but he does not elaborate it or the relation of these primitive categories to later perceptual processes.

A number of points of his further discussion of perception need not concern us in detail. His first proposition, that perception is a decision process, is a key one. Further propositions enlarge on the ways in which decision processes enter into the process of categorization.

Perception for Bruner, then, is dependent on the construction of a set of organized classes by which the stimulus input is categorized, identified, and given connotative meaning. Veridical perception (and perception may develop toward greater veridicality, though we cannot yet regard this as an experimental fact) depends on this process of constructing category systems. In the course of development (we may assume) greater perceptual readiness is achieved. That is, classes become progressively more accessible to the stimulus inputs—they can be more readily categorized, or the decision process becomes easier. It is evident at this point that the development of perception is intimately interwoven with the growth of the organism's ability to categorize and to decide. The development of both learning and cognitive processes is crucial here, and the matter cannot be further discussed without first dealing with this matter.

The conclusion of a review of developmental studies of perception should be a statement of the explanatory principle that unifies all these observations. Such a statement is not forthcoming, from me at least. There have been a number of attempts at such a statement—none of which is all-embracing as an explanation.

Werner speaks of a developmental shift in which young people see the world holistically, whereas in maturity it is seen analytically. Old people, he claims on the basis of studies (Wapner et al., 1960), revert to the holist style of perception. It is because mature individuals are not passive in their interaction with the world that they seek to analyze their experiences. One manner in which this analytic influence is seen is in the changes from childhood to maturity of both assimilation and contrast effects, both of which are dependent on holistic perception and are modified by analysis. A principle with such a high level of abstraction is difficult to apply as a conceptual tool having practical utility (for example, in designing educational procedures) and in any case seems inconsistent with other reported findings. It is contradictory, for one thing, to the report that young children do not readily make intersensory transfers. It might be argued that intersensory perception (e.g., recognizing by touch a previously seen shape) depends on analysis and recognition of essential elements, but such a statement is unsatisfying if one con-

siders that recombination of certain of the analyzed elements—holism—is necessary to the performance. In other words, mature perception involves both analysis and synthesis, the latter producing a new whole. Because children are not analytic, it is implied, they cannot resynthesize, and their perceptions differ from those of adults. Whether or not this is true, it seems too vaguely general a statement to be useful.

Fieandt (1958) has suggested that a unitary theory of perception will incorporate the fact that perceptions (in real life at least) are multidimensional and involve more than one modality: "the organism reacts as a whole to a relational system of stimulus-effects" (p. 317). If both this and Werner's theory are true, then we must have a different theory of perception for children and some account for the shift from one explanatory principle to the other. In addition to this is the probability that because the organization of the nervous system, caused in part by the varying degrees of maturation of regions, is different for children, an explanatory principle that is valid in maturity is not applicable to children. The theoretical issues in the development of perception are therefore complex in the extreme. We have at present only a very imperfect *description* of perceptual processes in childhood, and we are not within sight of an explanation of their changes with age.

A program of attack on this question would seem to involve, first, a much more intensive effort on developmental studies of auditory perception as well as of the other nonvisual modalities, but especially of audition. Second, it would involve studies of sensory interrelationships—multidimensional studies rather than studies of tiny segments of experience within a single modality. Thirdly, it would require much more knowledge of the neurological changes of childhood and the relation of these changes to perceptual processes.

A developmental theory of perception has been presented by Piaget (1961), and reference to certain aspects of it has already been made. He sees the development of perception as a continuous process in which it differs from the development of intelligence, which has definite stages. There is a· slow shift from outer to inner and from peripheral sensory processes to central ones. Flavell (1963a) has noted with regard to Piaget's formulations on perception, that there are two aspects, the theory *of* perception and the theory *about* perception.

One part of Piaget's dealings with perception concerns itself with some theoretical issues on the perceptual process, or, perhaps more accurately (in terms of our definitions), with the sensory processes that mediate perception. For instance, he speaks of *encounters* between the elements of the visual system and those of the stimulus—such as the ones that occur in the eye movements involved in scanning a point of a line. Thus Piaget attempts to account for certain of the illusions in terms of these encounters. For example, he sees the perceived length of a line as influenced by the number of encounters or brief scanning movements involved in examining it. He explains in this way the fact that a line seen in brief tachistoscopic presentation is perceived as shorter than the same line examined more fully; there are fewer encounters involved in the former case.

As already mentioned, these formulations of Piaget seem to be theoretical anticipations of the kinds of things Hubel and Wiesel (1963) are making more specific. Because the latter are tied much more to physiological mechanisms, they might be considered more appropriate to those psychologists of the "brass tacks" persuasion.

Another concept used by Piaget is *coupling* between the encounters on one line and those on another when they occur together, and these coincidences may be temporal or spatial. They permit a *transport* from one element to another and hence enter into the building up of a gestalt. Piaget uses this theory to explain such phenomena as those covered by the Weber-Fechner law, and Flavell (1963a) has pointed out that this introduces a phenomenon unusual in Piaget—quantification.

The centration hypothesis has already been mentioned. The perception of the younger child is dominated by (is centered on) aspects of the field that are determined by *field effects.* These are Gestalt features such as closure, good form, and continuity. As development proceeds, there is *decentration* in that these field effects no longer dominate, and perception becomes internalized. The development from sensations to perceptions may be seen here.

There are sequential activities (which Piaget does not apparently see as forming defined stages) related to age, among which are perceptual exploration, schematization, reorganization, anticipation, and transport.

The process of decentration occurs first in the earliest of these sequences, and a child who decenters in exploration may not yet be doing so in an activity requiring reorganization. The degree of decentration is also conditioned by the nature of the stimulus. A configuration with strong field effects (good closure) is less readily decentered than one with weaker Gestalt properties.

Piaget's theory *about* perception really fits better in the discussion of intellectual development. He sees both perception and intelligence as *adaptations,* but perception is, as it were, a lower level of adaptation (Flavell, 1963a). It should be noted, however, that what Piaget means by perception is more limited than what most others mean. His use corresponds more to *sensation* as the term is used in this chapter, but it is not precisely limited to raw sensation (Flavell, 1963a). In this sense it becomes quite understandable that he should see intelligence as something supraordinate to perception. To him, perception arises developmentally from sensory-motor intelligence rather than from the reverse. Hence the first perceptions have meaning to the infant not directly but by the mediation of sensory-motor schemes, the totality of which is an intellectual operation, but of which the sensations form parts. This formulation becomes consonant with the present argument if we extend Piaget's statement somewhat. We may modify his term *perception,* and speak of sensations being elaborated by intelligence into perceptions. In doing this, we introduce into perception more than he evidently intends, but it is useful to do this in anticipation of a return to the discussion in Chapter 17.

One general statement that does come from this review is that a considerable amount of perceptual organization is early in appearance and probably part of the innate equipment of the organism. Precisely what role learning has in the emergence of mature perceptual processes is not yet fully described. Its role is evidently important but to a considerable extent consists in the modification of sensory mechanisms already organized.

If early learning is as inefficient as has been suggested in Chapter 12, it may be asked what affect this has on early perceptual development. As already suggested, it may be that what occurs in the early stages is at most a kind of "half-learning" in which certain features of the environment complete already incipient organizations. To say that these perceptual phenomena depend on native factors or on learning is in either case only partly correct.

If learning were the only factor involved, it would be expected that there would be considerably more individual variation than there is in perceptual phenomena, whereas in fact there is remarkable (even if not complete) uniformity. Many of the illusions and constancies, and the general properties of form and space perception and so on, are consistent from individual to individual to an extent that would be surprising if learning alone were involved. Moreover, there is some evidence that this consistency may also extend across species, as, for instance, with certain of the illusions and constancies that are apparent in other species. We do not know, of course, whether a cat or a chimpanzee sees a cube as we see it, but assuming these animals can detect edge and straight line, it is difficult to imagine how they could see it differently.

They may be less able to abstract a shape from an embedding pattern, but under suitable figure-ground conditions they presumably sense what a man would sense. The idea that a considerable amount of early perceptual development is predominantly (if not exclusively) dependent on already existing organizational features of the CNS seems both more parsimonious and more consistent with the evidence than the notion that extensive learning is involved in the early stages.

The idea that complex sensory functions —certain of the constancies, for example—can be innately organized may seem incredible. Yet we have to accept the astounding facts of embryology as evidence of the innate organization of development. When one contemplates how innate propensities organize the development of a single cell into the intricate form of a wasp or a sparrow, with all its inbuilt behaviors, here is a marvel indeed. Nobody disagrees that a newborn human infant is the physical product of similar programs carried in some awe-inspiring manner in the two gametes from which it arises. In this context, is it quite indefensible to believe that just as the stickleback innately organizes the sensory input from its environment in particular ways, so does the human infant also?—or further, that mature perception is also an elaboration by learning of basic processes that are innate? There seems to be something to be said for Pastore's contention (1960) that the major features of perception are determined by the intrinsic properties of the nervous system. It is evident that aspects of perception can be improved by learning—we can learn to discriminate finer details and to organize the perceptual field (in reading X-rays, for example), but we can do this only within the limits imposed by our receptors and their neural hinterland. No amount of learning will enable a human to detect polarization of light with his native equipment. Man can circumvent such biological limitations, but that is a consideration for another context.

Fourteen

Origins of Emotions and Motivation

It might be said that infancy is a time of feeling and that feelings precede thoughts in development. It is surely true that an individual's emotional development has a profound influence on his effectiveness and happiness as a person.

The current majority view, according to Leeper (1965), is that motives are on a lower level of function than cognitive processes; this, he says, is generally true even though certain psychologists have questioned such a belief. This notion of the lower status of motives in the organizational hierarchy is based in part upon their phylogenetic antiquity, which makes them biologically more primitive than the cognitive processes. But whatever the merits of the high value placed on cognition, in discussing emotion we are dealing with a topic of importance. It may be that man's greatest asset, and his main distinction from the animals, is his capacity for intellectual activity—his ability to relate a vast number of perceptions to one another, to abstract, to learn, and to communicate. But these capacities make man no more than a highly developed computer and without emotion these powers are lifeless.

Numerous writers point out how man's emotions are destructive, and one is aware of the truth of this. Certainly some of the emotional components inherited from his animal ancestors have their disruptive aspects. Emotional experiences can be uncomfortable for the individual—at times acutely so. But on the other hand, emotional feelings can be pleasurable and sometimes ecstatic; it is these occasional experiences that make the difference between existing and living. This is the old truth of no good without evil to contrast it with.

The aim of child rearing—or one of several aims—should be to produce individuals who can meet the pain, sorrow, and frustration that are inescapable in this world without being overwhelmed but who can also appreciate to the full the beauty that is offered and be able to attain the joys that life can avail.

There seems to be no reason for supposing the pains and joys to be counterpoised, and that one must necessarily experience the profoundest sorrow to appreciate supreme joy. The acutely depressed psychotic is not the only one who can value ecstasy; indeed, he commonly does not know what it is. One does not have actually to starve to appreciate a good meal, even though a moderate state of hunger is the best appetizer. A proper emotional development prepares the individual to appreciate the pleasurable aspects of emotion and to cope adaptively with the unpleasant. The well-rounded personality is not flat or wholly intellectual but expressive and emotionally responsive in a disciplined manner.

Man shares the capacity for emotional responsiveness with the animals and has it as part of the legacy from his more primeval forebearers. But as with others of his inheritance, he elaborates and enriches it and is capable of a wider range and greater depth of emotional feeling than is any other creature. (One cannot prove this, but intuitively it is true.) It is not common in scientific writings to extol this aspect of man's nature, but it should be cherished as being among his greater assets.

In Chapter 4, with regard to the neoinstinctual theories, there is a discussion of the role of emotion in what might be called primitive motivational systems. It concerns the idea that in the higher animals emotion, or the feeling experience accompanying certain states of physiological need, serves to maintain goal-directed behavior toward satisfaction of those primitive needs.

This idea of emotion as the product of frustration, or the result of a lack of adequate means for the satisfaction of a need, is given by several recent writers, for instance, Bartley (1958), P. T. Young (1961), and Sartre (1962). In this view a situation with which one can cope skillfully arouses little emotion. (One might question if this is not too restrictive a view of emotion. Sailing up to a mooring in a crowded anchorage in a stiff breeze can certainly be an anxious experience for the novice helmsman, whereas the seasoned yachtsman can do it with aplomb; he ex-

periences only pleasure at a well-executed manoeuver; but such a feeling can, of course, be considered as an emotion.)

It may be expected that a child's reaction to frustration (or blocking of goal-directed activity) will change with age, both with respect to the response and to the events that cause frustration. Early frustration relates to the direct blocking of organic needs, but with increasing age the range of potentially frustrating circumstances increases and so, fortunately, do the capacities for coping with them. Douglas (1965) has demonstrated how children develop with age methods for dealing with frustration, becoming able to rationalize disappointments and thus able to face the reality of unfortunate facts, often by finding alternatives for unattainable goals.

We have no means of knowing what experiences the infant has, anymore than we have of knowing this for the animals. The feeling tones attributed to them in theorizing about the matter are derived from our own introspective knowledge. However, we can observe in infants (as in animals) behaviors and physiological changes that are like those correlated with the feelings reported by communicative individuals.

At first, emotional behaviors in infants appear only in connection with physiological need (e.g., crying when hungry) or in situations where the stimulus may reasonably be thought to trigger some innate response (for example, crying when wet or soiled and smiling in response to a face). Later, of course, motives beyond those satisfying a physiological need are acquired, in addition to those that might accompany some inbuilt response pattern. Indeed, some of this learning no doubt consists in inhibiting innate response patterns, for instance, in not fearing snakes and in controlling response to the urgings of sexual tensions.

Whether all motives are derived from basic ones and later become functionally autonomous, will be discussed later. The immediate concern is the state of emotions as seen in infants. In some young animals the motivational state (with its presumed accompanying feelings) that goes with hunger leads to movement toward the nipple. In helpless infants like the human, the only response available is one that is also considered part of the emotional expression—crying that brings the mother to the baby.

In the earlier discussion (Chapter 4) it was suggested that an emotional feeling arises when the satisfaction of a need state is thwarted. Emotion is, indeed, the driving force that enables the organism to overcome or circumvent a block to satisfaction. The infant whose hunger needs are skillfully anticipated does not cry; he presumably feels no emotion except the pleasurable one of satiation. If one could imagine an infant with the kind of omnipresent and all-attentive mother that some child-care experts recommend, what would be the effect on its emotional development? Indeed, on its total development? Possibly the self-stimulation that accompanies frustration-induced emotion in the infant might be an element in early stimulation with its developmental effects.

EMOTIONS IN INFANCY

Long ago Bridges (1932) found that attempts to distinguish between the emotional expressions of infants were unsuccessful, and Wenger (reported by Leeper, 1965) was disappointed to find that even with refined measures, the physiological reactions of adults to different emotional stimuli could not reliably be distinguished from one another. It would seem that at all stages of life the physical bases of emotion are somewhat undifferentiated. A tear-streamed face may express grief or joy.

In a paper on the ontogenesis of emotional behavior, Bousfield and Orbison (1952) have made the following two assumptions, based upon physiology, concerning the factors that influence the development of emotional behaviors:

1. The infant is essentially a precorticate organism and the establishment of cortical control, especially in the frontal lobes, is not achieved until adulthood.
2. The infant is relatively lacking in endocrine products which sustain some of the physiological responses to stress.

In developing their thesis, they adopt Hebb's distinction (1949) between the terms *emotion* and *emotional behavior*. For Hebb, emotion is a construct for "the neural process that is inferred from and causes emotional behaviour." His thesis emphasizes the neurological components. Emotional behavior is the activity that is correlated with the emotion and includes both emotional disturbance and organized emotional responses such as aggression or flight.

NEURAL INFLUENCES IN EMOTIONAL BEHAVIOR

It is known that the thalamus is an important center for mediating emotional behavior, as distinct from emotional experience. Thus Bard (1934) has shown that decorticate cats give a "sham rage reaction" in which the behavior is a gross, automatic, but poorly directed and poorly timed rage reaction. An observer of these rages gets the impression that the animal is going through the motions of anger without the angry feelings. It is, of course, somewhat anthropomorphic to try to deduce the experience of the animal, but a human situation that is somewhat parallel is found in the patient after frontal lobotomy; here we have a person who is operatively partly decorticate. Such patients show immediate and often excessive responsiveness to external stimulus, but their emotional behavior tends to lack depth, as their introspective reports testify. Their responses are of short duration, may alternate rapidly from one emotional state to another, be less inhibited than those of normal adults, and show a quicker return to a neutral level. A certain childishness in their emotional responses is evident. Similar changes often occur in persons with brain damage following an accident or disease, especially when the frontal lobes are involved. It appears from such observations that the cortex imposes important modifications on the gross emotional reactions mediated by the thalamus.

The role of the cortex in emotional expression is illustrated in a study by Bard and Mountcastle (1947). These workers found that cats can be made extremely placid by removing all of the forebrain except the amygdaloid complex and the transitional cortex of the midline, but that when either of these structures are removed, the cat becomes extremely ferocious. This ferociousness can also be obtained by removing only the amygdaloid complex and the pyriform lobe, the rest of the forebrain being left intact; these animals differ from the ones described earlier by Bard in that their rage reactions are better directed and better timed. As we go down the phylogenetic scale to animals with less cortex, we notice that emotional disturbances following stimulation get briefer and recovery to a "normal" state of functioning is more rapidly obtained.

It would appear from these various pieces of evidence that the cortex, particularly the frontal lobes, is involved in both the inhibition of emotional responses and the instigation and sustaining of them. Further, the emotional behaviors of the mature organism, at least higher up the phylogenetic scale, involve some kind of interaction between the thalamus and the cortex (particularly the frontal lobes). Hebb (1949) has observed that ascending the phylogenetic scale there is a progressive lengthening of the period of emotional disturbance following momentary stimulation, this lengthening being presumably correlated with the increasing importance of cortical functions.

At birth much of the cortex, and the frontal lobes in particular, is still immature and exerts little if any influence on the functions of the lower parts of the brain. The newly born child may be regarded as essentially a noncorticate organism, with emotional responses that are somewhat similar to those of the phylogenetically lower animals, who even in the mature state have a relatively meager cortex. The characteristics of these emotional responses is that they are quickly aroused but also short-lived; residual disturbances afterward are minimal, and the organism rapidly returns to a neutral state. The emotional responses of the young child are quite consistent with his immature cortex and lack of cortical component in emotional responsiveness.

The neurological bases of neonatal emotional responses have also been dealt with by Bronson (1965). He makes the same point that in the newly born the emotional responses are those mediated by the brain-stem RAS. Midbrain and cortical mediations are as yet undeveloped because of the immaturity of these regions (this is reviewed more fully in Chapter 6). He speaks of the role of the RAS at its various levels and proposes a "motivational hierarchy" in which the vegetative needs are basic. The developmentally early brain-stem RAS mediates a generalized arousal, which is not goal-oriented. The higher (and later) thalamic RAS has more specific sensitivity to input from the internal environment and directs activity toward more specific goals. "Higher" motives, which include learned ones, require cortical mediation and involve both downward and upward pathways from the RAS.

HORMONAL FACTORS IN EMOTIONAL BEHAVIORS

Hebb's theory of neurological mechanism in emotional disturbances does not adequately account for one fact, as Hebb himself acknowledges, and that is the increase in the vigor of emotional states with increasing age. The second of the proposals of Bousfield and Orbison (1952), that the infant is relatively lacking in endocrine products that sustain some of the physiological responses, may be very useful in completing Hebb's formulation.

They base their consideration mainly upon the adrenals, though they recognize that the pituitary as well as other glands may have a significant influence on emotional response and on emotional development.

The adrenal glands have a peculiar development: After birth they decrease rapidly in size until the age of two years when they are less than half their birth weight. From this point they abruptly start to gain in weight, the increase being fairly rapid up to the age of about five and then less rapid from five to about eleven. From about eleven onward until around the twentieth year there is another spurt that tends to get faster as the subject grows older. The birth weight is regained around the sixteenth year. This pattern of development is not typical of the endocrine glands as a whole (Lanman, 1953). It appears that the adrenal glands of the neonate are composed almost entirely of adrenal cortical tissue, the medulla being relatively small.

During fetal development there is very marked growth of the adrenal cortex, relative to that of the medulla. At birth the adrenal glands of the neonate are composed almost entirely of cortical tissue that differs histologically from that of the mature gland. Essentially, the adrenal cortex of the neonate consists of two layers, the inner of which is temporary and degenerates, and the outer of which becomes the true cortex of the adult. This degeneration of the inner layer starts immediately after birth, and the main structural features of the adult adrenal gland are developed by the end of the second month, but the gland is much reduced in size and continues to shrink until about the second year. It is generally assumed that there is some positive relationship between the size of a gland and the amount of its secretory activity. The adrenal loss of weight during the first two years of postnatal life presumably is accompanied by reduced secretion.

Cannon (1929) has made statements (that are well known) regarding the role of adrenaline, the secretion of the adrenal medulla, in emotion. In general he regards this hormone as being responsible for the sustaining of states of emotional arousal first triggered by the autonomic nervous system. Certain qualifications to Cannon's position may be necessary (see Arnold, 1945), but in general we can accept the view that the liberation of adrenaline into the blood stream increases the vigor of response and prolongs the emotional state. The relatively small adrenal medulla in the young child would account in part at least for the transitory nature of his emotional responses.

The adrenal cortex differs from the medulla in not being subject to direct neural regulation, but it is regulated by a secretion of the anterior pituitary, the adrenocorticotropic hormone (ACT); it is this hormone that brings about the release of the steroid hormones, including the 17-ketosteroids. Thus while the adrenal medulla has rapid influence by neural mechanisms, the cortex has a slower activation by the anterior pituitary and the hormone ACT.

It appears that during stress some tissues, and especially muscle, require the adrenal cortical hormone in increased amounts. It is not known just what change in these tissue cells is produced by stress that needs these hormones, but it is probably one related to increased metabolism. In other words, large secretions of adrenal cortical hormones appear to be necessary for the maintenance of prolonged states or prolonged reactions to stress (see Sayers and Sayers, 1948).

Evidence on the exact nature of adrenal cortical secretions during childhood is lacking. The secretion of the adrenal cortex, in the adult at least, contains twenty-five or more different steroids, including the most well known, 17-ketosteroid. The adrenal cortex is essential to life, but the essential functions are probably not dependent on all these steroids. The necessary functions must obviously be present throughout childhood. The 17-ketosteroids are not produced in measurable amounts until the ninth or tenth year of life. It is known that in mature individuals there is a direct relationship between stress and the output of 17-ketosteroids, the output increasing under stress. It is not unreasonable to suppose that the relative lack of the 17-ketosteroids in earlier childhood is one of the factors involved in the different emotional responses between the immature and the more mature individual.

Some interesting points are raised by Funkenstein et al. (1957) about the balance of adrenal secretions. The secretion of the medulla is not solely adrenaline, but contains noradrenaline as well (i.e., adrenaline without a methyl group). These two related substances have different physiological effects and their secretion is controlled by different areas of the hypothalamus.

These authors claim that adrenaline is related to passive reactions to stress, and that social and unaggressive animals such as the rabbit have a balance in which adrenaline tends to predominate over noradrenaline. The reverse is true of solitary and aggressive animals, such as the lion, in which noradrenaline predominates.

They also claim, on the basis of experiments done with medical students, that in human adults there are characteristic reactions, which they call "anger-in" and "anger-out," to stress or frustration. Those showing the former type tend to "bottle" emotions and to be self-blamers, whereas those showing the latter were more prone to outward expressions of anger and to blame others for frustrations. The "anger-inners" tended to have an excess of adrenaline over noradrenaline, whereas the reverse was true of the "anger-outers." The emotional reaction of the anger-outers tended to be of lower intensity, physiologically speaking, and to be accomplished by less anxiety.

During childhood, these authors claim, there is a predominance of noradrenaline in the medullary secretions, the balance later shifting toward equality and presumably pushing some individuals over to an opposite preponderance. If Funkenstein and his associates are correct in their assays, then there

are further physiological reasons why children differ from adults in their stress reactions.

The preceding assumes that the physiological processes are basic, and the psychological concomitants following; a further finding of these authors might lead one to ask whether this is necessarily the case, for they found significant differences in parental relationships between the two groups. The anger-out group tended to perceive the father as the chief authority figure and the role model, while the mother was the principal source of affection. Affectional relations with the father were poor, being hostile or strained. The father is also described as being angry frequently.

The anger-in group felt their mothers to be the more affectionate, but this group also had close and affectionate relationships with their fathers. There was not the same difference of authority between father and mother but rather a more balanced family. Funkenstein et al. take the differentiation between the groups to be a confirmation of Freud's and Alexander's views on paternal relationships, the lenient and indulgent father fostering an overstrict superego because the child in the face of this love can only turn its aggression inwardly.

In the midst of so physiological a study it is interesting, and perhaps a little surprising, to have a psychological explanation of its findings. Neural influences on the adrenal medulla by higher centers via the hypothalamus are not implausible. However, other explanations, such as a genetic one, are possible. The anger-outers tended to be authoritarian, as their fathers were; conversely the anger-inner fathers were more permissive, which could be the equivalent of the trait of non-dominance in their sons.

All of which serves to show how difficult explanations are in psychology; even physiological changes can be seen as psychologically instigated. I am inclined to interpret these findings as showing an initial physiological bias. Because of genetically determined tendencies, the young child is prone to certain patterns of reaction to the climate of care provided by the parents. This physiological bias gives a start and a direction to a whole complex of physiological-psychological interactions that determine development. Similar interaction patterns had determined the development of the parents, and the correlations between parental and child personalities arise from this similarity.

This treatment of the origins of emotional behavior places emphasis on the role of maturation, both in the nervous system and in the endocrine system. The differences in emotional responsiveness between children and adults is claimed to be partly caused by the cortical immaturity of the child and partly due to differences in his endocrine output. The differences may be not only in quantity but also in quality.

Heredity factors may also enter the picture, influencing the nature of the neural equipment, the hormonal secretions, or both, in certain strains or individuals. It is well known that in rats strains can be bred that are emotionally highly reactive or stolid and unreactive (Hall, 1941), and it is probable that in humans also susceptibility to stress and emotional responsiveness are influenced by genetic factors.

Another study that seems to point to a constitutional basis to emotional responsiveness is by Doerr and Hokanson (1965), who divided, on the basis of resting heart beat, children aged seven, nine, and eleven into three groups: low, medium, and high. This characteristic is presumably constitutional, though not necessarily innate. When exposed to a frustrating situation (the incorrect marking of an arithmetic exercise so that some right answers were not credited and verbal rebuke of the subject for poor performance), there was an increase in heart rate. On retest following frustration, the low-heart-rate group improved performance, whereas the high-rate group showed a decrease. The medium-rate group showed no marked change.

This was interpreted in the light of Malmo's inverted-U hypothesis (1958), which claims that performance increases as general activation level rises up to a moderate level but then decreases again. The low-rate group were assumed to have a low initial level of activation, so that arousal raises it to optimum levels, whereas the high-rate group was assumed to have their initially higher level raised into the decreasing part of the U function.

Infantile experiences have an influence on the later behaviors related to the satisfaction of basic drives. For instance, Hunt (1941), in a well-known experiment, reared young rats for a period of fifteen days following weaning under conditions in which food supplies were irregular and inadequate, so that there was not only frustration of hunger drives but also competition for the available resources. For the next five months they had unrestricted feeding. Compared with controls on unrestricted diets all along, these animals as adults showed an exaggeration of hoarding behavior, and this is typical of the normal behavior of the species under conditions of food scarcity. When food was plentiful, there was no difference, but on return to plenty following five days of bare subsistence feeding, the hoarding behavior of the deprived group rose markedly more than did that of the controls. These results were replicated (Hunt et al., 1947). It seems that early rearing influences the motives involved in hoarding behavior, and it is feasible that other drives are similarly modifiable by experience.

Another effect on emotionality, in rats at least, is the experience of the mother. The nonhandled offspring of mothers who had been subjected to gentling in their infancy showed less emotionality in open-field tests when compared with the nonhandled offspring of the nonhandled mothers (Denenberg and Whimbey, 1963). In the same situation there was also for the first group less rise of adrenocortical steroids in response to novel stimulation (Levine, 1967). However, the handled offspring of both nonhandled and handled mothers were no different from one another, and one does not apparently produce a compounded effect when both mother and offspring are early stimulated. Perhaps there is a ceiling to the effect. It is also of note that Levine found no difference between ten- and twenty-day early stimulated groups in this experiment; one may need to revise his earlier statements about the effect of too much stimulation.

PRIMARY DRIVES AND MOTIVATION

The motives of the young child are entirely drive-based, and Allport (1961) says that for the first two years of life drive theory is adequate to account for motivation. He does not state his reason for this particular time period, but in the absence of any direct evidence it is probably a good guess. Drive theory does not, of course, end here but remains at least a partial explanation of behavior throughout life.

However, one of the advantages of civilized living should be that basic needs are readily satisfied. In some societies (or some sections of society) the satisfactions of some basic needs is so time-consuming an operation that little remains for investment in derived needs. In others the basic drives (especially hunger) are so poorly satisfied that the constant frustration dominates other possible sources of motivation. Technological advances and the growth of a just society tend to ensure in principle that all individuals have the basic needs satisfied without undue effort, so that both leisure and energy are left for other derived motivations.

It may be oversimplifying, however, to assume that the untrammeled satiation of basic needs leads to a state in which they can be ignored as strong motivational sources. A good meal, elegantly prepared and well served, does much more than raise the blood sugar level. Even elimination can be one of the minor pleasures of life. Whether or not sex provides *the* profound satisfaction is perhaps a matter of viewpoint; it is certainly highly appreciated by many. All these show how the basic needs are embellished—a satisfying meal is not just a matter of calories and vitamins. There is a considerable amount of learned enrichment of both the alimentary and sexual needs in human adults, and all the other basic needs probably, to some extent, require more than minimum conditions for satiation.

The entire behavior of the infant is, we may presume, based on motivations derived from vegetative needs, and probably only on certain of them, on those that Klineberg (1954) has called the "absolutely dependable motives." These are hunger, thirst, rest and sleep, elimination, breathing, activity, and sensory hunger. Klineberg finds these motives universal to all individuals in all human cultures. Certain other widely distributed motives that (according to him) are not entirely universal are sex and postmaternal and self-protective behavior. Perhaps we should change postmaternal to parental behavior, because, as argued elsewhere in this book, males also have basic responses to infants; in any case this is obviously a later-emerging motive. How much later it emerges is open to question; if we limit it to manifestations consequent on actual parenthood, it is an adult motive, but precursors may be seen in childhood play.

Sex also is primarily an adult motive, though if we are to believe the psychoanalysts, manifestations of it are to be found at early ages—ridiculously early, even prenatally, according to some. The orthodox Freudians seem to regard early sexuality as essentially adult in character, though they produce no convincing evidence in support of this contention. It is difficult, on the other hand, to prove conclusively that this is not so; one can only say that from what he knows of mature adult sexuality, this is much richer and more complex than anything the child is capable of. Perhaps, indeed, one can reverse Freudian thinking and claim that rather than children having adult sexuality, too many adults have childish sexuality.

One manifestation that is commonly regarded as childhood sexuality is an interest in sex anatomy. Whether one should regard this as a specifically sexual interest or merely an aspect of general curiosity about the world around is an open question. In primitive communities where the outward differences between males and females are plain for all to see, no particular excitement accompanies the child's observations of them. Maybe the interest children in our society show is more a matter of concealment whetting curiosity than of any truly sexual arousal.

If we are to believe, as is maintained elsewhere in this volume, that males and females come equipped with certain ready-made responses to one another, then the Freudian contentions about the young child's emotions relative to the opposite-sexed parent are not entirely without credence. What does strain credibility is the description of their quality. As we speak of in another context (Chapter 8), the infant's first social responses are directed toward adults rather than toward his peers. If the precursors of heterosexual responsiveness are present in the young child, then it is understandable that these will be directed by the boy to the adult female most prominent in his environment. Similarly, for the girl, they will be directed toward the most available adult male. Moreover, psychoanalytic theory emphasizes the son-to-mother interaction rather more than the daughter-to-father one; this is perhaps consistent with the apparent fact that in primates the earlier and stronger manifestations of the sex drives occur in males (Harlow, 1962).

Play that involves the sex organs and which might be regarded as a manifestation of a sex drive is certainly common in primates and in human young. To what extent it is part of general play activity and how much it is truly

sexually motivated is impossible to say. Perhaps again in our society it derives an excitement from its forbidden nature, but whether this excitement is really sexual is another question. It may be that calling such play sex play is actually misleading, in that it implies the deeply erotic precoital activity that is a feature of adult sex behaviors. Children certainly are capable, from an early age, of showing the physiological and behavioral changes associated with sexual tension and detumescence, but how sustained these are, and how strongly motivating, is unknown. We really know very little about childhood sexuality as a specific source of motivation. However, it would seem from the evidence reviewed earlier in this chapter that the child's emotional responses are qualitatively different from those of the adult and that sex as a motivating factor is less sustained and as an energizer is small until it is boosted by endocrine secretions at puberty.

EXPLORATORY OR CURIOSITY DRIVES

The question of whether activity can be regarded as a drive has been considered by Cofer and Appley (1964), who they say that they find the idea of a drive to activity a difficult one to conceive. Other drives have a definite state of deprivation or depletion associated with them, but any such condition is difficult to detect in the case of activity, which often tends to be high in animals that are fully satiated for all the known physiological needs. Of course, activity is also found as generalized restlessness in states of want, but this is presumably an adaptation to need; the moving animal is more likely to find food than a stationary one, but hunger, rather than a "drive to activity," is the motive. There are probably two distinct and unrelated kinds of activity; this is one, and what Hebb has called the "curiosity drive" is another.

As outlined in Chapter 6, it may be that

exploratory behaviors develop from the primitive orientation reactions mediated in young infants by brain-stem mechanisms. Bronson (1965) has emphasized the role of maturation in this development. Neurologically, the development of curiosity depends on maturation in both the hypothalamus-thalamic-limbic systems (G. Bronson's level 2) and the neocortex (his level 3). However, it is evident from data (reviewed in Chapter 11) on the effects of early experience on such things as curiosity that extrinsic factors are also important to the proper functioning of motivational systems, and that they influence their development. Whether this influence is exerted via an effect on maturation is not known; it may be, because there seems to be a critical period involved, but it is not necessarily the case.

Among the earlier investigators of curiosity or exploration as a motivation was Nissen (1930), who found that rats would actually cross an electrified grid and then run a maze to gain access to a novel (and apparently interesting) goal box. This discovery went unnoticed, or even perhaps ignored, because it did not fit in with the then current theories of motivation. More recent work has confirmed that the satisfaction of curiosity alone can be rewarding and in suitable circumstances a strong motivation.

Rats will prefer that side of a Y maze leading to a further checkerboard maze over one leading to a blind alley (Montgomery, 1954) and will learn a black-white discrimination for the same reward (Montgomery and Segall, 1955). Monkeys will also learn and will work for a peep at a toy train (Butler, 1954). Kittens will learn position habits, or brightness discriminations, for exploration reward (Miles, 1958). Other things being equal, novelty (the least visited arm of the T maze) can be rewarding to rats (Denny, 1957).

Manipulation is another source of reward. Harlow et al. (1950) had rhesus monkeys busily disassembling a simple mechanical puzzle for no other reward than that inherent in the activity. This manipulatory behavior appears at about twenty to thirty days of age

in this species and increases in strength in the following month (Mason et al., 1959). Welker (1956a,b) observed in young chimpanzees playful manipulation of objects, which tended to decline in frequency as novelty wore off; differences of color and shape were more stimulating than homogeneity.

Using five-year-old children, Berlyne (1960) demonstrated a similar effect, the young subjects being seated in a darkened room while a picture was flashed by pressing a button. These children responded at higher rates than adults. "Surprisingness" was a critical variable. For example, given a simple series consisting of six consecutive red triangles, then a series showing five green circles and then a violet square, the seventh and twelfth stimuli were preferred, presumably because of the novelty introduced by their differing from the preceding ones.

Berlyne (1960) has coined a term new to psychology: *epistemic behavior,* or knowledge-augmenting behavior. He suggests that not knowing sets up a state of conflict or incongruity, which the organism diminishes by seeking knowledge. He offers some experimental support for this category of behavior, but there has been little work done with children on this. One might question whether artificial experimental verification is needed for what everyone knows from naturalistic observations, but this is one weakness of psychologists—their need to prove the obvious. And as J. E. Anderson (1948) has said, one of the most obvious things about children is that they seek stimulation. There is presumably an optimum level of stimulation, and presumably the optimum point changes with age. Whether it is raised or lowered does not seem to have been much studied, though from the amount of noise and bustle that young children can tolerate, one would not be surprised to find a decline in older ones. However, such evidence as there is does suggest an increase. Rosenzweig (1945) set up an experimental situation in which children were permitted to choose between an easy task and one that was difficult (in fact, it was insoluble). Younger children characteristically chose the easy task, but the older ones chose the more difficult one.

There is, thus, in children a basic and possibly innate motivation for learning and activity, and many educational theorists have capitalized on this need. Some (such as Rousseau) have even suggested that the main object of education is to preserve this inherent motivation from the destruction that it may suffer in more restrictive educational settings.

There are, as always, complexities to these problems that would take us far afield to discuss in detail here. Helson (1964) has treated in some fullness the question of contextual factors on affectivity and motivation. A modest piece of music, for instance, seems much better if it follows a poor piece. Sudden death to a close comrade is more damaging to morale in a soldier than that of a more distant one, and so on. Affective processes are, as Helson shows, subject to order, intensity series, and background influences. There are interactive effects that modify and establish levels of emotionality. As in perception (Chapter 13), there is a preference for intermediate levels of complexity of these various interactions that one may relate to Hebb's concept, already discussed, of optimum arousal.

Another theoretical discourse that is in the same general area of reasoning is that of McClelland et al. (1953) concerning the "achievement motive." These authors have emphasized the social factors in the development of this motive—the Protestant ethic that stresses achievement and the child-rearing practices that reinforce productivity. This is, of course, a real factor, though one might argue that the "striving-to-do" of this activity drive is a basic fact of life and what the Protestant ideal does is to foster (and even perhaps exaggerate) this aspect of human (and animal) nature. McClelland and his group have collected an impressive amount of data that show that this presumably innate strive-to-activity can be considerably modified by culture.

The implications, for the practice of teaching, of theorizing in these areas have been discussed by De Cecco (1968). He points out that one of the functions of the teacher is to provide motivation or create arousal and relates research and theory in the areas of incentive and reward and punishment to increasing achievement.

LOVE EMOTIONS

The most important emotion of all has been treated extensively by the poets but almost entirely ignored by psychologists, at least in recent years. Freud related all manifestations of liking, affection, or tender feeling to the *libido*—to the sex instinct. McDougall (1926) also discussed the question and recognized that sex love is a highly complex thing. He claimed that it has two main roots, in the sex instinct itself and in the parental instinct. He also speaks (1960) of the emotion of love as one having as a prominent quality the "tender emotion," but that is also a complex blend of the "sentiments." However, in conjoining sex and love even McDougall is implying that sexuality is an essential component of the emotion.

One might question whether love and sex are necessarily inseparable. It seems plain that there can be sex without love, but is the converse always possible? Freud was no doubt right in claiming that love is commonly expressed in sex, but is this necessarily so? The world is in need of a great deal of love that is not expressed in bed, but at the present there is little that can be said in this chapter about means of developing love between neighbors. (In other contexts one might suggest means of reducing prejudice or of increasing empathy between different social groups, but these are not germane to the present discussion.) Despite the psychoanalysts, one might ask whether parental love for children, or the converse, is necessarily tinged with a sexual emotion, but such queries are unanswerable.

As we have seen in Chapter 11 in discussing early stimulation, the child needs love for optimum development, and there is a considerable literature on the receipt of love as a factor in child psychology. When one attempts to describe the stimulus components of "love" in this context, it seems to narrow down to unromantic tactile stimulation, at least in the early months.

However, the main concern of this section is the growth of the child's ability to experience love and to give it, and on this the evidence is scanty. Watson and Morgan (1917) believed "love" to be one of the three innate emotional reactions detectable in early infancy; here again the sexual element is present, this reaction being elicited (they claimed) by stroking the erogenous zones of the body, gently tickling, rocking, and so on. However, this says nothing about the child's experiences, and in any case, as we saw earlier in the chapter, it is doubtful whether such differentiated emotional responses can be reliably elicited.

It is evident from the origins of the sociopathic personality, discussed in Chapter 11, that the early receipt of love has an important, indeed crucial, part in the development of the capacity to give love. It is difficult to believe that at the human level this capacity arises solely from the tactile stimulation that is apparently the salient element in the early receipt of love. These tactile experiences may play a critical role in starting the processes that lead to the development of loving, but it seems unconvincing that it is the sole factor after the process has commenced. Loving is a highly complex social skill; it involves not only the capacity to experience the emotion of love but also the ability to express the emotion and transmit it to a partner. It is of interest to note that some sociopaths seem to lack the former but not the latter; some of them can be most charming and attractive to the opposite sex, though because they do not experience the emotion, they lack the underlying motivation that would enable them to sustain a truly loving relationship. Sooner or later, and generally sooner, the partner finds

that the glitter is not gold. The sociopath has, in other words, acquired certain of the social skills involved in the relationship but lacks the motivational basis of it. This is an excellent illustration of the importance of emotion as a sustainer and motive force in behavior; it shows how emotion gives life to what is otherwise a mere set of actions.

On the other hand, there are some unfortunate individuals (and these are perhaps the more common) who experience the loving emotion strongly enough but lack the social skill to express it and elicit reciprocity. For saints it may be sufficient to give love and receive none, but for most this experience is unsatisfying (and one suspects that certain of the saints may have been the better for receiving some; one has suspicions, too, that not all were really givers of love).

A host of factors enter into the interpersonal aspects of loving, and because an important element of the matter is a relationship between a man and a woman, factors influencing this relationship are critical. Qualities of femininity in women are crucial to her attracting of the amorous attentions of a male, and who can say how many girls emotionally equipped for loving lack the actuality because no man approaches closely enough to release it. And despite what the advertising industry would have us believe, this probably has less to do with skin blemishes or body odor than with social ineptness. Possibly these social factors are more often lacking in males for whom social learning is more difficult. Constitutional factors may also operate against some; the diffident and nondominant male has his range of female companions limited and may have difficulty in finding one with whom he can establish mutuality.

In surveying the literature, this seems to be a virgin field insofar as experimental studies are concerned. There are practically no data to support the ideas presented here, nor is there much to tell us how the child eventually develops a mature kind of loving (nor, of course, do we have an adequate definition of maturity in this sphere). There is, of course, a considerable body of thought on the topic, as expressed by such writers as Freud, Allport, Erikson, Sullivan, Fromm, and Maslow, but this is based upon clinical rather than experimental observations. Where there is relevant but indirect data is in the research on empathy, self-concept, and attachment.

There is a growing literature on sexuality among adolescents; Hurlock (1967) reviews some of this, and it appears that we are producing a generation that attains experience in the techniques of sex more widely and earlier than was believed to be the case in previous generations. However, we still have no idea whether the level of sexual skill is rising, nor do we know whether these are young people with a greater range of sexual techniques and opportunities available to them but without any better ability to love in its wider meaning. Indeed, if one is to believe many of the popular commentators on the current scene, there is more activity but less experiencing.

In view of the amount of joy that the loving emotion can bring and of the immense amount of pain that arises when it is lacking in interpersonal relationships, this is a matter deserving much attention. We need to know how it develops and how it can be fostered, but as yet we have little idea. It is to be lamented that "hard" psychology has concerned itself so vastly with trivial issues, yet has failed to touch such a highly important one as this.

ANXIETY AS A SOURCE OF MOTIVATION

The idea of anxiety as a source of motivation was first discussed by Bechterev (1913) and later by Watson (1928), Dollard and Miller (1950), and others. It also forms an important part of Freud's approach to explaining human behavior—early psychic trauma implants anxieties into the growing child.

In the literature anxiety is commonly equated with fear (e.g., Mowrer, 1939) and fear is commonly taken to be learned (e.g., Mussen et al., 1963). The latter point may be questioned as a generality, but we can let that pass for the moment. The relation between fear and emotion needs no emphasis.

In Mowrer's formulation (1939) anxiety arises because of the anticipation of fear and has the adaptive function of avoiding or preventing the recurrence of painful stimuli. Fear reduction is thus a response-contingent stimulus event that is rewarding. This idea is developed in later works (Mowrer, 1950) in which he sees human beings as motivated not only by organic needs but also by the anticipation of these needs. From this develops the "need for security"—the impulse to ward off as far as possible any real privation. Thus anxiety, fear, or expectancy becomes highly motivating for the human adult. Even in the rat, he suggests, hunger and thirst are accompanied by fear of hunger and thirst. Thus anxiety arises not only from actually painful situations but also from the frustration of basic drives.

An important aspect of the arguments of both Dollard and Miller and of Mowrer is that the *energizing* and the shaping of behavior are consequences of learned anxiety. This anxiety is itself a conditioned response having stimulus consequences.

Whether or not one sees all children's fears as learned, there can be no doubt that many are. The celebrated Watson experiment by which fear of a white rabbit was induced (and removed) shows that fear may be acquired by simple classical conditioning, but this implies an unconditioned stimulus that is innate. Mowrer also describes a drive-reduction paradigm for the acquisition of fears by sign learning through contiguity (this kind of learning is discussed in another context in Chapter 17).

It may be that the best means of dealing with the relation of fear to anxiety is to follow Erikson (1950), who finds that in young children the distinction is difficult to draw, whereas in older ones the growing intellectualism makes possible the acquisition of internal or imagined fears, which are anxieties, and are contrasted with reactions to external or real dangers, which are fears.

The manner in which some anxieties are acquired in the young child is discussed by Dollard and Miller (1950). As an example they state that the masturbation taboo may quite easily lead to anxiety in boys; this happens when the pleasurable responses to manipulation of the penis are dissuaded with varying degrees of severity. Frustration of any of the drives may similarly lead to anxiety, but in our society, at least, sex is perhaps the drive most ill-satisfied.

The origins of anxiety in children are not clearly delineated by experimental studies. There are, of course, numerous psychoanalytically based theories about how anxieties are derived, but it is not proposed to review them here.

One source of origin may be genetic (Thompson and Bindra, 1952); presumably what are inherited are not anxieties per se but susceptibilities to the acquisition of the anxieties (though if certain fears are innate, there may be individual differences in the expressivity of this character). Another influence may be prenatal. Thompson (1957) has demonstrated higher levels of emotionality in the offspring of mother rats who were exposed during pregnancy to continual anxiety-provoking stimulation.

Developmental studies of the effects of anxiety on performance in children are not numerous (despite the many using adult subjects). Stevenson and Odom (1965) have reviewed some of these studies of children and find it reported that in some tasks performance has a direct relationship with anxiety level and in others an inverse relationship. Tasks that are already well learned, and also simple conditioning, vary directly and are enhanced by high anxiety. Tasks of the perceptual-motor or paired-associate type, in which the subject does not already have a repertoire of responses,

are performed better under low than under high anxiety. The situation also has an effect; when the task is perceived by the subject as a game, anxiety tends to facilitate learning, but when it is seen as a test, it may disrupt. Further performance on tasks in which a cautious approach is helpful is aided by some anxiety.

In their own experiment, Stevenson and Odom obtained results that were consistent with earlier findings. On tasks that involved verbal processes (paired associates, concept formation, and anagrams), anxiety was most disruptive of performance, whereas for discrimination tasks it had no significant effect. At the ages they used (grade four and grade six children), there was no difference with age and sex was not a variable. Another study is by Lipsitt and Spears (1965), who found that anxiety and stress have little effect on paired-associate learning in which the association value was high (that is, learning was easy) but that they had deleterious effects on the learning of more difficult associations.

The manner of functioning in relation to anxiety has broad implications for education. Some of these have been discussed by Sarason et al. (1960). Among their findings is that anxiety scores on the measures they used were higher in girls than in boys. They adopt a social explanation of this—that girls more readily admit to anxiety than boys do, cultural expectations being what they are. They go on to discuss the often unsuspected fears, worries, and anxieties that bedevil some children in our schools and their implications for pupil-teacher interaction and the general efficiency of the educational process.

In a further study coming out of the same long-term research program, Hill and Sarason (1966) reported that over time there is an increasing adverse effect of anxiety on both intellectual and academic performance. These authors assume that the high-anxious child has great difficulty in situations requiring independent action on his part. This may be related to the fact that low anxiety apparently fosters curiosity in children, whereas high anxiety inhibits it (Penney, 1965).

Grimes and Allinsmith (1961) have also considered the question in the context of school instruction. They point out that there are two main approaches to instruction in reading. One is the phonics method, which is basically a system of rules: The child learns to make up word symbols from an orderly building up of the letter elements. The other is the "whole-word" or "look-and-say" approach in which the child acquires a "sight vocabulary" by repeated exposure to a limited number of words which is gradually increased; phonics are taught later and incidentally. In this method the child is encouraged to guess at words from cues given in the text or in illustrations. The relative merits of the two methods have been ardently debated, but this need not concern us here; the important point is that taken overall neither method can claim exclusive superiority—some children seem to do well on one method and some on the other (Witty and Sizemore, 1955).

The phonic method is essentially a structural one, based upon rules. The whole-word approach is less structured and introduces more ambiguity for the student. Grimes and Allinsmith predicted that because the anxious child (like the compulsive one) is less tolerant of ambiguity, he would do better on the phonics method of instruction and less well on the whole-word approach. Using the Taylor Manifest Anxiety Scale, they demonstrated that children who rated high on this trait tended to better achievement in reading in schools using the phonics method than similar children in schools using the unstructured whole-word method. Under the conditions obtaining in the schools studied, low-anxiety children also did slightly better in the "structured" situation, but as the level of anxiety increased, performance declined in the "unstructured" school but increased in the structured one, so that the differences between high-anxiety students in the two settings was marked. This result is not apparent until the children have been followed over several grades. Thus there is a pervasive interaction between method of teaching and the personality characteristics of the child: the "best" mode of instruction can be stated only when the personality of the learner is taken into account. It seems in this instance that the level of anxiety in the population under consideration is the main factor in determining which method is the better.

The place of anxiety in the development of mature motivational systems is a little problematical. On the one hand, a total lack of anxiety is dangerous. There is survival value in a certain amount of cautiousness. Moreover, in humans at least, a lack of anxiety is one element in the pattern of unbridled consummation of drives found in the sociopath. This is undesirable from the viewpoint of society and hence maladaptive in the individual.

On the other hand, too much anxiety is emotionally crippling. To certain psychotherapists (e.g., Rogers) one of the aims of therapy is to enable the person to achieve the highest level of motivation, the drive to self-actualization (discussed in Chapter 19), and the removal of undue inhibition and anxieties is necessary to this aim.

A flavoring of anxiety is evidently desirable, but the delicate balance between too much and much too little is at present beyond our powers of definition. At some point anxiety turns from a positive to a negative motivational force, though perhaps this is not quite the way to state it; more accurately it turns from being a force that motivates adaptive activity to one that disrupts complex functioning (deranging, among other things, complex perceptions and their interpretation)—it hence becomes maladaptive. There are, no doubt, individual differences in the point at which this decline sets in, these differences being related both to constitutional factors and to early experiences.

The problem for the developmentalist is defining for the individual that level of anxiety necessary for optimum functioning and stating what early experiences will produce just this amount and no more (as well as what measures will correct too high a constitutional level). Because the optimum level probably depends on what function is under consideration, this promises to be a difficult matter to deal with.

EMOTION AND MOTIVATION

There is a tendency in the literature to regard emotions as distinct from motives, emotions being emotionally disrupting or disorganizing in character, whereas motives arouse and sustain activity and also organize and direct it (Leeper, 1965). The view being taken here is that emotions are in essence the feeling tone that accompanies a need state: They are psychophysiological concomitants of a state of motive arousal. While they *may* be disrupting when the level is too high, they are not necessarily so; indeed, typically they are sustaining of action, not destructive.

Drives have been described by Hebb (1955) as energizers: "the drive is an energizer, but not a guide; an engine but not a steering gear." Drives are (in some contexts at least) the same as motivations, and motives are therefore energizers of behavior. They have arousal functions.

Hebb speaks of the relationship between levels of arousal and efficient functioning, there being a level below which motivation is too low, but also a level at which arousal is so high as to be disruptive. There is thus an optimum level of arousal somewhere in the middle range. For learning, the optimum level of arousal is higher for simple situations than for more complex tasks (the Yerkes-Dodson Law). Presumably the same is true of many behaviors; where the achieving of consummation requires complex activity, the optimum level of motivation is lower than it is for a more easily attained goal. This is perhaps a paradox. A factor not taken into account by

Hebb is that a complex task (writing a book, for instance) may involve long-sustained motivation, even though it has to be at a moderate level, at least while the actual work is being done, though at some point a strong motive is needed. Maybe if one could measure the level of motivation during the performance of a long and complex task there would be peaks of high motivation during which actual production is low but sustained periods of more moderate arousal during which the best work is produced.

A question for the developmentalist is the course of growth of this phenomenon. At least a partial explanation, whereby early infantile stimulation alters the threshold for emotional arousal (see Chapter 11), has been offered by Denenberg. Unstimulated animals have as adults a lower threshold for arousal, and hence they sooner have performance disrupted by a raised drive level. The effect is less marked at simple task levels, and the results are to extend, as shown in Figure 14–1, the optimum portion of the inverted U spoken of by Malmo (1958).

The precise nature of the changes has not been explored, so it is not possible to say as yet whether the optimum portion of the curve continues as a longer plateau (as at *a*) or also rises to a new peak (as at *b*). Nor has the precise nature of the graph for differing types of task or different levels of difficulty been mapped out, though, as we have seen, there are indications of graphic functions changing with these variables. The whole question of relation of arousal to task and to developmental antecedents is highly complex.

The motivational aspects of emotion have also been emphasized by Leeper (1965). He points out that it is a fact of evolution that the higher animals are more emotional than lower ones; this is consistent with the viewpoint of the neoinstinctual theories discussed in Chapter 4. These higher species require a kind of motivation that can be modified by learning and adapted to varying conditions.

In saying this, Leeper is agreeing with

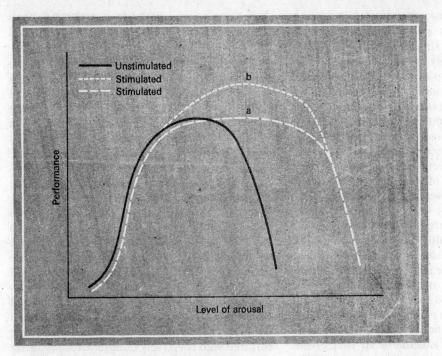

FIGURE 14-1. *Hypothetical curve of optimum arousal.*

Hebb (1955) that the emotions are not directors of behavior but rather alert, arouse, and energize; in Leeper's term, they invigorate the brain. This position is also taken by a number of recent authors in their discussions of the constructive nature of motivation (Bindra, 1959; Duffy, 1962; and Cofer and Appley, 1964).

These views arise from a knowledge of the role of the reticular activating system and the existence of motivational subsystems within the limbic system. Drives and their emotional concomitants produce not only specific autonomic effects but also psychological ones in producing a raised level of cortical arousal. The question of RAS involvement in emotion and motivation has been dealt with in greater detail by G. Bronson (1965), and his contribution is discussed more fully in Chapter 6. In brief, he shows how the RAS operates on three levels, the first or brain-stem level being

the only one mature enough at birth for functional operation. In the second or third month the midbrain or thalamic RAS begins to become functional, starting the changes from the gross, overall emotional reactions of the infant toward more differentiated and refined reactions mediated at midbrain levels. In turn the cortical level of motivational mediation reaches a functional degree of maturity instituting further refinements and permitting learned motivations and also the acquired modification of emotional responses.

PUNISHMENT AND MOTIVATION

The evidence on the effects of punishment on behavior has been reviewed by Church (1963). His review is mainly concerned with animal experimentation, and, as he says, the available evidence with humans is difficult to interpret. Furthermore, the results of animal experiments are not readily applied to practical child-rearing situations, because they usually involve highly artificial circumstances. The main conclusion of Church's overview is that punishment is more effective when it is contingent on the response than when contingent on the stimulus. Furthermore, the shorter the time between response and punishment, the more effective punishment is. In human terms this seems to say it is easier to extinguish the habit of reaching for the cookie than to produce aversion to cookies; it is more effective to slap the hand as it is reaching than to do so three hours later.

However, the results of punishment at both animal and human levels are highly varied (Church, 1963; Parke and Walters, 1967), and generalizations are not readily applied to specific situations: So much seems to depend on other circumstances. For instance, physical punishment by a generally warm and accepting mother is more effective than that given by a cold and hostile one (Sears et al., 1957). Some of the points raised here have been the subject of experiments by Parke and Walters (1967), and a detailed study of a number of interacting variables is made by Parke (1969), showing how complex the matter is.

In one sense the whole question of punishment is appropriate to more practically oriented treatises than this one. It is germane to the practical matter of child handling (which this book does not purport to deal with in any direct manner), to correcting errors rather than to guiding positive development. It is also a topic of considerable clinical interest—to the so-called behavior therapies, for instance. But again, this is not primarily a clinical treatise.

On the other hand, of course, punishment is a common experience in life, especially in early life as the more successful older person has learned to avoid it. But because the question is not central to any major issue in this book, it will not be discussed further.

SOCIAL FACTORS AND MOTIVATION

The emphasis on self-actualization to be made here rather neglects the social influences on motivation and these influences, in fact, are important. Even the hunger motive can be so influenced, as is shown when a hen satiated alone will recommence feeding when joined by hungry companions (Bayer, 1929).

It is not proposed here to review the literature on this topic but merely to acknowledge the importance of this factor. A recent study that has considered one aspect of the question is by Goldberg and Maccoby (1965), who showed that membership in a stable group was more effective in augmenting performance on a task requiring cooperation among second grade children than was membership in changing groups. Another difference that emerged was that the group with changing membership tended to favor the emergence of high-scoring children who coercively dominated low-scoring ones. It is probable that a whole complex of social factors such as these can influence motivation.

SEX DIFFERENCES IN MOTIVATION

In view of the extensive differences between the sexes (outlined in Chapter 10), which are presumed to influence the manner of organization of behavior, it would be expected that there are differences in the motivational systems of males and of females. Indeed, one might say that there must be such differences. The readily accessible literature to support this is meager; there are no doubt incidental statements about sex differences in studies of motivation, but because there have been few that have made this topic a main issue for investigation, they are not indexed in *Psychological Abstracts* or in other sources and hence are difficult to trace.

One could be on fairly safe ground in proposing that there are motivational differences between males and females in respect to specifically reproductive behaviors, and such a suggestion is made in Chapter 9. But these may extend to other behaviors also. For instance, Ross et al. (1955) have suggested that there are between male and female rats differences in hoarding behaviors that stem from different mechanisms.

Reference has already been made to the Hurlock studies on the effects of praise and reproof; her generalization that praise is the more motivating requires qualification, because Schmidt (1941) found that the results varied according to sex.

Much of the literature up to the early 1950's on motivational differences between boys and girls has been reviewed by Terman and Tyler (1954). The bulk of this material is related to what might be called social motivations (e.g., play and motivational aspirations), and all of it refers to acquired motives—interests and the like. There is nothing directly on differences in basic motivational patterns arising from organizational differences, though according to the argument being developed in this book, at least some of the acquired differences may get their initial fillip from more fundamental distinctiveness of organization.

A difference has been reported by Hartup (1958) in an experiment involving performance of nursery school children following the withdrawal of a nurturant adult. Girls typically showed a rise in performance after the adult withdrew, whereas boys showed mostly no change, the exceptions being highly dependent boys. These results presumably reflect a difference for the two sexes in the motivational effects of the change, though it is a little difficult to assess the precise nature of this effect. The fact that boys who show what might be considered a feminine trait, dependency, behaved like girls in this situation might be interpreted either as the result of type of rearing or of a constitutional trait, or perhaps (and more likely) as an interaction between the two. Because of the overlap of the distribution of traits for each set, some boys may on a given dimension be expected to behave like girls and vice versa.

According to Levin and Sears (1956), a factor such as severity of punishment affects manifest doll-play aggression differentially for sex and parental relationship; boys highly identified with the father and severely punished by him showed high aggression, whereas girls did not. Using somewhat older age groups—high school students—McClelland et al. (1953) reported sex differences in the effect of induced motivation by achievement-oriented conditions upon nAch. In boys these conditions raised nAch scores, but they did not do so in girls.

MOTIVATION AND MATURITY

One of the main points of Allport's theory of personality (1937, 1961) is that motives at first involved in the satisfaction of basic needs become functionally autonomous. That is, they lose their original connection with basic needs, and the behaviors become self-motivated. The man who first goes to sea (in his example) to satisfy basic needs eventually comes to love the sea and follow it even when he no longer depends on his career for sustenance. While this idea of functional autonomy is an intriguing one as a description of adult motives, it is unsatisfying to the developmentalist who asks just what is the course of this progress from basic to such highly derived motives. It seems to oversimplify what must in fact be a complex matter. Not all sailors come to honor Poseidon; many loathe his domain and look for easier ways to earn a living. Others are, as it were, predetermined to seafaring; they follow their fathers, or they build up some romantic notion before they ever set foot aboard a ship and have seriously to think about daily bread. Without denying the validity of functional autonomy, one needs some more detailed account of how it arises and operates.

In Allport's view (1961) some motives may become complete in the autonomy of their function, but Bindra (1959) has questioned this idea. He shows that motives may become autonomous with respect to a limited set of conditions, or achieve partial autonomy, but he doubts that complete autonomy occurs. This partial autonomy is achieved by such effects as substitution of new cues or the increased effectiveness of cues (lowering of threshold). This view would be consistent with the general philosophy of this book, that is, that early behaviors, and especially innate ones, continue to exert some influence throughout life, however much modified they are by interactions with the environment.

Another approach is to take Maslow's idea (1954) of growth motives. (This topic is discussed more extensively in Chapter 20.) He, like Allport (1961), says that in childhood all the basic drives (which he calls deficit motives) must be satisfied so that the child is freed to adopt the more evolved growth motives. These lead to self-actualization (a term he borrows from Goldstein, 1940). Maslow does not provide an explicit definition of the term as he uses it; it has to be deduced from how he describes the idea, as a state of mental health. The neurotic is bound to lower needs and more infantile motives. People at the self-actualization level of motivational development are spontaneous; their behavior is expressive. It is an end in itself rather than a means to an end (which coping behavior is). The self-actualizer is directed toward becoming what he has to be; he has the desire for self-fulfillment, to become actualized in what he is potentially.

One might ask if functional autonomy may not sometimes work in reverse: A student pursues a particular line of study for its intrinsic worth to him—he just wants to know the answer to some question that has intrigued him.

Having discovered this, and incidentally graduated in the course of doing so, he then uses this knowledge to earn a living. Of course, there could be further questions to tackle, but one wonders if too often the original drive is not diminished. This may happen especially with a subject like psychology, where seeking some personal knowledge may be the initial motivation for study. This discovered, the individual may really need to go on to some different field for his life's work but finds himself trapped in one that for his purpose is well enough explored. Self-actualization may then require him to paint or write music or be a photographer, and he may be the better person for doing so. But this is considered a waste of a Ph.D.!

Perhaps women are rather more favored than men in this matter, the expectation that, willy nilly, they make a career out of what they have studied may be somewhat less. There are, of course, grumbles in some quarters about an education being wasted in marriage, but what is really a waste of an education is its not leading to self-actualization, and the wastage in this sense might actually be higher among men than among women.

It will be evident from the brief outline of Maslow's theory that he views motives as hierarchically organized. As he points out, the order is not rigid, but self-actualization is the highest level, and this appears later in development. Gourevitch (1959) has suggested that the kind of reinforcement that is effective for the individual is an indicator of the level of motivational development achieved. Gourevitch and Feffer (1962) suppose that development goes through four stages, each distinguished by characteristically different reinforcers. In the first stage reinforcement is concrete and internal, that is, it is direct gratification of a physiological need state. In the second stage reinforcement is concrete but external, involving tangible rewards such as prizes, affection, or belongingness to a group. The third level involves abstract but external reinforcers—esteem of others, being thought well of. The final level involves active concern with self-actualization, reinforced by abstract and internal reinforcers, such as self-respect and moral rectitude. In a study of children aged six to thirteen years, added to previous work with adults, they showed a progression through their four stages, though in most of the children the second (rather than the third) was the most effective level of motivation.

If their results are correct (they need further replication), then abstract reinforcers are unlikely to be effective in preadolescence, and we cannot expect the child to be motivated by "learning for its own sake" or similar intangible rewards. "Self-realization" will have little appeal. As these authors point out, teachers should not expect this and should either make learning concretely enjoyable or provide concrete symbols of achievement. The same, no doubt, will be true in other settings. However, this perhaps requires wider consideration. Mozart was evidently a self-actualizer at a tender age, and whether lesser degrees of precocity are to be found more commonly needs to be examined.

This description of self-actualization motives seems rather highfalutin, and again one asks, how do people get this way? Further, one must ask do *all* develop these higher motives, and if not, why not?

A possible way of looking at the matter, and of making it somewhat more specific, is to assume that self-actualization evolves from the curiosity or manipulatory drives described earlier. It is not apparently a deficiency drive and results in behavior that is not useful, insofar as immediate gratification of basic needs is concerned.

One can readily see, however, the biological utility of this curiosity drive to higher organisms, which depend so much on learning. It impels, for one thing, the exploration of the environment and the acquisition of information that may suddenly become valuable—an escape route in some future emergency, for

instance, or a potential food supply. In the young, particularly, it is the root of play, with all the development of motor and other skills that this brings.

This manipulatory or curiosity drive appears only when more basic drives are reasonably satiated, and presumably self-actualization in humans can evolve only when the lower drives are well enough satisfied to allow exercise of this intermediate curiosity drive. We have seen elsewhere (Chapter 11) how early stimulation can affect emotionality, facilitating or inhibiting exploration and influencing later learning. We have seen how the deprived child has inhibited curiosity and lacks the motivational system that will lead to self-actualization.

There does not appear to be any experimental evidence to appeal to in testing this theory of self-actualization developing from the curiosity drive. It would suggest that adults who can be identified as high self-actualizers will as children have had the kind of early experiences, and perhaps the genetic endowment also, that make for a high level of curiosity drive. Conversely, those who are either by reason of constitution or early experience low in curiosity drive will tend to be low also in self-actualization. A whole field for exploration is opened up here.

If the stages of motivational development suggested by Gourevitch and Feffer are acceptable, it would seem that Skinner's types of reinforcement refer only to the first and second of these stages. A developmental problem is how progress from one stage to the other is brought about, and a practical question is whether an overemphasis on extrinsic reward can inhibit progress to higher orders of motivation.

HOW SHOULD MOTIVES BE NURTURED?

The question for the generation of motives is the extent to which educational and child-rearing systems should rely on punishment and reward, which are imposed on external sources of motivation. Skinnerian methods of reinforcement may be effective in their short-term results, but one might question the long-term influence.

Academic attainment by children in order to gain the approval of the teacher may in the long run produce a false attitude to the whole process. Do we thereby produce individuals who are other-directed? Is it not preferable to produce people who are inner-directed? Surely the ideal is to pursue education for its own intrinsic worth—for self-improvement rather than for tokens of external approval. Perhaps the widespread cheating that troubles educationalists today is a symptom of the fact that many students no longer regard an education as something worth pursuing for its own sake but merely as a means to an end. The idea that they are cheating themselves is lacking because the emphasis has been so much on the external rewards of teacher approval in the early stages and on the diploma in later ones.

This premise may be false, but it is worth investigating. If learning motivated by teacher approval becomes functionally autonomous, then the technique may not be undesirable; but we should be sure that it does and if necessary take steps to aid functional autonomy. The exploratory, curiosity, or activity drive provides a powerful alternative means of motivation that is intrinsic and hence preferable. Gourevitch and Feffer, in the study already outlined, are probably referring to this when they speak of making education concretely interesting to the pupil. But it is necessary to bear in mind that the aim in education should be to allow this basic property to flower into self-actualized motivations and to avoid procedures that will inhibit this process.

The study by Doerr and Hokanson (1965) (referred to earlier) suggests that the effects of emotional arousal and of motivating conditions differ for different individuals. For one thing, the amount of arousal necessary to assure optimum functioning may vary from

child to child, and some may even need a decrease from the normal to function best. Another question raised by this study is whether type of motivation is a varying factor. There is a considerable literature comparing negative and positive motivations—punishments and rewards—but little if any of this has gone into the question of individual differences in reaction to them. While, in general, rewards are considered to be more effectively motivating than punishments (e.g., Bandura, 1962), the question of whether some individuals are not better motivated by punishment is not considered; the low heart-rate group in this experiment apparently were effectively motivated by punishment, though the study does not tell us how they would have reacted to a rewarding situation.

It is evident that not all children react alike to reward or to punishment. One of the classic experiments in the field is by Hurlock, who found, in experiments involving intelligence tests (1924) and arithmetic tests (1925), that children who were either severely reproved or praised for their efforts both showed an improvement in retest scores as compared with unevaluated controls. However, what this experiment (and most of the many since) have not investigated is the characteristics of those who did not react in the general way. What of the children who declined on retest? Would the ones who declined with blame have increased with praise or vice versa? And what are the antecedents of the characteristic reaction? The Doerr and Hokanson experiment suggests that autonomic differences between children might be a significant prior influence to investigate.

Another variable, suggested by P. T. Young (1961), is self-confidence—the inferior-feeling child being more highly motivated by praise, whereas reproof may work better with the self-confident one (though presumably continued reproof would tend to lower confidence). Young points out that the relationship with the person giving praise or blame is also a variable.

It would seem that under certain conditions, at least, highly self-motivated children may function differently from those low on this trait. Battle (1965) used Riesman's categories of inner and other directedness. She showed in seventh, eighth, and ninth grade children that those who were inner-directed (as revealed by questions on their reasons for doing well in school) were more persistent in the face of a difficult task than those who were other-directed (under her experimental conditions the children worked alone; the other-directed children may well have performed more persistently under more social conditions).

EPILOGUE

Although emotion is not uncommonly regarded as a disruptive feature of psychology, and one at a lower level of functioning than the intellectual one, it is in fact a characteristic that makes the difference between existing and living. Emotion can be disruptive, but it is also necessary to constructive and truly human living.

There is a marked developmental change in the outward expression of emotional reaction, though what emotional *experiences* the infant and young child have are not really open to inspection. Certainly it would seem valid to say that early childhood is a time of *feeling* rather than of *knowing*.

The infant and young child are both neurologically and endocrinologically different from the older child in ways that markedly affect emotionality. Insofar as the neurological aspects are concerned, the neural mechanisms of the infant are more like those of lower animals, in which emotional changes are quick but brief. As discussed in Chapter 4, emotions become more important rather than less so as one ascends the scale to higher organisms, and the important sustained motivating effects of emotionality are not achieved

in the child until relatively late in development.

In animals a number of influences on the emotionality of offspring have been demonstrated. There are apparently genetic factors at work, mediating individual differences in the characteristic amount or level of emotionality, and such factors as prenatal stresses on the mother and postnatal stresses on the offspring are also influential. It may be presumed that similar factors operate in humans, though this is not well documented.

It is probable that, in keeping with the pervasive differences between males and females discussed in various contexts in this book, the motivational and emotional systems differ fundamentally between the two sexes. The differences in emotional reactivity of men and of women are commonly ascribed to upbringing and expectation, and these, of course, are factors. But beneath these cultural influences we may suppose that the physiological mechanisms of motivation differ for males and for females, and that the response differences are a result of organismic differences.

In civilized human societies the primary drives, with the exception of the sexual drive, are well satisfied, a fact that has had for a long time rather marked effects on the sexual functioning of adults and that has reflected on child rearing. What change the "sexual revolution" is really bringing into child development is not known. It seems that despite this mooted change children still do not obtain sexual information from the most reliable sources or from ones that are likely to give them a mature appraisal of their own impulses (Schofield, 1965). It will be most interesting to observe the sexual adjustment of the offspring of the "sexually liberated" generation. Certainly there is a major question here for devlopmental psychologists both to understand and to recommend child-rearing practices in the new atmosphere of sexual freedom.

Another realm of motivational power is provided by the "curiosity" or "exploratory" drive, which even in the lower mammals can be a strong source of motivation in its own right. It may be an introspective question to ask what emotion accompanies this motivation; it is perhaps not as clear-cut or as overwhelming as the feelings accompanying the sex drive may be, yet it can be viewed as one of the most significant of human sources of motivation, underlying all the inquiry that has brought man to his present state of cultural evolution. His curiosity may, of course, bring him to destruction, and the myth of Pandora's box has become reality. Be that as it may, curiosity is a drive with important implications to cognitive development and to human evolution.

Another source of motivation is anxiety or fear, the drive to avoid discomfort. Anxiety illustrates a fact that is true of all motives and emotions—that there is an optimum level that facilitates activity. At levels below this the organism may be ineffective and above it disorganized. A complete absence of anxiety can therefore be as little desirable as too much. It seems that there are individual differences in the level of anxiety at which functioning is optimum, this providing yet another dimension in which idiosyncratic needs apply. Punishment is a special case of imposed anxiety, and it, too, has different effects on different children.

Motivations are not, of course, purely internal in actions. That is, there are social influences that serve to modify the expression of motives and even to modify the emotional experience. This is especially evident in sex, where for many people in our own culture

satiation has not been a joyous experience but has been changed by guilt into a painful one. The atmosphere provided by childhood experiences is of obvious importance here.

The emotions are accompaniments of inner motives that have biological bases. There are also externally imposed sources of motivation. "Public opinion" is the common expression for one of these. Whether these have a biological base also is open to debate, though earlier psychologists (notably McDougall) insisted they had. In this view they stem from the biological tendencies of social species to congregate. It is quite obvious that for so highly evolved a social creature as man the inner directives of the basic drives must be subject to outwardly imposed controls, lest social life become impossible. This is not, of course, peculiar to man, because devices to control the inner urges—of aggression, for example—are found in most species.

Later in the book (and notably in Chapter 20) the virtues of inner directedness are praised. That is, it is suggested that a desirable child-rearing system will seek to foster inner rather than outer sources of motivation. These inner resources for energy will have their origin in the biological drives, but will be in refined forms of these. The exploratory drive will no doubt be important here. But perhaps it needs to be emphasized that only a hermit can be entirely inner-directed, and most people will have to temper inner directives with outward considerations. That is, we cannot educate children to self-fulfillment at the cost of others.

Fifteen

Development of Communication

A major feature of the human species distinguishing it from other species is the ability to use vocal speech as a means of communicating. All species of animals above the simplest communicate; it is, for example, a necessity to sexual reproduction to have the two partners come together and, once together, to coordinate their movements to fertilize the ova. This involves communication, which is sometimes vocal and sometimes uses other sense modalities. However, the more salient feature of human speech is that it communicates ideas and abstractions. Even here, if one wishes to be pedantic, is it possible to claim this ability as an absolute prerogative of humans?

The "language of the bees" is commonly cited as an instance of the communication of abstractions, and in a lowly invertebrate. The delightfully straightforward and replicable experiments of von Frisch (1967) have convinced many that the bees do indeed communicate the abstract notions of distance and direction, by gesture rather than by words. Now Science, in the persons of Wenner et al. (1969), has threatened this idyll by the prosaic suggestion

that it is all done by smell. I have personally found pleasure in the idea of a choreic language in bees, and regret its subjection by plain fact. Perhaps now I must place my faith in the porpoise as a fellow linguist in the animal kingdom.

The word *infant* is derived from the Latin *infans,* meaning "without speech." Many species of animals communicate vocally such bodily states as anger, alarm, and even pleasure (the purring of the cat, for example), but their communication is not speech. This is about the level of vocal communication in the human infant, and at several points throughout this book attention has been drawn to the fact that the human infant has much that is akin to phylogenetically lower species.

The matter of language among animals has been discussed by Bierens de Haan (1929), and he makes the point that there is no evidence of language in any of the species studied at that time. By a *word* he means a *conventional* vocal symbol made with the intent of communicating to another; language is the use of words to express an idea. He seeks to show that even in the chimpanzee there is no evidence of language, though there are a number of recognizable sounds that accompany certain emotional states; these sounds, he says, are innate. (This opinion may need revision in the light of new evidence.) The "talking" of birds is not, of course, language; it is merely a response, just as is the pecking of a pigeon at a disc for reward. He does not allow the "language" of bees as true language, because although it does communicate, it is innate and not a learned set of conventional symbols. The ethologists in recent years have described a large number of "signals," some of them vocal, that mediate certain responses in other animals, but these, too, are not language according to a definition such as Bierens de Haan's. More recent reviews of the topic of animal communication are by Hebb and Thompson (1954) and R. Brown (1958).

Referring to chimpanzees, Kellogg (1968) believes that a chimp's linguistic limitations are more specifically vocal, for the chimp lacks the neurological mechanisms for speech but can still acquire sign language. He describes experiments in which a chimpanzee has acquired a sign language based upon that commonly used by the deaf. (The experiment capitalizes on the fact that feral primates do gesture.) One female chimp has a well-established vocabulary of nineteen signs, denoting mostly nouns but also terms such as *hurry, sorry,* and *please.* This animal understands a greater number of signs but cannot use them all reliably.

The dolphin is a recent contender for sharing with man the characteristic of language. It is certainly not dumb (as Bierens de Haan believed), but whether the considerable range of noises it makes are language is as yet uncertain, despite claims, such as those by Lilly (1967), that it communicates fluently.

A parallel between animal "language" and that of infants has been drawn by Hobhouse (1915). He regarded the sounds of the child in the first year as akin to those of animals— sounds accompanying certain (and limited)

emotional states. The infant can respond to sounds as a dog does. If his master rises from his chair and says "Let's go for a walk" fairly consistently, the dog will come to respond in eager doggish anticipation, but he will respond in just the same manner if the words accompanying the action are "Boiled beef and carrots," said in the same tone of voice. In both animals and human infants the response is to gesture and tone, not to meaning. Only later can the human child put together two or more conventional vocal symbols to convey a thought. Insofar as we are aware, no animal ever can.

Language development in children has been reviewed by a number of authors. The surveys by McCarthy (1946, 1954) are among the more comprehensive ones of the earlier literature. A more recent though less exhaustive coverage is given by Ervin-Tripp (1966). Lenneberg (1967) also embraces much of the literature, though he does not purport to give an overview of the field but rather an argument for a particular thesis. His main arguments are succinctly presented in Lenneberg (1969).

PRELINGUISTIC VOCALIZATIONS

The salient features of prelinguistic vocalizations have been given by Ervin-Tripp (1966). In the first thirteen weeks the most common vocal sounds relate to "fussing," with crying and cooing second and third in frequency; over this period there is a shift, cooing becoming more common and crying less so. There is a relation of crying and cooing to specific and distinct situations, and some evidence of specific hunger and pain cries. She suggests that there may be patterns idiosyncratic to individuals. On this and other points more sophisticated spectrographic techniques may supply better evidence.

Babbling and cooing sounds change in quality and soon begin to approximate adult speech sounds, though there are also sounds unlike adult ones, perhaps because of the immaturity of the speech organs. The range includes sounds that are not those of the child's environment (though they might be found in some language other than those of the parents). Ervin-Tripp remarks that many studies have used English phonetic categories rather than neutral ones and hence have overlooked this point.

In the early months most of the sounds are vowels or vowel-like, consonants being infrequent. The first consonants are formed in the throat and back of the mouth, though these decrease in frequency later (at least in English-speaking environments). The voicing of consonants increases with age. Babbling includes many reduplicated sounds (e.g., "dada") and repetitions ("kaga," and "mibi," and so on). It also includes many sounds never used by the parents but also omits some sounds that are common in adult speech. Some sounds that are frequent in babbling may later be difficult to articulate. It seems that language does not emerge directly from babbling, and babbling may have no relation to organized language beyond "exercising" the neurological and motor mechanisms of speech.

With speech sounds, recognition precedes interpretation (as logically it must), and such aspects of speech as pleasure or displeasure in the tone of voice are early responded to by the young child, before there is actual understanding of content.

Menyuk (1968) notes that in kindergarten groups there is a facility for learning nongrammatical phonological sequences, which is lost at later grade levels. Because a foreign language is to the naive child a "nongrammatical" phonological sequence, Menyuk suggests that this might make it preferable to teach the auditory-vocal aspects of a second language at the kindergarten level, before the perception of oddity of stimuli becomes a competitive distraction to attention to sounds.

A question in the development of language is raised by the study by Warren et al. (1969) already mentioned in Chapter 13. It will be recalled that they found that adult subjects could not report the sequence of unfamiliar patterns of sounds even when presented at far slower speeds than those necessary to the recognition of sounds in speech or music. It was suggested in Chapter 13 that this may be because there is not enough time for the rehearsal and storage of these patterns. Speech reception, on the other hand, involves the recognition of patterns *already in storage,* a process apparently requiring less time than placing into storage.

Assuming the young child to be in an analogous position to the adults in the Warren study, the first learning of language might be thought to involve the recognition at slow speeds of patterns of sounds, just as the novice Morse Code operator learns dots and dashes in separate patterns at relatively slow speeds which later become faster. Also, of course, to the moderately skilled operator · – "disappears" as a pattern of distinct dot-dash. It is *A.* Hence there is a labelling phenomenon. For the highly skilled operator whole words and phrases (especially those in his working vocabulary) become merged into patterns which he recognizes as a whole, not as dots and dashes. Also important is learning the code is the motor element—sending is important to learning to receive. In speech too, the motor act of speaking is important in learning to *hear* speech.

VOCABULARY

There have been a number of studies of lexicon, though, as Ervin-Tripp (1966) remarks, many of the earlier ones were hampered by inadequate mathematical techniques for handling some of the sampling problems. This, in fact, remains a difficulty, despite some refinements, and estimates of vocabulary differ rather widely. Also, social factors and extraneous ones such as travel tend to increase vocabulary or to modify the actual usage of words and hence to affect estimates.

It is generally agreed that at twelve months the child typically has one or two words, this vocabulary increasing steadily, slowly at first but with increasing rapidity, until the child at school entry has maybe 2,500 words available to him (McCarthy, 1954).

As might be expected, the vocabulary of the preschool child is less abstract than that of adults and contains fewer superordinates. Thus while *truck* and *car* may both be in the vocabulary, *vehicle* is unlikely to be. When an abstract term, such as *animal,* is used by a young child, it does not have the full range of connotation that it can have for an adult but refers to a restricted number of members of this class (R. Brown, 1958).

GRAMMAR

Earlier work on the syntax of children made an analysis in terms of adult grammar and sampled the frequency of nouns, adjectives, prepositions, use of tense, and so on, at various ages. The excellent review by McCarthy (1954) summarizes the considerable literature that has taken this approach. This has been a valuable addition to useful knowledge and has, for instance, provided a basis for educational practice. It has not, however, been especially fruitful in providing a theory of language development.

The recent view, put forward by Chomsky (1965) and McNeill (1966), is that childish language is not merely a poor copy of the adult one but is in fact a different language. The child borrows much of its vocabulary from the language of the parents, though, as is well known, it frequently contains words of the child's own invention. Parents have to do their own linguistic research in order to understand their children. The grammar of this early childhood language follows its own rules of syntax, though apparently these rules are universally quite consistent and are independent of the locality and culture in which the child is growing. This point will be referred to again, though it is not necessary to the argument of this book to go into the details of childish syntax.

There are two kinds of competence, *communication competence* and *linguistic competence,* which must be distinguished. The former refers to the ability to use language as a means of communication, whereas the latter refers to the correct use of grammar to construct proper sentences, and to the ability to make transformations (that is, to express the same message in a variety of ways). Linguistic competence is acquired quite early. According to McNeill (1966), by the age of three and a half children have a considerable skill, which by seven or eight is comparable to that of an adult, though Krauss and Glucksberg (1969) place the age of leveling off of growth of linguistic competence somewhat later, beyond age ten. After this time growth is more in the increase of vocabulary and of more varied means of expression.

Communication competence is in some senses more than linguistic, since it involves role-taking skills, particularly the ability to appreciate the knowledge of the listener (Flavell et al., 1968). This kind of competence thus involves the social aspects of speech as a speaker-listener dyad, in addition to the more mechanical skills involved in linguistic competence. Comprehension involves competence in decoding speech, production involves encoding. As has already been mentioned, it is a common observation that children seem to comprehend before they produce, and the latter seems to lag behind in its development for some time. However, this matter has apparently received little attention in the way of controlled observation. One study is by Fraser et al. (1963), who confirmed that comprehension does indeed exceed production, often markedly. Glucksberg et al. (1966), studying nursery school children, found listener proficiency to precede speaker proficiency in development. Cohen and Klein (1968) noted an increase with age in communication accuracy in school children in grades three, five, and seven. The third-grade child is also relatively limited in associative repertoire, which is significantly increased in the later grades.

The fact that comprehension is ahead of production is of theoretical interest since it seems to refute those theories of language development that are based on the response, that say the uttering of words brings a reward such as parental attention, so that this class of response becomes shaped (e.g., Skinner, 1957; Mowrer, 1958). This refutation is made fairly conclusive by the observation that comprehension of language may be established in the absence of any ability to speak (Lenneberg, 1967). As a further disproof of the S-R theory of language development one might take the results of observations by Wahler (1969) of a single infant in interaction with his mother. The child's vocalizations during the first year underwent systematic changes despite the fact that the mother was observed to reinforce by social attention *all* classes of infant vocal behaviors, so that "shaping" could hardly be invoked as an explanation of these changes.

A question arises as to the part that formal instruction might play in the development of the construction of correct sentences. It is plain that perfectly understandable language can develop in the absence of any formal teaching of grammar or indeed of any formal attempt at all in teaching speech. Lenneberg (1967) comments that even with deaf children, where special efforts are needed, it is probably not grammatical instruction that is effective but rather it is the special measures (such as hearing aids) to give them contact with language that enable them to synthesize sentences for themselves.

If we follow Chomsky (1965) and others in believing that the child speaks its own exotic language (even though it borrows freely from that of the parents), then obviously no one could teach the child, because until recently the grammar of this language was unknown to adults (and indeed is still known imperfectly and only to a few). Whether this new

knowledge will have any practical effect in suggesting special training in language acquisition remains to be tested. If there are the critical periods in language development to be outlined later, then it may be that this development takes its own pace, which may already approximate the optimum.

It is evident that in early life the child is, as it were, bilingual. That is, he is comprehending the grammar of the adult, but producing juvenile grammar. Thus Herriot (1969) has shown that at three years of age normal children can comprehend future and past as well as present tense. As noted elsewhere, production is no doubt important to the acquisition of linguistic skill, and the fact that a child's production is so faulty (in terms of adult language) may well be a handicap to acquisition. However, despite this handicap, it does occur, and perhaps we should be surprised at its rapidity.

PSYCHOLINGUISTICS

In recent years the science of psycholinguistics has grown and has a rapidly expanding literature, though like many other "modern" approaches in psychology it had early beginnings and a long fallow period. An early reference is Humboldt (1836), though no doubt Aristotle had something to say on this topic. Psycholinguistics has looked afresh at the problems of the development of language but as yet has not established a versatile armory of experimental techniques and hence does not have a broad array of confirmed knowledge. Much of the literature seems to the outsider looking for statements about how we talk and how children learn to do so to be philosophical in nature and lacking in concrete information. However, the earlier approach provided concrete data without a usable philosophical or theoretical framework and was no more enlightening to understanding *how* language develops. This new attack on the problem has already brought some major insights and hopefully will produce more.

Two of these insights that appear especially interesting to the present context are the biological nature of the bases of language and the possibility of viewing childish language as something qualitatively different from that of the more mature speaker.

The new approach to the topic tries to analyze childish language not in terms of the grammatical rules of the adult but by discovering what rules the child uses and finding whether there is any universality in these, either between juvenile speakers or across languages. The modern view regards the child as fluent in an esoteric language, and the psycholinguist's task is the same as in studying any other language—to find the grammar of the speaker (McNeill, 1966).

One point that must be clear, McNeill insists, is the distinction between competence and performance. Competence is the knowledge of the language that a native speaker must have in order to produce or understand any of the indefinitely large number of grammatical sentences that can be made in that language. This is what the psycholinguists call the speaker's *linguistic intuition*. A sentence such as "the boy sailed the kite" is grammatical, whereas "the boy elapsed the kite" is not, even though it contains the subject, verb, and object that an uncritical application of the grammatical rules would demand. The competent speaker knows intuitively that it is incorrect.

Performance is the expression of this competence, either in speaking or in listening. Performance is limited by several factors, important among which are memory, which is relatively short and which imposes constraints on expression or understanding. Thus some sentences may be too long to be understood, even though they are perfectly acceptable by the grammatical rules of the language.

A considerable difficulty faces the developmental psycholinguist. He must not apply adult linguistic intuition to constructing a grammar for the child's language. In constructing a grammar for a foreign language, he can construct a sentence and ask a native speaker if this is correct. Anyone who attempts to carry on a dialogue of this kind with a two-year-old is courting frustration.

Language has been viewed by the behaviorists as a vast collection of habits. Staats (1968) has dealt with S-R learning in relation to language acquisition, and he considers the earlier efforts to relate the two to be too simple to account for all the complexities of language. He attempts to use the principles of both operant and respondent conditioning to explain language development, though it is perhaps too early to assess his claim that he has produced a satisfactory theory.

R. Brown (1958), on the other hand, regards some aspects of language as a system of rules. What the child has to acquire is a knowledge of these rules, and he does so not by formal instruction but by deducing them from the performance of others.

The same view of language development is put forward by Chomsky (1965) and Lenneberg (1967), who also say that what the child acquires is not a collection of linguistic habits but a set of rules for grammar. The acquisition of language is thus essentially the acquisition of certain concepts. However, these authors go beyond this in maintaining that there is an innate basis to the concept-forming abilities of the child; special sets of linguistic concepts are present:

[T]he child has an innate theory of potential *structural descriptions* that is sufficiently rich and fully developed, so that he is able to determine, from a real situation in which a signal occurs, which structural descriptions may be appropriate to this signal, and also that he is able to do this in part in advance of any assumption as to the linguistic structure of this signal [Chomsky, 1965, p. 32].

It is certainly an achievement for the young child to deduce the complex rules of language at the time he does. A card game such as eulesis, which involves the deduction of rules, is beyond the capacities of the child at a time when complicated linguistic rules are being mastered with apparent ease. This suggests that here we have a "preprogrammed" learning, which is entirely consonant with the views of Lenneberg and Chomsky. The human species, they claim, is already "programmed" for language acquisition, and this takes place easily when the environment provides the necessary stimuli at the proper stage of maturation.

Such a formulation would have been considered unthinkable a few years ago, because it would seem impossible to imagine a genetic mechanism that could underlie such a complex proposition. But the recent knowledge of the nucleic acids, and the possibility of virtually limitless program storage that they bring, makes the proposal feasible. It is also becoming evident that, in fact, there is an immense amount of programmed behavior to be found in animals; even the simple nervous system of the insect can store behavioral sequences that involve communication.

At the human level, too, it is becoming evident that much perception is preprogrammed (see Chapter 13), and it is not incredible, even if as yet unproved, that certain conceptual systems may be innate also. What the theories of the genesis of language are saying is not merely that a capacity for conceptualization is inherited but also that certain specific linguistic conceptual systems are so transmitted. Assuming these to be universal to the species (as apparently is the case), then there is a basic similarity in the pattern of all languages.

In passing it might be remarked that in most genetic characteristics where abnormalities are nonlethal (and the innate language-forming capacity is surely one of these) the range of variation is rather wide. It is interesting to note, therefore, that absence or very low expression of this trait is rare, and that the trait is present in almost all members of the human species. Perhaps speech has a "fail-safe" mechanism.

Elsewhere in this book it is suggested that

certain other cognitive systems are inherited, or at least are markedly influenced by inheritance—cognitive style, for instance (Chapter 16)—and that global expression of cognitive activity, intelligence, is also inherited. Within the framework being developed in this book, it is altogether reasonable to regard language as a biologically based phenomenon. (This implies more than that an organism has to be alive to have language, for most living organisms do not have language; it also implies that man has species-specific biological equipment that makes language possible.)

The foregoing does not deny the place of the environment in the emergence of language; indeed, it provides an excellent example of the essential interaction between the biological organism and its environment. Given that the child has the biological equipment for language, it is obvious that he needs exposure to a specific language in order to acquire a usable system of communication with his fellows. It would be interesting to know whether two infants brought up together in isolation from a linguistic community would develop a language of their own. Given the foregoing, one might expect that they would, and a simple but completely unethical experiment would decide the question. It is to be hoped the experiment will not be performed. If one day somebody comes across the normal children of deaf-mute parents in a completely isolated family, then perhaps some facts will be available.

BIOLOGICAL BASIS OF LANGUAGE

It will be plain that the account of language development given by Lenneberg (1967) is very much in sympathy with the general thesis of this book. Following such biologists as D'Arcy Thompson (1942) and Bertalanffy (1952), he takes the view that there is a relationship between form and behavior. Most behavior is species-specific; that is, it is determined by the reflexes, sensitivities, and motor patterns inherited by the species, even though it may be modifiable by learning. This is true even though often one cannot predict behavior from morphology; he can usually see the relationship only by hindsight. There is thus a necessary relation between language and its biological foundations.

There are certain morphological correlates of speech: The acoustics of human sounds depend on certain features of the structure of the face and vocal tract, which permit a greater control and range of sounds than is possible in the great apes. But more important yet in its influence on human speech is the high degree of specialization in the human brain. Certain aspects of this matter have already been discussed in Chapter 6. Lenneberg insists that it is not merely the size of the human brain that serves speech but also the whole organization of this organ and the way in which its parts are coordinated. Laterality is one aspect of this organization, as is an antereoposterior polarizing of function (motor elements of speech being anterior, sensory ones posterior). Further, speech is dependent not merely on the cortex but on subcortical and midbrain structures (see Chapter 6), and it is the peculiarities of the total organization of the human brain that make speech possible.

The evidence on animal language has been reviewed in a book by R. Brown (1958), which is an admirable example of lucid communication. He concludes that there are important differences between the communicative responses of animals and linguistic reference in humans. The first difference is that human language is acquired (which is true even if the biological bases upon which language rests are innate), whereas animal communication is instinctive. Second, there is no evidence of phonological structure in animals; there are no words built up from sound elements that can be recombined in a variety of ways. Third, these animal responses rarely name categories (which is not to say that animals cannot categorize but only that they have very limited

if any capacities for using "words" to denote categories), and the responses are not extended to new categories.

Lenneberg poses the rhetorical question, why do children usually begin to speak between their eighteenth and twenty-eighth months? He straightway rejects the notion that parents universally commence language training then or that there is some ubiquitous environmental change at that time. He sees the changes underlying this emerging development as lying within the child rather than in the outside milieu or in the availability of stimuli. This idea that language development depends on maturation at this time is not peculiar to Lenneberg, but an imitation hypothesis is more widely accepted (Ervin-Tripp, 1966). While imitation certainly occurs, recent evidence suggests that it is not, as some theories contend, the sole factor in speech development. Of course, a child who is cut off from language by deafness or social isolation does not speak, and in this sense exposure to language and some imitation of it is crucial. But the language that emerges from the child is not mere imitation; it is modified. For instance, in imitating an adult sentence, the grammar may be modified to be consistent with the child's grammatical structures; it is not merely a more or less accurate rendering of the sounds of the adult. This is said to be especially evident in a language such as Russian, where there are rather marked differences between the order regularities of childish grammar and the highly variable word order of the adult (Slobin, 1966).

One source of support for the maturation hypothesis is the regularity of onset; certain phases in speech development have a fixed sequence and occur at fairly constant ages. Speech is in part at least a motor activity, and it would not be surprising to find some interlocking between motor development and speech. Lenneberg claims this to be the case. However, it is not a necessary relationship for language development. Talking certainly requires motor control, but language understanding can develop independently of the motor skills necessary to articulation (Lenneberg, 1962). Furthermore, while articulation shows some relationship to motor development, it is not a close one, not at least to the grosser motor activities, such as crawling and walking, that form the usual developmental motor milestones. Lenneberg suggests that there is a maturational schedule specific to language.

About the time of the first tottering steps, or perhaps a little before, the child has two or three words and presumably has the motor skill to articulate more, even if rather clumsily. However, adding to the vocabulary is slow and is presumably handicapped by some factor other than motor skill. Similarly, Lenneberg points out, the child can babble endlessly but cannot combine the words he has into an utterance.

One factor that might be involved here is the competition of another skill that emerges about this time, walking. It could be that the effort of acquiring upright movement distracts attention from talking and requires a greater investment of energy than can be shared. It would be of interest to study the language development of children in whom walking is prevented at this time—by confinement in a cast for the correction of congenital hip abnormalities, for instance. On the other hand, by the age of three the highly complex coordinations of laryngeal and respiratory motor systems necessary to articulation are well developed, whereas many other kinds of motor skills are still far short of ultimate development. Speech seems to follow its own timetable.

As has already been mentioned, another feature of language development is the advance of language comprehension over production. The repeated observation that children seem to understand what is said to them several months before they can themselves reply or frame a satisfactory sentence is also true of an older person's early experience with a foreign language.

Another point that distinguishes the speech sequence from others is that in certain disease conditions, early muscular atrophy, for instance, language may develop normally, whereas other aspects of motor development may lag behind. Conversely in a small proportion of the normal population speech development may lag by as much as two years or more, while all other aspects of development proceed by the usual timetable. Lenneberg (1967) reviews a number of such pieces of evidence that show that there is no direct causal relationship between motor and speech development.

On the other hand, in conditions such as hypothyroidism or mongolism, which affect all developmental processes together, there is, between motor and language development, a synchrony which Lenneberg takes as most compelling evidence to support the idea that language acquisition is regulated by maturational processes.

Attention is drawn by Lenneberg to an interesting aspect of speech as a skill. Although with proper training most children can acquire some proficiency in skills such as sketching or piano playing, these are not usually well developed until adolescence. Moreover, there are very wide variations in the degree of proficiency attained. Language, on the other hand, is acquired much earlier with a high degree of proficiency and with no apparent effort. Further, there is a less marked range in individual skills, most individuals showing a high degree of aptitude, and an absence of skill is rare. It would seem that there is a natural aptitude for language shared universally by the human species.

From some observations of deaf children born of deaf parents (he does not say whether the deafness was total), Lenneberg (1967) reports that their early language development was hardly different from that of normal children. They went through the usual stages of cooing at about three months and spontaneous babbling at about six months. Their emotional sounds seemed indistinguishable from those of other children. The deaf children tended to persist on a given sound more than hearing children but on the whole showed very little difference in other aspects of communicative skill in the first two years, even though lacking verbal means. Another of his observations was of a child who had been tracheotomized for six months, but who, as soon as the tube was removed at fourteen months, produced normal sounds for his age. Similarly, some psychotically mute young children will suddenly commence unpracticed speech appropriate to their age level.

The actual onset of speech is relatively unaffected by environmental factors (Lenneberg, 1967), but subsequent developments may be affected. As already mentioned, the children of deaf parents go through the same early sequences of speech development as those of hearing parents who respond to their offsprings' utterances in the usual way. Also, the nature of the early speech development is apparently the same in all human cultures. Furthermore, Lenneberg claims, all natural languages are learned with equal facility. However incredible this may seem to foreigners, any language is equally easy to the young child. In short, he says, the age of onset of speech capabilities is surprisingly constant over a very wide range of environmental variation; this points strongly to a maturational basis.

As Lenneberg remarks, there is a considerable literature on the physiology of language, and he selects from it to illustrate his thesis that language is a manifestation of intricate physiological processes. One aspect of this is seen in the respiratory patterns of vocalization. Breathing shows changes in pattern that are peculiar to speech, and Lenneberg believes that man is endowed with special physiological adaptations that make possible the maintenance of a flow of speech depending on expired air. Although there are limits to other changes in respiration—hyperventilation, for instance—the periodic expiration necessary to talking can be maintained with little interruption for hours on end, even by a young child. Lenneberg analyzes in some detail various aspects which need not concern us here, of the physiology of speech production.

One problem he raises that must be mentioned is the organizing principle in speech. Lenneberg finds a rhythmic element in articulation, at a base rate of about six per second, so that one sixth of a second is the time unit in the programming of speech motor patterns. He believes this fits in with a number of observations on the sensory side also. For instance, in delayed auditory feedback, 180 milliseconds (or a trifle under one sixth of a second) is the delay that produces maximum interference with speech.

He also claims that the same time period enters into thought processes. Thus in silent counting or even thinking about numbers or letters the optimum rate is about six per second. The same is true of finger tapping.

It is evident from the EEG that rhythmic activity is a fundamental property of the brain of vertebrates, and Lenneberg (citing Brazier, 1960) notes that there is a steady rhythm of about seven counts per second detectable over the temperoparietal region; this area is closely related to speech. He also observes that children do not show much development of speech until this dominant rhythm reaches about seven counts per second—at around two years. There is other evidence produced by Lenneberg to support this idea of a six-per-second beat at the CNS level underlying the highly specialized activity of human speech.

CRITICAL PERIODS IN LANGUAGE ACQUISITION

The early acquisition of language cannot be hastened. The child goes through the initial changes with considerable independence of the environment and in due course enters the period of ripeness for acquiring words, grammar, and syntax. During the early years of life there is, from mere exposure to a given language (Lenneberg, 1967, 1969), a period of effortless acquisition which appears to end after puberty. This is not to say that another language cannot be learned but that now it can be learned only by conscious effort.

The matrix for language skills exists and can be used in learning but no longer in the effortless manner of the child. The accent of a foreign language is also difficult to acquire after puberty, and the losing of one's original accent is similarly difficult.

The evidence is not extensive, but it does seem plain that there is a fairly definite critical period in acquiring linguistic skills. Whether such periods apply equally to *all* aspects of language has not been studied, though the persistence of grammatical errors, even when embarrassing to the perpetrator, suggests that other aspects are also subject to critical periods.

One of the surprising features about speech is that it is acquired rapidly. Grammatical speech does not usually begin before about eighteen months of age, but the basic processes are complete by about three and a half years (McNeill, 1966). Compared with the time span for other cognitive functions, and the fact that there is still so much maturation to be achieved in the brain, this period is remarkable. Language development is not, of course, by any means complete at that time, but by then the infant has been transformed into a competently communicating person who has most of the basic requirements of highly complex linguistic skills of the adult.

It has been pointed out that the child has to learn to hear before he can learn to speak, and we may distinguish *reflex* from *comprehension* hearing (Whetnall, 1958). Reflex hearing is a primitive, protective hearing possessed by all mammals and present at birth. In animals there is a reflexive response to sound that poises ready for flight and includes movements of the eyes, ears, and body. This response is controlled by lower centers.

In humans the reflex centers are subordinate to higher ones, and there is considerable change in the pathways involved in hearing from those found in the animals (Beatty, 1932). Comprehension hearing, Whetnall says, is the result of learning in the early years and involves learning the distinction of sounds. Speech sounds are among the most difficult

the child has to learn because there are great variations in wave form; the same word spoken by father, mother, and sister are different in the wave motions produced, to which differences may be added accent, intonation, speed of production, a whisper, or a shout. Under these conditions, recognition is achieved by the skilled listener but not at first by the young child.

Among speech sounds there are differences in the ease of recognition. Vowels are easier than consonants, and "th" is the faintest and last acquired (Fletcher, 1929; Shirley, 1933).

The ability to recognize and interpret sounds, that is, comprehension hearing, must be developed before hearing can be said to be effective (Whetnall, 1958). This really implies distinguishing between the sensory aspects of hearing, that is, the mere ability to detect sounds, and perceptual hearing, which consists of interpreting these sensations. According to Fry and Whetnall (1954), there is in the the first year a period of a "readiness to listen," which is critical to this development. After the third year the ability to recognize new sounds diminishes. If a deaf child is not taught to hear (or perhaps, more accurately, given the opportunity for spontaneous learning) by means of a hearing aid during this period, the best time might be lost. By five, comprehension hearing becomes difficult to acquire and by seven almost impossible; hence at this point speech cannot be acquired. (From other evidence, reviewed by Lenneberg, 1967, one might question whether the cutoff is quite as early as this, though certainly for the practical matter of training the deaf to speak "the earlier the better" seems to be the maxim.)

Another critical period, from about twelve to eighteen months (Stinchfield and Young, 1938), had been described as one of "readiness to speak." Obviously this must follow the one of readiness to listen, and presumably if this is delayed, the later one is too.

The early learning of speech involves very fine kinesthetic control, and this has to become habitual before speech is established.

Speech necessitates auditory feedback and is in deaf children difficult to learn in the absence of hearing. After this control is acquired, auditory feedback is less important, and a degree of deafness that would not in an adult interfere markedly with the understanding of speech may prevent a child from learning.

A child becoming deaf in the first two years may show an immediate arrest of speech development and may lose what has been learned, but with increasing age there is less and less interference (Whetnall, 1958). This suggests that speech is but loosely established at the beginning of this period, becoming more firmly established later.

INDIVIDUAL DIFFERENCES IN LANGUAGE ABILITY

While it may be, as Lenneberg suggests, that the ability to acquire language is remarkably uniform, it is difficult to believe that there are no individual differences in the biological substratum; complete uniformity would be unique, and in most phenomena the range is rather wide. Certainly there are individul differences in the skill with which language is used. Some people are more fluent speakers than others, and this is something independent of fluency of ideas. Many a rapid, fluent, and lucid speaker has nothing much to say, and fluency of expression is distinct from having something to express. Similarly there seem to be individual differences on the receptive side; this does not appear to have been much studied. Some individuals seem able to follow a flow of verbal communication easily and accurately and others with more difficulty, despite normal hearing. Some, one suspects, are relatively unable to follow long verbal messages (though they may be intelligent and able to decode long and complex written messages).

It is also observable, even among children, that there are individual differences in the ease of acquisition of a second language. Whether these differences reflect differences in training, opportunity, or interest is difficult to say. In learning a first language, it seems that any normal environment provides more than enough opportunity, and training seems somewhat irrelevant. Only an extremely impoverished environment provides less than an adequate amount of opportunity (though it may provide a limited vocabulary and faulty standard grammar, but that is a separate issue). Hence it might be argued that the differences found are in the biological substratum rather than in the environment.

For a second language, opportunity may be more crucial. While few children fail to get enough stimulation to develop the language of their community, many lack the opportunity for learning another. Among school children being taught a second language where the only exposure is to the one teacher in the same classroom, and where no exposure is given outside school, wide individual differences still emerge. It could be, of course, that there are differences in parental exhortation even where they can give no direct help, and differences in motivation or interest may be held accountable. But one knows of children given every encouragement to learn a new tongue who find such learning arduous and of those with little external pressure who find it easy, and it is difficult to believe that there are no individual differences in the aptitude for a second language. One interesting point would be to see if it is the fluent natural speaker who readily acquires a second language also, a finding that would lend support to the idea of a high natural capacity for language in such individuals.

Linguistic ability seems to be a special talent somewhat independent of intelligence, and even a vocabulary test of intelligence is not a good prediction of achievement in learning a second language (Carroll, 1962).

SEX DIFFERENCES IN LANGUAGE DEVELOPMENT

As already mentioned (Chapter 10), there are widely reported sex differences in language functions, particularly in early life (McCarthy, 1959). In general the differences favor girls, who in most aspects of speech development are ahead of boys. Moore (1967) has confirmed some of these sex differences.

McCarthy (1954) suggests social explanations for these differences—that, because of closer identification with her, girls find it more rewarding than boys do to imitate the mother; that boys are discouraged because they can less easily imitate the father's deeper voice; that boys are encouraged to play away from the mother and also are verbally rebuked more often than girls are.

T. Moore (1967), in describing cognitive differences between boys and girls, comes closer to what I would consider the more probable explanation (though without making it specific how these differences might have originated). He points out that boys favor exploration and preoccupation with things—with cognitive activities, in fact, which encourage nonverbal abilities. They involve activities less readily shared with others. Girls, on the other hand, are concerned from an early age with interpersonal relationships and hence with the need to communicate.

The boy eventually (Moore suggests) acquires from his early concrete operations a foundation for the logical inductions later made possible by language; when he eventually does acquire sophisticated language, he can use this to extrapolate beyond immediate experience to mathematics, science, and philosophy. The girl is more concerned with intimate understanding of human reactions, leading to the "feminine intuitions" in this area. Rather than the logical rigors of science, this leads girls to prefer the more subtle disciplines of the humanities. Moore recognizes that biological predispositions underlie these

differences. One might (in the context of this chapter) wish to take this further and suggest that sex differences in the biological bases of language itself may also account for the differences in language development. Thus language development may take different courses in the two sexes not only because of differences in cognitive styles of functioning but for more direct reasons. The differences of style may serve to increase the linguistic distinctiveness, of course.

LANGUAGE RELATIVITY

In studying American Indian languages, Whorf (1956) noted that there was often considerable difficulty in translating them into English or into other European tongues, and he suggested (somewhat tentatively) that this difficulty arose from differences in the thought processes of the two sets of speakers, these distinctive styles of thinking arising from the characteristics of the language in which thought is carried. There is, in fact, little evidence to support this idea, and Lenneberg, among others, rejects it. He points out that another theory, that some languages require less mature cognition than others, has also been dismissed by linguists.

A species-specific characteristic of humans is a conceptual capacity, which Lenneberg sees as supraordinate to language. Some languages may somewhat favor certain cognitive modes, but the use of language is creative, and it can transcend the static aspects of language. This is, of course, a separate problem from that of vocabulary; there are things some people cannot talk about because they lack the words that label them, but given the need, they can soon enough invent words or import them from another language. From such evidence as there is, no difficulty in dealing with thought at a conceptual level exists because of the characteristics of a given language (Carroll, 1964).

Lenneberg also claims that during the biologically optimum period for language acquisition the degree of relatedness between a first and second language has no bearing on the ease with which the second language can be acquired. This statement may, however, be doubted, according to MacNamara (1966), who believes creolization to occur only when quite distinct languages are involved.

LANGUAGE AND EMOTION

Communication has not only an intellectual or factual content; we communicate not only ideas and specific facts but also emotional meanings. Communication of the latter can be by verbal means. One might make such a statement as "I am very happy," but if this is said in a flat voice accompanied by a sad face and a drooping posture, a witness would be confused in interpreting the total message and is likely to believe the nonverbal content rather than the verbal.

This transmission of emotional meaning is no doubt a very important aspect of communication but one that has received very little experimental attention (Davitz, 1964). One might regard the communication of emotional meaning as both phylogenetically and ontogenetically primitive. Most (but not all) animal communication is of emotional states, and infants apparently respond to emotional expressions in others long before they can understand verbal communication. (One says *apparently* because infants will respond fearfully to an angry tone, though perhaps this is because an angry voice is commonly louder than a soothing one; this may be merely the normal fear reaction to any loud sound.)

The literature on research on facial and vocal expressions of emotion has been reviewed in Davitz (1964). Almost all the work in this area has been with adults, and information on developmental aspects is meager indeed. There is a suggestion from cross-cultural studies that innate factors play a con-

siderable role in emotional communication in humans. Studies of the blind, for instance, suggest that certain emotional *expressions* are unlearned. The role of learning in emotional *recognition* is another question; there are indications that learning plays a part in the correct visual recognition of facial expressions (Davitz, 1964), but whether or not learning merely refines an innately present skill is not answered by the available evidence. A study by Wilcox and Clayton (1968) suggests that discrimination of social expressions is not present in young infants, but when or how this ability does develop is as yet unstudied.

Among the few experimental studies of the development of emotional meaning is one by Dimitrovsky (1964), who found between five and twelve a significant increase with age in the ability of children to identify correctly the meaning of vocal expressions. She found girls to be more accurate than boys in this. Interestingly, she also found that male adult speakers were more effective in their communication of specific emotional meanings to children than were females. This study does not tell us anything about development prior to age five; at that age children were already accurate at a better-than-chance level.

NONVERBAL COMMUNICATION

There is an important area of communication that has been largely neglected and on which I have been unable to find a single developmental reference. This is nonverbal communication. There are a few works, mostly anecdotal in nature, on this topic, but they have almost nothing to say about how nonverbal communication develops.

A great deal is obviously learned. Our society abounds in nonverbal signs—traffic signals, for instance—and a fairly extensive pictograph language is growing again. Expo '67 in Montreal had, in an attempt to avoid multilinguistic verbal signs, a number of these, though their messages were not always immediately clear. In primitive societies, too, one finds such signs—the flower worn over the left ear (or is it the right?) denotes the maid who is seeking a mate.

In addition to nonverbal signals of the kind conveying a fairly definite message, there is also a range of symbols conveying more abstract and less specific messages—the cross, hammer and sickle, national flags, and so on. The swastika, once a good-luck symbol, has radically changed its meaning since the 1930's.

In all these it seems safe to assume that the individual learns the connotation of the sign or symbol, though in pictographs there is an attempt to provide an obvious or readily deducible meaning. An interesting question is whether there are any innate signals to which we respond. The ethologists have provided considerable evidence in the animals of innate responses to signals having definite communicative value, and there have been suggestions of some operating in humans too. These are reviewed in Chapter 4.

Proving that the communicative value of these signals is unlearned may be difficult. The side-to-side movement of the head to express the negative and the nod for the positive seem so fundamental to us as to be natural. This does not necessarily prove the signals we use to be other than innate; it may be that the Chinese use an "unnatural" signal. The side-to-side negative gesture might arise from the replete child's refusal of the breast by a movement of the head to one side, though it would be necessary to show that infants customarily use a horizontal rather than vertical movement for this. The author has the impression this might be the case, though he has no systematic observation to support this hypothesis. The vertical movement would probably be more difficult for the infant to make.

Such speculations might be interesting, though it might also be questioned whether they would be fruitful. Whatever the origin of nonverbal communication, it is highly probable that subtle cues enter into social interaction and that an individual's skill in interpreting the actions of others depends to a considerable extent on his sensitivity to these nonverbal forms of communication. Whether he is born with this sensitivity or acquires it is unknown.

It is also the case that, to a considerable extent, ordinary conversational interchange is aided by nonverbal accompaniments—gestures of emphasis, the averted gaze, and so on. Conversational speech also contains much that is not properly speech itself but that adds to the informational content or to the nature of the messages, pauses, intonations, and the like. Part of linguistic skill is the correct execution and interpretation of these extralinguistic signs. How much of this is learned or how it is learned has not been explored insofar as I am aware. The observations that young children respond to tone of voice early, even before comprehension, makes one ask if this response might not be innate and whether certain aspects of extralinguistic communication are not also part of the biological equipment of the species.

WRITTEN LANGUAGE

The claim might be made, and has been made by Myklebust (1965), that written language represents the peak of man's linguistic achievement. Whether or not spoken language is unique to man, one would be fairly safe in claiming writing to be so. Myklebust points out that higher intelligence is necessary for the acquisition of reading and writing than of speech.

There is, in fact, very little known about the development of writing, and in spite of its considerable practical implications to education and its inherent interest there have been few studies of the matter (Myklebust, 1965).

There are two sides to language, the encoding and the decoding. Decoding is primary—children comprehend before they can express. The same is true of written language—reading precedes writing. By the same token, children who by reason of deafness or other causes are retarded in speech also have difficulty in learning to read or write (Myklebust, 1964). However, it is not clear whether there is some essential developmental link between the two processes or whether the explanation is merely the rather obvious point that a child who does not know what words are and what they can do is unlikely to appreciate the value of squiggles as a means of communication.

It has been claimed that there are biological bases for speech, both decoded and encoded. Whether the same can be claimed for writing is another matter, though there is little evidence of the kind reviewed by Lenneberg for speech to support the idea that writing is similarly preprogrammed.

LANGUAGE AND THOUGHT

A popular view of the relationship between language and thought is that language is a tool developed by man to aid thought. Lenneberg (1969) disagrees with this way of putting it. One might say that algebra is a thought-aiding invention, a devised tool, but one cannot say this of language. Rather, for Lenneberg, language and thought are intimately integrated activities. Language is an essential part of cognition, and is neither the cause nor the effect of it. Language is an operation of the mind.

One of the most important contributions to the question of the relation between thought and language was written by Vygotsky in the 1930's but was suppressed in Communist Russia until 1956, when it was revived, largely at the instigation of Luria. The following summary of Vygotsky's position is taken from the edited English translation (Vygotsky, 1962).

Vygotsky emphasizes the role of generalization in verbal communication; things must first be categorized, and only after this can the signs involved in language come to represent the categories. In this sense the development of communication becomes that of generalization.

In discussing the development of thought, Vygotsky takes issue with Piaget (though we have to bear in mind that it is the Piaget of the 1930's and not that of the 1960's who is being criticized). In contrast to the early Piaget, Vygotsky believed that egocentric speech (i.e., monologue or soliloquy, or speech not directed toward another) in the young child is functionally equivalent to inner speech and drops out as inner speech supplants it. To Vygotsky, speech is always social, whether communicative or egocentric, and he rejects Piaget's dichotomy between egocentric and socialized speech. Egocentric speech is a stage toward inner speech and plays an important development role.

The argument continues by a discussion of the genetic roots of thought. He points out that (as revealed by Köhler's observations) intelligence in apes (or other animals) is not related to speech. Even though these apes have a gesture language, can express affect, and will mimic actions, they make little attempt to mimic sounds. (Vicki, a chimpanzee reared in a family, acquired only five word sounds, but these were never used linguistically [Hayes, 1951].) Vygotsky claims that chimpanzees apparently cannot acquire even a visual sign language and also remarks that most of the spontaneous sounds and gestures occur during emotional states, that is, when intellectual functioning tends to be at a minimum. Hence he says thought and speech are apparently not functionally related, as they are in man. Kellogg's recent work, cited earlier, calls this opinion into question.

Vygotsky concludes that thought and speech have different genetic origins, that they at first develop independently, and that there is in the beginning no constant correlation between them. There is a prelinguistic phase in thought and a preintellectual phase in speech. At a certain point in development these two meet, and "thought becomes verbal and speech rational." Whether or not one should regard Lenneberg as in serious disagreement with Vygotsky on this point is debatable. Lenneberg has stated (1969) that cognition is *not* peculiar to man, but is panspecific, whereas language is human species-specific. This seems to imply a genetic difference between cognition and language at least in origins, even if the intimate relationship between thought and language, which both Vygotsky and Lenneberg emphasize, soon develops.

There is a sudden discovery by the child that speech has a symbolic function, but this discovery is possible only after some level of thought has been achieved. This occurs at about age two.

The concept of inner speech is important to Vygotsky's argument, and he rejects the Watsonian view (current in his day) that inner speech is vocal speech that has passed through the whisper to inaudibility. Vygotsky claims that speech turns inward because its function changes.

Vygotsky distinguishes several phases of the development of language and thought. First, there is a primitive stage of preintellectual speech and parallel but separate preverbal thought. The second stage involves accumulation of naive psychological experiences of his own body, of objects, and of the use of tools. In parallel, speech becomes grammatically correct, though the child does not yet understand the logic of grammar. He masters the syntax of speech before the syntax of thought. The third stage involves egocentric speech and, in thought, the use of external signs or operations (e.g., counting on fingers) to aid it. The fourth stage is one of "ingrowth," or inner speech, in which the operations are internalized, and thought and language converge. The child begins to use "logical memory" (such as mental counting) and to operate with inherent relationships and inner signs. For speech de-

velopment, this is the final stage of inner or nonverbal speech. There remains an interaction between inner and outer operations, with rapid shift from one to the other. Though so interrelated, inner speech and thought are not the same. Much thought can be wordless —even without inner words—as, for example, is the thought manifested in the use of tools.

However, Vygotsky insists that the later development of thought is largely determined by language and that the child's full intellectual growth is contingent on his acquiring language or the social means of thought.

The early stages of development of speech and of thought are thus separate. The later stages of inner speech and verbal thought are not merely continuations of these earlier phases; the development changes in nature. The first stages are biological, and the later are social.

Vygotsky outlines some of the experimental evidence (from his own laboratories and those of others) that detail the course of the development of concepts. These are topics for Chapter 16. It is noteworthy that mere practice in verbal expression does not necessarily promote the structuring of thought (T. Moore, 1967).

An interesting point has been raised by Meadows (1968), who found that deaf children of deaf parents were superior in both intellectual and social functioning to deaf children whose parents were hearing. This appears to be because the deaf parents were accustomed to communicating with the deaf, largely by sign language, and hence were much better able to communicate with their children than were the hearing parents. It would seem that any language system, not only the verbal, can facilitate the more advanced development of thought beyond the prelinguistic level. This is not to say, of course, that sign language is *as* effective as verbal language, which can presumably communicate more easily a wider range of abstractions and form a more efficient vehicle for complex thought.

Piaget's view of the development of language is that it proceeds from a stage of *egocentric speech,* which is nonsocialized, to *socialized speech* (Piaget, 1926). Egocentric speech has no real communicative aim. It is often used in the absence of a listener and even when another is present is not truly directed toward him. The practice of language utterance skills is no doubt the important function of this phase.

In socialized speech the child does attempt to communicate, though even at six years of age as much as half a child's utterances may be egocentric, and there is a transitional stage taking up to about seven years before socialized speech is well established.

From his studies of the child's handling of verbal material (as in the proverbs experiments, mentioned in Chapter 16), Piaget proposes the idea of *syncretism,* which is a typical aspect of child thought and a result of the egocentric nature of the child's language. In this state (at about seven to eleven years) the child merges logically separate elements of a sequence into a diffuse schemata that prevents an appreciation of the underlying logic. Thus logical thought depends on the emergence of advanced linguistic skills that enable the child to appreciate and separate the essential elements in a verbal statement.

Bruner (1966) makes the point that any kind of symbolic activity requires the organization of the world of experience in manners essentially similar to those involved in syntax. Any language involves several principles such as categorization and hierarchy. Categorization arises from the fact that almost all verbal labels refer to classes of objects, and the child has to be able to categorize to use language. Hierarchy refers to the fact that some words in an utterance are more important to the message than others are, and the "telegram" language of the young child indicates a grasp of this fact.

The child can use these organizational principles quite fluently in language before he can use them to organize the world of experience. Since (if Chomsky, McNeill, and Lenneberg are correct) these basic principles underlying language are innate, the child starts off with inbuilt principles that enable him to deal with symbolic thought. In this sense thought and language have common origins. However, Bruner insists that without further training in the symbolic representation of experience thought remains dependent on enactive and iconic modes of representation of the world rather than on symbolism. (These are discussed in Chapter 16.)

In brief, Bruner is saying that we have to conceptualize the world in ways constrained by our structure, by the nature of our neuromuscular system. The primitive properties of visual, auditory, and haptic space constrain our attempts to represent knowledge in imagery. Our representation of the world by means of language or symbols is also limited by our innate endowment for mastering symbolic systems.

The question of the relationship between thought and language has been discussed by Furth (1966), who draws on research on deaf persons but generalizes also to normal linguistic functions as well as to their implications for the education of the deaf.

Furth has pointed out that many of the statements that the deaf are poor in concept formation have been based upon the fact that they are poor in linguistic skills. That is, it is assumed that abstract thought *is* linguistic. As he says, for an operational definition of abstract thought one might be justified in labelling it "verbal thinking," but one is not thereby justified in explaining abstract thinking as causally related to linguistic skill.

When the thinking skills of the deaf are examined in detail, as they are by Furth, one finds some situations in which these people perform less well than hearing people, but others in which there is no difference. There are, it seems, differences in the approach to a task. Thus in the Logical Symbol Discovery Task (Furth, 1966) the deaf learned associations by rote and did not seek reasons behind the symbols. Because of this, they could not use the symbols in other situations, whereas hearing persons who comprehended the *meaning* of the symbols could do so quite readily. When, however, the deaf were shown the meaning of the symbols, they could use them in a new task quite as well as the controls. Thus the deaf were inferior in discovering a principle but in comprehension and use of the principle were no different. (It may be, of course, that discovery is a higher-order intellectual function than utilization, the deaf being handicapped in the more "powerful" functions.)

Furth is insistent that the differences between hearing and deaf people are due not to any necessary or direct relationship between language deficiency and intellectual functioning but that they are caused by social reasons. He outlines the several ways in which society treats the deaf differently from the hearing and the ways in which the deaf child is educationally disadvantaged. He points out that the parents of deaf children have difficulties in communicating with them, difficulties that are often compounded by the advice of educators. In this connection the study by Meadows (1968) showing less disadvantage in the deaf children of deaf parents is of interest.

Furth claims that thought without language is quite possible, though he recognizes that thought *with* language may be more efficient, more objective, and more flexible.

He also suggests that many of the difficulties in linguistic competence of the present generation of deaf persons may be caused by faulty teaching of language. He is not assuming that the deaf *cannot* learn language: "The deaf child fails to acquire language because it is taught too late, in an unreasonable medium, in an unnatural way, and by the wrong person" (p. 206).

Whether or not Furth is correct in claiming that conceptual deficiency is not a *necessary* accompaniment of hearing deficiencies, it apparently is a fact that deaf children are generally handicapped in conceptual performance under the conditions in which they

grow up. Pettifor (1968) has demonstrated that it is the higher levels of conceptual thinking that are most affected by linguistic deficiencies due to deafness; this is not surprising. Concrete levels of conceptual thinking (those involving, for example, manipulations of visual perceptions) are less dependent on language.

WORDS AND THE CHILD-REARING PROCESS

It could be asked whether we do not, in our child rearing, rely *too* heavily on words despite their importance. Lord Chesterfield wrote letters to his son, Philip Stanhope, to a total weight of five pounds. They were literate and cultivated and replete with excellent advice for the station in life that Philip was to occupy. Voltaire described these letters as forming the best book on education ever written. Yet Philip turned out sluggish, careless, awkward, and poor of speech. Fanny Burney, who had plenty of experience in these matters, said of Philip that he had "as little breeding as any man I met with."

Important as language may be to the educational process, it must be remembered that a considerable part of the shaping of the individual is by nonlinguistic means. Part of Philip's difficulty may have been that the words were applied at the wrong time—the fact that they were in letters rather than communicated more directly is noteworthy. But it is also the case that a significant part of the determinants of personality are genetic, and some of the most important environmental influences occur before language is well enough established to be potent. It might be claimed that the role of language in development is more to refine and extend than to initiate trends.

It is perhaps one of the sorry aspects of human development that for so many of its more cogent aspects words are not enough. For many things the child *can* make use of the linguistically encoded wisdom of the past. He does not have to recapitulate for himself the long process by which man has decided that the planets revolve around the sun. He can learn the periodic table without having to retread all the steps from alchemy to modern science.

Yet there is so much that he can only learn for himself. This applies not only to motor actions, such as swimming or riding a bicycle, which can never be taught linguistically, but also to interpersonal relationships and a host of similar affectively tinged functions that the child must experience for himself. Words have only limited power to substitute for experience. Sad as it may be to parents, we can tell our children our experiences and our errors, but so many of the errors they must make for themselves.

This is not to say that words are unimportant to development, for this is clearly not the case. Yet we do invest words with magical properties—traces of the abracadabras in the spells of witches have by no means disappeared. We need to keep in mind not only the power of words, but also their limitations in the developmental process.

Sixteen

Development of Cognitive Processes

The question of how the preconscious neonate becomes a thinking being is a crucial one to psychology, for it deals with the development of man as a rational being.

Some of the major issues have been indicated by Gallagher (1964), who has spoken of recent changes in viewpoint on cognitive processes. At one time an IQ score, provided it was valid in terms of competent administration and the absence of any circumstances disrupting to the child, was regarded as a sufficient measure of all important aspects of cognitive development. Creativity, productive thinking, and problem solving were all regarded as adequately assessed by intelligence tests. This idea may not be explicitly stated so blatantly, but it is implicit in a number of practices, for example, in the definition of mental retardation in terms of IQ alone. Similarly, the bright child is defined in terms of a high IQ, and little consideration is given to other factors that may make for "giftedness." This implicit assumption is also seen in the definition of underachievement: If the child's academic status does not compare with his IQ score, he is considered an underachiever,

which makes the assumption that the IQ score is and should be the major determinant of academic expectation. In terms of the history of intelligence testing, this is not surprising, but perhaps we should not be bound by history.

As Gallagher points out, intellectual development was considered to be mainly a process of maturation that would be altered only by extreme conditions. The idea of the constancy of the IQ is an expression of this point of view. A further assumption stems from this—that the training of mental abilities is not possible—and this assumption in fact discouraged any attempts at training.

In a conference on gifted children (Gallagher, 1963) there was a reevaluation of current views on cognitive abilities. It was concluded, first, that intellectual ability should be considered multidimensional. This is not, of course, by any means a novel idea, but it is one that has been tacitly ignored in much of the recent work in the area. The conference also emphasized the close relationship between motivational and personality variables in the growth of intellectual abilities, again, not an original statement, but one apt to be forgotten. A further point for attention is the fact that intellectual ability is capable of modification, which is a widely accepted notion at the present time, though the extent of this modification is not really known. As we shall see, it may be overestimated.

DEVELOPMENT OF INTELLIGENCE

How intelligence actually develops with age is a major problem for psychology. One source of difficulty in studying this comes from the fact that the instruments used need to change with age. If we conceive the abstract notion of some "pure" intelligence, then how is this measured? All we can observe is intelligent behavior, and the young child has limited capacities for *acting* intelligently. At this stage we can only observe and measure what Horn (1968) has called *sensory-motor alertness,* which is only slightly related to intelligence as it is measured at later stages of development (Bayley, 1965; Hofstaelter and O'Connor, 1956).

A concept that is especially valuable in the present context is Hebb's notion (1949) of two kinds of intelligence. What he calls *Intelligence A* is the potential or the capacity for development. This is innate and, as Hebb describes it, involves "the possession of a good brain and a good neural metabolism" (p. 294). This hereditary factor permits the elaboration of perceptions and conceptual activities. *Intelligence B* is the functioning of a brain that has been influenced by experience. It is the developmental outcome of the maturation of Intelligence A modified by the environment. It is this that more directly underlies the actual level of intelligent behavior of the individual, and it is this more than A that is measured by tests (though even B is only imperfectly measured by them).

We thus have the idea that there are certain innate "tendencies to intellectual func-

tioning" that differ among individuals. These are modified by experiences, and because experience also differs among individuals, a further dimension of differential development is introduced. As Ferguson (1954) has pointed out, different environments result in the overlearning of certain patterns of behavior, and because of this overlearning, these patterns tend to become fixed.

It is important to recognize, as Hebb does, that experience is necessary for the development of the innate potential and that the kinds of experience the young organism has may limit the manner of development of the potential, in ways such as Ferguson speaks of. But the innate potential also limits the extent to which experience can be effective. Thus there grows a complex system of checks and balances. A simplified schemata is illustrated by Figure 16-1.

The thick boundary line represents the

FIGURE 16–1. *Potential and functional intelligence.*

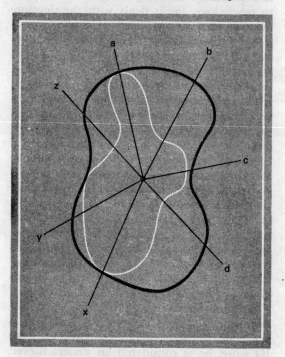

limits of "innate intelligence," and the "shape" of this boundary differs for different individuals. Within this boundary is another boundary (doubtless a more fluid one) determined by experiences and the kinds of overlearning Ferguson talks about. It represents the actual functioning level of intellectual activity. The individual represented in Figure 16–1 is not a very highly developed one, as the "area" of his functioning is considerably less than his potential. A fully developed individual would completely fill his potential area. But we must assume he cannot burst out of the genetic boundary.

It will be noted that this model implies a multifactorial concept of intelligence and implies further that individuals have non-uniform potentials along these sundry dimensions. A unitary concept of intelligence would imply that the genetic boundary is at all points equidistant from the center, that is, circular.

The early manifestations of intelligence are seen in *anlage* functions (Horn, 1968) or tendencies to act. These consist in elementary capacities for perception, retention, and expression. The span of apprehension, or the number of discrete elements that can be held in immediate awareness, is one such elementary capacity. Such capacities determine the level of intellectual functioning that is possible for the individual: For instance, the span of apprehension determines the length of sentence that the child can understand.

Later intellectual activities involve *anlage* functions but also more advanced devices such as concept formation (to be discussed later). The older child uses what Horn calls *generalized solution instruments* or *aids*. For instance, though the adult span of immediate awareness is about six or seven digits, a ten-digit long-distance telephone number is readily apprehended by grouping in two three's and a four, a device that circumvents the "natural" limit.

As discussed in Chapter 12, later learning tends to be influenced by earlier learning.

Ferguson (1956) proposes a theory of the manner in which learning forms accretions, and rather specific basic skills can be added together to form broad abilities. Transfer is the key variable here, though Ferguson declines to say anything about its psychological nature. He adopts a mathematical model and views transfer in terms of concomitant change. As one intellectual function changes, others change with it. This view emphasizes the experiential influences on the development of intellectual functions.

Thus we conceive of intellectual functioning as the outcome of two major sets of influences, the genetic and the environmental. The former sets limits on the latter, but experience also determines whether or not the genetic potential will be achieved and to what extent each of the factors presumed to make up "intelligence" is individually developed (not that it is conceived that each "factor" of intellectual functioning is a separate entity that can develop, or fail to develop, without widespread repercussions on other factors).

As might be expected, there is with age an increasing ability to process information. Linda Siegal (1968) has produced experimental evidence of this increase, which is based in part at least upon better coding of data by older subjects, which enables them better to handle more complexity.

SYMBOLISM AND THOUGHT

Bruner on Cognitive Growth

Piaget is quite clearly the dean of contemporary students of children's thinking and out of respect for his age and eminence should perhaps be given priority. But Bruner, who acknowledges his considerable debt to Piaget, forms a convenient link between this chapter and Chapter 15 and has been chosen as opening batsman (North American readers will pardon a metaphor from cricket).

Over the past several years Bruner and his associates have studied *concept attainment,* which is the process by which mature individuals arrive at concepts in particular instances by using already acquired cognitive skills (Bruner et al., 1956). More recently he has investigated *concept formation,* that is, the developmental process of acquiring the cognitive skills necessary to thinking and to attaining concepts.

Bruner (1960) has applied Piaget's theories in a specific situation in assuming that the child during the intuitive phase of concrete operations (which is approximately ages four to eight) is capable of grasping some of the basic ideas of mathematics, the sciences, the humanities, and the social sciences. To Bruner an operation is "a means of getting data about the real world into the mind and there transforming them so they can be organized and used selectively in the solution of problems" (p. 35). For a long time teachers have assumed that the child had to be able to present a formal argument, for instance, formulate the proof for a geometric theorem, in order to demonstrate his grasp of a concept. During the stage of concrete operations the child frequently cannot give formally organized theoretical ideas but nevertheless can solve many problems that depend on these ideas.

In Bruner et al. (1966) the author reports his own theorizing on cognitive growth and the results (of cross-cultural studies by his associates) that are derived from these theories.

For these authors cognitive growth is a series of psychological events influenced by genetic and linguistic factors and by the cultural environment. In discussing the growth of language, he is obviously sympathetic to the point of view of Lenneberg (discussed in Chapter 15), but as Lenneberg's book had not at that time been published, it is not referred to. Because the development of cognition is closely tied with the development of language, the constitutional factors that constrain language development must also influence thinking.

This view of cognition is organized around two central tenets. The first is that knowledge of the world is based upon a constructed model of reality and that this model can only be partially tested against input. The physical requirements of adaptive action may force us to conceive of the world in a particular way, a way that is constrained by the nature of our basic equipment. We are also constrained by the primitive properties of our perceptual systems in our effort to represent our knowledge in terms of imagery. Finally, our representation of reality in terms of language or symbolism is restrained by what seems to be our native endowment for mastering particular symbolic systems, systems premised on rules of categorization, hierarchy, predication, causation, modification, and so on. Bruner et al. (1966) view the growth of man as the process of internalizing the ways of acting, imagining, and symbolizing that "exist" in his culture, ways that amplify his powers. He then develops these powers in a fashion that reflects the uses to which he puts his own life.

Thus while Bruner takes a predominantly environmentalist point of view in discussing cognitive development, speaking, for example, of the differing influences of literate and illiterate cultures on the process, he is not entirely opposed to the idea that these depend on constitutional factors in their first emergence. The representation of the environment is filtered through perceptual lattices that in the young child at least are almost certainly innate. He quotes the work of Fantz, Bower, and others (reviewed in Chapter 13) on this point. However, he does emphasize the role of learned techniques in the representation of the environment. He regards culture as the chief instrument of survival for the human species; we depend, he says, more on the inheritance of characteristics acquired from the cultural pool than on those derived from the genetic pool. In a sense this is true, though it perhaps underestimates the degree to which the culture is molded by these biological contingencies (a point discussed more fully in

Chapter 18). He states that the human neo-natal brain is markedly immature—with which no one can disagree—and he also believes that it has few prepared response patterns. This book reviews a fair amount of evidence that I regard as contrary to the latter statement, though it has to be admitted that the evidence does not conclusively contradict Bruner, but neither does Bruner present conclusive evidence against the point of view taken in this book. Many of the prepared patterns may not be manifest immediately, but they are there, one can assume.

Mention of this difference of emphasis is not intended as a detraction from Bruner's theory. Indeed, it is valuable to discuss it here as a corrective to the biases of this book. One of the important conclusions of Bruner's researches is that cognitive growth *is* culture-bound. Language is a good example of a culturally determined behavior, and the child must often reorganize his way of viewing and imaging things in order to use language to describe what he knows. That is, language modifies the view of the world.

An important concept in this theory is *information seeking,* the means the individual uses to organize thoughts in order to answer a question. In Western culture at least, the mode of search changes in a rather regular way with growth. At first the child deals with single features of a problem one at a time; he uses images, seeking to match what is before him with some specification in his head. In time he comes to deal with several alternatives simultaneously. Eleanor Gibson (1966) is quoted as suggesting that increased informational efficiency is an important stage of perceptual development. After this stage is reached, and the alternatives can be arranged hierarchically, the child loses dependence on images (matching what he sees with some specification in his head) and commences information analysis. He becomes less and less dependent on redundancy of information.

A fundamental assumption in the position of Bruner and his team is that information

about the environment is coded in some manner. This is the idea of *representation.* The code is not, however, immutable, and in fact it changes with time; the use made of the code is one factor that modifies it. The authors distinguish three codes. The *enactive representation* is in terms of a specific habitual action and is the first perceptual scheme used by children. For the infant the actions evoked by stimulus events may serve in major parts to "define" them. At this early age it is difficult for the child to distinguish between a percept and a response. Specific actions become associated with a particular percept, and appearance of the original object can evoke the response. In proposing this theory, Bruner points out that the infant, even in the first few days of life, is capable of considerable response to features in the environment. (Much of the evidence on this was reviewed in Chapter 13.)

A second code is *iconic representation,* which is in terms of images. According to Bruner, this stage emerges by the end of the first year, when the child is able to represent the world to himself by an image or spatial schema that is relatively independent of action. By the time iconic representation is established, there should be a sharp separation between the child and world around him. When he "matches" something in his mind to something he has encountered, he does so by pointing to some particular sensory correspondence between the two. Only when the child can go beyond matching by direct correspondence can he learn to deal with "non-sensory" ideas such as the relations between quantities.

The third code is *symbolic representation* in terms of abstract schema, which are arbitrary; particular among them is language. Bruner views the establishment of this process as stemming from a form of primitive and innate symbolic activity, which through acculturation gradually became specialized into different systems, the most specialized of which is language. In this case symbolic representation refers to the nature of the proto-symbolic activity that supports language and all other forms of symbolization. The successful use of symbolic representation depends on the extent to which the sphere of experience has been prepared to bring it into some conformity with the requirements of language.

Bruner's theory of symbolic representation is briefly this: Language embodies the "ultimate structure of thought," but language matures earlier in child development than intellectual capacities do. Thus language anticipates symbolic representations. That is, rules used for language are the same as those used later on in stages of mature symbolic representation. Mature thought is verbalized and thus has features common to language—productivity, flexibility, discreteness, and transformality (this last being the rules of a language for rewriting, e.g., passive voice, interrogative, and so on).

When language becomes an instrument of thought, thought becomes verbalized and the conflict of language and thought is a *ratiocinative amplifier*. That is, it extends the capacities for thinking in an infinite variety of ways.

There is a developmental progression through the three codes of representation, from enactive through iconic to symbolic, though Bruner et al. recognize that adults may use all three in the representation of information.

For the child to use language as an instrument of thought, he must first bring the world of experience under the control of principles of organization. Without special training in the symbolic representation of experience, the child grows to adulthood still depending on enactive and iconic representation regardless of the language he speaks.

Language is not essential to thought, but is a *catalyst,* or, another term used by Bruner, a *ratiocinative amplifier.* It is a great convenience and is perhaps essential to the highest levels of abstraction. The conflicts necessary to development can only be provided by language; hence language is essential

to cognitive development. There is some need for the preparation of experience and mental operations before language can be used. After language has been applied, it can be used as an instrument to reach to higher levels. After experience has been coded into language, it is possible to read surplus meaning into experience by using the built-in implications of the rules of language.

In the conservation experiment, when the child perceives a discord between the statement "they are the same" and his perception of a difference in water level, he must rearrange his thinking to make this description true.

The use of language in thought is fostered by acculturation, and being told about things out of context is important to this process. Thus if a child lives in an advanced society such as North America, he becomes what Bruner calls *operational* (i.e., thinks symbolically), and by the age of five, six, or seven, given cultural support, he is able to apply the fundamental rules of language to the world as well as to his words. If, on the other hand, he grows up in a native village of Senegal, among Eskimos, or in a rural Mexican village, he may remain at a level of manipulation of the environment that is concretely iconic and lacking in symbolic structures, although his language is perfectly adequate.

In this statement Bruner is accepting the Whorfian hypothesis of language relativity, discussed in Chapter 15. As mentioned there, current opinion is skeptical of this idea, though Bruner's work might be taken as evidence in support of the theory.

It is clear that Bruner is impressed with the power of words. If it is true, as suggested in an earlier section, that children are, in fact, less touched by words than we might hope, then perhaps a necessary educational procedure is the improvement of the valence of words. They bring an enormous economy into cultural transmission, and it is an almost impossible task to set up an educational system that allows self-discovery of all needed concepts and total "learning by doing."

As already mentioned, the work of the Bruner team has drawn heavily on both Piaget's theories and his methods of studying child thought. Piaget was evidently somewhat ambivalent at having the recent book (Bruner et al., 1966) dedicated to him, for he finds himself compelled to criticize it strongly (Piaget, 1967). Much of his criticism concerns the methodology of the several studies and in particular the failure to ensure in the conservation experiments that the subjects really had this concept and not pseudoconservation. Here we have concentrated more on Bruner's theoretical premises, and Piaget also has criticisms of these. His main point, in effect, is that Bruner oversimplifies development: Piaget says that "cognitive development is a continuous building of new *transformational* structures and not the making of cameras or talking machines." He implies that Bruner's scheme supposes the latter. We need to determine, Piaget says, whether actions on reality performed by the subject consist simply in the construction of appropriate images and adequate language or whether the subject's actions and operations *transform* reality and modify objects.

Child Thought and Primitive Thinking

It is not uncommon to find in the literature statements that either say outright that adults in primitive cultures think in the prelogical manners of younger children in our own society or that imply this. The notion was propagated by Lévy-Bruhl (1922), who claimed from a study of the beliefs and customs of primitive peoples that their thinking is subjective in a manner that makes impossible the distinction between logically unrelated events, so that modes of thought are prelogical. Werner (1957) has also made a direct comparison between the thinking of children and primitive adults.

On the other hand, this idea has been vigorously attacked by Boas (1938), who claims

that there is no fundamental difference in the ways of thinking of primitive and of civilized man. He points out that the existence of superstitions and magicoreligious beliefs in primitive cultures is hardly valid evidence of a difference, because similar illogical ideas can be found among civilized peoples. Furthermore, many investigators who have attempted to study the matter more directly by the actual questioning of individuals have framed their queries in terms so uninteresting or so foreign to the people concerned that an impression of dullness has been obtained. They have often, in fact, asked stupid questions and received the stupid answers they deserved. Boas insists that within their own cultures and using their own frames of reference, primitive folk show no less initiative and foresight than civilized ones do.

The question is of some theoretical interest to the present discussion because if, in fact, primitive peoples retain a "childish" level of intellectual functioning, one might argue that this demonstrates the role of learning in the acquisition of the more mature modes of thought found among adults in complex societies; because primitive cultures do not train their children in logical thought, prelogical processes might be retained. Modern anthropologists reject this assumption (Piddington, 1950) and are strongly in support of the point of view put forward by Boas, but actual experimental data are hard to come by. There is, however, evidence of a more anecdotal nature that is interpreted by anthropologists as showing that the thinking of primitive adults is by no means similar to that of children in advanced societies and that the thought of the primitive adult develops from that of the primitive child in a manner comparable with the development in Western cultures. If illogical thoughts are to be found in the former cultures, these do not differ from the latter ones in this respect.

The study of the development of thinking has barely been started, but a cross-cultural study of changes, with age, in thinking would be a fruitful area of inquiry for anthropologically inclined psychologists. Such a study is provided by Bruner et al. (1966), and they claim to show that advanced cultures provide the special training necessary to symbolic representation, which is lacking in primitive ones. They point to the fact that in primitive societies a child's education is concrete. A primitive child learns to fish not from illustrated talks about fishhooks and techniques but by actually going and doing it. The whole of his education is specific and bound to actual performance. This is in sharp contrast to our own society, in which so much education is abstract and is provided through the medium of symbols. Bruner sees this as an advantage of our educational system because it fosters the development of the symbolic representation that is necessary to higher thought processes. By implication he seems opposed to the learning-by-doing theory of education (though presumably he would not object to some of this in earlier grades).

What Bruner and his associates have shown is that children in primitive societies (such as Senegal) think iconically at an age when our children are using symbolic representation. He also shows that within societies such as that of Senegal there are similar differences between children with schooling and those without. These studies do not, however, tell us how Senegalese unschooled adults think. It would be of interest to study this, because it would indicate whether symbolic representation can be achieved *only* through the kinds of abstract instruction provided by Western educational techniques or whether these techniques merely hasten a development which even unschooled individuals achieve at maturity. Thus we still do not know whether Boas is correct in believing that the cognitive processes of all adults are essentially the same, irrespective of culture.

It has been useful to discuss Bruner in order to balance the biological biases of this book. If, as he suggests, language plays such a crucial role not only in thinking but also in the development of thinking, then perhaps

the biological factors are less significant here than they are in some other aspects of development. It might even be that words can provide what the genes have neglected; I have strong reservations about this idea, but it is certainly not to be dismissed as wholly invalid.

Of course, as discussed in Chapter 15, we might follow Lenneberg in accepting a biological basis to language itself, but even granted this, language provides man with a means of transcending his biological bounds. The part played by language in stimulating the fulfillment of the biological potential should not be minimized—nor should it be exaggerated.

PIAGET ON COGNITIVE PROCESSES

The enormous outflow, from Piaget and his collaborators, of work on cognitive processes in children presents a problem to me. A chapter on the development of cognition can hardly ignore Piaget, yet how does one present an adequate short account of his vast work? On the other hand, because Piaget's philosophy of development is primarily biological, his approach would seem eminently in keeping with the point of view of this book.

The following is offered as a brief résumé of Piaget's theoretical premises; it makes no attempt to be comprehensive and relies somewhat heavily on secondary sources, notably Flavell (1963a), that have condensed Piaget's work. A more recent exposition of Piaget's theoretical foundations is given by Furth (1969), who also supplies an account of some of Piaget's latest writings which are not yet available in English.

In following Piaget's excursions into child thought, it is helpful to know that Piaget himself was initially a biologist who later became interested in epistemology. One can view Piaget's lifelong inquiries as an attempt to grapple with the old question, "What is knowledge?" He wished to know how we came to apprehend the world about us. As Tuddenham (1966) has said, Piaget's genius lay in avoiding the unanswerable question posed here, or the Berkeleyan query as to whether there is an external reality, and instead addressing himself to the more readily answered question, "How does knowledge develop and change?" Thus Piaget has an empirical epistemology that is to be approached developmentally. He has not concerned himself with the question of whether the world is real but has studied the changing processes by which the growing child copes with the world.

Although Piaget tells us that he is first a biologist and takes a biological approach to development, he is disappointing to me in that he says almost nothing more about the biology underlying the changes during growth. In this respect his accounts of development are not different from those of strict environmentalists. However, many of his concepts such as assimilation and adaptation, are biological in nature. Piaget (1967a) has written a book setting out his explicit views on the biological basis of knowledge. (At the time of writing it was not available in translation, and I have not seen a copy.) Furth (1969) provides a translation of the final section of this work.

From this section one finds that Piaget sees a biological organization as an open system which extends into the environment, but which at the same time must tend to close in order to preserve its own organization. Behavior is a kind of resultant of this double function. *Knowing* is an evolutionary advance which tends toward stabilizing this oscillation between opening and closing: Through knowing the biological organization tends to reach beyond itself; hence Piaget's epistemological search leads him to look at this biological organization.

To Piaget, cognitive functions are a specialized organ which regulate the interactions of the organism with its environment, but which are derived from a general biological organization.

Since for Piaget *knowing* is a biological phenomenon, the attainment of truth is also a biological urge, because it is a characteristic of knowledge to attain truth. Truth is not merely a copy of external reality (and failure to realize this has led to philosophical error), but it is, rather, an organization of the real. Hence one is led into the question of how this organization is organized, and this is a biological question. Piaget does not wish, however, to make knowledge exclusively biocentric, and certainly not anthropocentric. If I understand Piaget's argument correctly, he is saying that evolving is a part of truth, and since evolution is incomplete, knowledge of truth is at present incomplete, but we can continue to attempt to understand knowledge by observing its construction through the cognitive processes.

There are limitations in biological organizations, since these are basically homeostatic, though this equilibrium toward which they are directed is unattainable. Only cognitive mechanisms can reach the goal of achieving knowledge, and only man has the capacity for the social interactions that can transcend individual knowing.

Knowledge, says Piaget, is of three main kinds: innate know-how, or instinct; knowledge of the external world through the sense organs; and logico-mathematical knowledge. For Piaget, the instincts involve cognitive regulations, but these are preprogrammed and rigid. The third kind of knowledge is a late evolutionary innovation. For Piaget, instinct almost totally disappears in the primates (with which statement I am in obvious disagreement), but the new mode of knowledge does not replace instinct. Rather, it disassociates instinct and uses its components (so perhaps Piaget and I are not in great disagreement after all). Instinct is not exclusively preprogramming, Piaget recognizes, but is a basis for further modes of organization (which seems entirely consistent with the ideas presented earlier in this book). Intelligence and learning can modify instinctive adjustments, and new modes of regulation emerge. Since man lives in society and is responsive to the pressure of social groups, society is, in a sense, the supreme unity. Yet society is a product of life (a point discussed in Chapter 18), and depends upon the fact that each member of it has a nervous system.

Thus Piaget is hypothesizing that cognitive functions extend organic regulations and form a differentiated organ regulating exchanges with the external environment.

In his book, Piaget is pleading for an inter-disciplinary cooperation between biologists, psychologists, and epistemologists, a coopera-tion he finds too infrequent in the face of all the problems there are to tackle.

There s a most important consequence of Piaget's b ological presupposition and that is his conviction that development follows a strict sequence that is ordained by the in-herent nature of the organism. While his writings seem to emphasize ages, these are to be viewed merely as guides or estimates. He is much more interested in the fixed order of events and in their universality than in the age at which they occur in particular children.

Another feature of Piaget's philosophy is a lack of concern with individual differences. His age estimates represent means, but he is so little interested in variation that he gives no account of the range about the mean.

An important feature of Piaget's scheme, which is in agreement with the philosophy of this volume, is that the organism is not merely the passive recipient of a ready-made reality but organizes its own reality. In this it is consistent with Gestalt theory but is more dynamic than that theory.

There are fundamental difficulties in any stage theory, but as Kessen (1962) has re-marked, we seem to have a need to impose segmentation on the course of human develop-ment, and although it is usual to insist that development is continuous rather than salta-tory, we usually fall perforce into descriptions by "stages" or discrete steps. Kessen goes on to discuss how inevitable this is, because only by fragmentation can we break behaviors into pieces that we can describe precisely and make valid predictions about. Piaget and Freud are among the developmental theorists that have used the *stage* concept most clearly, but we are all forced into at least covert use of this device.

One of the great weaknesses of the stage concept is that it becomes difficult to account for the transition from one stage to the next. Piaget has attempted to do this, at least for some of the earliest stages, but Kessen sees a general failure to account for transition as one of the weaknesses of his position. Piaget's theory, Kessen suggests, is rather a "state" theory that examines the child at discrete points in time and finds him now in this state, now in that, but without a real account of the move from one to the other.

Learning theorists are in a sense students of transition rules, but their rules are not yet generally applied to movements between suc-cessive developmental stages (and, if the sug-gestions elsewhere in this book are valid, are not in any case applicable to *all* progressions).

Although the greater volume of Piaget's work has concerned intelligence, he has not entirely neglected other aspects. He has dis-cussed in a number of contexts (quoted by Flavell, 1963a) the question of the motivation underlying intellectual development. While recognizing the part played by the vegetative needs, Piaget maintains that these do not supply the real motive directing intellectual activity. He believes that there is an intrinsic tendency for cognitive structures, once formed by functioning, to become self-perpetuating. The need is inherent in their existence. For Piaget, assimilation is a major element in intelligence, and a prime attribute of assimi-lation is an intrinsic and repetitive tendency to reach out into the environment and in-corporate it. This idea is, of course, entirely consistent with the exploratory or curiosity drives proposed by others and discussed in Chapter 14.

He also sees affect and cognition as complementary, with affective life, like the cognitive, being a continuous process of adaptation, and the two being interdependent. Both loving and hating involve subtle judgments, and affective schemes are also intellectual ones (Piaget, 1951).

Piaget on the Structure of Child Thought

In the highly advanced mental processes often (but not invariably) shown by intelligent adults, we may see that conceptual relations are objective, impersonal, abstract, and general. Such qualities, Piaget's work shows, are lacking in early child thought, in which relations are egocentrically conceived and related to concrete perception and action.

For example, the child conceives objective relations such as *right* and *wrong* as concrete and egocentric concepts. Piaget gives the example of a child aged six who was informed that another child had added two and three to make six and was asked if this was right; the child replied "No, that's not right." "Why not?" "Because the boy reckoned wrong!" We see here that thinking is not directed toward the general mathematical truth involved but to the concrete situation and the fact that the boy had not worked out the problem correctly.

Children, then, are unable to think in terms of impersonal abstract statements. They cannot grasp the hypothetical. For instance, a six-year-old child, when asked the question, "If your brother is a year older than you, how old is he?" protested that he could not answer this question because he did not have a brother. Up to the age of ten years, three quarters of the children examined by Piaget were unable to grasp the relationships involved in telling just how many brothers and sisters each brother and sister in his family had.

To give an example from a conversation I was involved in, Pippa being six:

"Pippa, what is your sister's name?"
"Heather."
"And who is Heather's sister?"
"Heather hasn't got a sister."
"But who are you then? Aren't you Heather's sister?"
"No, I'm Pippa."

Such examples illustrate the difficulties that even simple relationships pose for young children and how much their thought processes are limited by immaturity.

Children, even as late as thirteen or fourteen, have difficulty in grasping simultaneously different aspects of a relationship or of a double relationship. A form of question common to some tests goes like this:

"Edith is lighter than Susan; Edith is darker than Lillie. Who is the darkest—Edith, Susan, or Lillie?"

Typical answers to such problems illustrate the limitation of child thought:

Godfrey, nine years: "Edith is darker than Lillie, but Susan is *heavier* than Edith." (A confusion from being too literal?)

Child, thirteen years and nine months: "Once Susan is the darkest, and once Edith is, so Susan is the same as Edith, and Lillie is the lightest."

The difficulty that the children have in solving this relationship is mainly in the fact that it depends on an understanding of the twofold relationship in which Edith stands.

Yet another example is given by the problem:

"If the animal has long ears, it is a mule or a donkey; if it has a thick tail, it is a mule or a horse. This animal has long ears and a thick tail. What is the animal?"

Boy, nine years: "The animal can be a donkey because you say that if it has long ears, it is either a donkey or a mule, but it can be a mule, for you say that if the animal has a thick tail it is either a mule or a horse."

The child evidently could not grasp the simultaneous two-way relationship.

Proverbs also provide a valuable insight into modes of reasoning:

"When the cat's away the mice will play."

Boy, eight and a half years: "Some people get very excited, but never get anything done." He explains this by saying, "people run around, but afterwards they never get anything done because they are tired. That's like the cat who runs after chickens. He rests in the shade and goes to sleep. There are many people who run around, but afterwards they can't go any more, and have to rest."

The implication is that the cat runs around, first after the chickens and later to find a place to rest, and because of this can catch no mice.

"You can't get white dust out of a bag of coal."

Boy, nine years: "Those who waste their time, neglect their affairs." According to his reasoning, both sentences mean the same thing, because he explains, "Coal is black and you can't make it white. Those who waste their time don't take care of their children, and then they get so black, you can't clean them."

We see in the answers given by these children that they have conceived concretely what the adult would have conceived as a universal content. The child shows literal, arbitrary, and idiosyncratic processes of reasoning, and the examples show that this thinking differs markedly in some respects from the sophisticated processes of which adults are capable.

Piaget, from whom some of the above examples are drawn, has devoted a great amount of effort to the study, from an analysis of responses to questions like those cited, of the development of thinking in children. From observations of practical test situations in which logical processes could be demonstrated, he has induced some developmental stages through which intelligence passes in its growth. This involves, of course, the reasonable and indeed necessary assumption that thought and intelligence are intimately related and that in his modes of thinking the individual manifests that abstract, intangible quality we call intelligence. It may be that the culture has an influence on the logical forms available to the child, but his underlying intellectual development limits his ability to grasp them.

The greater part of Piaget's work has concerned itself with intelligence. For Piaget, intelligence is a primarily biological concept, determined by both species and individual genetic endowment (Piaget, 1952), though it transcends these origins. Because of the biological nature of intellectual development, there are certain fundamental properties that give a constancy to functioning, and these Piaget has called *functional invariants*. They are *organization* and *adaptation*: All living matter adapts to the environment and possesses organizational properties that make this adaptation possible (Piaget, 1952).

Adaptation consists essentially in a balance or equilibrium between the two processes of *assimilation* and *accommodation*. Assimilation is the process whereby changing elements in the environment become incorporated into the structure of the organism. At the same time, the organism must accommodate its functioning to the nature of what is being assimilated. Thus intelligent activity is the active, organized process of assimilating the new to the old and of accommodating the old to the new (Flavell, 1963a). *Content* refers to raw, uninterpreted behavioral data—to what the child does (or says). *Structure* means cognitive structure, or the organizational properties of intelligence. *Function* creates structure; functions are the major features of intellectual activity, such as number and quantity, time, space, probability, logic, and so on.

Piaget on Developmental Stages in Intelligence

During its growth, intelligence passes through stages, so that the difference between the five- and fifteen-year-old is not merely a quantitative one but a qualitative one also. Piaget has attempted to trace the evolution and development of the use of logical symbols in the child; these, it may be assumed, parallel the development of intelligence itself. He has outlined the following stages.

1. Period of Sensory-Motor Intelligence (from Birth to Two Years). Before the appearance of language the child can perform only motor actions and not thought processes that depend on symbolic language, though because intelligence is adaptation, there is intelligence before the development of symbolic operations.

There is no evidence at this stage that the child recognizes the continued existence of an object outside the perceptual field; for instance, the child shows no attempt to find a hidden or concealed object: "Out of sight" is apparently completely "out of mind." This might be because the child is not yet capable of the motor movements necessary to explore the perceptual field, notably the arm and hand movements necessary to uncovering a covered object. It would seem from data reviewed in Chapter 13 that exploratory eye movements and fixations are possible early in life; the role of eye-hand coordination in the development of the concept of object permanence is discussed by Piaget (1952), who sees it as the first step toward the release from egocentrism. Whatever the reason, it is some time before the child discovers that objects do maintain a continuous existence, even though temporarily out of the perceptual field. If this is the case, then the solution of any "detour" type of problem, in which it is necessary temporarily to lose sight of the goal, is not possible. According to Piaget, during this period the child is building more and more complex responses that can be used in exploring the environment, in recognizing stimuli and stimulus differences, and during this stage the child reaches the limits of intelligence that are possible without language. By the end of this period object permanence is achieved, the human capacity for language is appearing, and the child is ready for the next phase.

2. Period of Concrete Operations.

A. Stage of Preoperational Thought (Two to Seven Years). Between eighteen months and two years symbolic functions appear. These are language, symbolic play, deferred imitation such as occurs quite some time after the original event, and mental imagery, which is a kind of internalized imitation. Because of these symbolic functions, the internalization of actions into thoughts becomes possible. Before, the child could only solve problems that he could manipulate concretely and behaviorally; now he begins to be able to solve problems that require psychological operations—that require thought—though much preparation is necessary before he can do this at all effectively.

The two-year-old can carry out a sensory-motor action quite skillfully but is still unable to do this in thought; direct perceptions still dominate. But from two onward there is further change, and during this stage the child learns to classify the stimulus patterns, differentiated in the first stage, into class concepts. To quote one of Piaget's examples, a child walking through a wood sees several snails; he does not know whether he sees the same snail repeatedly or a different snail each time; the distinction is, in fact, meaningless to him. The concepts of "snail in general" and "this snail in particular" are not yet learned, but such concepts are being acquired during this stage: The child is passing from preoperational thought to later kinds. Deductive reasoning of the form "all men have ears; Socrates is a man; therefore he has ears" is not possible before concepts of class membership are understood, and such reasoning is not possible to the child during the preoperational stages—nor is inductive reasoning from the particular to the general. Rather, the child reasons *transductively* (Piaget's term) from the particular to the particular (*A* is like *B* in one respect; therefore *A* must be like *B* in other respects, or *A* is *B*). Such reasoning may be valid in some circumstances, of course, but will lead to logical errors in others.

B. Stage of Intuitive Thought. Thought during this stage is intuitive, which is best described by Piaget's own example: In the presence of the child, beads are poured from a short wide glass into a tall narrow one; he sees that *all* the beads go from one to the other. He is asked whether there are now more beads or fewer. Most children of this age say either "more" ("because the pile is higher in the new glass") or "fewer" ("since the glass is narrower"). This error occurs because the children cannot yet separate perception from reasoning; they can see a change in the perceptual quality of the mass of beads but cannot yet reason about the "unseen" concepts of the volume of beads. Here, reasoning is dominated by perception. Another feature of this is an inability to take account of the several aspects of the situation (the height and width of the column of beads being inversely related to keep the amount of beads constant). Adults are not, of course, entirely free of such errors but yet are capable of higher-order reasoning.

The various types of thought activity in this phase are *irreversible*. The child can think from proposition A to proposition B but not back again from B to A. Thus a child shown a ball of clay that is rolled out into a sausage shape will likely say that there is "more clay there because it is longer." If the clay is then rolled back into the original ball, the child is unable to see, before the age of about seven years, according to Piaget, that this proves that the volume has not changed; he is unable to reverse the thought processes.

Abstract relationships present difficulty; thus, presented with two sticks of equal length with the ends level, the child can correctly identify them as equal in length. Move one ahead of the other, and he claims that it is now longer.

C. Stage of Concrete Thought (Seven to Eleven Years). The previous periods have been prelogical in the sense that the child was not yet capable of the sorts of logical operations accepted by logicians, but they were a preparation for development toward these operations. In this stage the child becomes capable of properly logical thought. Piaget calls these logical thought processes *operations,* and although there are several, his three most important are the following:

1. *Classes.* This operation is the ability to *think* of all objects with a common feature together as forming a class of objects with that characteristic. Younger children may be able manually to group objects of a class—for example, to put all the yellow ones together—but apparently cannot think of them as a class in the abstract.
2. *Relations.* This operation involves relationships of the sort "A is longer than B," "X is the son of Y." Again, while younger children may recognize such relationships in the concrete, they cannot, Piaget claims, manipulate them abstractly in thought. Whereas younger children fail the two-stick test described earlier, children this age can now see that the length remains constant.
3. *Numbers.* This operation involves both classes and relations; for example, the concept *thirteen* involves the grouping of thirteen objects in a class and of relating or ordering the concept *thirteen* between *twelve* and *fourteen.*

During this stage the child becomes capable of *reversible* logical processes, of reasoning an argument both ways. He can, for instance, now correctly state the constancy of the volume of the beads or of the clay. In Piaget's terms, he achieves conservation.

3. Propositional or Formal Operations (Eleven Years Onward to Adulthood). In this stage appears the ability to reason by hypothesis. In previous levels of development, a child presented with a problem such as the following item from Ballard's Nonsense-sentence Test

"I am very glad I do not like onions, for if I liked them then I would always be eating them and I hate eating unpleasant things."

would criticize the data, saying that onions are not unpleasant, or that it is wrong not to like them, or by means of some similar argument. At the present level subjects can accept the data as a hypothesis and concentrate on the contradiction between "if I liked them" and "onions are unpleasant." There is a change to hypothetical thinking and to hypothetical-deductive reasoning.

Beginning in this stage, the child becomes capable of adult logic. He can adopt a proposition "suppose X be true, then . . ." and follow the argument, whereas younger children would not get beyond arguing whether X is true or not. In his writings Piaget commonly ends this period at fifteen, though it continues to adulthood. Piaget's observations form a useful source of hypotheses for further experiments.

SOME SPECIFIC ASPECTS OF DEVELOPMENT STUDIED BY PIAGET

The tremendous output of experimentation from the Institut J. J. Rousseau at Geneva (together with the other laboratories directly or indirectly set into activity by Piaget) has covered a considerable range of topics—the development of judgment, causality, probability, and numerous others. It has investigated the acquisition of concepts of form, time, space, weight, volume, number, quantity, logic, velocity, and many others. It is not proposed to review these at all completely but to use a somewhat randomly selected few as examples of the method and the results. A review of some of the studies of concept acquisition has been given by Sigel (1964) and a very comprehensive one has been offered by Flavell (1963a), who also gives a complete bibliography of Piaget's writings to 1962.

Concept of Object Permanence

One of the most fundamental of concepts is that an object is different from oneself, being independently permanent; this is an essential prerequisite for conceptual thinking. Piaget (1954) has examined the attainment of this concept in some detail and shows that between eighteen and twenty-four months the child comes to realize that objects have substance, occupy space, and are permanent. At first an object or a sensation is regarded by the child as an extension of himself, and an object no longer in view ceases to exist. The attainment of the concept of object permanence is important in two ways. First, there is the realization that objects have their own integrity and independent existence; and, second, which follows from this, the child comes to understand that another individual is differentiated from himself and from the environment and can be treated as an object. The attainment of the concept of object permanency occurs at a time when verbal skills are hardly developed and few linguistic labels are available, but yet, according to Piaget, the child can think of the object independently of what he can do with it. That is, the child has developed representational processes and can imagine the object and its displacements in the absence of the actual object and hence in the absence of any physical action by the child in relation to the object.

Space and Spatial Relations

According to Piaget, at the same time as the child is attaining the concept of object permanence, he is also acquiring spatial concepts, and it is important to realize that several developments are occurring simultaneously. (A fruitful source of inquiry for the future will be the interlocking effects of these several simultaneous processes.) In Piaget's scheme the attainment of concepts of space is a complicated process going through six stages (Piaget, 1954). We have seen, from the material reviewed on the development of perception (Chapter 13), that the *sensing* of space appears very early and that the young child is able to operate in certain manners in space quite adequately. What Piaget is referring to here is a somewhat different matter: the development of the child's awareness of space, conceptually.

It is useful to review Piaget's findings on the development of the concept of space and spatial relations as an instance of the sequential and interlocking stages he proposes for development in general. Initially there exists a heterogeneous and unrelated set of perceptual clusters, each of which is a "space." Until three to six months of age, the infant merely analyzes the content of sensory images presented to him. Schemata develop that constitute a practical space in which the child can move and adapt himself to forms and dimensions; however, no spatial relations are conceived as being independent of action.

During the second stage the child is able to return to an object in the initial position in which he perceived it. The practical and the heterogeneous nature of the different spaces characterizes these first two stages. The child is neither aware of the spatial relation of one object to another nor of his own displacement in relation to anything external to himself.

The third stage involves the coordination of these unrelated and practical groups, beginning with the relating of sight and touch, or prehension. The subjective group, a step in the transition from the practical to the objective group, is formed as the child learns to use his hands in order to act upon things. He thus becomes aware of, and makes use of, the spatial relations between objects. He also begins to relate some of his movements to those of his environment and can find objects even when they move too quickly for his eyes to follow them. Still bound by perception, however, he cannot conceive of a complete rotation of an object and thus will not search for its reverse side if he has not seen it. Toward the end of this stage the child begins to perceive distant space as such.

The transition period from subjective to objective groups occurs in the fourth stage of development in which the child learns relationships between things themselves, unrelated to actions involving them. It is now

that he discovers reversible operations, acquires constancy of shape and dimension of objects, and discovers perspective by deliberately moving his head and noting the resultant changes in object shape. He can distinguish changes of position from changes in state and has achieved the use of the third dimension in space. Even though he has advanced in the direction of objectivity, the child still recognizes positions and displacements as being relative only to himself. He does not yet locate himself in a space common to himself and his environment.

During the fifth stage, the child attains full use of relationships between objects without reference to his own body. He now understands the relative displacement of objects and has succeeded in noticing sequential displacements of that which he seeks, no longer looking for it in its initial position. The child begins to be aware of his own movements as displacements of a whole, and now a common space organizes everything entering into direct perception.

However, it is not until the final stage that the child can represent himself, and his own displacements, as if he were to see them from the outside. The sixth stage, accordingly, adds imagined displacements to those directly perceived. The child now invents detours and performs acts of orientation. Space has become a motionless and ordered environment containing the child himself as an element.

Piaget, in examining the mechanisms by which the notion of space evolves in the child, reviews the nativism-empiricism interpretations. He concludes that it is the organism-environment interaction that prepares for the later interaction of the intelligence and "things," although no specific mechanism has as yet been determined.

Development of Conservation of Mass, Weight, and Volume

Some of Piaget's most well-known experiments have been carried out on the investigation of conservation. Russell (1956) has surveyed the literature that has stemmed from Piaget's suggestions. In summary, the findings show a steady improvement with age in the understanding of conservation of mass, weight, and volume, but the studies do not give much information about the actual development of these concepts. The prototype of these experiments is that by Piaget and Inhelder (1941) in which balls of clay were rolled out and altered in shape and the child invited to say whether the quantity or the weight or the volume remained the same. Elkind (1961a,b,c) and Lovell and Ogilvie (1960, 1961a,b) repeated Piaget's experiments and confirmed his statement of the developmental sequence for quantity and weight but found volume to be a more difficult concept. Kooistra (1963), studying children of four to seven years of age and of superior intelligence (mean IQ, 135), found results that were also comparable when mental age was used instead of chronological age. Fifty percent of the children had achieved the concept of conservation of quantity at age five, of weight at age six, and of volume at age seven. This study is of interest in suggesting that it is the mental rather than the chronological age of the child that is the important factor in determining the onset of a stage. As far as mass, weight, and volume are concerned, then, there does seem to be an invariant order in their development.

Using simple arrays of objects, Mehler and Bever (1967) have claimed to demonstrate concepts of "more" and "the same" in number of objects in children between two years and six months and three years and two months, which is earlier than conservation had been considered possible. They believe their results to indicate that the inability to conserve quantity is a temporary phase in development, the child first having conservation, then losing it and reacquiring it later (in the case of conservation of quantity, in the fourth year). Piaget (1968) has criticized the Mehler and Bever study on the grounds that it has nothing to do with conservation because it does not deal with transformations and equalities,

though nevertheless he admits it provides useful data on the development of quantification.

Piaget takes up the suggestion of a temporary phase of nonconservation and says that some innate mechanisms are "so poor and so fragile" as to manifest themselves only fleetingly and after difficulty but are then swamped. They reemerge later in childhood after new strategies and performances that permit their expression are acquired. Young children *do* conserve so long as the facts presented to them are within their expectations. A stage of nonconservation arises when they come across facts inexplicable to them and fall back on nonconservational explanations in an attempt to cope with events they cannot analyze. They later return to conservation as their capacities for dealing with the cognitive situation improve (Piaget, 1968).

He goes on to say that the child does not show nonconservation because he lacks the native endowment for conservation (Piaget seems to regard conservation as an innate property) but because his perceptual strategies do not allow him to take into account the several properties presented to him. The child interprets the data as best he can with the skills he has but falls back on "magical" thinking when faced with an incomprehensible situation (in which perhaps the adult does not differ from the child, except in the level at which the inexplicable is reached).

Concept of Causality

The concepts of space, form, color, and size are natural attributes of objects. Even the concept of object permanence is to be regarded as knowledge of the natural attribute of objects, certain of the philosophers notwithstanding. Cause-and-effect relationships are of a different order, though their attainment is extremely important to intellectual functioning. Piaget has undertaken a considerable amount of research into this question and has shown that although children in the first or sensory-motor period of intellectual development do show some awareness of cause-effect relationships, objective understanding of them is not attained until late in childhood (Piaget, 1928, 1930).

Piaget has described three fundamental approaches that children have to reality, each of which he claims arises from the lack of distinction by the young child between himself and the world. At first, children are egocentric and unable to discriminate between psychological and physical events: Human experiences, thoughts, feelings, and wishes are constantly confused with objective reality. This is seen when the child describes dreams or thoughts as possessing thing-like qualities; Piaget calls this type of conceptualization *realism.* At the same stage of development the child also shows *animism,* or the attributing of life to inanimate objects. There is also *artificialism,* or the tendency to regard physical phenomena as the products of human or divine creation.

Piaget (1930) describes the development of reality and causality as passing through the following stages: The first covers the first two or three years of life, in which the child confuses objective and subjective reality; there is the belief that desire can influence external objects, which can be obedient to these wishes; this is magical thinking. The second stage is precausal, during which time the child is thinking egocentrically, making no attempt at logical justification for his beliefs. Motive and cause, or psychological activity and physical mechanism, are confused. It is not until the third stage that logical and real categories develop and the child can give logical causal explanations.

There have been a number of attempts to replicate Piaget's findings, but the results are confusing. Some are consistent with Piaget's contentions; others are contradictory or inconclusive. Laurendeau and Pinard (1962) have reviewed and analyzed these studies on causality and have concluded that the differences and contradictions that have been reported are due to methodological matters.

Their own very exhaustive study of the question involved 500 children, an equal number of boys and girls, between the ages of four and twelve years. They found realism to last until approximately six and a half years of age, artificialism until about nine, and animism and dynamism until about ten. Various kinds of precausal thinking survived until this last age, but certain sorts of precausal explanations disappeared at various times before this. These authors observe that some areas of reality are more easily objectified than others, depending on the complexity of the phenomenon itself and the child's experience and the teaching he has received. Laurendeau and Pinard believe that the order of development is fixed but that experience may influence the onset of the various stages. All in all it would seem that Piaget's formulations on the development of a notion of causality have been neither conclusively proved nor disproved and still therefore form a tenable hypothesis.

Piaget's discussion of causality relates to the physical. Whiteman (1967) has investigated *psychological* causality and in an exploratory manner has found evidence of a parallel between the development of the two, with psychological causality being more strongly age-dependent than physical causality.

Probability Concept

One aspect of the immature thinking of the child in the stages of preoperational thought (roughly between three and six years) is that he does not distinguish possibility from necessity. He is influenced more by contiguity in space and time than by causality (Piaget, 1960). The notion of chance first develops in the concrete-operational stage, after the seventh year (Piaget and Inhelder, 1951), and the child begins to distinguish what is necessary from what is possible. From this follows the idea of multiple possibilities and the further distinction of the certain, the probable, and the merely possible. Thus in turn comes the concept of the relative probabilities of events. This concept is really understood only after about eleven years, during the stage of propositional or formal operations. Abstract concepts such as combinations, permutations, and proportions then become understandable.

The experiments upon which Piaget's theory is mainly based have been criticized on two chief grounds. One is the common complaint against his experimental method—that it involved too small samples and failed to control for a number of relevant variables (e.g., Messick and Solley, 1957). The other is that the experiments on probability required in the child a considerable degree of fluency to verbalize rather technical mathematical probabilities (Flavell, 1963a).

Davies (1965) attempted to expand on some of the issues related by Piaget's theory of the development of the probability concept in children. She used male and female subjects at each age from three to nine years. Each child was presented with a nonverbal test of probability and later a verbal test of probability, using red and white marbles of various proportions. The results support Piaget's interpretation of this concept as a developmental phenomenon. Davies also found that the nonverbal behavior of the preoperational child is consistent with the inference that the child is responding to event probabilities. The results also demonstrate that nonverbal behavior consistent with event probabilities precedes the ability to verbalize the probability concept. Thus Davies' study is in partial support of Piaget's conclusions. It modifies his thesis in showing that while verbalization may not begin to appear until the concrete-operational stage, nonverbal apprehension of the concept of probability may begin in the preceding one.

Verbal Fluency and Concept Grasp

Reference has been made by a number of critics to Piaget's heavy reliance on question and answer in his "clinical" experimental method, which demands verbal fluency. It may well be that in each of his concepts, nonverbal manipulation of the concept precedes the ability to use the concept verbally and to communicate it. But Piaget has in his more recent experiments used both larger samples and more careful checks on the child's real grasp of the concept. Indeed, he criticizes Bruner strongly for failing, in his series of experiments, to distinguish true conservation from pseudoconservation and for not using the checks he has developed to make this distinction (Piaget, 1967).

Critical Periods in the Acquisition of Concepts

At first sight Piaget's insistence on the necessity for each stage to be passed through before the next can be entered, together with his notion of a biological substratum underlying these stages, makes his theory consistent with the critical period hypothesis. However, there are difficulties and at least the appearance of an inconsistency in Piaget's reasoning. (It may be that somewhere in his vast writings he discussed this point, though I am unaware of such a discussion.)

According to Flavell (1963b), the content of Piaget's theory can be divided into three classes. First, there is the metatheory—in brief, his epistemological aims. Second, there is the stage-independent theory, which concerns itself with what kind of "device" the human thinker is, not at any given stage but fundamentally, and by what general principles he develops. The third is the stage-dependent theory, which considers the actual succession of genetic steps by which development proceeds.

Now it seems that critical periods are a well-established biological fact and that any theory which claims to be biological must take cognizance of these. The essence of critical periods (as the term is conceived in this book) is that they are maturational; that is, they rest on changes in the biological substratum even if their manifestations are psychological (and in this context the "psychological" may be considered a subclass of the "biological"). Thus critical periods are time-bound, at least for the individual, and presumably for the species there is, within the usual limits of variation, a fairly consistent time element. Thus for critical period phenomena there is both a sequential invariance and at least some rather marked tendency to chronological invariance.

Piaget is insistent on the first: The sequence of developmental steps is invariant, but the chronological age at which each occurs is not. I am not in the privileged position of knowing Piaget's thoughts and writings intimately and so cannot quote his latest views on this question. There are indications, however, that he might agree with the more orthodox views on critical periods. Piaget is skeptical of attempts by Bruner and others to teach children more sophisticated mathematical and similar symbolic concepts at an early age (Piaget, 1964a). One can suppose that he is sympathetic to the idea that critical periods not only impose a sequential pattern on development but a time element also. There is, of course, a further point: Agreeing that critical periods involve both a sequence and a chronology does not commit one to agreeing that cognitive developments involve critical periods. This is merely inferred. The outcome of experiments that attempt to alter the chronology of cognitive development will throw light on this question.

Role of Previous Experience

A question arises as to how a child progresses from one stage of development to another. Piaget does not really answer this question, though he does recognize that experiences are necessary to intellectual development and that both physical activity and social interactions are part of these experiences (Piaget, 1964b).

There have been a number of attempts at accelerating such concepts as conservation, and they have been reviewed by Almy et al. (1966). On the whole these attempts have been unsuccessful, but we still cannot be sure whether this is because we have not hit on the right experiences to give the child. These experiences are evidently part of the normal environment, but the problem is to isolate them and to focus on them in a didactic manner.

Some writers have doubted, on theoretical grounds, that such acceleration is possible, even if we do discover the salient experiences. Wohlwill (1964) believes that the absence of conservation in the younger child is due to his being in a perceptually dominated stage and that the development of conservation depends on the passing of this perceptual dominance and the emergence of language as a mediational process. A number of experiments (also reviewed by Almy et al., 1966) have attempted to study what is involved in the progress from perceptual to conceptual thought, though again without being conclusive.

In a study involving children in two schools, one with a predominantly middle-class enrollment and the other lower class, Almy et al. (1966) found a similar sequence in the development of conservation. The middle-class children, however, tended to be ahead of those from less privileged (and presumably less stimulating) homes, and Almy concludes that within whatever limits may be set by maturational factors experience makes an important contribution to the development of conservation.

A relationship between personality factors and conservation has been demonstrated by Goldschmid (1967), who found children with a high degree of conservation to be more objective in self-evaluation and more reflective; they were viewed as more attractive and described more favorably by their teachers. They were also more popular with their peers and less dominated by their mothers. The personality traits of objectivity and self-knowledge probably enhance cognitive functioning, and the popularity and independence of these children would tend to increase interactions with the environment. Also in keeping with these possibilities is the finding that emotionally disturbed children tend to be later than normal children in the achievement of conservation; this suggests that disruptive personality and social factors may retard cognitive development (Goldschmid, 1968b).

As Goldschmid points out, these findings do not contradict Piaget's age-dependent theory of cognitive development but do show that there are individual differences in the timing and point to some possible experiential correlates of these. It is also possible, of course, that these personality differences, and the differing reactions with the environment that they produce, are related to constitutional factors.

Special Training in Concept Attainment

There are a number of studies that have attempted special training in Piaget-type concepts. Smedslund (1961) has investigated the possibility of training a child to learn the concepts of conservation of quantity, weight, and volume. Beilin and Franklin (1962) attempted to teach the concept of conservation of area; Ervin (1960a,b) gave training in logical thinking; Welch (1940) gave training in hierarch-ordered concepts; and Wohlwill and Lowe (1962) gave training in the conservation of number. In each of these studies there was an attempt to teach the child some concept before he was naturally "ready," and the results were on the whole negative (though there were some positive ones). That is, they seem to show that the child cannot acquire a particular concept before he reaches the requisite stage of cognitive maturity. Flavell (1963a) has criticized these studies on the grounds that it was not previously ascertained in sufficient detail which sequences are a necessary prelude to such learning. Also, it is possible that the training periods were too short. Flavell, in fact, sees these negative results as confirming Piaget's

contentions that all the necessary sequences must be gone through before learning is possible.

As mentioned above, not all studies show training to be ineffective. Smedslund has reported positive results in the acquisition of the conservation of substance (1961). He suggests that the salient condition for the shift from nonconservation to conservation is the introduction of cognitive conflict. As a result of this conflict, there is a cognitive reorganization, which leads to the concept of conservation. In testing this hypothesis, Smedslund used thirteen children, of five and a half to six and a half years of age, who showed on pretest no evidence of the concept of conservation of substance. They were submitted to a training procedure in which they were presented with two pieces of Plasticine. One was left intact, and the other was changed in two ways, in shape and in quantity (by either removing a piece or adding a piece to it). To create conflict, the change in shape was always opposed to the addition or substraction. That is, the object would be both elongated to make it appear larger and have a piece taken from it to make it smaller, or would be altered conversely. During training, five of the thirteen subjects consistently answered only in terms of addition or subtraction and were able to ignore the change in shape. Four of these gave conservation responses in the post-training test and were able to give a logical explanation. The control group received no training and failed to show conservation. No rewards were given for correct responses, but the introduction of conflict improved the performance of the training groups as compared with the controls. This has some important applications to education, because it suggests that, in teaching concepts, the juxtaposition of two competing ones will force the child to reflect rather than to respond on the basis of what he already knows. Rewarding the child is apparently not necessary, the cognitive conflict being in itself motivating. (This study tests the equilibration theory, the idea of internal reorganization that is itself motivating, as against the learning theory, which depends on external reinforcement.)

As a criticism of the hypothesis of the trainability of concepts one might point to the fact that although some of the trained children did acquire the concept, most still did *not* have it at the end of the experiment. However, there are other studies by Fournier-Chouinard (1967) and Gellman (1967) that show positive effects of training. These studies showed generalization of the concept to non-trained tasks, and also maintenance of the concept on retest, which in the Fournier study was five months later. Goldschmid (1968b) has also reported with five-year-old children successful training of the concept of conservation which here occurs some two years earlier than the time given by Piaget for the "natural" acquisition of this concept. Goldschmid also noted retention of the concept after six weeks and the generalization of the concept to unrelated conservation tasks. Thus the effects of training appear to be stable and generalizable.

One of the studies by Smedslund (1961) contains a point of particular interest. He found that children who had acquired the concept of conservation as a result of their own experience were different from those who had obtained it by specific training. Those who had acquired conservation for themselves did not readily give up the concept when experimental conditions challenged their understanding of the concept. In this experiment subjects were shown two objects of Plasticine. One was changed in shape, but the experimenter covertly took a piece from it. When the child responded that the quantity was the same, even though the shape was different, the experimenter proved him wrong by weighing the object. The natural acquirers of the concept resisted this proof and attempted an explanation—that a piece of the object had fallen to the floor, for instance. The children who had acquired conservation by training reverted to nonconservation under these circumstances. The educational moral of this is

that one's own experience is a better teacher than formal training (and once again psychology gives experimental proof of a well-known fact).

This being the case, it would seem that training as such is inappropriate. What is needed is not special "lessons" in concepts but the provision of a milieu in which the child can discover them for himself. It may be that both parents and teachers place too much faith in words, though admittedly it is a heavy tax on ingenuity to arrange self-learning situations.

On the whole, it would seem that the evidence on the effects of special training is somewhat ambiguous. It is apparently possible for certain concepts and under particular conditions, but the generality (and the desirability) of such training needs further inspection. This question will be taken up again in another section.

COGNITIVE STYLE

Cognitive style has been defined as the manner in which an individual comes to grips with reality (Klein, 1951). It is perhaps a point of debate whether this topic should be discussed under perception, or here where intellectual processes are being considered, or as a personality attribute. In fact, cognitive style no doubt includes all three; that is, particular modes of perceiving the world, particular styles of integrating these perceptions, and typical manners of responding to the integrated perceptions.

Broverman and Lazarus (1958) have suggested that a cognitive style may manifest itself in two ways, as a directive influence on behavior or as an ability to resist disruption under interference conditions or distraction. In the case of directive cognitive styles certain responses have a greater probability of occurring in situations where the stimulus is ambiguous. Both instances may be interpreted in terms of response strength. In adults, task difficulty is apparently a variable in determining the style that is used.

It is thus suggested that cognitive styles involve complexities in operation, there being individual differences in the preferred style, and also factors, such as the nature of the cognitive task of the movement and the interplay of the various styles available to the individual, which are relevant to the outcome.

In discussing the nature and range of cognitive styles, it is useful to take a specific exemplar. Broverman and Lazarus (1958) have proposed and given experimental demonstration of three styles. One of these is *automatization,* which functions on a "weak" to "strong" dimension; the other two are *conceptual dominance* and *perceptual-motor dominance,* again on polar scales, so that conceptual dominance implies low perceptual-motor performance and vice versa.

Broverman (1960) has shown that the conceptual style is limited to tasks that are novel or difficult or demand concentration. In simple and highly practiced tasks, the style he calls automatization appears regardless of whether the task is conceptual or perceptual-motor in nature (*automatization* is defined below). Difficult conceptual tasks cannot be automatized. Because these styles are apparently independent, four groupings of style can be seen:

1. Conceptually dominant, strong automatizers
2. Conceptually dominant, weak automatizers
3. Perceptual-motor dominant, strong automatizers
4. Perceptual-motor dominant, weak automatizers

Cognitive styles may therefore be ordered on a number of parameters.

Thinking is thus seen as a process in which there are individual differences in the manner in which a problem is approached. For example, Harlow (1959a) has shown how different children obtain and employ different concepts. For some children the parts or apparent common elements are the bases of organization, while others organize materials by drawing inferences rather than by dealing

with what is immediately evident. The concept the child acquires is thus influenced by his predisposition to attend to particular features of the environment.

Two individuals who earn the same score on a standard measure of intelligence may in fact function very differently in their actual approach to intellectual tasks, and one of the fallacies of intelligence testing is the assumption that all individuals with the same score will be equal in their ability to solve all cognitive problems.

The focus of interest in the context of this book is the origin of these differences in cognitive style. As with almost all other such questions, there are three possible answers. The most popular is that early experiences determine them. An alternative appeals to constitutional and probably genetic differences. The third, or eclectic approach, assumes that differences in cognitive style result both from constitutional factors *and* from experience.

Constitutional Approach to Development of Cognitive Style

In terms of the principles guiding theorizing in this book it is appropriate to look for constitutional factors underlying the development of style. There is not, in fact, much factual information available. One approach toward the relating of cognitive style to more basic matters has been given by Klaiber et al. (1965) who suggested the factors underlying the *automatization* style. At this stage their suggestions must be regarded as speculative, though they are speculations of a type that those wedded to a physiological viewpoint in psychology may find quite reasonable (but that those who are not so biased will find, perhaps, entirely flighty). Automatized behaviors are those that have been so highly practiced that a minimum of mental and physical effort is required for their execution. Based upon earlier investigators, these authors argue that the automatization of simple habits is a necessary condition for the acquisition of new and more complex abilities. Such learning reduces the attention necessary for the performance of a task, thus making possible greater concentration on the new elements of a problem. On this reasoning, individuals who are highly automatized in everyday routine and repetitive behaviors should have an advantage in meeting more complex nonautomatized situations (provided their automatized repertoire forms a positive platform for the more advanced behavior). Support to this contention is given in a study by Broverman (1964) in which adult males with strongly automatized routine behaviors were shown to have a higher occupational level than individuals of similar age, education, and intelligence who were weakly automatized.

Klaiber et al. related automatization as a cognitive style to androgen level. The biochemical reasoning here is as follows: A relationship has been shown by Zeiler (1965) between androgen and monoamine oxidase (MAO) activity in rats. This relationship is an inverse one, castration raising brain MAO and testosterone administration lowering it. MAO is believed to be the principal inactivator of the catecholamines in the brain (Brodie et al., 1959). These substances, which include norepinephrine, are associated with behavioral activity. Hence, the more androgen, the less MAO and the greater availability of norepinephrine.

In addition to biochemical assays of androgen output, these authors also studied body hair and other anthropometric indices known to be associated with androgen secretion. For psychological measures they used a battery of tests consisting of two *restructuring* tasks and two automatization tasks. Restructuring tasks are those that require an initial response to an obvious stimulus to be set aside in favor of response to hidden and less obvious stimulus relations. (Tasks used were the Wechsler Adult Intelligence Scale [WAIS] block design subtest and the Witkin embedded figures test.)

It was argued that strong automatizers would perform less well on restructuring tasks. The automatization tasks consisted in speed of naming repeated objects and speed of reading repeated color names. On such a task, strong automatizers would be expected to do well.

Using male college students as subjects, the expected results were obtained. There was a positive relationship between androgen output and strong automatization as a cognitive style.

Klaiber et al. have also found the automatization cognitive style to be related to physical development in male preadolescents and adolescents as well as in adults (Broverman et al., 1964; Broverman et al., 1965). One should not seek too much capital out of a study based upon theoretical premises that some may find questionable and that in any case stand in need of replication. The study may, however, be seen to point to the way in which some aspects of cognitive style might be related to fundamental conditions in the bodily economy, and presumably it is the *early* presence of these biological factors that influence the development of this style.

The practical applications of automatization have not been worked out in detail, though it might well prove to be a style with important educational implications. Mathewson (1967) has shown that boys who are poor oral readers are characterized by being weak automatizers, whereas the good readers in her study were strong automatizers.

There are other studies that relate aspects of cognitive functioning to personality characteristics without making clear the causal link, if any, between them. They leave open the question of whether the style develops as a consequence of the personality trait or whether the style is merely the expression in the cognitive realm of a pervasive general mode of functioning (that is, whether the processes are developmentally sequential or parallel). A number of such studies have been reviewed by Freeberg and Payne (1967). Sontag et al. (1958) found emotional dependence on parents, aggressiveness, self-imitation, and competitiveness in the preschool years to be predictive of intellectual growth. An attempt to define a consistent and specific difference in the individual's approach to his environment was made by Kagan et al. (1963). They established for grade school children measures of distinctive cognitive (conceptual) styles that indicate *analytic* and *relational* (nonanalytic) approaches and that differentiate between males and females. These resemble the field-dependent/field-independent dimension of Witkin.

The approach to cognitive style espoused by Broverman and his associates emphasizes the biochemical factors that determine its development. The alternative approach, and that which probably has the majority support, emphasizes the child-rearing and cultural influences on the development of style.

Cultural Influences on the Development of Cognitive Style

Much of the available literature on cultural influences on cognitive style relate to another dimension, the field-dependency one of Witkin and his associates. Shaffer et al. (1957) found that ten-year-old children using the field-dependent cognitive style differed markedly in background from field-independent children. The parents of the field-dependent children had used more severe and aggressive modes of punishment, with withdrawal of love as a means of control. They had inhibited assertive or independent behavior. The parents of the field-independent children, on the other hand, had encouraged decision making and were more likely to reprimand passive or irresponsible behavior than initiative. This study suggests that one aspect at least of cognitive style may be influenced by child-rearing procedures.

A conceptual tempo dimension they call *reflection-impulsivity* has been described by Kagan et al. (1964). This factor has an influence on performance; for example, the impulsive child makes more errors in reading than the reflective one and is more likely to form incorrect solutions to inductive reasoning problems. This dimension appears in the preschool years and becomes a consistent and fixed characteristic of the child. The tendency to an impulsive tempo is modifiable, at least in first grade children, by a training method that encourages reflection (Kagan et al., 1966).

More recently Witkin (1967) has suggested the *global-articulated* dimension as one providing a useful approach to cross-cultural studies of the effects of rearing on cognitive functioning. Witkin sees the cognitive styles as a personality attribute. They are the characteristic and self-consistent modes of functioning in the cognitive sphere but are also manifestations of broader facets of personal functioning.

The global-articulated dimension of cognitive functioning has at one pole the ability to organize the perceptual field. The *articulated* perceiver is able readily to abstract an element from an organized field and to impose structure on a field that is not inherently organized. The *global* perceiver is relatively less able to do this. Developmentally there is a progression from the global to the articulated style of functioning. This is reflected also in the development of the concept of self, for at the beginning the child experiences the self and the environment as a continuous body-field matrix, that is, globally. Articulation emerges as the child begins to differentiate the body boundaries from the environment. The development of articulation is thus a process of differentiation.

This process of articulation is likewise present in the growth of thinking where symbolic representations are involved. An articulated cognitive style, an articulated body concept, and a sense of separate identity are all taken as indicators of developed differentiation. The experiences that help shape a child's cognitive development include to a large extent the social influences of the surroundings in which he grows up. The contribution of ecology (in this case the person-environment interaction) in cognitive development is not readily separable from the contribution of socialization.

Witkin (1967) has reviewed the cross-cultural studies that examine cognitive development in different cultures. Witkin et al. (1962) and Dyk and Witkin (1965) found, for example, that boys who were field-independent tended to have mothers who interacted with them in ways that had fostered differentiation. Evidence has been found to support the assumption that the patterns of mother-child interaction associated with the development of greater or more limited differentiation are operative in the first months of life as well as at a later age (Escalona, 1965). It is apparent, Witkin et al. claim, that some very specific aspects of mother-child interaction are important to the development of cognitive style even at an early age.

There is some evidence of cross-cultural differences in cognitive style. A study by Dawson (1963) investigated aspects of the development of cognitive functioning among various African tribes. His findings extend those of American studies on the relationship between development along global-articulated cognitive dimension and involvement in particular socialization experiences while growing up. A study by Berry (1966) further delineates this relationship. Berry examined the Temne of Sierra Leone and the Eskimos of Baffin Island. The strict child-rearing practices of the Temne and the permissive rearing of the Eskimo children were reflected in differences among individuals in perception of the severity of the discipline to which they had been subjected while growing up. Ecological backgrounds were likewise very different. Berry found evidence of marked field independence in the Eskimos, and compared with the field-dependent Temne, they showed a generally high level of differentiation across psychological areas. Dershowitz (1966) made a study of cognitive functioning of two subcultures in the United States, Jewish boys from a Hebrew School with an Eastern European background and Protestant boys of Anglo-Saxon origin. Jewish boys were found to be more field-dependent than the Protestant boys and gave evidence of a more global body concept.

In discussing the origin of these cognitive styles, Witkin et al., as we see, do recognize that there may be an inherited basis, some aspects of which may be related to a genetic factor. On the whole, boys and men tend to be more field independent than are women and girls. However, the expectations of society are different for the two sexes (e.g., in America, the commonly held view is that women are dependent and that men are independent). Therefore, according to Witkin et al., sex differences in cognitive functioning cannot be explained by genetic factors alone, and they implicitly give greater weight to cultural factors.

The global-articulated cognitive style is claimed by Witkin to be of considerable value in cross-cultural studies because research has shown it to be an important dimension of individual differences in cognitive functioning. Witkin's review stresses the fact that the performance of cognitive tasks such as tests of field dependence reflect the individual's social background. Biological differences may also, through the role they play in individual psychological development, contribute to sex differences in differentiation, but their influence is complex and indirect. Group differences in cognitive style may be based, in part at least, upon genetic differences. Adaptive selection may play a role in groups that have lived in the same environment over a long period and have remained in sexual isolation from other groups. But, these authors believe, development of the articulated cognitive style appears to be more under the influence of the *quality* of the relationships with critical persons early in life.

There are other studies that relate style to environmental factors. For example, Hess and Shipman (1965) related the child's style of response to problem-solving situations to the mother's ability to utilize verbal concepts in her interaction with him.

A Rapprochement

The eclectic approach will regard cognitive style as a basically constitutional character that is subject to environmental modification. This differs from the preceding formulation only in its emphasis; as we have seen, Witkin and his co-workers admit the possibility of constitutional factors but place the main weight on environmental ones. The approach to the question being advocated here admits that the environment plays a part—indeed a critical one—but insists that constitutional factors are also important. One avoids saying *equally* important because it is in fact impossible (and not especially meaningful) to attempt to apportion the relative weights of the two realms of influence. What is assumed is that the organism starts off with certain inherent "tendencies to style" that differ among individuals and on which the environment operates. It may operate to increase or to decrease these tendencies. An aim of child rearing should be to identify the child's tendencies to cognitive style and in general to provide an environment that will develop them, on the assumption that cognitive functioning will be most efficient when it follows the innate style. (Some tendencies might, of course, be disadvantageous to thinking and hence are to be circumvented.)

In discussing parental roles in the development of cognitive style, a number of questions arise. The reader will be sufficiently familiar with my biases to know what these questions will be. Why do some parents encourage autonomous behavior in their offspring, whereas others discourage it? Are there genetic factors involved, these characteristics tending to run in strains? Do self-assertive, field-independent parents tend to *inhibit* their children by reason of their own self-assertiveness? If transmission is cultural, one might expect to find a reversal in each generation, whereas consistency from generation to generation could be regarded as an indication favoring genetic transmission.

One question that arises here is whether the two ranges of influence overlap, and this is a matter that is not specific to cognition, but is general to all the areas in which a constitution-environment interaction may operate. Assuming, for the sake of argument, that field dependence is an inherited trait, but also subject to environmental influence, can a strong field-dependence-inducing environment produce a degree of this trait that is phenotypically the same as field dependency produced by genetic influences? At present there is no answer to this question. But one thing we may assume is that it is developmentally more efficient to produce a particular cognitive style in an individual with the potential for it than to induce it by environmental pressures in one not so predisposed. Another facet of this same question was discussed in Chapter 10, when it was assumed that field dependency is a feminine sex-linked trait. Nevertheless, it was suggested, both males and females may, despite their constitutional predispositions to field independency/field dependency, respectively, vary on these dimensions as a result of environmental influences. But we lack the data to know whether (for instance) a girl made field independent by a "masculinizing" environment is indistinguishable on this trait from the male norm for this style. It may be that in our present lack of sophistication the question is hypothetical because we lack the practical techniques for answering it, but perhaps in the future the question may become practical and meaningful.

We may assume that an individual with a genetic tendency to a particular cognitive style will most economically develop that style to its highest degree. One aspect of maximum self-fulfillment for this individual is such development. Furthermore, if we also assume that society needs individuals with a wide divergence of cognitive skills, then the fostering of this supreme development is socially desirable. One cannot say in the abstract that certain cognitive styles are better than others; one can only say that for certain types of problems, certain cognitive approaches are more suitable than others. In an increasingly specialized society, the development of more specialized cognitive skills seems demanded. Education in the future should become more diversified, identifying early a greater range of potential cognitive styles and providing a variety of educational environments to foster these. The aim should be the maximizing of individual differences rather than the present tendency to minimize them. (One recognizes that a suitable social and political climate, in which these differences are not made the basis for ethical inequality, is needed.)

We see that there are the two approaches to the origin of cognitive style: that exemplified by Broverman, which regards it as constitutional in origin, and that represented by Witkin, who places most weight on the environmental influences of its development. As already mentioned, an eclectic one might regard both approaches as right, and they can be so in two senses. On the one hand, it could be that there is a class of styles, of which automatization is an instance, which are constitutionally determined, and another class, of which field dependence is one, in which the determinants are environmental. The other sense that combines both views is that all styles depend on both constitution and environmental elicitation. It is obvious that this is the view taken here. There is, however, a possible qualification to this position. It could be that certain styles (such as automatization) are strongly determined by constitution and relatively impervious to environmental influences. Others (such as field dependence) also have a constitutional basis but are more subject to influence by child-rearing or cultural influences. The former will be modified relatively little by the environment and the latter to a greater extent.

There is a point that arises from Witkin's idea that there is a developmental progression from the global to the articulated style. Are we to assume that an adult who functions globally is arrested in his development? This may be the case and Witkin certainly thinks so. If the suggestions made earlier are valid, then it seems that an individual is constitutionally a "weak" or "strong" automatizer, and children do not start off "weak" and develop toward "stronger" automatization. Evidently one cannot make universal statements about the developmental course of cognitive styles, and different styles may have differing developmental histories.

Sex Differences in Cognitive Style

There was a review in Chapter 10 of the evidence that shows that the two sexes adopt differing approaches to intellectual tasks. Broverman et al. (1968) reviewed a number of studies (many of them also referred to in Chapter 10) that show that males and females adopt different strategies or operations in functioning intellectually.

In their review of a considerable literature, Broverman et al. (1968) cover a number of biochemical studies that can be interpreted as indicating the physiological factors underlying the cognitive sex differences, and they conclude that these differences are related (at least in part) to the sex steroid hormones. These hormones have effects on the neural processes of activation and inhibition. The details of this study need not concern us in this section, but in brief the hypothesis is that the adrenergic nervous system has a mobilizing function in preparation for activation and that the cholinergic system functions in ways promoting protection, conservation, and relaxation or inhibition of activity. Cognitive functioning is the result of an interplay between these competing systems. The *ergotropic* functions that promote wakefulness and sensory reactivity facilitate simple perceptual-motor tasks. The *trophotropic* functions promoting inhibition of activity contribute to the cognitive ability to delay initial response tendencies to obvious stimulus attributes in favor of response to less obvious stimulus relationships.

Males are cholinergic or trophotropic, the androgen steroids tending to produce a balance of biochemical factors favoring the cholinergic type of neural functioning. Females tend to be ergotropic.

It may seem paradoxical that males are characterized in this scheme by such terms as *conservation* and *inhibition* and females by such a term as *activation*. This seems in direct contradiction to the *behavioral* traits that tend to characterize the two sexes. It may be that Broverman et al. have not chosen the least ambiguous terms, but they are referring to characteristics of neural functioning, not to behavioral outcomes. The female nervous system in this scheme is fast-acting and has the advantage, at least in simple perceptual-motor tasks. The male system is slower, but because of this the male is more reflective, drawing in (we may presume) and coordinating a wider range of correlated neural actions—for example, allowing time for the linking up of *diverse* previous experiences. Thus (if the argument is correct) females are more conservative behaviorally because neurally they act rapidly on established habits. The slower male system allows the time necessary for switching to more novel behaviors.

According to Broverman et al. (1968), the behaviors in which males are superior to females are those involving an inhibition or delay of initial response tendencies to the more obvious aspects of the stimulus in favor of less obvious attributes (e.g., in the embedded figures test). Males are also better in those behaviors involving extensive mediation of higher processes in contrast to those requiring automatic or reflexive stimulus-response connections. They also claim males to be superior in tasks requiring novel solutions as opposed to those involving speed or accuracy of repetitive responses.

Females are superior in tasks requiring drawing on similar past experience or learning (e.g., color naming, talking, reading) as distinct from those involving novel relationships or problem solving. Females are thus better in tasks that involve a minimum of mediation but extensive prior practice. This shows up in typing and similar tasks that become reflexive automatic responses. Another area of feminine superiority is in tasks requiring attentional and perceptual processes and fine muscle coordination and also in tasks requiring speed and accuracy in repetitive responses.

One cannot at this stage regard the matter as conclusive, but there is in the matters reviewed here at least a reasonable basis for the thesis that cognitive styles may be influenced by biochemical factors and may tend to cluster in distinctive patterns in males and females. As Broverman et al. put it, "rational physiological explanations of cognitive sex differences are not only possible, but probable" (1968, p. 41). That is, while there are wide individual differences in cognitive styles, certain of them at least are represented markedly more heavily in one sex or the other.

The relationship between biochemical factors and cognitive style may not be a simple one. At this stage, when the possibility of a relationship is only beginning to be explored, any hypotheses put forward have to be tentative. A style already discussed is automatization. Strength of automatization appears to be related to androgen secretion, having a positive correlation with hair distribution and other bodily indices of androgen influences on physical development (Klaiber et al., 1967). All the work so far published on automatization has used male subjects, and strong automatization might be considered a male trait. However, one must not be misled into hasty conclusions. It might be assumed from the correlation between androgens and "strong automatization" that females would be "weak automatizers," but this may not be so, because, according to Broverman et al. (1968), estrogens are more effective than androgens in inhibiting MAO activity, and may contribute to the greater activation of females. It therefore becomes of considerable interest to know how the automatization style operates in women. If the biochemical arguments put forward by Broverman et al. are valid, it might be found that women are stronger automatizers than men are. However, it would seem from the suggestions made by Broverman that females may tend to be perceptual-motor-dominant rather than conceptually dominant. If this is so, then in the four cells suggested by Broverman (p. 371) females will tend to cluster in the perceptual-motor/strong automatizer cell, with relatively few in the other three cells. Males will tend to be more evenly distributed between the conceptually dominant/strong automatizer and the conceptually dominant/weak automatizer cells, though perhaps with a preponderance in the former. Both males and females will, of course, appear in the other two cells, but overall one would expect more males in the two conceptual cells and more females in the perceptual-motor ones.

The possibility of direct genetic influences on cognitive style has been discussed by Freeberg and Payne, based upon evidence from several different sources, e.g., Kagan et al. (1963) and Witkin et al. (1962) who both report persistent evidence of sex differences along cognitive style dimensions. Witkin et al. (1966) have reported significant differences in the verbal and performance IQ's of girls with the Turner syndrome, a genetic abnormality (and this has been discussed in Chapter 10).

Findings of a consistent discrepancy between verbal and nonverbal areas in the retarded have provoked some research, and Shaffer (1962) has reported on studies of girls with the Turner syndrome in which one of the female (X) chromosomes is missing. Often the abnormality is not detected until puberty. Shaffer found the general IQ of these girls to be average, but performance scores were considerably lower than verbal scores. If verbal-comprehension and analytical scores of the Wechsler tests are considered, the discrepancy is even more apparent. It is consistent when individual cases are considered.

The point of theoretical interest is the possibility that the Turner cases present a cognitive pattern that is to some extent at least under the influence of the sex chromosomes (Witkin et al., 1966). The possibility of a linkage between sex chromosomal make-up and cognitive characteristics is of special interest in view of the consistent finding that men are superior to women in analytical ability. Investigations of Turner patients and other cases have obvious potential for exploring the possible genetic basis of patterns of cognitive growth and of sex differences in these patterns.

Epilogue to Cognitive Style

This section has not attempted an exhaustive survey of the question of cognitive style. Some styles have been described, but it is not supposed that the list is exhaustive either of those mentioned in the literature or of the total range of differing styles that in fact exist. The range of unidentified styles may be considerable, and here is an area for future research. Some of these styles tend to be sex-linked. This is not to say that they are exclusive to either sex but that they tend to appear more frequently or in greater degree in one sex or the other.

One practical implication of their existence is that because cognitive styles are an important aspect of intellectual functioning they no doubt influence how the child learns and what kinds of strengths and weaknesses he will display. Children with differing styles will learn different things with individual facility. It is not sufficient merely to know how bright a child is; one must also know what kind of cognitive dimensions his intelligence operates in. For remedial work, for instance, one needs to know not merely his IQ but also a great deal more about what we may call "his style of intelligence." We need to know what cognitive operations cause him difficulty and also which ones he operates facilely.

A point about remedial efforts should be mentioned. We have at present an educational system that conceives of a kind of standard child to whom all should conform. The child that does not match must be "remedied" toward a match. In a more diversified system it might be possible to assess a child's deficits and the degree of handicap this causes and in some cases, if not in all, to ignore these and to allow him to specialize in his areas of strength. There is, of course, some possibility of this in a gross manner by subject choice, but often such a choice limits the future of the child. To get into a university, for instance, the child has to be able to jump through a rather standard hoop, whereas other talented candidates for higher education may not receive it because they cannot conform to this particular initial pattern. Educational reforms to accommodate greater diversity will have to be broad and effective over the whole range of education.

The practical details of such an ambitious revision of our educational system need to be worked out, and obviously much further research is needed. But already some general principles are emerging. For example, it seems on present knowledge that in general it is an advantage to be a strong automatizer, because it frees one from attending to the trivia of activity to concentrate instead on more advanced production. Therefore it would seem desirable to train children in automatized styles. Now it is suggested here that some children are natural automatizers because this is part of their constitutional makeup. It is unnecessary to train them, and in terms of educational economics it is wasteful to do so. What one should do is direct efforts toward the children who are weak automatizers. We do not know, of course, that this cognitive style can be trained, but at least one could hope to bring *some* improvement in the autom-

atization habits of children who lack them. If it turns out that automatization is not readily acquired by training, then two educational strategies are possible. One is to find means of circumventing any disadvantages that may attach to weak automatizing. An alternative is to capitalize on any advantages that may come from being a weak automatizer. Until we know in greater detail the implications for cognitive activity of the two styles, we are not in a position to say which alternative is preferable.

Thus in the future, with an improved educational system, there will be a highly diversified program that assesses the strengths and weaknesses of the individual child and makes decisions about which of his attributes can be safely left to flower for themselves and which need extra encouragement. Each child enters a program tailor-made for himself. In practice, of course, it is probable that there will be enough children with similar patterns of needs to make such a scheme feasible. Though in theory to implement such an educational philosophy one needs as many programs as there are children, it is likely that most children could be fitted into a more limited number of standard but flexible programs. Special provision might be necessary only for the small remainder of children with uncommon special talents or unusual deficits.

IMAGERY AND THOUGHT

A long time ago, up to the 1930's and before most of us could spell psychology, imagery was a topic of considerable interest to the mental philosophers. Francis Galton in his *Inquiries into Human Faculty* (1883) described individuals whose mental imagery was mainly visual, and others whose imagery was auditory. According to Galton a majority of people are visual, that is, their most vivid imagery conjures up "seen" experiences; less than a third of the population are auditory; and a small number are kinaesthetic. There are individual variations in the amount of each kind of imagery and in the vividness of images in either modality. Some of Galton's auditory subjects were unable even to understand what a visual image might be, and some visualizers could conjure up only the "faintest" of auditory experiences. Beethoven evidently had superlative auditory imagery.

A number of esoteric kinds of imagery were also reported; an example is *synaesthesia,* where modalities are mixed—music might be "seen" as a flow of colored images. Another kind that aroused interest, particularly among child psychologists, was *eidetic imagery;* Jaensch (1930) was one of many who investigated the phenomenon, and Klüver (1931) reviewed the literature. Eidetic imagery was thought to be common in childhood, but uncommon in adults (and many studies claimed a general decrease with age in the vividness of all kinds of imagery). In eidetic imagery the subject apparently has a "picture" of unusual accuracy, in which he can "see" complete detail. In one of the early studies reported by Jaensch, children could "read" from the image the letters of a long word that was in the original picture; since it was a word the children could not spell, it seemed that something more than memory may have been involved. A recent study by Haber (1969) quotes the case of an eidetic boy who after thirty seconds' exposure to a fairly complex picture could "see" the image of that picture with sufficient clarity and accuracy to count off the sixteen stripes on a cat's tail when questioned. Since he had no idea what details he would be asked about, it is most unlikely that he counted when the picture was actually before him, and sixteen is well beyond the number that can be apprehended without counting.

For more than thirty years eidetic imagery has fallen almost completely out of interest as a topic of concern. Haber's study revives interest in it, though from his data it seems to be less common than once believed.

Piaget and Inhelder (1966) have discussed imagery in relation to perceiving and knowing. (This untranslated material is summarized in Furth, 1969.) These authors suggest that imagery and linguistic signs are used in the service of operative knowing, and this occurs not only in the pre-operational period but also later. Language is to the child as much a part of the real situation as is perception or imagery, and for this reason it would seem to Furth (1969) that language, like images, is a figurative instrument to the growing child, and perhaps is no easier to use in the service of rational thought.

For Piaget, an image has symbolic and significative properties, just as words have. Piaget, then, is concerned with the "semantic" aspects of images, and sees words and images not as unrelated entities, but as intricately related ones.

As we have already seen, Bruner et al. (1966) have spoken of iconic images in relation to thought, and the thesis that imagery enters into cognitive processes. They refer to an unpublished study by Kuhlman (1960), who supposed that the major means of thought in children is by means of images. She found individual differences in elementary school children in the use of images. Children with a high degree of imagery performed better at tasks which involved applying arbitrary verbal labels to pictures, whereas children with low imagery were better at concept formation. The child who relies on vivid perceptual cues finds concept attainment more difficult, and language is evidently a more efficient mode of thinking, which is consistent with the idea that intellectual growth includes (among other things) a moving away from images.

Robertson and Youniss (1969) carried out a study of imagery in deaf and hearing children, aged eight years in one group and eleven years in another, using the technique of Piaget and Inhelder (1963) (involving, for one instance, saying how the water level would appear in a tilted, but imagined, bottle). They found that the older children (both deaf and hearing) performed better than the younger ones, and they attribute this performance to the better use of visual symbolism in the older children. An alternative explanation might, of course, be that the older children did better because they did not use visual imagery. It is likely that imagery of all kinds may have some theoretical importance to perception and to thinking, reviving another old controversy about the role of imagery in thinking and the alleged superiority of "imageless thought" in abstract conceptualization. An image that is taken as a reality is an hallucination, a symptom of disease when found in an adult. To what extent do children confuse perceptions and images? Since images are mental counterparts of perceptions, what role (if any) do images have in modifying perceptions? In the practical field, one might ask —though apparently few have—what role differences in imagery play (or should play) in educational practice. A number of other questions arise, like the relationship of imagery to cognitive style, and a whole field of inquiry is opened up.

CREATIVITY

In reading the literature on creativity one has the impression of banality in the discussion. This is noticeable in other special cases. The layman might expect the scientific literature on humor to twinkle with wit, but it does not. It is not that the literature on laughter is really duller than that on other topics, but merely that the context arouses expectations that are unjustified in the realm of scientific discourse. The same contrast effect seems to apply when the subject under discussion is creativity.

Creativity is the subject of considerable psychological importance as well as being of great social significance. In the sciences as well as in the arts, progress depends upon individuals who are able to generate new concepts. The fostering of creativity is regarded by some (though not universally) as one of the important aims of education, and the shortage of creative individuals may be seen as a factor

handicapping man's progress. Whereas at one time the arts might have been regarded as the outlet for creativity, industry as well as the sciences are recognizing the value of this subtle quality and are seeking means of recruiting individuals possessing it. One might consider it a travesty to use this quality to boost the sales of toothpaste, or worse still of cigarettes, but that would be a judgment in values. The question to the developmental psychologist is what are the antecedents of this particular quality and to what extent can it be fostered in the growing child? Reviewing the literature on this topic makes it plain that little is known for certain about what causes individuals to differ in the extent to which they show this capacity. Presumably it is a trait like most others, shown to some extent by all, but to a greater extent by a few. Some educational theories imply that *all* children start with a high degree of creativity, which diminishes with age if the child's experiences do not support and foster the quality. This question must be examined.

Definition of Creativity

Like so many other terms of psychology, *creativity* is difficult to define, and there is no universally accepted statement of what it is. Wallach and Kogan (1965), in common with most others, see creativity as an aspect of thinking, and they define it in terms of the individual's ability to generate cognitive associations in quality and with uniqueness. Other writers, such as Getzels and Jackson (1962), adopt an operational definition for particular experimental purposes. These authors used tests of the ability to deal inventively with verbal and numerical symbols and with spatial relationships. Obviously such an operational definition will leave out many areas of what are commonly regarded as creative abilities.

Definitions that emphasize the cognitive aspects might give a false impression of this quality. One could equally well regard creativity as an aspect of personality, and indeed many studies have focused on the personality attributes of creative individuals. Any distinction between the two areas is, of course, arbitrary, though one might regard personality as the more embracing concept. Styles of thought are but one aspect of personality.

There is some inconclusive debate about the structure of creativity. Sultan (1962), Getzels and Jackson (1962), and Ward (1968) believe creativity to be a unitary trait, whereas Guilford and Merrifield (1960) and Torrance (1962b) consider it multifactorial. In view of the complexity of the attribute, the latter view seems more probable, but it is unproved as yet.

There are certain things that creativity is not. Gerard (1959) has suggested that people with the "quiz kid" kind of mind, who can fix things easily in memory and retain them, are usually lacking in flexibility and are rarely imaginative or creative. Another attribute that is not necessarily associated with creativity is fluency. Some individuals, as we all know, are verbally fluent and produce many words but banal content. Whether there is any statistical relationship between output and creativity is unexamined. Presumably the greater the output, the greater the likelihood of making some original statement by chance, but such accidental productions presumably do not qualify an individual for the accolade *creative*.

A point for debate (but not yet for any conclusion) is whether creativity is to be considered a cognitive style or some special faculty. The cognitive styles tend to be pervasive; that is, they appear in most if not all of the cognitive operations of the individual. Whether creativity can really be considered a style of cognition in this sense is uncertain. We do not know whether creative individuals share this attribute in all their actions or more specifically. Apart from the rare "all-rounders," it seems likely that creativity (when present) will show up most clearly in areas of special ability or be absent in areas of dis-

ability. Thus the creative individual who lacks a flair for mathematics will probably not master the groundwork of this subject and hence is unlikely to produce any creative innovations. His "originality," in fact, is likely to consist in erroneous calculation, and whether or not one wishes to consider unusual errors as signs of creativity is a matter of definition. Presumably a creative act should perform some useful function, even if this is only the "usefulness" of a clever joke, and a good mathematical joke no doubt demands a considerable grasp of mathematics.

The question is of some interest to the developmentalist, because if we are to consider child-rearing means of fostering this attribute, we need to know whether we are dealing with a broad characteristic that will generalize or whether we must seek to identify and encourage it in special contexts.

Genetics of Creativity

A topic that seems to be somewhat overlooked in the literature on creativity is the part played by genetic factors. Neither Getzels and Jackson nor Wallach and Kogan even comment on this question, and the recent literature proceeds on the assumption that creativity is unquestionably the result of early experiences and training. Older writers, and notably Galton, had quite the opposing assumption that this is a quality that runs in families and is inherited. In the absence of data one is free to adopt any hypothesis that seems reasonable. The premise that creativity is an acquired trait is reasonable and also contains the hopeful premise that it can be increased. However, because of my disposition toward biological explanations, I adopt what is at present the equally reasonable (if more pessimistic) hypothesis that creativity is a genetically transmitted character, similar to intelligence though not invariably linked to it. Indeed, it seems to be a rarer quality than high intelligence. Furthermore, there is evidence to suggest that it is sex-linked, being more common in males. In stating this, one is assuming that creativity has limited dispersion in the population and that for any individual the maximum potential is fixed. As is the case with intelligence, the environment determines the level, up to this potential, at which the individual will, in fact, function, but the environment cannot (by any means known at present) raise this upper limit. Thus, however favorable the environment may be to the development of creativity, it is predicted that individual differences in this trait will exist, though the mean level may be raised. This last point is important. We must assume that there is, in fact, a wastage in creative potential, a proportion (and perhaps a large one) of potentially creative individuals functioning below their limit. Hence an environment more conducive to the realization of potential would raise the *mean* of the population, but it would also be expected to raise the upper extreme. The amount of possible increase in the mean is not unrestrained and is probably fairly limited.

Age Changes in Creativity

There are difficulties in assessing individual differences in creativity in young children because of the lack of any reasonable external criteria of achievement such as can be applied, roughly at least, to adults (for example, public acclaim as a productive artist). These problems have been discussed by Ward (1968), who also provides a technique for measurement.

Some of the developmental studies of creativity have been reviewed by Torrance (1962b). As is true in so many areas, there is a lack of consistency in method and kinds of measures used that makes comparison between studies very difficult. Ribot (1906) was one of the earlier students of the topic, and he suggested that imagination and reason are in some regards mutually antagonistic. At first,

he said, imagination develops more rapidly, but reason catches up and stifles the growth of imagination, so that for most adults it either declines or provides nothing new. Another early writer (not mentioned in Torrance's review) was Rank, who in 1907, and before he met Freud, produced a book on the development of artistic creativity, which he later rewrote in the light of his psychoanalytic experiences (Rank, 1932).

McMillan (1924) has a rather poetic view of the development of imagination going through three stages. In the first, the young child has a sense of beauty that is the route to knowledge. In the second stage, he becomes aware of reality and begins to inquire into cause and effect and in particular to notice the absence of beauty in the world. During the third stage the child begins to work out some creative compromise between his first vision and the world as it is.

E. G. Andrews (1930), in a more systematic investigation, traced the development of imagination in the preschool years. He found that total imaginative scores were highest between four and four and a half, with a sudden drop at about five, when the child entered kindergarten. The ability to restructure or recombine showed a peak between three and four years and then decreased; analogy reached its peak during the fourth year and declined during the fifth. The most creative types of imagination were at their height during three and a half to four and a half and at their lowest during the fifth year. This decline, coincidental with kindergarten, might arouse suspicious interest, though it may be natural decline independent of schooling. Markey (1935) found an increase in imaginative behavior throughout the preschool years. Grippen (1933), contrary to these studies, concludes that creative imagination is rare in children below the age of five years. Evidently what one chooses to regard as creative and imaginative must have considerable influence on what one finds.

Kirkpatrick (1900), using imaginative responses to ink blots, found a decline in imaginative production in the fourth, fifth, and sixth grades as compared with the first three grades. A rise again appeared in the seventh and eighth grades. Colvin and Meyer (1906), using compositions as criteria, found a steady decline in imagination from grades 3–12. R. M. Simpson (1922) reported a sharp increase in creative imagination at the end of grade 3, as compared with the beginning of the year, but this was followed by a decline at the beginning of the fourth grade; there was again an increase to a peak in the second half of the sixth grade, followed by a decline in the seventh and eighth grades. Mearns (1941) found a rapid decline in creative activity in the sixth and seventh grades as compared with the first five grades, the greatest activity being during grades 1–3.

Coming to more recent works, Vernon (1948) studied *constructive imagination* by means of the ability of the child to understand pictures and to interpret them as a whole. It was not until the age of eleven that the child could incorporate the thoughts, emotions, and activities of the characters into an invented explanation of the scene. Another is that by Ligon (1957), who studied the development of imagination from birth to sixteen years. Out of this investigation he also produced recommendations for the fostering of imagination. He believes that the development of imagination begins in the first year, though it would seem that this conclusion is based upon the fact that the child is curious and eager for experience through touch, taste, sight, and sound and later when he asks for the names of things. To what extent one can regard these well-known characteristics of the young child as evidence of the working of imagination is another question. He also believes that during this period creative growth can be encouraged by games and various sorts of play material. In effect, he recommends the setting up of an enriched environment.

Ligon discusses the topic in convenient two-year periods from two until eighteen, and it

is not until this last age that the capacity for creative problem solving is well developed and permits working in terms of abstractions or the creative channeling of emotional energy. At all stages the need for perceptive understanding by adults is emphasized.

Barkan (1960), in an intensive study of a relatively small number of teachers and children in art classes in elementary schools, found a spurt in creativity in the first to second grade. Wilt (1959) has related the decline in creativity to the "gang-age," which she calls a stage of "realism." She points out that at about the fourth grade the child is concerned with conformity to the peer group norms and that many aspects of thinking become stiff and stereotyped, with a consequent reduction in creative output. According to Wilt, this stage puts an end to creativity in most children, only a few being able to withstand group pressures to conformity and to return to creativity after this stage is past. If this is true, any attempts to foster creativity must offset the effects of group pressures.

Torrance (1962b) has summarized some of the results of the Minnesota studies from kindergarten through to grade 12 and beyond. These have shown a steady increase from the first through to the third grade in overall creative thinking as measured on a wide variety of tasks making up the Minnesota Test of Creative Thinking. This increase was followed by a sharp decline during the third and fourth grades (causal thinking being an exception here, it alone showing no decrease). There was some further increase during the fifth and sixth grades, and another sharp drop between the sixth and seventh, although followed again by growth until the end of the school years. It will be noted that this study is consistent with some of the others, which also show the fourth and seventh grades as times of decline in imaginative or creative activity.

The Minnesota group has attempted to explain these decreases in the fourth and seventh grades (Torrance, 1962b). Longitudinal studies have shown that these decrements are typical of most children, but that some individuals do maintain creative growth over these periods. They also claim that many of those showing this dip in creativity do not regain it, and there is a permanent loss. Following H. S. Sullivan (1953), they point out that the third- and fourth-grade period is one in which there are considerable pressures toward socialization; there is a strong dependence on group validation of ideas, and unusual ideas may bring ridicule and humiliation. The transition into adolescence at about the seventh grade is another time at which there are social pressures toward conformity, with feelings of inadequacy and insecurity as new roles are being assumed, and again an inhibition of productive thinking. They also mention the possibility of physiological changes underlying the decline at these stages. They quote an unpublished observation by R. W. Lowry that suggests that at about age nine (grade 4) there is a stage in the development of vision in which children are in what might be described as a state of visual disorganization. Defects (presumably of a temporary nature) are commonest at this age, and any kind of visual training is most difficult at this time. The physiological changes coincident with the second dip in creative imagination at the onset of puberty need no elaboration. It would seem, then, that there are probably social and possibly physiological factors that influence the development of creativity.

Using his newly developed measure of creativity, Ward (1968) found individual differences in the trait in boys of seven and eight years. He found this trait to be undetectable in kindergarten children.

It seems evident from these various studies that there is no close agreement on the age at which creativeness first appears, whether it generally decreases or increases with age, and what developmental patterns it follows. No doubt, some, if not all, of the discrepancies between studies arise from lack of agreement of what constitutes creativity and how it should be measured.

The age change that has received most attention is the apparent decline in the prepubescent period. In view of the importance, in socialization, of this phase of development this finding is not unexpected. This is a stage of emphasis on the group, and on group thinking, and to think like others is by definition uncreative.

Theories of the Origins of Creativity

In theorizing about the basis underlying creativity, the Minnesota group (Torrance, 1962b) followed Kubie (1958) in stressing the role of preconscious mental processes in creative function. Kris (1952) has regarded ego regression as crucial to preconscious thinking; the types of ego regression found in sleep, in the twilight stage preceding sleep, and in intoxication and psychotic conditions have, according to him, something in common with that involved in productive thinking. To produce, the subject must assume a naive or childlike attitude, but without losing control of thought processes or becoming swamped by tension.

Torrance summarizes from his review of the literature five conditions that are necessary to the proper functioning of the preconscious mental processes that are said to underlie creativity:

1. The absence of threats to the self and the willingness to take risks
2. Self-awareness, appreciating one's own feelings
3. Self-differentiation, or awareness of distinctiveness
4. Openness to the ideas of others together with confidence in one's own ideas and perceptions of reality
5. Mutuality in interpersonal relations, or a balance between sociability and pathological associability

In general, to foster creativity, these conditions should be encouraged, but whether all of them must be present, or what combination is sufficient, is not stated. Furthermore, the question of whether these are the conditions necessary and sufficient for creativity or whether they are environmental conditions that permit the flowering of some more basic quality is unknown.

MacKinnon (1962) has pointed out that the creative person is not only open to experience but is intuitive about it. As he says, we can train students to be accurate in their perceptions, but can we train them to be intuitive also? Sense perception, he suggests, can be improved by rote learning, drill, and concern for memorizing. On the other hand, he believes that intuitive perception as well as intuitive thinking can be increased by emphasis on transfer of training from one subject to another, by training in the search for common principles, and by the stressing of analogies, similarities, and metaphors. These are tasks that he describes as a seeking for symbolic equivalence of experience in a variety of sensory and imagery modalities, training in imaginative play, and viewing facts in perspective. However, experimental evidence on this point is lacking, and it is still questionable whether effective training that can be generalized in new situations can be achieved in these matters. Obviously considerable and difficult long-span experiments are necessary to establish whether this is the case or not.

Further evidence supporting Torrance's view that creativity is related to openness of perception is provided by Shulman (1966), who gave creativity and perceptual tests to fourth grade children and found a significant correlation between the two. Other data were interpreted as suggesting that creativity is dependent on "perceptual openness," that is, the ability to see the world from several different vantage points and in a playful manner. The more open the person is, the better he sees the properties and the possibilities of what is perceived; there is flexibility and expansiveness of action. Again, like MacKinnon (1962), Shulman stresses the importance of developing tests of creativity and the need for perceptual experiences in school.

Another theory of the creative process has been proposed by Mednick (1962), who suggests it is an advanced association process, bringing remote ideas into contiguity. Laughlin (1967) has taken up this idea to suggest that incidental learning and these creative associative processes have much in common, so that there is a relationship between the capacity for incidental learning and creativity. The creative person has greater perceptual sensitivity to apparently irrelevant stimuli and retains memories of these in more accessible form and hence can use them in later problem solving. Laughlin tested this hypothesis on undergraduate students and found that there was a positive relationship between creativity (as measured by the Mednick technique) and the ability to form, retain, and utilize remote associations.

In view of the suggestion, in Chapter 11, that one feature of children reared in an impoverished environment is a deficiency in incidental learning, it is possible that this deficiency may be one factor that would suppress the development of creativity in individuals who have a potential for it. It is not necessarily true, of course, that providing an enriched environment will stimulate creativity in those who lack the potential, but such an environment might be expected to further its development in those who do have the potential.

A "stop theory" of creativity has been proposed by C. C. Anderson (1966), though perhaps it should be called a "nonstop theory," because "stops" are inimical to creative production. He points out how rules of various kinds, of thought or of conduct, inhibit creative output and how lack of assimilation of such rules is, in fact, conducive to productivity. He goes on to outline the practical application of such a theory in a school setting and the effects on students of teachers who might or might not emphasize the "stop rules." It would be interesting to assess originality of students before and after the different teaching methods were applied.

Creativeness and Intelligence

Although he does not specifically state this, Hunt (1961) seems to imply that originality *is* intelligence, or is at least an aspect of certain kinds of intelligent behavior; he speaks of the child discovering new means of action through active experimentation motivated by an interest in novelty and in these activities manifesting "the constructive, original element characteristic of intelligence. . . ."

A study by Cropley (1966) supports Hunt's implicit view that originality is intelligence. A battery of tests, some divergent and some convergent, was administered to grade 7 children, the divergent tests being scored for originality. Correlations between the tests were subjected to factor analysis. The results indicated that the special divergent factor, creativity, showed a significant correlation with the factor defined by more normal tests of intelligence.

In the popular mind, and perhaps in the view of many psychologists, this relationship between intelligence and creativity is generally assumed. This assumption is questioned by some. Dearborn, as long ago as 1898, observed that high intelligence and creativity do not necessarily go together. Getzels and Jackson (1962) have reviewed some of the literature on this topic since that time, and Dearborn's remark seems to be substantiated, but some qualifications are needed.

However, another way of looking at the question is given by C. W. Taylor (1959), who regards the lack of a relationship between IQ and creativity as an artifact of our cultural views on intelligence. Western culture, he says, stresses the speed at which relatively unimportant problems can be solved without making errors, whereas other cultures might estimate intelligence in a manner more consistent with a high level of creativity. Guilford (1950) has claimed that a study of the content of intelligence tests shows very little in them that is of a creative nature. He suggests that this is because some of the primary abilities important for creative work are not represented in intelligence tests. (One reason for this may be that creative answers are of necessity difficult to score objectively and test designers would find such items troublesome to handle, even if they felt them worthy of inclusion.) Part, then, of the lack of relationship between intelligence and creativity reported might be referable to the nature of the instruments used to measure the former.

Nonetheless, a number of researchers have produced evidence that they interpret as showing that the two are at least to some degree genuinely independent. Getzels and Jackson (1962), in their study of high-intelligence adolescents have shown that their group could be divided into two categories of individuals, those that are bright but conventional and those that are bright and creative. Herr et al. (1965) also found no correlation between creativeness as measured by the Guilford tests and intelligence in junior high school students. MacKinnon (1962) has reported in his group of creative architects an absence of correlation between intelligence and creativity, and he claims that this is not due to the narrowly restricted range of intelligence with which he was dealing. He acknowledges that over the whole range of intelligence and creativity there is some positive relationship, because feebleminded individuals do not usually show up in creative groups. There is necessary to creativity a certain required minimum level of intelligence, which varies in different fields, but above this level high intelligence does not guarantee creativeness.

There are some views supporting the idea that the correlation between creativity and intelligence does depend on the level of intelligence with which one is concerned. At a certain level, it is suggested, intelligence becomes unimportant to creativity. Meer and Stein (1955) state that this cutoff point is the ninety-fifth percentile and Barron (1961) quotes a comparable figure of 120 as the approximate point at which a correlation between IQ and creativity no longer holds.

However, Wallach and Kogan (1965) are critical of the studies that show low correlations between the two factors. Referring to the Getzels and Jackson study, they point out that the five creativity tasks used were in fact only weakly correlated among themselves and showed low correlations with intelligence, so the indicators of creativity used by these authors measured nothing in common that could be regarded as distinct from general intelligence. Their review of other studies in the field revealed a similar state of affairs, and they conclude that the various measures that have been regarded as indicators of creativity do not reflect some single dimension. Hence they argue it is invalid to assume that "creativity" (as defined operationally) is a homogeneous entity with a range of individual variations that is unrelated to the range of differences in intelligence.

In the most ambitious study so far of the relationship between creativity and intelligence, Wallach and Kogan (1965) used a technique that they have described as being intermediate between the intensive clinical study of the single case and the extensive sampling of subjects, with a small amount of information on each.

Using five measures of creativity based upon their idea of associational modes of thinking, Wallach and Kogan produced a battery having moderately high intercorrelations (an average of .4 and rather higher than within previously used instruments). They felt justified in assuming they were tapping a kind of thinking ability that could be called "creativity." Applying this to the entire fifth grade population of a suburban middle-class school system, they found essentially the same results as other studies, with only a .1 correlation between the creativity measures and intelligence. A point of special interest is that even though part of their battery was verbal (a skill usually highly associated with intelligence), this low correlation was still found.

They selected eight distinct groups (as nearly equal as the numbers allowed): those high in both, those low in both, and those high in one and low in the other—boys and girls separately. They then studied and described the behavior in the school setting of these groups, as well as certain personality characteristics of the groups.

These authors examined the question of whether there is an aspect of cognitive function that can be labeled "creativity" and that stands apart from general intelligence as traditionally defined. They review a considerable amount of evidence and conclude that there is little support for the idea that creativity can be conceptualized as a general cognitive dimension, similar to general intelligence but apart from it. Thus the two assumptions that are current in the literature, that creativity is not intelligence and that individual differences in creativity are as pervasive as are those in general intelligence, must both be held in question. As they point out, it might have been inferred at this stage that there are indeed no individual differences in creativity that are independent of those in general intelligence. However, they saw another alternative, that an incorrect approach had been taken to the measurement of creativity and that too diffuse a set of operations had been subsumed under the term. In their experiment they used an associative conception of creativity in which the process of creating refers to the generation or production of associations, and their experimental method consisted of observing a number of associational responses that the subject could make under various conditions and of assessing the uniqueness of these responses.

In discussing the role of intelligence in

creativity, Wallach and Kogan point out that many psychologists have viewed creative thinking as a special class of highly productive problem solving (for example, Bartlett, 1958). For such authors a novel, harmonious, and elegant solution to a problem is evidence of creative thinking. To Wallach and Kogan, such productive problem solving would represent a combination of creativity and intelligence. The novel and elegant solution to a problem will involve both associative and evaluative ways of thinking, and the individual with the larger associative ability will generate more alternatives, among which the elegant solution is likely to appear. But it is also necessary that the individual recognize the most appropriate fit between problem and solution, and it is here that intelligence enters the picture. Therefore, creativity and intelligence do not of necessity involve cognitive processes that are orthogonal to each other. Some problems involving what might be called "adventurous thinking" require associative processes to be brought to bear on the problem in order to reach an elegant or novel solution. Restructuring of the problem may be necessary before solution is possible. Most intelligence tests involve "closed-system" processes in which all the information necessary to the solution of the problem is contained in its structure. This given information must be manipulated in order to produce the correct solution (as defined by the test-maker), but nothing new needs to be added. Wallach and Kogan recognize the importance of closed-system thinking, and it is evident that children need to learn to think in structured ways, there being many cognitive operations that must follow formal rules and that allow little scope for associative modes of thinking. They do suggest, however, that the ability to think within closed systems is not necessarily related to ability to think in open systems.

This idea that a closer look at the nature of intelligence in relation to creativity might be profitable is given support in a study of nine-year-old boys by O'Bryan and MacArthur (1969), who found that Piaget's concept of reversibility is actually of two types, and that these two are differentially related both to intelligence and to creativity. Possibly more refined methods of looking at both will reveal new dimensions of relatedness.

An important question that is not made clear is whether the creative productions of low-intelligence subjects are qualitatively the same as those of high-intelligence ones. Wallach and Kogan, for instance, do not tell us this.

In summary, it is not possible on the present evidence to make a definitive statement about the relationship between intelligence and creativity. However, it does seem reasonably clear that being intelligent does not guarantee creativeness, and this fits with the common observation that many intelligent people are quite unoriginal. Indeed, one might suspect that creativity is relatively uncommon, even among the intelligent. A second conclusion is that creativity is probably (though not certainly) proscribed by low intelligence, and, as seen, there are studies that suggest a fairly direct relationship between creativity and intelligence up to a certain level, after which there is a plateau on the curve of intelligence. To be highly creative, the individual needs to be on this plateau (the figure of 120 has been suggested as its approximate beginning), though just where is not particularly significant. But in addition he requires certain other attributes (as yet ill-defined) that enable this intelligence to be used in the flexible and productive manner typical of creation. These supraintelligence attributes are the subject of the next section.

One might ask if there is not the possibility of a cultural factor that makes creativity increasingly more difficult to attain. It may be that some current phenomena in the arts are a reaction to the feeling that everything that can be done has been done, and originality can be achieved only by bizarreness. This may not yet apply to the sciences, at least in some fields.

Personality and Intellectual Characteristics of the Creative Individual

Not only is there no great body of research on the question of creativity in children, but it is also difficult to obtain any leads from the published work on creativity in adults as to what might be crucial areas worthy of investigation here. Wallas (1926), for example, described four stages in the forming of a new thought, the alliterative phases of preparation, incubation, illumination, and verification. One might take incubation as the crucial phase here, and the problem then becomes how to foster this process in children. This is a tough proposition for study; although the preceding phase of preparation and the succeeding illumination may be available to investigation, incubation is necessarily a private phenomenon. Ghiselin (1956) has said that insight is the crucial mental process in creation. And while he believes that the creative process might consist in discrete steps, he says, in effect, that in the nature of creativity no amount of knowledge of these steps will make a person creative.

If C. W. Taylor (1959) is correct in stating that the rules of logic and scientific method form a psychological straitjacket that inhibits creative thought, then these subjects should be kept out of the school curriculum if we are to foster creativity (though it might be premature to accept this notion without further questioning).

Golann (1963) has reviewed the literature on creativity—almost exclusively on adults—and describes a considerable range of personality characteristics of the creative person. And, as he makes clear, the ingredients of creativity are extremely elusive. He suggests that it is now possible to isolate a number of criterion variables, such as tolerance for ambiguity, openness to experience, self-actual-

ization or expression, internal frames of evaluation, independence of judgment, and child-like traits (or Kris' ego regression, p. 385). These are theoretically based descriptive concepts that frequently appear in the literature. The development of these criterion variables in the child might, he suggests, throw light on the growth of creativity. While "openness to experience" may be a necessary condition for creativity, it may not be a sufficient one (E. T. Fitzgerald, 1966).

Maslow (1954) has described creativeness as the universal characteristic of his group of "self-actualizing" people to which further reference is made in Chapter 20. Although creativity is, according to Maslow, one of the outstanding characteristics of the self-actualizing person, it is evident that the achievement of self-actualization is not a necessary prerequisite to creativity, because this is a characteristic that is to be found in immature individuals, whereas, according to Maslow, self-actualization is achieved later in life. The role of the achievement of self-actualization in creative activity might well be the subject for further research, but at present there are little, if any, data on this question. But that there may be some important relationship between self-actualization and creativity in its most developed forms is suggested by the fact that Maslow's descriptions of the self-actualizing person are very similar to those described elsewhere as characteristic of the creative one.

Maslow holds that creativeness is a fundamental property of human nature, present in all at birth but lost by most in the process of enculturation. This is a point of considerable importance. If it is true, then we have only to seek the child-rearing practices that will preserve this pristine quality unmarred.

Discussing the personal characteristics of the creative person, Wallach and Kogan (1965) proposed that the essential elements in the creative process are twofold: first, the production of an abundant and unique associative content, and, second, the presence in the individual of a playful, permissive attitude toward the task. (This they derive from a remark by Einstein about "combinatory play.") One of the points they emphasize in assessing creativity is the necessity of freedom from any temporal pressure. Their associative approach to creativity, then, emphasizes an attitude of playful entertaining of possibilities in an environment that is centered on a task rather than on a person and is free of time pressure.

In their study of school children, testing was individual. Pains were taken to remove any suggestion of examination, and the experiment was conducted in a game-like atmosphere. They used ten indicators of general intelligence, taken from verbal and performance subtests of the WISC and the school and college ability tests. They also used ten creativity indicators, which consisted of a uniqueness and a productivity measure for each of the five procedures they used. They found the ten intelligence measures to be highly intercorrelated among themselves, as were the ten creativity measures, but the correlations between the creativity and the intelligence measures were low. They expressed considerable surprise that such a dimension should prove independent of general intelligence, though in view of the previous literature on this subject, they should hardly have been unforewarned. One of the points that intrigued them was that the creativity processes mostly called for verbal facility, which is a highly basic element of the concept of general intelligence. They were also interested to find this independence of creativity and intelligence in elementary school children who were expected to show less differentiation in their modes of cognitive functioning than would adults.

Having isolated in children this mode of thinking that is pervasive but independent of intelligence, Wallach and Kogan then sought to understand its psychological significance. To do this, they formed eight groups of children, taking boys and girls separately and making groups high in both intelligence and creativity, high in intelligence but low in creativity, high in creativity but low in intelligence, and low in both characteristics. They observed a number of behavioral and quantitative differences between these groups of children. They were observed in the classroom and rated, independently by two experimenters, on a number of dimensions.

They summarize their clinical information on these children as follows:

1. *High creativity—high intelligence.* These children show both control and freedom and adult-like and child-like kinds of behavior.
2. *High creativity—low intelligence.* These children are in angry conflict with themselves and their school environment and have feelings of unworthiness and inadequacy but can flower in a stress-free milieu.
3. *Low creativity—high intelligence.* These children are described as "addicted" to school achievement. Academic failure to them would be extremely painful, and they constantly strive for excellence.
4. *Low creativity—low intelligence.* These children are bewildered and engage in various defensive maneuvers such as passivity or psychosomatic symptoms.

The question arising here is whether these observed characteristics of the four groups were necessary and basic to the type of cognitive functioning they show or the result of it; presumably the latter is the case.

Wallach and Kogan believe that the broad modes of thinking that are revealed by the intelligence and creative dimensions may have a very wide significance in the life of the child, influencing not only his academic performance but also his social relationships and his evaluation of himself.

The role of "risk taking" in creative productivity has been discussed by Torrance (1962b), and he claims that willingness to take a calculated risk is one of the characteristics that distinguishes the creatively productive person from the merely clever. He bases this in part on a study by himself and his associates of highly successful jet fighter pilots with a record number of MIG "kills." One might hesitate to regard this as a criterion of creativity—or, if it is such, it represents creativity unhappily applied—but be this as it may, the idea of risk taking and creativity having something in common is a notion with at least high face validity.

This study also quotes the results of the work in Minnesota. Torrance and his associates found three personality characteristics that differentiated the highly creative child from the less creative but equally intelligent one; the former had a reputation for wild and silly ideas (especially the boys) and both teachers and their peers rated them this way. They were also characterized by the production of ideas that were unusual (without being silly), for example, including unique details in drawings of the human figure. Torrance remarks that one of the reasons such children do not show up particularly well on standardized tests of intelligence is simply because the norms do not take account of these unusual details. There is some tautology in these two characteristics, because they are just what one would expect of creative persons, who would by definition show them. The third set of characteristics are more enlightening; their work was characterized by humor, playfulness, relative lack of rigidity, and relaxation. This confirms the results of other studies.

The personalities of artistically gifted adolescents were studied by Hammer (1961), who compared five who were rated as "truly creative" with five who were rated as "merely facile." Using an extensive psychological evaluation, he found that the creative ones differed from the facile in exhibiting greater feelings, greater original responsiveness, preference for the observer role over being a participant, stronger determination and ambition, integration of feminine and masculine components, greater independence, rebelliousness and self-awareness, stronger needs for self-expression, greater tolerance for discomfort, and a fuller range of emotional expression.

Weisberg and Springer (1961) compared creative and noncreative children and found the creative children to be rated significantly higher than the noncreative on the following points: strength of self-image, ease of early recall, humor, availability of Oedipal anxiety, and uneven ego development. "Availability of Oedipal anxiety" is presumably to be interpreted as psychiatric jargon for "self-awareness." Uneven ego development is described by such things as an enthusiasm for Shakespeare and dolls and impulsive behavior alternating with mature control. On the Rorschach they showed a tendency toward unconventional responses, unreal percepts, and imaginative treatment of the material, which can presumably be interpreted in cognitive rather than in personality dynamic terms. They also showed more human movement and color responses than the less creative children or than adult norms. This was interpreted as signs of both greater sensitivity and greater independence.

Genius has been defined as an infinite capacity for taking pains. This is touched on in several of the studies of the creative personality. Hammer (1961), for instance, notes determination and drive as a characteristic of creative adolescents. MacKinnon (1962b) found his creative architects to be tenacious, staying with a task and not being discouraged by adverse criticism of their ideas.

Another feature mentioned by MacKinnon is that creative individuals are reality-oriented; one definition of creativity could be realistic problem solving. There might, of course, be a difference here related to the area of creative endeavor. In the sciences there must be a strong element of realism in productive endeavors, and for architects realism is presumably mandatory. But in the arts the reality principle may be less binding, and perhaps the necessary personality characteristics differ with the field of creative effort.

Creativity and Femininity

A number of writers speak of sex-role characteristics in connection with creativity, the more common being references to feminine characteristics in the personalities of creative men.

This matter of equating creativity and femininity is one that requires some elaboration. It constantly appears in the literature and seems to be an argument from tradition rather than science. Helene Deutsch (1945), in the second volume of her work on the psychology of women, expresses this idea, and in such contexts, it would seem, the argument is that because women produce children they are the true creators, and therefore creativity is a feminine characteristic. On the other hand, it could be said that it is precisely because the woman is the child-bearer that she is uncreative. For child rearing, she seeks stability and conservation, not daring ventures and innovations.

Allowing some other grounds for regarding creativity as a feminine trait, such an assumption would lead one to predict that more women than men are creatively productive and that the most feminine women would be the most productive ones. Torrance (1962b) has claimed that an emphasis on sex role creates problems for highly creative children. He suggests that this emphasis has stifled the creativity of women and is an explanation of the rareness of their creative achievements in the sciences and the arts. However, he also maintains that a misplaced emphasis on sex role is inimical to creativity in both males and females and places handicaps to creative achievements in the sciences and the arts. He claims that a misplaced emphasis on sex role makes problems of adjustment for creative individuals of both sexes. Creativity, he says, requires sensitivity and independence, and in our culture sensitivity is defined as feminine, whereas independence is a masculine trait. This being so, it might be expected that the creative boy will be more effeminate than his peers, whereas the creative girl will be more masculine.

Hammer (1961) has also commented on the feminine component in the personality of the productive male. In his study of a small group of artistically creative adolescents, he noted the frequent projections in the Rorschach, particularly in card III, of female images. He sees this as uncertainty, on the part of these creative male subjects, in their masculine identification, the reverse occurring with female creative subjects. However, other evidence shows that these subjects have a high degree of strength and masculinity, with typical masculine traits such as confidence, determination, ambition, and power. Hammer speaks of the fusion of the feminine with the masculine, this fusion allowing the necessary sensitivity and intuitiveness that, combined with purpose of action and determination, fosters creative artistry. Again, the emphasis is not on the artistic male being "effeminate" or the artistic female "masculine" but rather that both incorporate into the unity of their personalities certain broad characteristics that are normally absent from other individuals of the particular sex.

MacKinnon (1963, 1965) has also spoken of the femininity dimension in the personalities of his group of highly creative architects. When one examines what he is really saying, however, it is not that these men were effeminate but rather that the highly creative person is one whose personality is widely and fully developed, one not constricted by cultural stereotypes, among which sex-role typing must be included. Because of this they do, as it were, unashamedly show characteristics that our society regards as feminine as well as those that are masculine. In this sense their creativity stems from, or perhaps more properly is released by, their being well-rounded and fully developed individuals and is not dependent on their "femininity" as its source. As pointed out in another context, it is a historical fact that the overwhelming majority of people who have been regarded as highly creative have been men, and this fact alone should make it difficult to equate creativity with femininity in any strong manner. Indeed, a study by Helson (1965) shows that women rated as creative tend in personality makeup to be masculine rather than ultrafeminine, and this would further support the idea that it is being extensively developed rather than being masculine or feminine that is the crucial factor.

Family Relationships of Creative Children

There are two ways in which the family environment of the creative child is of interest, but unfortunately at present there is no means of knowing for sure which is the proper way of looking at it. On the one hand, if creativity is something that is fostered by the child's environment (and presumably his early one in particular), then family dynamics may well be critical; it is implied that any parents who choose to mimic these conditions can produce a creative child. On the other hand, it may be that to beget creative offspring, parents must themselves be creative and carry whatever genetic or constitutional basis provides this condition. The constellation of family relationships are, in this view, incidental and not causal.

Stein (1956) has reported that individuals rated as creative were more likely to feel that their parents were inconsistent in their attitudes to them. More creative individuals also preferred solitary activities as children, while less creative subjects were more prone to engage in group activities. R. B. Cattell (1959) has reported similar trends from biographical studies. It might be naive to suppose, however, that parents should be advised to be inconsistent toward their children and to discourage group activities in the hopes of fostering creativeness in them. We are not told whether the parents of creative children are themselves creative and whether being creative tends to make one inconsistent as a parent; it is not unreasonable to suppose that the latter might be the case.

Weisberg and Springer (1961) studied gifted fourth-grade children and their families. Comparisons were made of highly creative children in the group with those who were less so, using as a criterion certain tests from the Minnesota battery. Personalities were studied through psychiatric interviews and projective tests. The family pattern for the highly creative children was distinctive from that of the others. Parental values did not stress conformity; the family unit was not a close one; and there was little dependence of individuals on one another. Characteristically, the marriage was not especially well adjusted; there was overt and sometimes stormy expression of feeling. The father was found to interact strongly and positively with the child, whereas the mother interacted strongly and ambivalently. The fathers tended to be in occupational positions that gave them autonomy and independence. The creative child was often an older sibling but not a favorite one. This study did not, unfortunately, rate the parents themselves on creativity, so it leaves unanswered the question of whether this trait runs in families.

MacKinnon (1962) has commented on the family backgrounds of his group of creative architects and presents a similar picture. There was often a lack of any intensely close relationship between parent and child, and neither strongly positive nor strongly negative ties existed. MacKinnon points out that this may have had a liberating effect and left the child free to develop himself. Another characteristic was in fact the degree to which the parents permitted the freedom necessary to such self-development. Although not generally having strong and close ties with their sons, the fathers of these boys did present a model of effective and resourceful behavior in the community. The mothers were also autonomous, leading active lives with independent interests. Another notable characteristic was that (in contrast to some other studies) the family discipline was consistent and predictable, though rarely harsh. These families frequently moved, so that close community roots were not usually developed. In this particular group another feature was an early development of skill and interest in drawing and painting, a matter having obvious relevance to the later profession. MacKinnon is committed to the view that creativity can be nurtured, though he acknowledges that we lack the information necessary to say just how this can be done. The measures that he cites, however, might be regarded as ones to use to avoid suppressing creativity that is already there rather than to germinate it. He speaks, for example, of the necessity of avoiding too-early and too-frequent criticism of first efforts.

Getzels and Jackson (1962) found certain characteristics of the families of their two groups to be distinctive. The parents of the high-IQ but uncreative children tended to be concerned about financial security, class status, and good behavior and high academic performance in their children. They tended to minimize risks and to show limited individual divergence. The parents of the high-IQ but creative children, on the other hand, tended to be unconventional and willing to take risks; they emphasized their children's values, interests, and responsiveness to experience.

Holland (1961), in a study of nearly a thousand talented high school juniors, found that the parents of the high but uncreative academic performers tended to emphasize perseverance, self-control, and good behavior and to be rigid and somewhat authoritarian. The parents of the creative children were relatively permissive, and their children were expressive and independent in social behavior.

Recently Datta and Parloff (1967) have also investigated the kind of family in which the creative individual is likely to develop. Previous studies have isolated the relevant dimension to be autonomy-control. The creative child was more likely to perceive both parents as providing a "no rules" situation in which his integrity and responsibility were assumed rather than one in which expectations were enforced by authoritarian controls.

It will be noted that there is a certain consistency in these reports on the families of creative children. The parents seem to show some of the characteristics of self-actualizers, though the reports are not sufficiently detailed in all cases to know whether they can really be described thus. One important question is again whether the parents of these creative children were themselves creative, but it is not answered clearly. One can believe they might be from the descriptions of them. Another point is that while there is some correlation between certain family patterns and creativity, this does not necessarily mean a causal relationship. We are not yet in a position to say whether creative children are so because they are reared in this kind of family or whether this kind of family holds the genes that may underlie creativity.

The development of IQ, creative abilities, and academic achievement and their relationships to family size, birth order, sibling sex, and age difference between siblings have been investigated by Cicirelli (1967). He found no significant relation between family size and measures of ability and achievement. It was found, however, that verbal creative abilities, reading, and arithmetic were improved for those subjects with siblings of like sex who were close in age. In three- and four-child families birth order was found to be unrelated to ability and achievement.

Mental Health of the Creative Individual

The idea is still current that the creative person is neurotic and indeed that neuroticism is a prerequisite for creativity. Both Kubie (1958) and Roe (1959) have discussed the folklore of the neurotic creator, which they believe to be false. It is not to be denied that many creative people have been neurotic, but it may be that they have been creative in spite of rather than because of their neuroticism. Kubie has described neurosis as banal and says that only the individual untrammeled by fear and guilt can allow the preconscious processes that he believes to be basic to creativity to operate. Nevertheless, Torrance (1962b) has claimed that both parents and teachers as a rule prefer a child to be "well adjusted" rather than creative and different, and the idea of creativity being unhealthy apparently still lingers on.

Hammer (1961) also separates the two in saying that emotional disturbance and creative ability are clearly not synonymous but goes on to cite the instances of a number of highly creative individuals who have had their productivity related either by themselves or by others to their emotional state. Freud is among these. In MacKinnon's study, the most creative architects were intermediate in neuroticism between the low creative group (who were least neurotic) and the moderately creative group (who were most neurotic).

The creatively gifted person has an ability for synthesis that is lacked by the merely "sick," and this may enable him to compensate for a neurosis, but a neurosis is not a necessary condition for creative production, and may be a handicap.

Training in "Creativity"

There are a number of studies that purport to show an improvement in creativity following training. Covington and Crutchfield (1965) have provided one of these. They used an *autoinstructional program* consisting of detective and mystery stories, each lesson comprising a mystery problem for solution and a succession of clues leading to the final solution. Following training, they used three criterion measures to test creative functioning. One consisted of problem-solving tasks (such as how to get out of a deep pit without tools —the kind of predicament familiar to television heroes). Another involved tests of *divergent thinking,* such as thinking of unusual uses for tin cans or bricks. The final criterion consisted of attitude and self-evaluation measures tapping self-confidence in problem solving and values regarding creative thinking.

Using elementary school children in the fifth and sixth grades, the experimental groups did markedly better than the controls. These results were repeated in a second study. Another study showing the effects of training is by Cartledge and Krauser (1963), who found an improvement in first grade children following a program designed to increase creativeness.

A question that these studies raise, but do not answer, is whether individual differences in "creativity" remain after training; it would be surprising if they did not. If they do remain, it would suggest that some preexisting skill or potential was improved by the training. Covington and Crutchfield recognize this point. They ask if the training program had produced new skills or whether it had sensitized the child to using skills already possessed. They believe the latter is the more likely possibility.

Creativity and Child-Rearing Policy

A question that the foregoing raises is whether a child-rearing and educational system should set out to foster creativity in *all* children or whether its aim should be the more limited (but possibly more realistic) one of identifying the child who already has what it takes to be creative and then seeing that it does not destroy this quality. As Wallach and Kogan point out (somewhat inconsistently with their suggestions for training), creativity may be a delicate flower that may be withered by attention, and they point out that the concern about creativity—particularly in the sciences—which followed the shock of Sputnik in 1957, may in fact destroy what it seeks to foster. There are some very intriguing questions here for the psychologist, who may need enough self-discipline to recognize that his best contribution to creativity is to leave it alone.

A point that needs examination, supposing we are prepared to risk the dangers of self-consciousness about creativity, is whether the conditions that are best suited to the creative child are necessarily the most satisfactory ones for noncreative children. (Some will protest, of course, that there is no such thing as a noncreative child, so perhaps this is a preliminary question to clear up: My thesis assumes that there *are* children relatively lacking in creativity.) The question is, first, one of economics. Creative education is not easy, and creative teachers are in short supply. Just as it is uneconomic to insist on teaching music even to the tone deaf and musical morons, so plain economics may require restriction of "creative training" to those who can most benefit.

Apart from practical questions of this sort, it might be asked whether the conditions in which the creative child will flourish are necessarily those that should apply generally. To insist that they do might be to hold the idea of eighteenth-century aristocrats who believed that all their children were equally able to benefit from a classical education and (metaphorically) like them to flog the laggards who perversely fail to assimilate it.

The jokes about children in "free expression" schools who ask plaintively "But do we really *have* to do as we please?" may be an expression of a reality. Some children find ambiguity intolerable and prefer a well-structured situation. Creative children may be unusual not only in their productivity but also in the kind of environment in which they flourish best, and we should not assume (at least without further inquiry) that the environment that best suits them is the desirable model for all children.

The Teacher and the Creative Child

Following on the discussion of earlier sections, it is interesting that Torrance (1962b) has claimed, perhaps justifiably and certainly on the basis of wide experience, that schools show little interest in recognizing and encouraging the creative child; many teachers are suspicious of him and believe him to be in some sense unhealthy.

He documents instances of the way in which unimaginative teachers have stifled the lively mind of the imaginative and creative child, who is discouraged from stepping out of line and who in due course gives up the effort. Instances are also given of teachers who are themselves creative and who encourage this trait in their students, but the implication of his writings is that the unimaginative teachers are in the majority and by and large there is wastage of stifled creative talent among our school children. It is difficult to say where the balance lies, but it is not unlikely that it does fall to a negative side. Today, one suspects with dismay, the alert and imaginative high school student and undergraduate can find much more challenging and exciting courses to follow than those offered by many teacher training programs; the better students do not go in for, but avoid, teaching as a profession. Getzels and Jackson (1962) have implied that the climate of anti-intellectualism in the age of the "organization man" has cast a chill over our schools and has led to an attitude of hostility in them to the creativity-gifted child. The emphasis is on "success" as measured by good, conforming grades.

Epilogue on Creativity

Creativity, like intelligence and many other psychological concepts, is an ill-defined cognitive quality, and for this reason there is insufficient consistency between studies to relate those qualities clearly to one another. It is thus difficult to know when creativity first manifests itself in the child or what its developmental course may be. What has been taken to be creativity has been described in young children, though just how it relates to the quality in maturity has not been adequately described. There is some evidence of two periods of developmental relapse in creativity, one at about age nine to ten and another at about twelve to thirteen years. The latter one may be a kind of negative critical period, insofar as this quality is concerned, because it corresponds to a particular stage of formation of group conformity that is inimical to creativity. Many individuals apparently do not survive this second period with productivity intact and become relatively uncreative as adults, though none of the studies are longitudinal ones and hence do not tell us whether high-creative children are (as one would suppose) less liable to loss at this stage.

There is extensive but inconclusive debate about the relationship between creativity and intelligence. On the whole the consensus seems to be that creativity is possible with low intelligence, though there is a tendency for the two to be related in that increasing intelligence is conducive to creative productivity, but only up to a certain level. In persons of superior intelligence (an IQ of about 120 or better) there is little or no relationship between creativity and intelligence. The most creative individuals are in this intellectual range.

Some personality characteristics of creative individuals have been described. An intellectual adventuresomeness, variously described by such terms as *risk taking,* a tolerance of ambiguity, and a distaste for structure or routine are among the attributes mentioned. A tendency to certain opposite-sex characteristics is also discussed in a number of studies as a marked feature of the creative personality and is considered important to the operation of creativity. Psychic good health is also conducive to creativity, though neurosis does not necessarily suppress it. Psychosis presumably tends to loosen the reality testing that is necessary to creative production in some fields (notably science), though it may not be so handicapping in artistic creation.

There are certain family constellations that appear to be frequently correlated with creativity, though what the causal relationship may be is not clear. There is in the family life of creative individuals, a looseness of structure and freedom, with an absence of dependent child-parent relationships and a tendency to easy discipline and autonomy for the child.

However, this kind of family constellation is probably more common than is creativity; that is, one can find many families that apparently fit this description and that do not produce creative children. Such a family setting might be a necessary condition for creative development but seemingly cannot be a sufficient one.

Few of the studies discuss the creativity of the parents of creative children, though the personality descriptions of the parents are similar to those of creative adults. This leads one to ask whether creative parents tend to have creative children and whether there may not be a genetic basis to the character.

The crucial question is whether creativity is an attribute that can be *inculcated* by training. Most authors either state or imply that this is the case. If this is so, then by replicating the family relationships and educational practices said to be related to creativity, one should produce creative children at will.

This conclusion may be viewed skeptically, and the hypothesis is proposed that creativity is, in fact, a temperamental quality and presumably has a genetic basis. If this is so, creative individuals cannot be produced by training, at least at present or in the foreseeable future. What "training" can do is to bring out maximum expression in those with the potential for creativeness, and suitable conditions can avoid wastage of this scarce talent.

TIME AND RATE IN COGNITIVE DEVELOPMENT

Critical Periods

Critical periods have been described in a number of aspects of growth and development, and it is quite clear from material reviewed in Chapter 7 and elsewhere that experiences, or the lack of them, during certain times in development markedly influence intellectual functioning. We have, however, little data on such periods in more specific aspects of cognitive development—whether, for instance, the various cognitive styles are subject to periods of special development.

It may be just coincidental, a matter dictated by extraneous factors rather than some insight, but all educational systems start the formal teaching of children between five and seven years of age. This age range corresponds to watersheds in several descriptions of development. There are four major theoretical approaches to cognitive development, and S. H. White (1965) has made the point that each of them attaches special importance to the five to seven period.

Piaget finds age seven to be a major transitional point at which the child obtains an "intuitive" understanding of relations between objects and, consequently, what he calls "concrete operations" become possible.

The Russian theorists represented by Luria (1960) note that around the fifth year is the time at which speech is internalized, and that this process is a prelude to a decisive stage in cognitive development.

The stimulus-reaction theorists are represented by Kuenne's experimental finding on transposition of response in the period (1946). She regards the preverbal child as, like the nonverbal animal, functioning in the discrimination learning situation and unable to transpose. The acquisition of language as a mediator makes possible a shift to transposition of learning; that is, for example, the ability to verbalize a concept like "smaller" and consistently choose on the basis of this concept even when the relative sizes and differences of sizes are markedly different from those on which the child is trained. Kendler and Kendler (1962a) and Reese (1962) have also argued on similar lines.

White goes on to state that Freud claimed a transitional period, between five and seven,

when the Oedipal situation has been worked through and sexuality is inhibited, leading to the latency period. Also at this time the superego is developed by the internalization of parental values. For Freud, latency is one stage in which psychosexual development is slow, but social and cognitive development proceed rapidly.

White suggests a synthesis of these various approaches by accepting the five to seven period as a time when maturational development (in a modal environment) inhibits a broad range of first-level functions to permit a new, higher-level of function. Thus there is a shift from what White calls an "associative level" of mental processes to a "cognitive level." The associative level is relatively fast-acting but limited. The cognitive level is slower to act and to process information but is capable of greater power. As White points out, the associative level tends to be overlaid or inhibited but is still available to adults and may be used in appropriate learning situations. It does not necessarily cease developing at age seven.

Effects of Training on Concept Attainment

Because it is Piaget's idea that the time at which a child enters a given stage of development is influenced by the experiences he receives, it is appropriate to expect that special training will have some influence. This statement is not necessarily inconsistent with the idea of critical periods. If we assume that psychological critical periods involve both a maturational base and the necessity for some experience, then the timing of this experience is a variable. In Chapter 7 it was suggested that critical periods in humans are not of the dramatic start-stop nature found in such instances as lower-species imprinting, but that they have a slower decline that may never reach zero. The experience is most effective at the peak but not wholly ineffective afterwards. Thus there is a preperiod in which the experience is ineffective but a latitude after the maturational readiness is reached. Hence the timing of consecutive experiences necessary to some acquisition can be foreshortened to a minimum determined by the maturational changes underlying them but not compressed beyond this limit. On the other hand, in a "slow" environment it may be prolonged. The optimum state of affairs exists when each experience impinges just at the moment of peak in the substratum.

The situation is depicted in Figure 16–2, in which the changes in the maturational substratum are represented by the curves 1, 2, and 3 and in which A, B, and C represent consecutive events necessary to the attainment of some concept. The arrows A, B, and C represent the optimum timing and spacing of these events, and the ease of acquisition is represented by the shortness of these arrows; a, b, and c, and a', b', and c', represent early and late events that are relatively less efficient as

indicated by the lengths of line. Too long a spacing may mean that consecutive events get out of phase with the biological substratum, as is the case in a'', b'', and c''.

According to this model there are a number of possible variations in timing: for example, if the first event is late, as at a', and the second is early, as at b, then the interval between them is reduced, though neither occurs at the optimum time. In particular, b is too early and may require a disproportionate amount of effort for impression upon the organism. In other words, reduction of the interval is possible but inefficient. Another variation is to apply A at the optimum time and then advance b and c, but again this can be done only at the cost of increased effort in the last two.

There is one point that this model lacks and that is the possibility of environmental influences modifying the biological substratum itself. This matter is discussed in Chapter 7. However, it is being assumed that the degree of alteration in either the susceptibility to a

FIGURE 16–2. *Maturation and the timing of experiences.*

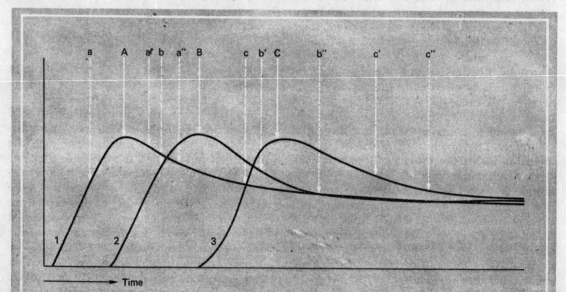

given event or the timing of it is limited and that the organism must function within the constraints imposed by its biology. These constraints are not inflexible, but neither are they so fluid as to be immaterial.

DO WE HAVE A REVOLUTION IN LEARNING?

A question that has been repeatedly asked in this chapter and touched on at several points elsewhere in this book is to what extent can intellectual development be accelerated? This is distinct from another question; should it be?

The first question may need qualifying by making it more specific to particular aspects of development. It may or may not be the case that *total* development can be speeded. To some extent the answer to the question depends on how much the aspect of development under consideration is bound to maturational processes. As mentioned in several contexts, maturation is not immutable, and the kinds of stimulation to which the organism is exposed can accelerate or retard the rate of maturation; reduction of stimulation can lead to permanent insufficiency in the maturational substratum of development (e.g., an impaired visual system may follow gross infantile understimulation). However, so far as present evidence goes, the amount of change in the rate of maturation appears to be relatively small. Hence maturationally based developments can be changed in rate, but only within somewhat narrow limits. It may also be the case that it is easier to retard than to accelerate, because the normal environment for most organisms may provide more than enough stimulation for development.

In recent years there has been considerable interest, in North America at least, in the acceleration of one aspect of development, the intellectual one. In this connection, reference has already been made to J. McV. Hunt (1961) and Bruner (1960). A "talking typewriter," by which three- and four-year-old children can self-learn to read, write, and compose poetry, has been developed (Moore and Anderson, 1968). Pines (1966) has written an enthusiastic popular account of the discoveries of the "mind builders," and she looks forward to the revolution in learning that she believes is about to overthrow traditional educational methods.

There seems to be a confusion between two distinct matters in this field. One is the acceleration of the lagging development of children growing up under conditions of cultural deprivation and a low level of stimulation. The other is the production of advanced development in children who already have a high level of stimulation.

Insofar as the underprivileged child is concerned, there is optimistic (but not yet conclusive) evidence that enrichment of the environment of young deprived children, even in somewhat limited sessions, can lead to an improvement in development. Blank and Solomon (1969) discuss the kinds of teaching techniques needed for teaching the disadvantaged preschool child, and they point out that the usual methods with traditionally trained nursery school teachers may be inappropriate, and that a one-to-one technique has to be used for effectiveness.

Despite some successes, there have also been some disappointing results. For one thing, a Hawthorne effect seems to set in—almost anything new goes well and produces results for about a year but then goes stale (see, for instance, Gray et al., 1966a,b). Similar findings are reported elsewhere. In assessing the results of a three-year experimental "head start" program with underprivileged Negro children of borderline intelligence, Weikart (1967) found the results to be "not as encouraging as some might have hoped nor as bleak as some might have predicted" (p. 1). The disappointment arose because about half the children failed to benefit—and the encouragement from the fact that half did benefit. On Stanford-Binet scores, the experimental group showed a small but significant rise in the IQ in the first year, but at the completion of the third year both experimental and control groups showed a small increase in IQ (about seven points) with no significant difference between them. On the California Achievement Tests there were moderately significant increments for the experimental group. The experimental group as a whole showed social improvements.

The successful half of the experimental group showed a sixteen-point mean rise of IQ and educational achievement commensurate with their intellectual level; they were coping with the elementary school curriculum.

Weikart asks why is there this marked difference in response to the program, but the information necessary to a reply is as yet lacking. Obviously more research effort is needed.

Incidentally, one of the more interesting but little exploited possibilities of a "head start" program is that of making the parents themselves the sources of stimulation (Weikart et al., 1964). One fears it may not be universally possible to arouse the parents, but where it is so, this no doubt represents the happiest (and cheapest) solution to the problem. Another notable effect is diffusion, the tendency for more children than actually attend the program to benefit by some osmotic process (Gray et al., 1966a, b).

Despite the discouragements, there are both theoretical and factual reasons for supposing that early stimulation contributes significantly to development (as discussed in Chapter 11) and that supplying extra stimulation in an impoverished environment will have its effects. But, as suggested earlier, the laboratory-reared rat may be an environmentally deprived one and comparable to the culturally deprived child. The assumption that we produce a "super-rat" by early stimulation may be false. What we produce is one approximating the liveliness of the normal feral rat, or in other words, one that exploits its potential more fully. Similarly, by enriching the environment of the underprivileged child, we enable him to develop his potential but not to reach super-levels.

In passing it is worth noting that the effects of educational manipulation are subtle. Rosenthal and Jacobson (1968) have shown how teacher expectations that underprivileged children will underperform may result in just such performance. These authors even suggest that a less expensive method of achieving the effects of a "head start" program may be obtained not by direct manipulation of the children but by working on the expectations of teachers.

On the question of the long-term effects of extra stimulation for infants in privileged homes, there are few data upon which to base any sound conclusions. As we have already stated the rat data do not provide satisfactory comparative-experimental evidence because of the possibility that the laboratory rat is an underprivileged animal. Reference has been made to the Moore and Anderson experiments with the talking typewriter, but here the small group of children so far involved were from superior homes, and some at least were of exceptionally high native intelligence. They might have learned to read anyway at the age they did, and the results so far supply no warrant for supposing that any healthy child taken at random would show such startling achievements in intellectual performance.

In the absence of concrete evidence, one must rely on anecdotal clues. Against the experiment by James Mill that produced, by early and rigorous training, John Stuart Mill, one must place the case of Herbert Spencer, who reputedly received no formal education until he was forty. It is true that J. S. Mill's philosophy has had a deep effect on the society that we in the West live in today and in this sense has been much more consequential than Spencer's, but one could not really make a convincing case for the proposal that the difference lies in the early cramming of J. S. Mill. Other influential social philosophers have not had this kind of early rearing.

The story of one juvenile genius may carry a moral. (A brief account is given in *Intelligence,* the Mensa journal, January 1968.) This boy's father, described as a brilliant professor of abnormal psychology, started by suspending the letters of the alphabet over his crib and reciting them hour by hour and day by day. A relentless program of tuition followed this and bore results. At two the boy could read high school texts. At three he was writing treatises in both English and French and at four produced a profound paper on anatomy. By nine he had qualified for entry to Harvard but delayed his studies until he was eleven, filling in the time by writing a geometry text, among other efforts. At fourteen he was lecturing on the fourth dimension.

The astonishing effect of this experiment in education is marred by the fact that this prodigy was socially inept and shunned by his colleagues. His brilliant lectures were interrupted by uncontrollable fits of giggling. He vanished from the academic scene to work as a clerk, dying unknown and embittered.

It is not necessarily true that every child exposed to early stimulation of this kind will repeat this history, but it would seem worthwhile to ponder the matter before advocating a too rigorous approach to early training. It is notorious that, in the field of music at least, child prodigies rarely achieve their promise as adults, though whether the effect here is primarily intellectual or motivational or social is not known.

In discussing music in the context of accelerated development, the case of Mozart comes to mind. Here indeed is an exception to the rule that child prodigies in music rarely flower into adult musicians of note. Mozart's Symphony K16 in E-flat was composed at the age of eight, and while it may not be among the greatest of the musical productions of the eighteenth century, it is still very good. In his teens he produced a hundred or more works of good quality, some showing excellence.

Against this, one must contrast Beethoven, Schubert, Brahms, and indeed almost all other great composers, few of whom produced anything of note until maturity (a single exception is Schubert's *Gretchen am Spinnrade,* a flash of fire at seventeen).

It is also noteworthy that the young Mozart developed his early talents and produced his early works not as the result of some strict regime of musical head start but in disregard of parental injunctions that he play with toys and not harpsicords. Just what factors underlay the early expression of this genius are not known, but it does seem certain that whatever they were, they were highly unusual and provide little reason for supposing that this achievement can be a common phenomenon. It may be true that most children can learn to give a recognizable rendering on the piano of *Men of Harlech* or the *Blue Danube Waltz.* This does not mean that every child can become a Rubenstein, or even a Liberace. We need to retain a realistic understanding of the genetic or constitutional limitations on the development of special skills.

Modern technology has increased tremendously the amount of stimulation that comes into our daily lives. Part of this is what might be called stimulus pollution, the scream of jet planes and sonic booms, the incessant noise of traffic, and the visual stabbings of neon signs. In addition there is the bombardment of television—much of it low-level intellectually but nonetheless a stimulus input. Some of it is in fact informational, and we might indeed face the situation of information overload.

Before we are in a position to know whether superenrichment of early education is feasible, we need more data on the information input capacities of the young child and some assurance that a high level of stimulation will not defeat its purpose by reducing motivation, as is suggested by some of the animal work discussed in Chapter 11. Furthermore, we need to know whether the successes of an enrichment program are the unusual child who would have achieved highly even under less special conditions and whether the more average child is really untouched by such experiences. Further, we need long-term knowledge of the overall effects on adult functioning of early intellectual hothousing. This will be discussed more fully in Chapter 20.

EPILOGUE

Reverting to the conclusions of the Conference of Research on Gifted Children (Gallagher, 1963) mentioned at the beginning of the chapter, it is evident that intellectual ability is indeed multidimensional. Here we have considered only a fraction of the aspects of intellectual functioning that have been mentioned in the literature. It is obvious that within this rich variety of forms of cognition there is great scope for individual variation. A topic for the future to consider is the interaction between various cognitive styles and the final pattern of functioning that emerges in maturity from this interplay of forces. It seems that the variety in what might be called the units of cognitive action is sufficiently great to allow for a virtually infinite variation in the pattern of functioning of each individual, so that each person may be unique in his particular constellation of cognitive activities.

Within this variation, it is suggested, males tend to resemble other males more than they do females and vice versa, so that there is a tendency toward a distinctiveness between the sexes in cognitive functions. Within males and females it is also possible to group individuals according to predominating aspects of their cognitive styles, though this grouping has in the past been carried too far (e.g., in the assumption that all with IQ's of 70 act alike or that they follow the same developmental patterns, and that all with 100's or 140's have a common pattern distinctive to their level).

A number of personality variables related to various sorts of intellectual functioning have been described. Again the coverage of these in this chapter has been selective and is certainly not exhaustive. It is, in fact, only by a quite unrealistic process of dissection that one can consider cognitive functions apart from personality variables at all. Cognitive style is a part of personality. Motivational factors as they influence cognition have been discussed, perhaps less extensively than they might have been, in Chapter 14. There is no doubt that high motivation can compensate to some extent for low ability, though the size of this effect is probably limited. It is also the case that low motivation may offset the effects of high ability, and this is perhaps a commoner and more marked event. It is, in fact, a special instance of the general effect noted elsewhere: that it is easier to retard functioning or development than it is to accelerate it.

It has been seen also that intellectual activity can be modified. Males can function like females and vice versa. Low automatizers no doubt can learn to masquerade as high ones (and, again, vice versa). But for each individual the more efficient means of functioning is in accordance with those styles dictated by his constitution. The assumption made in this chapter has been that each individual starts with innate tendencies that the environment fosters, retards, or modifies, but the aim of child rearing should be to permit the maximum development of the individual potential. This demands not a uniform educational system but a highly flexible one allowing wide scope for individual rates and styles of growth.

It would seem that some intellectual characteristic and cognitive styles may be more valued than others, which is not the same as being more valuable. For instance, there would be considerable (though perhaps not universal) agreement that high intelligence is valued. But let us consider the effects on society, under our existing economic conditions, of having an entire population with IQ's between 140 and 200. A very large part of the daily activities of people, even in an advanced technical society, do not demand this level and would in fact be painful to the gifted. The 140 IQ grocery clerk, bus driver, gandy dancer, plumber's mate, or waitress would have to "switch off" or go crazy. As society is at present organized, the aim of producing a genius in every child is not only unrealistic in the developmental sense but also in the social sense. We cannot provide appropriate occupations for trainloads of Einsteins with nobody to drive the train or make their trousers or provide them with potatoes and drinking water, to say nothing of desks and chairs and pens to write with or even calculators to calculate with. The last may be designed by clever men, but most of the labor in their actual construction is skilled though not exceptional. Regrettable as this may be, the fact is that for most people in the world as it is a less than superb intelligence could be regarded as an advantage. Similarly, strong automatization may seem an advantage at first sight, but we need to know more about the disadvantages that may go with it and bear in mind the possibility of some advantage in weak automatizing.

It may be that the twenty-first century will bring social changes in which the disadvantages of having too many people with high IQ's and boundless creativeness are removed. But despite the promise of an automated hothouse, we have not yet achieved one.

Seventeen | Identification

It is common in the literature to ascribe all instances of a similarity between children and parents to identification; as we shall see, this means attributing them to learning.

There are some questions aroused by speaking of identification as having the essence of learning. For one thing, it is not an explicit assumption in some discussions of identification that learning is involved, even though it is surely an implicit one. The psychoanalysts, social learning theorists, and attachment theorists all use the term, without in most cases explicitly calling it a learning process.

Most of these approaches describe identification in terms of its consequences rather than its mechanisms. Sears et al. (1965) have named four general sets of consequences: (1) acquisition of sex roles, (2) acquisition of adult roles and attitudes, (3) acquisition of self-control (e.g., resistance to temptation in low-risk settings), and (4) acquisition of guilt reactions to deviations once committed. It is the third and fourth sets that cause the greatest troubles for learning theorists (at least for those using reinforcement models) because they involve self-denial and intropunitive behaviors rather than "rewarding" actions.

The consequences of identification are discussed more fully in Chapter 18. This chapter is concerned more particularly with the process of identification. While the earlier parts of this book have emphasized the biological transmission of traits, including temperamental ones, we are now dealing with transmission that is probably not genetic. It is an observed fact that there are phenomena of the type covered by concepts such as *superego,* but their mechanisms are difficult to explain. The notion of identification was invented to account for such experientially induced changes in children, who develop from hedonistic motivations toward altruistic motivations (even if not all reach them; few outside the ranks of the saints achieve them fully).

The child develops from being asocial to becoming prosocially oriented and ready to pass on the social heritage of self-restraint to the next generation. One important consequence of identification that should be added to those listed above is the production of child-rearers.

While no doubt few would deny that traits may be transmitted genetically, this possibility is tacitly ignored by many writers. The genetic transmission of temperamental traits has been discussed elsewhere in this book, and it is not appropriate to do so again in this chapter, which is more concerned with the role of learning in transmission. However, it is necessary to point out that we can be sure that learning is solely involved only when similarities appear between unrelated individuals (which is the case in many experimental demonstrations of identification and no doubt in real life, too). But within the family, traits appearing in parent and child may be the result of genetic factors alone—or perhaps, more commonly, the result of learning augmenting a genetic tendency.

Elsewhere it is suggested that a range of traits are sex-linked with maleness and femaleness. That is, a boy and his father share a common core of "maleness" that tends to make them more alike than are the boy and his mother. The girl, for her part, has a similar concordance with her mother.

Thus sex-role behaviors may not be exclusively the result of learning but may be in part at least the product of both sex-specific behaviors common to males or females and to particular variations of these in the genetic strain of the father or mother.

This chapter concerns itself with learning that is not imposed on a *tabula rasa* but on a biased organism. Learning may elaborate this bias or it may obliterate it, though it is presumably easier to do the former than the latter. In other words, it is being asserted here that sex typing involves the kind of preprimed learning spoken of in earlier chapters. An interesting question arises here. It has already been suggested (Chapter 10) that the mammalian brain is fundamentally female and is hence, presumably, programmed for female-type behaviors. In the presence of testosterone during fetal life it is masculinized, and normally, of course, masculinization is associated with the XY chromosomal makeup. This masculinization obliterates the tendency to female-type behaviors and overlays them with a predisposition to male-type ones. It could be claimed, therefore, that females will have

greater difficulty learning male-type behaviors than males will have in learning female-type ones, and this would be consistent with the observations that psychosexual disturbances and difficulties over sex-role identification are more prevalent among males. Against this, it can be recalled that the Y chromosome is strongly masculinizing insofar as the development of *physical* sex characteristics are concerned, though whether this also extends to psychological development is problematical. On what little evidence there is so far, one would favor the view that *normal* females are more resistant to (or less susceptible to, depending on how one wants to state it) learning male-type behaviors than males are to learning female-type ones.

It would be interesting in this context to study the degree of male-type behaviors shown by girls masculinized by testosterone administered to the mother during pregnancy. The animal work (Levine, 1966) suggests that a masculinizing of behavior would be found. This is not inconsistent with the statement in the last paragraph, because these masculinized females are not normal but more like males.

Thus sex typing and the development of masculinity and femininity are the product of constitutional factor and identification, and one should speak of a constitution—identification complex of interactions rather than treating the factors in separation (or dealing with the latter alone, as is common). When one does for convenience discuss them in isolation, as in this chapter, it should be recognized that it is a convenience of discourse that introduces an artificiality into the discussion.

In Chapter 10 the idea was proposed that males and females are biologically different organisms that respond distinctively to the environment. Moreover, they require different sorts of experiences in the environment in order to develop optimally their differing potentialities.

Among the environmental influences that are important to development is identification. Indeed, identification covers one of the most important factors in development. The biological maleness of the boy gives a directionality to his development that requires a masculine environmental *field* to foster its optimum growth. Quite obviously the father will be a prime influence on the generation of this male field. Similarly, the feminine field necessary to the girl's development is provided by the mother. But the two processes are not merely mirror images of one another. Freud believed the identification processes of boys and girls to differ, and others have taken up the same point, though not always seeing the same process. Freud thought the process to be more difficult for the girl, whereas Mowrer (1950) and others have suggested it must be more difficult for the boy. One reason given for this is that he starts off with an "identification" with the mother that he later has to substitute for one with the father. It is suggested elsewhere in this chapter that this early or *anaclitic* period may not actually involve any identification in the true sense, but nevertheless if we assume that an emotional attachment is important to the identification when it does occur, this early period must have powerful influences on such identification. Others supporting the analytic contention, though for different reasons, are Mussen and Rutherford (1963), who believe that the development of sex typing in boys is easier because the male role is more highly valued and the proper behaviors more clearly defined. This belief might be questioned on the grounds that our child-rearing system is matricentric (Nash, 1965) and fails to provide adequate access to the father or other male models.

There are some indications that mothers tend to think in neuter terms of children rather than of boys and girls (E. W. Goodenough, 1957; Johnson, 1963) and to be less differentiated in their influence (Brodbeck, 1954). If this is so, it follows that a matricentric system will tend to minimize sex differences and to provide poor conditions for the development of masculinity; perhaps surprisingly, it may not provide proper conditions for the development of femininity either, as we shall see.

The literature on sex typing is considerable, and it is not proposed to review it in detail here. One extensive review is by Kagan (1964). Most of the work in this area refers to the acquisition of sex-appropriate behaviors, and most of it takes the view, either implicitly or explicitly, that these are learned. This is not being denied in this chapter, but merely modified by the suggestion that this learning is superimposed on a biological substratum of masculinity or femininity.

The literature makes it clear that male sex typing is mediated largely by the father (or other males in his place) and that female sex typing is acquired largely from the mother. But there are also cross sex effects that are less generally recognized.

IDENTIFICATION AND IMITATION

People tend to become like those with whom they have contact, and in particular children tend to show the personality characteristics of their parents. This homely observation has been the subject of numerous learned treatises and is widely known as identification. This term is descriptive, and these treatises elaborate with varying degrees of detail and clarity the statement of the observed facts. Relatively little has been written about the way in which identification actually occurs.

Identification is a Proteus of psychology; it appears not only with frequency but in so many shapes that one can never with certainty recognize any given instance as an unequivocal manifestation of the phenomenon. One thing that is apparent is that vague and nebulous as it is, it is still a concept that is indispensable. This makes all the more urgent the task of rendering it precisely.

Certain writers use the terms *imitation* and *identification* as if they were synonymous. It would be preferable to draw a distinction, using *imitation* for the copying of the overt behavior of another person—it is the act, not the person, that is being copied. The change in the action of the imitator may be only temporary and specific to the situation, as when in a foreign social situation one is uncertain of the etiquette and copies that of someone else. What one acquires is merely a motor act.

The distinction between imitation and identification is rather subtle and not easy to define tightly, but it would seem useful to distinguish between the learning of motor acts, which is often wittingly done, and the unwitting acquisition of the *qualities* of other people, their characteristic tolerance of frustration, for instance, or their attitudes to fluoridation. It is the transmission of the qualitative aspects of personality that constitutes identification. In many situations (if these definitions are used) imitation and identification may be seen together, as when a child acquires both the quality of a parent's reaction to frustration and a pattern of motor action as well.

This usage of identification·may seem to correspond to the psychoanalytic term *introjection,* but the latter includes in its definition reference to id and ego and other concepts that I want to avoid. In this book, the usage of the term *identification* is not unlike Freud's original use, apart from the omission of terms such as ego from the definition, but later psychoanalysts seem to have developed an explanation of the mechanisms underlying identification that would imply some different process from that intended here. Knight (1940), for example, has spoken 'of it as involving an interaction of introjective and projective mechanisms. The latter term involves *unacceptable unconscious tendencies; unconscious tendencies* might be allowed in the definition, but *unacceptable* is not appropriate, and between this and id, ego, and oral patterns, it would seem that the later psychoanalytic usage of the term describes something different from what is intended in this work. One is tempted to coin some new word.

Another way of stating the distinction drawn between imitation and identification is that the former is the acquisition of a specific pattern of motor behavior, whereas the latter involves the acquisition of sets or what might be called *cognitive principles.* That is, when a boy walks with just the stance that characterizes his father, he is imitating; he is imitating when he speaks with the accent and intonation of those around him (because these speech patterns arise from subtle vocal-motor habits). But when he displays the same attitude toward Negroes as does his father, this is identification. Imitation, as it were, guides overt behavior, whereas identification influences ways of thinking; attitudes and interests are not gained by imitation but by identification. Lazowick (1954) has expressed this distinction in defining identification in terms of similarities of meaning systems between subject and model and imitation in terms of such similarities of behavior patterns.

Imitation may, of course, serve identification or form a part of it. Adopting the dress or outward mannerisms of a person or a group may be an expression of the inner adoption of a value system. It is a sign of identification. However, it is presumably possible to imitate without identifying and also to identify without overt imitation.

The S-R inclined psychologist may possibly retort that separating imitation and identification is making a distinction without a difference, internalized s's and r's, token acts, or what have you making all psychological reproduction from one·individual to another essentially imitative. One has to be something of·a Gestaltist to regard identification as something more than imitation. However, the distinction is considered possible within the S-R frame of reference developed by Lazowick (1955), for whom identification is a developmental outgrowth of imitation

Stoke (1950) has spoken of two kinds of identification, *behavioral* and *emotional*. In the frame of reference being constructed here, behavioral identification is imitation, and all identification is emotional because the fulfillment of some motive, the satisfying of an affectional need, or the giving of psychological comfort is essential to the process.

Imitation refers to the acquiring of specific motor acts with little if any power of generalization; identification is the acquisition of sets, which may be highly generalizable. Imitation is not characteristically emotionally toned, whereas identification typically is. It is obvious that these differences may be important in a number of contexts, and for this reason the difference will be justified.

Whether or not the same principles of learning underlie the boy's blowing his nose with the mannerisms of his father (imitation) and the adoption of his father's attitude to race or pacifism (identification) is a question that cannot be answered at the present time. Even if future knowledge does show them to be the same, the distinction may still remain a proper one in some contexts. The learning theorist may find learning to ride a bicycle and acquiring an anti-Semitic prejudice to be indistinguishable in essence within *his* frame of reference, but there will no doubt remain some contexts in which to see that a difference exists may be useful. And because at present the possibility that these forms of learning may be different even in the learning-theory framework still exists, it may be disadvantageous to conceal the possibility. For present purposes it is proposed to adopt the hypothesis that the same or similar learning processes underlie both imitation and identification. This may prove to be wrong, but because there is yet no proof of this, Ockham's razor must be used.

NONPERSONAL IDENTIFICATIONS

It is common in the literature to find the term *identification* applied to attachments formed with material objects or to organizations, as when a man is said to identify with his own possessions or with an institution. If, as is done here, identification is defined as the fact of having acquired some personal quality from some other person, then it is clearly impossible to identify with objects;

they are excluded by the definition. Institutions, however, are not so easy to decide on because they involve people. When we say that a sailor has identified himself with his ship, or a boy with his college, do we really mean that it is the object of steel or stone to which the attachment has been formed or is it to the ship's crew or to the alumnus that the tie has been made?

One can imagine that a captain might form an attachment to his ship and regard the crew merely as creatures necessary to working it; some boys might be as cats are said to be, attached to places and not to people, and for them the college is the fabric and not its members. Freud has used the terms *object choice* and *object cathexis*. In his usage the *object* may be another person, particularly when the infant not yet capable of appreciating the animate and personal nature of his parents *uses* them as comforting objects, but it may also be objects in the usual sense of the word. Here the psychological mechanism is object cathexis, not identification.

It might be expected, however, that in some cases, and probably in most, the psychological ties that arise with an institution are mediated by the personal relationships that develop, and it would seem likely that the processes that form these ties are similar to those involved in identification between two persons. Indeed, it would seem possible that institutional identifications arise by generalization, the newcomer first identifying with one or few of the established members and through these extending his identification to the institution as a whole. If this is so, then it is quite proper to speak of identification in such a context.

Another distinction that is useful to keep in mind is between identifying as a process and identifying as a response, which is the result of this process. Most of the literature, in fact, deals with the latter, describing the existence of similar patterns of behavior in model and identifier rather than dealing with the process by which this similarity comes about. An explanation of identification, as distinct from a demonstration of its existence, requires concentration on the process aspects.

FREUDIAN IDENTIFICATION

The term *identification* originated with Freud, who used it to describe the process whereby a person molds his own ego upon another that has been taken as a "model" (Freud, 1948). Bronfenbrenner (1960) has reviewed Freud's own use of the term, for as with others of the Freudian ideas, this one developed over a lifetime and changed as it grew, and this review is valuable in drawing together the scattered references to the concept. Bronfenbrenner shows that Freud distinguished three aspects of the parent on which the child may pattern himself: the overt behavior, the parent's motives, and the parental aspirations for the child.

There is some confusion of terminology in Freud's account. One important process in his scheme is *anaclitic object choice,* which is not identification but a device for warding off the possibility of loss of love. It is based upon the feeding and nurturance dependency relationship and hence usually involves the mother as an "object" to be cathected.

He speaks of two forms of identification. One has been called by his daughter *identification with the aggressor* (Anna Freud, 1937). In modern social learning and socialization theories identification with the aggressor is more commonly called *defensive identification.* This occurs simultaneously with object cathexis but is a separate process.

Another feature of the Freudian hypothesis is that somewhat different processes of identification are found in boys and in girls. In the Freudian scheme, the child's first identifications, irrespective of its sex, are of the anaclitic kind, principally involving the mother as (in his view) the chief source of love because she is the main source of sustenance and comfort; the father might also share this alimental role, but in Freud's thinking the mother is much the more prominent figure. Later, the arousing of the Oedipal situation, in which this anaclitic identification by the boy develops into a sexual involvement with the mother, leads to the necessity of resolution for fear of the father, who is a stronger competitor in this triangle. Any anaclitic identification formed with the father changes to hostility. This is brought out in his essay *Dostoevski and Parricide* (Freud, 1950) and in other contexts. The father becomes (in the perception of the boy) an obstructive and hostile figure but far too powerful to be attacked openly. Identification, this time of the second kind, provides a psychological mechanism of escape (Freud, 1948). In developing the notion, the threat of castration comes to play a major role in the mechanisms proposed by Freud (see, for instance, his essay *The Passing of the Oedipus Complex* [Freud, 1924]), and hence the alleged fear element in the boy's relationship with his father becomes correspondingly important to the theory.

Even with the mothers there is an ambivalence in the anaclitic identification, and the universal ambivalence toward the mother in the "oral phase" is basic to the whole of Freud's theorizing about the origins of ego and the reality principle.[1]

Because the girl has already suffered "castration," she has no need to identify with the aggressor (see Freud's essay *Some Psychological Consequences of the Anatomical Distinction between the Sexes* [Freud, 1950]), and therefore anaclitic identification is a sufficient mechanism.

The resolving of the Oedipus complex plays an essential role in the formation of the superego, which "inherits the parental function." The aggressive type of identification is therefore intimately involved in the process.

[1] In Freudian theory the *ego* is an organization imposed on the *id* by the environment. The id operates by the *pleasure principle* and the environment by the *reality principle.* The incorporation of the external world (mainly represented by parental strictures) develops the *superego* (or conscience).

This has consequences for the formation of the superego in girls, who have no motive for aggressive identification and thus lack the main driving force for superego development. This notion that identification with a feared authority figure is the prime stimulant of superego growth was developed by Anna Freud, and her writings have markedly influenced the subsequent thought on this topic. The neo-Freudians make use of the concept; Sarnoff (1962), for example, has listed four psychological processes involved in varying circumstances in the establishment of the superego: (1) identification with the aggressor, (2) classical conditioning, (3) instrumental learning, and (4) concept formation. In his account identification is most significant.

Bronfenbrenner, in the article cited, distinguishes two manners in which Freud uses the term *identification*. In most contexts he treats it as a process and as interplay of internal and external forces that motivate the child to take on characteristics of the parent, as in the Oedipus situation. The two kinds of identification, anaclitic and aggressive, are processes. However, on occasion he also uses the term for the *result* of the process, as when similarities between the characteristics of the child and his model are being described. This overworking of the term is to be found in the writings of later authors also, and it might be desirable to adopt some other name for the result to distinguish it from the process leading to it.

Identification, as the term is generally used, implies a measure of dependency or a submission-dominance relationship between the identifier and the person identified with. This is expressed in Ausubel's use of the term *satellization* (1954) for the learning that (in his view) is incidental to the child's dependency relationship with older persons. During adolescence, if he is to achieve maturity, the derived status acquired by satellization must be replaced by independent self-evaluation and a self-generated status. Ausubel calls this process *desatellization.*

Post-Freudian Usage

Stoke (1950) has criticized the Freudian concept of identification on the grounds that it is scientifically unverifiable, which alone would be sufficient to justify its rejection as a hypothesis. He finds it inconsistent in its applicability to boys and girls; it fails to account for the differences between identifier and model and does not distinguish emotional from behavioral identification. He also finds it not useful as a clinical guide.

A number of approaches to a theory of the dynamics of identification have been made. Most of them are consonant with either psychoanalytic or social-psychological concepts. Burton and Whiting (1961) have proposed what they call a *status envy* hypothesis in which identification consists of learning a role by rehearsal in fantasy or play rather than by actual performance, the motive for this learning being envy of the privileged status of the model. The implications of this theory have not been fully pursued as yet. The point about learning through fantasy and play may have an appeal for those who find the *latent learning* hypothesis, of learning without doing, an unconvincing one.

Kagan (1958) has defined identification as an acquired, cognitive response. Other writers also speak as if the process is a conscious one; Slater, for instance, says, "The child who identifies . . . with a parent is saying in effect: 'I want to be like you. If I were, I would have you (and your virtues) with me all the time, and I would love myself as much as I love you . . .'" (1961, p. 113).

A number of writers have followed the Freudian lead in speaking of two kinds of identification. Jacobson (1954) has called the two kinds *ego identification* and *infantile identification.* The difference is as follows: "The first are realistic in so far as they result in lasting changes in the ego which justify the feeling of being at least partly like the love object. The latter are magic in nature; they represent a temporary-partial or total-blending of magic self and object images, founded on fantasies or even the temporary relief of being one with, or becoming, the object, regardless of reality" (p. 43).

Lair (1949) and Mowrer (1950) have used the terms *developmental* and *defensive* identification for the same two processes; Stoke (1950) speaks of *emotional* and *behavioral* identifications, and Lazowick (1955) uses the terms *true identification* and *imitation. Defensive identification* is near enough to *identification with the aggressor* to be covered by the arguments below, which make the Lair and Mowrer term redundant, and the distinction between identification and imitation drawn by Lazowick and followed here covers behavioral identification also. The cognitive nature of Jacobson's discussion of the question places it in another plane of discourse, different from that attempted here.

Lazowick (1955) relates imitation and identification sequentially, imitative behavior forming the developmental roots of identification. As already mentioned, he distinguishes the two terms, the former referring to specific behavior patterns and the latter to *meaning systems*. He proposes a mediation theory of identification in which there are similarities in mediating processes between subject and model, some reduced portion of the total behavior of the model representing this set of meanings and being incorporated as a set of meanings by the identifier. The difficulty with such an explanation is that *sets of meanings* would seem to be some matter internal to the model and not accessible to the identifier in many instances. Certainly there may be situations in which the model may make manifest his sets of meanings in observable actions, as in genuflecting to the altar or shaking his fist at a civil rights worker, but much of the stuff of identification is more abstract. In this case it is presumably the words of the model expressing his sets of meanings that are the observable actions, and the identifier incorporates these words into his behavioral repertoire. But all this seems to nullify the

distinction between imitation and identification and to bring us no nearer an explanation of either. Lazowick's definition of identification in terms of meanings and his statement that learning is involved are entirely acceptable: his learning paradigm is clear, logical within a stimulus-response frame of reference, but unconvincing. (His interesting experimental findings [Lazowick, 1953] will be discussed elsewhere. These give some descriptive facts about identification without revealing its mechanics.)

ANACLITIC IDENTIFICATION

Freud viewed anaclitic identification as the earliest type to arise. While he recognized that the father, who could be a nurturant figure, might provide some basis for this form, anaclitic identification is usually with the mother. This position has been taken explicitly by other writers, for example, Parsons (1958), and most accept implicitly the idea that early identification is maternal.

The definition of anaclitic identification is open to criticism; is there really any such thing? Because identification has been defined as involving the integration of qualities of personality derived from a model, it is debatable whether or not the infant in fact does this. A perusal of the literature reveals no experimental evidence on this point. Anaclitic identification refers essentially to the earliest period of life, and there is no mention of when this period comes to an end. Weaning may represent a key event in either starting or terminating this period.

Because identification may be considered as a learning process and since the child at this age is limited in his capacities for learning (Chapter 12), it is questionable whether the child is capable of true identification. At such a young age it is difficult to demonstrate personality similarities between parent and child, and because any that could be shown might be genetic in origin, rather than learned, it might be more appropriate to assume that the former is so. In fact, the kinds of "personality" traits that could be studied would be more temperamental (i.e., constitutional factors such as reactivity, speed of response, amount of activity, and prevailing mood) and do not require learning.

The definition of anaclitic identification can, therefore, be debated on theoretical grounds. Although there is an early "anaclitic" period involving an intense relationship, usually with the mother, identification as defined here may not occur. That is, there is no incorporation by learning of maternal personality attributes. The boy's first identification can, in fact, be with the father, and under ideal conditions we might assume it is with him. However, the early relationship with the mother may hinder achieving a relationship with the father and the cultural hindrances of a matricentric society may also impede such a relationship.

A possibility that seems to have escaped notice in the literature is that boys might form an early anaclitic relationship with the father rather than with the mother. The author has observed a number of such instances, including one involving his own son. This has happened despite breast feeding, and these infants were much like Harlow's monkeys that fed from the wire mother surrogate but went for comfort and security to the nonfeeding cloth one. These boys would fall asleep more readily with the father, needed him for comfort when distressed, and would later, when frightened, run to him in preference to the mother. There is no record of how common this phenomenon may be; it seems never to have been studied. It would be interesting to know what the later identifications of these boys would be. One would suppose a strong identity with the father, though whether this identity would show any qualitative difference from that of boys without this early anaclitic paternal relationship is unknown.

IMPRINTING AND ANACLITIC IDENTIFICATION

Anaclitic identification might be related to imprinting and the theories of Lorenz and others discussed in Chapter 8. In this idiom one could redefine anaclitic identification with the caretaker in ethological terms. If we are to regard identification as a learning process and try to relate it to the two-stage development of learning outlined in Chapter 12, then we have again the problem of explaining how the first steps in this learning process are started. Imprinting could be invoked as providing a non-set-influenced learning. It is pre-primed and is the initial "fuse" that sets in motion the whole process of identification.

Imprinting, it will be recalled, provides both a mechanism for the establishment of ties to specific individuals (usually the parents) and also by generalization from these initial parental ties to the species as a whole. This being so, imprinting might be seen as the precursor of all the effects subsumed under identification. The set-influenced learnings, or second-stage learnings, that are involved in identification cannot occur unless imprinting has provided the preliminary stage-one conditions.

It will also be recalled that imprinting is pertinent to both parents, who need to imprint to the child, as well as to the child. Hence parental imprinting is salient to the development of the nurturant relationship, discussed more fully elsewhere, as an essential element facilitating the identification process.

IDENTIFICATION WITH THE AGGRESSOR

The concept of identification with the aggressor has already been mentioned. It raises certain problems, however, and these should now be examined. One question is whether it is a necessary concept at all.

It has seemed to some psychologists that the behavior of hurting another can not be acquired by social learning from an adult who is himself aggressive. This is because an aggressive person usually punishes rather than rewards the behavior of another; this is especially true in the case of the aggressive behavior of a child and the response of an aggressive parent to such behavior.

Most of the instances of identification with the aggressor given in the literature are of the acquisition of "negative" traits (as judged by middle-class morality), such as aggressivity itself. Such attributes could be eliminated by fiat, simply by defining identification in terms of positive traits only, but because the negative qualities of one group or culture might be the positive ones of another, this might not be a satisfactory manner of escaping the dilemma; and even if we make the definition of *positive* culturally relative, we cannot say that only "good" traits are obtained by identification.

A key point in the explanation of identification, as will be seen, is that it depends on a positive and rewarding relationship between identifier and identificand. It could be argued that in some of the clinical instances of identification with the aggressor there could still be a rewarding element involved in what to outward appearances is an unsatisfactory relationship. (Again, "unsatisfactory" is by the standards of mental hygienists.) Other situations that have been cited as instances of identification may be interpreted differently. For instance, Bettelheim's observations in concentration camps (1943), where inmates have been said to "identify" themselves with the guards and have acted in the same brutal manner toward their fellow sufferers, could perhaps better be interpreted by some other mechanism. Identification seems to be a universal phenomenon, and it then becomes difficult to understand why not all but only a minority of the inmates took on the characteristics of the guards. It might be more accurate to consider the behavior as the expression of a preexisting potentiality. All human communities (it is to be feared) contain individuals who would sadistically exploit their fellows. As Bettelheim (1943) and Frankl (1959) have said, survival under concentration camp conditions demands a tenacious hold on what Allport would call the *style of life,* the central unifying core of personality. For the majority of people, we trust, this style is such that it does not demand the sacrifice of others, but there are some in whom the style of life is brutish, though this fact is hidden under normal conditions of civilized living. The wheel of fate made some of them guards of concentration camps and some of them inmates, and circumstances were such as to show the true character of each. Perhaps it was not a case of one group identifying with the other but of both groups revealing their common style of life.

Returning to the question of identification with the aggressor, there is a need to clarify the concept. Stoke (1950) has recorded the case of a lad, Frank, who had difficulties in his relationships with his aggressive father when the father returned from active service after the war but who yet showed a pattern of aggressive behavior similar to that of his father. This might readily be interpreted as an instance of identification with the aggressor, but Stoke also mentions that Frank had shown clear signs of aggressive reaction to frustration even before the father returned, so we could regard this situation as involving the common expression of a similar trait that may have been genetically determined in both rather than being dependent on one individual learning it from the other. Had he not been reared apart from his father, we might have supposed that Frank learned his pattern from him, and it could be that other apparent instances of identification with the aggressor (and of plain identification) are really examples of the genetic transmission of traits and not of transmission by example.

This mechanism may be illustrated by a study by Poffenberger and Norton (1959), who found that the attitudes of college freshmen toward mathematics reflected the paternal attitudes, but those students who were "close" to their fathers were no more like them in attitude than those who were "distant." Such a finding is inexplicable if we regard "attitude to mathematics" as a phenomenon of identification, but it can be explained genetically. There is evidence that numerical ability is inherited (Carter, 1932), and, furthermore, some form of sex linkage appears to be involved. Whether or not attitude to mathematics is entirely independent of identification cannot be decided on the available evidence, but there is reason to suppose that genetic factors may be the more crucial ones.

A further possibility is that in some cases it is a misjudgment when a parent or other model for identification is viewed negatively. It might generally be assumed that if a man beats his wife, he does not love her; he would be judged negatively by most social scientists. Yet in Czarist Russia, we are told, if a man refrained from beating his wife she assumed she had lost his affections (things no doubt are different now). In other words, it is not always easy to assess how a given interpersonal pattern of behaviors is seen subjectively by those involved, but this subjective view, rather than the objective facts that the social scientist believes he records, is presumably the crucial one. The parent judged negatively by the scientist may in fact be a more positive figure to the child and may supply sufficient gratification to be rewarding to him. It could even be that the needs of a masochistic child might be satisfied by a sadistic parent and thus provide a basis for reward in learning theory terms. Indeed, Stoke (1950) gives an example of a mother-daughter relationship that could be interpreted in this way (though he does not interpret it so).

The upshot of these arguments is that identification with the aggressor may be in some instances a misnomer and that an apparent or real correspondence of traits in two individuals can be explained by mechanisms other than learning. However, identification may result in the transmission by learning of both positive or negative traits (those culturally desirable or undesirable), but when either occurs, the same mechanism, to which rewards are crucial, is involved. The term *identification with the aggressor* implies an unwarranted value judgment on the part of the psychologists (that is, unwarranted from the subjective viewpoint of the identifier), and because there is redundancy in the expression, it should be dropped.

FACTORS IN IDENTIFICATION

Stoke (1950) describes the following factors that influence identification:

1. The biological fact of sex and its predisposition to some forms of behavior
2. The social pressures on children to identify with their own sex
3. The degree of affection accorded to the child by the person with whom identification is attempted
4. The extent to which the child's needs are gratified by this person
5. The degree of acquaintance that the identifier has with the identified person
6. The clarity of the role of the person with whom identification is attempted
7. The attitude of influential people toward this person
8. The capacity of the child to be like the person with whom he is to identify
9. The temperament of the child in relation to the person to be identified with
10. The existence in the child of strong needs that conflict with or coincide with the pattern provided by the model

The first factor implies the assumption that for some kinds of behavior the process of identification is easier when the identifier and the model are of the same sex because they already have a basic potentiality in common. (This is a special instance of factors 8 and 9.) This factor is reinforced by the second factor —by the pressures that society place in the same direction. The third and fourth factors both refer to rewarding ones in identification, and the assumption, by Stoke, Mowrer, and others, that reward is the important element in identification leads to theoretical difficulties when one considers the sort of process often called *identification with the aggressor*.

The fifth factor is one having a high face validity and it also corresponds with the clinical evidence to be discussed in another section. Degree of acquaintance implies amount of actual face-to-face contact, and J. P. Scott (1963) has suggested that rather than affection being the important factor in the formation of social relationships, prolonged contact is the only crucial one, the nature of the experiences in these contacts, whether rewarding or punitive, being immaterial. This opinion is based upon an unpublished animal study by Fisher (quoted by Scott) and would require further confirmation before it could seriously influence the theory of identification being discussed here; if it is confirmed, then some modification might be called for, but a possible explanation that would reconcile the two points of view might be that *any* social relationship is rewarding in certain circumstances. Under conditions of deprivation, values change, as when university undergraduates in sensory deprivation experiments repeatedly ask for a recitation of "Mary Had a Little Lamb," such banalities becoming "rewarding" when compared with continued silence. Clinicians have stated that children, or some anyway, find punishment preferable to being ignored. Some of the brainwashing techniques seem to depend on a reversal of the more usual evaluation of what is "punishing" and what "rewarding." A further point emerges from the experiment by Bandura and Huston (1961) in which the acquisition of aggressive patterns of behavior was independent of whether re-

lationships with the model were nurturant or nonnurturant, while other patterns did depend on nurturance. It appears that different patterns might require differing conditions for their acquisition. Scott supplies insufficient details of Fisher's experimental technique for one to judge whether either or both of these possible explanations could be applied to his data.

A number of studies do show a positive relationship between nurturance and degree of identification (P. S. Sears, 1953; Payne and Mussen, 1956; Mussen, 1961; Lynn, 1962; Mussen and Rutherford, 1963; R. R. Sears, 1965b). Even though a warm and positive emotionally tinged relationship may not be the only factor involved in identification, it would seem to be one of considerable importance to the process. There is an extended discussion of the *dependency theory* in relation to identification in R. R. Sears et al. (1965), together with experimental data on the topic. This question will be taken up again later, and it is sufficient for the present to point out that the parents' satisfaction of the child's dependency needs creates an affective climate that fosters identification. Conversely, failure to supply dependency satisfactions in general hinders identification.

Where the nurturant relationship is with the parent of the opposite sex, it may encourage opposite-sex identification (Nash, 1965; R. R. Sears, 1965b), though this is a statement requiring some qualifications, which will be made later.

On the sixth point, the clarity of the model role, one of the questions that arises is whether the model for identification must be physically present or whether an absent or even mythological person may not form a model. Diamond (1957) quotes the case of a young man whose father had divorced his mother when he was two and a half and over the years the boy had heard his father discussed disparagingly by his mother and his grandmother, who saw his father as a selfish and shiftless character. This was the model the boy had accepted for himself, and he in turn saw himself as irresponsible, especially in relationship to his own wife. This boy's "acquaintance" with the absent father was apparently extensive, though by proxy.

While it is feasible that absent persons or unreal ones may provide a model for identification, one would expect serious limitations in their effectiveness. A fantasy figure can provide only fantasy rewards and place only fantasy restraints. There may be a danger that instead of the identifier becoming like the model, the model is made to fit the needs of the identifier. On the other hand, some of the heroic characters of television and motion pictures display a consistency that is almost unearthly and that it is certain few parents could match. These models are never out of temper with their audience, nor do they frustrate them; they may have advantages. Apart from anecdotal evidence from clinical studies, such as that quoted above, there seems to be little in the literature on the role of incorporeal figures in identification, and this would seem to be an area for further study.

The idea in Stoke's seventh point—that the attitude of influential persons toward a potential model may affect the course of identification—is one having at least face validity and probably some genuine validity also. Stolz et al. (1954) and Baxter et al. (1964) are among the investigators who report evidence that the attitude of the mother toward an absent father materially affects the course of the child's relations with him on his return and hence affects identification with him. The mother is no doubt an influential person in these matters even when the father is no more absent than is customary in our culture. Some writers, for example, Slater (1961), have suggested that identification with the father takes place only through the mother. While this might possibly be a common state of affairs, there is no good reason for regarding it as a necessary one. The statement is a reflection of the matricentricism of the child-rearing practices of an industrial society rather than a statement of the natural ordering of things.

The eighth and ninth items in Stoke's list are really the same thing. The capacity of a child to be like his model is an aspect of identification often overlooked in the literature, and Stoke has been apposite in drawing attention to it. It is a factor that can either hinder or aid the process or can give a spurious appearance of identification where the mechanism is genetic rather than learned (though it may often be both).

The case of intelligence is an obvious example of an innate capacity that may influence the extent to which a child may be able to identify with certain of the parental attributes. A dull girl may be hindered in her identification with her bright mother, whereas her more intelligent sister may readily be in accord with her mother's intellectual qualities. However, it is to be questioned whether intelligence is crucial as a factor, because it is the early years (after infancy) that are of greatest importance in the development of identification; there is no experimental evidence on this point, but one may suspect that in general intellectual factors in parent and child are of small significance at this time. Identification is a conative as well as a cognitive phenomenon, and in the earlier years the affective elements probably predominate. In later years, of course, consonance between parent and child may be furthered by intellectual similarities or dissonance created by differences, but broad matters such as sex-role identification will already be established. This is not to deny that in particular cases intelligence may play a crucial but indirect part (as when a parent rejects an obviously retarded infant and thereby hinders the identification process), even in matters, such as sex-role identification, to which intellectual factors are largely irrelevant. On the average, however, differences will be less extreme and perhaps not noticed for some years.

The range of behaviors to which genetic mechanisms are important is reviewed elsewhere. There are a number of temperamental traits, such as "emotionality" (a broad and in some respects inaccurate term), that are inherited and that can influence the degree of likeness in personality between individuals. Such traits can both lead to similarity independently of identification and also increase the ease of identification between two individuals sharing the trait. Because parents and their offspring tend to have similar genetic equipment, they will show some traits in common even without identification operating, but the fact of this communality will also tend to facilitate identification when it occurs. For this reason identification between related persons might in general be easier than that between unrelated ones, and may be so quite apart from other extraneous factors that may retard identification between the latter.

It is not infrequently claimed that in modern Western society parental roles lack clarity—because, for one reason, male and female roles are not so clearly differentiated as they are in some cultures. As a consequence of this the roles of the father and mother in relationship to the child are less clearly demarked. While there does not appear to be any direct experimental evidence on this, it is to be assumed that the clarity with which a role is presented does affect the efficiency of identification, for there is a great deal of evidence in other learning situations that ambiguity in what is to be learned retards the learning process. If sex roles are indistinct, then sex-role learning by identification may be handicapped. The consistency with which the model displays other aspects of personality will presumably influence the ease with which the identifier acquires these aspects.

Referring to the tenth point, one important area of corresponding needs that we might consider in the present discussion is that mentioned in the first, the boy's "need" or inherent tendency to develop in a masculine way and the girl's "need" to develop femininity. This is dealt with more fully in a later section. One instance of a contrary "need" would be this same tendency, in the boy, that makes identification with his mother more difficult (and correspondingly for the girl with her father). This will also be elaborated.

IDENTIFICATION AS A LEARNING PROCESS

Among the early psychologists who attempted to apply learning theory to personality development and the acquisition of social behaviors was Holt (1931). He tried to explain social learning in terms of conditioning. He pointed out that the responses made by an infant may stimulate not only others but himself; the baby *feels* his bodily movements, he *sees* his hands move, and he *hears* the sounds he makes. Holt also noted the repetitive character of much of the infant's behavior, as seen in babbling, for one example. He conceived the notion of reflex circles in which the response-produced stimulation reactivates the neural pathways just fired and the behavior is repeated and the habit is thereby strengthened; a behavior pattern is acquired. If then another person provides the same stimulus (says "dada," for instance), the reflex is again triggered, and the infant manifests the same behavior: He appears to imitate the action. Of the several dissatisfactions with such an account, the most damaging is that it does not provide for cessation of an action; there is no explanation why the infant does not go on uttering dada's until it drops into exhaustion.

Another theory of imitation is that proposed by N. E. Miller and Dollard (1941), who acknowledge their debt to Holt's pioneering work in this field but try to produce a theory that avoids the shortcomings of his. In the Miller and Dollard theory the chance coincidence of similar actions is the first step to imitative learning; one individual happens to be doing the same thing as another at the time a drive is reduced or a reward given. These authors illustrate the argument by the example of a young boy learning from imitation of his older brother; their father (so the illustration goes) was in the habit of bringing candy when he came from work. The older boy would listen for his father's return and run to get his candy; the younger, not having yet associated the cues perceived by his brother with the reward, would remain playing. One day, by chance, the younger boy was running behind his brother when the latter perceived the father's return; the sophisticated one changed direction and ran to greet his father, and the naive child followed him: Both were rewarded. On subsequent days the younger showed increasing tendency to run when the older ran to the father, and each time he was rewarded; he also began to run whenever his brother did, even when the father was not about; he had learned to imitate his brother's actions but had not learned the cues to which his brother was responding.

Miller and Dollard called this kind of imitation "matched-dependent behavior"; that is, the behavior is like that of the model but is dependent for its stimulus on him and not on the cues that stimulate the behavior in the model. They distinguish a more highly evolved type, copying, in which there is a deliberate attempt by the imitator to mold his actions on those of the model. The advantage of imitation is the economy of effort it brings, because solutions to problems can be achieved by its use without the trial and error necessary to unaided attempts. Whereas the Holt explanation of imitative learning depended on the principle of contiguity, that of Miller and Dollard was based upon reward —on the reduction of a drive. These authors all use the term *imitation* to cover what we are calling *identification* as well as imitation more narrowly defined. The next author to be considered, Mowrer, does not explicitly make the distinction either. He uses the terms *identification* and *imitation* interchangeably, though his discussion implies the acquisition of qualities rather than motor acts. Lazowick's distinction of imitation and identification (1955) has already been noted, but the criticism of his position perhaps illustrates how difficult it is to maintain the distinction.

Mowrer (1950, 1953) has proposed a two-factor theory of learning in which there are two distinct processes, *sign learning* and *so-lution learning*. Sign learning occurs through contiguity or conditioning as elaborated by Pavlov, and Mowrer sees it as having some relationship (not very clearly specified) with the activity of the autonomic nervous system and the visceral-vascular systems. The learning of feelings and attitudes is mediated thus. Solution learning exemplifies the law of effect formulated by Thorndike and elaborated by Hull, and by its means are acquired the instrumental response patterns usually called *habits*. This kind of learning involves a relationship between the CNS and the skeletal muscles.

Mowrer has produced evidence that he interprets as showing that emotional responses (viscerovascular reactions) depend for their acquisition solely on the principle of contiguity, reward being irrelevant. He has found experimentally that fear is learned by the temporal coincidence of a signal and the *onset* of a painful stimulus rather than with the cessation of such a stimulus as was predicted by Hull. Hence sign learning is the operative principle in situations involving the acquisition of emotionally toned mechanisms. Reward reinforces only overt skeletal behaviors or their symbolic equivalents; therefore solution learning as such is applicable exclusively to behavior of this type. The appearance of solution learning of emotional responses may be obtained in certain situations, but here it is a contiguity element, not the reward, that is effective, and hence solution learning is not strictly involved.

One of the basic assumptions of the two-factor theory is that not only does the organism learn solutions to problems but he also learns problems. The organism is motivated by primary drives, and also by secondary drives that are acquired on the basis of association, by the paired presentation of two stimuli, the original and potent one and a new and neutral one. The individual's experience includes both types of learning, sign learning giving him fears, aversions, appetites, and other secondary drives. Experience also includes solution learning whereby the individual tries to find ways of reducing, satisfying, or avoiding the primary and secondary drives. Through solution learning the organism can profit from the fact that some of its responses produce beneficial results while others do not and can select those that are effective and discontinue those that are not.

As a special case of two-factor learning Mowrer (1950) proposes an alternative theory of imitative learning that compounds the theories of Holt and of Miller and Dollard. He describes Holt's theory as monistic, with *contiguity* as the key factor and *reward* ignored. Although Miller and Dollard explicitly mention four factors as essential to learning, Mowrer correctly describes their theory as monistic also, with *reward* as the key factor and *contiguity* neglected. Both theories suffer disadvantages, which Mowrer believed could be avoided by the use of both factors of contiguity and reward.

Mowrer also supplies a concrete instance to illustrate his theory, this time from observations on talking birds. With hopes of finding some clues to the psychology of language, he delved into the writings of bird-fanciers, who have found that to teach a bird to talk one of the first prerequisites is that the bird should like the teacher, who must feed it, tend it, and caress it. He found no evidence of an innate or instinctive drive to mimicry, for the bird that is treated impersonally does not imitate the voices it hears. (What it does possess innately is a vocal and neural apparatus that makes the memorization and reproduction of human sounds possible, and most species of animals lack this apparatus.)

The Holt theory is inadequate to account for the "talking" of birds on the basis of iterative reflex circles, because reward seems to be an essential factor. On the other hand, although the Miller and Dollard theory invokes reward, it, too, is inadequate; it requires that the bird happen to make a response (e.g., "pretty polly") and get a reward at the same time as it hears another organism make the same response. This assumes the thing it tries

to explain: How does the bird learn this improbable response in the first place?

Mowrer suggests that the learning goes through two stages. In the first the bird, because of the association of the trainer with reduction of thirst and hunger drives (and possibly because he is associated with satisfaction of social needs too), comes to like the presence of the trainer. The sights and sounds (in this context the latter particularly) of the trainer become secondarily rewarding, this occurring through contiguity learning of the Holt variety, or, in Mowrer's terms, sign learning with its viscerovascular component. (The reward that is apparently present in the situation is irrelevant, the temporal relationship being the crucial factor.) The second stage involves learning of the kind suggested by Miller and Dollard, or solution learning in Mowrer's terminology. The appearance and appurtenances of the trainer have become, by the process described, secondarily rewarding to the bird. Of the various characteristics of the trainer, the sound of his voice is the only one that the bird can call up for itself. Any sound resembling that of the trainer is secondarily rewarding, and by trial and error the bird may, in its repertoire reminiscent of the trainer, select and perfect those; no direct cooperation from the trainer is necessary (though presumably it may facilitate the process), and for this reason Mowrer calls the process *autistic*. When the bird has acquired, on this basis, some elements of speech, these elements may have instrumental value; for one thing they may tend to encourage increased attention from the trainer and from other humans as well.

In this new statement the key-word is *generalizes;* generalization and the concept of mediation as put forward by Mowrer would seem to have important relevance to the understanding of a number of aspects of human behavior, including identification. Another important feature of the theory is that it allows for the facilitation, extinction, or inhibition of behavior without the necessity of that behavior actually occurring. Mowrer cites a number of the studies that support this view, and a more extensive review has been given by Thistlethwaite (1951). It is this that makes Mowrer's proposal more attractive than that of Lazowick (1955), already cited. This idea is useful in explaining some other developmental phenomena that otherwise would be inexplicable. The idea that organisms can learn only by doing is too restrictive and makes too mysterious the emergence of some behaviors that may be learned, not innate, but that have never previously been performed by the individual. (For instance, the manner in which the behavior, toward his spouse or his children, of a long-dead father may reappear in his son, who obviously as a child had no means of practicing these roles nor after his marriage had any opportunity of direct learning.)

Mowrer uses mediation as a hypothetical construct by which we can make the transition from simple behaviors to complex symbolic processes. He discusses the idea that latent learning is dependent on mediation (and indeed *mediated* learning might be an alternative term); the transfer of training, or generalization, is mediated by a common element, which is stimulus similarity.

Since proposing the original two-factor theory in 1950, Mowrer made further revisions, and ten years later Mark III of the theory was produced (Mowrer, 1960a). In brief, he decided that solution learning is a special instance of sign learning, so the two-factor theory turns out to be one-factored in the sense that only one type of learning is proposed, but it remains two-factored in that there are two types of reinforcement. These are *incremental* and *decremental* reinforcement. (The terms are rather confusing, because, unexpectedly, incremental reinforcement refers to the type involved in punishment; that is, it induces drives toward avoidance behavior. Decremental reinforcement is associated with reward and tends toward drive reduction.) Secondary reinforcement of the same types are important to the theory.

Mowrer (1960b) has discussed his excursions into the psychology of avian speech in the light of the revised two-factor theory. The new statement of the process seems essentially similar to the earlier one but differs in certain respects: through conditioning the words uttered by the trainer in association with a primary reinforcement (feeding or petting) become secondary reinforcers (of the decremental type), and they then generalize to the stimulus provided by the sound as made by the bird itself. This does not require the bird adventitiously to make the sound in association with a reward before the process can start (as Holt's theory did), for the bird acquires the habit of uttering a particular sound by hearing it made and not of necessity by actually making it.

LATENT LEARNING AND IDENTIFICATION

The notions presented here lead us to a consideration of a paper by Bandura and Huston (1961), who have looked at identification as a form of incidental or latent learning. In an experiment involving nursery school children the apparent task was the learning of a two-choice discrimination problem, but in the course of demonstrating the task the experimenter performed some distinctive actions (e.g., marching across the room, saying "march, march, march") that were quite irrelevant to the solution that the child was to learn. There was a marked tendency for the children to reproduce these actions as well as perform the required task. In spite of its title, this study concerns imitation and not identification, but, as discussed earlier, similar learning processes for the two are being temporarily presumed. It is likely that incidental learning provides the mechanism for much identification, and it is, in fact, probably true that much more is gained by this means than by direct ones.

In a study based upon the Bandura and

Huston hypothesis, Mussen and Parker (1965) showed that the amount of incidental learning of the task-irrelevant behavior of their mothers was greater in girls who had a nurturant relationship with her than in those lacking such a relationship. However, in direct imitation of task-relevant actions there was no difference. We may assume that much of the learning involved in identification is not of actions immediately relevant to some specific task but of the overtones surrounding it, and which reflect attitudes and other personality traits. Thus a son may *imitate* the actions of his father in painting a wall, but he also may *identify* with the gusto and enthusiasm the father brings to the task or with the father's attitude that this is a menial task unworthy of his attention. This mainly unconscious incidental learning is dependent on the relationship with the father in a way that mere imitation is not.

INDIVIDUAL DIFFERENCES IN IDENTIFYING

If identification involves learning, it might be expected that groups in whom the capacity for learning is reduced will show less of it. This is supported in a study by Biller and Borstelmann (1965), who found that both boys and girls in the educable range of retardation showed greater appropriate sex-role preference than retardates in the lower trainable range. At the other end of the continuum of intelligence, Kohlberg and Zigler (1967) found brighter children in the four to eight range to be developmentally more advanced in measures on a male-female scale and in sex-role attitudes than were children of average intelligence. These authors believe that their results support a cognitive-developmental theory of psychosexual development rather than a libidinal-maturational one, or a social-learning theory.

An interesting feature of the Biller and Borstelmann study is that the relationship between IQ and sex-role preference was stronger for boys than for girls, supporting the idea that learning is more important to the former in their adoption of sex role.

As suggested elsewhere (Chapter 11), there are individual differences in the capacity for incidental learning that are related to early experiences. There are no doubt differences related to genetic factors also.

As already insisted, males are better equipped for learning male-type behaviors than are females and vice versa. However, for the variety of reasons mentioned, individual males and females will differ in the ease with which they identify with models. For example, the boy who is high in dominance (a genetic trait) will identify more readily with a father also high in this trait than will his brother who happens to be low in genetic dominance. Similarly, the boy who is high in those genetic aspects of masculinity will more readily identify with the masculinity of his father. Or put another way, the boy high in genetic masculinity will develop these aspects of behavior with less exposure to a masculine model; his learning is more efficient and requires less environmental sustenance. Similarly, such a boy will identify less readily with a feminine model; he would have to overcome more innate resistance to this model. The boy low in genetic masculinity, on the other hand, requires more intensive learning experiences from the environment and will more readily form feminine identifications if these are what the environment provides.

In this view, individual differences in identifying stem from a number of variables, some constitutional and others environmental. In each case the outcome of childhood identifications is a complex interaction between these diverse influences.

IDENTIFICATION, POSITIVE AND NEGATIVE

There are numerous examples of children acquiring attitudes and attributes from parents, and these we may call positive identification. Ausubel (1959) spoke of a kind of negative identification, or *desatellization* as he called it. There is the well-known phenomenon of adolescence in which certain attitudes are adopted that are directly in opposition to those of the parents; attitudes to Hippies, long-haired boys, premarital sex, and war are the current examples. Shall we see a puritanical revolt of our grandchildren against the sexual laxity in the attitudes of their parents, the present young generation?

CROSS SEX RELATIONSHIPS

The father has an important part to play in the development of femininity in the girl, as is evident from a number of studies reviewed by Nash (1969). It may be questioned, however, to what extent *identification* with the father enters into this picture. Rather, it may be suggested, the girl uses him as an available and mature male on whom to practice and develop the social techniques of femininity she acquires genetically and by identification from the mother. Actual identification with the father would hinder this process.

It is difficult to say whether a similar situation applies to the boy. A number of studies suggest that identification with the mother may underlie the development of homosexuality (Nash, 1965; Nash and Hayes, 1965), but this identification normally occurs only when the father is absent or inadequate. Most theories of identification assume that the boy, like the girl, starts off with an identification with the mother, though this assumption has been questioned earlier in this chapter. Whether the boy needs the mother as a female toward whom he acts as a male and practices masculine roles is an open question. Mussen and Distler (1959) and Mussen (1961) have suggested that where a boy's relationships with the father are sound, his relationship with the mother is not particularly influential on the development of masculinity.

If one takes the independence-dependence, active-passive, or dominance-submission dimensions as elements in the masculinity-femininity interaction, there is an obvious difference in cross sex behaviors between boys and girls. The girl can practice the dependency-passive-submissive aspects of femininity with her father, but the boy has greater handicaps in practicing independence-active-dominance behaviors toward the mother. This may be especially true in a matricentric society in which the mother plays an authority role. This could explain why peer-group activities play a more crucial role for the boy than for the girl (Chapter 18). It could be claimed (even if not proved on present evidence) that girls practice feminine behaviors toward males (especially the father) at an earlier stage of development than boys practice masculine behaviors toward females. The boy initially practices and develops these behaviors in a masculine milieu, only later directing them toward females, at which time they no doubt undergo refinement. Psychoanalytic theorizing notwithstanding, it might be asked to what extent overtures toward the mother are important in the boy's development of masculinity and whether adolescent relationships with girls are not more critical. The boy's first social-sexual approaches to girls are markedly influenced by his paternal relationships.

EPILOGUE

At several points in this volume it has been suggested that individuals function most efficiently when they operate according to their basic potentialities. In this view the male functions best in masculine ways and the female in feminine ways. The male operating in "feminine" ways, as in some forms of homosexuality, introduces a stress, and while to do this may be within the capacities of the highly modifiable human organism, it is not done without effort and is wasteful of energy. Similarly the female can function in "masculine" manners, but again only with greater effort than is required for feminine operations.

This may seem obvious enough when applied to specifically sexual behaviors and to the social behaviors that stem from them, but there is some evidence to support the notion that more general effects may be found. For example, Mussen (1961) found that adolescent boys who were well identified with their fathers and high in masculinity were more exuberant, calmer, smoother in social functioning, and generally happier and more relaxed than boys low in masculinity. This smoother functioning of high masculine boys might be expected to result in a greater efficiency that generalizes, and Mutimer et al. (1966) have shown a relationship between father identification in boys and achievement in reading. Anastasiow (1965) found the more masculine boys in a kindergarten to be superior to less masculine ones in a number of both cognitive and social measures. *They were also rated by their teachers as more ready for promotion to grade 1.* In this grade, they performed better in reading. (This is, incidentally, a nice example of self-fulfilling prophecy and the manner in which the social environment selectively reinforces appropriate sex-role learning.)

It is possible, of course, that these more masculine boys were superior in some more fundamental respects of which masculinity and achievement were both results. There is more research needed here to tease out the lines of influence, but at least it is a reasonable hypothesis that boys who are allowed to develop fully their masculine potential will operate more efficiently in many other aspects of functioning.

There are not many data on the corresponding situation with girls. The Mutimer study showed achieving girls to be mother-identified, which is consistent with the theory that fem-inine girls will function generally in a more effective manner. It is interesting in this connection to note Piaget's observation that emotional disturbance in children hinders the acquisition of mathematical concepts. In other words, a high-order cognitive operation is handicapped by a generalized inefficiency of functioning such as is represented by a neurosis.

In the view put forward in this chapter, identification is a learning process that plays an important role in developing certain innate tendencies of the child. Some of these predispositions are sex-linked, and the same-sex parent plays a crucial role in their development. Indeed, these sex-related aspects of development tend to dominate the question, so that identifications with the opposite-sex parent have influences on development that cast a baleful effect on a wide range of behaviors.

It is not claimed that identification is a vehicle for the fostering and transmission of sex-related behaviors only. It is the mechanism of transmission of the cultural heritage as well as a factor in the full emergence of innate behaviors. Included in this cultural heritage are certain sex-related matters, ranging from customary patterns of coitus to attitudes to premarital sex but also including much more. As well as attitudes to love, there are those to war, work, money, race, witchcraft, democracy, and so on. Even attitudes to the pill are part of a wider set of beliefs that includes sex but much else besides. If this chapter has tended to give some emphasis to identification as a mechanism for the elaboration of innate tendencies to behavior, it is because these aspects are generally neglected. That identification is also a vehicle of transmission of nonbiologically determined behaviors is acknowledged, but this is well discussed in other works.

Eighteen

Some Social Influences on Personality Development

The main concern of this book has been the biological influences that direct development. In taking this standpoint a whole range of social influences that are important in developing the personality have been somewhat underplayed. These influences have, in fact, been the main concern of psychology, in North America at least, for the past several decades. By its own bias, this book may serve as a corrective to this bias.

This chapter is not intended as a systematic account of social influences on development, but rather as a discussion of certain topics relating to cultural and family influences that strike me as relevant to the major themes of this work. In particular it examines the idea that the form of human cultures is to a marked degree influenced by the biological nature of man.

One has to distinguish between social organization by instinct and modification of individuals by culture. Ants, as but one instance, have a social organization, but it would be farfetched to suppose that this imposes itself on the personalities of the individual insects. One might, however, see the beginnings of an influence of "culture" on

"personality" in such phenomena as the pecking order of hens. Dominance hierarchies are evident in many species, including the primates (Katz, 1953).

Among primates there are some clearer indications of culture and of cultural influences on personality. A study by Imanishi (1957) of the Japanese monkey from the Kyoto Primate Research Group refers to the acquisition of status in the dominance hierarchy by young males from association with their dominant mothers. The troop consists of an inner group of dominant males and their attendant females (who attain status by this association) and an outer group of low-status members, mostly young males. With the females in the inner circle are the infant monkeys. Although most or all of the females are in the central "in-group" of the troop, a dominance hierarchy exists among them, and the lower-dominance ones tend to occupy the fringes of the inner circle.

A feature of these troops is that each shows patterns of behavior peculiar to itself (Imanishi, 1957; Kawamura, 1959), so that one can speak of cultural differences among them. Some of these are in diet itself; others are in food-related behavior, such as is the case with one troop that customarily washed sweet potatoes before eating them; this is apparently quite unusual. (The articles by Imanishi and Kawamura seem to imply other patterns, too, in which there are differences from troop to troop, but these are the specific examples given.) Now it is the in-group members that most consistently show the shibboleth; the males in the out-group do not display the troop characteristic so markedly, and they are much more likely than "inner-groupers" to leave the troop to join another. Imanishi (1957) has suggested that the concept of identification is applicable to the case. He says that through their identification with the mother the offspring of high-status females have direct access to the leaders (who display most strongly the cultural peculiarities of the troop), are able to identify with them also, and thus become acculturated.

The question arises as to whether one can admit this as an instance of identification as the term is used in Chapter 17. If, of course, one is to be thoroughgoing in acceptance, then in the light of the discussion of sex-role identification (p. 424), one would expect these mother-identified males to be homosexual, but perhaps this is being too anthropomorphic! It could be argued that the behavior is merely imitation, the acquisition of motor patterns, and not the acquiring of sets or principles as in identification. There is insufficient information in the published reports to be decisive on this point, and in any case the distinction would be no easier to decide than in the case of human identifications. But from the available descriptions it would seem certain that this is imitation and might even be an infrahuman instance of identification.

Culture may therefore be seen as a feature of life having discernible existence below the human level, though it is a mechanism of adaptation to the environment which is so highly developed in man as to be one of the major marks of the species.

It is being assumed that man is by nature a social species. That is, man has what Mc-Dougall called "gregarious instincts" that cause him to seek affiliation, to group with others of his own kind. Some of the earlier manifestations of these innate behaviors have been discussed in previous chapters—the imprinting phenomenon, for instance.

A number of social scientists have taken the view that human personality is infinitely malleable and that given the required kind of environment, any sort of personality can be produced. Ruth Benedict (1934) might be taken as one of the earlier proponents of this argument and one whose influence is still strong. This view is widely accepted among psychologists.

One of the most well-known and forceful statements of the relationship between culture and personality is by Margaret Mead. (She actually uses the term *temperament,* but because the word is being used in this book to mean the biologically determined traits from which personality is developed, it is preferable to use the term *personality,* which is what she really refers to. Mead, in fact, implies that temperament, as conceived here, does not exist.) She studied three New Guinea tribes, the Arapesh, the Mundugumor, and the Tchambuli (Mead, 1935). The aspects of personality that interested her related to masculinity and femininity, and she sought to show that these are the result of the cultural expectations of men and women. The Arapesh is a "feminine" society in which both males and females display the traits of this sex. In consequence the children grow up in a milieu that produces these traits in both boys and girls. The Mundugumor, on the other hand, are all "masculine," and girls grow in an environment that suppresses their femininity. The Tchambuli show (she says) a reversal, the men being "feminine" and the women "masculine."

In discussing the questions raised by such formulations, it is necessary to distinguish two matters in this area. One is the process of acculturation, by which the individual becomes a conforming member of his society, accepting its value systems and absorbing its traditions.

Here the emphasis is on socialization, on the group and on the individual only as a member of it; interest is focused on the group rather than on the individual.

The other process involves the development of the individual within the society and the influence society has on his personality. It deals with the individual's genetic potential, his particular experiences, and the interaction between these and the pressures of society.

The former assumes a standard individual and focuses attention on the features of the society; it is the sociological approach. The latter attends more to the individual, and is the psychological approach. The two are, of course, complementary and not clearly separable in practice. The anthropologist takes the first of these approaches. Mead, for instance, seeks to show how the Tchambuli culture makes men within it "feminine." It is seemingly implied that *all* men are feminized and all equally. The psychologist, on the other hand, should attend more to individual reactions to this feminizing milieu, describing its influence on the growing child but also noting and attempting to account for the fact that individuals will differ in their response to this influence.

In considering anthropological data, the psychologist finds a somewhat different realm of discourse. Throughout much of this book the attempt has been made to draw on relevant experimental data. Anthropology is not an experimental science, and there is a marked element of subjectivity in the reports of even the most competent of anthropologists. The difference in idiom will be apparent in this chapter.

PRINCIPLE OF CULTURAL RELATIVITY

One of Ruth Benedict's contributions to social science is the principle that human behavior in any culture can be understood and evaluated only in terms of the particular assumptions and values of that culture. This is a valid and very useful scientific concept, though Benedict herself weakened it by her assumption that cultures can be adequately described by simple characterizations, such as, for example, the "paranoid" Dobu. She describes Dobuian culture as a kind of hell on earth in which no one trusts anyone else and in which life is spent in perpetual suspicion, leading to cruel retaliation.

I had occasion twice in one week to meet passengers from ships at the ocean terminal in Sydney. One ship was the *Southern Cross,* from Southampton, and the other was the *Galilai Galileo* from Milan. In the one case the dockside was crowded with a throng of people, babies and grandparents, laughing, weeping, shouting. Men embraced and kissed; women shrieked and rushed into passionate greetings. There was tumultuous confusion. From the other ship the passengers passed sedately down the gangplank, in orderly groups; there were waves of the hands and smiles, polite handshakes, and impassive greetings such as "How nice to see you again." The reader should have no difficulty in telling which scene corresponds to which ship.

The Benedict-Mead approach to culture notes the dockside behavior of the Englishman and sees him as controlled and reserved; it epitomizes the British character in these terms. Any such simple characterization of a culture is false. If one says that Americans are competitive, smoke cigars, and drive Cadillacs, an Arapesh might believe it, but few North Americans will be misled by the statement and take it as a true epitome of the culture of the United States. The Ford Motor Company would certainly not accept the idea that all *its* customers are deviants.

Many anthropological studies have tended to point to the differences among peoples, often with surprise and delight at the strange mores and exotic customs that one can find. In emphasizing the novel, it has been overlooked how similar human beings are the world over, after one looks beneath the differences that catch the eye and excite the imagination.

It is perhaps an illustration of cultural factors in science that Piddington, an Australian-anthropologist whose initial training was in the British tradition of psychology, has been among the strongest critics of the supposition that cultures can be epitomized in the ways illustrated above or that culture is so absolute a determinant of personality (Piddington, 1957). In saying this, one is admitting that cultural factors are significant, and it is by no means the purpose of this chapter to deny it. What is intended is to bring the question into perspective.

Piddington (1957) has pointed out how Mead's fieldwork in the particular three cultures she describes is poorly documented and really provides no warrant for the conclusions she draws. The human organism, as Piddington insists, is subject to certain universal determinants, and the variability of personality development is limited by the inborn physiological character of the species. Because man has certain universal biological needs and tendencies that society must recognize and cater to, human societies tend to take on a universal pattern.

Culture is the medium within which man satisfies his biological needs. Basically, these are the needs for food and shelter, necessary to survival of the individual, and sex, necessary to survival of the species. Beyond these minimum survival needs there are certain needs that though not essential to bare existence are a part of the human condition. The need for affiliation, or belongingness to a social group, is one of these. One might regard this as part of the genetic inheritance of a social species. Allied to these are the satisfaction of broader reproductive needs.

BASIC UNIFORMITY OF MAN

This chapter makes the assumption that fundamentally men are alike the world over.

There is one human species (Harrison, 1958). By *alike* one does not mean to imply that all men are the same; a major emphasis of this book has been the individuality of men. What is implied is that the range of variation is approximately the same in all groups of men and that insofar as we are aware there are no important racial differences in psychological functions. Man is the same, though men may differ.

It cannot be denied, of course, that there are physical differences among races quite apart from obvious ones such as skin color. There are, for example, differences in the distribution of blood groups in various parts of the world; American Indians have a particularly high incidence of group A, but so do other peoples as far separated as Scandinavians and Australian aborigines (Harrison, 1958). The important thing is that while there are local differences of incidence of this kind, the ABO blood groups are universal. Men are so much alike physically that the practice of medicine and surgery can be essentially similar the world over.

Almost nothing is known about the distribution of psychological traits, but it may be assumed that here, too, there is universality, without much likelihood of unique traits being possessed by any race of man. The uncanny tracking ability of the Australian aborigine is almost certainly a matter of special training of standard perceptual equipment rather than the possession of some peculiar faculty, just as pitch discrimination in musicians is a question of training. There are, of course, individual differences in the basic ability for pitch discrimination, and some could never develop this skill to the highest degree. It may well be that there are individual differences among Australian aborigines in the perceptual processes underlying tracking ability, and it may even be that in the rigors of life in this genetically isolated population there has been some degree of natural selection so that there is an unusually high proportion of individuals carrying the upper ranges of this trait, but we may assume they do not possess a unique trait found nowhere else.

It could be that among the Dobuians there is an unusually high proportion of individuals carrying the genetic basis of paranoia (assuming there is such a basis), but because a society of the mentally ill would be unlikely to survive, one must presume that most individuals in Dobu are in fact sane and that even if they are under some stress from their sick relatives they function much like other men in similar circumstances.

Nearer home, the racial origins of whites in North America with ancestors from Europe are so mixed from generations of migration and intermarriage that genetic differences between ethnic groups are minor, even if some of these tiny differences are magnified by certain cultural considerations. This is not to deny that there may be special pockets of genetic concentration. For instance, the more energetic and intelligent inhabitants of Dogpatch may tend to migrate, so that there is downward selection in those that remain. But even if Dogpatch has a rather higher proportion of idiots than is found elsewhere, idiocy is not peculiar to it.

DYNAMICS OF SOCIAL CONFORMITY

As Piddington points out, many of the dictates in the mores of a society run counter to individual desires, such as lust, ambition, greed, or jealousy, while others impose long hours of irksome effort and demand courage or self-sacrifice. In spite of the fact that most individuals are from time to time tempted to evade or even defy the rules of their society, only a very small proportion of people actually do so, and the vast majority are conforming to the normative system of their culture.

In primitive communities a number of factors contribute to social conformity. One of the most important of these is the pressure of public opinion. Such societies are usually small and compactly organized, and everybody knows everybody else and his business. There is little privacy, and no member can err without the serious risk of detection. Even though no material results may follow transgression, there is still the loss of esteem, and other intangible pressures of public opinion will keep a man conforming. But further than this, public opinion may take many practical forms, not only in outright punishment of unconformity but in ostracism, which may even be so severe as to force an offender to commit suicide or to retire to exile. Added to this, a man may be dependent on the goodwill of his neighbors for assistance in many of the tasks of life, such as the heavy work of building a house or other undertakings that cannot be done alone.

In addition to public opinion, practically all primitive communities have a system of mythology that embodies the magicoreligious beliefs of the society. Such mythology usually accounts for the manner in which the world came into existence and often contains legends about the formation of the local landmarks and geographical features. Not uncommonly these beliefs place the particular culture in a specially favored position relative to the rest of mankind, and often the myths explain how the gods at the formation of the world gave certain advantages to these people; the idea of being a chosen race is not uncommon in primitive thought. Usually firmly embedded in this mythological system are maxims or rules for the conduct of life, and these contain the moral code of a particular people (Piddington, 1950, 1957).

Coupled with such a code and mythology, there is often some idea of supernatural beings who may punish wrong doing. Not infrequently these are the ancestors, who keep a watch on the present generation and may be angered by transgressions or failure to preserve the way of life that has been handed down. The concept of sin as an offense against the supernatural powers is not uncommon, and the fear of visitation by sickness or calamity has a normative influence. Incidentally, few primitive societies have ideas of hell fire, and damnation in the hereafter; in most cases they think in terms of immediate here-and-now punishment for wickedness.

A further normative factor is the belief in sorcery and witchcraft, which is very widespread among primitive people. Chiefs and headmen and deceased ancestors in particular are frequently believed to have powers of sorcery or at least have access to sorcerers who will perform at their behest. The authority of chiefs is not infrequently supported by such beliefs. By these various means, the adult is induced to conformity, and this conformity is essential to the welfare, and often to the survival, of the community.

It is of interest to note the fundamental belief in causality revealed here. Man seems to need to explain, and the scientific attitude has given a whole new approach to causality. To what extent the adult can fully outgrow the early "magical" concept of causality described by Piaget is an open question. Even trained scientists can show traces of magical thinking, outside the laboratory even if not within it.

It is often said of our urban society that it is anonymous and that the pressure of public opinion is less than in those communities where everybody is known to everyone else. There is some truth in this, and for many people one of the advantages of city life is being allowed to mind his own business. This attitude can, unhappily, go too far, as in the instance of the young woman in New York who was murdered in the sight of some thirty or forty neighbors who declined to become "involved."

This is not to say that urbanized man is entirely immune to public opinion, and indeed most people are said to remain "other-directed" (Riesman, 1950). The numerous experiments of the type that set up "stooges" to aver some patently incorrect statement (i.e.,

that an obviously shorter line is longer) show that a considerable proportion of people, even intelligent ones, will disavow their own judgments in the face of contrary group pressures. The way in which advertisers will use the statement that eight out of ten people prefer their product as a criterion of its excellence is another illustration of the importance of conformity in modern living.

The fact is that most people belong to at least one group whose opinions matter to him and that molds his attitudes, and indeed "public opinion" may be seen as too vague and abstract to be strongly influential. In primitive communities public opinion is really the beliefs of recognizable and nameable individuals and, because communities are generally small, includes almost everybody with whom the individual has contact. There is no mass of faceless people.

Out of the faceless mass of our cities, most individuals have some group with faces whose opinions matter to him. But the opinions of these subgroups may not be those of society as a whole and may in some instances be highly deviant from the vague corpus of "public opinion," as is the case in a delinquent gang.

Public or group opinion is not, of course, the only force tending to conformity. Fear of legal reprisal is another, though even here it could be argued that the law is but the codification of public opinion.

The primitive child grows up in an environment in which he has a quite intimate contact with adults, most particularly, of course, with his own parents. He absorbs the cultural norms of his society not by abstract tuition but by observation of events around him. The child does not learn the techniques of his society by writing things in books or history by sitting in a school room. He learns to fish by fishing, he goes with his father and assists him in the task, and he quite soon realizes that if the task fails he may go hungry; most primitive children know the meaning of hunger. Similarly, he learns the history of his people as he walks with his father, and his father points out to him natural features and the legends that go with them.

He learns the rules of etiquette of his people by observing his father performing them, and in a similar fashion a girl learns from the mother the feminine code of conduct. Almost everything that a child learns he does so as part of some activity directed toward ends that do not primarily concern the young. Thus he learns incidentally, as part of the task in helping his father obtain the family's dinner, to make a net or to fish.

Aside from actual participation in the activities of the adults, play forms an important learning situation for children in primitive societies, as in our own, but such play is usually patterned much more on the activities that the child will actually perform as an adult than is the case in our culture. Much of a child's play in our society involves activities, such as cowboys and Indians, that he will never perform in real life, and there is more unreality in our children's play than there is in that of primitive children.

Because primitive education involves participation in adult activities, children acquire at an early age the adult values and outlook with regard to these activities. Many of these are concerned with obtaining food, and where technical incompetence may mean an empty stomach, the motivation to learn is high. The need for imposed discipline is little, because failure to learn carries its own punishment.

An important educational institution in many primitive societies and one of the few in which people outside the family may take part are initiation ceremonies. These are more common for boys than for girls and not infrequently involve telling the child the secret folklore of which he may yet have been kept ignorant. Sometimes this is done by a priest or some other individual outside the family. The initiation may also include ordeals to test the boy's fitness for manhood. Not infrequently the badge of initiation consists in some bodily mutilation, such as circumcision or the making of scars or other distinctive marks that will last throughout the rest of life. Because initiation gives tangible witness to the laying aside of childish things and the taking up of adult status and responsibilities, it strengthens identification with the adult culture and its values.

An element in the social conformity of the child is thus his identification with socially conforming parents. Primitive societies, at least in pre-culture-contact [1] days, were characterized by a uniformity of public opinion. A feature of more complex societies is a diversity of opinions. In one family a child may absorb the opinion that birth control is a sin, while in another the child is exposed to the notion that it is a social duty. In primitive cultures (again in the primeval state) the corpus of public opinion of the juvenile peer culture is not markedly dissonant from that of the society as a whole, whereas we in Western society are facing the gap between the mores of the generations. However, the teenagers of our culture *are* subject to pressures to conformity, even if these pressures are less well controlled by the parents.

Child rearing in our culture in recent years has been changing. Revisions in the kinds of advice on child training given by the U.S. Department of Labor Children's Bureau have been reviewed by Wolfenstein (1951). She shows a shift between 1914 and 1951 in the content of the *Infant Care Bulletin* from a puritanic ethic in the earlier editions to a "fun morality" in the 1940's. The early issues gave strongly worded warnings about the damaging effects of autoerotic practices and the necessity of rigorously preventing them, by tying the infant's hands if need be. There were stern admonitions not to respond to mere attention seeking crying and the necessity of strict routine. In general the idea that anything that is pleasurable to the child is necessarily sinful was strongly implied if not actually stated.

By the 1940's the concern over masturbation

1 See pp. 430-431.

had subsided, and the mother was recommended to regard this practice lightly; distraction to other things by presenting a toy is the kind of action suggested. The idea that bathing, feeding, and other aspects of care can be fun for both the child and the parent was introduced, and the whole tone of the recommendations were more liberal and relaxed.

As Wolfenstein points out, one does not know how closely the recommendations of the bulletin represent expert opinion, nor does one know how much they were followed by parents. But because there was certainly this kind of movement from a Calvinistic strictness toward a liberal permissiveness in society as a whole over this period, it seems likely that similar changes did take place in child-rearing practices, probably irrespective of the bulletin, which merely reflected a cultural trend.

An essential function of society is to provide a stable platform on which child rearing can be rested. A stable platform is not necessarily a motionless one, but it should not move so violently or unpredictably that all sense of direction is lost.

There is repeated evidence in the anthropological literature of the effects of culture contact on indigenous societies, and these effects are usually deleterious in their short-term effects (see, for example, Piddington, 1957). Whether the long-term effects are constructive is open to debate. Historically, the modification of one culture by another has gone on for a long time, and British society is but one of many instances of a culture built-up from a series of contacts with alien ones.

In the past century or so the pace of expansion of Western technological culture has steadily increased, until today there is probably nowhere in the world a culture entirely untouched by it. In general the short-term effects have been a disruption of the old cultures. In particular, the authority structures of these cultures have usually been weakened and but rarely replaced immediately by effective new ones.

The struggle between the generations is probably a universal phenomenon, common to all past and present societies. It is, however, especially marked at times of social change when the sanctions that supported the authority of the older generation are removed. Thus in some societies (and not only illiterate ones) the father stands in a priestly relationship to his family and is regarded as an intermediary with the gods. When these gods are slain and replaced by none, or replaced by the god of the missionaries, who does not operate through the father, the father's hold may be weakened. The extent to which his hold over his children is based upon this authority or on affection will be one factor determining the outcome of family relationships at a time of cultural upheaval.

Today we have a culture in rapid change —but no clear indication of the direction of change. We also have a dead God, or so some theologians are telling us. The impact of the death of God on children and on their rearing has not been described; it may have had little effect. The churches and Sunday schools are, it is reported, increasingly well attended, though the extent to which they perform a social rather than a religious function is difficult to say; perhaps the two functions are in any case inseparable.

In previous generations men praised God for their creation, though an impartial observer of the lives of many of them might certainly wonder why. Children, in turn, praised their parents for bringing them into the world to enjoy its blessings, though again the observer might find this surprising when these blessings are counted. The rationale was, of course, that this life gave the opportunity of eternal bliss.

To what extent this still holds true today is not really known. Certainly some children now do remind their parents that they did not ask to be born, and they are aware that contraceptive devices have placed the onus of decision on the parents. For many, the idea of God's will governing the conception no longer holds. We really do not know how many children regard their existence as an unnecessary accident or willful error, but if this attitude is at all widespread, it will obviously color relationships between parents and children. It is clear that the modern family can survive its present stresses and face the dimly seen changes of the future only if it is held together from within by ties of affection. External or supernatural sanction cannot be relied on.

An essential element in any culture is a code of rules to govern life, and without such a code there cannot be enough stability for a culture to exist at all; anarchy is an impossible form of human society. It is repeatedly stated today by Jeremial speakers and writers that morals are in decay. One might question whether this is so and ask whether morals are now more honest. We are perhaps attempting to replace an authoritarian code with a personal one in which life is no longer governed by an arbitrarily defined set of rules backed by religious authority but by rules for which each person becomes his own authority.

A code of this kind is much more difficult to live by than is an authoritarian one, and it might be questioned what proportion of the population can in fact live this way. Certainly it must impose a strain on children, for Piaget has shown how young children use a highly concrete and arbitrary definition of delinquency: Wrong is that which is punished.

In due course children begin to question the given code by which "wrong" is defined. However, it is a notable feature of teenage rebellion that it tends to replace the abhorred rules of the "square" world by rules of its own that are often no less arbitrary and no more original.

The fact is, and children will readily enough recognize this, that order is essential to a tolerable human existence. It has also been a fact that man in the past had not reached a stage of social evolution and intellectual development in which a rational authority could be widely accepted. Most men have depended on mythological sanctions to support their belief in the code that defines

order, though almost invariably these mythological sanctions have been backed up by temporal ones. Whether we are now evolved enough to accept rational authority is open to question, but we are now, ready or not, being forced into an era in which a rational code has to be adopted and transmitted to children.

Any code based upon a reasoned appraisal of man's potential and respect for individual dignity will bear a recognizable resemblance to the essential elements of the Judeo-Christian ethic and other religious systems (as distinct from the dogma of a church). Taking into account the fact that established religion has had in the past to pitch its teachings to the level of an illiterate mass of peasants rather than to the small group of intelligentsia, its emphasis on magical beliefs and superstitious sanctions is understandable, even if not commendable. In our culture, as in others, the church has also repeatedly been made a political tool, which has occasioned many of its more sordid episodes, among which has been the suppression of thought and the maintenance of the status quo. Be that as it may, much of the teaching of Judeo-Christian thought makes very sound social sense, and at its best this has been presented in a highly aesthetic manner. Perhaps the moral instruction of children in the future should be in a historical perspective, outlining man's thinking about his moral nature and leading to the culmination of this thought that we now adopt, not superstitiously but because it represents the most advanced code for a humanitarian society.

METHOD VERSUS CONTENT IN CHILD REARING

The assumption that it is the method rather than the content of the process of conditioning that is primarily important in determining personality is implied in many educational theories. According to this view, *how* the child is taught rather than *what* he is taught is the important shaper of personality. Anthropological observations do not particularly support this view, because, for example, the over-indulged and physically undisciplined children of Samoa grow into good Samoan adults, while the Chaga child, subject to vigorous discipline reinforced by physical punishment, grows into a respectable Chaga adult. What is taught appears to be more important than the method of teaching. As Little (1950) has pointed out, we find instances of the same types of adult character being produced in cultures whose child-rearing practices are quite different. If there is an inevitable causal relationship between child-rearing methods and adult personality, we would expect to find that similar child-care practices lead invariably to similar types of adult personality, but in fact we find that similar adult character types may be found in societies having different child-rearing techniques and that similar child-rearing methods may lead to different types of adult personality.

There are some obvious qualifications needed to the statement that content is the important matter in child rearing. Neither the content nor the method of Chaga upbringing will prepare a person to fit adaptively into a Samoan village, and the Samoan rearing would ill-prepare an individual to take a place in Chaga society.

Furthermore, it may be in many cases that method and content are inseparable; in the terms of Marshall McLuhan, the medium is the message. The Chaga are a militaristic people by necessity, for their neighbors are the Zulus, and the former have to protect themselves from this aggressive group. They also have to protect themselves and their cattle from lions and other predatory animals. Thus their whole philosophy emphasizes discipline and fortitude, and aggressive forms of punishment can be seen as part of the content as well as of the method of socialization. The Samoans, on the other hand, can afford to be easygoing. They have no aggressive neighbors and no lions; the climate is mild, and while there might be occasional famines, the obtaining of

food is not usually arduous. A more relaxed way of life and a relaxed child rearing practice go together.

Another point is that while it may be that the same results can be produced by differing means, it is still possible that some means are more efficient than others. Moreover, it is hardly necessary to say that the content of some cultural teachings may be undesirable. The teaching of the Aryan myth in Nazi Germany was undesirable by any scale of values that abhors genocide and deplores militarism.

CHILDHOOD IN OTHER CULTURES

The comparative approach to the study of child rearing has in principle a great deal to offer to our understanding of how children become adults integrated with their society. In practice the lessons to be learned are often ambiguous.

We are too close to the society in which we are embedded to form an unbiased opinion of it or even to perceive it accurately. I have commented on an instance of this (Nash, 1965): Our society has a mother-centered system of child rearing, and many psychologists seem to have taken it for granted that this is the only possible form of child rearing. Some, indeed, have ignored the father so completely that one might wonder if they are aware of the facts of life. But one brought up in a culture that makes this assumption that the mother is the agent of child rearing can quite readily accept this assumption as the *only* possible manner of carrying out such practices. To be exposed to cultures that do not make such assumptions can therefore be revealing.

Another problem for the psychologist in our stratified society is that he generally is from the middle classes himself and has difficulty in perceiving life as it is for those in other strata. Our society, in fact, is too vast and complex to be seen whole. The same is true of many of the greater non-Western cultures. One might go to India or China with the proper frame of objectivity and freedom from preconceptions from his own childhood but still be hopelessly confused by the diversity within these ancient and complex societies.

Primitive societies offer a more manageable object of study. Communities are commonly small enough to be seen whole and also sufficiently homogeneous for one to make reasonably valid statements about the society as a whole. A rough definition of *primitive* is "illiterate"; these cultures are without a written language in which knowledge and tradition are passed on by word of mouth. Despite the fears that psychologists might entertain about the changes that may be introduced into tradition by this method of transmission, anthropologists seem convinced that such shifts are not important because the tales embodying the history, folklore, and beliefs are well known to all, and errors in recounting are corrected by the hearers.

There are now few cultures in the world that have not been contaminated (if that is the appropriate word) by Western culture. It was unfortunate that the earlier anthropologists, who had the opportunity of studying cultures having little if any contact with our own, did not interest themselves more in the children within them. Many did, of course, provide incidental observations of children, but they mostly tended to concentrate on special events such as initiation ceremonies, and few gave a detailed and well-rounded account of child-rearing practices and interactions between parents and children.

Among some of the earlier accounts of childhood in primitive societies is that of the African Bantu by Kidd (1906). Other studies, of African communities, that include data on children are by Fortes (1949) for the Tallensi, and Raum's descriptions (1940) of childhood among the Chaga, a particularly vivid account, because he himself grew up as a boy among these people, his parents being missionaries.

Studies of children in Pacific societies include Hogbin (1931) on education in Ontong, Java, and his observations on the first eight years of life in Wogeo, New Guinea (1946). Malinowski (1927, 1929) gives some data on child care in the Trobriands, which is particularly interesting in that these people did not recognize biological paternity, yet valued social paternity highly. Margaret Mead's book (1929) on Samoan childhood is well known; it gives more data on girls than on boys.

There are a number of studies of indigenous North American societies, which include that by Dennis (1940) on the Hopi. References to others are given by Whiting and Whiting (1960).

In the symposium Six Cultures, Whiting (1963) presents detailed accounts of child rearing in a variety of societies, which show graphically that there can be marked differences in childhood experiences in different cultures. But what these studies do not tell us with any clarity is what results these experiences have on adult personality. Of course, we can infer that the adults of each community will be the kind of people that will give this kind of child-rearing experiences to their offspring, and they were presumably brought up this way themselves, but this inference gives only a very hazy picture of the adult personality.

An interesting experiment in child rearing in a designed culture has been provided by the kibbutz. Using Rorschach and Thematic Apperception Test (TAT) responses as a measure, Rabin (1961) compared kibbutz-reared adolescents with a group reared in Israeli villages of the more conventional type. He found no difference between the groups in adjustment; the kibbutz group was certainly not less well adjusted, he claims, and was rather more spontaneous. The kibbutz adolescents were less "self-motivated" and not so ambitious as the other children. They were also more rigid in their sexual morals than the normal-family-reared group.

It is also interesting to note that there was evidence of less conflict with the parents and less involvement with them in fantasy productions. These findings were also supported in a study of ten-year-old children (Rabin, 1959) in which the kibbutz children also had more positive attitudes to the parents and the family. It might be that in a social setting where parents are freed from the more irksome aspects of parenthood discipline, for instance, but on the contrary are encouraged to spend a couple of hours each evening with their children, there might actually be more time, and more effective time, spent together in a relaxed atmosphere than in families where contact is less structured. Malinowski's observations (1927, 1929) of the Trobriand Islands, where fathers were not regarded as biological kin of their children and were not responsible for their discipline (which is the duty of the mother's brother), are in keeping with this finding for the kibbutz children. There, too, father-child relations were free and friendly.

A discussion of cross-cultural studies has been given by Holtzman (1965), who outlines the history of this approach to understanding personality development and mentions some of its shortcomings. He points out that many of the cross-cultural studies consist in an unsystematic replication of American research in another literate society, and the methodological problems related to sampling and examiner variability are not commonly controlled. Also, the difficulties introduced by linguistic differences of meaning and cultural variation in response set are insufficiently appreciated.

He illustrates a more systematic approach o cross-cultural comparison by a study of children involving a long-term coordinated program between Austin, Texas, and Mexico City, Mexico. A number of tests are used, including the embedded figures test, the WISC, and objective personality tests. Unfortunately for present purposes this study is an ongoing one, and no results are yet available. A point that he does mention is that in Mexico there is a marked emphasis on sex roles and that conscious efforts are made to rear girls in a feminine manner and to develop masculinity in boys. In view of the suggestions, made elsewhere in this book, that this is a desirable aim of child rearing, data on the results of this emphasis will be of great interest.

CHILD CARE IN AN INDUSTRIAL SOCIETY

Despite a higher level of technology, something akin to the primitive system of child rearing exists in some literate communities today. It existed in Europe before the Industrial Revolution and in the early days of Pre-Revolutionary America. In these agrarian communities the men tended the horses, tilled the fields, carted the produce, and built walls and ditches. The women made the clothes, cooked and made preserves, and did the dairy work. There were no schools, except for the upper classes, and the boys early joined their fathers and the girls their mothers. The trades were commonly carried from generation to generation, boys learning the skills from their fathers.

Our culture has been dominated for the past 150 years by the Industrial Revolution that has dictated its form and modified its child-rearing system. The cooperative family economy with its sex division of labor and its inbuilt education was replaced at first by a system of near-slavery in which men, women, and children all worked (but usually separately) in the factories and under such conditions that must have made any real family life almost impossible. Gradually legislation removed the women and children but left the father to work long hours in separation from his family. He became the sole, but virtually absentee, economic support for the family. The mother cared for and educated both the boys and the girls. Thus the matricentric system of child care evolved. Compulsory education in due course further modified the family's role.

Characteristically, Mead (1954) sees in the

emphasis on the mother's role an antifeminist plot, men fostering this notion in order to confine women to the nursery and the home. She makes the valid point that most primitive societies do not demand such an exclusive relationship but provide care by many people. She suggests that our insistence on close mother-child ties may be a good preparation for lifelong monogamous marriage. However, it is perhaps more reasonable to see this matricentric system as an accidental by-product of the Industrial Revolution rather than a planned policy. (One might even claim that men do not desire lifelong monogamy and therefore deplore the situation as much as Mead, but that would take the argument beyond the scope of this book.)

It is evident that the more primitive method of child rearing has much to recommend it from the psychological point of view. But it is equally evident that it is quite unpracticable in a highly developed technological society. If, however, one is to consider how a technological society might be modified to provide the optimum child-rearing system possible within its structure, then there may be something to learn from a study of other cultures.

If, as is insisted in other places in this book, one element in optimum development is to maximize sex differences and to develop masculinity in males and femininity in girls, then the primitive system is ideal. Indeed, one can see it as a direct adaptive response of culture to the differing natures of men and women.

SEX DIVISION OF LABOR

According to Sahlins (1959), the sex division of labor and the establishment of the family on this basis is one of the critical evolutionary advances of man over the other primates. It is important among the factors that made human cultures possible.

It has been insisted at several points in this book (especially in Chapter 10) that cultures have different expectations of males and females because man's observations of the natural world show him that males and females *are* different. These expectations are not some arbitrary imposition perpetuated throughout history by cultural inertia but a dynamic expression of a biological fact inherent in the nature of men and women. Just as no realistic society could be based upon the premise that all men are identical, that is, that any individual could occupy the role of any other without the change being noticed, so it is unrealistic to suppose that male and female roles are interchangeable.

Sex differences in humans show up in more different contexts and areas of behavior than in lower animals (e.g., in cognitive style), but the differences found are probably less sharply distinct than in lower species. This greater range of sex differences has had its influence on the evolution of culture.

All human societies, in fact, recognize these differences. Some have exploited them to the disadvantage of women as judged by certain ethical philosophies. However, as Piddington (1950) points out, most primitive societies do not judge the question on an ethical basis. The differences are accepted as a fact of life, and the woman is valued both for her economic contribution and as a person.

Primitive economies are essentially cooperative, and a practical reason that has fostered the extended family is that it increases the cooperative labor force and makes possible many tasks that a nuclear family could not undertake for itself. Furthermore, *all* members are integrally involved in the economic (i.e., food-getting) activities, and in most parts of the world concerted efforts, at least at certain times of the year, are necessary to survival. Thus even the children play a part in the economic well-being of the family and make a significant contribution to the work. How early children are involved depends on a number of factors, chief among which is the amount of labor necessary to survival. Because of the absence of mechanization and crude techniques of agriculture or hunting, survival is generally a struggle, and there are few parts of the world where Rousseau's noble savage can lead an idyllic life of ease, plucking an effortless living from a bountiful nature. In most places the struggle is keen and constant, and the harder it is, the earlier do children have to become productive members of the economy.

The widespread sex division of this labor assigns different tasks to men and to women. Just what these tasks are differs from culture to culture, but in general men are assigned the heavier and more dangerous tasks that require the greater physical stamina which they generally possess. Women perform the lighter tasks, and in particular those that interfere least with the demands of pregnancy and suckling (Piddington, 1950). The strictness with which the sex division is enforced differs a good deal from culture to culture. Some tasks are more or less neutral, to be performed by anyone who happens to be available at the time; some child-care tasks are often included here. In others the division is more formal; for example, gardening may be considered a woman's job, but the men do the heavy work of clearing the land initially. Not uncommonly there are strict sanctions reinforced by mythological beliefs that make certain tasks rigidly exclusive. For example, in certain Polynesian societies canoe building is an exclusively male occupation; for a female, even a young girl, to so much as touch a canoe before it is completed brings disaster and the building is abandoned (Firth, 1936). Similarly, among most of the Bantu of Africa, cattle rearing is a strongly male occupation. Evans-Pritchard (1940) has described this in detail for the Nuer.

Similarly, there are certain tasks that are exclusively feminine. An interesting and revealing case in point is in connection with cattle rearing among the Nuer. Although men own, pasture, and tend the cattle, only women can milk them, and terrible consequences are expected to follow any attempt by a male to perform this chore. One effect of this taboo is to guarantee the woman her place in society. A wife who is displeased with her husband may refuse this service, and he has shamefacedly to beg a female relative to perform the task for him. In the Polynesian culture, the women have an essential part in the ritual attending the launching of a new canoe, and without this feminine blessing the men consider the craft ill-fated and will refuse to sail it.

One effect of the sex division of labor is that men and women have clearly defined roles to play in society, and the child grows up in a milieu in which these roles are unambiguously presented. They are acted out before his eyes.

Another consequence follows from the child's involvement in the economic pursuits of his parents. Because most of these activities separate the sexes—the man goes to the sea to fish, the woman to the fields to plant—the boy leaves the feminine care of his mother to follow his father in his work. In many societies he will commonly do this before he is really able to make a serious contribution (and when indeed he may even be a hindrance) because the father considers it his duty to train the child. There are no specialist teachers, and in general parents teach their own children (sometimes a classificatory parent, for instance, the mother's brother, may have a duty to impart certain information, but even here the duty is within the family). Thus the boy acquires the greater part of his knowledge directly from his father and the girl hers directly from her mother, whom she accompanies in her activities.

The consequences of this to identification and sex typing need no emphasis. Each child from an early age has a clear conception of his role as a male or her role as a female. The young boy can say, "I am a man, and I build the canoe." To which his sister replies, "And I am a woman, and it must have my blessing."

One fact of primitive communities is the

general absence of formal schooling. While there may be some degree of specialization found in such societies, it is the exception, and generally each man is his own Jack-of-all-trades. Among these trades is that of teacher to his children, and the general rule is for the children to learn directly from their parents much if not all of the knowledge and skills they require in life (Piddington, 1950). For this reason child rearing is less diluted by nonfamilial influences, and one might suppose that similarities between parents and children are for this reason somewhat stronger than in societies that bring nonrelatives into child rearing. The sex division of labor extends into the parents' roles as pedagogues teaching tribal lore and technical skills.

A Sex Division of Contribution to Society?

It would be an abandonment of the reality principle to advocate that our society should divide the occupations between the sexes and say that only men can do some and only women others. What is more appropriate is to ask that when men and women do the same job they bring to it a different approach and produce from it distinct contributions to society. In some occupations this may be difficult. If a woman cannot bring some unique contribution to engineering, then she is misplaced in this profession. This may be, indeed, why so few women do enter it, because in this profession she cannot really fulfill herself as a person, for being a person involves being a woman or a man, and an occupation that does not allow scope for both sexes to develop within it should not be popular with the disadvantaged sex. (Of course, the feminist may insist she *has* a unique contribution to make to *any* profession, including engineering; then let her define it.)

It is true, unhappily, that there are occupations that give little scope for the individual touch, male or female. It is difficult to see how the female bank teller can bring to the job a contribution distinctive from her male colleague, unless it is to smile pleasantly at the male clients while he flatters the female ones.

Because we are on the verge of cultural changes in which the tasks that allow no scope for individual contribution will be performed by machines, perhaps we may be approaching a time when most people can have a vocation rather than an occupation. If this is so, then the time is approaching to give earnest consideration to the ideas proposed here and to direct the development of our culture accordingly.

The distinctive approaches of males and females is most evident in the social sciences and in the professions that rest on them. It is perhaps no accident that the representation of the two sexes in these fields tends to be more nearly equal than in some other professions, and it may be that the proportion of men and women in the various occupational groups does represent in a rough manner the extent to which one sex or the other can make a distinctive contribution.

There is, however, one important exception to this, and that is education. Because roughly half the children in school are boys, half the teachers should be men. This is not to suggest that boys should be taught exclusively by men or girls by women. What is suggested is that no boy should be taught exclusively by women (nor, for that matter, any girl exclusively by men, though this, one supposes, rarely happens). In education, above all professions, the two sexes can make unique contributions and in an ideal society would be able to make this contribution each to both boys and girls. This requires as many men in the profession as there are women.

However, our society is far from ideal, and among the nonideal aspects of it is its public educational system. For a long time teaching has been a low status occupation with corresponding standards of pay. Today the pay for teachers, in many places at least, is not too far from other professions with comparable educational prerequisites. But what is still lacking is a selection procedure that will encourage a high quality of intake to the profession. The regrettable fact seems to be that many teacher training colleges are so sterile that anybody with a creative bent and a distinctive contribution to life keeps away from them if he or she is forewarned. When a bright and lively teacher becomes disenchanted with the system as it is, she writes *Up the Down Staircase* and departs for more intellectually rewarding fields. Graduate schools contain many excellent teachers fleeing into other professions. The profession that should be the spearhead or battering ram for the cultural changes our society must make if it is to survive is, in fact, not fulfilling this function, and this is a serious problem. Perhaps it is unfair to lay all the blame on teachers. The present sorry state of affairs is the result of public attitudes, and historically it is these attitudes that have generated the system as it is.

CULTURE OF LEISURE

An important need is that for recreation. One could typify the life of many species of animals as satisfying the survival needs; any time not occupied in their pursuit is spent in sleep. On the other hand, there are many species of animals in which what might be called a recreative need is evident.

Play is a common feature of the childhood of numerous species and is probably universal in the higher ones. This play has a crucial role in the development of motor and other skills necessary to adult functioning. But a feature of most of the highest species is the amount of time the adult will spend in nonutilitarian activities; Huizinga (1955) has suggested that our species might be renamed *Homo ludens*. Leisure for play does, of course, require an environment that provides satisfaction of the basic needs with sufficient ease to leave spare time for recreation, and one of

the assets of a well-organized industrial society is that it does make such an environment.

It is not machinery and technology that make a society great. While society may be founded on the digging of ditches and the growing of turnips, or the production of automobiles and can openers, being only a producer in this sense is not a truly human enterprise. To dig ditches and grow turnips merely to be alive next week to dig more ditches and grow more turnips is an inhuman existence and unworthy of man's potential. The promise of the industrial society—in part realized—is to give man ample leisure, after producing what is necessary to his own and community survival, for the pursuit of more human activities.

This idea of leisure for the cultivation of the arts and for the contemplation of the universe and philosophical consideration of man's place in it is by no means new in human history. The ancient Chinese held this view, perhaps long before the Greeks. However, what is new is the possibility of this being shared widely in the community. Until industrialization, this creative leisure was confined to the very few, who depended on the toiling masses to make their leisure possible. The important social change has been the distribution of greater amounts of leisure over wider segments of the population. When one looks at the standards of mass entertainment, he might well doubt the capacity of the present mass-man to utilize leisure. If he uses this leisure to listen to the caterwauling of banal ditties or to get excited over some fellow hitting a white ball with a wooden stick, one may think he might as well be digging ditches. But we do in fact enjoy a considerable advance over the Roman circuses, because it is probably true that a markedly greater proportion of the population than ever before are using leisure constructively. But even though this proportion is increasing, it is still far too small.

Maybe one day all the menial and repetitive tasks will be performed by machines, leaving all men free for creative and satisfying activity. We have not yet achieved this, and most people still have to earn a living in ways that are not very satisfying. Satisfaction in living must come for most from outside their occupations.

There is an aspect of the trend toward total leisure that needs to be faced once again; it was faced once at least before in human history, in Roman times, and then unsuccessfully. By definition, one half the population has an IQ of 100 or less (the actual figure is slightly more, because of the skew in the distribution). Can this half of mankind fulfill the lofty ideal of creatively productive leisure? Indeed, what proportion of the other half can do so?

The Roman experiment suggests that a society that attempts to amuse masses that are unable to amuse themselves will court disaster. It also seems, from the record of history, that even the small elite of leisured classes tend to become unproductive, however brilliantly they may start. Their activities tend to become formalized into mere variations on traditional themes. And when the Dark Ages were ended by the Renaissance, it was not by the emergence of new ideas but by a revival of ancient Greek ones.

If we can avoid annihilation, we are already on the verge of the leisured culture, and we must add to our growing list of problems the problems of leisure. It is not proposed to discuss this further here, but one contribution the developmentalist must be prepared to make is in suggesting manners of child rearing that will prepare the individual to live in such a culture. This book contributes to this in the general sense by suggesting that when we fully understand man's potential, and can aid the individual to achieve the maximum potential of his being, this fulfilled person will be able to fit comfortably but productively into the culture of leisure.

One of the moral problems for a philosophy of leisure in the past has been that leisure for some could be obtained only by the labor of others. In Greek and Roman times leisure depended on slave labor. At the beginning of the Industrial Revolution it depended on a system that was technically not slavery but in which the conditions of life for the workers were no better and perhaps worse than those for Greek and Roman slaves. We now, we are told, have sight of the technical possibility of escaping this moral dilemma. Whether we can evolve the social structure to do so is another matter.

One aspect of the age of leisure that is especially pertinent here is that it could provide the opportunity for parents really to fulfill their roles, and one highly constructive use of this time could be in having a close and extensive relationship with their children. However, one doubt does suggest itself. The amount that children have to learn in school is increasing rapidly. Are we to replace a situation in which children wait at home for the brief sight of a weary father by one in which the father waits for the late return of his tired children? Perhaps in the age of leisure the adults will once again be the privileged generation.

THE FAMILY

The Family in Culture

Older social philosophers, for example, Lloyd Morgan (1894, 1896), believed that the social organization of early man did not include the family. Human social organization, as they described it, consisted of groups of women and children. The men lived apart and visited the primitive horde only to rape the women. In this uncharitable view of the early male he apparently had no inbuilt feelings of tenderness toward either women or children and no innate tendencies that would predispose him to protect or nurture a family. The present structure of the family, insofar as the father at least is concerned, is thus seen as an acquired cultural characteristic. This is at variance with the view being proposed in this book, that males no less than females have a biological basis for parental behaviors and through the family and child care satisfy not merely the gross sexual needs but other needs that are no less biological but more altruistic.

Another theory of the family implied that originally there was a happy state of primitive communism that extended to group marriage in sexual relations. Within the tribe, any man mated as the flesh or the spirit moved him with any cooperative woman, and the resulting offspring were reared indiscriminately by the community (Engels, 1902). Only later, when the advent of private property dispelled the primitive state of natural collectivism, did the family as we understand it emerge as a feature of social organization.

The fact is that we have virtually no knowledge of early man's social organization, and our information goes back only as far as written records—some four or five thousand years. From what we know of present or recent primitive societies, the family is universally the unit of social structure and possibly always has been, though because there is no evidence it is idle to debate this point. (Although there is no evidence of the Engelian type of social organization in humans, it is of interest to note that among chimpanzees in the wild there is no "marriage" or stable male-female-child unit. These apes live in small groups in a territory and the males copulate indiscriminately with the females [Lawick-Goodall, 1965]. Engel's theory might then have been true of man's earlier ancestors.)

The adult members of the family, who largely shape its character, are themselves in general acculturated members of their society. They bring to the family society's values and assumptions. Thus the family provides a microcosm of the culture, and through it the child is exposed to the wider culture of which he is a member.

The child in our culture is exposed to at least two major acculturating agencies, the family and the school, though in relative importance the former is probably the stronger. Not infrequently there is a dissonance between them, which may adversely affect the efficacy of one or the other, or perhaps of both. One might ask whether it would not be strengthening of the family to have the schools concentrate on academic instruction and the fostering of intellectual skills and leave morality and other matters of cultural transmission to the parents. This is not an easy question. For example, the schools are in some places becoming involved in sex education because parents are not providing it; but even though sex education is obviously desirable, usurping the function of the family is not. Perhaps the answer is to make it clear that this is a one-generation effort, the present generation being given it so that they can do it themselves for their children.

It is worth mentioning, because it is obvious enough to be overlooked, that the family provides not only the immediate cultural milieu within which the child develops, but in general it provides the genetic inheritance of the child also. (The exceptions to this are adoptive families; in some societies, such as the Manus, adoption is widespread and many children in the family are, in fact, biologically unrelated to their social parents. Families composed wholly of adopted children are not uncommon in our society. Despite such exceptions, the norm for human families is for parents and children to be directly related genetically.)

Thus any similarities observed between parents and children may be the result either of transmission by learning or of genetic transmission. In many developing features one has no difficulty in deciding which is the explanatory principle. If a child in a Catholic family recites the catechism and attends mass and confession, one is hardly likely to consider this as an instance of genetic transmission. Some other things one observes might be less easily ascribed. If the child of acrobats starts showing a propensity for balancing and tumbling, is this evidence of learning or of genetic inheritance? It is probably the former, but one cannot be so sure. There is fairly good evidence that a genetic factor underlies superior musical ability; when musical talent runs in families, there is some reason for assuming that genetic transmission is at work, even if it is not the only factor involved. And when a community, such as Vienna, has a considerable number of accomplished musicians, we may have not only a cultural milieu that favors musical interests and aptitudes but also one in which there is a high concentration of musical genes.

Not only may there be special instances, such as the ones cited, of familial genetic transmission, but there are also certain features of human societies that are the result of genetic inheritance common to the species. The fact, to take a very obvious example, that intelligent activity may be seen in all human societies is because this capacity is part of the genetic endowment of *Homo*.

Some writers have suggested that man shares with the animals certain territorial instincts that are not allowed proper expression under conditions of urban living and that one of the stresses of city life is the unfulfillment of what might be called a "private space need."

One might ask whether there may not be an innate basis to some behaviors that are commonly thought to be culturally determined. Obviously in the narrowest sense, feeding behavior is innate and so is reproduction. The need for shelter is perhaps not, in the same sense, for man originated as a species in climates where shelter is not essential to survival. But in many aspects of human behavior one can ask if transmission of customs is purely cultural. For example, modesty seems a universal human reaction. Some of the earlier travelers (and especially clerical ones) were scandalized by the immodesty they imputed to some cultures, but they failed to see the essential modesties that actually existed. Even though some cultures consider a naked female face immodest and others see no shame in bare bosoms, almost all show some kind of reticence, particularly in concealment of the genitalia (and often in the act of elimination), even though in some this may be minimal. One may note that even the most casually brought up children in our society seem to display a natural modesty around the eighth or ninth year (I know of no studies of this, but anyone can verify this by his own observations). The interesting thing is that this is also mentioned at about the same time in primitive cultures, where by our standards adults are casual and relatively immodest, though again there are no systematic data.

An instance of this universal modesty has been given by Whiting (see Whiting and Whiting, 1960), who describes how when he first visited Kwoma in New Guinea, where no clothing is worn, he found himself gazing at the maidens until he noted that he was offending etiquette by doing so. In practice, at a gathering the women sit behind the men. If a man meets a woman on a path, she would step aside and turn her back; if they stopped to converse, the conversation would be conducted with each turned away from the other.

Similarly, the "gang phase" in boys shortly before puberty seems a universal phenomenon, even in those cultures, such as the Trobriands, that impose no obvious pressures on boys and girls to separate. Indeed, it seems that it is the girls who initiate this move into one-sex activities rather ahead of the boys, though actual gangs are less common among the girls.

Are such things transmitted solely by culture, or could they be the expression of innate tendencies that are part of the human equipment? Another feature common to human cultures is the incest taboo, which might also be the cultural embodiment of a biological fact. It is well known to cattle breeders that a bull kept with a few cows loses interest in them but will rush lecherously to a fresh one;

male rats that have copulated to satiation with one female will respond immediately to a new one (Fisher, 1958). Marriage counselors sometimes report (though not always with approval) that extramarital experiences will revive a flagging marital relationship by allowing the partners (especially the husband) to return to a renewed relationship. Some possibly innate factors of this kind were discussed in Chapters 9 and 10.

It seems to be a fundamental fact, of male psychology at least, that the familiar loses in attractiveness. This may be an inbuilt mechanism of birth control and may also have the effect of reducing (if not eliminating entirely) intrafamilial matings, thus forming a biological "incest taboo."

The family thus has three functions. One is to transmit the species-specific genetic characteristics that are common to mankind. Another is to transmit strain-specific genetic characteristics that, as the expression goes, run in families. (These are not always advantageous.) The third function is to transmit the cultural inheritance of the community to which the family belongs.

It should also be mentioned that insofar as the second of these functions is concerned there are mechanisms that tend to ensure that characteristics do not run *too* strongly in families. As discussed in Chapter 3, sexual reproduction in fact ensures *differences* between offspring and parents, as well as leading to some measure of similarity between them. In human communities the incest taboos act to further the dissimilarities (Lindzey, 1967).

Structure of the Family

The family as we understand it consists of a father and a mother, who is married to the father in some manner prescribed by custom or by law, and the offspring of this union. This is the *nuclear family*. It is, of course, variable in manners not directly important to the present discussion, as when there is a second marriage and there are children biologically unrelated to one of the partners.

The norm for the structure of the family differs from what we are accustomed to in most parts of Western society. Murdock (1949) examined over 500 cultures throughout the world and found that the *extended family* was most numerous; in this kind of family the unit is made up of two or three generations. Commonly such families are either patriarchal or matriarchal and also patrilocal or matrilocal. That is, the patriarchy invests authority in the males, and the family consists of a grandfather and his wife together with his sons, their wives and children, and his unmarried daughters. If the society is also patrilocal, his married daughters leave to go to their husband's extended family, while his sons bring their wives from another locality. (Patriarchy and patrilocality usually but not invariably go together.)

The matriarchal family, on the other hand, consists of the oldest-generation woman and her husband, her daughters and their husbands, their children, and the unmarried sons. As already mentioned in Chapter 10, while authority may be ceremonially invested in the woman, it is usually, in fact, exercised by the men.

However, Murdock has argued that the extended family really consists of two or more nuclear families and that even polygamous units consist of nuclear families in which one of the spouses is common to both.

The terms *Western society* and *culture* are used at various places in this book and should be defined: They refer to European cultures (including the U.S.S.R. in general) and those societies in Africa, Australia, and North and South America that are historically derived from Europe. These are admittedly vague terms covering cultures that differ in many respects but that also have much in common, perhaps because of a Judeo-Christian ethic that is a historical core to most of them. Be that as it may, the fact is that a child's experience in an extended family, or in a polygamous family, will be different from that in an isolated nuclear one. In the patriarchal extended family the child's father's brothers all stand in a paternal relationship to him, and they are commonly addressed by the title of father also (this relationship is known as classificatory kinship). He has no cousins, only "brothers" and "sisters." In the matriarchal family he has several "mothers."

The nuclear family exists where the conditions that favor the extended family do not apply. Among the Eskimos the nuclear family is the norm, because available food supplies in any given locality will support only a few individuals, and in consequence families have to move apart to increase their chances of survival. There might be some credence to Engels' view that the nuclear family is the product of our economic system, because it is a feature of societies which emphasize private property and that at the same time have economic systems that favor individual rather than collective effort. However, private property is no less appreciated in extended families. These families do, on the other hand, depend on cooperative effort for economic well-being, especially in primitive conditions where such effort is often necessary to survival.

The persistence of the family as a feature of human social organization is illustrated by the Russian experiment. In view of Engels' influence on Marx, it is not surprising to find in Russia a deliberate attempt in the 1920's to abandon the nuclear family as a bourgeois feature of the capitalist society. Marriage was denigrated and divorce a matter of simple request ratified by postcard. Illegitimacy was abolished by fiat and abortion made free. But by 1935 it was felt necessary to impose a deterrent fee on divorce, with extra penalties for second and subsequent ones. The freedom of abortion was abolished, and by the early 1940's there was a concerted attempt to restore marriage and the family (Timasheff, 1960).

Primitive communism, at least as it applied to the rearing of children, was found unworkable. One of the effects was that the children it produced were unsocialized. After the revolution children were granted rights and privileges above the older generation, but it became evident that a viable society demanded a restoration of parental authority. Whether or not this renegation on Engels' social theories started the movement of the Soviets away from orthodox Marxism is difficult to say; one of the bourgeois notions to be restored was the right to dispose of property at death. Communism had faced the reality principle to the extent of observing that people work better for private gain that they can control and that parental authority is upheld by the right to disinherit. Furthermore, it has accepted the fact that honoring the father and the mother is an essential ingredient to a sound child-rearing system.

It will be interesting to see how the other great experiment in family living will evolve. Spiro (1960) has proposed that the kibbutz is really a "familial" society whose members see each other psychologically as kin. In this sense it is a kind of extended family, though it lacks the authority structure typical of most families of this kind.

One would predict that the reemergence of the nuclear family will be slower in kibbutz society. For one reason, kibbutz living is voluntary, so disenchanted members can withdraw. Moreover, there is authority in the group, if not in the parents as such, so the wilder extremes of the early communist experiment are avoided. Whether this is sad or not depends on one's point of view, but he may suspect that there are a number of factors that would make this style of life fundamentally unattractive to most people, and it is unlikely to become widespread. The nuclear family is a highly viable phenomenon, because it satisfies certain fundamental (and biologically based) features of human psychology. There may already be a shift in the kibbutz, because Gerson (1966) has reported the family there to be similar in character to the modern family, though tending to greater emotional intensity. He noted a marked familial trend in second-generation kibbutz members.

Parental Practices and Personality

There is a considerable literature on parental child-rearing practices as related to the personality of the child. It is not proposed to review these studies here because many of the extant works on child psychology have already done this in detail but merely to discuss some general questions using a few recent studies as a point of departure.

One study of preschool children contrasted the rearing of those whose personalities were described as assertive, self-reliant, self-controlled, buoyant, and affiliative with that of two other groups, one described by the adjectives discontented, withdrawn, and distrustful and the other as low in self-control and self-reliance and as retreating from novel experiences (Baumrind, 1967). Rearing practices were assessed by interviews.

The parents of the happy first group were described as controlling, demanding, communicative, and loving. The parents of the unhappy discontented group were controlling and detached; those of the low self-esteem children were noncontrolling, nondemanding, and warm.

A companion study by Baumrind and Black (1967) studied what they call *competence behaviors* in relation to parents' rearing practices. They found that various aspects of competence depend on parental rearing techniques that are intellectually stimulating and mildly tension-producing; these include making demands on socialization and maturity of behavior and firmness (even punitiveness) in discipline. The parents who demanded self-control and good performance and encouraged independence of action had self-reliant offspring.

There was, however, one of those sex differences in response to similar environmental influences mentioned in Chapter 10. Firm home discipline did not produce dependent, conforming behavior in nursery school by girls, whereas it did so in boys.

Although this study did interview both fathers and mothers in assessing rearing practice, the data are not presented in a manner that enables any clear indication of the separate effects of the four possible combinations of interaction, which is regrettable because this would be a point of considerable interest.

Another study, by Hatfield et al. (1967), investigated only mothers but made direct observations of the mother-child interaction in a standardized playroom setting; the children were from a nursery school and of middle-class families. The investigators concerned themselves with those aspects of maternal behavior that they considered antecedents of child behavior (e.g., reinforcement procedures, maternal pressure, restriction, reward or punishment of aggression or independence, maternal warmth or hostility, and so on). Observations and verbal interchanges were tape-recorded, and behavior was categorized according to a specified rating scale. Child behavior variables included in the evaluation were dependency, independence, warmth, achievement standards, various forms of aggressive behavior, sex-type role, and adult role playing.

Consistency of child and mother behavior was investigated by the split-half method. Consistency was low from one session to the other, suggestive of the influence of differences between the two sessions and situations within each session. Mothers' behavior was less consistent than that of the children, indicating mothers to be more responsive to situational differences.

Certain socialization effects were independent of the sex of the child. Among these, maternal permission for assertive behaviors was associated with independence and warmth in the child of either sex.

There were, however, frequent sex differences in both child variables and maternal behaviors, an important one being greater incidence of aggressive behavior in boys in response to their mother's demonstration of the belief that aggression in boys is an appropriate form of behavior. In contrast, girl's aggression was not rewarded by mothers and led to a type of frustrated dependency.

The analysis of children's behavior in the role-playing situations again revealed two rather distinct patterns for boys and girls; these were related to "masculine" and "feminine" patterns respectively. A factor analysis of the variables involved in this study gives further evidence to support the assumption of the importance of the mother-child interaction (socializing process) on the child's personality.

The kinds of concepts commonly employed in socialization studies has been illustrated by H. Thomae (1965), who in a longitudinal study (in Germany) related certain personality ratings—for example, activity, emotional responsiveness, feeling of security, and so on—to certain social variables—socioeconomic status, integration of family, work of mother, legal status, number of siblings and birth order, displacement of family, and breast feeding. It is perhaps salient that the most significant results related to the vaguest of the variables, that is, socioeconomic status. Whether the child is breast-fed or not and the number of siblings he has are more objective and limited facts, whereas the socioeconomic standing of his family is a vague condition carrying with it a whole gamut of overtones, class mores, and the like. Presumably the vaguer a category, the more likely is it to produce correlations with other variables, just as the vaguer a fortune-teller is in her readings of the palm, the more likely she is to say something that appears significant. If she talks about "crossing water," this could mean anything from a trans-Pacific voyage to a walk on the bridge over the creek at the back of the town. So vague a prediction is likely to be fulfilled, one way or another, whereas a specific statement such as crossing the Vistula is much less likely to be so.

Of course, some of the other variables are only slightly less vague psychologically. For instance, legal status can be expressed in a highly specific manner—legitimate birth or illegitimate. But a whole range of psychological variables attach to the distinction.

Several points may be noted in connection with these studies. One is that highly global child-rearing dimensions are related to equally global personality characteristics in the child. Because *global* is a scientific euphemism for vague, this may be taken as criticism. Another evident point is that there is little comparability between the studies, so we do not know whether the results are specific to the populations involved or have more general applicability. Yet another matter is that these studies show a *tendency* for certain parental practices to be correlated with certain personality attributes of the child, but such a correlation tells us nothing about the *causal* relationship between these practices. One *could* argue that the relationship is entirely genetic: Parents show certain child-rearing behaviors because they are genetically predisposed to them. Because of this genetic predisposition passed on to the children, they show certain behavioral characteristics also. We need not suppose that these behaviors are the same as in the parents, because the juvenile form of an adult behavior may not necessarily be recognizable as such. Of course, no one would argue that this purely genetic transmission really occurs, for the actual outcome of parental practices is surely the resultant of the parents' behavior and the temperamental or biological tendencies of the child (one might ignore for this purpose whether the parental behavior is innately determined or not). Two parents who gain the same label, for example, "controlling," may in fact differ quite markedly in the manner in which they exercise this control, and moreover they direct this control toward children that differ in their temperamental reactivity. In other words, in trying to study parental practices and child personality outcomes, one is involved in a multidimensional field of effects of immense complexity.

Something might be gained from the study of child-rearing outcomes in adoptive families; here at least the factor of genetic communality between parent and offspring is eliminated, so one could argue that transmission is more purely environmental. However, the fact of adoption itself introduces another set of variables, and one still does not eliminate the temperamental reactivity of the child, even if it is genetically unrelated to that of the adoptive parent.

Despite these difficulties, some consistent results of child-rearing practices are emerging. For example, there is a general consensus over a considerable number of studies that "masculinity" in the boy is related to certain constellations of paternal modes of rearing. Although "masculinity" is ill-defined and what it means differs from study to study, there is an appreciable measure of overlap between what is taken as "masculinity" in most, if not all cases.

What is required to study the effects of parental practices is, on the one hand, some closely defined parental *behavioral* attributes (e.g., "controlling" in "cold" and "warm" parents, all three labels being suitably defined). On the other hand, we require better categorization of the temperamental characteristics of children as related to better defined personality outcomes on specifiable dimensions. Thus one might use some definable temperamental attributes in the child (such as Sheldon's types) and relate them to a particular and at least operationally definable personality character, such as dependence-independence of judgment measured in a structured situation. This is schematized in Figure 18–1. (An imaginative and effective use of structured situations for measurement and assessment has been made by Sears et al., 1965.)

As with so many other problem areas in psychology, we need some agreed on dimen-

FIGURE 18–1. *Example of interaction effect between child-rearing behavior of the parent and temperament of the child.*

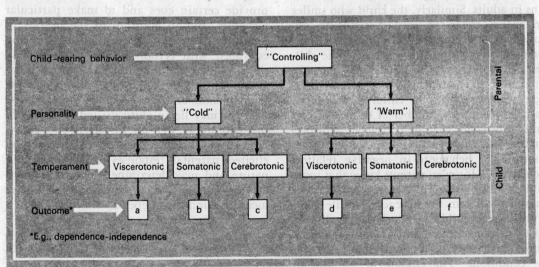

*E.g., dependence-independence

sion at various levels that can be replicated in numerous studies. Only thus are we going to gain real advances in knowledge (as opposed to the proliferation of papers).

Child-Parent Interactions

The literature on interactions between the generations has concentrated almost exclusively on the parents' influences on their children (and largely on that of one parent, the mother). The reverse flow of influences, the effects of children on their parents, has received very little attention. There are, of course, a number of studies showing that parents tend to react differently to boys and to girls, and some of these studies have been referred to elsewhere, but there is little on the question of temperamental or personality attributes in children as an influence on parental behaviors (and even on parental personality).

Mention has been made in earlier chapters of some rather basic influences, for instance, there is the possibility that the child presenting more marked "kewpie-doll" features may the more readily trigger basic parental reactions in adults. Similarly, the child who smiles and makes eye-to-eye contact tends to encourage and reinforce parental reactions. Common observation suggests that some children are more rewarding to parents than are others and that parenthood is a more satisfying experience with some children. Reference has been made to a number of dimensions of parental behavior that are correlated with personality attributes in children, for example, "controlling" behaviors in negative relation to creativity. However, parents know that some children seem to require more control than others and that in the absence of quite rigid controls some children reduce family life to chaos, whereas others can remain tolerable within the family under much more permissive conditions. The climate of opinion in psychology tends to the view that it is the parents alone who set the initial pattern of interaction, which then builds up into reciprocating relationships that magnify, for good or ill. But one can note that within the same family the same parents interact differently with their various children, which leads one to ask what part the child himself plays in the reactions he elicits; whether, for example, a parent encourages independent behavior in a particular child may rest, in part at least, on attributes of the child as well as on those of the parent. It is, of course, quite valid to study the results of particular patterns of parent-child interactions on the personality of the child, but in considering the developmental origins of these patterns of interaction, the role in the child of temperamental factors that tend to elicit certain responses from adults is one factor that has to be taken into account. In other words, the child is not merely the passive recipient of parental actions but is also the provider of stimuli to the parent, and right from the beginning there is an active two-way reciprocation of stimuli and responses. The parent is to a considerable extent disposed by learning and experience to certain patterns of action, whereas the infant is largely predisposed by temperamental or constitutional factors to provide certain cues and to make particular responses. But in addition to the overlay of learning, the parent (it is suggested) is also equipped with certain biological predispositions to react to the child. The social interactions within the family are thus a two-way phenomenon, and the origins of some of these patterns may lie in child-elicited responses of the parents as well as in parent-elicited responses of children. Certain of these child-elicited parental responses are biological in nature and may determine the earliest interactions between the two, on which their later social relationships depend.

THE PEER CULTURE

At all stages of life except the first a person's peer group, that is, his age-mates, are of great importance to him. Only the young infant directs his social attentions solely toward another age group, showing no interest in his peers.

In many human societies there is a clear division between two main peer groups, the uninitiated children and the initiated adults (further subdivisions of the latter need not concern us). A number of writers have pointed out that individuals in cultures with this kind of formalized division have the advantage of knowing just where they stand in the social hierarchy (e.g., Piddington, 1950). This is in contrast to our society, where adult status is given, as it were, piecemeal and not too explicitly.

As already mentioned, some dissonance between the generations is a feature common to all human societies, though it is probably more prominent in those that do not mark the transition to adulthood by a ceremony of initiation. The initiate who is formally acknowledged by society to be an adult is rather more likely to identify with the adult culture; he has less need to draw protesting attention to himself. Conflict between the generations is most marked in societies in flux in which the old standards are crumbling and the sanctions that supported them are in disrepair. Our own society might be seen as one that discourages consonance between the generations on two scores: in not clearly awarding adult status and in being in a state of change.

Bronfenbrenner (1969) has commented on an increase in the United States in the distance between generations, because in the United States children spend an increasing amount of time (compared with earlier generations) in the company of peers. This is in contrast to Germany, where children still spend much time in the family. In England, according to his findings, peer groups are highly autonomous —that is, independent of adult society and developing their own norms for behavior. In contrast, the "children's collectives" of the U.S.S.R. are carefully regulated by the adult society and are a deliberate attempt to inculcate adult norms. In this article, Bron-

fenbrenner discusses a number of influences in North American society that tend to segregate the ages and to produce increasing disruption in the socialization process.

Peer-Culture Influences in Infrahuman Animals

It is evident from the studies from the primate laboratories referred to elsewhere in this book, and especially from those at Wisconsin, that early peer experiences have a marked influence on social development below the human level. Some of these studies, and a number of other observations of primate social behavior, have been collected by Southwick (1963).

It will be recalled that primates reared in isolation from peers show marked ineptness in social relationships as adults and are also markedly unskillful at a particular form of social behavior, copulation. This is especially true of males, for whom the peer culture and the experiences it provides seem crucial to social learning, though females also are handicapped, particularly in maternal behavior toward an infant (Hansen, 1966).

An interesting and significant effect of early social experience has been revealed by Pratt and Sackett (1967), who found that monkeys reared under varying conditions of isolation and consequently showing abnormal behavior of different kinds tended later to prefer social interactions with peers of a similar degree of social abnormality. It seems that these animals learn patterns of social cues and prefer "friends" that display similar patterns.

Function of the Peer Culture

The peer culture plays a critical role in the social development of the child in providing a medium in which the child can practice the emerging social skills. In providing this medium it is also, of course, playing a critical part in the development of personality.

The mother-dependent and effeminate boy may be discouraged by rejection from the male peer group and perhaps forced into the girls' peer group, though he is liable to eventual rejection (even if less forceful) by that group also as the girls become less tolerant of boys, which they do at about eight or nine (Northway, 1944). The boy may thus be driven back into an even closer maternal relationship, and this withdrawal further increases his effeminacy.

It is interesting to note that the separation of the sexes in prepuberty is apparently a widespread phenomenon in human societies. It has been mentioned, for example, by Mead (1935) for Samoa, Hogbin (1946) for Wogeo in New Guinea, and Malinowski (1927, 1929) for the Trobriands; it appears in African communities, among the Tallensi (Fortes, 1949) and the Chaga (Raum, 1940). It thus appears across societies with a wide spectrum of social organizations, including some, such as the Trobriands, that are highly permissive of sex play among children and apply no pressure to separate boys and girls. Yet even here the spontaneous separation of the sexes occurs at about the same age as elsewhere. It is also of interest to note that in all societies where this is reported it is apparently the girls who separate first. This suggests that this separation is not a cultural phenomenon imposed by the males but a maturational stage that girls reach earlier.

During this time of separation the two sexes, it would seem, practice and consolidate their masculinity or femininity, respectively. They are acquiring social skills that they are not yet ready to practice on the opposite sex (or at least not on their opposite-sex peers, though they may on their parents, especially in the case of the girl's behavior toward her father [Nash, 1969]).

There are sex differences in this essential phenomenon. In girls the groupings are more usually twosomes or threesomes, whereas for boys there are frequently larger groups. This has, indeed, been called the gang phase.

It is evident, however, that relationships with the adult generation, and especially with the parents, are important over this period. Thrasher (1927) long ago noted that *delinquent* ganging was rife among boys whose paternal relationships were poor, a finding supported by Crane (1951, 1955), whereas boys with a sound relationship with the father tended to constructive, socialized ganging. One might suppose that boys at this stage are practicing male typing and masculinity. Boys who lack an adequate and mature model adopt immature concepts of masculinity that emphasize "toughness" and contain a "masculine protest" against feminine domination, a domination that the well-fathered boy does not feel. Because the former perceive some values of society, such as the sanctity of property and tenderness toward the weak, as "feminine" (because they have been transmitted by mothers and women teachers rather than by men), they reject these and become antisocial.

The lesser incidence of such delinquency among females may be related to several factors. For one, there is the biological fact that girls are less equipped for overtly aggressive types of behavior, but they are also less prone, in a matricentric child-rearing system, to reject maternal standards as inconsistent with their self-image. When they do, sex delinquencies are the most common form of misbehavior.

Thus the peer culture provides reinforcement for desirable or undesirable social learning. The activities of this stage are based upon earlier formed relationships with the parents (especially those with the parent of the same sex) and depend heavily on the learning acquired then. The function of this stage is to confirm and elaborate this initial learning. It is of interest to recall the animal studies that suggest the particular importance of peer-culture relationships in the male and note some trend toward this in the human male.

This gang phase of peer culture activity at the beginning of adolescence gives way to heterosexual groupings at the beginning of adolescence (Tryon, 1944). At first these tend to be groups of boys who meet with groups of girls, but gradually there is pairing off as serious dating begins.

Quite obviously a child's relationship with his peers involves a two-way interaction. The kinds of activity initiated by the child toward others influences the quality of the activity others reciprocate back to him (Kohn, 1966).

Sex Typing and Peer-Culture Relations

There is some evidence that a boy's peer relationships are rather radically influenced by his display, or lack of it, of sex appropriate behaviors and masculinity (Nash, 1965). It seems that this is rather less true for the girl. While the effeminate boy is likely to be severely rejected by the peer group, the tomboy girl is less likely to suffer severely at the hands of her peers. Because a crucial element in the development of the boy's sex typing and masculinity rests in his relationship with his father (Nash, 1965, 1969), this relationship has an important bearing on the boy's development of adequate peer relations.

Siblings and Acculturation

The family contains not only parents and their influences but commonly provides siblings also. In a sense siblings are part of the peer culture, but they, needless to say, stand in a special category and have different effects from nonrelated peers.

A consistent finding is that firstborn children end up in the ranks of the eminent markedly more frequently than would be predicted by chance. This was first noted by Galton in 1869 and has been confirmed in a number of studies since, including the one by Schachter (1963). A review of some of the literature has been given by Altus (1966), and

a more comprehensive review has been provided by Warren (1966). The general conclusions on the greater achievement of firstborns (especially males) has been supported by Lunneborg (1968), and the importance of sex in birth-order effects is also supported by this study.

Studies also show that firstborn children are more intelligent than those born later (Chopra, 1966; Warren, 1966), and it is therefore not surprising to find that they attend college more frequently than would be predicted on a chance basis (Schacter, 1963; Warren, 1966). In college, firstborns tend to do better than those in other ordinal positions (Altus, 1966). There may also be cognitive style differences with ordinal position that could influence intellectual functioning. Wright (1969) has reported a highly significant tendency for firstborn boys to score *reflective* and ones born later to score *impulsive* on some of Kagan's cognitive-style tests.

It would seem that an explanation of these findings must be environmental rather than biological, though it is possible that being born of younger parents confers some biological advantage. But a purely biological explanation seems contradicted by the finding that the sex of the next sibling is also influential. In two-child families, the firstborn children, either male or female, with younger brothers are significantly more intelligent than those with sisters (Altus, 1963, 1964). Furthermore, independently of birth order, in a two-child family children of either sex who have a brother are brighter than those with a sister (Koch, 1954). It is difficult to think of a biological explanation for these findings, and it would seem that a brother somehow stimulates intellectual development more than does a sister. To be firstborn in a family of three children is apparently more advantageous than to be so in families of two, four, or five children (Nichols, 1966). The only child also has an advantage in getting to college (Schachter, 1963), but it may be that an economic factor applies to this particular case.

Assuming that the birth-order effects on intellectual functioning are environmental, they presumably operate on that part of intellectual variance subject to environmental influence (Chapter 16). The difference between individuals in various ordinal positions are significant but not great.

One may look at the question from the other end. It may be true that firstborns are represented in positions of eminence more often than would be expected by chance, but it is surely also the case that of the considerable numbers of firstborns in the population most do not achieve excellence. Altus (1966) attempts to explain this in terms of special parental child-training attitudes that will tend to foster excellence but that are so stringent that relatively few parents will be able to supply them. Another line of explanation is that excellence requires certain innate qualities, high intelligence among them. If one happens to have these qualities (and few do), then being firstborn will give an added advantage to achievement if not to other matters. But being firstborn does not of itself guarantee excellence.

Ordinal effects have been reported in perceptual phenomena; for instance, a birth-order effect in preferences for polygons of varying degrees of complexity has been reported by Eisenman (1967), who found firstborn males to prefer more complexity than those born later, whereas later-born females preferred greater complexity than firstborn ones. Whether this is really a perceptual difference, or some subtle projective effect of a personality difference, is impossible to say on present evidence.

There are also some indications of personality differences related to ordinal position. This again is not a new belief; Adler (1928) described the firstborn as a "power-hungry" conservative, though Altus finds no support for this notion from his studies.

According to Sears et al. (1957), the firstborn is reared more strictly than are later children, and they also make the interesting suggestion that the father is more likely to discipline the firstborn than he will others. In consequence conscience development in the firstborn is greater. Dean (1947) has reported firstborns to be more cooperative and more curious, whereas children born later are more pugnacious and affectionate.

Differences in "affiliative needs" are reported by Schachter (1959), who found the firstborn child to need to share anxiety with another to a greater extent than those later born and to seek out company in circumstances of danger or stress. Another possibly related finding is that firstborns, more often than others, volunteer for psychological experiments (Capra and Dittes, 1962; Altus, 1966); this points to a possible source of bias in experiments using volunteer subjects.

It is not unreasonable to expect that the sex of siblings should have effects on personality, though the findings are contradictory and not easy to interpret. The study by Koch (1954), already mentioned, found that five- and six-year-old boys from two-child families who have an older sister are more effeminate than those with older brothers. Altus reports similar findings in college students. However, there are a number of studies that have found that male homosexuals tend to have significantly more brothers than would be expected from the usual sex ratio. These studies have been reviewed by Nash and Hayes (1965), who also confirmed these findings in a population of Australian homosexuals. As already mentioned in Chapter 9, a biological explanation of these findings in terms of genetic females being apparent males and incorrectly reared as such has been proposed (Lang, 1940, 1960), but this is untenable (Pritchard, 1962). Nash and Hayes prefer a primarily environmental explanation, or rather several explanations, some or all of which may apply to specific instances. One is the "dilution" of the fathers' influence and hence of sex-role identification in larger families (in which case one would expect the homosexual to be a later-born child). Another is a "disappointment" factor in families already having several boys and where a girl has been desired; the "disappointing" boy is reared as a girl. (This rearing is more likely to be dominated by the mother, and the case of Oscar Wilde is an illustrative example.) On this basis one would predict a predominance of later-born children in the male homosexual population, but none of the available statistics permit an analysis of this prediction.

Another but contrary line of explanation is that absentee fathers will tend to have small numbers of children (at least in their legal families), so there will be a preponderance of only children who will be reared by their mothers. As discussed in Chapter 17, the rearing of a boy by the mother alone is conducive to homosexual development. If both kinds of explanations are valid to them, one would predict that homosexuals will tend to be either firstborn or to be late in a large family and less often middle children.

It may be irrelevant to this particular question, but Hodges and Ballow (1961) have noted that boys with learning difficulties tend to have more brothers than sisters. Because it is seen elsewhere that boys well identified with the male role do better in school than those uncertain of sex-role identity, some common factor may possibly be involved in the two observations. The question of sex differences in birth-order effect were studied by Carrigan and Julian (1966) in sixth-grade children. They investigated their conforming behavior under neutral and socially threatening conditions. The subjects first rated fellow classmates on a sociometric questionnaire, thus arousing Need Affiliation. They hypothesized that firstborn or only children would be more subject to this influence than later-born children and also that females would be more susceptible than males. This sex difference is contrary to previously found ones, though it does agree with Staples and Walters (1961). These differences increased under conditions of heightened affiliative arousal. They point out that there is an interaction effect between ordinal position and sex. They also relate the

differences from other studies to differences in the experimental situation. Hence the factors entering into an interaction of this kind are very complex.

In addition to those mentioned here, a variety of birth-order effects on conformity, alcoholism, delinquency, and schizophrenia have been described in the literature, though the trends are not so marked as for eminence and college attendance (Warren, 1966). It seems, overall, that both ordinal positions and the sex of siblings have some effect on development. As a general factor it may not be strong, though in individual cases it may be a highly significant effect.

As already indicated, the explanation of these various effects is probably social rather than biological. The first child usually has, for a time, the undivided attention of his parents but against that has inexperienced parents and also the discomfort of being supplanted by a rival. The succeeding children come into a dynamically changing family. They have older siblings to emulate as well as to compete with, while the older ones have younger children to nurture or bully according to their disposition.

Physiological explanations of some birth-order differences are not entirely ruled out. The intrauterine environment and birth process itself may differ for firstborn and later-born children. However, as we have seen, some of the effects of birth order do not seem explicable by biological factors unless they are of the kind described by Lehrman (1962) in ring doves. He has shown how certain endocrine changes necessary to the emergence of reproductive behaviors in these birds are dependent on the visual stimulation provided by a mate; in the absence of this social stimulation the endocrine changes do not occur, and neither does reproductive activity. No such mechanism has been described in the mammals. In the light of other evidence on the physiological effects of early stimulation, it is not, however, impossible that the social stimuli provided by siblings may induce physiological changes that have psychological effects, though there is as yet no evidence of such an interaction.

CAN CULTURE CHANGE?

One of the arguments of this book is that man has to make a deliberate, self-conscious attempt to further his own evolution. Moreover, because of the threat of annihilation incipient in the technological age, this must be done quickly.

There is an important warning to be gained from the communist experiment, which shows the danger of basing a revision of the culture upon inadequate information. Engels was an armchair philosopher, and his theories were based upon rumination rather than upon facts that give a clear understanding of man as he is. It is not supposed that the account of man presented in this book is the final and definitive one, for we are far from such knowledge. However, it is hoped that the description may give an account that is accurate enough to produce a workable model that can be improved without having to be scrapped altogether.

There are some disquieting matters that are commonly ignored in psychology books and do perhaps belong more in political treatises. But as Bertrand Russell has said, psychology is the science that embraces the whole of human experience, and all subjects are therefore within its scope.

A visitor from Mars who hopped from his UFO to collect some evidence of life on earth and happened to obtain as his specimen a copy of *Parents' Magazine* would describe to the Martian Academy of Sciences how earth families live in ranch-type houses on treed lots. They have two cars and a stable of horses. The children are immaculately dressed and attend private schools; they are well fed, but some have problems of adjustment and others wet the bed. There are highly paid professionals who solve these problems.

Many of the texts on child psychology give almost as false a picture of life as it really is for the large majority of human beings. The hunger, dirt, squalor, and ignorance are passed over. This book repeatedly utters phrases such as the "realization of the human potential" as if the author was unaware of the snotty-nosed, potbellied waifs that are so many times more numerous than the well-brushed heads of *Parents' Magazine*. These children have as much chance of realizing their human potential as they have of growing wings; they need a meal much more than psychology.

We wade through a morass toward *1984* and *Brave New World*. If we dislike the Orwellian idea of a society of numerous proles or the Huxlian prophecy of masses of gammas and deltas, then radical changes both in human societies and in their educational procedures are called for. And if indeed the potentiality of some is such that no promotion is possible, then perhaps we have to accept that "all men are equal, but some are more equal than others." Society has to be realistic in its values, but there are signs of vastly unrealistic thinking. It is, for example, unrealistic in the 1960's to expect the American Negro to sit docilely in the slums awaiting some distant and uncertain relief, yet large sections of the white population seem to expect just that. At the other end of the scale the democratic idealism of the equality of man in all respects is just as mistaken, even though it is a thoroughly honorable error. The developmental psychologist has a part to play in suggesting how we might form a just and humane society that permits each to fulfill his potential but which does not stray so far from reality as to be unworkable. To aim high is necessary in order to advance, but the trick is to gauge the target that will stimulate growth without producing hopelessness.

We have to accept the reality that few men have the potentiality of an Aristotle, a Voltaire, or a Bertrand Russell. No matter how perfect society may become and how ideal its educational system, individual differences will persist and giants will dominate the scene. The American ideal of a college education for everyone can be achieved only by radically broadening and individualizing the value of higher education.

The potential that all men share is dignity, and if this is assiduously preserved, then we can acknowledge the inequality of man without fulfilling the prophecies of Huxley and Orwell.

It would be naive to suppose that the pleas for changes in human societies that are suggested at various points in this book—perhaps glibly suggested—will be at all easy to implement. We are surrounded by so many instances of resistance to change, even when one would suppose that the advantages are so obvious as to be overwhelming. In underdeveloped societies a constant source of frustration to visiting experts is the unwillingness, so frequently encountered, to initiate change. Among the Bantu of Africa, for example, the *number* of cattle a man possesses is the only criterion by which wealth is judged; their condition is immaterial. In consequence much of the land is overstocked and the cattle half-starved; yields of meat or milk are poor, and the true economic value (as opposed to prestige value) of the beasts is low. Disease and actual starvation take toll of the numbers, but this is a risk the Bantu are prepared to take. In terms of the value system of this culture and the part cattle play in the social organization of the community, this attitude is comprehensible, though irrational. In the past perhaps, when populations were smaller and land more plentiful, these attitudes may even have been adaptive and valuable, but now they are socially dangerous.

The Baiga of India present a similar example. They have a religious objection to the use of the plough. Their agricultural technique consists of clearing a forested hillside, gardening it for a few years until it becomes unproductive, and then clearing more land. This wasteful method has denuded much of the land, and the Baiga now face starvation but still resist proper farm technology that would involve the plough. The depredations of the sacred cow constitute another example of irrationality from India.

However, it cannot be supposed that such self-destructive inflexibility is peculiar to primitive folk in far lands. We have plenty of examples right at home. As one cynic has put it, the general public won't worry about air pollution until it interferes with television reception. Nor should it be supposed that expert suggestions, no matter how wise and advantageous, will be hailed with public acclaim and acted on with expedition. The fate of the Moynihan Report on the Negro family (1965) is a case in point. This was a genuine attempt to make social science theory and the facts derived from research available to policy-makers. It analyzed the social factors that have contributed to the disadvantaged position of the Negro and that have influenced the family in Negro life. It pointed out, among other things, how the matriarchal structure of the Negro family has undermined the self-esteem of the Negro male and contributed to his psychological distress. It contained many concrete suggestions that, if energetically followed, could alleviate a condition so serious that any constructive approach might be expected to be welcomed by rational policy-makers.

The fate of this report has been analyzed by Rainwater and Yancey (1967), who show how any action on this report has been inhibited by political controversy. It is not intended to be overcritical here. It is possible that the opponents to the implementation of the report may be right (though I suspect they are wrong). What is intended to be made of this instance is the warning that the social scientist cannot expect an eager rush to translate social theory into action. Rainwater and Yancey's book also contains the warning that both scientific theory and established fact may be misinterpreted or distorted to suit policy.

The outlook is not entirely depressing. Lopez (1967) is heartened by signs that the

United Nations Charter of Human Rights is, in fact, having an influence even on governments that scoffed at it twenty years ago when it was first adopted (South Africa is one exception to this trend). He claims that societies *are* becoming more concerned to give to every individual a sense of personal worth and dignity.

EPILOGUE

This chapter reviews a somewhat miscellaneous collection of topics. It attempts to draw attention to the fact that certain social forces acting on the developing personality have their origins in biological directives. Firstly, many of the broad features of human cultures contain tacit acknowledgment of man's biological needs and nature. Culture may indeed be viewed as a medium within which man expresses his biological nature in manners consistent with survival and comfort. Thus the main aspects of human cultures are biological in origin.

Culture in the first place controls or contains the biological motivations, but it supplies more than the rather negative disciplining of what are disparagingly referred to as "man's

animal instincts." It also provides the medium within which the biologically based potential of man can be developed and his biology transcended. Culture not only suppresses man's animal nature (an aspect that has appealed to moralists) but also permits its flowering. This is illustrated in the current change in attitudes to sex in our society—from an evil necessity to be curbed to an aspect of human potentiality to be experienced and enjoyed. That is, our culture is acknowledging the positive as well as the negative aspects of man's biological nature. (This may be new to our society but certainly not to others; some societies have long held this view.)

In this sense, culture and its institutions (major among which is the family) are to be seen as a medium in which the initially *biological* infant develops into a *social* adult. At the beginning of the individual's life there is a marked predominance of biological directives of development, though social forces increasingly enter the constellation of influences. But because culture itself is biologically shaped and acts on an organism that remains a biological one despite modification, these basic forces remain operative, even if not invincible, throughout life.

Nineteen

Development of the Concept of Self

Man has only a few attributes that he can claim are his. Language is one attribute that may be unique to man, though this claim can be disputed. Another attribute, with possibly a stronger case to support it, is the possession of a concept of self. A number of writers have pressed the claim for self-awareness or a self-concept as man's distinguishing attribute.

To quote Fromm (1964),

Man has intelligence, like other animals, which permits him to use thought processes for the attainment of immediate practical aims; but man has another mental quality which the animal lacks. He is aware of himself, of his past and of his future, which is death; of his smallness and powerlessness; he is aware of others as others—as friends, enemies or strangers. Man transcends all other life because he is, for the first time, life aware of itself. Man is in nature, subject to its dictates and accidents, yet he transcends nature because he lacks the unawareness which makes the animal part of nature—as one with it.

On the same line of thought, Bidney (1953) has said,

Man is a self-reflecting animal in that he alone has the ability to objectify himself, to stand apart from himself, as it were, and to consider the kind of being he is and what it is that he wants to do and to become. Other animals may be conscious of their affects and the objects perceived; man alone is capable of reflection, of consciousness, of thinking of himself as an object.

The geneticist Dobzhansky (1967) also emphasized self-awareness as a fundamental, and possibly the most fundamental, characteristic of the human species. Self-awareness, he says, is an evolutionary novelty. Man descended from species that had only the rudiments of self-awareness, if they had this at all. While self-awareness covers those attributes most characteristic of man as a distinctive species, it also involves a certain negative aspect, such as fear, anxiety, and death awareness. This self-awareness has far-reaching implications to human experience. Dobzhansky says,

Among the two million or more species that are living on earth, man is the only one who experiences the ultimate concern. Man needs a faith, a hope and a purpose to live by and to give meaning and dignity to his existence. He finds himself in this world not by his own choice; he wants at the very least to avoid excessive suffering and to capture the joys that may be within his reach. He desires to experience beauty and to shun ugliness. Above all, he yearns for love and relatedness to other persons; he wants to gain and to hold his self-respect, and if possible the respect and admiration of others. For this respect and self-respect, he may forego pleasures and accept pain and ordeal [1967, p. 108].

This "ultimate concern" of which Dobzhansky speaks is the search for the meaning of life. Only a self-aware creature is capable of this ultimate concern, though as we must recognize, it could be that not all humans are aware of this concern—indeed, it may be that only a minority are. However, for those who have considered the question of the meaningfulness of human existence, it becomes crucial:

If mankind is meaningless then my personal existence cannot be meaningful. I must discover a hope for mankind in its historical development. The purpose of my life can only be a small part of mankind's larger purpose. It is, furthermore, inconceivable for mankind to have meaning if the universe has none. Mankind is involved in mankind, mankind in life, life in the planet earth and earth in the universe. The universe of which man is a part must be meaningful [p. 108].

As a biologist, Dobzhansky is necessarily keenly aware of man's biological roots and the recency of his emergence from the long stream of evolutionary development. He sees self-awareness as a trait that has come out of this evolutionary process. As Dobzhansky says, many people find degrading the idea that man and the world in which he lives are the products of an evolutionary development, but this is not really degrading, because to have the potentialities of being actualized man must first of all have the potentiality of evolving.

There is a difficult question in knowing how the stream of consciousness and self-awareness originated from the physiological processes of man's animal ancestors. There are two oversimplifications that must be avoided: one of them is to assume a complete break in the evolutionary continuity between life and nonlife and the other to assume such a break between humanity and animality.

At several points in this book it has been said that the human neonate is an animal organism. It is an incompletely developed animal and, now we must add, a peculiar one in having the potentiality for developing self-awareness. In this view the ultimate task of the developmentalist is explaining how the unaware neonate becomes the self-aware adult —how the self-concept emerges and changes over childhood.

BODY SCHEMA, BODY IMAGE, AND SELF-CONCEPT

Body schema, body image, and self-concept are three expressions that are found (along with variations of them) in the literature discussing the self. The terms body schema, body image, and self-concept (and its synonym self-awareness) are used by a variety of authors in various ways and sometimes as if they were interchangeable.

The term body schema originated with Head (1920). He was concerned with its role in the motor coordination of purposeful movements and orientation in space. Schilder (1950) has given the most well-known analysis of the body image and the questions related to it. In many ways his concept is similar to that of Head, in that to him the body image is formed from proprioceptive impulses, but is really more inclusive than Head's concept in that it also involves awareness of this body, and an awareness of the continuity of it, its locations, and positions, and its basic identity as one's own body as distinct from objects or other bodies. Self-concept is something more again than either of these in that it involves not merely awareness of the identity of one's body but also of one's psychological identity as a person.

Possibly we would not have realized that these differing aspects of selfhood exist and present problems if it were not for the fact that in certain conditions of brain damage or mental illness these things that we normally take for granted may be disarranged, so that we do find individuals who appear to be unaware of the boundaries of their own body, or who show such bizarre notions as denying that their own hand is theirs, and even persons who have lost the awareness of their own identity as individuals. Gerstmann (1958) is well known for his exposition of these matters.

Studies of disturbance of the body schema, such as may happen in brain damage, suggest that aspects of body functioning, and in particular the integration of voluntary activity, are heavily dependent on it. But beyond this, the body schema appears to have profound psychological overtones that affect not merely the motor functioning of the body but also the individual's concept of himself as a self. This body schema forms the physical basis of self-awareness.

A distinction is drawn here between the body schema and the body image. The body schema is the "diagram" of the body that, it is believed, is built up in the brain (probably in a definite location) by which coordinated, purposeful movements are carried out and by which the body parts and the body itself are oriented in space. The function of this higher coordinative center differs, of course, from those unconscious coordinative functions carried out by the cerebellum: they involve mainly the coordination of muscle groups and involuntary movements rather than the purposeful behaviors that are controlled by the body schema. Possibly the most accurate sources of bodily awareness are from haptic and kinesthetic cues, and these probably also play the most important part in the early development of the body image.

According to the ideas put forward at the opening of this chapter, being self-aware is the essence of being human, and on this assumption one might say that self-awareness is what development is toward. It could be that the animals are determined in their behavior because of lack of self-awareness, and that man is free only to the extent that he is self-aware and understands this self. At several points in the book we have spoken of the end product of development in maturity, and one definition of psychological maturity could be a high degree of self-awareness. In this scheme the person is psychologically mature to the extent that he knows himself and has a useful working understanding of both his assets and limitations. Further, the individual is mature to the extent that he can use this concept of himself toward greater understanding. No one lives long enough to attain perfect understanding, but to aspire constantly to greater knowledge of oneself is perhaps the closest to perfection it is humanly possible to become.

Development of Body Schema, Body Image, and Self-Concept

Because the bodily schema seems fundamental, and there is apparently a hierarchical progression from the body schema to the body image, with the self-concept supraordinate to both, it would seem possible to propose a developmental sequence from schema to image to concept.

Body Schema. As mentioned already, the body schema, or "diagram" of the body that is built up in the brain, is highly important for the carrying out of coordinated purposeful movements and also has some important effects on the individual's ability to orient himself in space.

The effects of disruption of the body schema may be strikingly demonstrated in cases where the brain is damaged. For example, in certain kinds of brain damage, usually those of sudden onset such as might be caused by a cerebrovascular accident, there may arise a one-sided paralysis of the body, or of part of the body, accompanied by a psychological phenomenon known as an anosognosia. In this condition the patient may deny that there is anything wrong with his body and apparently completely ignores the fact that the limbs of one side are paralyzed. Thus one woman suffering from this condition denied the fact that her left arm was immobilized and without any sensations. At one time when her own paralyzed left arm was lying across her chest, she interpreted it as her husband's arm caressing her. Because this arm did lack any sensations referred to itself, it would, of course, feel to her very much like somebody else's arm lying on her body, which did retain touch sensations. Though this condition fairly commonly accompanies hemiparesis, it does not do so in the majority of cases, and this suggests that in those cases in which it does occur there has been not only disruption of the motor and sensory nerve supply to the limb but also some disruption of part of the body schema, the part affecting that limb. It also suggests that the body schema may have a definite location in the brain and probably in the parietal lobe (Critchley, 1953). In other cases the sense of body location may be impaired so that the individual cannot locate the position of a limb by the usual cues and has to look at it to see where it is.

It is difficul to know how this body schema arises, though there is some evidence that it is basically innate, but is doubtless modified from the myriad of sensations that impinge on the infant, gradually "filling out" this schema of the body. We can only conjecture as to the child's first experiences of his own body, though we may assume that the sensations from it play a very important part in the child's building up of his concepts of the boundaries of his body.

If one watches small babies, he is struck by the fact that they often seem to treat their bodily parts just as they do other objects in the environment. The way they examine them and even try to manipulate them does suggest to the observer that they are unaware of body organs as parts of themselves. This becomes particularly clear when a baby bites his hand or other part of his body, seemingly without realizing that he is biting himself. But doubtless something is learned from this experience,

in that biting this object (which is part of himself) leads to a distinct (and unpleasant) sensation that differs from those he receives on biting objects not part of himself. It may be incorrect to assume, however, that the body schema arises only from these experiences.

Penfield has suggested a *sensory homunculus* in which the various regions of the body are represented according to their sensory importance. The lips and the hands, for instance, have a relatively huge representation in the sensory-motor cortex, whereas the upper arm or the back, which contribute so much less to the sensory input, have only small areas allotted to them.

The "phantom limb" phenomenon is most fascinating in connection with the body image. Amputees commonly report that they can still "feel" the absent limb as if it were present, and when the last sensations from the limb were painful, a painful phantom may remain. This usually fades with time. Hebb (1960) discusses the phantom limb and points out how it shows that normal awareness of the body is not a direct percept; it depends (he says) on learning and can continue in the absence of sensory input. Simmel (1962) also regards the phantom limb as the product of learning, and there is certainly evidence to support this viewpoint.

It may be questioned, however, whether learning is the only factor involved. Weinstein and Sersen (1961) and Weinstein et al. (1964) have produced evidence, from the phantom limb sensations of patients with congenital aplasias, that the sensory homunculus may be innate. These subjects reported phantom limb sensations from limbs they never had possessed. Moreover, the nature of the phantoms corresponded to the nature of the deformity; terminal aplasias (which correspond to areas of greater cortical representation) were accompanied by phantoms more often than were intercalary aplasias. The evidence presented by Weinsten et al. depends on subjective reports and cannot be regarded as conclusive proof, but it does bring the interesting suggestion that the sensory homunculus may be innately present, at least in a rudimentary form. Both from the additional evidence of these authors and from what we know of development in general, we can be sure that experiences modify the preexistent elementary homunculus. For instance, in deformed rather than absent limbs the phantom, after removal of the deformed limb, tends to correspond with the deformity, as if the supposed innate standard sensory "model" is changed to correspond to the body that actually develops.

In the study by Simmel (1962) already referred to, phantoms are reported only in children who had actual experience of movement of the limbs, and it is concluded that this proprioceptive input is critical to the development of the body image. Weinstein et al. regard their method of inquiry as better and account thereby for Simmel's failure to find phantoms in very early amputees.

It is not to be denied that proprioceptive feedback may be very necessary to the full development of bodily awareness and manipulation. The work of Held and others, reviewed in Chapter 13, shows that sensory-sensory feedback does have a role in the development of visually guided behaviors and no doubt in other actions that depend on complex intermodality transfers. The body schema is implicated in these functions. But the precise role of this *reafference* (which is the newer term for sensory-sensory feedback) may be open to question. Howard and Templeton (1966) suggest that Held and his collaborators should have concluded that reafference is sufficient rather than necessary for visual-motor coordination. The work of Taub et al. (1966, 1968) also supports this idea. They have found in a series of experiments that have removed sensations from various parts of the bodies of monkeys by severing the afferent nerve fibers, that these afferents are not essential to all learning. Evidence of this kind does not prove that there is some innate schema that the brain can use in the absence of an imposed or acquired schema, but it is consistent with the

notion. While it would seem from some of the evidence that reafference (which is an ingredient of this learning) has a definite role in building up the mature body schema, there is also some ground for supposing a preexisting *archetypical* schema, a kind of general diagram. The role of learning is presumably to modify this innate schema so that it is consistent with the particular body in which it is operating. One such modification that may occur by learning is "dropping" an amputated limb from the diagram. Phantoms usually disappear eventually.

Thus we are suggesting that there is an innate body schema, which is a kind of standard diagram of the body for the species. It requires modification to be an accurate schema for a particular body, and this is where learning comes in. This learning continues over childhood.

There are many studies of early childhood concerned with the child's learning, by his explorations, about position and space. Gesell (1945), for instance, regards the eye-hand coordination as very important in the child's early experiences, experiences that effect the development of manipulative and other forms of behavior. As already noted, Piaget also finds this eye-hand cooperation important and attributes the child's earliest cognitive schemata to it. Spatial coordination in early life is also related to body image; things such as left-right, up-down, and front-back are all judged from the point of view of the body position in early life, and it is not until the ninth or the tenth year that any independence of spatial coordinates is developed. Many individuals, even after this age, have great difficulties in locating left and right without first referring to their own body.

Body Image. The infant, we suggest, has only an innate body schema but shortly begins to modify this by his experiences with his body. In so doing, he begins to become aware of this body. *Body image* is used here as a term distinct from *body schema,* for those concepts of his own body that the individual builds up are constructed, mostly, we may be sure, during childhood. The body image is doubtless related developmentally to the body schema from which it is derived. The body image is, as it were, the image that the individual has of himself as a physical person. It involves his own estimation of himself as strong or puny or herself as beautiful or ugly. Younger children are frequently most accepting of their bodies as they are, even apparently accepting defects without serious question. There are periods, however, when the body becomes a matter of considerable interest to the individual. This commonly happens in adolescence. One situation in which it may be a particular cause of concern is that of the child whose maturation is markedly behind that of his peers; some problems may also arise for the child who is ahead of them in physical development, though those are usually not so keenly felt. At adolescence defects may be the source of considerable embarrassment and unhappiness to the individual. Even normal variations, such as protruding ears or freckles, may be felt as defects at this time; there may even be entirely imaginary bodily defects.

As noted earlier, Hebb (1960) has suggested that body awareness is not a direct percept but can continue in the absence of sensation. However, it seems it cannot continue indefinitely without a sensory input. It was observed by Bexton et al. (1954) that the sensory stream seems important to the sense of selfhood. In their sensory isolation experiments, a common report of the subjects after a day or so of reduced sensory input was that they lost their sense of selfhood. Hebb (1960) also quotes the "depersonalization" of pilots in high altitude flying, and this may be an analogous phenomenon (though oxygen lack may contribute). This might be taken as indication that the body image remains a constant part of the self-concept, which is not, as it were, an abstraction that has become autonomous from its bodily origins.

There are numerous problems connected with the body image (or percept) and its development, and they have been reviewed by Wapner and Warner (1965). It does not seem imperative to digress into these questions at this stage, though many of them will need to be examined in a fuller consideration of the relationship between the development of bodily awareness and self-awareness.

The child's concept of himself as a physical person is difficult to separate from the concept that he builds up of himself as a total person. There are periods in development when emphasis on the physical qualities of the individual become particularly marked, and at these times his physical attributes or deficiencies (whether actual or imagined) may have a considerable influence on the development of his concept of himself as a person.

In discussing the body schema, we are in the realm of neurophysiology. In a sense these matters form a conceptual link between the content of Chapter 6 and of this chapter. We move from this physiological basis through the body image in a developmental hierarchy to the self-concept. Here we get into the quite different realm of ego psychology, and the nature of the discussion changes markedly.

THEORIES OF SELF-CONCEPT

There have been numerous approaches to a theoretical exposition of the nature and development of the self-concept. Among these is Freud's three-part model of personality, with the id, the ego, and the superego. The self-concept (or ego) arises from the interplay between the biological or instinctual urges of the id and the modifying influences of the culture and parental strictures forming the superego.

Adler spoke of the *life style,* which is the characteristic manner of coping with life's problems that is molded by the child's evaluation of himself and of society. This evaluation arises from his experiences, though it is based in part upon his heredity. Adler seems to imply a high level of self-awareness, the child asking "Who am I?" and "How can I achieve my goals?"

The phenomenological psychologists, represented by Coombs and Snygg (1959), have a perceptual approach in which the crucial element is the manner in which the individual sees or interprets reality. The objective facts of a situation are not especially significant. In this approach behavior is always reasonable and purposeful, though the definition of what is reasonable is individual, not objective. The individual selects the manner of behaving which is the most effective manner to him in the light of how he interprets his experiences. All behavior is determined by the perceptual field. Among the psychologists influenced by this point of view is Rogers, whose psychotherapy involves the restructuring of the person's view of reality, and Maslow, who speaks of self-actualizing as the realization of the potential the individual sees within himself.

Sullivan, in his view of the development of the self-concept, also recognizes the perceptual element but emphasizes the role of "significant others" in the development of this self-concept. Self-concept is thus in his view not so much an emergence of nascent potentials as a process of external molding.

For Erikson (1963), adolescence is the crucial period in the development of self-identity. He proposes eight stages in the development of personality. In brief, they are as follows:

1. The child develops trust and security (or if conditions are unfavorable, mistrust and anxiety). He becomes able to tolerate temporary parental absence.
2. In the second stage the child acquires autonomy (or shame and doubt as its converse). This he relates to toilet training. In this stage the child learns self-assertion.
3. The next stage develops initiative (or guilt). The child broadens his skills and learns cooperation. He begins to become independent.
4. The fourth stage corresponds with school entrance, and in it he acquires "industry" or inferiority, according to whether his work efforts are appreciated or unrecognized.
5. This stage corresponds with puberty and is crucial in the development of identity (or its negative, role diffusion). The child seeks answers to the question "Who am I?" and the attainment of self-concept. Failure to do this results in role diffusion or uncertainty of identity.
6. Having established an identity, the adolescent enters the stage of intimacy; being certain of his identity, he can now abandon it in situations of intimacy—such as those involved in deep friendship or marriage. If incompletely sure of his identity, self-abandonment is threatening and results in isolation.
7. The stage of "generativity" versus "stagnation" extends the sixth stage. Generativity is concerned with responsibility (mainly parental) and the ability of the individual to work productively. Without it there is regression and stagnation.
8. The culminating stage is of "ego integrity" versus despair—the ability to face reality and to accept a realistic self-concept and evaluation of achievements that the individual can live with constitutes the former. The lacking of this leads to despair.

Development of Self-Concept

If one accepts the notion that self-awareness, or the development of self-concept, is the prime characteristic of the human species, then it would seem that this is both the most interesting and the most important area of psychological study. However, the *principle of inconsequentiality* (Nash, 1968) operates here. This principle states that the scientific acceptability of any technique of psychological investigation is inversely related to the importance of the question being asked, or, in other words, that the maximum of technical power and methodological elegance can be achieved only with questions of minimal importance to mankind.

In consonance with this principle, the self-concept and its development have received relatively little attention from experimental psychologists, and studies reaching any high degree of sophistication or conclusiveness are somewhat uncommon. This is not to be taken as a criticism of psychologists but as a commentary on the techniques of investigation available to us. Everybody realizes the significance of the question.

An extensive review, by Wylie (1961), of the literature on the self-concept has shown how little coherent knowledge there really is on the topic. The bulk of the literature deals with adults, and there is relatively less on children. What there is seems to describe the state of the concept of self at various ages rather than provide any real data on the unfolding of this aspect of development. The same appears to be true of the more recent literature. Thus while there is a literature on the self-concept and a number of theories about its origins, there is no extensive body of experimentally derived facts to document these theories. The difficulties involved in the study of the self-concept have been analyzed by Allport (1961). One of these sources of difficulty—a familiar one—is that the term *self* is so variously used by different authors that there is virtually no consistency from account to account. Second, the self is a private matter and so pervasive that its boundaries are indistinct. Third, it involves many philosophical problems that psychologists in general would prefer to ignore.

Despite these difficulties, there are studies of the factors underlying the development of the self-concept, self-esteem, or self-evaluation. A few of the more recent ones will be discussed.

Allport (1961) has suggested the concept of the *proprium*. The term is intended to cover the self as the object of knowing and feeling —to include, in fact, the subjective elements that are essential to the concept. As he so rightly points out, people's behavior varies greatly depending on whether or not they are self-involved. Learning, for instance, is, as has long been known and experimentally verified, much more effective when the material is self-relevant (e.g., Razran, 1936, 1957).

It is a difficult question to decide just when the child becomes aware of himself as distinct from objects or from others. It is often claimed that the "you" precedes the "I"; that is, parents and other familiar persons are recognized before self-awareness begins. According to Spitz (1957), the awareness of self begins at about fifteen months. However, if the confusion over personal pronouns is any indication (and it is commonly claimed that it is), then this bewilderment continues for some time. The two-year-old still misuses first-, second-, and third-person pronouns and seems to have most difficulty with the first person (Ames, 1952).

It would seem, however, that after the concept of self is acquired, it dominates the personality for a time. The "selfless" infant becomes the "egocentric" young child, described by Piaget, in which all manners of psychological functioning are dominated by this self-reference. For a time objectivity or non-self-reference in thinking or action is difficult for the child. (In using the term *egocentric*, one has to avoid the value-laden connotation of *selfishness* or *self-centeredness*. True, the child is "selfish" at this stage, but this characteristic becomes a matter for evaluative comment only when carried excessively into later development.)

The *age of negativism* is one consequence of the emergence of selfhood and its temporarily dominating nature (Ausubel, 1950). Between about two and three (with rather wide individual variation) the child responds negatively to a considerable proportion of the demands made on him, be they ever so gently made.

A number of unpublished studies (reviewed by Wattenberg and Clifford, 1964) have shown a relationship between poor self-concepts and academic progress in school. Wattenberg and Clifford also found measures of self-concept (particularly those relating to feelings of competence and personal worth) in kindergarten children to be significantly predictive of their progress in reading two and a half years later. On the other hand, the relationship between self-concept and intelligence test measures was insignificant (which is an interesting observation that would most further exploration; in some respects this is a puzzling finding). Goldschmid (1967) has also reported that a high level of conservation in first and second grade children is related to personality variables, and of particular interest in this context is that those children with an understanding of conservation were also more objective in self-evaluation. The causal sequence here is not yet explicated, but Goldschmid suggests that constructive personality characteristics favor cognitive development—that is, being more stable and self-evaluative favors the development of the cognitive concept of conservation rather than vice versa.

In discussing the antecedents of self-esteem, Coopersmith (1968) has mentioned a number of factors apparently *unrelated* to this characteristic, at least for the subjects of his long-term study (normal, middle-class urban boys of ten to twelve years). Some of these non-relationships are surprising. They are physical attractiveness, height, family size, early trauma, suckling technique, and whether the mother worked or stayed at home. Moreover, family social position and income seemingly had no influence (this is of interest in view of the low esteem of Negro groups mentioned elsewhere, but presumably, as of the *middle*-class, these boys' families all enjoyed a life above the poverty level and its humiliations). Coopersmith suggests that these findings may mean that personal success is measured in rather direct terms of day-to-day personal relationships rather than by external standards.

On the factors related to self-esteem, Coopersmith and his associates noted that the appraisal of the parents was highly important. The interest shown in the children, their knowledge of their friends, and in general the manner in which they regarded the boy as a significant person reflected on his own self-evaluation.

Another notable finding was that parents of high-self-esteem boys were *less* permissive than those of boys with low self-esteem. They were strict but consistent and demanded high standards; they gave the boys challenging goals to achieve. The parents of low-esteem boys were mostly permissive but harsh when the children went beyond the limits they would tolerate. Boys high in self-esteem tended to set markedly higher levels of aspiration for themselves, whereas lower-self-esteem boys tended not only to set lower goals but to lag farther behind in their achievement. Coopersmith and his group also noted that superior ability, in athletics or academics, does not of itself bolster self-esteem. Indeed, the more able are liable to set very high standards and to be more conscious of failure to reach them, even though their actual achievement may be well beyond the average.

The influence of the rate of maturation at puberty on the self-concept has been studied by Peskin (1967). He notes that an early puberty implies a short latency period, and he discusses the question in the light of psychoanalytic theory. The longer latency period of the later maturer gives (in this view) greater opportunity to explore and amplify both motor and intellectual skills. A number of authors, including Erikson (1956), have argued that this is the case. Some others have argued against this (e.g., Eichorn, 1963), saying that an early puberty may also mean an early start to the latency period and hence no shortening of it (this could mean, though, that early childhood is cut short). Peskin discusses the physiological data contrary to this and notes that early physical development is necessarily less variable because it takes place in a relatively short time anyway; hence early puberty almost inevitably results in a short latency period.

Taking subjects (all males) who were early or late in pubertal onset (as measured by the appearance of secondary sex characteristics and other indices, including skeletal age), Peskin found the two groups to differ in certain marked respects. He confirmed the statement by Rapaport (1946) that early maturers perform best on tasks having lesser ideational or affective relevance but requiring concentration or restricted attention. He also, in general, confirmed the findings by Mary Cover Jones (1965) that the early maturers tend to be poised and responsible but conventional in attitudes and in cognitive patterns: They are conforming achievers. The later maturers in Jones' study were active and exploratory; they were independent and insightful but also impulsive. (The two samples of Jones and Peskin were both drawn from the Oakland Growth Study [OGS], though Peskin does not state whether any of his subjects were the same as in Jones' group.)

The major question that arises from these studies is whether the kinds of personality associated with early or late maturing are causally related to the rate of maturation. That is, by artificially accelerating the physical development of any child at random, do we produce a conforming achiever, or by lengthening the latency period, do we produce the more insightful and independent individual? On the other hand, is the relationship less direct, rate of maturation and the personality characteristics described being both related to some more basic thing and only indirectly to one another? (One should not perhaps at this stage ignore the possibility that the relationships reported are artifacts and that perhaps further replication is called for.) It is also worth noting that certain of the characteristics of the early-maturing boys (particularly the lesser ideation and conformity and the more effective performance on tasks involving restricted attention) are reminiscent of the feminine characteristics discussed elsewhere. Girls also have short latency periods. For the present one can only note the similarity, but the suggestion that masculinity is slow-growing and needs a longer latency period might merit closer study.

White et al. (1967) have confirmed the old idea that adolescence is a time of marked extension of the limits of self and that the concept of self develops on through this period. These authors examined Allport's (1961) idea of the proprium, with its seven aspects of "becoming." As might be expected, there are indications of sex differences in the course of self-concept development. In particular the girls showed greater anxiety about acceptance by the opposite sex, and greater dissatisfaction in the self-concept arose when they doubted their abilities in this area.

Social Influences on Self-Concepts

There are many social influences on the development of self-concept, important among which is membership in a disadvantaged group. Often such groups are minorities (such as the Jews in North America) and often their disadvantages are social-psychological rather than inherent (the North American Jews, for instance, being in many other respects an advantaged group, perhaps because of selective factors in migration). Sometimes disadvantaged groups are majorities, such as is the case with the Negro in many parts of Africa. The influence that white domination has had on collective self-esteem is evident in much of the reactive nationalism of the newly emerging states.

A minority group that is receiving considerable interest at the present is the Negro in America. Among several writers who have reviewed this question is Goldschmid (1969). He notes that a major factor in the present unrest of black Americans is the quest for identity. The Negro has a traditional role model of passive restraint and patience, one of "flunky" to "whitey." The "black power" movement is rejective of this, and emphasizes an aggressive and active confrontation with "white power." The Negro child emerging from the ghettos to interact with the white community has to learn new value systems. For some this involves "identification with the aggressor," adopting white middle-class norms as a protective device and in so doing rejecting their own origins and culture. The European immigrant has some identity problems when integrating into a new culture, but at least he has old world values to support him. For the Negro, there is only slavery and oppression to look back on, and even when he breaks free of the psychic bonds these entail, he has the color of his skin to hinder his integration with the prevailing culture.

These factors form the broader social milieu in which the Negro child develops, but it seems that the negative self-concept he tends to derive is learned at home rather than directly from the community. In one study it was found that the relationship with the father is an important factor. Negro college students who had a positive relationship with their fathers were more likely to reject anti-Negro statements and to be active in the civil rights movement, whereas those with a poor paternal relationship had a generalized fear of rejection and were accepting of anti-Negro statements. In another study, Negroes were found to be less accurate than whites in self-evaluation. They were more discrepant with fact in their estimates of their own IQ, and such self-esteem factors may influence their intellectual development (these studies are collected in Goldschmid, 1969).

Not only are there the negative effects of low-status minority group membership, there are also the positive effects of membership in high-status groups. The effortless self-assurance of the upper-class Englishman has been a source of irritation (tinged no doubt with envy) for generations to many outside this upper crust. Today, of course, one notes some interesting phenomena reactive to these attitudes such as the inverted snobbery of a non-U accent carefully cultivated. However, here again it is not group membership, but family mores, that seems to be the crucial factor. Coopersmith (1968), for instance, noted that it was not class membership per se, or family income, but rather it was the attitudes of the parents that directly influenced self-esteem. Thus lower-class low-income families do produce high-self-esteem children if the parents' self-esteem is high. The Negro's problem is that most of the parents have low self-esteem, and this tends to be a self-perpetuating disability. Of considerable help to breaking this cycle of effects would be knowing how

high-esteem parents come about in low-esteem groups. There is also a converse effect; what Adler called "feelings of inferiority" are not unknown among aristocrats despite the group support of superiority. The origins of such things must be in the immediate child-rearing situation. And perhaps we should not overlook the fact that for some an admission of inferiority may be an objective self-appraisal.

Constitutional Factors Influencing Self-Concept

It is an obvious enough point requiring only mention and not extensive elaboration that innate and constitutional qualities may markedly influence a person's concept of himself. Thus the intellectually dull child in a gifted family must have his self-evaluation affected by his differences from the family norm. This is not to say that this is of necessity a negative effect (though it may commonly be so), but the child must derive a different self-concept from those of his more alert siblings. Such instances could be listed at length: the clumsy child in a society that extols athletic prowess, the female child in a society that favors males, the pigmented child in a society that considers a relatively unpigmented skin a virtue. On the other hand, the very bright child in an environment that neither values intellectual pursuits nor trusts book learning may actually find his talents a liability to group acceptance and hence possibly to self-acceptance. The body, the nervous system, and the constitution are basic influences on the developing self-concept. They form the foundations on which the self-concept is built.

Male and Female Self-Concept

An aspect of self-concept is the concept of being a masculine or a feminine person. The animals are, presumably, not self-aware of their maleness or femaleness. These concepts are, indeed, so highly pervasive in humans as to influence a considerable range of functions outside the purely sexual realm or even the specifically social one. As mentioned in Chapter 17, there are studies showing successful sex-role identification to be related to good personal-social functioning (e.g., Mussen, 1961) and even to school performance in subjects such as reading (Anastasiow, 1965; Mutimer et al., 1966). Moreover, as noted in several contexts, physical maleness and femaleness carry with them a considerable range of perceptual, cognitive, and personality characteristics. It would be no exaggeration to say, therefore, that self-concept is essentially the concept of oneself as a male or female person. No matter what aspect of the self-concept he takes, this concept is always of a personality of a given sex—self-image as a stupid *man,* an intelligent *woman,* an aggressive *man,* or an attractive *woman.* Whatever the self-description the individual builds, this aspect of being a male or female colors it and pervades it. The self-concept is never neuter.

This is true even though some individuals are in conflict over the sex of their self-description. There are some males who desire femininity and who seek to build up a feminine rather than a masculine self-image. There are some women (probably fewer than the males) who seek a masculine rather than a feminine self-concept, yet even here, one may suppose, the concept is never neuter, never sexless. The sexual ambivalence becomes a part of the self-description. It may be that these persons are even more constantly self-conscious about the sex of the self-concept than are those who are more assured in their masculinity or femininity. The assured individual can in many aspects of functioning push such preoccupations into the background. But whenever the self-concept becomes a matter for consciousness, the sex of this concept is always there.

Male and Female Body Image

The developmental origins of the male and female self-concepts are no doubt in the early stages related to the body image. As the Freudians have insisted, the discovery of the anatomical difference between the sexes is a critical event in the ontogeny of sex identity. Whether it is necessarily the *traumatic* event, especially for the girl, that they believe it to be is another matter. The possibility that there is an innate difference in the body schemata of males and females is an unexplored (and possibly unexplorable) question. In the light of the kinds of sex differences described in previous chapters it would not be surprising to find that within the differing nervous systems of males and females there are distinctive body schema for each, but this is entirely speculative. Certainly the body image in maturity must differ. Articulate men and women can describe what it feels like, bodily, to be a man or a woman, though it is very difficult for the one really to appreciate how it feels to be the other. Whether these physical feelings predate puberty is unknown. That is, is maleness or femaleness in early childhood a kind of intellectual awareness of being one or the other or has it a physical concomitant? Presumably boys and girls, though aware of their anatomical differences, are never aware at this stage that they *feel* different—maybe many never are aware.

As discussed in Chapter 9, boys, even in infancy, show tumescence and detumescence accompanied by widespread bodily correlates of tension and orgasm. What sensations go with these phenomena, and what part they play in the development of the body image, is unknown. In later childhood there is a marked sex difference in masturbation that may also influence body image development, overdeveloping, as it were, the representation of the genitalia in the body image of boys. Another area in which a difference might arise to consciousness is in the early feeling of "growing up" that girls have. There are also neuromuscular differences, in the manner of running or throwing, for instance, that may well give rise to differences in the "feel" of being a boy or a girl.

In all these questions we are dealing with phenomenological matters that have for some time been considered improper questions for psychological investigation. Even though there are signs of a readmission of phenomenology to scientific study, the future for a developmental phenomenology does not seem extensive. The questions raised here seem likely to remain questionable. But it seems a reasonable presumption that girls and boys do have differing body images underlying the *sex self-concept*.

The idea being presented here is that this sex self-concept develops from within outward. That is, the young boy already has certain predispositions to maleness and the girl to femaleness, and these predispositions are biological in origin. These inbuilt trends are soon subject to external influence, and it is these that are the major concern of this section.

Sex Self-Concept

As already stated, the self-concept is considered of necessity a sex-related one: Whatever one does, whatever attributes one incorporates, whatever view of the self one holds, it is always a male or a female that is doing or being. In this sense the term "sex self" is a tautology as the self is always male or female. Nonetheless, it is convenient for purposes of discussion to abstract the sex identity of the person as a topic for separate examination.

There are two main sources of external influence on the development of the internal directives of the sex self, or of sex identity. One of these is the culture, and the other is the parental dyad. These external influences modify the innate directives and may in some cases obliterate them.

The influence of the culture has been discussed in the previous chapter. As stated there, all human cultures assign differing social roles to males and to females and have different behavioral expectations for each sex. These expectations (it was suggested) are themselves a result of the nature of males and females.

The cultural pressures are to a large extent mediated through the parental dyad, particularly in the early years. It may be, in fact, that direct cultural influences, through peers and other sources outside the immediate family, only become at all powerful after the initial sex-typing influences of the parents are well established. The parents themselves are, of course, the product of the culture and subject to its influences.

North American society has been epitomized as matricentric (Nash, 1965), having a system of child care that revolves around the mother and leaves the father somewhat peripheral, though there are signs of a change toward a system of care that involves the father to a greater extent than has been the case for several generations. The developmental consequences of these changes remain to be observed.

Father-Son Relationships and Masculine Identity. It is now fairly clear that the relationship with the father is of critical importance to the boy's development of a masculine identity. To a considerable extent the boy derives his male self-concept from his father. The literature on this has been reviewed by Nash (1965, 1969). The process here is one of identification, as discussed in Chapter 17. By this process the father acts as a "facilitator" of the biological tendencies toward masculinity of the boy. Where the father-son relationships are inadequate, because of the physical absence of the father or his "psychological" absence or because of an incompatibility between him and his son, then his facilitatory function may be lost or weakened. In these instances the boy is liable to form an identification with the remaining available parent, the mother. In this case he may acquire from her elements of a feminine sex-role identity, with consequent confusion of his self-concept. This may go to the extent of a reversal of psychological sex, the boy developing a homosexual self-concept (Nash and Hayes, 1965). However, as remarked in Chapter 9, boys have a biological predisposition to masculinity, that is, to adopt a male self-concept. Moreover, it was suggested there that there are individual differences in the potency of this innate masculinity. In some it is strong, and the facilitatory influence of the parent is relatively less important to the boy's development. Such boys will derive an adequate male self-concept from relatively little fathering, or in the absence of the father will resist the feminizing influences of the mother. Others with less strong biological directiveness to masculinity will require more fathering for adequate development, and in the absence of this fathering may be more susceptible to feminizing influences from the mother. This accounts for the observations that some boys do develop adequately in the absence of the father and that not all boys reared by mothers become homosexual. A host of factors contribute to the development of the self-concept, and though very important, neither father nor mother alone are indispensable—though one or the other is needed. (It should be noted that this is a theoretical statement. Because we have at present no means of predicting which infant boys have strong propensities to "spontaneous" male self-concept development, as a practical matter one must recommend adequate paternal attention for all. And moreover, even the boy who develops adequately without a father might have developed better with one.)

Father-Daughter Relationships. According to Freudian theory, the girl at first identifies with the mother but later forms a basically incestuous relationship with the father, and her feminine self-concept is molded to a marked extent by her paternal relationship.

On marrying, she transfers her relationship with her father to her husband, but after she herself becomes a mother she revives her initial identification with her mother and becomes covertly hostile to her husband. One is reminded of Oscar Wilde's remark in *The Importance of Being Earnest:* "All women become like their mothers. This is their tragedy." The extent to which this is really the case has not been carefully studied, though it is one of those statements that rings true.

Some authors have suggested that the father is critical to the feminine identity development of girls as well as of boys (e.g., Johnson, 1963; R. R. Sears, 1965b; Wright and Tuska, 1966). In brief, it seems that the girl practices with the father certain of the feminine social approaches she will later use toward boys, and her development of a feminine self-concept is to a considerable extent influenced by her *early* relationships with the father (Forrest, 1966).

Mother-Daughter Relationships. The foregoing statements that the father is important to the development of the self-concept of both masculinity in boys and femininity in girls should not be taken to mean that the mother's role is negligible. A rewarding, nurturant relationship with the mother has been shown, in a number of studies, to correlate with femininity in the daughter (P. S. Sears, 1953; Payne and Mussen, 1956; Mussen, 1961; Mussen and Rutherford, 1963).

Mother-Son Relationships. It has been suggested that the girl "practices" her femininity on the father (Forrest, 1966). To what extent the converse holds for the boy is problematical. If, of course, one is to accept the theorizing of Freud, Bowlby, and others (reviewed elsewhere), then there is no question. But at various points in this book and elsewhere (Nash, 1965; Nash and Hayes, 1965) I have spoken of the negative aspects of mother-son relationships. To what extent one should emphasize these negative aspects is a matter for further research to decide. As was said in discussing the peer culture, the boy may take a considerable part of his male concept from his father but then practices this concept at first with his peers rather than with the opposite-sex parent as the girl does (or at least is said to do). It will be noted that the peer culture is apparently less significant to the girl than it is to the boy. It might be that, provided there is a sound and nurturant early relationship with the father, the postweaning relationship with the mother is not especially salient to the boy. Whether research will support such heresy is a question to be decided in the future.

Sex Differences in Self-Concept Development

It would seem to follow from the suggestions made not only in brief in this chapter but in more detail at various points in preceding ones, that the processes of self-concept attainment differ for boys and girls. Not only do they commence with differing basic equipment, but they are subject in many respects to differing cultural influences. Indeed, it could be said that even when the culture does not make an ostensible distinction in its influences on boys and girls, the same influence is phenomenally different for the two sexes because they react differently to similar events. Furthermore, the two parents have differing saliences as facilitators of the biological tendencies and differing roles to play in the development of their sons and daughters.

"Masculine" Protest. As so many people have said, our society is male-oriented. While we men do not all utter the traditional Jewish prayer of praise to God that we were not born women, most of us, we can be sure, feel that way. No doubt some women are thankful they are not men, but it seems that more girls show a preference for the male role than males do for the feminine role. This may be related to the fact that our society shows a

multitude of signs of preference for the male. In view of the emphasis on masculinity from the Deity Himself down to the more mundane matters of life, it is perhaps surprising to find males needing so much reassurance of their maleness.

The clue may indeed be found in the Jewish custom mentioned, for the strongly mother-centered child rearing of that culture may well set up a situation in which the boy has to protest his masculinity to escape the smothering toils of the maternal family. For some other cultures, including our own, this masculine protest is also a real phenomenon. A rather common feature of such matricentric cultures, then, is a deficiency in the male self-concept, which takes the form of a compensatory overconcern or self-consciousness about masculinity. According to the analytic literature, there is not a corresponding "feminine protest" but instead a self-deprecating phenomenon—the so-called "penis envy."

One symptom of the male overcompensatory self-concept is delinquency (Nash, 1965). The familial history of delinquency in boys has been noted by Jonsson (1967), who found a record of increasing delinquency from grandparents through parents to grandson to be a common feature; he comments that just as it is said to take three generations to make a gentleman, perhaps it requires the same to make a delinquent. It may be that a kind of family tradition, that tends to create unsatisfactory conditions for the development of the boy, builds up.

Some of the literature on the relationship between delinquency and the loss of a parent has been reviewed by Gregory (1965). Most of these studies were retrospective. Some of them confirm the relationship between the loss of the father and a variety of psychiatric conditions (but not all the studies differentiate the effects of the parents). In an extensive study of orphanhood in Minnesota, Gregory found delinquency among boys to be closely related to the loss of the father (though Gregory raises certain reservations about the rural bias in his population). The highest rate of delinquency was among those boys of divorced parents, especially when the boy was living with the mother alone. He interprets his findings as suggesting that, in the origins of delinquency, the loss of the father is more significant than the loss of the mother.

In Gregory's study, delinquency among girls was markedly less than among boys, as one would expect from the well-known statistics to this effect. There was, however, a higher rate among girls who had lost the mother than among those without the father.

Among nondelinquents in this study there was a high rate of high school dropout, again related mainly to the loss of the parent of the same sex. While economic factors might account for this dropout rate to some extent, Gregory suggests that problems of identification are also causal. As noted elsewhere, self-concept and cognitive development are related.

A number of other authors have commented on an overemphasis on masculinity in delinquent boys (for example, W. B. Miller, 1958) and have related this to overmothering and a lack of identification with an adequate male model. For boys with a warm affectionate relationship with the father, the relationship with the mother has little influence on masculinity (Mussen and Distler, 1959; Mussen, 1961), but it seems that the boy who lacks this paternal influence and perceives himself as under feminine domination may react into antisocial activities. This may result from being forced to adopt peer-culture standards of what is "masculine," standards which give a necessarily immature concept of what its quality is. Tenderness, succorance of the weak, and mannerliness are virtues taught by women; ergo, masculinity is toughness, brutality, and uncouthness. However, because not all mother-dominated boys become delinquent, some additional factors are evidently at work. Milieu is no doubt important among these. The family background of aggressively delinquent boys has been studied by McCord et al. (1963), who concluded that neglect and punitiveness together with a deviant-aggressive paternal model produces antisocial aggressiveness in boys.

A cross-cultural study of crime, involving forty-eight nonliterate societies, showed a defective father-son relationship to be a significant correlational factor (Bacon et al., 1963). These authors review a number of papers that see crime in the light of revolt against feminity in males reared without adequate identification with their fathers and hence with uncertainty about their own masculinity. They also suggest that the same may be true of certain cultural groups within our own society.

This idea of a masculine protest against feminine domination has also been discussed and supported in a study by Siegmann (1966), who obtained self-ratings of early childhood misdemeanors from groups of male medical students and found a significantly higher report of antisocial behavior in those whose fathers had been absent on war service during their childhoods.

A statistical comparison of the family characteristics of a population of delinquent and nondelinquent boys in Sweden has been presented by Jonsson (1967). He says that the term best describing the parents of the delinquents, and the fathers in particular, is *failure*. The family is characteristically an economically marginal one and contains signs of pathology, such as alcoholism, irregular marriages, and illegitimacy. Both mental and physical disease is more common than in normal families, and there is a high incidence of disharmony among all family members. Absence of the father (who is sometimes replaced by a stepfather) is common.

Early separation from the mother is one factor of note, some period of separation in the first six years occurring in no less than 84 percent of the delinquents (compared with 38 percent of the controls). But as Jonsson points out, separation from the mother almost always means from the father also, and only 25 percent of the delinquents (compared with 83 percent of the controls) had a constant relationship with a father figure. He discusses his data in comparison with other studies, both in Scandinavia and elsewhere, and remarks on the general consensus of data showing a clear relationship between the absence of a constant father and delinquency.

Because his study is essentially a statistical one, there is not much information in it about the actual dynamics of father-son interaction (or its failure) in generating delinquency. However, it does produce certain figures that reflect some of the underlying factors. For example, punishment in the delinquent families was commonly severe and often brutal; the parents' attitudes were authoritarian.

Another feature was the fact that the delinquent boys, markedly more often than the nondelinquents, grew up in homes in which the mother dominated. This finding was based upon the parents' own statements as to who made decisions. However, the delinquent boys themselves did not perceive this dominance pattern any more frequently than did the nondelinquents. In both cases about 45 percent gave the father as master of the family, which is itself an interesting social comment, because Jonsson notes that some of the delinquent boys who never had a father in the home still rated a father figure as the decision-maker! This must represent wishful thinking. From other evidence Jonsson concludes that the delinquents commonly had an unfavorable image of the father, and that this image was often contributed to by the mother.

The Father and the Peer Culture. There are a few indications (reviewed by Nash, 1965) that suggest that a boy's peer relationships are markedly influenced by his relationships with his father. The normal peer group is somewhat intolerant of deviants, and the boy who is immature, effeminate, or submissive is liable to rejection by the peer culture. This may mean that the deviant boy either seeks a deviant peer group or remains outside any male group.

This may be a factor in delinquent ganging

where the boy who is uncertain of his masculinity engages in overcompensatory expressions of "toughness" (an immature concept of maleness) and a rejection of the social standards that he perceives as feminine because they have not been transmitted to him by an admired male. This matter has been discussed more fully under the heading of "Masculine Protest."

A somewhat different slant on the same question is provided by Lois Hoffman (1961), who notes that a wife-dominated father does not provide a satisfactory male model to the boy, whose peer relationships are thus adversely affected. According to Hetherington (1966), father-absent boys tend to be more dependent on their peers than those with fathers present, but because the peer group is itself immature, it may be unable to provide a satisfactory substitute model of mature masculinity, and this relationship exists quite apart from the suggestion that father-absent boys tend to have difficulties in their incorporation with the peer culture.

Kagan (1964) has reviewed much of the literature, up to 1964, on sex typing and the developing of the sex-role identity. One dimension that Kagan discusses is the masculinity of the father as an influence on the development of masculinity in the boy. He points out that two fathers, even though equally nurturant, might display sex-typed behavior to differing degrees. The boy with the less masculine father is likely to find himself less able to meet the expectations of society (as represented by the peer culture) of him as a male. His behavior will be less sex-typed, and dissonance is likely to be a consequence.

Self-Concept, Self-Objectification, and Humor

The Socratic rule for the good life is *know thyself,* a dictum repeated by many wise men, from Chaucer's "Ful wys is he that kan hym-selven knowe" (the Monkes Tale) to Burns'

Oh wad some Pow'r the giftie gie us
To see oursels as others see us!
It wad frae monie a blunder free us
An' foolish notion:

One question that arises here is the extent to which "oursels as others see us" is a valid mirror for self-objectification. If one is to appeal to the poets, then the sentiments of independence expressed in Kipling's *If* come to mind: "If you can trust yourself when all men doubt you. . . ."

The opinions of others, the kinds of feedback they provide, are no doubt important in the forming of self-knowledge, but to be molded too closely by these influences is to produce the other-directed person—one, in fact, who has no personality of his own and is merely a copy of the group personality.

Allport (1937, 1961) has spoken of the role of humor in the process of self-objectification. To him, a sense of humor is the core of the mature personality, and the most striking correlate of insight (he says) is this sense of humor. This is because humor and self-objectification are basically the same thing: "The man who has the most complete sense of proportion concerning his own qualities and cherished values is able to perceive their incongruities and absurdities in certain settings" (1961, p. 293). But as Allport is careful to point out, an exclusively humorous philosophy leads to mere cynicism, in which everything is trivial. The unifying philosophy of life demands a purpose to life that humor alone cannot supply but will only inhibit.

It is interesting to note (as Allport does) that few people will admit to lacking a sense of humor. He quotes that other McGill professor, Stephen Leacock: "There is no quality of the human mind about which its possessor is more sensitive than the sense of humour. A man will freely confess that he has no ear for music, or no taste for fiction, or even no interest in religion. But I have yet to see the man who announces that he has no sense of humour.".

If the matters of these paragraphs are com-

petent, then the development of a sense of humor is of considerable interest to the ultimate development of the mature personality. There is not, in fact, a great deal of data to appeal to, though there is a certain amount of speculation. As Allport notes, the sense of humor is a subtle aspect of personality that so far we have had little success in measuring.

Some of the literature on children's humor has been reviewed by Kappas (1967). She notes rather well-defined changes with age in the kinds of humor appreciated, and these shifts have been described by Gesell and his associates (Gesell et al., 1946, 1956) and by others.

In a study of third, fifth, and seventh grade children, Zigler et al. (1967) found cognitive challenge to be a factor in humor appreciation. The greatest mirth scores were found to correspond to jokes of moderate difficulty. They proposed two possible explanations of their findings, the second or alternative being of special interest here (the data do not yet permit a choice between them on empirical grounds). This theory proposes that the individual prefers stimuli at a complexity level congruent with his cognitive structure (which doubtless changes with age); this is in keeping with material discussed in earlier chapters, particularly in Chapter 13. It is also consistent with the finding that there is some correlation between intelligence and humor appreciation in children (e.g., Mones, 1939).

However, a number of studies find either no *close* relationship between humor and intellectual capacity or that intelligence is only one of several temperamental factors that are relevant for humor (this question is reviewed by Zigler et al., 1966). A purely cognitive theory of a sense of humor is evidently too simple. It may well be that a certain cognitive level is a necessary but not a sufficient condition for a developed sense of humor, just as in the case of creativity.

There does not appear to be much experimental work on the origins of humor. The earliest systematic observations relate to about year five. At this age the child has only limited capacities to deal with abstractions, and hence humor that depends on word play, whimsy, or other more abstruse cognitive processes is unappreciated. Humor at this stage is essentially slapstick. As Allport says, the child at this stage has a sense of the comic rather than a sense of humor. (This type of humor seems persistent, and even mature adults brought up on Laurel and Hardy still appreciate them, seemingly as much as their children do in the revivals of their films.) As the child becomes able to understand physical relationships of size and space, exaggerations of these relationships begin to become mirthful.

By nine years there is an extension in what is considered humorous. Slapstick is still funny, but verbal jokes, puns, and riddles as well as practical jokes and those involving the misfortune of others become appreciated, as are jokes invoking "taboo" matters. More significant to the present context is the fact that at this stage *some* children begin to show a capacity for self-objectification and the ability to laugh at themselves, but this is apparently unusual.

By fourteen there is considerable intellectual development beyond the nine-year-old level. The increased logical capacity permits more sophisticated humor, but "corny" and ridiculing humor tends to predominate. Much of it is smutty. Verbal wit becomes increasingly common. With increased self-appraisal and critical judgment, laughter at oneself becomes more frequent and acceptable.

There are, however, at all stages considerable individual differences in at least the overt response to humorous situations, and these differences widen with age. The developmental origins of these differences have not been described, and their developmental consequences have not been explored.

We have here the same question as has been asked in other contexts. Given that a sense of humor correlates with certain desirable personality characteristics, do we by fostering humor in children encourage the development of these traits? And apart from

this, can a sense of humor be taught? A positive answer to the first question is doubtful and to the second one is highly doubtful. A joke explained is an emasculated thing. We might give a child some cues as to when he should make the motor actions of laughter, but to inculcate spontaneous and felt humor is quite another matter. However, if our aim is to produce self-objectification, then perhaps developing a sense of humor is not the only route to this end. Humor is a condition favoring this trait but it may not be a necessary one for its attainment. The individual who can accept the fact that he lacks a sense of humor has achieved self-objectification—if we are to believe Leacock, on a heroic scale—and has no need of humor, at least as a route to that end.

Religion and Self-Concept

At one time every book on child psychology discussed religion as an aspect of development, especially during adolescence, a period that was frequently described as one of religious turmoil. Today it is not usual to find reference to the topic, and where it is found, the discussion is usually brief (see, for instance, Jersild, 1968). In fact, it has to be brief, because the modern style derives discussion from experimental facts, and there are very few of these available on the topic.

To the earlier writers, such as William James and McDougall, the bases of religious experience were instinctual. That is, a tendency to awe, reverence, or sentiment was seen as part of the inherited character of man, and such a notion is consistent with the ideas expressed earlier in this chapter. Self-awareness (which we have called a species-specific characteristic of humans) leads almost unavoidably to a consideration of the self on a cosmic scale and to thoughts about the origin of this self, its history before birth, and its survival after death. Man being both self-aware and intelligent, some religious concepts are inevitable and are a feature of all human societies.

There can be little doubt that in the past religious ideas played a significant role in the development of the self-concept—and not always a positive one. The Judeo-Christian religion has set up an ideal model for the self that was in some senses too much at variance with man's nature to be attainable by many people, and much self-devaluation has resulted. On the other hand, the considerable positive influence of religion should not be forgotten.

There can be little doubt (even if no experimental proof) that, as Allport (1937) has insisted, religious ideas play an important role in the development of the mature "philosophy of life" and the self-concept this implies. What is largely unexplored in modern psychology is the influence on self-concept development of current reevaluations in religious thought —the "death of God" controversy and so on. It is not, of course, that such ideas as the death of God are new—Nietzsche wrote about it long before our time—but that the dissemination of ideas such as this is now much wider and discussion is freer. Recent changes in both the technology and the philosophy of communication mean that children are potentially open to a greater range of influence than they were in the past. (This change is not restricted to religious ideas either.) The actual impact of this on child development is little understood. It might be that the ease of propagation of ideas defeats its purpose in that children are subjected to more than they can cope with and perhaps end by accepting nothing. But given that man is biologically disposed—because he is self-aware, intelligent, and susceptible to beauty and to a sense of awe—to formulating religious ideas, we may expect some form of religion to continue to play a part in shaping the personality.

Religion implies some kind of code for the conduct of life and hence contains ideas about right and wrong. The more advanced religions involve highly abstract ethical notions that are quite beyond the intellectual capacities of the child. Piaget (1932) has studied the development of the child's ideas on morality and has shown how these parallel intellectual development. A problem for free-thinking parents who wish to communicate rational ideas on religion to their younger children is this concreteness in their thinking, for instance, the following exchange with my son (aged nine):

"Daddy, what does God look like?"
"God is a black woman."
"No, he's a man. He has a white beard."
"How do you know?"
"Cos."
"Why cos? Why do you say he's a man with a beard?"
"I saw a picture in church."

Then followed an attempt to explain to the boy that God is what you want to conceive "it" as and that it is perfectly competent to think of God as a Negro woman or as an Eskimo boy (at this stage I carefully avoided the complications of God as a spirit or as purely imaginary). But this left him still convinced that God is Santa Claus in a white robe instead of red. Similar (but varied) preconceptions about God have been documented by Maurer (1967).

It is perhaps not surprising that these kinds of concretizations of the abstract concepts of religion get carried over into many adult lives. Whether or not the "hell-fire" preachers have a sound theology is one question, but perhaps there is less question that their psychology is sound, or at least realistic. However, many adults do acquire the ability for abstract thought despite the highly concrete beginnings of intellectual processes, and the same developments no doubt enter into the grasp of advanced religious ideas. But religious abstractions are necessarily tinged with emotional overtones in a manner that abstract thought is not, and one cannot explain the development of religious ideas in terms of cognitive growth alone.

EPILOGUE

This chapter has considered the manner in which biological bases are evolved into a self-concept. Self-awareness is taken as an inherited and species-specific human characteristic, and without this biological capacity for knowing the self there can be no self-concept. At the lowest level of the ontogenetic hierarchy is the body schema, and this we must presume man shares with the animals; it is part of the basic equipment of the higher orders, though just where in evolution it emerged need not concern us. Nor is it really necessary to debate whether or not animals have a body image, but it is assumed that man alone has self-awareness.

The child starts with the biological tendencies to behavior that have been detailed in previous chapters. These give him certain potentialities that may aid or hinder the developing self-concept. The dominant and naturally aggressive young boy, for instance, has a better start in acquiring the self-concept of an active male than does a more retiring and less assertive one. While both aggression and self-effacement may be learned, there is reason to believe they are often temperamental traits.

In the course of his development each child discovers himself by a process of action and feedback. An early and significant event is the discovery of sex, and following this the considerable range of sex-related aspects of the self-concept begin to emerge. Other qualities that make for concordance or discordance are discovered, to a considerable extent by feedback provided in the family, though since the family is itself molded by the culture, cultural forces soon begin to operate. As the child becomes more independent and mobile, direct cultural influences are felt, though these are perhaps largely the modification of features already laid down by intrafamilial influences. The father's role in self-concept development is perhaps rather generally underestimated but can be shown to be important, especially in relation to the self-concept as male or female. The process of identification plays an important part in this finding of the self.

A characteristic of maturity is the ability to be objective about the self, and it seems a sense of humor is useful to self-objectification. A successful life involves knowledge of one's assets and their full exploitation but also involves knowing the limitations within which one must operate.

Twenty

Epilogue: Synthesis and Projection

Nietzsche, in his book *The Birth of Tragedy out of the Spirit of Music,* proposed a synthesis of Dionysius and Apollo, a fusion that was the secret of the vitality of Greek culture. In his own life, his friend Wagner was the Dionysius the Apollonian Nietzsche would so much have liked to be. This book, too, has spoken of such a duality in human development. On the one hand, we have the instincts and ecstatic emotions as motivating forces for mankind, forces which lead to action and adventure and joy in action. From these come song and music—the Bacchus facet of Dionysius, a vigorous, masculine spirit. On the other hand, there is the Apollonian ideal, feminine aestheticism, peace, leisure, and repose. From this arises intellectual contemplation, logic, and philosophy. Man at his best, we propose, is both Dionysian and Apollonian. He enjoys and appreciates what he gains from his evolutionary origins but interprets and expresses these gains in the specifically human ways that go beyond these origins.

The sympathy, in the later chapters of this book, with the kinds of existential statements made by Sartre, Maslow, and others may be surprising to the reader after the earlier chapters with their heavy emphasis on the biological determinants of behavior. Sartre in particular is in strong protest against the view of man that regards him as helplessly swept along by historical forces, his destiny predetermined by the natural laws. I should not necessarily be regarded as perverse or illogical in thinking, and as confusing apparently irreconcilable concepts. It may be, of course, that existential philosophy is illogical—hence the case that any system that attempts to reconcile it with anything is necessarily illogical. I do not propose to argue this point. I merely state that I take the existential position as valid and regard it as a kind of axiom. The reader who cannot accept this can still read most of the book with profit, even if he disagrees with those sections that attempt to deal with the wider human condition.

The point is that it is an incontestable fact that man *is* a biological organism, and any view of man must take realistic account of this fact. This book is an attempt to explore the evidence on man's biological nature, the limitations this nature imposes on his functioning, and the potentials that it gives him. It may seem to the reader that the argument goes unnecessarily far in emphasizing these biological factors and that it might be more comfortable to accept the current notions that tend to underplay biology—which emphasize, for example, the role of learning, rather than innateness, in the development of perception or motives. But in the light of the evidence, as I see it, it is unrealistic to maintain such an emphasis.

On the other hand, many of those who *do* agree with this position will wish to go to what seems the logical conclusion—that all psychology ultimately disappears into cellular microbiology. The synthesis attempted here depends on the assumption that the whole is more than the sum of its parts. This question has been discussed by Dobzhansky (1967), who suggests that (at the risk of some oversimplification) one can approach the study of the living world in two ways. They are equally valid but ask different questions and therefore command different answers. The first is the reductionist or Cartesian approach, which in essence attempts to reduce biological processes to their chemistry. The other approach is the Darwinian, which attempts to make life explicable in terms of its origins and of the phylogenetic development of species. In contrast to the reductionist approach, the second may be called compositionist. The reductionist approach regards man as what Dobzhansky calls a "conglomeration of groceries," which is true in one sense but which in another sense is ridiculous. Dobzhansky describes the origins of life and the origin of man as evolutionary crises or turning points in the actualization of forms of being. He calls these radical innovations *transcendencies* in the evolutionary process. The human mind did not arise, he says, from some kind of rudimentary mind in the molecules and atoms, and evolution is not simply an unpacking of things that were present in the ancestral state.

The same thing, we may suggest, is true not only of phylogeny but of ontogeny. The personality of the individual at maturity is not merely as Descartes tried to maintain, the mechanical outcome of mathematical laws, nor is there, as Liebnitz believed, an algebra of life whereby one can explain personality fully in terms of an interaction between biological forces and environmental influences. But on the other hand, this interaction does play a major role in the molding of the individual —even if the final outcome is creative—and this interaction is well worthy of study. It is, in fact, within the realm of the developmentalist to study it.

This means that there is an indeterminancy principle in psychology, which no doubt covers a much wider range of phenomena than the same principle does in physics. Indeterminancy does not imply that events are lawless, but merely that, because with certain events we cannot at any given moment study all the factors entering a situation, the outcome of these events is unpredictable. Thus we have to tolerate a measure of unpredictability as a fact of life when dealing with such vastly complex phenomena as developmental psychology does. In this sense, when we say that an outcome is creative, we mean that it is unpredictable, and we must accept the fact that certain developmental events are likely to remain so.

One of the main theses of this book has been that humans cannot be considered as merely reactive to the environment. As the Scottish philosopher MacMurray (1961) has said, "human behavior cannot be understood, but can only be caricatured, if it is represented as an adaptation to environment" (p. 86). One can equally well say that neither can it be understood as solely directed internally by genetic and other biological influences. The careless reader of this book may believe that the latter is being suggested here, but this is not the case. What is being insisted is that these biological directives or organizers interact with the environmental forces to produce, as a resultant, patterns of actions. Moreover, it would be insisted that creative resultants

—resultants that are not merely the predictable mechanical outcome of a pattern of forces —can emerge from this interaction. Man's intelligence (a biological trait), together with other species-specific biological characteristics such as self-awareness, makes it possible for man to assess himself and his environment and to choose to change either. Man not merely adapts to the environment, but he adapts the environment to himself. Man evolves machines that enable him to transcend his biological limitations. He can choose *how* he will react to the environment or to what aspects, and he can choose the kind of environment in which he wishes to mold his children.

Looking at history, one must be aware that while man *can* do these things, he does not always do so. Indeed, one may feel that man exercises his options rather rarely and that unless he is careful, he will lose control of his destiny. But the potential is there, and one of the tasks for developmental psychology is to foster this potential.

A SYNOPSIS OF DEVELOPMENT

The early part of this book deals with the Dionysian, the instinctual man, or man as a biological organism. For each species, structure and biology determine modes of action and impose a pattern norm on function. The most efficient functioning for the species is consistent with this pattern norm, though the higher organisms in particular are capable of modifications of behavior that permit "non-normal" modes of function. Dogs and horses *can* learn to walk on their two hind legs, as every circus shows, but this activity is a highly inefficient mode of locomotion in terms of their structure. Similarly, it is suggested, this concept of optimum functioning extends to the nervous system and results in optimum modes of psychological functioning. Each kind of organism has its own species-specific peculiarities of structure and of neural action that

result in its particular patterns of behavioral functioning. This is true, it may be assumed, of the human organism, though its great range of plasticity makes possible wide variations in function, both structurally (that is, in motor actions) and also psychologically. But again, in both realms we must assume that there is within this range of possible variation a point at which functioning is most efficient.

Not only are there species norms for action, but within the species there is a range of individual differences. Each individual, in fact, is unique in the details of its structure, biochemistry, and mode of function. This is true even in the invertebrates: The nuptial flight of the queen bee bears witness to this; the males follow her and fall out one by one as each reaches his own limit; only the remaining highest-flying male mates with her. As the organism grows more complex, the range of individual variation increases. In man it is great, especially in psychological functions. In intelligence, for instance, the gap between the least and the most bright is enormous; to indicate this range, IQ's should perhaps be expressed on a logarithmic scale rather than an arithmetic one. But it still holds, presumably, that each individual has his own optimum level of operation.

Furthermore, this uniqueness of the individual extends to his developmental history. While there are for many aspects of development fairly distinct sequences and timings, each individual follows his own timetable and program of change. The extent to which the program can vary has not yet been adequately described.

Man is the product of evolution, and much of his present state can be understood in the light of this fact. Most of his psychological characteristics can be observed in the sub-human species. Man does have certain anatomical characteristics peculiar to himself, but it is rather more difficult to find uniquely species-specific psychological characteristics. Language is possibly one and self-awareness another.

Many of man's psychological traits are presumed to be the product of genetic modes of transmission, so the neonate comes into the environment already predisposed to react in particular ways to it. However, a high degree of plasticity is one of the characteristics of the primates, and man shows this trait to a degree unrivaled by any other species. Because of this *biological* general character of plasticity, the human can react variously to the environment and may even override *some* of his genetic tendencies (but not all of them). Nevertheless, he develops most economically to himself when growth is consistent with the genetic code. (The demands of social living may require more or less forcible "pruning" of certain innate tendencies, but these are particular cases.) To understand human development properly, one must consider both the history of the species and the particular inheritance of the individual.

Parts of the genetic inheritance of man that are of particular interest to the psychologist are the built-in tendencies to react with more or less specific responses to particular stimulus patterns: These are the instincts. Man's continuity with the rest of the animal kingdom is well illustrated here, though again there are important differences in the degree of determination between man and most other species; man is less rigidly predetermined to action by these instincts. His inherited traits of intelligence and modifiability permit some freedom of action. Man *can* act in counterinstinctual manners, and in some instances he *must* do so if he is to survive. But not all the instincts are destructive or undesirable, and some of them form highly constructive functions even in the artificial conditions of modern living. The emotions, which are an element of instincts, make the difference between existence and living, and far from disparaging the "animal instincts" as some have in the past, we must regard them as an enrichment of the human condition.

The instincts have a major directive influence on development, and certain of the selective manners in which the young organism responds to environmental stimulations have a profound importance to the developmental process. The study of instinct is therefore a major concern for developmental psychology.

It might appear that the suggestions that such highly involved patterns of behavior with prolonged time sequences are preprogrammed into the nervous system rather than imposed on it by learning are too farfetched for credibility. But when one comes to consider just what must be involved in modifying the nervous system by learning so that it retains complex patterns of behavior involving precise time sequences, it becomes questionable whether this supposition really has the merit of greater simplicity. Because learned sequences are encoded in the nucleic acids, the genetic transmission of similar patterns seems perfectly feasible.

Furthermore, it is becoming evident that complex behavior patterns are in fact encoded, even in quite elementary nervous systems. As Wilson (1968) has said, until recently it was thought that relatively simple behaviors, such as locomotion in insects, are mediated by a direct transfer of sensory information from preceding movements, that is, by peripheral control. Wilson has shown, however, that there is a central control of such behaviors that is probably innate or already present in the nervous system of insects. That is, the output pattern of motor impulses controlling locomotion can be generated by the CNS without proprioceptive feedback. We still do not know just *how* information that is coded and genetically transmitted is translated into temporal sequences of behavior, but it is becoming clear that this translation does happen. And if it can happen in the rudimentary nervous system of insects, presumably more complex systems can encode even more intricate patterns.

Not only are certain behavioral patterns inherited more or less directly as previously encoded "programs," but certain rather unspecific mechanisms, such as those spoken of by the "constitutional psychologists" as under-lying the temperamental aspects of personality are also inherited. These are less specific "tend-encies to behaviors" than the instincts, but they determine rather broad manners of re-action to the environment. Mood, speed of re-sponse, "introversion-extroversion," and other behavioral patterns are of this kind. Some of these may be mimicked by purely environ-mental procedures—a child's experiences alone may make him timid in·his approach to life —but more generally these temperamental traits are the expression of genetic rather than environmental influences.

The infant is a neurologically different kind of organism from the adult. The human in-fant is in some respects more akin to phylo-genetically inferior organisms with very meager cortices, because in its state of neurological immaturity many of the functions of the cortex are ill-formed or even absent. Though we lack much specific information at present, a great many of the developmental events of childhood are directly related to the matura-tion of the CNS.

Especially pertinent here are the critical periods. During development the organism passes through phases at which it is partic-ularly susceptible to given environmental in-fluences. Before and after this period it may be considerably less amenable to an environ-mental event—in some cases totally uninflu-enced by it. One aspect of developmental efficiency is ensuring that the positive critical events·impinge on the organism at the time of maximum susceptibility (there are also cer-tain negative effects particularly to be avoided at these times). Not all the critical periods are related to neural changes; some relate to en-docrinological ones (or perhaps more likely to an interaction between the two types).

A considerable amount of human behavior is programmed in the nervous system. This is not, however, the only source of constitu-tionally derived behaviors. Endocrine influ-ences are also important. This is especially true of the lower animals in·which certain behaviors are absolutely dependent on hor-mones and cease in their absence. This is found in a broad range of behaviors, includ-ing those related to reproduction and the care of offspring.

The role of the hormones seems to be to "prime" the nervous system, and one effect of them is the lowering of the threshold to appropriate stimuli. Motivation and its emo-tional accompaniments are also affected.

Among the higher animals the dependence on hormones is less, and there is, in fact, a steady reduction in the relative salience of hormonal influences as one ascends the phylo-genetic scale. Thus the higher mammals can continue sex behaviors in the absence of the priming of the nervous system. There is some evidence that this is less true of the female, who, even in the primates, remains rather more dependent than the male on the hor-mones for the continuation of these behaviors.

Although in the higher animals the hor-mones may not be essential to the continua-tion of sex behaviors in the adult, they are apparently essential to the *learning* of these behaviors during the juvenile stage. Because in the higher animals (and especially in the higher primates) learning is of crucial im-portance to the consummation in the adult of skilled sexual performance, this means that the endocrine secretions are of prime im-portance to the development of these be-haviors. Once learned and well established, the experienced animal (and this applies par-ticularly to the male) can maintain activity without the priming and energizing of the endocrines, but even though the endocrine secretions of the immature organism are much lower, this low level is evidently critical to making the nervous system receptive to learn-ing.

Though at present there is no clear evi-dence on this point, it is likely, in view of the widespread differences that are found in practically every biological function, that there are differences in these juvenile endocrine secretions. Such differences might serve to produce individual differences in the capacity for learning sex behaviors. Because of these endocrine differences, some children will learn sex-appropriate behaviors with facility, or stated another way, will require a minimum of exposure to whatever experiences in early life contribute to the learning of these behaviors. (We do not know in any detail what these experiences are, though they doubtless relate in part to socializing activities in play. Identification with the same-sex parent is also of crucial importance.) Other children less well endowed with these chemical primers will require more experience or greater environmental support in acquiring these social skills. Such children will also be more susceptible to adverse environmental influences, such as those predisposing to homosexual rather than heterosexual developments. While sex hormone secretions may vary from zero (or a low level) upward, there is no mechanism known whereby opposite-sex hormones can induce homosexual development in humans. Indeed, in man the androgens and estrogens are seemingly less specific in their influence on sexual motivations than they are lower in the scale.

Though little is known about this at present, it may be that the chemical priming of the nervous system by other hormones also influences the sensitivity of the nervous system in particular ways and hence affects the susceptibility of the developing organism to environmental forces.

The phenomenon of imprinting is an important one in forming the first sequence in the development of social behaviors. It is a biologically based phenomenon in that the organism is preprogrammed to make the kinds of response to the special stimulus patterns that are appropriate to its species. Particularly in the higher organisms there is a great deal of learning in the social interactions of maturity, but the first steps in the learning process are triggered by the innate "tendencies to learn" that are the imprinting phenomenon. It is assumed that this is the case at the human level as well as in other species and

that the highly complex social learning over childhood is "primed" by imprinting.

A major emphasis of this book has been on the fact that males and females are essentially distinct organisms. They have (it is claimed) differently organized nervous systems and different biochemical economies. They therefore react differentially to the environment and act on the environment in distinctive manners. The tendencies to behavior that result from these differences are not so strong that they cannot be overridden by learning, but in keeping with the principle that the most efficient development is obtained when it is consistent with the pattern norm of the organism, then male and female children have different courses of development, following different schedules and having different requirements of the environment. An ideal child-rearing system will take account of these differences.

In part because of the neurological immaturity of the young child, learning processes in early life are different from those of the neurologically more mature organism. It has been suggested that in some respects the infant is comparable in its learning processes to lower animals. This has some merit as a pedagogical phrase but should not be taken too literally. For one thing, it should not be taken to imply that the human adult has processes of learning that are distinct from anything found among nonhuman species. What it is intended to underline is the fact that the infant is to a considerable degree a procorticate organism and in its learning capabilities resembles (but is not necessarily identical with) those species without extensive cortices.

We are as yet too ignorant of the neurology of learning, and of the developmental history of those elements of the CNS involved in learning, to draw anything more than a vague parallel between the growth of learning and the growth of the nervous system. A careful comparative study of kinds of learning (for example, of conditioning, instrumental, and latent learning) might throw light on the sorts of developmental sequences that may be found in learning over childhood.

Learning and changes in learning capability are not merely the result of neural processes and maturation. The experiences of the organism enter in. The act of learning itself, we may presume, affects the maturation of the CNS. Furthermore, learning affects learning; that is, all learning depends on previous learning. The logical paradox this entails is answered by the supposition that the first learning depends on preprogramming or innate learning (if an oxymoron may be allowed) —the kind of thing of which imprinting is a prime example. The environment plays its part not only in passively providing the material to be learned but also in being an active agent in stimulating the maturation of the CNS and in actively influencing the successive accumulation of the prior experiences that constantly interplay between constitutional and environmental factors in the development of learning. The fact of immaturity will at times make the organism insusceptible to certain experiences, and at other times, in critical periods, it will produce heightened susceptibility to experience.

Learning is intimately related to perception and vice versa. Most of what is learned comes in via the exteroceptors. The development of the sensory mechanisms therefore greatly influences learning. The infant senses but does not perceive. That is, he does not interpret the sensory data. In early life certain tendencies to sense particular stimulus patterns are related to the innate tendencies to learn. Early learning, in fact, proceeds by the linking up of stimulus patterns, to which the young organism is innately selective, to specific responses that it is preprogrammed to make. The "intervening" mechanisms between the two are already there, at least in some rudimentary form, and development at first proceeds by completing these half-formed links.

Early learning and early perceiving are thus both limited to such primitive mechanisms. As both proceed, they become more sophisticated and in the higher organisms less and less tied to ready-made stimulus response connections. Perception (as distinct from sensing) involves learning, and the greater capabilities of the higher organism permits more complex perception, which in turn in a leap-frog manner permits more advanced learning. If we take Bruner's idea of perception as a process of categorization, then the greater categorizing ability of the more advanced organism permits more complex perception, which in turn facilitates greater learning. Any advance in one area increases the other area.

Man has a long childhood, and the leap-frogging progression of learning and perception continues over a long time—two decades, perhaps. The higher forms of learning, such as latent learning, are not possible until perceptual processes are highly developed, but one could also say that the higher forms of perception (such as abstracting elements from complex arrays, as in studying a microscopic slide) are not possible until latent learning is well developed.

One of the major emphases of the environmental approach has been the effects of early stimulation. Repeatedly throughout this book I have taken issue with the idea that the organism is the passive recipient of environmental influences, a yielding clay to be molded, a *tabula rasa* to be printed upon.

The organism is not merely the recipient of stimulation but is also the seeker of it. In the most deprived of environments (rare outside experimental situations) the organism may actually inflict painful stimulation on itself when no other source is available. The organism is, moreover, normally selective of the stimulation it will admit and may be rejective of stimulation above the optimum levels the input channels will cope with.

Stimulation does not have purely psychological effects (indeed, what is a "pure psychological effect"?). In the immature organism at least, the effects of stimulation are physiological as well—stimulation influences maturation, and maturation influences the organism's capacity to receive more complex stimulation, and once again we have the leap-frog effect. Having received stimulation, the organism has increased capacity not merely to receive but also to seek more. The phenomenal environment of the organism changes with stimulation. Without any increase in its real complexity, it becomes in effect more complex for that organism, which can now apprehend a greater segment of the total range of stimuli the milieu can provide.

Though not explicitly stated, so far as I am aware, it seems to be implied by the environmentalists that by presenting increased levels of stimulation one can produce a "supernormal" organism. The idea arises in part from the fact that most of the research has been done on deprived species. Most of the animal work has been on the laboratory rat, and it has been suggested that the "normal" laboratory environment is an impoverished one compared with the natural ecology of the species, and that the so-called "enriched environment" experiments merely approach the complexity of the normal environment of the feral rat. Hence these "enriched" environments do not produce a "super-rat," but one that exploits more fully than the usual laboratory rat the potentialities of the species.

Similarly, the observation that children reared under less than optimum conditions in an underprivileged environment are restrained has led to the logically unjustified assumption that rearing in a "super-environment" produces a "super-child." What is argued here is that there is a limit to the amount of stimulation the organism can cope with and that the normal middle-class home in North American society probably comes close to this limit. Stimulation above the optimum is ineffectual and may even be deleterious; we may not be far from the optimum in the more privileged ranks of our society, so we cannot expect any startling increases there. It is, of course, a quite different question with underprivileged groups, and here increased stimulation will pay dividends. (As noted in Chapter 16, the actual effects of "head start" programs have been less than one

would desire, but this should not discourage effort. It is probable that so far the attacks on the problem have not taken into account all the complexities—the broader social effects of understimulation, for instance.)

We have discussed the role of the biological drives in development. First, there is, over childhood, a marked change in the physiological factors underlying the biological drives and their accompanying emotions. In the young child this whole motivational system is different, and it is only as he approaches maturity that the long-sustained motivational systems of the adult are formed. This development is basically maturational, but experience is also significant, though mainly perhaps in modifying the stimuli that excite motives and the kinds of actions that ensue rather than in changing the emotional feeling itself. Thus by his learning over childhood a male may come to be excited sexually by males rather than by females and to direct his actions toward males, but the emotional experience he undergoes is unaltered.

There have been two approaches to child development, the mental health approach, which has emphasized emotional development, and the educational approach, which has stressed cognitive development. The current ethos of North American psychology is rather noticeably favorable to the latter. Sputnik no doubt had some influence on this state of affairs. But we must recall to ourselves the fact that a well-developed individual is not merely an effective intellectualizer but is also able to control and to enjoy emotionality. While the idea of emotions as pleasurable may still have overtones of indelicacy, we have to recognize that emotions are a legacy from our animal ancestors and not a liability they have bequeathed to us. Moreover, it is suggested, the most efficient intellectualizer is one whose emotional life functions best. We do not subscribe to the view that neuroticism aids cognition.

At a number of points in this book parallels are drawn between the human infant and infrahuman animals. This similarity (but not necessarily identity) is rather strikingly noted in language. For most of the first year the child is prelinguistic. After language (in the sense of words as conventional symbols denoting objects) appears around the end of the first year, there is a fairly rapid rate of language development, and by the time he enters school the child is a competent linguist, at least insofar as communicating and being communicated with on everyday and rather concrete matters are concerned. The more abstract uses of language are still only weakly developed at this stage.

Earlier investigators of language development have (on this continent at least) taken a behavioristic approach and have viewed language growth as the accumulation of linguistic *habits*. Recent works have emphasized the growth of language as the accumulation of *rules*. If this is so, then language development and cognitive development must be closely related. This newer view is not, of course, inconsistent with the idea that habit formation does enter into language development; it only claims that the acquisition of habits does not form a sufficient explanation of it.

Two basic ideas emerge. One is that discussed by Chomsky, that the child speaks a language of his own, a language which differs from that of the mature speaker. It is not so much in vocabulary as in the rules of its grammar that childish language differs. Moreover, this juvenile language is universal. Its actual vocabulary differs from place to place, but the basic grammatical construction is essentially the same for all children everywhere. The psycholinguists also claim a universality in adult language; that is, the basic structure of all human languages are the same, even though vocabulary and the details of linguistic structure differ markedly. However (though this is not stated explicitly), it seems to be assumed that juvenile language is more uniform than is adult language.

The second major assumption is that language is a species-specific character of humans and has definite biological bases. These are more particular bases than the obvious general ones that the organism must have an appropriate mouth and a tongue, neural storage mechanisms, and so on in order to be able to act linguistically. This view claims much more than this; it claims that the human organism has direct and specific neurological mechanisms serving speech. The human is, in fact, preprogrammed for speech, and (as it were) a blueprint for linguistic development is part of the basic inherited equipment of the child. The role of the environment is to stimulate and set going this "readiness to speak" and to provide the particular sounds and constructions of the child's locality. Thus the neonate is not a *tabula rasa* insofar as speech is concerned but is already biologically biased to language acquisition, and speech development consists of the environmental facilitation of this innate propensity. Speech development is highly efficient because speech is part of the biological "pattern norm" for the species.

As already mentioned, speech and cognitive development are closely related. One cannot say that thought *is* language, but it is certainly the case that one process facilitates the other and that again there is a leap-frog progression in which linguistic development aids thought and increased thought in turn facilitates the development of speech at increasingly abstract levels.

Intellectual development is a highly involved matter. (It would, like a number of other topics discussed here, require at least a book itself for complete coverage. Intellectual functioning is multidimensional, and here we have considered only some sample areas.) Each individual has a unique constellation of cognitive abilities. Males, however, tend to have patterns of abilities that are somewhat alike and that are distinctive from female patterns. Similarly, females on the average are more like one another than they are like males.

The intellectual capacities of the individual develop from basic tendencies that are innate. The environment provides the kinds of stimulation and experiences necessary to develop these nascent potentialities. In the imperfect world we inhabit, it is perhaps too often a matter of chance whether the environment favors, disfavors, or is merely indifferent toward a particular individual's potentials. The aim of an ideal educational system would be to reduce this randomness and ensure a milieu that fully develops the unique potential of each, though we are a long way from realizing this ideal. For one thing, we cannot as yet identify with certainty a given individual's potentials in the detail this aim implies; for another, we do not have anything approaching the flexibility and diversity of educational facilities that this aim requires. It is, however, an objective to strive for, even if it will require much research, on the one hand, and a considerable amount of political maneuvering, on the other, to attain it.

In discussing the relative influences of the internal and external factors on intellectual development, it is essential to avoid oversimplification. For instance, a number of authors (Burt is perhaps the most insistent of these) have stated that "intelligence" is mainly determined by heredity (and some, like Burt, quantify at such figures as 75 to 85 percent). But this oversimplifies by assuming that "intelligence" is some unitary thing. It is doubtful that this is the case; there are probably many varieties of intelligence and a number of components of it. It is also entirely possible that different aspects of this multiphasic entity are differently influenced by innate and environmental factors. Some aspects may be largely determined by heredity and others much more by environment. It is obviously important to know if this is really the case, because this knowledge would materially affect the design of the ideal educational system. It would influence the selection procedures and the practical questions of implementation.

It may be that even where a particular aspect of cognition is weakly represented in an individual, he can learn to mimic its operations. It has been suggested, for instance, that the potentially weak automatizer may learn to organize his cognitive activities like a strong automatizer, but he will not do this as effortlessly as one who is predisposed to do so. It might be that for some the effort to do so is disproportionate to the advantages that follow.

One might be dubious of the extent of such mimicry. The 100-IQ individual, for example, may in some respects function like a 140-IQ individual (and vice versa), though one suspects that such large discrepancies will be rare. It is almost certainly the case that the 100-IQ individual, even if he does have some 140 peaks, cannot learn to mimic the 140-IQ person in his *overall* functioning. And the stress of mimicking even a 120 level of performance may be too severe and too expensive to other aspects of functioning to warrant the effort. In other words, development, in this area as in others, must follow the design of the organism to be most efficient, and because individual human organisms differ widely in design, there must be wide differences in the kinds of environmental facilitations of basic potentialities that are supplied.

If it is true, as insisted throughout this book, that biological maturation rates impose a limit on educational acceleration, should we not accept this as a fact of life? Man can circumvent natural limitations. We cannot with our natural equipment detect polarization of light, but this has not prevented man from discovering that light can be polarized or from readily detecting polarization by artificial extensions of his natural equipment.

Similarly it may be unnecessary to shorten human childhood; it may be sufficient to merely improve the efficiency of education. For instance, much of the great amount of memorization that is still part of education is surely an anachronism in an age when artificial data storage is readily available. One part of the revolution in learning that is obviously appropriate is the insistence on principles rather than facts, though even here a certain minimum of facts is necessary to appreciate principles.

I suspect that an efficient educational system with properly trained pedagogues (as distinct from teachers banalized by normal schools) could easily teach all that is given in each of the elementary grades in six to twelve weeks. The rest of the school year is wasted. But even if this is true, it is not necessarily an argument for teaching the content of grades 1 to 7 between six and seven years of age. There is a host of things that could profitably be done with the balance of the time—such as listening to symphony concerts or exploring the Adirondacks or sailing. In other words, the extra time could be given to learning to live.

In considering human development, it might be asked whether emotional development is not, in fact, slower than intellectual development. In accelerating intellectual growth, we may produce a disharmony in the total process by allowing the various aspects to get out of phase. There are questions here that need very careful thought (and more data) before we embark on any wide-scale efforts to rush human development and to shorten childhood.

As already mentioned, almost the whole animal kingdom shows in the species two forms, male and female. These forms are innately different, develop differently, and display behavioral differences, not merely in reproductive behaviors but often in a wide range of behaviors not directly related to reproduction or care of offspring. This is especially true of the higher animals and is most true of humans. The boy and the girl therefore commence life with different potentialities and modes of functioning.

The environment acts upon the two sexes differently, and at the same time the sexes are distinctive in their reactions to the environment and in the manner in which they act back to modify it.

Important among the environmental influences on the masculine and feminine development of boys and girls are the father and the mother. The same-sex parent is a facilitator of the innate potentials for sex-appropriate behaviors. A major mechanism involved here is identification, which is es-

sentially a learning process, even though much of masculine and feminine behaviors are of the "preprimed" or "ready-to-go" variety also found in other forms of development. The boy has ready-made propensities to male-type behavior which the father (under suitable conditions) elicits and facilitates. If the assumption is valid that girls are rather less dependent on learning for the development of their sex-appropriate behaviors than are boys, the corresponding identification process between mother and daughter may be less salient. Indeed, it is possible, as some writers suggest, that father-daughter relationships (which may not be of the nature of identifications) are the critical ones in the development of social femininity in girls.

Important to the identification process is a nurturant relationship between the child and the parent. This must at present be taken as an observation and not as an explanation. That is, it is not explained *how* the affectional relationship between the two mediates the process, though apparently it is salient. Although it would seem that cultural devices to encourage this relationship are desirable, certain aspects of our society at the present time are not maximally conducive to father-child interactions.

Because there is evidence to suggest that maximum developmental efficiency is achieved when the male or the female develops along sex-appropriate lines, the encouragement of the identification process with the same-sex parent is desirable to realizing the aim of producing the fullest potential of the individual.

An important secondary effect of identification is on peer group relationships. Insofar as present evidence goes, this effect seems more significant to boys than to girls. The boy with a satisfactory identification with his father is aided in his acceptance by the peer culture and hence in acquiring the important range of experiences that this segment of the environment can provide. This effect is especially salient to the juvenile social activities that are involved in the learning of masculine sex behaviors.

The culture is a major source of influence in child development and has been the main concern of developmental psychologists, especially in North America. Among these cultural influences, the family is the most important. It is, in fact, a microcosm of the main culture in which it is embedded and provides the immediate matrix in which the child develops. Another highly significant influence is the peer culture.

There are similarities among all human cultures, because all are based upon biological needs that are common to all men. Culture is not independent of man's biology but in a fairly direct manner is molded by it. This is seen, for example, in the manner in which all human cultures have different expectations of males and females, expectations that are an expression (conscious or unformulated) of the fact that the sexes *are* different.

Human culture is an evolutionary innovation. Though cultures must reflect man's biological nature, they also give him an opportunity of transcending the baser elements of this nature, and they provide the medium in which his further evolution must occur. As Hallowell (1961) has said, cultural adaptation is the great novelty in the evolution of the primates and has brought a psychological restructuring that makes possible further cultural adaptation and change. Whether man will ultimately outgrow his biology altogether is a hard question. Unless he takes careful stock of his present nature and takes his further evolution in hand, the question will simply not arise. But if a value judgment may be made, there are some positive aspects to being a biological organism. Man does not have to be ashamed of being an animal, and much that is most beautiful and noble in human life derives rather directly from man's biology. What we really need of human cultures is the fullest development of what is best in man's biological potential.

A number of questions of value must be faced here. To take an example, we have suggested that sex differences should be fostered, though maybe this should be considered carefully. Thus a male trait is aggressivity, and this is one that threatens the very existence of the human race. Should this be advanced as an argument for the suppression of *all* sex differences? Femininity, no doubt, is entirely desirable and to be fostered in its completeness. Masculinity perhaps is good only in parts and should be encouraged only in parts. The above argument assumes that aggressivity is wholly bad and directed only to evil ends, which patently is not the case. It is a trait that can be used constructively as well as destructively, and the problem is not to eliminate aggressivity but to direct it into channels which are preferably useful ones.

The race to the moon is a classic example of alternative channeling. Possibly it was better in the early 1960's for Russia and the United States to become aggressively confronted in this enterprise than in some others that might have developed, but it may be questioned whether we really need this kind of lunacy at this stage of human history. All this intense energy could have been more constructively directed against famine. We are more likely in the later 1970's to be aggressively facing the Chinese, and the moon channel may already have outlived its usefulness.

If we think of aggression not in terms of physical combat but in terms of overcoming obstacles to the achievement of some worthwhile goal, then there is an abundance of nonviolent channels to accommodate the drives of males. A really aggressive approach to poverty and hunger could make this earth a fit place for human habitation.

It has been suggested already that a potent source of destructive aggressivity in the male is uncertainty about masculinity. The demasculinized male is under stress, which sometimes erupts into destruction. One might expect that a society that confirmed the male's masculinity might more readily harness his aggressivity to constructive ends. A number of authors have mentioned the "masculine protest" as a major factor in Negro rioting in the United States. A considerable proportion of Negroes are reared in mother-centered families, and absentee fathers are almost the norm. Under these conditions appreciable numbers of Negro youths and men are uncertain of their masculinity and protest it in the violent forms that have become familiar. Economic hopelessness and feelings of injustice are one ingredient in the present unrest, but this masculine protest is apparently another and a major factor. This aggression is not, however, a phenomenon peculiar to Negroes.

This situation illustrates very well the effects of dissonance between biological tendencies to behavior and the facilities the enviroment provides for their development. The Negro male (in common with many white males also, let it be remembered) develops in a milieu that does not provide the optimum conditions for the realization of his potential as a male. This engenders stress and produces behavioral deviation, which perhaps has the effect of releasing tension but really fails as a means of self-actualization.

If one is to ask what the aim of child rearing may be, then one will receive a variety of answers. Ask the question in the Pentagon, and the answer will be "to produce a young man who will cherish his draft card as his dearest possession." Ask Dr. Spock, and the answer will be different.

The answer given here is that the aim is to produce an individual who is self-aware, who knows himself, or herself, and who has a realistic self-concept. Such a definition can be disputed. For instance, there are some people who can say, and perhaps who do say, that their realistic self-appraisal is that they are inferior and will act accordingly. One then is obliged to introduce some qualifier, such as self-knowledge of the *best* that is within him—but this introduces a value judg-

ment as to how to define *best*. To avoid such a judgment, one can only follow Pollonius' advice, "To thine own self be true," and leave the individual to define this truth for himself. In an ideal society the judgment of what is desirable will be implicit and followed. Even in a rather less than ideal society there are standards that will influence most.

Self-awareness is the peak of evolution so far. It is man's prime mark of distinction as a species. To be fully self-aware is the achievement of the zenith of the individual's biological potential. To form a mature self-concept, man needs to know his assets and his liabilities and how to realize the former to the full and how to offset the latter.

To achieve this understanding, it is necessary to have some supraordinate scale of reference, and some kind of religious concept is needed here—not necessarily a deist religion, but some conception of man in relation to the universe, some philosophy that gives both hope and meaning to human existence. The search for meaning is the cardinal motive of man, a motive unique among life on this planet, and who knows whether or not it is unique in the universe?

MAN, HIS FUTURE, AND THE DEVELOPMENTALIST

The view of the content of developmental psychology being taken here is that it includes not only ontogenetic aspects, the growth and development of the individual, but phylogenetic ones also. That is, man's evolutionary past, as well as the short time span involved in the child's growing up, is properly the concern of the developmentalist. But further than this, man's evolutionary future is a competent concern. Moreover, it is considered that attempts to predict and measures to guide this evolutionary process are proper for the psychologist. This may appear to be an inflated evaluation of his role, but it must be accepted if we believe that man's fate is not in his stars but in himself. Not by any means is it suggested that the psychologist alone is able to direct man's evolution; that would indeed be a conceit that should not be countenanced. But it can hardly be denied that psychology has an important contribution to make to the understanding of man's nature and the defining of his potentials.

In the view of science man is the product of evolution; his body, its biochemistry, his nervous system and its workings, are in direct lineage with that of his animal ancestors. To many this has been an unacceptable notion. Science from the time of Copernicus onward has seemed to downgrade man by removing him from the exalted position "a little less than the angels" given to him by the Christian view of man. Darwin is frequently accused of producing the final degradation. Dobzhansky (1967) regards this view as wholly mistaken and sees evolution as a source of hope for man. Certainly, modern evolution has not restored the earth to the center of the universe, but Dobzhansky claims that even if the universe is not geocentric it may yet be anthropocentric. He is not impressed by the idea that throughout the universe there may be many inhabited planets and numerous hominoid species. He believes that this unique event in the universe, the evolution of man, may in this sense make the earth a focus in evolution. Moreover, on this earth there is evolutionary flow, and there is still change and development to take place.

The evolutionary process has, in fact, produced in man certain species-specific characteristics—his advanced intelligence, language, self-awareness—that in a sense enable him to transcend his biology. He still has the primitive instinctual modes of reaction but also the capacity to refine and make exquisite this aspect of his nature. Schopenhauer has taught us that the intellect is but one aspect of man and that the all-pervasive instincts are subtle and beautiful. Thoughts have not the impersonal qualities other philosophers claimed for them—they become active only when touched by desire. Genius, said Schopenhauer, is truly objective, but then genius is rare. And perhaps we should heed Schopenhauer even when considering man scientifically. As Anshen has put it in her introduction to Dobzhansky's book (1967):

The "objectivity" of science cannot help man in his present human predicament, since for science in this sense there can be no commitment. So that in the end we know everything but understand nothing [p. vii].

The ideal of the objective, impartial scientist who makes no value judgments is a dangerous one at this stage of human evolution. Only the most arid of pedants can remain entirely aloof, and for science today there must be concern and commitment.

It is important to define the present state of man in trying to forecast and mold his future. As has been suggested, there is no reason for regarding man as a finally evolved species but rather as a species in evolution. What relation does man of the future bear to man of the present? It is suggested here that the present species is misnamed: It is *homo faber*, not *sapiens*. We have entered a phase in man's existence in which the emphasis is on technology, on making for the sake of making rather than because it enhances man's nature. The race to the moon exemplifies this emphasis to its highest degree. Enormous amounts of talent and the cleverest of devices are being used to collect a handful of lunar dust without any apparent concern as to whether this is a worthwhile venture *at this point in history*. At a time when illiteracy is increasing rather than decreasing, when primitive methods of agriculture over most of the world are meaning that more and more of the increasing population gets too little to eat, one might ask whether the attempt to reach the moon is not a frivolous dissipation of effort. The United States has a race situation that seems more worthy of attention —not that it is entirely neglected, but maybe the cleverness being squandered at Cape Kennedy might more fittingly be added to the efforts to solve this problem. Russia, no doubt, has its more urgent matters for attention, but each nation is in the race because the other is. With so many problems involving man directly on the earth, this attention to a non-man-centered achievement is indicative of the fact that man is bemused by his ability to make and too little concerned with his ability to live and to enjoy living and too little concerned with ensuring that *all* can share this fullness.

This attitude of obeisance to technology is seen in so many facets of modern life. We see it in aviation. Because it is technically possible for large planes to fly at supersonic speeds, it is assumed without question that they *have* to, despite the certainty that they will produce broad swaths of sonic boom that will disturb millions. So that a few can save an hour or two, whole cities must suffer noise pollution, and few ask if it is justified. The industrialists consider that their ability to *do* gives them a sacred right to act. It seems that the education of man to think about technology critically, and to restrain it where necessary, is a matter of urgency.

The changes of the machine age are exemplified by the railway locomotive. The steam locomotive, for all its impressiveness, was completely "unintelligent." It relied entirely on men's brains, and without constant regard for its operation, it would run down and stop within a few miles or even destroy itself with a burnt-out boiler. It required, in fact, the coordinated intelligence of two men to keep it going. The diesel "thinks" for itself to a considerable extent, and there are already the technical means for making it completely self-operating. The crew are really redundant, and within a few years we will no doubt have crewless trains operating as a matter of routine. The same trend is to be found in almost all industries. We are producing a society in which fewer and fewer people can lead nonrobotized lives. There are (as discussed elsewhere) positive aspects to auto-mation in that it frees man from dull chores to permit truly human activities, but we need also to be aware of the dangers, lest they outweigh the advantages.

In a sense, it could be said that driving a steam locomotive was a more truly human and dignified activity than operating a diesel, because the man was master and without the man the powerful machine was powerless—only man gave the machine life. Now the man is largely superfluous and may well become more so. Even self-reproducing machines are already a theoretical possibility, and with the speed of technical changes one cannot dismiss them as a practical impossibility.

The influences of these technologically derived social changes on child rearing have not been much explored, though there are some who see a marked impact on the patterns of childhood. As Erikson (1959) warned us,

Our child-training customs have begun to standardize modern man, so that he may become a reliable mechanism prepared to adjust to the competitive exploitation of the machine world. In fact, certain trends in child-training seem to represent a magic identification with the machine, analogous to identifications of primitive tribes with their principal prey.

Some of these trends have been described by Schwarcz (1967), who believes there is a pervasive theme of anthropomorphism of machines in recent children's literature, accompanied by a dehumanization of man in relation to the machine. If these authors are right, then we require some consistent facet of education that will prepare the child to master the machine and not be mastered by it.

In discussing earlier man's place in the evolutionary scale, it was suggested that at a physical level his survival is reasonably assured. That is, famine, widespread disease, and climatic changes are unlikely to overwhelm the species, though they may take a toll of its numbers. It is not in the biological sphere but in the social one that man faces his greatest challenge to survival. It is social changes, not physical changes, that will tax his ability to adapt and threaten the extinction of the species. Thus again we have the fact that man is an aggressive animal, and conflict has been a prominent feature of his social activity; but he has modified his environment to the point where there must be a change in this aspect of his behavior, or it will destroy him. The dropping of war making as a feature of social behavior is an adaptation of the most pressing moment to the survival of the species. Prejudice may be part of man's biological nature—the tendency to eschew differences and avoid nonimprinted objects—but it is a tendency inimical to the close-packed social organization that has evolved. These are among the biological features of man's nature that must be modified if he is to survive as a species. Man has available to him the means for avoiding famine and disease that might extinguish the species, but the use of these means will involve social changes (such as the free international movement of food surpluses) that are apparently not feasible under present conditions. The limitation of family size and hence of population is technically possible, but its widespread use involves considerable social changes in many groups and societies.

In the use of the term *evolution* here, it is being given a broader meaning than in the purely genetic sense. We know, admittedly, rather little about the genetics of psychological characteristics and have less evidence of what changes have taken place. The physical anthropologists tell us that there has been no detectable change in the size or characteristics of the cranium in the past ten thousand years or so, but this tells us nothing about changes in its contents. There is no evidence of any change in the higher ranges of intelligence in historical times. One difficulty is that we can make estimates only for the most gifted—the Aristotles—and have nothing much to indicate the general level, except that the anonymous work of forgotten artisans seems to suggest the presence of manual and artistic skills no less than those common today. But

what the average level was is unknown. Shifts have been reported in certain mental diseases that are probably inherited, but it is impossible to say whether these are genuine changes or merely changes in fashions of labeling. Nor do we know of any changes in other psychological characteristics. (See Figure 20–1.)

While the height of the peaks of human achievement are unchanged, it could still be that such peaks are more numerous today, though greater educational opportunity might well account for the whole of this apparent increase. In any case, the population is so much greater that one would expect an increase in the number of Aristotles without a proportional change.

In speaking of evolution here, the question of a genetic component must be sidestepped, and the term is used rather for changes in attitudes and ideas. To take an example, if one can regard accent as a psychological characteristic, accent illustrates the point. In some societies (present-day Britain is an instance) accent has important social consequences. A cockney accent is a disadvantage in certain situations and seriously restricts the social mobility of an individual. Yet phoneticians tells us that in the time of Queen Elizabeth I the accent we now call cockney was that of the upper classes and probably that of the Virgin Queen herself. Gradually it became adopted by the masses and lost its function as a badge of good breeding and privilege; the upper classes evolved new ways of speech. Now quite obviously there have been no genetic changes involved here; there is not a gene for cockney speech or for the modern upper-class intonations known to phoneticians as RP (or received pronunciation). Evolution, as the term is being used here, implies the transmission from generation to generation, by learning, of ways of thought and learned behavioral characteristics. The example of accent is in many respects an unimportant characteristic, though it is locally important in the respect of having

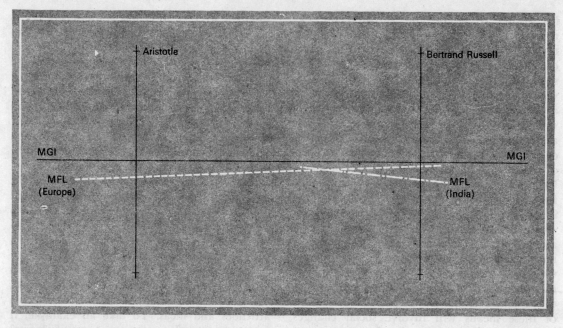

FIGURE 20-1. *Estimated trend of intelligence from the Age of Pericles to modern times (MGI: Mean Genetic Intelligence; MFL: Mean Functional Level).*

social consequences—a fact used tellingly in Shaw's play *Pygmalion*.

However, it is not altogether impossible that evolution in the genetic sense may also occur, though there is little evidence of much change in the human gene pool in historical times. It is not denied that evolution in the more biological sense is still possible, for it is, in fact, probable—but at this stage of knowledge there is little to say on the topic. The eugenics movement, active earlier in this century, was based upon the idea that human populations should be subject to selective breeding, whereby desirable traits, such as intelligence, should become more frequent and undesirable ones, like mental deficiency, should be eradicated, the evolutionary process being speeded. Little is heard of this today because it has been realized that quite apart from the social difficulties and questions of ethics involved the matter is not as simple as restricting the breeding of the unfit and en-

couraging that of the fit. Because of the phenomenon of regression to the mean, dull parents tend to have children brighter than themselves and bright ones to have less bright children—even mentally retarded ones. Not even the most ruthless control of man's reproduction would fully achieve the aims of a Eugenics Society.

Mention has already been made of aggressivity as an undesirable characteristic that threatens the survival of the species. Now there is from animal studies some evidence that aggressivity may be an inherited character. Certainly it is possible to breed strains of rats for aggression and docility, and it might be genetically possible to do so with humans also, though this would be impractical for other reasons. What is feasible is to evolve a social structure in which this tendency is channeled constructively and in which aggression as means of personal or international manipulation is not practiced. Even in rats, social conditions such as overcrowding influence the amount of aggression. There are certain biological tendencies that are amenable to acquired modification. Each generation has to acquire this modification anew, but it is the function of culture to provide the medium with which the growing child does acquire it.

In this sense, human evolution is the evolution of culture and its aim that of setting up a culture that minimizes the undesirable features of man's nature and encourages those features that are most desirable. The place allotted to the psychologist in this process is in helping to define what man's nature may be; the developmentalist is more specifically concerned with the development of this nature and is in a key position to suggest the means of aiding the flowering of the best.

The idea of continuing evolution implies that at any given time there are newly emerging desirable traits that are necessarily confined to a limited number of the population. Because these traits are advantageous, this implies that this small group constitutes an elite. This seems to conjure up the alphas of Huxley's *Brave New World*. But in the course of time the trait spreads throughout the population and is shared by the majority; it hence loses its distinguishing properties, though there is now likely to be a small group who *lack* the trait and constitute an underprivileged group. Again, these might seem to be the omegas. However, there is a constant flux that should tend to offset this effect. For one thing, we are not (or should not) be conceiving an aristocracy with one distinctive badge. The alphas in one trait may well bear omega endowments in others and vice versa.

In using terms such as *undesirable* or *not desirable,* there is a value judgment that is foreign to current scientific thinking. Scientists are not supposed to make such judgments. Nevertheless, it is patent that society cannot exist without some scale of values, and these have to come from somewhere. There was a time when it was considered that there was an absolute standard of values—

that inherent in God. Perhaps at no time has man been quite confident of knowing precisely what God's value system might be, but there have at least been times when man felt he had a working knowledge of it and could make value judgments, genuinely believing himself to have divine approval.

Today we no longer have any real confidence in divine sanctions; even though most of the Western nations officially recognize God, none of them conduct their affairs in much concordance with this belief. Most of the reasons for the present state of affairs are outside the scope of this work, though there is one that has some implications to the present discussion. A fatal defect in the Christian ethic, as interpreted by St. Paul and elaborated by later theologians, is its failure to take account of man's biological nature. So far as one can gather from the recorded statements of Jesus, and certainly this seems inherent in the spirit of his message, he was completely accepting of human nature as it is. He was in sympathy (it would seem from the Dead Sea Scrolls) with a liberal movement in Judaism, that had occupied two or three centuries before his time. However, Paul brought in the orthodox Judaic ideas, especially those on sexual morality, which implied man's basic nature to be something reprehensible. One may see in the present rejection of religion a revulsion from this austere view of man. Perhaps St. Paul has finally achieved what Saul of Tarsus set out to do. This is unfortunate, because contained within the Judeo-Christian code is a value system that makes good social sense and would form a basis for a workable human society.

The lesson from this would seem to be that any attempt at defining an ideal culture should not be left dependent on a scale of values decided by any one point of view. We should not ignore the transcendental side of man's nature, but we must also accept fully his biology. The scientist cannot abdicate his responsibility in this matter by pleading that values are outside his scope. He can describe the physical world as it is and he can describe plants and animals as they are, but he must be prepared to do more than describe man: He must be willing to make a judgment about how man ought to be.

The question of directed social evolution raises, however, some difficult issues. Who is to plot the direction it should take? There is merit to the argument that any attempt to plan man's development is open to abuse and should not be attempted. The fault with this argument is that it is too late to apply it. The fact is that man's destiny is being planned —not tidily perhaps, but rather surely. It is being decided, piecemeal no doubt and without an overall direction, by politicians and economic and military leaders, aided by dehumanized science. Sometimes these plans are dictated by genuine short-term needs of limited value to mankind as a whole. Otherwise, and possibly more often, they are directed by the material ambitions of individuals and small groups, with no reference whatever to man's overall welfare.

Maybe it would be aesthetically more satisfying to allow man to grow and flower in his own good time, but such time is not availed us and we are not faced with the choice of an ideal but with a choice between two evils. Planned evolution is markedly the lesser of the two and wisely handled need not be bad at all. Indeed, it could be seen as the speeding up by self-conscious effort of a process that must eventually occur if we can make one assumption—that human nature is inherently good.

This may seem to imply free will, and to do so will involve a bitter and fruitless hassle with the philosophers who maintain that this fallacy has been laid to rest for all time. The issue can perhaps be evaded (because argument with philosophers is a frustrating undertaking) by saying that there is no reason for supposing that man is predetermined to failure as a species. Maybe he is predetermined to success, and maybe the writers who express a hopeful belief in man's ability to control his destiny are merely perceiving the determined pattern.

The point of all this is that in studying the development of the individual we must have in mind what he is developing toward. Further, if developmental psychology is to be more than merely descriptive, it must be prepared to make some statement about the optimum direction of development—that which makes for the fullest flowering of the human potential.

BEHAVIORISM AND CHILD REARING

There is an influential line of approach to child development that has not received much attention in this book, and most of the attention that it has received has been critical. This is the "behavioristic" approach, with J. B. Watson as its prime mover, but more recently developed by Skinner.

It must be quite evident to the reader, especially from what has been said in this chapter and in Chapter 19, that the behavioristic approach arouses cognitive dissonance in me. The emphasis here on self-actualizing and the implied responsibility for one's own psychic fate is quite at variance with the "schedules of reinforcement" that Skinner sees as the shapers of behavior. I place positive value on "autonomy" and negative value on "other-directiveness."

In dealing with my own children I have said, "Why should I reward you for getting A's on your report? The reward is inherent in the getting; it is to *your* advantage, not mine, to do well in school."

Partly on the basis of my own experience with this self-directed approach, I am prepared to concede that Skinner's thesis has merit. Some children *are* Skinnerians and need constant external reinforcement, and no doubt all children need some positive feedback of this nature in order to commence the self-actualizing process. It may even be that only a minority of children are sufficiently self-directed to be able to function autonomously, although this hypothesis needs verification.

The relative failure of traditional methods of psychotherapy, such as psychoanalysis, which have heavy emphasis on cognitive restructuring, might also be taken as evidence supporting the Skinnerian position. The so-called "talking therapies" rely very much on the patient's own ability to be self-directed, to restructure from within. The fact that they fail with so considerable a proportion of those that undertake them is perhaps an indication that the ability to be self-directed is limited, at least in the population that seeks psychiatric treatment. (One is also led to wonder what proportion of the successes of these therapies are with people having the inner resources to solve their existential problems anyway, so that the connection between visits to the therapist and change is merely fortuitous.) The reported successes of the "behavior therapies," particularly in cases where the "talking therapies" have failed, may be evidence that some people are in fact more molded by external rewards and punishments than by inner directives. What division of the population at large there may be between the two types, the autonomous and the other-directed, is unknown.

It seems to me that the Skinnerian approach underestimates the potential of the child's natural curiosity—what has been spoken of in earlier chapters as the "exploratory" drive and the seeking of novelty and stimulation. These are persistent and powerful sources of motivation and ones that generate increasing intellectual and personality development from within. Reinforcement is inherent in achievement, and does not exist merely in teacher approval or candy rewards. It may well be that children differ innately in the strength of these biological "curiosity drives" and that these differences will lead to differing approaches to the environment and strivings to master it. But it is also evident from material reviewed in previous chapters that early experiences may considerably modify these biological tendencies. A stimulating environment may foster them, and an unfavorable one may suppress them.

There are several lines of inquiry that arise here. Are Skinnerian techniques in fact more (or less) effective in the long run? Is it the case that children brought up on schedules of reinforcement become dependent on them for continued performance, or do they progress on to higher levels of inner motivation? Are there individual differences in response to inner and outer sources of motivation? It could be the case that Skinnerian methods are necessary and suited to repairing the results of early deprivation and that the best responders to external reinforcement are those whose inner resources have been stunted.

Even if Skinner is more nearly correct than I am prepared to concede here, it would seem politically desirable to emphasize in child rearing the self-directed approach. I have the uncomfortable feeling that *Walden II* and *1984* are too much alike to be encouraged.

On reflection about the implications of behaviorism for child rearing, it would seem that there are some important issues that have not been adequately discussed in this book. Throughout the book there is repeated the plea that education should be individual and that different children will respond better to certain methods of child rearing than to others. It could be that the setting up of a universal milieu dependent on self-direction will disadvantage some children who cannot respond to this kind of situation. It may be false to assume that this is the case, but at least it seems an assumption that needs to be examined. It may even be that to avoid the political dangers of too great other directiveness we need to further the evolution of self-directors and minimize behavioristic modes of response in children.

CAN REARING BE CONSISTENT?

One problem in producing a blueprint of a child-rearing system is that some requirements are mutually exclusive. For instance, we have seen that "permissiveness" in child rearing may produce children of low self-esteem. On the other hand, permissiveness is necessary to producing creativity (or put somewhat differently, structured rearing is inimical to creativity). The fact is that the correlation between permissiveness and low self-esteem is not a perfect one, so some children reared permissively do achieve high self-esteem—possibly because they are creative children who can realize *their* particular potential best under these conditions.

The highly variegated system of rearing being advocated here may be expected to contain many contradictions, and what is desirable for one child may not be so for another. It may even be that for a particular child there are potentialities having different and mutually exclusive requirements. For instance, the personality of a particular child with creative potential may be such that an unstructured environment makes him impossible to live with, and that a judgment has to be made as to whether to provide the conditions to foster his creativity and let his neighbors stand the inconvenience or to limit his behavior and risk suppressing his creativeness.

There are no simple recipes for child rearing, and an approach to this problem needs to be highly sophisticated. The developmentalist needs to be tolerant of ambiguity and to make quite opposing recommendations in particular cases.

THE AIM OF CHILD REARING

In attempting to conceptualize human development, it is necessary to have some idea of the goal of development. This schematic target model could take the form of a description of man as he is—a study of that ubiquitous fiction, the average man. We could assume that today's children will turn out to be like this, and such an assumption has some measure of validity, though it gives a necessarily mediocre model.

On the other hand, can we adopt the comfortable assumption of previous generations of parents and educators that the world as we know it is the one our children are to live in as adults? This may not be the case, and the rapid changes of the past half-century may well continue, so that to take man as he is will give only an imperfect picture of man of the future.

This raises the further question of the limits of change. *How* different can human beings become? The question leads into a discussion of the biological basis of development and the constraints (if any) that these impose on human change, either over the life span of an individual or from generation to generation. It raises, in fact, the question of the pattern norm and the human design.

With these questions in mind, one approach to a philosophy of development could be to set up some ideal concept of man—not necessarily man as he is, but as he might be—and then examine the process by which the child can achieve this end result.

A wide variety of descriptions of the ideal man are available, and there could be interminable debate, with little hope of arriving at any unanimity of opinion, as to which is the appropriate one. In choosing a model one need not be influenced by the popularity of the appeal of what he chooses, but one must make a choice that there is some reasonable hope of attaining. In other words, the choice must take realistic account of both man's potential and his limitations and man's pattern norm. The limitations must be regarded, though not too pessimistically. It is well known that men can respond to demands with unexpected achievements, but the idea that faith can move mountains has to be taken metaphorically and not literally. Perhaps we must agree, with Sartre, that man is not perfectible but has a duty to become the best he can. If man cannot win outright, then at least he can be a good loser.

As the ideal model for man as he should be it is proposed to take Maslow's "self-actualizer," which is realistic in that some men achieve it, though it is also lofty in that many men do not (Maslow, 1954).

It is, of course, a blatant value judgment to claim that this, rather than some other, is the appropriate model, but for the purpose of argument some arbitrary assumptions must be made. The reader with some alternative model can readily fit *his* into the general theme of this book.

In his book Maslow does not give a clear definition of self-actualization, but to him it is the highest level of motivational organization. He derives the term from Goldstein (1939) but uses it in a more specific and limited manner. For Maslow, it refers to man's desire for self-fulfillment—his desire to actualize in himself what he is potentially. There is, of course, an enormous range of individual difference in the direction that this "becoming everything that one is capable of being" will take. A necessary prerequisite for the development of self-actualization is the satisfaction of basic physiological needs and also the supplying of certain fundamental psychological needs, which Maslow describes as safety, love, and esteem.

In a study of self-actualizing people, Maslow reports that almost all the subjects he could find to meet his criteria of being self-actualizers were older subjects; in extensive screening of 3,000 college students, only a handful were found. This may be taken as consistent with the idea that psychological development continues after physical maturity is reached. One of the primary characteristics of the self-actualizer is acceptance of himself, including his animal self, for he can enjoy his appetites in a hearty and unashamed manner. He is an Apollonian Dionysius.

Another characteristic of the self-actualizing person is spontaneity in both behavior and in inner life. This does not consist of a striving for unconventionality for its own sake, for the value of some convention is recognized, and conventions will often be observed out of respect for the feelings of others. Rather, the self-actualizer is unconventional when he can be constructively so; he is not merely a bohemian concerned with trivial rebelliousness. Maslow quotes Fromm (1941), stating that the average, normal well-adjusted person often has not the slightest idea of what he is or what he wants or what his opinions are. Maslow finds the self-actualizing person to be profoundly different from this and suggests that we may need a different psychology of motivation for such individuals. He suggests, in fact, that the concept of motivation might apply only to non-self-actualizers, because they no longer strive but rather just develop. The motivations of "ordinary men" (Maslow's term) involve striving for basic need gratifications, whereas self-actualizing persons have achieved these gratifications in self-acceptance. They do not lack impulses, but their impulses are toward maturation, development, and self-growth.

Maslow asks whether self-actualizing people are not more human, more in keeping with the original nature of the human species, whereas the non-self-actualizers are over-domesticated. This is perhaps one way of looking at it, but in some ways the reverse might be more accurate; that is, that those whom Maslow has called "ordinary" men are the present species, and the self-actualizers are an evolutionary development beyond this stage. This would seem more in keeping with the use of the species concept in biology in which majority characteristics are taxonomic.

Another characteristic of the self-actualizer is found in what Maslow calls "problem centering"; these people are focused on problems outside themselves—not egocentric or introspective problems, such as are characteristic of the insecure person, but problems related to a mission in life or a task to be fulfilled. In saying this, Maslow follows Angyal (1941). In general, self-actualizers are concerned with basic issues and questions that are usually called philosophical or ethical. They tend to see in breadth rather than being concerned with the minute or the trivial.

A further quality of self-actualizers is one of detachment or a need for privacy. Because of this detachment, they may appear aloof and reserved, but they are also able to view even their personal misfortunes with serenity and without undue reactions. They are less dependent on social relationships than are others and much better able to tolerate (and indeed to require) a degree of isolation. Such qualities are not, of course, without their problems, and they lead to difficulties in acceptance by others. But Maslow suggests that the introvert-extrovert dichotomy is not really applicable to this situation and that self-actualizers should not be thought of as introverts.

Autonomy, or the independence of cultural environment, is another characteristic of the self-actualizers, who are directed by growth motivations rather than by deficiency motivations. They are not dependent for satisfactions on the real world, or on other people, or on culture, but instead are dependent on their own potentialities and latent resources. Deficiency-motivated people must have others available because their need gratifications for love, safety, respect, prestige, and belongingness can come only from other humans. The growth-motivated person, on the other hand, has achieved satisfaction of these and is strong enough to be independent of the good opinions of other people. Maslow is careful to point out that this independence can only be arrived at after having received love and respect in the past and that no doubt the early childhood experiences are a necessary preparation for the achievement of self-actualization. The individual who has not received these in earlier life is presumably severely handicapped in achieving self-actualization in later life.

A characteristic of the self-actualizing person (which has also been described as characteristic of the creative person) is the capacity to appreciate the basic things of life, freshly and naively and with awe, pleasure, and wonder; ecstasy is a common experience for these people. This is true even of such things as the beauties of nature, which have paled for others. For some such people, Maslow suggests, sexual experiences may have a mystical quality that is revitalizing. The kinds of mystic experiences described by William James (1943) are common in Maslow's sample of self-actualizers, not only in connection with sexual orgasm but in other contexts also.

The self-actualizing person has a feeling for mankind, for which Maslow adopts the term, by Adler (1939), *Gemeinschaftsgefühl* as being the only one available that describes it. There is a deep feeling of identification simply in affection for mankind, even though this is tempered by anger, impatience, or disgust at some of the manifestations of humanity. He has what Adler has called the "older brother" attitude.

Although Maslow has described self-actualizing persons as being relatively independent of interpersonal relationships, he also finds them to be capable of more profound personal relationships than are other adults. There is also a selective factor, in that these close relationships are likely to be with other individuals also high in self-actualization, a fact that, according to Maslow, restricts the circle of possible close friends, because the number of these people is limited.

These people are democratic in the true sense of the word, in that they are untied by the usual boundaries of class, education, race, color, and so on. They find it possible to learn from anyone who has anything to teach, and they respect other human beings because they are human. Means and ends are clearly distinguished by self-actualizing people, and in general the attention is fixed on ends rather than on the means. It is not entirely clear what Maslow means by this, but he comments that none of his subjects were unsure about the diffe ence between right and wrong (even though their conceptions of right and wrong were often not the conventional ones) and that they generally had a truly religious outlook—for the most part they rarely were confessed atheists, but, on the other hand, they did not contribute to orthodox religion. Again, this is similar to the position taken by certain of the existential philosophers, notably Sartre, who despite a nonreligious attitude of mind have a strongly binding code of morality based upon respect for the individual.

The importance of a sense of humor as forming the core of a mature and well-adjusted personality has been emphasized by Allport (1937) and discussed in Chapter 19. Maslow also sees this as characteristic of the self-actualizer. But it is unlike that of other people. For one thing, hostile humor (laughter at the expense of others or at someone else's hurt) is not amusing to them, and neither is superiority humor or laughter at someone else's inferiority. Similarly, merely smutty jokes without elements of genuine humor are not appreciated. Maslow regards Abraham Lincoln's humor as an example, for he never made a joke that hurt anybody, but most of his jokes had something to say—and they had values beyond that of producing a laugh.

Yet another characteristic, already covered by much that has been mentioned, is the resistance of the self-actualizing person to enculturation. One might say that they are in the culture but not of it; that is, they get along well enough with the mores and demands of society, yet they retain detachment from them. Riesman (1950) has pointed to the importance to Western civilization of this saving remnant who are resistant to molding by culture, and this resistance may well be a socially important attribute of these individuals. The dissent that is so deplored by some sections of American society may, in fact, be its salvation. We can only hope so.

One of the most characteristic features of the self-actualizer is creativity, and Maslow says this characteristic was universal in the subjects in his study. Not all, of course, showed creativeness of the genius variety, but all, in some field or another, showed originality or inventiveness. In fact, in viewing the other characteristics that Maslow described for these people, one might see creativeness as the keystone quality that gives each of the others its place: Without creativeness we may suppose that none of the other qualities can function in the constellation of traits that make up self-actualizing.

Maslow is not blind to the fact that his group of self-actualizing individuals have their faults. They are not so good as to be paragons, but, as with other people, they have flaws that often stem from their virtues.

It may be felt that the picture of the ideal man painted by Maslow is a somewhat smug one. Other models might be taken—for example, the astronaut, as an intelligent, clean-living all-American, well trained and dutiful, and from all accounts terribly dull. Or another might be the Aryan ideal of the Nazis—the efficient military man—and there is a warning here. Implicit in Maslow's ideal, indeed in any that one chooses to set up, is the notion of a superior class, a race of men apart from the ordinary. One draws close to the idea of Nietzsche and the master race, and we know too well where such notions can lead. But the self-actualizer, even as a superman, would be benevolent—too liberal for intolerances, too concerned with other issues to seek autocratic power over his fellows.

In view of the limitations on certain aspects of development discussed in various preceding chapters, it may be questioned to what extent —even with the most ideal child rearing—all individuals can become self-actualizers. (The same applies to almost any other ideal one sets up that is not merely banal.) It would seem probable that even in an ideal society many and perhaps most individuals will be non-self-actualizers. However, the self-actualizer (assuming he is in control, which does not perhaps follow of necessity) would seem to be one eminently trustworthy of ensuring a dignified and happy life for those unlike himself.

This book has spoken of man as he might be, and it may well be asked if an instance, in flesh and blood, of this ideal might be pointed to. Is this man only in the abstract, of which there is no living example? Many, no doubt, will provide their own paragons; others will protest, maybe, that no living instance exists. I believe there are several living instances, and I wish to conclude with a quotation from one man whose life exemplifies the best in humanity—one of the finest humans of the twentieth century. Here we have a superb intellect—self-aware, self-actualizing, an Apollonian—yet warm and fully appreciative of beauty and the joy of life—a Dionysian too. He said:

There is no reason why life on earth should not be filled with happiness. There is no reason why imagination should have to take refuge in myth. In such a world as men could now make, if they chose, it could be freely creative within the framework of our terrestrial existence. In recent times, knowledge has grown so fast that its acquisition has been confined to a tiny minority of experts, few of whom have had the energy or the capacity to impregnate it with poetic feeling and cosmic insight.

The Ptolemaic System of astronomy found its best poetic expression in Dante, and for this it had to wait some fifteen hundred years. We are suffering from undigested science. But in a world of more adventurous education this undigested mass would be assimilated and our poetry and art could be enlarged to embrace new worlds to be depicted in new epics. The liberation of the human spirit may be expected to lead to new splendours, new beauties and new sublimities impossible in the cramped and fierce world of the past. If our present troubles can be conquered, Man can look forward to a future immeasurably longer than his past, inspired by a new breadth of vision, a continuing hope perpetually fed by a continuing achievement. Man has made a beginning creditable for an infant—for, in a biological sense, Man, the latest of species, is still an infant. No limit can be set to what he may achieve in the future. I see, in my mind's eye, a world of glory and joy, a world where minds expand, where hope remains undimmed, and what is noble is no longer condemned as treachery to this or that paltry aim. All this can happen if we will let it happen. It rests with our generation to decide between this vision and an end decreed by folly [Bertrand Russell, 1961, p. 126].

Bibliography

AARONSON, B. S. 1959. A comparison of two MMPI measures of masculinity-femininity. *J. Psychol.,* **15:** 48-50.

ABEL, S. 1945. Androgenic therapy in malignant disease of the female genitalia: preliminary report. *Amer. J. Obstet. Gynecol.,* **49:** 327-342.

ABERCROMBIE, BARBARA, and JAMES H. ABERCROMBIE. 1961. The stability of the domestic chick's response to visual flicker. *Anim. Behav.,* **9:** 205-212.

ABERCROMBIE, M. L. J. 1968. Some notes on spatial disability: movement, intelligence quotient and attentiveness. *Develop. Med. Child Neurol.,* **10:** 206-213.

ABRAVANEL, E. 1967. Developmental changes in the intersensory patterning of space. *Proceedings of the 75th Annual Convention of the American Psychological Association,* **2:** 161-162.

———. 1968. The development of intersensory patterning with regard to selected spatial dimensions. *Monogr. Soc. Res. Child Develop.,* **33** (2): Serial No. 48.

ADER, R. 1962. Social factors affecting emotionality and resistance to disease in animals. III. Early weaning and susceptibility to gastric ulcers in the rat. A control for nutritional factors. *J. Comp. Physiol. Psychol.,* **55:** 600-602.

ADES, H. W. 1946. Effects of extirpation of para-striate cortex on visual discrimination in monkeys. *J. Neuropathol. Exp. Neurol.,* **5:** 60-65.

ADLER, A. 1928. Characteristics of the first, second, third child. *Children,* **3:** 14, 52.

———. 1939. *Social interest.* London: Putnam.

ADRIAN, E. D. 1928. *The basis of sensation: The action of the sense organs.* London: Christopher.

AGRANOFF, B. W. 1967. Memory and protein synthesis. *Sci. Amer.,* **216**(6): 115-123.

AGRAWAL, K. G. 1966. Age and color codability. *Mannas.,* **13:** 33-39.

AINSWORTH, MARY. 1962. The effects of maternal deprivation: a review of findings and controversy in the context of research strategy, in *Deprivation of maternal care: A re-assessment of its effects.* Geneva. World Health Organization Publication, Health Papers, 14.

———, D. SALTER, and BARBARA A. WITTIG. 1969. Attachment and exploratory behavior of one-year-olds in a strange situation, in B. M. Foss, ed., *Determinants of infant behavior.* IV. London: Methuen.

ALLEE, W. C. 1936. Analytical studies of group behaviour in birds. *Wilson Bull.,* **48:** 145-151.

———. 1942. Group organisation among vertebrates. *Science,* **95:** 289-293.

ALLEN, C. 1949. *The sexual perversions and ab-*

normalities: a study in the psychology of paraphilia. London: Oxford Univ. Press.

———. 1962. *Textbook of psychosexual disorders.* London: Oxford Univ. Press.

ALLEN, J. 1904. The associative processes of the guinea pig. *J. Comp. Neurol. Psychol.,* **14:** 293-359.

ALLPORT, G. W. 1937. *Personality: A psychological interpretation.* New York: Henry Holt.

———. 1961. *Pattern and growth in personality.* New York: Holt, Rinehart and Winston.

ALMY, MILLIE, E. CHITTENDEN, and PAULA MILLER. 1966. *Young children's thinking.* New York: Columbia Univ. Press.

ALTMAN, J., G. D. DAS, and W. J. ANDERSON. 1968. Effects of infantile handling on morphological development of the rat brain: an exploratory study. *Develop. Psychobiol.,* **1:** 10-20.

ALTUS, W. D. 1962. Sibling order and scholastic aptitude. *Amer. Psychologist,* **17:** 304 (abstract).

———. 1963. Some birth-order parameters related to verbal and quantitative aptitude. *Amer. Psychologist,* **18:** 361 (abstract).

———. 1964. Birth order and a brief (ten-point) measure of aptitude. *Amer. Psychologist,* **19:** 506.

———. 1966. Birth order of the omnibus personality inventory. *Proceedings of the 74th Annual Convention of the American Psychological Association,* 279-280.

AMBROSE, J. A. 1963. The concept of a critical period for the development of social responsiveness, in B. M. Foss, ed., *Determinants of infant behavior,* Vol. II. New York: Wiley.

AMES, LOUISE. 1952. The sense of self in nursery school children as manifested by their verbal behavior. *J. Genet. Psychol.,* **81:** 193-232.

———, and FRANCES ILG. 1964. Sex differences in test performance of matched girl-boy pairs in the five-to-nine year old range. *J. Genet. Psychol.,* **104:** 25-34.

AMTHAUER, R. 1963. Über das "Spezifische" und das "Kompensatorische" beim Zustandekommen von Leistungen, aufgezeigt an Ergebnissen einer Untersuchung zur Frage der Leistungsunterschiede der Geschlecter. (The contribution of "special intelligence" and "compensatory skills" to achievement as demonstrated by an investigation of achievement differences of the sexes.) *Psychol. Rdschr.,* **14:** 151-170.

ANASTASI, ANNE. 1958. Heredity, environment and the question "how?" *Psychol. Rev.,* **65:** 197-208.

ANASTASIOW, N. J. 1965. Success in school and boy's sex role patterns. *Child Develop.,* **36:** 1053-1066.

———, and J. P. FOLEY. 1953. *Differential psychology.* New York: Macmillan.

ANDERSON, C. C. 1966. A cognitive theory of the nonintellective correlates of originality. *Behav. Sci.,* **11:** 284-294.

———, and A. J. CROPLEY. 1966. Some correlates of originality. *Aust. J. Psychol.,* **18:** 218-227.

ANDERSON, E. C., and W. H. LANGHAM. 1959. Average potassium concentration of the human body as a function of age. *Science,* **130:** 713-714.

ANDERSON, J. E. 1948. Personality organization in children. *Amer. Psychologist,* **3:** 409-416.

ANDREW, R. J. 1965. The origins of facial expressions. *Sci. Amer.,* **213**(4): 88-94.

ANDREWS, E. G. 1930. The development of imagination in the pre-school child. *Univ. Iowa Stud. Character,* **3**(4): 64.

ANGULO Y GONZALEZ, A. W. 1929. Is myelinogeny an absolute index of behavioural capability? *J. Comp. Neurol.,* **48:** 459-464.

ANGYAL, A. 1941. *Foundations for a science of personality.* New York: Commonwealth Fund.

ANSHEN, RUTH. 1967. In T. Dobzhansky, ed., *The biology of ultimate concern.* New York: New American Library.

AREY, L. B., M. G. TREMAINE, and F. L. MONZINGO. 1935. The numerical and topographical relation of taste buds to human circumvallate papillae throughout the life span. *Anat. Rec.,* **64:** 9-25.

ARNOLD, M. B. 1945. Physiological differentiation of emotional states. *Psychol. Rev.,* **52:** 35-48.

ATTARDI, D. G., and R. W. SPERRY. 1963. Preferential selection of central pathways by regenerating optic fibres. *Exp. Neurol.,* **7:** 46-64.

AUSUBEL, D. P. 1950. Negativism as a phase of ego development. *Amer. J. Orthopsychiat.,* **20:** 796-805.

———. 1954. *Theory and problems of adolescent development.* New York: Grune & Stratton.

———. 1959. Viewpoints from related disciplines. Human growth and development. *Teacher's Coll. Rec.,* **60:** 245-254.

BAAR, H. S., and A. M. GABRIEL. 1966. Sex linked

spastic paraplegia. *Amer. J. Ment. Defic.*, **71**: 13-18.

BACHRACH, D. 1964. Sex differences in reaction time to late auditory feedback. *Percept. Motor Skills*, **19**: 81-82.

BACON, MARGARET K., I. L. CHILD, and H. BARRY, JR. 1963. A cross-cultural study of correlates of crime. *J. Abnorm. Social Psychol.*, **66**: 291-300.

BAERENDS, G. P., and J. M. BAERENDS-VAN ROON. 1950. An introduction to the ethology of Cichlid fishes. *Behaviour, Suppl.*, **1**: 1-243.

BAILEY, P., D. N. BUCHANAN, and P. C. BUCY. 1939. *Intercranial tumors of infancy and childhood.* Chicago: Univ. Chicago Press

BAILEY, P., and E. W. DAVIS. 1942. Effects of lesions of the periaqueductal grey matter in the cat. *Proc. Soc. Exp. Biol. Med.*, **51**: 305-306.

BAKWIN, H. 1942. Loneliness in infants. *Amer. J. Dis. Child.*, **63**: 30-40.

BALAZS, R. 1969. Report on meeting of Neurochemical Group of the Biochemical Society. *Nature*, **221**: 808.

BALDWIN, A. L. 1955. *Behaviour and development in childhood.* New York: Dryden.

BALL, J. 1939. Male and female mating behavior in prepubertally castrated rats receiving estrogens. *J. Comp. Psychol.*, **28**: 273-283.

BANDURA, A. 1962. Punishment revisited. *J. Psychol.*, **26**: 298-301.

———, and ALETHA C. HUSTON. 1961. Identification as a process of incidental learning. *J. Abnorm. Social Psychol.* **63**: 311-318.

BANHAM, K. 1950. The development of affectionate behavior in infancy. *J. Genet. Psychol.*, **76**: 283-289.

BARCLAY, A., and D. R. CUSUMANO. 1967. Father absence, cross-sex identity and field-dependent behavior in male adolescents. *Child Develop.*, **38**: 243, 250.

BARD, P. 1934. Emotion: 1. The neurohumoral basis of emotional reactions, in C. Murchison, ed., *Handbook of general experimental psychology.* Worcester, Mass.: Clark Univ. Press.

BARD, T., and V. B. MOUNTCASTLE. 1947. Some forebrain mechanisms involved in the expression of rage with special reference to the suppression of angry behavior. *Res. Publ. Ass. Nerv. Ment. Dis.*, **27**: 362-404. Quoted by C. T. Morgan and E. Stellar. 1950. *Physiological psychology,* 2nd ed. New York: McGraw-Hill.

BARKAN, M. 1960. *Through art to creativity.* Boston: Allyn & Bacon.

BARR, M. L. 1957. Cytologic tests of chromosomal sex. *Progr. Gynaecol.*, **3**: 131-141.

BARRON, F. 1961. *Creative vision and expression in writing and painting, in the Conference on the Creative Person.* Berkeley: Univ. Calif., Institute of Personality Assessment and Research.

BARRY, H., JR. 1956. The critical ages for maternal bereavement in psychoneuroses. *J. Nerv. Ment. Dis.*, **123**: 495.

BARRY, H., III, M. K. BACON, and I. L. CHILD. 1957. A cross-cultural survey of some sex differences in socialization. *J. Abnorm. Social Psychol.*, **55**: 327-332.

BARTLETT, D. J., W. P. HURLEY, C. R. BRAND, and E. W. POOLE. 1968. Chromosomes of male patients in a security prison. *Nature*, **219**: 351-354.

BARTLETT, F. 1958. *Thinking: an experimental social study.* New York: Basic Books.

BARTLEY, S. H. 1958. Emotion and the evaluative feature of all behavior. *Psychol. Rec.*, **8**: 39-41.

BATTLE, ESTHER S. 1965. Motivational determinants of academic task persistence. *J. Personality Soc. Psychol.*, **2**: 209-218.

BAUM, M. J. 1968. Pineal gland: influence on development of copulation in male rats. *Science*, **162**: 586-587.

BAUMRIND, DIANA. 1967. Child care practices anteceding three patterns of preschool behaviour. *Genet. Psychol. Monogr.*, **75**: 43-88.

———, and A. E. BLACK. 1967. Socialization practices associated with dimensions of competence in pre-school boys and girls. *Child Develop.*, **38**: 291-328.

BAXTER, J. C., D. L. HORTON, and R. E. WILEY. 1964. Father identification as a function of mother-father relationship. *J. Individ. Psychol.*, **20**: 167-171.

BAYER, E. 1929. Beiträge zur Zureikomponententheorie des Hungers. *Z. Psychol.*, **112**: 1-54.

BAYLEY, NANCY. 1943. Size and body build of adolescents in relation to rate of skeletal maturating. *Child Develop.*, **14**: 47-90.

———. 1949. Consistency and variability in the growth of intelligence from birth to 18 years. *J. Genet. Psychol.*, **75**: 165-196.

———. 1955. On the growth of intelligence. *Amer. Psychologist*, **10**: 805-818.

————. 1965. Comparisons of mental and motor test scores for ages 1-5 months by sex, birth order, race, geographical location and education of parents. *Child Develop.*, **36**: 379-411.

————, and M. H. ODEN. 1955. The maintenance of intellectual ability in gifted adults. *J. Gerontol.*, **10**: 91-107.

BEACH, F. A. 1945a. Bisexual mating behavior in the male rat: effects of castration and hormone administration. *Physiol. Zool.*, **18**: 390-402.

————. 1945b. Current concepts of play in animals. *Amer. Naturalist*, **79**: 523-541.

————. 1947. A review of physiological and psychological studies of sexual behavior in mammals. *Physiol. Rev.*, **27**: 240-307.

————. 1948. *Hormones and behavior.* New York: Hoeber.

————, and A. M. HOLZ. 1946. Mating behavior in male rats castrated at various ages and injected with androgen. *J. Exp. Zool.*, **101**: 91-142.

————, and A. M. HOLZ-TUCKER. 1949. Effects of different concentrations of androgen upon sexual behavior in castrated male rats. *J. Comp. Physiol. Psychol.*, **42**: 433-453.

BEACH, F. A., and J. JAYNES. 1954. Effects of early experience upon the behavior of animals. *Psychol. Bull.*, **51**: 239-263.

————. 1956a. Studies of maternal retrieving in rats: I. Recognition of young. *J. Mammal.*, **37**: 177-180.

————. 1956b. Studies of maternal retrieving in rats. III. Sensory cues involved in the lactating female's response to her young. *Behaviour*, **10**: 104-125.

BEATTY, R. T. 1932. *Hearing in man and animals.* London: Bell.

BECHTEREV, V. M. 1913. *La psychologie objective.* Transl. from the Russian by N. Kostyleff. Paris: Alcan.

BECKER, W. C., and R. S. KRUG. 1965. The parent attitude research instrument—a research review. *Child Develop.*, **36**: 329-365.

BEECHER, H. K. 1959. *Measurement of subjective responses.* New York: Oxford Univ. Press.

BEERY, JUDITH W. 1967. Matching of auditory and visual stimuli by average and retarded readers. *Child Develop.*, **38**: 827-833.

BEILIN, H. 1968. Cognitive capacities of young children: a replication. *Science*, **162**: 920-921.

————, and I. C. FRANKLIN. 1962. Logical operations in areas and length measurement, age

and training effects. *Child Develop.*, **33**: 606-618.

BELL, R. Q., and NAOMI S. COSTELLO. 1964. Three tests for sex differences in tactile sensitivity in the newborn. *Biol. Neonat.*, **7**: 335-347.

BELL, R. Q., and J. F. DARLING. 1965. The prone head reaction in the human neonate. *Child Develop.*, **36**: 943-949.

BENEDICT, RUTH. 1934. *Patterns of culture.* Boston: Houghton Mifflin.

BENNETT, E. L., MARIAN C. DIAMOND, D. KRECH, and M. R. ROSENZWEIG. 1964. Chemical and anatomical plasticity of brain. *Science*, **146**: 610-619.

BENNETT, E. L., D. R. KRECH, M. R. ROSENZWEIG, H. KARLSSON, N. DYE, and A. OHLANDER. 1958a. Cholinesterase and lactic dehydrogenase activity in the rat brain. *J. Neurochem.*, **3**: 153-160.

BENNETT, E. L., M. R. ROSENZWEIG, H. KARLSSON, N. DYE, and A. OHLANDER. 1958b. Individual strain and age differences in cholinesterase activity of the rat brain. *J. Neurochem.*, **3**: 144-152.

BENNETT, O. K., H. G. SEASHORE, and A. G. WESMAN. 1952. *Manual for differential aptitude tests*, 2nd ed. New York: Psychological Corp., 75.

BENTZEN, FRANCES. 1963. Sex ratios in learning and behavior disorders. *Amer. J. Orthopsychiat.*, **33**: 92-98.

BEREITER, C. 1960. Verbal and ideational fluency in superior 10th grade students. *J. Educ. Psychol.*, **51**: 337-345.

BERLYNE, D. E. 1960. *Conflict, arousal and curiosity.* New York: McGraw-Hill.

BERMAN, PHYLLIS, H. A. WAISMAN, and FRANCES GRAHAM. 1966. Intelligence in treated phenylketonuric children: a developmental study. *Child Develop.*, **37**: 731-746.

BERNARD, G., and L. W. SONTAG. 1947. Foetal reactivity to tonal stimulation. A preliminary report. *J. Genet. Psychol.*, **70**: 205-210.

BERNER, G. E., and D. E. BERNER. 1953. Relation of ocular dominance, handedness and the controlling eye in binocular vision. *A.M.A. Arch. Ophthal.*, **50**: 603-608.

BERRY, J. W. 1966. Temne and Eskimo perceptual skills. *Int. J. Psychol.*, **1**: 207-229.

BETTELHEIM, B. 1943. Individual and mass behavior in extreme situations. *J. Abnorm. Social Psychol.*, **38**: 417-452.

BEVER, T. G., J. MEHLER, and J. EPSTEIN. 1968. What children do in spite of what they know. *Science,* 162: 921-924.

BEXTON, W. A., W. HERON, and T. H. SCOTT. 1954. Effects of decreased variation in the sensory environment. *Canad. J. Psychol.,* 8: 70-76.

BIDNEY, D. 1953. *Theoretical anthropology.* New York: Columbia Univ. Press.

BIERI, J. 1960. Parental identification, acceptance of authority and within-sex differences in cognitive behavior. *J. Abnorm. Social Psychol.,* 60: 76-79.

———, WENDY M. BRADBURN, and M. D. GALINSKY. 1958. Sex differences in perceptual behavior. *J. Personality,* 26: 1-12.

BIERENS DE HAAN, J. A. 1929. Animal language in its relation to that of man. *Biol. Rev.,* 4: 249-268.

BILLER, H. B., and L. J. BORSTELMAN. 1965. Intellectual level and sex role development in mentally retarded children. *Amer. J. Ment. Defic.,* 70: 443-447.

BINDRA, D. 1959. *Motivation: a systematic reinterpretation.* New York: Ronald.

BINGHAM, W. E., and W. J. GRIFFITHS. 1952. The effect of different environments during infancy on adult behavior in the rat. *J. Comp. Physiol. Psychiat.,* 45: 307-312.

BIRCH, H. G., and LILLIAN BELMONT. 1964. Auditory-visual integration in normal and retarded readers. *Amer. J. Orthopsychiat.,* 34: 852-861.

———. 1965. Auditory-visual integration, intelligence and reading ability in school children. *Percept. Motor Skills,* 20: 295-305.

BIRCH, H. G., and A. LEFFORD. 1963. Intersensory development in children. *Monogr. Soc. Res. Child Develop.,* 28 (5): Whole No. 89.

———. 1967. Visual differentiation, intersensory integration and voluntary motor control. *Monogr. Soc. Res. Child Develop.,* 32(2): Serial No. 110.

BIRCH, H. G., A. THOMAS, S. CHESS, and M. E. HERTZIG. 1962. Individuality in the development of children. *Develop. Med. Child Neurol.,* 4: 370-379.

BITTERMAN, M. E. 1965. The evolution of intelligency. *Sci. Amer.,* 212: 92-100.

BLANK, MARION, and W. H. BRIDGER. 1964. Cross modal transfer in nursery school children. *J. Comp. Physiol. Psychol.,* 58: 277-282.

BLANK, MARION, and FRANCES SOLOMON. 1969. How shall the disadvantaged child be taught? *Child Develop.,* 40: 47-61.

BLAUVELT, H. 1955. Dynamics of the mother-new-born relationship in goats, in B. Schaffner, ed., *Group processes. Transactions of the First Conference.* New York: Josiah Macy, Jr. Foundation.

BLEWETT, D. B. 1954. An experimental study of the inheritance of intelligence. *J. Ment. Sci.,* 100: 922-933.

BLUNDELL, J. E. 1967. Personal communication.

BLURTON JONES, N. G. 1967. An ethological study of some aspects of social behaviour in children in nursery school, in D. Morris, ed., *Primate ethology.* Chicago: Aldine.

BOAS, F. 1938. *The mind of primitive man,* rev. ed. London: Macmillan.

BOLING, J. L., and R. J. BLANDAU. 1939. The oestrogen-progesterone induction of mating responses in the spayed female rat. *Endocrinology,* 25: 359-371.

BOLWIG, N. 1959. A study of the behavior of the chacma baboon, Papio ursinus. *Behaviour,* 14: 136-163.

BOOK, HANNAH M. 1932. A psychophysiological analysis of sex differences. *J. Soc. Psychol.,* 3: 436.

BOSS, W. R. 1943. Hormonal determination of adult characters and sex behavior in herring gulls *(Larus argentatus). J. Exp. Zool.,* 94: 181-209.

BOUQUET, A. C. 1950. *Comparative religion.* Harmondsworth, England: Pelican.

BOUSFIELD, W. I., and W. D. ORBISON. 1952. Ontogenesis of emotional behavior. *Psychol. Rev.,* 59: 1-7.

BOUTERLINE YOUNG, H. 1963. Ageing and adolescence. *Develop. Med. Child. Neurol.,* 5: 451-460.

BOVARD, E. W. 1958. The effects of early handling on the viability of the albino rat. *Psychol. Rev.,* 65: 257-271.

BOWER, T. G. R. 1965. Stimulus variables determining space perception in infants. *Science,* 149: 88-89.

———. 1966a. Slant perception and shape constancy in infants. *Science,* 151: 832-834.

———. 1966b. Heterogenous summation in human infants. *Anim. Behav.,* 14: 395-398.

———. 1967. Phenomenal identity and form perception in an infant. *Percept. Psychophys.*, 2: 74-76.

———. 1968. *Vision in infancy.* Colloqium at McGill University, Montreal.

BOWLBY, J. 1946. *Forty-four juvenile thieves: their characters and home life.* Paris: Baillière.

———. 1951. *Maternal care and mental health.* Geneva: W.H.O. Monogr. Ser., No. 2.

———. 1953. Critical phases in the development of social responses in man. *New biology*, Vol. 14. London: Penguin.

———. 1960. Grief and mourning in infancy and early childhood. *Psychoanal. Stud. Child.*, 15: 9-52.

———, MARY AINSWORTH, MARY BOSTON, and DINA ROSENBLUTH. 1956. The effects of mother-child separation: a follow-up study. *Brit. J. Med. Psychol.*, 29: 211-247.

BOWLES, J. W., and N. H. PRONKO. 1960. A new scheme for the inheritance of intelligence. *Psychol. Rec.*, 10: 55-57.

BRACKBILL, YVONNE, GAIL ADAMS, D. H. CROWELL, and M. LIBBIE GRAY. 1966. Arousal level in neonates and preschool children under continuous auditory stimulation. *J. Exp. Child. Psychol.*, 4: 178-188.

BRACKBILL, YVONNE, H. F. FITZGERALD, and L. M. LINTZ. 1967. A developmental study of classical conditioning. *Monogr. Soc. Res. Child Develop.*, 32(8): Serial No. 116.

BRADLEY, N. C. 1947. The growth of the knowledge of time in children of school age. *Brit. J. Psychol.*, 38: 67-78.

BRADWAY, CATHERINE P., and CLAIRE W. THOMPSON. 1962. Intelligence at adulthood: a 25-year follow-up. *J. Educ. Psychol.*, 53: 1-14.

BRAIN, RUSSELL. 1961. The neurology of language. *Brain*, 84: 145-166.

BRAINE, M. D. S. 1963. The ontogeny of English phrase structure: the first phase. *Language*, 39: 1-13.

BRAINE, M. D. S., CARYL B. HEIMES, HELEN WORTIS, and A. M. FREEDMAN. 1966. Factors associated with impairment of the early development of prematures. *Monogr. Soc. Res. Child Develop.*, 31(4): Serial No. 107.

BRAZIER, M. A. B. 1960. Long-persisting electrical traces in the brain of man and their possible relationship to higher nervous activity, in H. H. Jasper and G. D. Smirnov, eds., On electroencephalography of higher nervous activity. *EEG J. Suppl.*, 13: 347-358.

BREMER, J. 1959. *Asexualization: a follow-up study of 244 cases.* New York: Macmillan.

BRESSLER, D. E., and M. E. BITTERMAN. 1969. Learning in fish with transplanted brain tissue. *Science*, 163: 590-592.

BRIAN, C. R., and F. L. GOODENOUGH. 1929. Relative potency of colour and form perception of various ages. *J. Exp. Psychol.*, 12: 197-213.

BRIDGES, K. M. B. 1932. Emotional development in early infancy. *Child Develop.*, 3: 324-341.

BROADBENT, D. E. 1958. *Perception and communication.* New York: Pergamon Press.

———. 1963. Flow of information with the organism. *J. Verbal Learn. Verbal Behav.*, 2: 34-39.

BRODBECK, A. J. 1954. An exploratory study on the aquisition of dependency behavior in puppies. *Bull. Ecol. Soc. Amer.*, 35: 73.

BRODIE, B. B., S. SPECTOR, and P. A. SHORE. 1959. Interaction of drugs with norepinephrine in the brain. *Pharmacol. Rev.*, 11: 548-564.

BRONFENBRENNER, U. 1960. Freudian theories of identification and their derivatives. *Child Develop.*, 31: 15-40.

———. 1969. On the making of new men: some extrapolations for research. *Canad. J. Behav. Sci.*, 1: 4-24.

BRONSON, G. 1962. Critical periods in human development. *Brit. J. Med. Psychol.*, 35: 127-133.

———. 1963. A neurological perspective on ego development in infancy. *J. Amer. Psychoanal. Soc.*, 11: 55-65.

———. 1965. The hierarchical organization of the central nervous system: implication for learning processes and critical periods in early development. *Behav. Sci.*, 10: 7-25.

———. 1968. The development of fear in man and other animals. *Child Develop.*, 39: 409-432.

BRONSON, WANDA C. 1966. Central orientations: a study of behavior organisation from childhood through adolescence. *Child Develop.*, 37: 125-155.

BROOKS, R. M., and A. G. GOLDSTEIN. 1963. Recognition by children of inverted photographs of faces. *Child Develop.*, 34: 1033-1040.

BROOM, L., and P. SELZNICK. 1957. *Sociology: a text with adapted readings,* 3rd ed. New York: Harper & Row.

BROVERMAN, D. M. 1960. Dimensions of cognitive style. *J. Personality*, 28: 167-185.

———. 1964. Generality and behavioral correlates of cognitive styles. *J. Consult. Psychol.,* **28:** 487-500.

———, A. BLUM, and E. L. KLAIBER. 1965. The automatization cognitive style and physical development in pre-adolescent males. Worcester State Hospital Library, Worcester, Mass.

BROVERMAN, D. M., I. K. BROVERMAN, W. VOGEL, R. D. PALMER, and E. L. KLAIBER. 1964. Physique and growth in adolescence. *Child Develop.,* **35:** 857-870.

———. 1968. Roles of activation and inhibition in sex differences in cognitive abilities. *Psychol. Rev.,* **75:** 23-51.

BROVERMAN, D. M., and R. S. LAZARUS. 1958. Individual differences in task performance under conditions of cognitive interference. *J. Personality,* **26:** 94-105.

BROVERMAN, D. M., W. VOGEL, I. K. BROVERMAN, R. D. PALMER, and E. L. KLAIBER. 1964. The automatization cognitive style and physical development. *Child Develop.,* **35:** 1343-1359.

BROWN, ANNE M., R. E. STAFFORD, and S. G. VANDENBERG. 1967. Twins: behavioral differences. *Child Develop.,* **38:** 1055-1064.

BROWN, D. G. 1958a. Inversion and homosexuality. *Amer. J. Orthopsychiat.,* **38:** 424-429.

———. 1958b. Sex-role development in a changing culture. *Psychol. Bull.,* **55:** 232-242.

BROWN, J. S. 1961. *The motivation of behavior.* New York: McGraw-Hill.

BROWN, M. H., and G. ELIZABETH BRYAN. 1957. Sex as a variable in intelligence test performance. *J. Educ. Psychol.,* **48:** 273-278.

BROWN, R. W. 1958. *Words and things.* New York: Free Press.

BROWN, R. W., and V. BELLUGI. 1964. Three processes in the child's acquisition of syntax, in E. H. Lenneberg, ed., *New directions in the study of language.* Cambridge, Mass.: M.I.T. Press.

BROWN, R. W., and C. FRASER. 1963. The acquisition of syntax, in C. N. Cofer and B. S. Musgrave, eds., *Verbal behavior and learning.* New York: McGraw-Hill.

BRUN, R. 1951. *General theory of neurosis.* New York: International Univ. Press.

BRUNER, J. S. 1957. On perceptual readiness. *Psychol. Rev.,* **64:** 123-152.

———. 1960. *The process of education.* Cambridge, Mass.: Harvard Univ. Press.

———. 1964. The course of cognitive growth. *Amer. Psychologist,* **19:** 1-15.

———. 1965. The growth of mind. *Amer. Psychologist,* **20:** 1007-1017.

BRUNER, J. S. et al. 1966. *Studies in cognitive growth: a collaboration at the Center for Cognitive Studies.* New York: Wiley.

BRUNER, J. S., JACQUELINE J. GOODNOW, and G. A. AUSTIN. 1956. *A study of thinking.* New York: Wiley.

BRUNER, J. S., JEAN MATTER, and MIRIAM PAPANECK. 1955. Breadth of learning as a function of drive level and mechanization. *Psychol. Rev.,* **62:** 1-10.

BRUNSWICK, E. 1956. *Perception and the representative design of psychological experiments.* Berkeley: Univ. California Press.

BUDOFF, M., and D. QUINLAN. 1964. Auditory and visual learning in primary grade children. *Child Develop.,* **35:** 583-586.

BUGENTAL, J. F. T. 1967. The challenge that is man, in J. F. T. Bugental, ed., *Challenges of humanistic psychology.* New York: McGraw-Hill.

BÜHLER, CHARLOTTE. 1930. *The first year of life.* New York: John Day.

BULLOCK, T. H. 1958. Evolution of neurophysiological mechanisms, in Anne Roe and G. G. Simpson, eds., *Behavior and evolution.* New Haven: Yale Univ. Press.

BURGHARDT, G. M., and E. H. HESS. 1965. Food imprinting in the snapping turtle, Chelydra serpentina. *Science,* **151:** 108-109.

BURKE, R. J. 1965. Sex differences in recognizing the correct answer to a problem. *Psychol. Rev.,* **17:** 532-534.

BURKS, B. S. 1928. The relative influence of nature and nurture upon mental development. *Yearbook Nat. Soc. Stud. Educ.,* **27**(1): 219-316.

BURT, C. 1946. *The backward child.* London: Univ. London Press.

———. 1955. The evidence for the concept of intelligence. *Brit. J. Educ. Psychol.,* **25:** 158-177.

———. 1966. The genetic determination of differences in intelligence: A study of monozygotic twins reared together and apart. *Brit. J. Psychol.,* **57:** 137-153.

———, and R. C. MOORE. 1912. The mental differences between sexes. *J. Educ. Pedagogie,* **1:** 273-284 and 355-388.

BURTON, D., and G. ETTLINGER. 1960. Cross-modal

transfer of training in monkeys. *Nature,* **186:** 1071-1072.

BURTON, R. V., and J. W. M. WHITING. 1961. The absent father and cross-sex identity. *Merrill-Palmer Quart.,* **7:** 85-95.

BUTLER, R. A. 1954. Incentive conditions which influence visual exploration. *J. Exp. Psychol.,* **48:** 19-23.

CAMPBELL, B. A., and D. K. CANDLAND. 1961. Effects of prior shock on the emotionality of young rats in an open field. *Canad. J. Psychol.,* **15:** 1-5.

CANELLI, P. E., S. WAPNER, and H. WERNER. 1959. Perception of verticality in middle and old age. *J. Psychol.,* **47:** 259-266.

CANNON, W. B. 1929. *Bodily changes in pain, hunger, fear and rage.* New York: Appleton.

CAPRA, P. C., and J. E. DITTES. 1962. Birth order as a selective factor among volunteer subjects. *J. Abnorm. Social Psychol.,* **64:** 302 (abstract).

CARLSON, E. R., and R. CARLSON. 1960. Critique and notes: male and female subjects in personality research. *J. Abnorm. Social Psychol.,* **61(3):** 482-483.

CARLSON, R. 1965. Stability and change in the adolescent's self-image. *Child Develop.,* **36:** 659-666.

CARMICHAEL, L., ed. 1954. *Manual of child psychology,* 2nd ed. New York: Wiley.

CARR, H. 1935. *An introduction to space perception.* London: Longmans, Green.

CARRIGAN, W. C., and J. W. JULIAN. 1966. Sex and birth order differences in conformity as a function of need affiliation arousal. *J. Pers. Social Psychol.,* **3:** 479-483.

CARROLL, J. B. 1962. The prediction of success in intensive foreign language training, in R. Glaser, ed., *Training and education research.* Pittsburgh: Univ. Pittsburgh Press.

———. 1964. *Language and thought.* Englewood Cliffs, N.J.: Prentice-Hall.

CARTER, A. C., E. J. COHEN, and E. SHORR. 1947. The use of androgens in women. *Vitamins Hormones,* **5:** 317-391.

CARTER, H. B. 1932. Family resemblances in verbal and numerical abilities. *Genet. Psychol. Monogr.,* **12:** 1-104.

CARTERETTE, E. C., and MARGARET H. JONES. 1967.

Visual and auditory information processing in children and adults. *Science,* **156:** 986-988.

CARTLEDGE, CONNIE J., and E. L. KRAUSER. 1963. Training first-grade children in creative thinking under quantitative and qualitative motivation. *J. Educ. Psychol.,* **54:** 295-299.

CASSEN, D., and R. NEFF. 1960. Blood-brain barrier behavior during temporary concussion. *Amer. J. Physiol.,* **198:** 1296-1298.

CATTELL, PSYCHE. 1933. Do the Stanford-Binet IQ's of superior boys and girls tend to decrease or increase with age? *J. Educ. Res.,* **26:** 668-673.

CATTELL, R. B. 1959. The personality and motivation of the researcher from measurements of contemporaries and from bibliography, in C. Taylor, ed., *The 1959 University of Utah Research Conference on the Identification of Creative Scientific Talent.* Salt Lake City: Univ. Utah Press.

———, D. B. BLEWETT, and J. R. BELOFF. 1955. The inheritance of personality. *Amer. J. Hum. Genet.,* **7:** 122-146.

CHAMOVE, A., H. F. HARLOW, and G. MITCHELL. 1967. Sex differences in the infant-directed behavior of pre adolescent rhesus monkeys. *Child Develop.,* **38:** 329-336.

CHARLES, D. C. 1953. Ability and accomplishment of persons judged earlier mentally deficient. *J. Genet. Psychol. Monogr.,* **47:** 3-71.

———, and SUZANNE T. JAMES. 1964. Stability of average intelligence. *J. Genet. Psychol.,* **105:** 105-111.

CHARLES, M. S., and J. L. FULLER. 1956. Developmental study of the electroencephalogram of the dog. *EEG Clin. Neurophysiol.,* **8:** 645-652.

CHASE, R. A., S. SUTTON, D. FIRST, and J. ZUBIN. 1961. A developmental study of changes in behavior under delayed auditory feedback. *J. Genet. Psychol.,* **99:** 101-112.

CHASE, W. P. 1937. Colour vision in infants. *J. Exp. Psychol.,* **20:** 203-222.

CHOMSKY, N. 1965. *Aspects of the theory of syntax.* Cambridge, Mass.: M.I.T. Press.

CHOPRA, S. L. 1966. Family size and sitting position as related to intelligence test scores and academic achievement. *J. Soc. Psychol.,* **70:** 133-137.

CHOW, K. L., and H. W. NISSEN. 1955. Interocular transfer of learning in visually naive and experienced infant chimpanzees. *J. Comp. Physiol. Psychol.,* **48:** 229-237.

CHURCH, R. M. 1963. The varied effects of punishment on behaviour. *Psychol. Rev.,* **70:** 369-402.

CICIRELLI, V. G. 1967. Sibling constellation, creativity, I.Q., and academic achievement. *Child Develop.,* **38:** 481-490.

CLARKE, A. D. B. 1968. Learning and human development. *Brit. J. Psychiat.,* **114:** 1061-1077.

CLEGG, M. T., and L. L. DOYLE. 1967. Role in reproductive physiology of afferent impulses from the genitalia and other regions, in L. Martini and W. F. Ganong, eds., *Neuroendocrinology.* Vol. II. New York: Academic Press.

COFER, C. N., and M. H. APPLEY. 1964. *Motivation: theory and research.* New York: Wiley.

COHEN, B. D., and J. F. KLEIN. 1968. Referent communication in school age children. *Child Develop.,* **39:** 597-609.

COHEN, L. D., D. KIPNIS, E. C. KINKLE, and P. E. KUBZANSKY. 1955. Observations of a person with congenital insensitivity to pain. *J. Abnorm. Social Psychol.,* **51:** 333-338.

COHN, R. 1951. On certain aspects of sensory organization of the human brain: a study of rostral dominance in children. *Neurology,* 1: 119-122.

COLBY, M. G., and J. B. ROBERTSON. 1942. Genetic studies in abstraction. *J. Comp. Physiol. Psychol.,* **33:** 385-401.

COLLIAS, N. E. 1952. The development of social behaviour in birds. *Auk.,* **69:** 127-159.

———. 1956. The analysis of socialization in sheep and goats. *Ecology,* **37:** 228-239.

———, and E. C. COLLIAS. 1956. Some mechanisms of family integration in ducks. *Auk.,* **73:** 378-400.

COLLINS, T. B. 1965. Strength of the following response in the chick in relation to degree of "parent" contact. *J. Comp. Physiol. Psychol.,* **60:** 192-195.

COLVIN, S. S., and I. F. MEYER. 1906. Imaginative elements in the written work of school children. *Pedagog. Sem.,* **13:** 84-93.

COMMINS, W. C., and C. P. STONE. 1932. Effects of castration on the behavior of mammals. *Psychol. Bull.,* **29:** 493-508.

CONEL, J. L. 1939, 1941, 1947, 1951, 1955, 1959, 1963. The postnatal development of the human cerebral cortex. I: Cortex of the newborn. II: Cortex of the one-month infant. III: Cortex of the three-month infant. IV: Cortex of the six-month infant. V: Cortex of the fifteen-month infant. VI: Cortex of the twenty-four-month infant. VII: Cortex of the four-year child. Cambridge, Mass.: Harvard Univ. Press.

CONNOLLY, C. J. 1950. *External morphology of the primate brain.* Springfield, Ill.: Thomas.

CONRAD, H. S., and H. E. JONES. 1940. A second study of family resemblances in intelligence. *Yearbook Nat. Soc. Stud. Educ.,* **39**(Part II): 97-141.

COOK, W. M. 1931. Ability of children in colour discrimination. *Child Develop.,* 2: 303-320.

COOMBS, A., and D. SNYGG. 1959. *Individual behavior,* rev. ed. New York: Harper & Row.

COOPER, M., and L. ARONSON. 1958. The effect of the adrenalectomy on the sexual behavior of castrated male cats. *Abstract of the Proceedings of the American Society of Zoology. Anat. Rec.,* **131:** 544.

COOPERSMITH, S. 1968. Studies in self esteem. *Sci. Amer.,* **218**(2): 96-107.

CORTÉS, J. B., and FLORENCE M. GATTI. 1965. Physique and self-description of temperament. *J. Consult. Psychol.,* **29:** 432-439.

COSTELLO, C. G., and H. M. BRACHMAN. 1962. Cultural and sex differences in extraversion and neuroticism reflected in responses to a children's personality inventory. *Brit. J. Educ. Psychol.,* **32:** 254-257.

COULES, J., and D. L. AVERY. 1966. Human performance and basal skin conductance in vigilance—type task with and without knowledge of results. *Percept. Motor Skills,* **23:** 1295-1302.

COVINGTON, M. V., and R. S. CRUTCHFIELD. 1965. Experiments in the use of programmed instruction for the facilitation of creative problem solving. *Program. Instruct.,* 4: 3-5.

COX, V. C., J. W. KAKOLEWSKI, and E. S. VALENSTEIN. 1969. Ventromedial hypothalamic lesions and changes in body weight and food consumption in male and female rats. *J. Comp. Physiol. Psychol.,* **67:** 320-326.

CRAIG, W. 1912. Observations on doves learning to drink. *Brit. J. Anim. Behav.,* 2: 273-279.

———. 1914. Male doves reared in isolation. *Brit. J. Anim. Behav.,* 4: 121-133.

CRANE, A. R. 1951. A note on pre-adolescent gangs. *Aust. J. Psychol.,* 3: 43-46.

———. 1955. Pre-adolescent gangs: a socio-psychological interpretation. *J. Genet. Psychol.,* **86:** 275-279.

CRESSEY, D. R. 1963. Crime and delinquency, in L. Broom and P. Selznick, eds., *Sociology: a text with adapted readings,* 3rd ed. New York: Harper & Row.

CRICK, F. H. C. 1954. The structure of the hereditary material. *Sci. Amer.,* 191(4): 54-61.

CRITCHLEY, M. 1953. *The parietal lobes.* London: Arnold.

CROPLEY, A. J. 1966. Creativity and intelligence. *Brit. J. Educ. Psychol.,* 36: 259-266.

CRUTCHFIELD, R. 1961. The creative process, in Conference on the creative person. Berkeley: Univ. California Institute for Personality Assessment and Research.

CULLEN, E. 1960. Experiment on the effect of social isolation on reproductive behavior in the three-spined stickleback. *Anim. Behav.,* 8: 235 (abstract).

CURTIS REPORT. 1946. *Report of the Care of Children Committee,* Myra Curtis, Chairman. London: H. M. Stationery Office (Parliamentary Papers Cmd. 6922).

DALLENBACH, K. M. 1914. The effect of practice upon visual apprehension in school children. I and II. *J. Educ. Psychol.,* 5: 321-334 and 387-404.

DARLING, F. F. 1938. *Wild country.* London: Cambridge Univ. Press.

DARWIN, C. 1877. A biographical sketch of an infant. *Mind,* 2: 285-294.

DATTA, LOIS, and M. B. PARLOFF. 1967. On the relevance of autonomy: parent-child relationships and early scientific creativity. *Proceedings of the 75th Annual Convention of the American Psychological Association,* 2: 149-150.

DAVENPORT, R. K., JR., E. W. MENZEL, JR., and C. M. ROGERS. 1961. Maternal care during infancy: its effect on weight gain and mortality in the chimpanzee. *Amer. J. Orthopsychiat.,* 31: 803-809.

DAVIDSON, J. M. 1966. Cited in S. Levine, Sex differences in the brain. *Sci. Amer.,* 214(4): 84-90.

DAVIDSON, May A., R. G. MCINNES, and R. W. PARNELL. 1957. The distribution of personality traits in seven year old children: a combined psychological, psychiatric and somatotype study. *Brit. J. Educ. Psychol.,* 27: 48-61.

DAVIES, A. D. M., and G. W. H. LEYTHAN. 1964. Perception of verticality in adult life. *Brit. J. Psychol.,* 55: 315-320.

DAVIES, CAROLYN M. 1965. Development of the probability concept in children. *Child Develop.,* 36: 779-788.

DAVIS, K. B. 1926. Periodicity of sex desire. *Amer. J. Obstet. Gynec.,* 12: 824-836.

DAVISON, A. N. 1969. Report on meeting of Neurochemical Group of the Biochemical Society, *Nature,* 221: 808.

DAVITZ, J. R. 1964. A review of research concerned with facial and vocal expressions of emotion, in J. R. Davitz, ed., *The communication of emotional meaning.* New York: McGraw-Hill.

DAWSON, I. L. M. 1963. Psychological effects of social changes in a West African community. Unpublished doctoral dissertation. Oxford: Univ. Oxford. Quoted in H. A. Witkin. 1967. A cognitive-style approach to cross-cultural research. *Int. J. Psychol.,* 2: 233-250.

DAYTON, G. O., M. H. JONES, P. AIN, R. A. RAWSON, and B. STEELE. 1964. Developmental study of co-ordinated eye movements in the human infant. *Arch. Ophthalmol.,* 71: 871-875.

DEAN, D. A. 1947. Thesis, Ames, Iowa: State Univ. Iowa. Quoted in W. D. Altus. 1966. Birth order of the omnibus personality inventory. *Proceedings of the 74th Annual Convention of the American Psychiatric Association,* 279-280.

DEARBORN, G. V. 1898. A study of imagination. *Amer. J. Psychol.,* 5: 183-190.

DE CECCO, J. P. 1968. *The psychology of learning and instruction: educational psychology.* Englewood Cliffs, N.J.: Prentice-Hall.

DE CILLIS, O. E., and WM. D. ORBISON. 1950. A comparison of the Terman-Miles M-F test and the M-F scale of the MMPI. *J. Appl. Psychol.,* 34: 338-342.

DELL, P. C. 1958. Some basic mechanisms of the translation of bodily needs into behavior, in G. E. W. Wolsteinholme and C. M. O'Connor, eds., *Symposium on the neurological basis of behavior.* Boston: Little, Brown.

DENENBERG, V. H. 1964. Critical periods, stimulus input, and emotional reactivity: a theory of infantile stimulation. *Psychol. Rev.,* 71: 335-351.

———, and G. G. KARAS. 1959. Effects of differential handling upon weight gain and mortality in the rat and mouse. *Science,* **130:** 629-630.

——. 1960a. The interactive effects of age and duration of infantile experience on adult learning. *Psychol. Rep.,* **7:** 313-322.

——. 1960b. Supplementary report: the Yerkes-Dodson law and shift in task difficulty. *J. Exp. Psychol.,* **59:** 429-430.

——. 1961. Interactive effects of infantile and adult experience upon weight gain and mortality in the rat. *J. Comp. Physiol. Psychol.,* **54:** 685-689.

——, K. M. ROSENBERG, and S. F. SCHELL. 1968. Programming life histories: an experimental design and initial results. *Develop. Psychobiol.,* **1:** 3-9.

DENENBERG, V. H., and A. E. WHIMBEY. 1963. Behavior of adult rats is modified by the experiences their mothers had as infants. *Science,* **142:** 1192-1193.

——. 1968. Experimental programming of life histories: toward an experimental science of individual differences. *Develop. Psychobiol.,* **1:** 55-59.

DENENBERG, V. H., J. M. WOODCOCK, and K. M. ROSENBERG. 1968. Long-term effects of pre-weaning and postweaning experience on rats' problem-solving behavior. *J. Comp. Physiol. Psychol.,* **66:** 533-535.

DENGROVE, E. 1961. *Sex difference in sexual behavior,* Vol. II. London: Heinemann.

DENNIS, W. 1940. *The Hopi child.* New York: Appleton.

——. 1941. Spalding's experiments on the flight of birds repeated with another species. *J. Comp. Psychol.,* **31:** 337-348.

——, and P. NAJARIAN. 1957. Infant development under environmental handicap. *Psychol. Monogr.,* **71**(7): Whole No. 436.

DENNY, M. R. 1957. Learning through stimulus satiation. *J. Exp. Psychol.,* **54:** 62-64.

DERSHOWITZ, Z. 1967. Influences of cultural patterns on the thinking of children in certain ethnic groups. A study of the effect of Jewish sub-cultures on the field-dependence-independence dimension of cognition. Unpublished doctoral dissertation. New York: New York Univ. Quoted in H. A. Witkin. 1967. A cognitive-style approach to cross-cultural research. *Int. J. Psychol.,* **2:** 233-250.

DESCOUDRES, A. 1914. Couleur, forme, ou nombre. *Arch. Psychol.,* **14:** 304-344.

DEUTSCH, HELENE. 1945. *The psychology of women. A psychoanalytic interpretation.* Vol. II. New York: Grune & Stratton.

DEUTSCH, J. A. 1960. *The structural basis of behavior.* Cambridge: Cambridge Univ. Press.

DEUTSCH, M., and H. PROSHANSKY. 1961. Information and opinion during an international crisis. *J. Soc. Psychol.,* **54:** 169-174.

DE VORE, I. 1963. Mother-infant relations in free ranging baboons, in H. L. Rheingold, ed., *Maternal behavior in mammals.* New York: Wiley.

DIAMOND, S. 1957. *Personality and temperament.* New York: Harper & Row.

——, and W. C. YOUNG. 1963. Differential responsiveness of pregnant and nonpregnant guinea pigs to the masculinizing action of testosterone propionate. *Endocrinology,* **72:** 429-438.

DiCARA, L. V., and N. E. MILLER. 1968a. Instrumental learning of peripheral vasomotor responses by the curarized rat. *Commun. Behav. Biol.,* **1:** 209.

——. 1968b. Instrumental learning of vasomotor responses by rats: learning to respond differentially in two ears. *Science,* **159:** 1485-1486.

DiCARA, L. V., and J. M. WEISS (in press). *J. Comp. Physiol. Psychol.*

DICKERSON, W. L. 1966. A study of illogical choice behavior on concept learning tasks among bright, normal and retarded children. *Dissert. Abstr.,* **27**(2A): 386.

DICKINSON, R. L., and L. BEAN. 1931. *A thousand marriages: a medical study of sex adjustment.* Baltimore: Williams & Wilkins.

DIMITROVSKY, LILLY. 1964. The ability to identify the emotional meaning of verbal expressions at successive age levels, in J. R. Davitz, ed., *The communication of emotional meaning.* New York: McGraw-Hill.

DIXON, J. C. 1957. Reactions of superior and feeble-minded children to an illusion. *J. Genet. Psychol.,* **21:** 458.

DOBZHANSKY, T. 1967. *The biology of ultimate concern.* New York: New American Library.

DODEK, O. I. 1966. Testicular feminization. *Gen. Practitioner,* **34:** 104-109.

DOEHRING, D. 1960. Color-form attitudes of deaf children. *J. Speech Hear. Res.,* **3:** 242-248.

DOERR, H. O., and J. E. HOKANSON. 1965. A relation between heart-rate and performance in children. *J. Pers. Soc. Psychol.,* **2**: 70-76.

DOLLARD, J., and N. E. MILLER. 1950. *Personality and psychotherapy.* New York: McGraw-Hill.

DORIS, J., MYRA CASPER, and R. PORESKY. 1967. Differential brightness thresholds in infancy. *J. Exp. Child Psychol.,* **5**: 522-535.

DOUGLAS, VIRGINIA I. 1965. Children's responses to frustration: a developmental study. *Canad. J. Psychol.,* **19**: 161-171.

DREES, V. 1941. The effects of practice on memory performance. *Cath. Univ. Amer. Educ. Res. Monogr.,* **12**(4).

DREIFUSS, S. E. 1963. Delayed development of hemispheric dominance. *Arch. Neurol.,* **8**: 510-514.

DREVER, J. 1917. *Instinct in man.* Cambridge: Cambridge Univ. Press.

———. 1955. Early learning and the perception of space. *Amer. J. Psychol.,* **68**: 605-614.

DRIESCH, H. 1914. *History and theory of vitalism.* Transl. by C. K. Ogden. London: Macmillan.

DUBOIS, P. H. 1939. Sex differences on the color-naming test. *Amer. J. Psychol.,* **52**: 380-382.

DUFFY, ELIZABETH. 1962. *Activation and behaviour.* New York: Wiley.

DUPERTUIS, C. W., and N. B. MICHAEL. 1953. Comparison of growth in height and weight between ectomorphic and mesomorphic boys. *Child Develop.,* **31**: 203-214.

DUSTMAN, R. E., and E. C. BECK. 1966. Visually evoked potentials: amplitude changes with age. *Science,* **151**: 1013-1015.

DYK, L. B., and H. A. WITKIN. 1965. Family experiences related to the development of differentiation in children. *Child Develop.,* **36**: 21-55.

EASON, R. G., P. GROVES, C. T. WHITE, and D. ODEN. 1967. Evoked cortical potentials: relation to visual field and handedness. *Science,* **156**: 1643-1646.

EBERT, ELIZABETH, and CATHERINE SIMMONS. 1943. Brush Foundation's idea of child growth and development: I. Psychometric tests. *Monogr. Soc. Res. Child Develop.,* **8**(2): Whole No. 35.

EDWARDS, D. A. 1969. Mice: Fighting by neonatally androgenised females. *Science,* **161**: 1027-1028.

EELS, J. F. 1961. Inconsistency of early handling and its effect upon emotionality in the rat. *J. Comp. Physiol. Psychol.,* **54**: 690-693.

EIBL-EIBESFELDT, I. 1961. The interactions of un-learned behavior patterns and learning in mammals, in J. F. Delapresuaye, ed., *Brain mechanisms and learning. Symposium of Council for International Organisations of Medical Sciences.* Oxford: Blackwell.

EICHENGREEN, J. M., S. COREN, and J. NACHMIAS. 1966. Visual-cliff preference by infant rats: effects of rearing and test conditions. *Science,* **151**: 830-831.

EICHENWALD, H. F., and PEGGY C. FRY. 1969. Nutrition and learning. *Science,* **163**: 644-648.

EICHORN, DOROTHY H. 1963. Biological correlates of behavior, in H. W. Stevenson, ed., *Yearbook Nat. Soc. Stud. Educ.,* **62**(Part): 4-61.

EISENBERG, RITA B., ELIZABETH J. GRIFFIN, and D. B. COURSIN. 1964. Auditory behavior in the human neonate: a preliminary report. *J. Speech Hear. Res.,* **7**: 245-269.

EISENMAN, R. 1967. Complexity-simplicity: II. Birth order and sex differences. *Psychonomic Sci.,* **8**: 171-172.

ELKIND, D. 1961a. Children's discovery of the conservation of mass, weight and volume: Piaget replication study, II. *J. Genet. Psychol.,* **98**: 219-227.

———. 1961b. The development of quantitative thinking. *J. Genet. Psychol.,* **98**: 37-46.

———. 1961c. Quantity conceptions in junior and senior high school students. *Child Develop.,* **32**: 551-560.

———. 1964. Ambiguous figures for study of perceptual development and learning. *Child Develop.,* **35**: 1391-1396.

———, R. R. KOEGLER, and ELSIE GO. 1964. Studies in perceptual development: II. Part-whole perception. *Child Develop.,* **35**: 81-90.

ELKIND, D., and L. SCOTT. 1962. Studies in perceptual development: I. The decentering of perception. *Child Develop.,* **33**: 619-630.

ELLINGSON, R. J. 1958. Electroencephalograms of normal, full-term newborns immediately after birth with observations on arousal and visual evoked responses. *EEG Clin. Neurophysiol.,* **10**: 31-50.

———. 1960. Cortical electrical responses to visual stimulation in the human infant. *EEG Clin. Neurophysiol.,* **12**: 663-677.

———, and R. C. WILCOTT. 1960. Development of evoked responses in visual and auditory cortices of kittens. *J. Neurophysiol.,* **23**: 363-375.

ELLIOT, O., and J. O. SCOTT. 1961. The development of emotional distress reactions to separation in puppies. *J. Genet. Psychol.*, **99**: 3-22.

ELLIS, H. 1926. *Man and woman*, 6th ed. London: Black.

EMERSON, L. L. 1931. The effect of bodily orientation upon the young child's memory for position of objects. *Child Develop.*, **2**: 125-142.

ENGELS, F. 1902. *The origin of the family, private property and the state.* Chicago: Kerr.

ENGLE, E. T. 1942. The testes and hormones, in C. V. Dowdry, ed., *Problems of ageing*, 2nd ed. Baltimore: Williams & Wilkins.

EPSTEIN, W. 1964. Experimental investigations of the genesis of visual space perception. *Psychol. Bull.*, **61**: 115-128.

ERIKSON, E. H. 1950. *Childhood and society.* New York: Norton.

———. 1956. The problem of ego identity. *J. Amer. Psychoanal. Ass.*, **4**: 56-121.

———. 1959. Identity and the life cycle: selected papers. *Psychol. Issues*, **1**: 1-171.

———. 1963. *Childhood and society*, 2nd ed. New York: Norton.

ERLENMEYER, K. L., and LISSY F. JARVIK. 1963. Genetics and intelligence: a review. *Science*, **142**: 1477-1478.

ERVIN, S. M. 1960a. Training and illogical operation by children. *Child Develop.*, **31**: 537-554 and 555-563.

———. 1960b. Experimental procedures of children. *Child Develop.*, **31**: 703-719.

———. 1964. Imitation and structural change in children's language, in E. H. Lenneberg, ed., *New directions in the study of language.* Cambridge, Mass.: M.I.T. Press.

———, and W. R. MILLER. 1964. Language development. *Child Psychology*, 62nd Yearbook. *Nat. Soc. Stud.* Chicago: Univ. Chicago Press.

ERVIN-TRIPP, SUSAN M. 1966. Language development, in L. W. Hoffman and M. L. Hoffman, eds., *Review of child development research*, Vol. II. New York: Russell Sage Foundation.

ESCALONA, S. K. 1965. Some determinants of individual differences. *Trans. N.Y. Acad. Sci.*, **27**: 802-816.

ETTLINGER, G. 1960. Cross-modal transfer of training in monkeys. *Behaviour*, **16**: 56-65.

ETZIONI, A. 1968. Sex control, science and society. *Science*, **161**: 1107-1112.

EVANS-PRITCHARD, E. 1940. *Nuer. A description of the modes of livelihood and political institutions of a Nilotic people.* New York: Oxford Univ. Press.

EWER, R. F. 1959. Suckling behaviour in kittens. *Behaviour*, **15**: 146-162.

EYSENCK, H. J., and D. B. PRELL. 1951. The inheritance of neuroticism. *J. Ment. Sci.*, **97**: 441-465.

FABRICIUS, E. 1951. Zur Ethologie junger Anatiden. *Acta Zool. Fennica*, **68**: 1-175.

FAISZT, J., and A. GYÖRGY. 1968. Role of different RNA fractions from the brain in transfer effect. *Nature*, **220**: 367-368.

FANTZ, R. L. 1957. Form preferences in newly-hatched chick. *J. Comp. Physiol. Psychol.*, **50**: 422-430.

———. 1958a. Depth discrimination in dark-hatched chicks. *Percept. Motor Skills*, **8**: 47-50.

———. 1958b. Pattern vision in young infants. *Psychol. Rec.*, **8**: 43-47.

———. 1961a. A method for studying depth perception in infants under six months of age. *Psychol. Rec.*, **11**: 27-32.

———. 1961b. The origin of form perception. *Sci. Amer.*, **204**: 66-72.

———. 1963. Pattern vision in new-born infants. *Science*, **140**: 296-297.

———. 1964. Visual experience in infants: decreased attention to familiar patterns relative to novel ones. *Science*, **146**: 668-670.

———, and SONIA NEVIS. 1967. Pattern preferences and perceptual-cognitive development in early infancy. *Merrill-Palmer Quart.*, **13**: 77-108.

FANTZ, R. L., J. M. ORDY, and M. S. UDELF. 1962. Maturation of pattern vision in infants during the first six months. *J. Comp. Physiol. Psychol.*, **65**: 907-917.

FARBER, S. M., and R. H. WILSON, eds. 1966. *The challenge to women.* New York: Basic Books.

FEINDEL, W. 1961. Response patterns elicited from the amygdala and deep temperoinsular cortex, in D. E. Sheer, ed., *Electrical stimulation of the brain.* Austin: Univ. Texas Press.

FERGUSON, G. A. 1954. On learning and human ability. *Canad. J. Psychol.*, **8**: 95-112.

———. 1956. On transfer and the abilities of man. *Canad. J. Psychol.*, **10**: 121-131.

FERGUSON-SMITH, M. A. 1966. Sex chronation, Klinefelters' syndrome and mental deficiency, in K. L. Moore, ed., *The sex chromatin.* Philadelphia: Saunders.

FERSTER, C. B. 1964. Arithmetic behavior in chimpanzees. *Sci. Amer.*, **210** (5): 98-106.

FIEANDT, K. 1958. Toward a unitary theory of perception. *Psychol. Rev.*, **65**: 315-320.

FILLER, W., and N. DREZNER. 1944. Results of surgical castration in women over forty. *Amer. J. Gynecol.*, **47**: 122-124.

FINK, M., and M. B. BENDER. 1953. Perception of simultaneous tactile stimuli in normal children. *Neurology*, **3**: 27-34.

FIRTH, R. 1936. *We, the Tikopia*. New York: American Book.

FISCHE, GLORIA J. 1966. Distribution of practice effects on imprinting. *Psychon. Sci.*, **5**: 197-198.

FISHER, A. E. 1955. The effects of differential early treatment on the social and exploratory behavior of puppies. Unpublished doctoral dissertation. University Park: Pennsylvania State Univ. Quoted by J. P. Scott. 1963. The process of primary socialization in canine and human infants. *Monogr. Soc. Res. Child. Develop.*, **28** (1): Serial No. 85.

———. 1958. Effects of stimulus variation on sexual satiation in the male rat. *Amer. Psychol.*, **13**: 382 (abstract).

FISHMAN, R., and R. B. TALLARICO. 1961a. Studies of visual depth perception: I. Blinking as an indicator response in prematurely hatched chicks. *Percept. Motor Skills*, **12**: 247-250.

———. 1961b. Studies of visual depth perception: II. Avoidance reaction as an indicator response in chicks. *Percept. Motor Skills*, **12**: 251-257.

FISKE, M. 1941. Effect of light on sexual maturation, estrous cycles, and anterior pituitary of the rat. *Endocrinology*, **29**: 187-196.

FITZGERALD, E. T. 1966. Measurement of openness to experience. *J. Pers. Soc. Psychol.*, **4**: 655-663.

FITZGERALD, H. E. 1968. Autonomic pupillary reflex activity during early infancy and its relation to social and nonsocial visual stimuli. *J. Exp. Child. Psychol.*, **6**: 470-482.

FLAVELL, J. H. 1963a. *The developmental psychology of Jean Piaget*. Princeton, N.J.: Van Nostrand.

———. 1963b. Piaget's contributions to the study of cognitive development. *Merrill-Palmer Quart.*, **9**: 245-252.

———, P. T. BOTKIN, C. L. FRY, J. W. WRIGHT, and P. E. JARVIS. 1968. *The development of role taking and communication skills in children*. New York: Wiley.

FLECHSIG, P. 1927. *Meine Myelogenetische Hirnlehre mit Biographischer Einleitung*. Berlin: Springer.

FLETCHER, H. 1929. *Speech and hearing*. Princeton, N.J.: Van Nostrand.

FLETCHER, R. 1957. *Instinct in man*. London: Allen & Unwin.

FLINT, BETTY M. 1966. *The child and the institution: a study of deprivation and recovery*. Toronto: Univ. Toronto Press.

FOIS, A. 1961. *The electroencephalogram of the normal child*. Springfield, Ill.: Thomas. Trans. and ed. N. Low, from (1956) *L'electroencefalogramma del bambino normale*. Pisa: Instituto di richerche V. Baldacci.

FOLCH-PI, J. 1952. The chemical constituents of brain during development and in maturity, in *The biology of mental health and disease, the 27th Annual Conference of the Milbank Memorial Fund*. New York: Hoeber.

———. 1955. Composition of the brain in relation to maturation, in H. Waelch, ed., *Biochemistry of the developing nervous system. Proceedings of the First International Neurochemical Symposium*. New York: Academic Press.

FORBES, H. S., and H. B. FORBES. 1927. Total sense reaction: hearing. *J. Comp. Psychol.*, **7**: 353-356.

FORD, C. S., and F. A. BEACH. 1951. *Patterns of sexual behaviour*. New York: Hoeber.

FORGAYS, D. G., and JANET FORGAYS. 1952. The nature of the effect of free environmental experience in the rat. *J. Comp. Physiol. Psychol.*, **45**: 322-328.

FORREST, TESS. 1966. Paternal roots of female character development. *Contemp. Psychoanal.*, **3**: 21-28.

FORSSMAN, H., and G. HAMBERT. 1967. Chromosomes and antisocial behavior. *Excerpta Criminol.*, **7**: 113-117.

FORTES, M. 1949. *The web of kinship among the Tallensi*. London: Oxford Univ. Press.

FOSS, B. M., ed. 1961. *Determinants of infant behaviour*, II. (Proceedings of the 2nd seminar held under the auspices of the C.I.B.A. Foundation, London, September 1961.) London: Methuen.

———. 1969. *Determinants of infant behaviour*, Vol. IV. (Proceedings of the 4th Tavistock study group on mother-infant interaction, London, 1965.) London: Methuen.

Foss, G. L. 1951. The influence of androgens on sexuality in women. *Lancet*, 1: 667-669.

Fournier-Chouinard, E. 1967. Un apprentissage de la conservation des quantités continues par une technique d'exercices opératiores. Unpublished doctoral dissertation. Montreal: Univ. Montreal.

Fowler, W. 1962. Cognitive learning in infancy and early childhood. *Psychol. Bull.*, 59: 116-152.

Fox, M. W., O. Inman, and S. Glisson. 1968. Age differences in central nervous effects of visual deprivation in the dog. *Develop. Psychobiol.*, 1: 48-54.

Frankl, V. 1959. *From death camp to existentialism.* Boston: Beacon.

Fraser, C., U. Bellugi, and R. Brown. 1963. Control of grammar in imitation, comprehension and production. *J. Verbal Learn. Verbal Behav.* 2: 121-135.

Fraser, G. R. 1965. Sex-linked recessive congenital deafness and the excess of males in profound childhood deafness. *Ann. Hum. Genet.*, 29: 171-196.

Freeberg, N. E., and D. T. Payne. 1967. Parental influence on cognitive development in early childhood: a review. *Child Develop.*, 38: 65-87.

Freeburne, C. M. 1949. The influence of training in perceptual span and perceptual speed upon reading ability. *J. Educ. Psychol.*, 40: 321-352.

Freedman, D. G. 1965. An ethological approach to the genetical study of human behavior, in S. G. Vandenberg, ed., *Methods and goals in human behavior genetics.* New York: Academic Press.

———, J. A. King, and O. Elliot. 1961. Critical period in the social development of dogs. *Science*, 133: 1016-1017.

Freedman, J. L. 1965. Increasing creativity by free-association training. *J. Exp. Psychol.*, 69: 89-91.

Freedman, L. Z., and Anne Roe. 1958. Evolution and human behavior, in Anne Roe and G. G. Simpson, eds., *Behavior and evolution.* New Haven: Yale Univ. Press.

Freeman, F. N., K. J. Holzinger, and B. C. Mitchell. 1928. The influence of the environment on the intelligence, school achievement and conduct of foster children. *Yearbook Nat. Soc. Stud. Educ.*, 27: 103-217.

Freeman, J. A. 1966. Sex differences and target arrangement. *J. Parapsychol.*, 30: 227-235.

Freud, Anna. 1937. *The ego and mechanisms of defence.* London: Hogarth.

Freud, S. 1924. *Collected papers,* Vol. II. London: Hogarth.

———. 1948. *Group psychology and the analysis of the ego.* London: Hogarth.

———. 1950. *Collected papers,* Vol. V. London: Hogarth.

Friedman, S. R. 1965. Developmental level and concept learning: confirmation of an inverse relationship. *Psychon. Sci.*, 2: 3-4.

Fromm, E. 1941. *Escape from freedom.* New York: Holt.

———. 1964. *The heart of man.* New York: Harper & Row.

Fry, D. B., and Edith Whetnall. 1954. The auditory approach to the training of deaf children. *Lancet*, 1: 583.

Fuller, J. L. 1950. Situational analysis: a classification of organism-field interactions. *Psychol. Rev.*, 57: 3-18.

———. 1966. Transitory effects of experimental deprivation upon reversal learning in dogs. *Psychon. Sci.*, 4: 273-274.

———, C. A. Easler, and E. M. Banks. 1950. Formation of conditioned avoidance in young puppies. *Amer. J. Physiol.*, 160: 462-466.

Fuller, J. L., and W. Thompson. 1960. *Behaviour genetics.* New York: Wiley.

Fuller, J. L., and M. B. Waller. 1962. Is early experience different? in E. L. Bliss, ed., *Roots of behavior: genetics, instincts, and socialization in animal behavior.* New York: Harper & Row.

Funkenstein, D. H., S. H. King, and M. E. Drolette. 1957. *Mastery of stress.* Cambridge, Mass.: Harvard Univ. Press.

Furth, H. G. 1966. *Thinking without language: psychological implications of deafness.* New York: Free Press.

———. 1969. *Piaget and knowledge.* Englewood Cliffs, N.J.: Prentice-Hall.

Gagné, R. M. 1968. Contributions of learning to human development. *Psychol. Rev.*, 75: 177-191.

Gaito, J., 1961. A biochemical approach to learning and memory. *Psychol. Rev.,* 68: 288-292.

———. and A. ZAVALA. 1964. Neurochemistry and learning. *Psychol. Bull.,* 61: 45-62.

GAITONDE, M. K. 1969. Report on meeting of Neurochemical Group of the Biochemical Society. *Nature,* 221: 808.

GALAMBOS, R., G. SHEATZ, and V. G. VERNIER. 1956. Electrophysiological correlates of a conditioned response in cats. *Science,* 123: 376-377.

GALL, M., and G. A. MENDELSOHN. 1967. Effects of facilitating techniques and subject-experimenter interaction on creative problem solving. *J. Pers. Soc. Psychol.,* 5: 211-216.

GALLAGHER, J. J. 1964. Productive thinking, in Emil Hoffman and Lois W. Hoffman, eds., *Review of Child Development Research.* New York: Russell Sage Foundation.

———. 1966. Sex differences in expressive thought of gifted children in the classroom. *Personnel Guid. J.,* 45: 248-253.

———, ed. 1963. A report on a conference of research on gifted children. Washington, D.C.: Co-operative Research Branch, U.S. Office of Education.

GALLUP, G. 1955. Gallup Poll. Princeton, N.J.: Audience research.

GALTON, FRANCIS. 1869. *Hereditary genius.* London: Macmillan.

———. 1883. *Inquiries into human faculty.* London: Macmillan.

GARDNER, D. B., G. R. HAWKES, and L. G. BURCHINAL. 1961. Non-continuous mothering in infancy and development in later childhood. *Child Develop.,* 32: 225-234.

GARDNER, D. B., D. PEASE, and G. R. HAWKES. 1961. Responses of two-year-old children to controlled stress situations. *J. Genet. Psychol.,* 98: 29-35.

GARDNER, R. W. 1961. Cognitive controls of attention development as determinants of visual illusions. *J. Abnorm. Social Psychol.,* 62: 120-127.

———. 1964. Development of cognitive structures, in C. Scheerer, ed., *Cognition theory, research, promise.* New York: Harper & Row.

GARRISON, S. C. 1922. Additional re-tests by means of a Stanford-revision of the Binet-Simon test. *J. Educ. Psychol.,* 13: 307-312.

GATES, A. I. 1925. Function of flashcard exercises in reading: an experimental study. *Teachers Coll. Rec.,* 27: 311-327.

———, and GRACE A. TAYLOR. 1925. An experi-

mental study of the nature of improvement resulting from practice in a mental function. *J. Educ. Psychol.,* 16: 583-592.

GATTESMAN, I. J. 1960. The psychogenetics of personality. Unpublished doctoral dissertation. Minneapolis: Univ. Minnesota.

GAURON, E. F. 1965. Specificity-generality of early experience effect. *Psychol. Rep.,* 16: 353-354.

GAUTENBEIN, M. M. 1952. Recherches sur le developpement de la perception du mouvement avec l'age (movement apparent, dit stroboscopique). *Arch. Psychol.* (Geneve), 33: 197-294.

GAYDOS, H. F. 1956. Intersensory transfer in the discrimination of form. *Amer. J. Psychol.,* 69: 107-110.

GAZE, R. M., M. JACOBSON, and G. SZEKELY. 1965. On the formation of connections by compound eyes in Xenopus. *J. Physiol.,* 176: 409-417.

GEDDES, P., and J. A. THOMSON. 1897. *The evolution of sex.* London: Scott.

GELLMAN, R. 1967. Conservation, attention and discrimination. Unpublished doctoral dissertation. Los Angeles: Univ. Calif.

GERARD, R. W. 1953. What is memory? *Sci. Amer.,* 189(9): 118-126.

———. 1959. Brains and behavior, in M. Spukler, ed., *The evolution of man's capacity for culture.* Detroit: Wayne State Univ. Press.

GERSON, H. 1966. Al yatsivut hamishpaha bakibuts (On the stability of the family in the kibbutz). *Megamot,* 14: 395-408.

GERSTMANN, J. 1958. Psychological and phenomenological aspects of disorders of the body image. *J. Nerv. Ment. Dis.,* 126: 499-512.

GESCHWIND, N. 1964. The development of the brain and the evolution of language. *Monogr. Ser. Language Linguistics,* No. 17.

GESELL, A. 1945. *The embryology of behavior.* New York: Harper.

———, and C. S. AMATRUDA. 1941. *Developmental diagnosis: normal and abnormal child development.* New York: Hoeber.

GESELL, A., and FRANCES L. ILG. 1946. *The child from five to ten.* New York: Harper.

———, and LOUISE B. AMES. 1956. *Youth: the years from ten to sixteen.* New York: Harper.

GETTY, J. P. 1968. The educated executive. *Playboy,* 15(9): 143.

GETZELS, J. W., and P. W. JACKSON. 1961. Family environment and cognitive style: a study of the sources of highly intelligent and highly creative adolescents. *Amer. Sociol. Rev.*, **26:** 351-359.

———. 1962. *Creativity and intelligence.* New York: Wiley.

GETZELS, J. W., and J. J. WALSH. 1958. The method of paired direct and projective questionnaires in the study of attitude structure and socialization. *Psychol. Monogr.*, **72** (1): Whole No. 454.

GHENT, L. 1960. Recognition by children of realistic figures presented in various orientations. *Canad. J. Psychol.*, **14:** 249-256.

———. 1961a. Form and its orientation: a child's eye view. *Amer. J. Psychol.*, **74:** 177-190.

———. 1961b. Developmental changes in tactual thresholds on dominant and non-dominant sides. *J. Comp. Physiol. Psychol.*, **54:** 670.

———, and L. BERNSTEIN. 1961. Influence of the orientation of geometric forms on their recognition by children. *Percept. Motor Skills*, **12:** 95-101.

GHISELIN, B. 1956. The creative process and its relation to the identification of creative talent, in C. Taylor, ed., *The 1955 University of Utah Research Conference on the Identification of Creative Scientific Talent.* Salt Lake City: Univ. Utah Press.

GIBBY, R. G., and R. GABLER. 1967. The self-concept of negro and white children. *J. Clin. Psychol.*, **23:** 144-148.

GIBSON, ELEANOR J. 1966. Perceptual development and the reduction of uncertainty. Paper read at the International Congress of Psychology, Moscow, 1966. Quoted by J. S. Brunner et al. 1966. *Studies in cognitive growth.* New York: Wiley.

———, and VIVIAN OLUM. 1960. Experimental methods of studying perception in children, in P. H. Mussen, ed., *Handbook of research methods in child development.* New York: Wiley.

GIBSON, ELEANOR J., and R. D. WALK. 1960. The "visual cliff." *Sci. Amer.*, **202:** 64-71.

GIBSON, ELEANOR J., and A. YONAS. 1966. A developmental study of the effects of visual and auditory interference on a visual scanning task. *Psychon. Sci.*, **5:** 163-164.

GIBSON, J. J. 1950. *The perception of the visual world.* Boston: Houghton Mifflin.

———, and ELEANOR J. GIBSON. 1955a. Perceptual learning: differentiation or enrichment? *Psychol. Rev.*, **62:** 33-40.

———. 1955b. What is learned in perceptual learning? A reply to Professor Postman. *Psychol. Rev.*, **62:** 447-450.

GILBERT, J. A. 1894. Researches on the mental and physical development of school children. *Stud. Yale Psychol. Lab.*, **2:** 40-100.

GILL, N. T. 1966. The relationship between modes of perception and selected variables in young children. *Dissert. Abstr.*, **27**(3A): 673.

GINSBERG, M. 1944. *The psychology of society.* London: Methuen.

GLANZ, Y. 1966-1967. Mimtsaim sotsyometrium bekhitot meoravot uvekhitot viltimeocravot. (Sociometric findings in co-educational and non-co-educational classes). *Hackinuch*, **39:** 1-20.

GLANZER, M. 1962. Toward a psychology of language structure. *J. Speech Hear. Res.*, **5:** 303-314.

GLASS, S. J., and R. W. JOHNSON. 1944. Limitations and complications of organotherapy in male homosexuality. *J. Clin. Endocrinol.*, **4:** 540.

GLIDEWELL, J. C., ed. 1961. *Parental attitudes and child behavior.* Springfield, Ill.: Thomas.

GLOOR, P., and W. FEINDEL. 1963. Affective behavior and temporal lobe, in M. Monnier, ed., *Physiologie und Pathologie des Vegetativen Nervensystems.* Stuttgart: Hippocrates-Verlag.

GLUCKSBERG, S., P. KRAUSS, and R. WEISBERG. 1966. Referential communication in nursery school children: method and some preliminary findings. *J. Exp. Child Psychol.*, **3:** 333-342.

GLUECK, S., and ELEANOR GLUECK. 1950. *Unravelling juvenile delinquency.* New York: Oxford Univ. Press.

GOINS, JEAN T. 1958. *Visual perceptual abilities and early reading progress. Suppl. Educ. Monogr.*, No. 87. Chicago: Univ. Chicago Press.

GOLANN, S. E. 1963. Psychological study of creativity. *Psychol. Bull.*, **60:** 548-565.

GOLDBERG, M. H., and ELEANOR E. MACCOBY. 1965. Children's acquisition of skills in performing a group task under two conditions of group formation. *J. Personality Soc. Psychol.*, **2:** 898-902.

GOLDBERG, SUSAN, and M. LEWIS. 1969. Play behavior in the year-old infant: early sex differences. *Child Develop.*, **40:** 21-31.

GOLDFARB, W. 1944a. Infant rearing as a factor in foster home replacement. *Amer. J. Orthopsychiat.*, **14:** 162-166.

———. 1944b. Effects of early institutional care on

adolescent personality: Rorschach data. *Amer. J. Orthopsychiat.*, 14: 441-447.

———. 1945a. Effects of psychological deprivation in infancy and subsequent stimulation. *Amer. J. Psychiat.*, 102: 18-33.

———. 1945b. Psychological privation in infancy and subsequent adjustment. *Amer. J. Orthopsychiat.*, 15: 247-255.

———. 1947. Variations in adolescent adjustment of institutionally-reared children. *Amer. J. Orthopsychiat.*, 17: 449-457.

———. 1961. *Childhood schizophrenia*. Cambridge, Mass.: Harvard Univ. Press.

GOLDIN, P. C. 1969. A review of children's reports of parent behaviors. *Psychol. Bull.*, 71: 222-236.

GOLDSCHMID, M. L. 1967. Different types of conservation and non-conservation and their relation to age, sex, IQ, MA, and vocabulary. *Child Develop.*, 38: 1229-1246.

———. 1968a. The role of experience in the acquisition of conservation. *Proceedings of the 76th Annual Convention of the American Psychological Association*, 361-362.

———. 1968b. The relation of conservation to emotional and environmental aspects of development. *Child Develop.*, 39: 579-589.

———. ed. (in press). *Black Americans and white racism: theory and research*. New York: Holt, Rinehart and Winston.

———, and P. M. BENTLER. 1968. Dimensions and measurement of conservation. *Child Develop.*, 39: 787-802.

GOLDSTEIN, A. G., and E. J. MACKENBERG. 1966. Recognition of human faces from isolated facial features. A development study. *Psychon. Sci.*, 6: 149-150.

GOLDSTEIN, K. 1939. *The organism*. New York: American Book.

———. 1940. *Human nature in the light of psychopathology*. Cambridge, Mass.: Harvard Univ. Press.

———, and M. SCHEERER. 1941. Abstract and concrete behavior: an experimental study with special tests. *Psychol. Monogr.*, 53 (2): Whole No. 239.

GOLDSTEIN, R., and B. ROSENBLÜT. 1965. Factors influencing electrophysiologic responsivity in normal adults. *J. Speech Hear. Res.*, 8: 323-347.

GOLLIN, E. S., and P. LISS. 1962. Conditional discrimination in children. *J. Comp. Physiol. Psychol.*, 55: 850-855.

GOODDY, W., and W. MCKISSOCK. 1951. The theory of cerebral localisation. *Lancet*, 260: 481-483.

GOODENOUGH, D. R. 1963. Sex differences in psychological differentiation. Paper read at the Society for Research in Child Development, biennial meeting, Berkeley.

———, and CAROL J. EAGLE. 1963. A modification of the embedded-figures test for use with young children. *J. Genet. Psychol.*, 103: 67-74.

GOODENOUGH, E. W. 1957. Interest in persons as an aspect of sex differences in the early years. *Genet. Psychol. Monogr.*, 55: 287-323.

GOODENOUGH, FLORENCE L. 1956. Measurement of mental growth, in L. Carmichael, ed., *Manual of child psychology*, 2nd ed. New York: Wiley.

GOTTESMAN, I. I. 1963a. Heritability of personality: a demonstration. *Psychol. Monogr.*, 77(9): Whole No. 572.

———. 1963b. Genetic aspects of intelligent behavior, in N. Ellis, ed., *Handbook of mental deficiency*. New York: McGraw-Hill.

———. 1966. Genetic variance in adaptive personality. *J. Child. Psychol. Psychiat.*, 7: 199-208.

GOTTLIEB, G. 1961a. Developmental age as a baseline for determination of the critical period in imprinting. *J. Comp. Physiol. Psychol.*, 54: 422-427.

———. 1961b. The following response and imprinting in wild and domestic ducklings of the same species. *Behaviour*, 18: 105-208.

———. 1963. Imprinting in nature. *Science*, 139: 497-498.

GOUREVITCH, VIVIAN. 1959. Motivation and social adequacy. Unpublished doctoral dissertation. New York: Teachers College, Columbia University.

———, and M. H. FEFFER. 1962. A study of motivational development. *J. Genet. Psychol.*, 100: 361-375.

GOY, R. H., and W. C. YOUNG. 1957. Somatic basis of sexual behavior patterns in guinea pigs. *Psychosomat. Med.*, 14: 144-151.

GRAHAM, FRANCES, CLAIRE B. ERNHART, D. THURSTON, and MARGUERITE CRAFT. 1962. Development three years after perinatal anoxia and other potentially damaging new-born experiences. *Psychol. Monogr.*, 76(3): Whole No. 522.

GRANIT, R. 1955. *Receptors and sensory perception.* New Haven: Yale Univ. Press.

GRAY, P. C., and K. I. HOWARD. 1957. Special recognition of humans in imprinted chicks. *Percept. Motor Skills,* **7**: 301-304.

GRAY, P. H. 1958. Theory and evidence of imprinting in human infants. *J. Psychol.,* **46**: 155-166.

———. 1960. Evidence that retinal flicker is not a necessary condition of imprinting. *Science,* **132**: 1834-1835.

———. 1963. A checklist of papers since 1951, dealing with imprinting in birds. *Psychol. Rec.,* **13**: 445-454.

GRAY, SUSAN W., R. A. KLAUS, J. O. MILLER, and BETTYE J. FORRESTER. 1966a. *Before first grade: the early training project for disadvantaged children.* New York: Columbia Univ. Press.

GRAY, SUSAN W., J. O. MILLER, and R. HINZE. 1966b. *Demonstration and research center for early education.* Mimeo. report. Nashville: George Peabody College for Teachers.

GREEN, J. D. 1956. Neural pathways to the hypophysis, in W. S. Fields, R. Guillemin, and C. A. Carton, eds., *Hypothalmic-hypophysical interrelationships: a symposium.* Springfield, Ill.: Thomas, 3-14.

GREENBLATT, R. B. 1943. Testosterone propionate pellet implantation in gynecic disorders. *J. Amer. Med. Ass.,* **121**: 17-24.

GREGORY, I. 1965. Anterospective data following childhood loss of a parent. I. Delinquency and high school dropout. *Arch. Gen. Psychiat.,* **13**: 99-120.

GRIFFIN, G. 1965. The effects of three months' total social isolation upon learning and social behaviors in rhesus monkeys. Unpublished master's thesis. Madison: Univ. Wisconsin. Reported in G. P. Sackett. 1965. Effects of early rearing conditions upon the behavior of rhesus monkeys (Macaca Mulatta). *Child Develop.,* **36**: 855-868.

GRIFFITHS, W. J., and W. F. STRINGER. 1952. The effects of intense stimulation experienced during infancy on adult behavior in the rat. *J. Comp. Physiol. Psychol.,* **45**: 301-306.

GRIMES, J. W., and W. ALLINSMITH. 1961. Compulsivity, anxiety and school achievement. *Merrill-Palmer Quart.,* **7**: 247-271.

GRIPPEN, V. B. 1933. A study of creative artistic imagination in children by the constant contact procedure. *Psychol. Monogr.,* **45**(1): 63-81.

GROHMAN, J. 1938. Modifikation oder Funktionsreifung. Ein Beitrag zur Klarüng der wechselseitigen Beziehungen zwichen Instinkthandlung und Erfahrung. (Modification or maturation. A contribution to the clarification of the mutual relationship between instinct and experience.) *Z. Tierpsychol.,* **2**: 132-144.

GROSS, FRANCES. 1959. The role of sex in perception of the upright. *J. Personality,* **27**: 95-103.

GRUMBACH, M. M., and M. L. BARR. 1958. Cytologic tests of chromosomal sex in relation to sexual anomalies in man. *Recent Progr. Hormone Res.,* **14**: 255-334.

GRUNKER, R. R., P. C. BUCY, and A. L. SAHS. 1959. *Neurology.* Oxford: Blackwell.

GRUNT, J. A. C., and W. C. YOUNG. 1952. Psychological modification of fatigue following orgasm (ejaculation) in the male guinea pig. *J. Comp. Physiol. Psychol.,* **45**: 508-510.

———. 1953. Consistency of sexual behavior patterns in individual male guinea pigs following castration and androgen therapy. *J. Comp Physiol. Psychol.,* **46**: 138-144.

GUILFORD, J. P. 1950. Creativity. *Amer. Psychol.,* **5**: 444-454.

———, and P. R. MERRIFIELD. 1960. *The structure of intellect model: its uses and implications.* Los Angeles: Univ. Southern California Press.

GUITON, P. 1959. Socialization and imprinting in Brown Leghorn chicks. *Anim. Behav.,* **7**: 26-34.

GUNTHER, M. 1955. Instinct and the nursing couple. *Lancet,* **1**: 575-578.

GURNEE, H. 1937. Maze learning in the collective situation. *J. Psychol.,* **3**: 437-443.

GUROWITZ, E. M. 1968. *Molecular basis of memory.* Englewood Cliffs, N.J.: Prentice-Hall.

GYLLENSTEN, L., M. TORBJÖRN, and M. L. NORRTIN. 1966. Growth alteration in the auditory cortex of visually deprived mice. *J. Comp. Neurol.,* **126**: 463-470.

HABER, R. N. 1969. Eidetic images. *Sci. Amer.,* **220**(4): 36-44.

HAITH, M. M. 1966a. The response of the human newborn to visual movement. *J. Exp. Child Psychol.,* **3**: 235-243.

———. 1966b. A semiautomatic procedure for

measuring change in position. *J. Exp. Child Psychol.*, **3**: 289-295.

———, W. KESSEN, and DOROTHY COLLINS. 1969. Response of the human infant to level of complexity of intermittent visual movement. *J. Exp. Child Psychol.*, **7**: 52-69.

HALL, C. S. 1941. Temperament: a survey of animal studies. *Psychol. Bull.*, **38**: 908-943.

HALLOWELL, A. I. 1960. Self-society and culture in phylogenetic prospective, in S. Tax, ed., *Evolution after Darwin*, Vol. II. Chicago: Univ. Chicago Press.

———. 1961. The protocultural foundations of human adaptation, in S. Tax. ed., *Evolution after Darwin*, Vol. II. Chicago: Univ. of Chicago Press.

HALSTEAD, W. C. 1947. *Brain and intelligence*. Chicago: Univ. Chicago Press.

———. 1951. Brain and intelligence, in L. A. Jeffress, ed., *Cerebral mechanisms in behavior*. New York: Wiley.

HAMBURGER, V. 1963. Some aspects of the embryology of behavior. *Quart. Rev. Biol.*, **38**: 342-365.

HAMILTON, G. V. 1929. *A research in marriage*. New York: Liveright.

HAMILTON, V. 1966. Size, constancy and intelligence: a re-examination. *Brit. J. Psychol.*, **57**: 319-328.

HAMMER, E. F. 1961. *Creativity*. New York: Random House.

HAMPSON, J. L., and JOAN G. HAMPSON. 1961. Ontogenesis of sexual behavior in man, in W. C. Young, ed., *Sex and internal secretions*, 3rd ed., Vol. II. Baltimore: Williams & Wilkins.

———, and J. MONEY. 1955. The syndrome of gonadal agenesis (ovarian agenesis) and male chromosomal pattern in girls and women: psychologic studies. *Bull. Johns Hopkins Hosp.*, **97**: 43-57.

HANLEY, C., and D. J. ZERBOLIO. 1964. Application of the up-and-down method in measuring perceptual development. *Child Develop.*, **35**(3): 979-984.

———. 1965. Developmental changes in five illusions measured by the up-and-down method. *Child Develop.*, **36**: 437-452.

HANSEN, E. W. 1966. The development of maternal and infant behavior in the rhesus monkey. *Behaviour*, **27**: 107-149.

HARLOW, H. F. 1949. The formation of learning sets. *Psychol. Rev.*, **56**: 51-65.

———. 1953. Mice, monkeys, men and motives. *Psychol. Rev.*, **60**: 23-31.

———. 1958a. The evolution of learning, in Anne Roe and G. G. Simpson, eds., *Behavior and evolution*. New Haven: Yale Univ. Press.

———. 1958b. The nature of love. *Amer. Psychol.*, **13**: 673-685.

———. 1959a. Learning set and error factor theory, in S. Koch, ed., *Psychology: a study of a science, Vol. II. General systematic formations, learning and special processes*. New York: McGraw-Hill.

———. 1959b. Love in infant monkeys. *Sci. Amer.* **200**(6): 68-74.

———. 1962. The heterosexual affectional system in monkeys. *Amer. Psychol.*, **17**: 1-9.

———, and KUENNE HARLOW. 1962. The effect of rearing conditions on behavior. *Bull. Menninger Clin.*, **26**: 213-224.

HARLOW, H. F., and M. K. HARLOW. 1962. Social deprivation in monkeys. *Sci. Amer.* **207**(5): 136-146.

———. 1965. The effect of rearing conditions of behavior, in J. Money, ed., *Sex research: new developments*. New York: Holt, Rinehart and Winston.

HARLOW, H. F., and MARGARET K. HARLOW. 1969. Effects of various mother-infant relationships on rhesus monkey behaviors, in B. M. Foss, ed., *Determinants of infant behavior*. IV. London: Methuen.

———, and D. R. MEYER. 1950. Learning motivated by a manipulation drive. *J. Exp. Psychol.*, **40**: 218-234.

HARLOW, H. F., and T. JOHNSON. 1943. Problem solution by monkeys following bilateral removal of the prefrontal areas. Pt. III. Test of initiation of behavior. *Psychologist*, **32**: 495-500.

HARLOW, H. F., and R. R. ZIMMERMAN. 1958. The development of affectional responses in infant monkeys. *Proc. Amer. Phil. Soc.*, **102**: 501-509.

———. 1959. Affectional responses in the infant monkey. *Science*, **130**: 421-432.

HARRIS, G. W. 1964a. Sex hormones, brain development and brain function. *Endocrinology*, **75**: 627-665.

———. 1964b. The central nervous system and the endocrine glands. *Triangle*, **6**: 242-251.

———, and R. P. MICHAEL. 1958. Hypothalamic mechanisms and the control of sexual behavior in the female cat. *J. Physiol.*, **142**: 26.

———, and P. Scott. 1958. Neurological site of action of stilboestral in eliciting sexual behavior, in G. E. W. Wolstenholme and C. M. O'Connor, eds., *CIBA Foundation Symposium on the Neurological Basis of Behaviour*. London: Churchill.

HARRISON, R. J. 1958. *Man the peculiar animal*. London: Penguin.

HART, B. L. 1968. Neonatal castration: influence on neural organisation of sexual reflexes in male rats. *Science*, **160**: 1135-1136.

HARTUP, H. W. 1958. Nurturance and nurturance-withdrawal in relation to the dependency behavior of pre-school children. *Child Develop.*, **29**: 191-202.

HARVEY, O. J., D. E. HUNT, and H. M. SCHRODER. 1961. *Conceptual systems and personality organization*. New York: Wiley.

HATFIELD, J. S., LUCY R. FERGUSON, and R. ALPERT. 1967. Mother-child interaction and the socialization process. *Child Develop.*, **38**: 365-414.

HAYES, K. 1951. *The ape in our house*. New York: Harper.

HAYWOOD, H. C., and D. W. ZIMMERMAN. 1964. Effects of early environmental complexity on the following response in chicks. *Percept. Motor Skills*, **18**: 653-658.

HEAD, H. 1920. *Studies and neurology*, Vol. II. London: Hodder and Stoughton and Oxford Univ. Press.

HEATH, R. G. 1964. Pleasure response of human subjects to direct stimulation of the brain: physiologic and psychodynamic consideration, in R. G. Heath, ed., *The role of pleasure in behavior*. New York: Hoeber.

HEBB, D. O. 1937. The innate organization of visual activity: Vol. I. Perception of figures by rats reared in total darkness. *J. Genet. Psychol.*, **51**: 101-126.

———. 1946. On the nature of fear. *Psychol. Rev.*, **53**: 259-276.

———. 1949. *The organization of behavior*. New York: Wiley.

———. 1953. Heredity and environment in mammalian behavior. *Brit. J. Anim. Behav.*, **1**: 43-47.

———. 1955. Drives and the CNS (conceptual nervous system). *Psychol. Rev.*, **62**: 243-254.

———. 1958. The motivating effects of exteroceptive stimulation. *Amer. Psychologist*, **13**: 109-113.

———. 1960. The american revolution. *Amer. Psychologist*, **15**: 735-745.

———. 1963. The semi-autonomous process: its nature and nurture. *Amer. Psychologist*, **18**: 16-27.

———. 1966. *A text of psychology*, 2nd ed. Philadelphia: Saunders.

———, and W. R. THOMPSON. 1954. The social significance of animal studies, in G. Lindzey, ed., *Handbook of social psychology*, Vol. I. Reading, Mass: Addison-Wesley.

HEDIGER, H. 1938. *Wild animals in captivity*. London: Butterworth.

HEIDER, F., and M. GRACE HEIDER. 1940. A comparison of color sorting behavior of deaf and hearing children. *Psychol. Monogr.*, **52**(2): 6-22.

HEINSTEIN, M. I. 1963. Behavioral correlates of breast-bottle regimes under varying parent-infant relationships. *Mongr. Soc. Res. Child Develop.*, **28** (4). Ser. No. 88.

HELD, R. 1965. Plasticity in sensory-motor systems. *Sci. Amer.*, **213**(5): 84-97.

———, and J. A. BAUER. 1967. Visually guided reaching in infant monkeys after restricted rearing. *Science*, **155**: 718-720.

HELD, R., and S. J. FREEDMAN. 1963. Plasticity in human sensorimotor control. *Science*, **142**: 455-462.

HELD, R., and A. HEIN. 1963. Movement produced stimulation in the development of visually guided behavior. *J. Comp. Physiol. Psychol.*, **56**: 872-876.

HELLER, C. G., and W. O. MADDOCK. 1947. Clinical uses of testosterone in the male. *Vitamins Hormones*, **5**: 394-475.

HELLER, C. G., and W. O. NELSON. 1945. Treatment of testicular failure. *J. Clin. Endocrinol.*, **5**: 27-33.

HELSON, H. 1964. *Adaption-level theory*. New York: Harper & Row.

HELSON, RAVENNA. 1965. Childhood interest clusters related to creativity in women. *J. Consult. Psychol.*, **29**: 352-361.

HENDERSON, N. D. 1966. Inheritance of re-activity to experimental manipulation in mice. *Science*, **153**: 650-652.

HERNANDEZ-PÉON, R., R. H. SCHERRER, and M. JOUVET. 1956. Modification of electric activity in the cochlear nucleus during "attention" in unanaesthetized cats. *Science*, **123**: 331-332.

HERR, E., G. D. MOORE, J. C. HANSEN, and C.

CASTELLI. 1965. Creativity, intelligence and values: a study of relationships? *Exceptional Child*, **32**: 114-115.

HERREN, R. Y. 1933. The effect of high and low female sex hormone concentrate on the two-point threshold of pain and touch and upon tactile sensitivity. *J. Exp. Psychol.*, **16**: 324-327.

HERRIOT, P. 1969. Comprehension of tense by young children. *Child Develop.*, **40**: 103-109.

HERSHENSON, M. 1964. Visual discrimination in the human newborn. *J. Comp. Physiol. Psychol.*, **58**: 270-276.

HERSHER, L., A. MOORE, and J. B. RICHMOND. 1958. Effect of post partum separation of mother and kid on maternal care in the domestic goat. *Science*, **128**: 1342-1343.

HESS, E. H. 1950. Development of the chick's responses to light and shade cues of depth. *J. Comp. Physiol. Psychol.*, **43**: 112-122.

———. 1957. Effects of meprobamate on imprinting in waterfowl. *Ann. N.Y. Acad. Sci.*, **67**: 724-733.

———. 1959a. Imprinting. *Science*, **130**: 133-141.

———. 1959b. The relationship between imprinting and motivation. *Nebraska Symp. Motivation*, **7**: 44-77.

———. 1961. Shadows and depth perception. *Sci. Amer.*, **204**: 138-148.

———. 1964. Imprinting in birds. *Science*, **146**: 1128-1139.

———. 1965. Attitude and pupil size. *Sci. Amer.*, **212**(4): 46-65.

———, and H. H. SCHAEFFER. 1959. Innate behavior patterns as indicators of the "critical period." *Z. Tierpsychol.*, **16**: 155-160.

HESS, R. D., and VIRGINIA SHIPMAN. 1965. Early experience and the socialization of cognitive modes in children. *Child Develop.*, **36**: 869-886.

HESS, W. R. 1943. Das Zwischenhirn als Kordinationsorgan. *Helv. Physiol. Acta*, **1**: 549-565.

———. 1944. Das Schlafsyndrom als Folge Dienzephaler Reinzung. *Helv. Physiol. Acta*, **2**: 305-344.

———, and M. BRÜGGER. 1943. Das subkortikale Zentrum der affektiven Abwehrreaktion. (The subcortical center for affective defense reactions.) *Helv. Physiol. Pharmacol. Acta*, **1**: 33-52.

HETHERINGTON, E. MAVIS. 1966. Effects of paternal absence on sex-typed behaviors in negro and white pre-adolescent boys. *J. Pers. Soc. Psychol.*, **4**: 87-91.

HILDEN, A. H. 1949. A longitudinal study of intellectual development. *J. Psychol.*, **28**: 187-214.

HILDRETH, GERTRUDE. 1949. The development of training of hand dominance. I. Characteristics of handedness. II. Developmental tendencies and lateral dominance. *J. Genet. Psychol.*, **75**: 197-220, 221-254, and 255-275.

HILL, K. T., and S. B. SARASON. 1966. The relation of test anxiety and defensiveness to test and school performance over the elementary school years. *Monogr. Soc. Res. Child Develop.*, **31**(2): Series No. 104.

HIMMELSTEIN, P. 1964. Sex differences in spatial localisation of the self. *Percept. Motor Skills*, **19**: 317.

HIMWICH, H. E. 1960. Functional organization of the brain, past and present. *J. Nerv. Ment. Dis.*, **130**: 505-519.

HINDE, R. A. 1962. Some aspects of the imprinting problem. *Symp. Zool. Soc. London*, **8**: 129-138.

HINGSON, R. J. 1960. Cortical electrical responses to visual stimulation in the human infant. *Electroenceph. and Clin. Neurophysiol.*, **12**: 663-677.

———, and R. C. WILCOTT. 1960. Development of evoked responses in visual-auditory cortices of kittens. *J. Neurophysiol.*, **23**: 363-375.

HIRSH, IRA J. 1967. Information processing in input channels for speech and language: The significance of serial order of stimuli, in Frederic L. Darley, ed., *Conference of brain mechanisms underlying speech and language, Princeton, N.J., 1965, Proceedings*. Chairman: Clark H. Millikan. New York: Grune & Stratton, 21-36.

HIRSCH, J. 1962. Individual differences in behaviour and their basis, in E. L. Bliss, ed., *Roots of Behaviour*. New York: Harper.

———. 1963. Behavior genetics and individuality understood. *Science*, **142**: 1436-1442.

———. 1967. Behavior-genetic or "experimental" analysis: the challenge of science versus the lure of technology. *Amer. Psychol.*, **22**: 118-130.

———, R. H. LINDLEY, and E. C. TOLMAN. 1955. An experimental test of an alleged innate sign stimulus. *J. Comp. Physiol. Psychol.*, **48**: 278-280.

HOAGLAND, M. B. 1959. Nucleic acids and proteins. *Sci. Amer.*, **201**(6): 55-61.

HOBHOUSE, L. T. 1896. *Theory of knowledge: a contribution to some problems of logic and metaphysics.* London: Methuen.

———. 1901. *Mind in evolution.* London: Macmillan.

———. 1915. *Mind in evolution,* 2nd ed. London: Macmillan.

———. 1921. *Principles of sociology. Vol. 2. The rational good.* London: Allen & Unwin.

———. 1924. *Principles of sociology. Vol. 41. Social development.* London: Allen & Unwin.

———. 1927. *Development and purpose.* London: Macmillan.

———. 1951. *Morals in evolution: a study in comparative ethics,* 7th ed. London: Chapman and Hall.

HOCKETT, C. P. 1967. Review of E. H. Lenneberg. Biological foundations of language. *Sci. Amer.*, **217**(5): 141-144.

HODGES, A., and B. BALLOW. 1961. Learning disability in relation to family constellation. *J. Educ. Res.*, **55**: 41-42.

HOFFMAN, H. N. 1955. Study in an aspect of concept formation with sub-normal, average and superior adolescents. *Genet. Psychol. Monogr.*, **52**: 191-239.

HOFFMAN, L. R., and N. R. F. MAIER. 1961. Sex differences, sex composition and group problem solving. *J. Abnorm. Social Psychol.*, **63**: 453-456.

HOFFMAN, LOIS W. 1961. The father's role in the family and the child's peer-group adjustment. *Merrill-Palmer Quart.*, **7**: 97-105.

HOFSTAETTER, P. R., and G. P. O'CONNOR. 1956. Anderson's overlap hypothesis and the discontinuities of growth. *J. Genet. Psychol.*, **88**: 95-106.

HOGBIN, H. I. 1931. Education in Outong Java. *Amer. Anthropol.*, **33**: 601-614.

———. 1946. A New Guinea childhood: from weaning till the eighth year in Wogeo. *Oceania.* **16**: 275-296.

———. 1967. Personal communication.

HOLLAND, J. 1961. Creative and academic performance among talented adolescents. *J. Educ. Psychol.*, **52**: 136-147.

HOLT, E. B. 1931. *Animal drive and the learning process.* New York: Henry Holt.

HOLTZMAN, W. H. 1965. Cross-cultural research on personality development. *Hum. Develop.*, **8**: 65-86.

HONIGMANN, J. J. 1954. *Culture and personality.* New York: Harper.

HONKAVAARA, S. 1958a. The "dynamic-affective" phase in the development of concepts. *J. Psychol.*, **45**: 11-23.

———. 1958b. A critical re-evaluation of the colour and form reaction and disproving of the hypothesis connected with it. *J. Psychol.*, **45**: 25-36.

———. 1958c. The colour and form reaction as a basis for differential psychotherapeutic approach. *J. Psychol.*, **46**: 39-51.

HONZIK, MARJORIE P. 1963. Sex difference in the age of onset of the parent-child resemblance in intelligence. *J. Educ. Psychol.*, **54**: 231-237.

———, JEAN W. MACFARLANE, and LUCILE ALLEN. 1948. The stability of mental test performance between 2 and 18 years. *J. Exp. Educ.*, **17**: 309-324.

HORN, J. L. 1968. Organization of abilities and the development of intelligence. *Psychol. Rev.*, **75**: 242-259.

HORNER, F. A., C. W. STREAMER, L. L. ALEJANDRINO, LINDA H. REED, and F. IBBOLT. 1962. Termination of dietary treatment of phenylketonuria. *New England J. Med.*, **266**: 79-81.

HOWARD, I. P., and W. B. TEMPLETON, 1966. *Human spatial orientation.* New York: Wiley.

HUBEL, D. H., and T. N. WIESEL. 1962. Receptive fields, binocular interaction and functional architecture in the cat's visual cortex. *J. Physiol.*, **160**: 106-154.

———. 1963. Receptive fields of cells in striate cortex of very young, visually inexperienced kittens. *J. Neurophysiol.*, **26**: 994-1002.

HUIZINGA, J. 1955. *Homo Ludens.* Boston: Beacon.

HUNT, E. E., and W. H. BARTON. 1959. The inconstancy of physique in adolescent boys and other limitations of somatotyping. *Amer. J. Physiol. Anthropol.*, **17**: 27-35.

HUNT, J. McV. 1941. The effects of infant feeding-frustration upon adult hoarding in the albino rat. *J. Abnorm. Social Psychol.*, **36**: 338-360.

———. 1961. *Intelligence and experience.* New York: Ronald Press.

———. 1966. Towards a theory of guiding the learning of the young. Paper read at the 27th Annual Meeting of the Canadian Psychological Association, Montreal, June.

———, H. Scholsberg, R. L. Solomon, and E. Stellar. 1947. Studies of the effects of infantile experience on adult behavior in rats. I. Effects of infantile feeding frustration and adult hoarding. *J. Comp. Physiol.,* **40**: 291-304.

Hunter, I. M. L. 1954. Tactile-kinaesthetic perception of straightness in blind and sighted humans. *Quart. J. Exp. Psychol.,* **6**: 149-154.

Hurlock, Elizabeth B. 1924. The value of praise and reproof as incentives for children. *Arch. Psychol.,* **11** (71): 1-78.

———. 1925. An evaluation of certain incentives used in school work. *J. Educ. Psychol.,* **16**: 145-159.

———. 1967. *Adolescent development,* 3rd ed. New York: McGraw-Hill.

Hurst, C. C. 1932. A genetic formula for the inheritance of intelligence in man. *Proc. Roy. Soc. London,* **B112**: 80-97.

———. 1934. The genetics of intellect. *Eugen. Rev.,* **26**: 33-45.

Hutt, Corinne, and C. Ounstead. 1966. The biological significance of gaze aversion with particular reference to the syndrome of infantile autism. *Behav. Sci.,* **11**: 346-355.

Hutt, C., H. von Bernuth, H. G. Lenard, S. J. Hutt, and H. F. R. Prechtl. 1968. Habitation in relation to state in the human neonate. Nature, **220**: 618-620.

Huxley, J. 1937. *Ends and means.* New York: Harper.

———. 1958. Cultural process and evolution, in Anne Roe and G. G. Simpson, eds., *Behavior and evolution.* New Haven: Yale Univ. Press.

Hymovitch, B. 1952. The effects of experimental variations on problem solving in the rat. *J. Comp. Physiol. Psychol.,* **45**: 313-321.

Imanishi, Kinji. 1957. Social behaviour in Japanese monkey, *Macaca fuscata. Psychologia: Int. J. Psychol. Orient.,* **1**: 47-54. (Also reproduced in C. H. Southwick, ed., *Primate social behaviour.* Princeton, N.J.: Van Nostrand.)

Ingram, V. M. 1958. How do genes act? *Sci. Amer.,* **198**(1): 68-74.

Inhelder, Bärbel. 1944. *Le diagnostique du renseignement chez les debiles mentaux.* Neuchâtel, Switz.: Delachaux et Niestlé.

———. 1957. Developmental psychology. *Ann. Rev. Psychol.,* **8**: 139-163.

Itani, J. 1959. Paternal care in the wild Japanese monkey, *Macaca fuscata. J. Primatol.,* **2**: 61-93.

Jackson, D. N. 1957. Intellectual ability and mode of perception. *J. Consult. Psychol.,* **21**: 458.

Jacob, F., and J. Monod. 1961. On the regulation of gene activity. *Cold Spring Harbor Symp. Quant. Biol.,* **26**: 193-209.

Jacobsen, C. F. 1935. Functions of the frontal association areas in primates. *Arch. Neurol. Psychiat.,* **33**: 558-569.

Jacobson, Edith. 1954. Contributions to the metapsychology of psychotic identification. *J. Amer. Psychoanal. Ass.,* **2**: 239-262.

Jacobson, M. 1969. Development of specific neuronal connections. *Science,* **163**: 543-547.

Jaensch, E. R. 1930. *Eidetic imagery and typological methods of investigation.* London: Kegan Paul Trench, Trubner and New York: Harcourt Brace & Co.

Jahoda, G. 1956. Sex differences in preferences for shapes: a cross-cultural replication. *Brit. J. Psychol.,* **47**: 126-132.

James, W. 1943. *The varieties of religious experience.* New York: Modern Library.

———. 1950. *Principles of psychology.* New York: Dover.

Jasper, H. H., L. Carmichael, and C. S. Bridgman. 1937. An ontogenetic study of cerebral electrical potentials in the guinea pig. *J. Exp. Psychol.,* **21**: 63-71.

Jay, P. 1963. The Indian Langur monkey (Presbytis Entellus), in C. H. Southwick, ed., *Primate social behavior.* Princeton, N.J.: Van Nostrand.

———. 1965. The common Langur of North India, in I. DeVore, ed., *Primate behavior.* New York: Holt, Rinehart and Winston.

Jaynes, J. 1956. Imprinting: the interaction of learned and innate behavior. I. Development and generalization. *J. Comp. Physiol. Psychol.,* **49**: 201-206.

———. 1957. Imprinting: the interaction of learned and innate behavior. II. The critical period. *J. Comp. Physiol. Psychol.,* **50**: 6-10.

Jeffrey, W. E., and D. D. Kluppel. 1962. Mediational variables in concept formation. *Psychol. Rep.,* **10**: 191-202.

Jersild, A. T. 1946. Emotional development, in L. Carmichael, ed., *Manual of child psychology.* New York: Wiley.

————. 1968. *Child psychology*, 6th ed. Englewood Cliffs, N.J.: Prentice-Hall.

JOHNSON, BETH, and L. F. BECK. 1941. The development of space perception. I. Stereoscopic vision in preschool children. *J. Genet. Psychol.*, **58**: 247-254.

JOHNSON, D. M., and CHARLEEN A. O'REILLY. 1964. Concept attainment in children: classifying and defining. *J. Educ. Psychol.*, **55**: 71-74.

JOHNSON, MIRIAM M. 1963. Sex role learning in the nuclear family. *Child Develop.*, **34**: 319-333.

JOHNSON, R. C., and C. W. THOMPSON. 1962. Incidental and intentional learning under three conditions of motivation. *Amer. J. Psychol.*, **75**: 284-288.

JONES, H. E. 1913. Mental differences between the sexes. *Pediat. Sem.*, **20**: 401-404.

————. 1938. The California adolescent growth study. *J. Educ. Res.*, **31**: 561-567.

————. 1946. Environmental influence on mental development, in L. Carmichael, ed., *Manual of child psychology*. New York: Wiley.

————, and NANCY BAYLEY. 1941. The Berkeley growth study. *Child Develop.*, **12**: 167-173.

JONES, H. E., and H. S. CONRAD. 1933. The growth and decline of intelligence: a study of a homogenous group between the ages of 10 and 60. *Genet. Psychol. Monogr.*, **13**: 223-298.

JONES, H. E., and M. C. JONES. 1928. A study of fear. *Child. Educ.*, **5**: 136-143.

JONES, MARY C. 1965. Psychological correlates of somatic development. *Child Develop.*, **36**: 899-912.

————, and NANCY BAYLEY. 1950. Physical maturing among boys as related to behavior. *J. Educ. Psychol.*, **41**: 129-148.

JONSSON, G. 1967. Delinquent boys, their parents and grandparents. *Acta Psychiat. Scand. Suppl.*, **43**: 195.

JOSEY, C. C., and C. H. MILLER. 1932. Race, sex and class differences in ability to endure pain. *J. Social Psychol.*, **3**: 374-376.

JOSS, ETIENNE, EDNA H. SOBEL, and K. A. ZUPPINGER. 1963. Skeletal maturation in rats with special reference to order and time of epiphysial closure. *Endocrinology*, **72**: 117-122.

JOSSO, NATHALIE, et al. 1965. True hermaphroditism with XX/XY mosaicism. *J. Clin. Endocrinol.*, **25**: 114-126.

JUNG, R., and R. HASSLER. 1960. The extrapyramidal motor system, in J. Field, ed., *Handbook of physiology*, Section I, Neurophysiology, Vol. II. Washington, D.C.: American Physiological Society.

KAGAN, J. 1958. The concept of identification. *Psychol. Rev.*, **65**: 296-305.

————. 1964. Acquisition and significance of sex-typing and sex role identity, in M. L. Hoffman and Lois W. Hoffman, eds., *Review of child development research*, Vol. I. New York: Russell Sage Foundation.

————, and F. A. BEACH. 1953. Effects of early experience on mating behavior in male rats. *J. Comp. Physiol. Psychol.*, **46**: 204-208.

KAGAN, J., BARBARA A. HENKER, AMY HENTOV, JANET LEVINE, and M. LEWIS. 1966. Infants' differential reactions to familiar and distorted faces. *Child Develop.*, **37**: 519-532.

KAGAN, J., and J. LEMKIN. 1961. Form, color, and size in children's conceptual behavior. *Child Develop.*, **32**: 25-28.

KAGAN, J., and M. LEWIS. 1965. Studies of attention in the human infant. *Merrill-Palmer Quart.*, **11**: 95-128.

KAGAN, J., H. A. MOSS, and I. E. SIGEL. 1963. Psychological significance of styles of conceptualization. *Monogr. Soc. Res. Child Develop.*, **28**(2): 73-112.

KAGAN, J., L. PEARSON, and LOIS WELCH. 1966. Modifiability of an impulsive tempo. *J. Educ. Psychol.*, **57**: 359-365.

KAGAN, J., B. L. ROSMAN, D. DAY, I. ALBERT, and W. PHILLIPS. 1964. Information processing in the child: significance of analytic and reflective attitudes. *Psychol. Monogr.*, **78**: 1-37.

KANNER, L. 1949. Problems of nosology and psychodynamics of early infantile autism. *Amer. J. Orthopsychiat.*, **19**: 416-426.

KAPPAS, KATHERINE H. 1967. A developmental analysis of children's responses to humor. *Library Quart.*, **37**: 67-77.

KARAS, G. G., and V. H. DENENBERG. 1961. The effects of duration and distribution of infantile experience on adult learning. *J. Comp. Physiol. Psychol.*, **54**: 170-174.

KARNABY, K. J. 1945. Premature sexual precocity in a young girl. *J. Clin. Endocrinol.*, **5**: 189.

KATZ, D. 1953. *Animals and men*. London: Pelican.

————, and G. RÉVÉSZ. 1921. Experimentelle Studien zur Vergleichenden Psychologie. Versuche mit Hühnern. *Z. Angew. Psychol.*, **18:** 307-320.

Katz, Phyllis A., and M. Deutsch. 1963. Relation of auditory-visual shifting to reading achievement. *Percept. Motor Skills,* **17:** 327-332.

Kawamura, Syunze. 1959. The process of subculture propagation among Japanese macaques. *J. Primatol.*, **1:** 43-60. Excerpted English edition appears in C. H. Southwick, ed., *Primate social behavior.* Princeton, N.J.: Van Nostrand, 1963.

Kaye, S. M. 1965. Primacy and recency in imprinting. *Psychon. Sci.*, **3:** 271-272.

Kelleher, R. T. 1956. Discrimination learning as a function of reversal and nonreversal shifts. *J. Exp. Psychol.*, **51:** 379-384.

Kellogg, W. N. 1968. Communication of language in the home-raised chimpanzee. *Science,* **162:** 423-427.

Kelly, A. H., L. E. Beaton, and H. W. Magoun. 1946. A midbrain mechanism for faciovocal activity. *J. Neurophysiol.*, **9:** 181-189.

Kendler, H. H. 1964. The concept of the concept, in A. W. Melton, ed., *Categories of human learning.* New York: Academic Press.

———, and M. F. D'Amato. 1955. A comparison of reversal shifts and nonreversal shifts in human concept formation behavior. *J. Exp. Psychol.*, **49:** 165-174.

Kendler, H. H., and T. S. Kendler. 1962a. Vertical and horizontal processes in problem solving. *Psychol. Rev.*, **69:** 1-16.

Kendler, T. S. 1961. Concept formation. *Ann. Rev. Psychol.*, **12:** 447-472.

———, and H. H. Kendler. 1959. Reversal and non-reversal shifts in kindergarten children. *J. Exp. Psychol.*, **58:** 56-60.

———. 1962b. Inferential behavior in children as a function of age and subgoal constancy. *J. Exp. Psychol.*, **64:** 460-466.

———. 1966. Optional shifts of children as a function of number of training trials on the initial discrimination. *J. Exp. Child Psychol.*, **3:** 216-224.

———, and B. Learnard. 1962. Medicated response to size and brightness as the function of age. *Amer. J. Psychol.*, **75:** 571-586.

Kendler, T. S., H. H. Kendler, and D. Wells. 1960. Reversal and non-reversal shifts in nursery school children. *J. Comp. Physiol. Psychol.*, **53:** 83-88.

Kennard, M. A., and L. F. Nims. 1942. Changes in normal electroencephalogram of Macaca mulatta with growth. *J. Neurophysiol.*, **5:** 325-333.

Keppel, G. 1964. Verbal learning in children. *Psychol. Bull.*, **61:** 63-80.

Kessen, W. 1962. 'Stage' and 'Structure' in the study of children, in W. Kessen and Clementina Kuhlman, eds., Thought in the young child. *Monogr. Soc. Res. Child Develop.* 27(2): Serial No. 83.

Kidd, D. 1906. *Savage childhood.* London: Adam and Charles.

Kimble, G. A. 1961. *Hilgard and Marquis' conditioning and learning,* 2nd ed. New York: Appleton.

Kimmel, H. D., and E. Kimmel. 1965. Sex differences in adaptation of the GSR under repeated applications of a visual stimulus. *J. Exp. Psychol.*, **70:** 536-537.

Kimura, Doreen. 1961. Cerebral dominance and the perception of verbal stimuli. *Canad. J. Psychol.*, **15:** 166-171.

———. 1963. Speech lateralization in young children as determined by an auditory test. *J. Comp. Physiol. Psychol.*, **56:** 899-902.

King, C. D. 1945. The meaning of normal. *Yale J. Biol. Med.*, **17:** 493-501.

Kinsey, Alfred C., W. B. Pomeroy, and C. E. Martin. 1948. *Sexual behavior in the human male.* Philadelphia: Saunders.

———, and P. H. Gebhard. 1953. *Sexual behavior in the human female.* Philadelphia: Saunders.

Kirkpatrick, E. A. 1900. Individual tests of school children. *Psychol. Rev.,* **5** (7): 274-280.

Kistyakovskaya, M. Yu. 1965. O stimulakh vyzyvayushchikh polozhitel'nye emotsii u rebenka pervykh mesyatsev zhizni. (Stimuli that elicit positive emotions in infants.) Pediatric Institute, USSR Acad. Med. Sci., Moscow: *Voprosy Psikhologii,* **2:** 129-140. *Psychological Abstracts,* 1965, **39:** 11912.

Kitay, J. I. 1967. Possible functions of the pineal gland, in L. Martini and W. F. Ganong, eds., *Neuroendocrinology,* Vol. II. New York: Academic Press.

———, and M. D. Altschule. 1954. *The pineal gland.* Cambridge, Mass.: Harvard Univ. Press.

Klackenberg, G. 1956. Studies in maternal deprivation in infants' homes. *Acta Pediat.*, **45:** 1-12.

Klaiber, E. L., D. M. Broverman, and Y. Ko-

BAYSHI. 1965. The automatization cognitive style, androgens and monoamine oxides. Unpublished ms. Worcester, Mass.: Worcester State Hospital Library.

———. 1967. The automatization cognitive style, androgens and monoamine oxidase. *Psychopharmacologia*, **11**: 320-336.

KLEIN, G. S. 1951. The personal world through perception, in R. R. Brake and G. V. Ramsey, eds., *Perception: an approach to personality*. New York: Ronald Press.

KLEITMAN, N., and T. G. ENGLEMAN. 1953. Sleep characteristics of infants. *J. Appl. Physiol.*, **6**: 266-282.

KLINEBERG, O. 1954. *Social psychology*, rev. ed. New York: Holt, Rinehart and Winston.

KLOPFER, P. H. 1962. *Behavior and ecology*. Englewood Cliffs, N.J.: Prentice-Hall.

———. 1968. From ardrey to altruism: a discourse on the biological basis of human behaviour. *Behav. Sci.*, **13**: 399-401.

———, and J. P. HAILMAN. 1964. Basic parameters of following and imprinting in precocial birds. *Z. Tierpsychol.*, **21**: 755-761.

KLUPPEL, D. D., and W. E. JEFFREY. 1964. Stimulus labelability as a factor in concept formation. *Psychol. Rep.*, **15**: 918.

KLÜVER, H. 1931. The eidetic child, in C. Murchison, ed., *A handbook of child psychology*. Worcester, Mass.: Clark Univ. Press.

KNIGHT, R. P. 1940. Introjection, projection and identification. *Psychoanal. Quart.*, **9**: 334-341.

KOCH, H. L. 1954. The relation of primary mental abilities in five- and six-year-olds to sex of child and characteristics of his sibling. *Child Develop.*, **25**: 209-223.

———. 1956. Sissiness and tomboyishness in relation to sibling characteristics. *J. Genet. Psychol.*, **88**: 231-244.

KOCH, J. 1961. An attempt to analyse the influence of the environment of children's homes on the neurophychic development of four to twelve month old children. *Cesk. Pediat.*, **16**: 332-340.

KOFFKA, K. 1935. *Principles of Gestalt psychology*. New York: Harcourt.

KOHLBERG, L. 1963. The development of children's orientations towards a moral order. I. Sequence in the development of moral thought. *Vita Humana*, **6**: 11-33.

———, and E. ZIGLER. 1967. The impact of cognitive maturity on the development of sex-role attitudes in the years four to eight. *Genet. Psychol. Monogr.*, **75**: 89-165.

KÖHLER, W., and H. WALLACH. 1944. Figural after-effects. *Proc. Amer. Phil. Soc.*, **88**: 269-357.

KOHN. M. 1966. The child as a determinant of his peer's approach to him. *J. Genet. Psychol.*, **109**: 91-100.

KOOISTRA, W. H. 1963. *Developmental trends in the attainment of conservation, transitivity, and relativism in the thinking of children: a replication and extension of Piaget's autogenetic formulations*. Unpublished doctoral dissertation, Detroit: Wayne State Univ.

KOPPENAAL, R. J., A. KRULL, and H. KATZ. 1964. Age, interference, and forgetting. *J. Exp. Child Psychol.*, **1**: 360-375.

KOSTICK, M. M. 1954. Study of transfer: sex differences in the reasoning process. *J. Educ. Psychol.*, **45**: 449-458.

KOVACH, J. K., E. FABRICIUS, and L. FALT. 1966. Relationship between imprinting and perceptual learning. *J. Comp. Physiol. Psychol.*, **61**: 449-454.

KOVACH, J. K., and E. H. HESS. 1963. Imprinting: effects of painful stimulation on the following response. *J. Comp. Physiol. Psychol.*, **56**: 461-464.

KRAUSS, R. M., and S. GLUCKSBERG. 1969. The development of communication: competence as a function of age. *Child Develop.*, **40**: 255-266.

KRECH, D., M. R. ROSENZWEIG, and E. L. BENNETT. 1960. Effects of early environmental complexity and training on brain chemistry. *J. Comp. Physiol. Psychol.*, **53**: 509-519.

KRETSCHMER, E. 1925. *Physique and character*. London: Kegan Paul.

KRIS, E. 1952. *Psychoanalytic explorations in art*. New York: International Univ. Press.

———. 1961. Notes on the development and some current problems of psychoanalytic child psychology. *Psychoanal. Stud. Child.*, **26**: 24-26.

KUBIE, L. S. 1958. *Neurotic distortion of the creative process*. Lawrence: Univ. Kansas Press.

KUENNE, M. R. 1946. Experimental investigation of the relation of language to transposition behavior in young children. *J. Exp. Psychol.*, **36**: 471-490.

KUHLMAN, CLEMENTINA. 1960. *Visual imagery in children*. Unpublished doctoral dissertation. Cambridge, Mass.: Harvard Univ.

KUN, H. 1934. Psychische Feninierung und Herma-phrodisierung von Mannchem durch weibliches Sexualhormon. *Endokrinol.*, **13**: 311-323.

KUO, Z. Y. 1930. The genesis of the cat's responses to the rat. *J. Comp. Psychol.*, **11**: 1-35.

———. 1938. Further study of the behavior of the cat towards the rat. *J. Comp. Psychol.*, **25**: 1-8.

KUTNER, B. 1958. Patterns of mental functioning associated with prejudice in children. *Psychol. Monogr.*, **72**: 1-48.

KVALE, J. N., and J. R. FISHMAN. 1965. The psychosocial aspects of Klinefelter's syndrome. *J. Amer. Med. Ass.*, **193**: 97-102.

LABRIOLA, J. 1953. Effects of caesarean delivery upon maternal behavior in rats. *Proc. Soc. Exp. Biol. N.Y.*, **83**: 556-557.

LACK, D. 1953. *The life of the robin.* London: Pelican.

———. 1968. *Ecological adaptations for breeding in birds.* London: Methuen.

LAIR, W. S. 1949. Psychoanalytic theory of identification. Unpublished doctoral dissertation. Cambridge, Mass.: Harvard Univ. Quoted by O. H. Mowrer. 1950. *Learning theory personality dynamics.* New York: Ronald Press.

LANDAUER, T. K. 1964. Two hypotheses concerning the biochemical basis of memory. *Psychol. Rev.*, **71**: 167-179.

———, and J. W. M. WHITING. 1964. Infantile stimulation and adult stature of human males. *Amer. Anthropologist*, **66**: 1007-1028.

LANDMARK, MARGRETE. 1962. Visual perception and the capacity for form construction. *Develop. Med. Child Neurol.*, **4**: 387-392.

LANG, T. 1940. Studies on the genetic determination of homosexuality. *J. Nerv. Ment. Dis.*, **92**: 55.

———. 1960. Homosexuality as a genetic problem. *Acta Genet. Med.* (Roma), **9**: 370.

LANGWORTHY, O. R. 1933. Development of behavior patterns and myelinization of the nervous system in the human fetus and infant. *Contrib. Embryol.*, **24**(139): Carnegie Inst. Pub. No. 443.

———. 1966. The neurophysiology of motivation. *Amer. J. Psychiat.*, **122**: 1033-1039.

LANMAN, J. 1953. The fetal zone of the adrenal gland. *Medicine*, **32**: 389-430.

LANSDELL, H. 1962. The sex-difference in effect of temporal lobe neurosurgery on design preference. *Nature*, **194**: 852-854.

———. 1964. Sex differences in hemispheric asymmetrics of the human brain. *Nature*, **203**: 550.

LASHLEY, K. S. 1938. The mechanism of vision. XV. Preliminary studies of the rat's capacity for detail vision. *J. Genet. Psychol.*, **18**: 123-193.

———. 1942. An examination of the "continuity theory" as applied to discrimination learning. *J. Genet. Psychol.*, **26**: 241-265.

———. 1950. In search of the engram. *Symp. Soc. Exp. Biol.*, **4**:454-482. Also reprinted in F. A. Beach, D. O. Hebb, C. T. Morgan, and H. W. Nissen. 1960. *The neuropsychology of Lashley.* New York: McGraw-Hill.

LAUGHLIN, P. R. 1967. Incidental concept formation as a function of creativity and intelligence. *J. Pers. Soc. Psychol.*, **5**: 115-119.

LAURENDEAU, MONIQUE, and A. PINARD. 1962. *Casual thinking in the child.* New York: International Univ. Press.

LAZOWICK, L. M. 1953. *A quantitative investigation into the nature of identification.* Unpublished Ph.D. thesis. Urbana: Univ. Illinois. *Dissert. Abstr.*, **14**(1): 407 (1954).

———. 1955. On the nature of identification. *J. Abnorm. Social Psychol.*, **51**: 175-183.

LEEPER, R. W. 1935. A study of a neglected portion of the field of learning—the development of sensory organization. *J. Genet. Psychol.*, **46**: 41-75.

———. 1965. Some needed developments in the motivational thory of emotions, in D. Levine, ed., *Nebraska Symposium on Motivation.* Lincoln: Univ. Nebraska Press.

LE GROSS CLARK, W. E. 1951. The CNS, in *Cunningham's Textbook of anatomy*, 9th ed., J. C. Brash, ed. New York: Oxford Univ. Press.

———. 1958. *The tissues of the body*, 4th ed. Oxford: Clarendon Press.

LEHNINGER, A. L. 1960. Energy transformation in the cell. *Sci. Amer.*, **202**(5): 102-114.

LEHRMAN, D. S. 1953. A critique of Konrad Lorenz's theory of instinctive behavior. *Quart. Rev. Biol.*, **28**: 337-363.

———. 1961. Gonadal hormones and parental behavior in birds and infra-human mammals, in W. C. Young, ed., *Sex and internal secretions.* Baltimore: Williams & Wilkins.

————. 1962. Interaction of hormonal and experiential influences on development of behavior, in E. L. Bliss, ed., *Roots of behavior*. New York: Harper.

LE MAGNEN, J. 1952. Les phénomenes olfactosexuals chez l'homme. *Arch. Sci. Physiol.*, **6**: 125-160.

LENNEBERG, E. H. 1962. Understanding language without ability to speak: a case report. *J. Abnorm. Social Psychol.*, **65**: 419-425.

————. 1967. *Biological foundations of language*. New York: Wiley.

————. 1969. On explaining language. *Science*, **164**: 635-643.

LENNOX, B. 1966. The sex chromatin and hermaphroditism, in K. L. Moore, ed., *The sex chromatin*. Philadelphia: Saunders.

LERNER, I. M. 1954. *Genetic homeostasis*. Edinburgh: Oliver & Boyd.

LESTER, D. 1967a. Sex differences in exploration: toward a theory of exploration. *Psychol. Rec.*, **17**: 55-62.

————. 1967b. Sex differences in exploration of a familiar locale. *Psychol. Rec.*, **17**: 63-64.

LEVENE, H. I., B. T. ENGEL, and F. R. SCHULKIN. 1967. Patterns of autonomic responsivity in identical schizophrenic twins. *Psychophysiology*, **3**: 363-370.

LEVIN, H., and R. R. SEARS. 1956. Identification with parents as a determinant of doll play aggression. *Child Develop.*, **27**: 135-153.

LEVINE, S. 1956. A further study of infantile handling and adult avoidance learning. *J. Personality*, **25**: 70-80.

————. 1960. Stimulation in infancy. *Sci. Amer.*, **202**: 80-86.

————. 1962. Psychophysiological effects of infantile stimulation, in E. L. Bliss, ed., *Roots of behavior*. New York: Harper.

————. 1966. Sex differences in the brain. *Sci. Amer.*, **214**(4): 84-90.

————. 1967. Maternal and environmental influences on the adrenocortical response to stress in weanling rats. *Science*, **156**: 258-260.

————. 1968. Influence of infantile stimulation on the response to stress during preweaning development. *Develop. Psychobiol.*, **1**: 67-70.

————, and M. ALPERT. 1959. Differential maturation of the CNS as a function of early experience. *Arch. Gen. Psychiat.*, **1**: 403-405.

————, and G. W. LEWIS. 1958. Differential maturation of an adrenal response to cold stress in rats manipulated in infancy. *J. Comp. Physiol. Psychol.*, **51**: 774-777.

LEVINE, S., S. C. HALTMEYER, S. S. KARAS, and V. H. DENENBERG. 1967. Physiological and behavioral effects of infantile stimulation. *Physiol. Behav.*, **2**: 55-59.

LEVINE, S., and G. W. LEWIS. 1959. Critical period for the effects of infantile experience on the maturation of a stress response. *Science*, **129**: 42-43.

LEVINE, S., and L. S. OTIS. 1958. The effects of handling before and after weaning on the resistance of albino rats to later deprivation. *Canad. J. Psychol.*, **12**: 103-108.

LÉVY-BRUHL, LUCIEN. 1922. *La mentalité primitive*. Paris: Libraire Félix Alcan.

————. 1923. *Primitive mentality*. Trans. Lillian A. Clare. London: Allen & Unwin and New York: Macmillan.

LEWIS, D. G. 1966. Commentary on "The genetic determination of differences in intelligence. A study of monozygotic twins reared apart," by Cyril Burt. *Brit. J. Psychol.*, **57**: 431-433.

LEWIS, M., and SUSAN GOLDBERG. 1969. The acquisition and violation of expectancy: an experimental paradigm. *J. Exp. Child Psychol.*, **7**: 70-80.

LEWIS, M., J. KAGAN, and J. KALAFAT. 1966. Patterns of fixation of the young infant. *Child Develop.*, **37**: 331-341.

LEWONTIN, R. C., and J. L. HUBBY. 1966. A molecular approach to the study of genetic heterozygosity in natural populations. *Genetics*, **54**: 595-609.

LIGON, E. M. 1957. *The growth and development of Christian personality*. Schenectady, N.Y.: The Union College Character Research Project.

LILLY, J. C. 1967. *The mind of the dolphin: a nonhuman intelligence*. New York: Doubleday.

LINDHOLM, B. W. 1964. Changes in conventional and deviation I.Q.'s *J. Educ. Psychol.*, **55**: 110-113.

LINDZEY, G. 1967. Some remarks concerning incest, the incest taboo, psychoanalytic theory. *Amer. Psychol.*, **22**: 1051 and 1059.

————, H. D. WINSTON, and M. MANOSEVITZ. 1963. Early experience, genotype and temperament in Mus musculus. *J. Comp. Physiol. Psychol.*, **56**: 622-629.

LIPSITT, L. P., and W. C. SPEARS. 1965. Effects of

anxiety and stress on children's paired-associate learning. *Psychon. Sci.*, 3: 553-554.

LISK, R. D. 1967. Sexual behaviour: hormonal control, in L. Martini and W. F. Ganong, eds., *Neuroendocrinology*, Vol. II. New York: Academic Press.

LITTLE, K. 1950. Methodology in the study of adult personality and "national character." *Amer. Anthropologist*, 52: 279-282.

LIVINGSTON, W. K. 1943. *Pain mechanisms.* New York: Macmillan.

LIVSON, N., and D. McNEILL. 1962. Physique and maturation rate in male adolescents. *Child Develop.*, 33: 145-152.

LOCKE, N. M. 1938. Perception and intelligence: their phylogenetic relation. *Psychol. Rev.*, 45: 335-345.

LODGE, ANN, J. C. ARMINGTON, ANN B. BARNET, BETTY L. SHANKS, and C. N. NEWCOMB. 1969. Newborn infants' electroretinograms and evoked electroencephalographic responses to orange and white light. *Child Develop.*, 40: 267-291.

LOEVINGER, JANE. 1959. *A theory of test response.* Proceedings of the 1958 invitational conference on testing problems. Princeton, N.J.: Education Testing Service.

LONDON, I. 1960. A Russian report on the postoperatively newly seeing. *Amer. J. Psychol.*, 73: 478-482.

LONG, BARBARA H., and E. H. HENDERSON. 1967. Social schemata of school beginners: some demographic correlates. *Proceedings of the 75th Annual Convention of the American Psychological Association*, 2: 329-333.

LONG, L. 1940. Conceptual relationships in children: the concept of roundness. *J. Genet. Psychol.*, 57: 289-315.

———. 1941. Size discrimination in children. *Child Develop.*, 12: 247-254.

LOPEZ, S. P. 1967. The internationalization of human rights. *Amer. J. Orthopsychiat.*, 37: 859-863.

LORENZ, K. Z. 1935. Der Kumpan in der Umwelt des Vogels. *J. P. Ornithol. Lpz.*, 83: 137-213.

———. 1937. The companion in the bird's world. *Auk*, 54: 245-273.

———. 1943. Die angeborenen Formen möglicher Erfahrun. (The innate conditions of the possibility of experience.) *Z. Tierpsychol.*, 5: 235-409.

———. 1950. The comparative method in studying innate behavior patterns, in K. Z. Lorenz et al., Physiological mechanisms in animal behaviour. *Symp. Soc. Exp. Biol.*, 4: 221-268.

———. 1952. *King Solomon's ring.* London: Methuen.

———. 1953. *Passim* in J. M. Tanner and Bärbel Inhelder, eds., *Discussions of child development.* Proceedings of the World Health Organization study group on psychological development of the child. New York: International Univ. Press.

———. 1955. Morphology and behavior patterns in closely allied species, in B. Schaffner, ed., *Group processes.* New York: Macy Foundation.

———. 1956. The objectivistic theory of instinct, in *L'Instinct dans le comportement des animaux et de l'homme.* Paris: Masson.

———. 1957. Companionship in bird life, in C. H. Schiller, ed., *Instinctive behaviour.* New York: International Univ. Press.

———. 1960. Imprinting, in R. C. Birney and R. C. Teevan, eds., *Instinct: an enduring problem in psychology: selected readings.* Princeton, N.J.: Van Nostrand, 52-64.

———. 1966. *On aggression.* New York: Harcourt.

LOUTTIT, C. M., and EMILY C. HALLS. 1936. The Indiana Speech Survey. *J. Speech Disord.*, 1: 73-80.

LOVELL, K., and E. OGILVIE. 1960. A study of the conservation of substance in the junior school child. *Brit. J. Educ. Psychol.*, 30: 109-118.

———. 1961a. A study of the conservation of weight in the junior school child. *Brit. J. Educ. Psychol.*, 31: 138-144.

———. 1961b. The growth of the concept of volume in junior school children. *J. Child Psychol. Psychiat.*, 2: 118-126.

LUBAR, J. F., C. J. SCHOSTAL, and A. A. PERACHIO. 1967. Non-visual functions of visual cortex in the cat. *J. Physiol. Behav.*, 2(2): 179-184.

LUDWIG, D. J., and M. L. MAEHR. 1967. Changes in self-concept and stated behavioral preferences. *Child Develop.*, 38: 453-467.

LUNDY, R. M., R. J. SCHLAFER, and G. CALDEN. 1959. Sex differences in body concepts. *J. Consult. Psychol.*, 23 (4): 378.

LUNNEBORG, PATRICIA W. 1968. Birth order, aptitude and achievement. *J. Consult. Clin. Psychol.*, 32: 101.

LURIA, A. R. 1957. The role of language in the formation of temporary connections, in B.

Simon, ed., *Psychology in the Soviet Union*. Stanford: Stanford Univ. Press.

———. 1960. Verbal regulation of behavior, in Mary A. B. Brazier, ed., *The central nervous system and behavior*. Report of the 3rd Macy Conference. Madison, N.J.: Macy Foundation.

———. 1961. *The role of speech in the regulation of normal and abnormal behavior*. New York: Liveright.

LYNN, D. B. 1962. Sex-role and parental identification. *Child Develop.*, 33: 555-564.

LYNN, R. 1961. Introversion-extraversion differences in judgments of time. *J. Abnorm. Social Psychol.*, 63(2): 457-458.

MAAS, H. S. 1963. *The young adult adjustment of twenty wartime residential nursery children*. New York: Child Welfare League of America.

MCCALL, R. B., and J. KAGAN. 1967. Attention in the infant: effects of complexity, contour perimeter and familiarity. *Child Develop.*, 38: 939-952.

MCCANCE, R. A., M. C. LUFF, and E. E. WIDDOWSON. 1937. Physical and emotional periodicity in women. *J. Hyg.*, 37: 571-611.

MCCARTHY, DOROTHEA A. 1930. The language development of the pre-school child. *Inst. Child Welfare Monogr.* Series No. 4.

———. 1946. Language development in children, in L. Carmichael, ed., *Manual of child psychology*, 1st ed. New York: Wiley.

———. 1954. Language development in children, in L. Carmichael, ed., *Manual of child psychology*, 2nd ed. New York: Wiley.

———. 1959. Research in language development: retrospect and prospect. *Monogr. Soc. Res. Child Develop.*, 24: Whole No. 74, 3-24.

MCCLEARN, G. E. 1962. The inheritance of behavior, in L. Postman, ed., *Psychology in the making*. New York: Knopf.

———, and W. MEREDITH. 1966. Behavioral genetics. *Ann. Rev. Psychol.*, 17: 515-550.

MCCLELLAND, D. C., J. W. ATKINSON, R. A. CLARK, and E. L. LOWELL. 1953. *The achievement motive*. New York: Appleton.

MCCLELLAND, W. J. 1956. Differential handling and weight gain in the albino rat. *Canad. J. Psychol.*, 10: 19-22.

MACCOBY, ELEANOR E. 1966. *Development of sex differences. Stanford University studies in psychology*. Stanford: Stanford Univ. Press.

MCCORD, JOAN, W. MCCORD, and A. HOWARD. 1963. Family interaction as antecedent to the direction of male aggressiveness. *J. Abnorm. Social Psychol.*, 66: 239-242.

MACDONALD, G. E., and A. SOLANDT. 1966. Imprinting effects of drug-induced immobilization. *Psychon. Sci.*, 5: 95-96.

MCDOUGALL, W. 1926. *Outline of abnormal psychology*. New York: Scribner.

———. 1948a. *The energies of men*, 7th ed. London: Methuen.

———. 1948b. *An introduction to social psychology*, 29th ed. London: Methuen.

———. 1960. *Introduction to social psychology* (Universities paperback series). London: Methuen.

MCFARLAND, W. J. 1966. An analysis of the influence of male participation in first grade instruction. *Dissert. Abstr.*, 27: 1714.

MCFIE, J. 1961a. The effect of hemispherectomy on intellectual function in cases of infantile hemiplegia. *J. Neurol. Neurosurg. Psychiat.*, 24: 240-249.

———. 1961b. Intellectual impairment in children with localized post infantile cerebral lesions. *J. Neurol. Neurosurg. Psychiat.*, 24: 361-365.

MCGEOCH, J. A. 1942. *The psychology of human learning*. London: Longmans, Green.

———, and A. L. IRION. 1952. *The psychology of human learning*, 2nd ed. London: Longmans, Green.

MCGRAW, MYRTLE B. 1935. *Growth: a study of Johnny and Jimmy*. New York: Appleton.

———. 1946. Maturation of behavior, in L. Carmichael, ed., *Manual of child psychology*. New York: Wiley.

MACKINNON, D. W. 1962a. The nature and nurture of creative talent. *Amer. Psychol.*, 17: 484-495.

———. 1962b. The personality correlates of creativity: a study of American architects, in J. S. Neilsen, ed., *Proceedings of the XIVth International Congress of Applied Psychology, Copenhagen, 1961*, Vol. 2. Copenhagen: Munksgaard, 11-39.

———. 1965. Personality and the realization of creative potential. *Amer. Psychol.*, 20: 273-281.

MACLEAN, N., W. M. COURT BROWN, PATRICIA A. JACOBS, D. J. MANTLE, and J. A. STRONG. 1968. A survey of sex chromatin abnormalities in mental hospitals. *J. Med. Genet.*, 5: 165-172.

MacLean, P. D. 1962. New findings relevant to the evolution of psychosexual function of the brain. *J. Nerv. Ment. Dis.*, **135**: 289-301.

————, B. W. Robinson, and D. W. Ploog. 1959. Experiments on localization of genital function in the brain. *Trans. Amer. Neurol. Ass.*, **84**: 105.

MacMeeken, A. M. 1940. *The intelligence of a representative group of Scottish children.* London: Univ. London Press.

McMichael, R. E. 1961. The effects of pre-weaning shock and gentling on later resistance to stress. *J. Comp. Physiol. Psychol.*, **54**: 416-421.

McMillan, Margaret. 1924. *Education through the imagination.* New York: Appleton.

McMurray, G. A. 1950. Experimental study of a case of insensitivity to pain. *A.M.A. Arch. Neurol. Psychiat.*, **64**: 650-667.

————. 1955. Congenital insensitivity to pain and its implications for motivational theory. *Canad. J. Psychol.*, **9**: 121-131.

MacMurray, J. 1961. *Persons in relation.* London: Faber.

MacNamara, J. 1966. *Bilingualism in primary education.* Edinburgh: Univ. of Edinburgh Press.

McNeil, J. D. 1964. Programmed instruction versus usual classroom procedures in teaching boys to read. *Amer. Educ. Res. J.*, **1**: 113-119.

McNeill, D. 1966. Developmental psycholinguistics, in F. Smith and G. A. Miller, eds., *The genesis of language.* Cambridge, Mass.: M.I.T. Press.

————, and N. Livson. 1963. Maturation rate and body build in women. *Child Develop.* **34**: 25-32.

MacNeill, M., and J. P. Zubek. 1967. Effects of prolonged visual deprivation (dark-rearing) on the weight of the sensory cortex of the rat. *Canad. J. Psychol.*, **21**: 177-183.

McNiven, M. A. 1960. "Social-releaser mechanisms" in birds: a controlled replication of Tinbergen's study. *Psychol. Rec.*, **10**: 259-265.

Maier, N. R., and R. J. Burke. 1967. Response availability as a factor in the problem-solving performance of males and females. *J. Pers. Soc. Psychol.*, **5**: 304-310.

Malinowski, B. 1927. *Sex and repression in savage society*, 2nd ed. London: Kegan Paul.

————. 1929. *The sexual life of savages.* London: Routledge.

Malmo, R. B. 1958. Measurement of drive: an unsolved problem in psychology, in M. R. Jones, ed., *Nebraska Symposium on Motivation, 1958.* Lincoln: Univ. of Nebraska Press.

Mamiya, Takeshi. 1956. Sei-Teki Hattatsu No Rinkaiki ni Kansuru Mondai: Chukan Hokoku (Problem of the Critical Period of Psychosexual Development). *Jap. J. Educ. Psychol.*, **4**: 21-27.

Mann, I. C. 1928. *Development of the human eye.* New York: Macmillan.

Markey, F. V. 1935. Imaginative behavior in preschool children. New York: Bureau of Publications, Teachers College, Columbia Univ.

Marler, P., and M. Tamura. 1964. Culturally transmitted patterns of vocal behavior in sparrows. *Science,* **146**: 1483-1486.

Marquis, D. G. 1935. Phylogenetic interpretation of the functions of the visual cortex. *Arch. Neurol. Psychiat.*, **33**: 807-815.

Maslow, A. H. 1954. *Motivation and personality.* New York: Harper.

Mason, W. A. 1961. The effects of social restriction on the behavior of rhesus monkeys: III. Dominance tests. *J. Comp. Physiol. Psychol.*, **54**: 694-699.

————, H. F. Harlow, and R. R. Rueping. 1959. The development of manipulatory responsiveness in the infant rhesus monkey. *J. Comp. Physiol. Psychol.*, **52**: 555-558.

Masters, W. H., and Virginia E. Johnson. 1966. *Human sexual response.* Boston: Little, Brown.

Mathewson, Suzanne. 1967. *Oral reading problems in children: a cognitive style approach.* Unpublished M.Sc. thesis. Montreal: McGill Univ.

Maurer, Adah B. 1967. Children's conceptions of God, in J. B. T. Bugental, ed., *Challenges of humanistic psychology,* New York: McGraw-Hill.

Mead, Margaret. 1929. *Coming of age in Samoa.* London: Cape.

————. 1935. *Sex and temperament in three primitive societies.* New York: William Morrow.

————. 1947. Age patterning in personality development. *Amer. J. Orthopsychiat.*, **17**: 231-240.

————. 1953. Discussion of the cross-cultural approach to child development problems, in J. M. Tanner and Bärbel Inhelder, eds., *Discussions of child development.* Proceedings of the meeting of W.H.O. Study Group on Psychobiological Development of the Child, Vol. I., Geneva.

——. 1954. Some theoretical considerations on the problem of mother child separation. *Amer. J. Orthopsychiat.*, **24:** 471-483.

——. 1961. Cultural determinants of sexual behavior, in W. C. Young, ed., *Sex and internal secretions*, Vol. II, 3rd ed., Baltimore: Williams & Wilkins.

——. 1962. A cultural anthropologist's approach to maternal deprivation, in *Deprivation of maternal care: a re-assessment of its effects*. Geneva: World Health Organization Publication, Health Papers, 14.

MEADOWS, KATHRYN P. 1968. Early manual communication in relation to the deaf child's intellectual, social and communicative functioning. *Amer. Ann. Deaf*, **113:** 29-41.

MEARNS, H. 1941. *The creative adult*. Garden City, N.Y.: Doubleday.

MEDAWAR, P. B. 1947. Cellular inheritance and transformation. *Biol. Rev.*, **22:** 360-389.

——. 1957. *The uniqueness of the individual*. London: Methuen.

——. 1963. Onwards from Spencer, evolution and evolutionism. *Encounter*, **21:** 35-43.

MEDNICK, S. A. 1962. The associative basis of the creative process. *Psychol. Rev.*, **69:** 220-232.

MEER, B., and M. I. STEIN. 1955. Measures of intelligence and creativity. *J. Psychol.*, **39:** 117-126.

MEHLER, J., and T. G. BEVER. 1967. Cognitive capacity of very young children. *Science*, **158:** 141-142.

MELZACK, R. 1965. Effects of early experience of behavior: Experimental and conceptual considerations, in P. H. Hoch and J. Zubin, eds., *Psychopathology of perception*. New York: Grune & Stratton.

——, and T. H. SCOTT. 1957. Early experience and response to pain. *J. Comp. Physiol. Psychol.*, **50:** 155-161.

MELZACK, R., and W. R. THOMPSON. 1956. The Scottish-Terrier experiments. *Canad. J. Psychol.*, **10:** 82-90.

MELZACK, R., and P. D. WALL. 1962. On the nature of cutaneous sensory mechanisms. *Brain*, **85:** 331-356.

——. 1965. Pain mechanisms: a new theory. *Science*, **150:** 971-979.

MENDEL, GISELA. 1965. Children's preferences for differing degrees of novelty. *Child Develop.*, **36:** 453-465.

MENYUK, PAULA. 1968. Children's learning and reproduction of grammatical and nongrammatical phonological sequences. *Child Develop.*, **39:** 849-859.

MERMELSTEIN, E., and L. S. SHULMAN. 1967. Lack of formal schooling and the acquisition of conversation. *Child Develop.*, **38:** 39-52.

MERRELL, D. J. 1957. Dominance of eye and hand. *Hum. Biol.*, **29:** 314-328.

MERRILL, F. E., and H. W. ELDREDGE. 1952. Culture and society. Englewood Cliffs, N.J.: Prentice-Hall.

MESSICK, S. J., and C. M. SOLLEY. 1957. Probability learning in children: some exploratory studies. *J. Genet. Psychol.*, **90:** 23-32.

MEYERS, W. J., and T. N. CANTOR. 1966. Infants observing and heart responses as related to novelty of visual stimuli. *Psychon. Sci.*, **5:** 239-240.

——. 1967. Observing and cardiac responses of human infants to visual stimuli. *J. Exp. Child Psychol.*, **5:** 16-25.

MICHAEL, R. P. 1962. Estrogen-sensitive neurons and sexual behavior in female cats. *Science*, **136:** 322-323.

MILES, R. C. 1958. Learning in kittens with manipulatory, exploratory, and food incentives. *J. Comp. Physiol. Psychol.*, **51:** 39-42.

MILLER, J. C. 1932. Race, sex and class differences in ability to endure pain. *J. Soc. Psychol.*, **3:** 374-376.

MILLER, N. E. 1958. Central stimulation and other new approaches to motivation and reward. *Amer. Psychol.*, **13:** 100-108.

——. 1960. Motivation effects of brain stimulation and drugs. *Fed. Proc.*, **19:** 846-854.

——. 1966. Extending the domain of learning. *Science*, **152:** 676 (abstract).

——. 1969. Learning of visceral and glandular responses. *Science*, **163:** 434-445.

——, and J. DOLLARD. 1941. *Social learning and imitation*. New Haven: Yale Univ. Press.

MILLER, O. J. 1961. Developmental sex abnormalities, in L. S. Penrose and H. L. Brown, eds., *Recent advances in human genetics*. Boston: Little, Brown.

MILLER, W. B. 1958. Lower class culture as a generating milieu of gang delinquency. *J. Soc. Issues*, **14:** 5-19.

MILNER, B. 1958. Psychological defects produced

by temporal lobe excision, in *The brain and human behaviour. Res. Publ., Ass. Nerv. Ment. Dis.,* 36: 244-257.

MILTON, G. A. 1957. The effects of sex-role identification upon problem-solving skill. *J. Abnorm. Social Psychol.,* 55: 208-212.

MINER, J. B. 1905. The case of vision acquired in adult life. *Psychol. Rev. Monogr. Suppl.,* 6(5): 103-118.

MISCHEL, W. 1961a. Delay of gratification, and need for achievement, and acquiescence in another culture. *J. Abnorm. Social Psychol.,* 62: 543-552.

————. 1961b. Father-absence and delay of gratification, cross cultural comparisons. *J. Abnorm. Social Psychol.,* 63: 116-124.

MOGENSON, G. J., and D. J. EHRLICH. 1958. The effects of early gentling and shock on growth and behavior in rats. *Canad. J. Psychol.,* 12: 165-170.

MOGENSON, G. J., G. A. McMURRAY, and L. B. JACQUES. 1957. Effects of stress and administration of cortisone on weight gain in gentled rats. *Canad. J. Psychol.,* 11: 123-127.

MOLTZ, H. 1960. Imprinting: empirical basis and theoretical significance. *Psychol. Bull.,* 57: 291-314.

————. 1962. The fixed action pattern: empirical properties and theoretical implications, in J. Wortis, ed., *Recent advances in biological psychiatry,* Vol. 4. New York: Plenum Press.

————. 1963. Imprinting: an epigenetic approach. *Psychol. Rev.,* 70: 123-138.

————. 1965. Contemporary instinct theory and the fixed action pattern. *Psychol. Rev.,* 72: 22-47.

————, and L. J. STETTNER. 1961. The influence of patterned-light deprivation on the critical period for imprinting. *J. Comp. Physiol. Psychol.,* 54(3): 279-283.

MONES, L. 1939. Intelligence and a sense of humor. *J. Except. Child.,* 5: 150-153.

MONEY, J. 1960. Components of eroticism in man. III. Cognitional rehearsals, in J. Wortis, ed., *Recent advances in biological psychiatry.* New York: Grune & Stratton.

————. 1961a. Components of eroticism in man. I. The hormones in relation to sexual morphology and sexual desire. *J. Nerv. Ment. Dis.,* 132: 239-248.

————. 1961b. Components of eroticism in man.

II. The orgasm and genital somesthesia. *J. Nerv. Ment. Dis.,* 132: 289-297.

————. 1961c. Sex hormones in human eroticism, in W. C. Young, ed., *Sex and internal secretions,* 3rd ed., Vol. II. Baltimore, Williams & Wilkins.

————. 1963. Developmental differentiation of femininity and masculinity compared. *Man and civilization: the potential of women.* New York: McGraw-Hill.

————. 1966. The sex chromatin and psychosexual differentiation, in K. L. Moore, ed., *The sex chromatin.* Philadelphia: Saunders.

————, ed. 1962. *Reading disability, progress and research needs in dyslexia.* Baltimore: Johns Hopkins Press.

MONEY, J., J. G. HAMPSON, and J. L. HAMPSON. 1957. Imprinting and the establishment of gender role. *Arch. Neurol. Psychiat.,* 77: 333-336.

MONTESSORI, MARIA. 1912. *The Montessori method of scientific pedagogy as applied to child education in "The children's houses."* Trans. from the Italian by Anne E. George. New York: F. A. Stokes.

MONTGOMERY, K. C. 1954. The role of exploratory drive in learning. *J. Comp. Physiol. Psychol.,* 47: 60-64.

————, and M. SEGALL. 1955. Discrimination learning based upon the exploratory drive. *J. Comp. Physiol. Psychol.,* 48: 225-228.

MOORE, J. E. 1939. *Children and movies.* Chicago: Univ. Chicago Press.

————. 1940. A further study of sex differences in speed of reading. *Peabody J. Educ.,* 17: 359-362.

MOORE, J. G., J. L. van CAMPENHOUT, and W. W. BRANDKAMP. 1964. Chromosome analysis in abnormal sexual differentiation and gonadal dysfunction. *Int. J. Fertility,* 9: 469-491.

MOORE, K. L. 1966a. Sex chromatin and gonadal dysgenesis, in K. L. Moore, ed., *The sex chromatin.* Philadelphia: Saunders.

————. 1966b. The development of clinical sex chromatin tests, in K. L. Moore, ed., *The sex chromatin.* Philadelphia: Saunders.

————, ed. 1966c. *The sex chromatin.* Philadelphia: Saunders.

MOORE, K. L., and M. L. BARR. 1953. Morphology of the nerve cell nucleus in mammals with special reference to sex chromatin. *J. Comp. Neurol.,* 98: 213-227.

MOORE, O. K., and A. R. ANDERSON. 1968. The responsive environments project, in R. D. Hess and Roberta M. Bear, eds., *Early education: current theory, research and action*. Chicago: Aldine.

MOORE, T. 1967. Language and intelligence: a longitudinal study of the first eight years. I. Patterns of development in boys and girls. *Hum. Develop.*, 10: 88-106.

MOREL, F., and J. WEISSFEILER. 1931. La commissure grise: étude anatomo-clinique. *L'Encéphale*, 26: 659-670.

MORGAN, C. L. 1894. *Introduction to comparative psychology*. London: Scott.

——. 1896. *Habit and instinct*. London: Arnold.

——. 1905. *Interpretation of nature*. Bristol: Arrowsmith.

MORGAN, C. T. 1951. The psychophysiology of learning, in S. S. Stevens, ed., *Handbook of experimental psychology*. New York: Wiley.

MORGAN, G. A., and H. N. RICCIUTI. 1969. Infants' responses to strangers during the first year, in B. M. Foss, ed., *Determinants of infant behavior*. IV. London: Methuen.

MORRELL, F. 1961. Electrophysiological contributions to the neural basis of learning. *Physiol. Rev.*, 41: 443-494.

MORRIS, D. 1954. The reproductive behaviour of the zebra finch (Poephila guttata), with special reference to pseudofemale behaviour and displacement activities. *Behaviour*, 6: 271-322.

——. 1955. The causation of pseudo-female and pseudo-male behaviour—a further comment. *Behaviour*, 8: 46-56.

MOSELEY, D. 1925. The accuracy of the pecking response in chicks. *J. Comp. Psychol.*, 5: 75-97.

MOWRER, O. H. 1939. A stimulus-response analysis of anxiety and its role as a reinforcing agent. *Psychol. Rev.*, 46: 553-565.

——. 1941. Motivation and learning in relation to the national emergency. *Psychol. Bull.*, 38: 421-431.

——. 1950. *Learning theory personality dynamics*. New York: Ronald.

——. 1953. *Psychotherapy: theory and research*. New York: Ronald.

——. 1958. Hearing and speaking: an analysis of language learning. *J. Speech Hear. Disord.*, 23: 143-152.

——. 1960a. *Learning theory and behavior*. New York: Wiley.

——. 1960b. *Learning theory and the symbolic processes*. New York: Wiley.

MOYNIHAN, D. P. 1965. *The Negro family: the case for national action*. Report to U.S. Department of Labor.

MUNN, N. L. 1954. Learning in children, in L. Carmichael, ed., *Manual of child psychology*, 2nd ed. New York: Wiley.

MUNSINGER, H. 1967. Developing perception and memory for stimulus redundancy. *J. Exp. Child Psychol.*, 5: 39-49.

——, and M. W. WEIR. 1967. Infants and young children's preference for complexity. *J. Exp. Child Psychol.*, 5: 69-73.

MURDOCK, G. P. 1949. *Social structure*. New York: Macmillan.

MURIE, A. 1944. The wolves of Mount McKinley. U.S. Department of the Interior, Fauna Series No. 5.

MURPHY, G. 1947. *Personality: a biosocial approach to origins and structure*. New York: Harper.

MUSSEN, P. H. 1960. *Handbook of research method in child development*. New York: Wiley.

——. 1961. Some antecedents and consequents of masculine sex-typing in adolescent boys. *Psychol. Monogr.*, 75(2): Whole No. 506.

——, J. J. CONGER, and J. KAGAN. 1963. *Child development and personality*. New York: Harper & Row.

MUSSEN, P. H., and L. DISTLER. 1959. Masculinity, identification and father-son relationships. *J. Abnorm. Social Psychol.*, 59: 350-356.

MUSSEN, P. H., and A. L. PARKER. 1965. Mother nurturance and the girls' incidental imitative learning. *J. Pers. Soc. Psychol.*, 2: 94-97.

MUSSEN, P. H., and E. RUTHERFORD. 1963. Parent-child relations and parental personality in relation to young children's sex-role preferences. *Child Develop.*, 34: 589-607.

MUTIMER, DOROTHY, L. LOUGHLIN, and M. POWELL. 1966. Some differences in the family relationship of achieving and under-achieving readers. *J. Genet. Psychol.*, 109: 67-74.

MYKLEBUST, H. R. 1964. *The psychology of deafness*. New York: Grune & Stratton.

——. 1965. *Development and disorders of written language*. New York: Grune & Stratton.

NASH, J. 1952. Fathers and sons. A neglected aspect of child-care. *Child Care*, 6: 19-22.

——. 1965. The father in contemporary culture

and current psychological literature. *Child Develop.*, **36**: 261-297.

———. 1968. Personal communication.

———. (in press). The father in child development, in Bettye Caldwell and H. N. Ricciuti, eds., *Review of research in child development,* Vol. III. New York: Russell Sage Foundation.

———, and T. HAYES. 1965. The parental relationships of male homosexuals. Some theoretical issues and a pilot study. *Aust. J. Psychol.*, **17**: 35-43.

NEALEY, S. M., and BARBARA J. EDWARDS. 1960. Depth perception in rats without pattern vision experience. *J. Comp. Physiol. Psychol.*, **53**: 468-469.

NEWMAN, H. H., R. N. FREEMAN, and K. J. HOLZINGER. 1937. *Twins: a study of heredity and environment.* Chicago: Univ. Chicago Press.

NICHOLS, R. C. 1966. Birth order and intelligence. Unpublished study quoted in W. D. Altus. 1966. *Birth order and the omnibus personality inventory.* Proceedings of the 74th Annual Convention of the American Psychological Association, 279-280.

NISSEN, H. W. 1930. A study of exploratory behavior in the white rat by means of the obstruction method. *J. Genet. Psychol.*, **37**: 361-376.

———. 1954. The nature of drive as innate determinant of behavioral organization, in *Nebraska Symposium on Motivation*. Lincoln: Univ. Nebraska Press.

———, K. L. CHOW, and J. SEMMES. 1951. Effects of restricted opportunity for tactile, kinaesthetic and manipulative experience on the behavior of a chimpanzee. *Amer. J. Psychol.*, **64**: 485-507.

NISSEN, H. W., S. MACHOVER, and E. F. KINDER. 1935. A study of performance tests given to a group of native African negro children. *Brit. J. Psychol.*, **25**: 308-355.

NISSEN, H. W., and R. M. YERKES. 1943. Reproduction in the chimpanzee: report on forty-nine births. *Anat. Rec.*, **86**: 567-578.

NOBLE, G. K., and M. WURM. 1940a. The effect of testosterone propionate on the black-crowned night heron. *Endocrinology*, **26**: 837-850.

———. 1940b. The effect of hormones on the breeding of the laughing gull. *Proc. Amer. Soc. Zool., Anat. Rec.*, **78**(Suppl. 1: 50), abstract.

NORTHWAY, M. L. 1944. Outsiders; a study of the personality patterns of children least acceptable to their age mates. *Sociometry,* **7**: 10-25.

OAKDEN, E. C., and MARY STURT. 1922. The development of the knowledge of time in children. *Brit. J. Psychol.*, **12**: 309-336.

O'BRYAN, K. G., and R. S. MACARTHUR. 1969. Reversibility, intelligence and creativity in nine-year-old boys. *Child Develop.*, **40**: 33-45.

O'CONNOR, N. 1956. The evidence for the permanently disturbing effects of mother child separation. *Acta Psychol.* **12**: 174-191.

———, and B. HERMELIN. 1963. *Speech and thought in severe abnormality.* New York: Pergamon Press.

OETSEL, R. 1962. Selected bibliography on sex differences. Mimeo. report. Stanford: Stanford Univ.

OLDS, J. C., and P. MILNER. 1954. Positive reinforcement produced by electrical stimulation of septal area and other regions of rat brain. *J. Comp. Physiol. Psychol.*, **47**: 419-427.

OLDS, M. E., and J. OLDS. 1962. Approach-escape interactions in rat brain. *Amer. J. Physiol.*, **203**: 803-810.

OLUM, VIVIAN. 1956. Developmental differences in the perception of causality. *Amer. J. Psychol.*, **69**: 417-423.

OPPENHEIMER, J. H. 1967. Abnormalities of neuroendocrine functions in man, in L. Martini and W. F. Ganong, eds., *Neuroendocrinology,* Vol. II. New York: Academic Press.

ORLANSKY, H. 1949. Infant care and personality. *Psychol. Rev.*, **46**: 1-48.

OSBORNE, R. T., and A. J. GREGOR. 1966. The heritability of visualization, perceptual speed and spatial orientation. *Percept. Motor Skills,* **23**: 379-390.

OSLER, S. F., and M. W. FIVEL. 1961. Concept attainment. I. The role of age and intelligence in concept attainment by induction. *J. Exp. Psychol.*, **62**: 1-8.

OSLER, S. F., and G. E. TRAUTMAN. 1961. Concept attainment. II. Effects of stimulus complexity upon concept attainment at two levels of intelligence. *J. Exp. Psychol.*, **62**: 9-13.

OTOMO, E., and M. MICHAELIS. 1960. Penetration of radioactive phosphorus into normal and shocked rats' brains. *Proc. Soc. Exp. Biol. Med.*, **104**: 259-260.

OURTH, L., and K. B. BROWN. 1961. Inadequate mothering and disturbance in the neonatal period. *Child Develop.*, **32**: 287-295.

OVER, R., and JOAN OVER. 1967. Detection and recognition of mirror-image obliques by young children. *J. Comp. Physiol. Psychol.*, **64**: 467-470.

OWENS, W. A. 1953. Age and mental abilities: a longitudinal study. *Genet. Psychol. Monogr.*, **48**: 5-54.

PADILLA, S. G. 1930. Further studies in the delayed pecking of chicks. *J. Comp. Psychol.*, **20**: 413-443.

PANTLE, A., and R. SEKULAR. 1968. Size detecting mechanisms in human vision. *Science*, **162**: 1146-1148.

PARE, W. P. 1964. Relationship of various behaviors in the open-field test of emotionality. *Psychol. Rep.*, **14**: 19-22.

PARKE, R. D. 1969. Effectiveness of punishment as an interaction of intensity, timing, agent nurturance and cognitive structuring. *Child Develop.*, **40**: 213-235.

————, and R. H. WALTERS. 1967. Some factors influencing the efficacy of punishment training for inducing response inhibition. *Monogr. Soc. Res. Child Develop.*, **32** (1): Series 109.

PARKER, G. H. 1922. *Smell, taste and allied senses in the vertebrates.* Philadelphia: Lippincott.

PARKES, A. S., and H. M. BRUCE. 1961. The olfactory stimuli in mammalian reproduction. *Science*, **134**: 1049-1054.

PARNELL, R. W. 1958. *Behaviour and physique.* London: Arnold.

PARSONS, T. 1942. Age and sex in the social structure of the United States. *Amer. Social Rev.*, **7**: 604-616.

————. 1958. Social structure and the development of personality. Freud's contribution to the integration of psychology and sociology. *Psychiatry*, **21**: 321-340.

————, and K. B. CLARK, eds. 1966. *The Negro American.* Boston: Houghton Mifflin.

PARTANEN, J., K. BRUIN, and T. MARKKANEN. 1966. Inheritance of drinking behavior. A study of intelligence, personality and use of alcohol of adult twins. *Finnish Foundation for Alcohol Studies*, **14**: 159.

PASTORE, N. 1949. *The nature-nurture controversy.* New York: King's Crown.

————. 1960. Perceiving as innately determined. *J. Genet. Psychol.*, **96**: 93-99.

PAVLOV, I. P. 1927. *Conditioned reflexes.* Oxford: Milford.

————. 1928. *Lectures on conditioned reflexes.* New York: International Univ. Press.

PAWLOWSKI, A. A., and J. P. SCOTT. 1956. Hereditary differences in the development of dominance in litters of puppies. *J. Comp. Physiol. Psychol.*, **49**: 353-358.

PAYNE, D. E., and P. H. MUSSEN. 1956. Parent-child relations and father identification among adolescent boys. *J. Abnorm. Social Psychol.*, **52**: 358-362.

PECHSTEIN, L. A. 1921. Massed vs. distributed effort in learning. *J. Educ. Psychol.*, **12**: 92-97.

PEIPER, A. 1925. Sinnesempfindungen des Kindes vor seiner. *Geburt. Wschr. Kinderheilk.*, **29**: 236-241.

PENFIELD, W., and P. PEROT. 1963. The brain's record of auditory and visual experience. *Brain*, **86**: Part 4.

PENFIELD, W., and L. ROBERTS. 1959. *Speech and brain mechanisms.* Princeton, N.J.: Princeton Univ. Press.

PENNEY, R. K. 1965. Reactive curiosity and manifest anxiety in children. *Child Develop.*, **36**: 697-702.

PESKIN, H. 1967. Pubertal onset and ego functioning. *J. Abnorm. Psychol.*, **72**: 1-15.

PETERS, R. S., ed. 1953. *Brett's history of psychology*, abridged ed. London: Allen & Unwin.

PETERS, W. 1927. Die Entwicklung von Wahrnehmungsleistungen beim Kind. *Z. Psychol. Physiol. Sinnesorg.*, **103**: 129-184.

PETERSON, G. M., and PATRICIA E. BARNETT. 1961. The cortical destruction necessary to produce a transfer of a forced-practice function. *J. Comp. Physiol. Psychol.*, **54**: 382-385.

PETERSON, K. 1903. On the inheritance of mental and moral character in man and its comparison with the inheritance of physical character. *J. Anthropol. Inst.*, **33**: 179-237.

PETTIFOR, J. L. 1968. The role of language in the development of abstract thinking. *Canad. J. Psychol.*, **22**: 139-156.

PFAFF, D. W. 1965. Cerebral implantation and auto-radiographic studies of sex hormones, in J. Money, ed., *Sex research: new developments.* New York: Holt, Rinehart and Winston.

PHOENIX, C. H., R. W. GOY, A. A. GERALL, and

W. C. YOUNG. 1959. Organizing action of prenatally administered testosterone propionate on the tissues mediating mating behavior in the female guinea pig. *Endocrinology,* **65:** 369-382.

PIAGET, J. 1926. *The language and thought of the child.* New York: Harcourt.

————. 1928. *Judgment and reasoning in the child.* New York: Harcourt.

————. 1930. *The child's concept of physical causality.* New York: Harcourt.

————. 1932. *The moral judgment of the child.* London: Kegan Paul.

————. 1946. *Le developpement de la notion de temps chez l'enfant.* Paris: Presses Univ. France.

————. 1951. *Play, dreams and imitation in childhood.* New York: Norton.

————. 1952. *The origins of intelligence in children.* New York: International Univ. Press.

————. 1954. *The construction of reality in the child.* New York: Basic Books.

————. 1959. *Judgment and reasoning in the child.* Paterson, N.J.: Littlefield, Adams.

————. 1960. *The psychology of intelligence.* Paterson, N.J.: Littlefield, Adams.

————. 1964a. Development and learning, in R. E. Ripple and V. N. Rockcastle, eds., *Piaget rediscovered: a report on the conference on cognitive studies and curriculum development.* Ithaca, N.Y.: School of education, Cornell Univ.

————. 1964b. Cognitive development in children: the Piaget papers, in R. E. Ripple and V. N. Rockcastle, eds., *Piaget rediscovered: a report on the conference on cognitive studies and curriculum development.* Ithaca, N..: School of Education, Cornell Univ.

————. 1967a. *Biologie et connaissance.* Paris: Gallimard.

————. 1967b. Review of studies of cognitive growth. *Contemp. Psychol.,* **12:** 532-533.

————. 1968. Quantification, conservation and nativism. *Science,* **162:** 976-977.

————. 1969. *The mechanisms of perception.* Trans. from the French by G. N. Geagrin. New York: Basic Books.

————, and BÄRBEL INHELDER. 1941. *Le developpment des quantites chez l'enfant.* Neuchâtel: Delachaux et Niestle.

————. 1951. *La genese et l'idee de Hasard chez l'enfant.* Paris: Presses Univ. France.

————. 1963. *The child's conception of space.* London: Routledge & Kegan Paul.

————. 1966. *L'image mentale chez l'enfant.* Paris: Presses Univ. France.

PIAGET, J., and A. MORF. 1958. Les isomorphismes partiels entre les structures perceptives, in J. Piaget, ed., *Études d'epistemologie genetique, Vol. VI. Logique et perception.* Paris: Presses Univ. France.

PIAGET, J., et al. 1956. Recherches sur le developpement des perceptions. Recherches I à XXXII. *Arch. Psychol., Geneve,* 1942 to 1956.

PICKFORD, R. W. 1949. The genetics of intelligence. *J. Psychol.,* **28:** 129-145.

PIDDINGTON, R. 1950. *An introduction to social anthropology,* (Vol. I). Edinburgh: Oliver & Boyd.

————. 1957. *An introduction to social anthropology,* Vol. II. Edinburgh: Oliver & Boyd.

PINES, MAYA. 1966. *Revolution in learning: the years from birth to six.* New York: Harper & Row.

PINNEAU, S. R. 1950. A critique on the articles by Margaret Ribble. *Child Develop.,* **21:** 203-228.

————. 1955. The infantile disorders of hospitalism and anaclitic depression. *Psychol. Bull.,* **52:** 429-462.

PISHKIN, V., A. WOLFGANG, and ELIZABETH RASMUSSEN. 1967. Age, sex, amount and type of memory information on concept learning. *J. Exp. Psychol.,* **73:** 121-124.

PISTOR, F. 1940. How time concepts are acquired by children. *Educ. Method.,* **20:** 107-112.

PITTS, F. N. 1969. The biochemistry of anxiety. *Sci. Amer.,* **220**(2): 69-75.

PITZ, G. R., and R. B. ROSS. 1961. Imprinting as a function of arousal. *J. Comp. Physiol. Psychol.,* **54:** 602-604.

POFFENBERGER, T., and D. NORTON. 1959. Factors in the formation of attitudes towards mathematics. *J. Educ. Res.,* **52:** 171-176.

POLANYI, M. 1968. Life's irreducible structure. *Science,* **160:** 1308-1312.

POLT, J. M., and E. H. HESS. 1964. Following and imprinting: effects of light and social experience. *Science,* **143:** 1185-1187.

————. 1966. Effects of social experience on the following response in ducks. *J. Comp. Physiol. Psychol.,* **61:** 268-270.

PRATT, C. L., and G. P. SACKETT. 1967. Selection of social partners as a function of peer contact during rearing. *Science,* **155:** 1133-1135.

PRATT, J. P. 1942. A personal note on methyl testosterone in hypogonadism. *J. Clin. Endocrinol.,* **2**: 460-464.

PRATT, K. C. 1946. The neonate, in L. Carmichael, ed., *Manual of child psychology.* New York: Wiley.

PRECHTL, H. F. R. 1958. The directed head turning response and allied movements of the human body. *Behaviour,* **13**: 212-242.

PRIBRAM, K. H. 1966. A neuropsychological analysis of cerebral function and informal program report of an experimental program. *Canad. J. Psychol.,* **7a**(4): 324-367.

———. 1967. *The new neurology and the biology of emotion: a structural approach.* Paper presented at the eastern Psychological Association Meeting, Boston.

———. 1969. The neurophysiology of remembering. *Sci. Amer.,* **220**(1): 73-87.

PRICE, W. H., and P. B. WHATMORE. 1967. Behaviour disorders and pattern of crime among XYY males identified at a maximum security hospital. *Brit. Med. J.,* **1**: 533-536.

PRITCHARD, M. 1962. Homosexuality and genetic sex. *J. Ment. Sci.,* **108**: 616-623.

PROVENCE, S., and R. C. LIPTON. 1962. *Infants in institutions.* New York: International Univ. Press.

PUROHIT, A. P. 1966. Personality variables, sex difference, GSR responsiveness and GSR conditioning. *J. Exp. Res. Pers.,* **1**: 166-173.

RABIN, A. I. 1959. Attitudes of Kibbutz children to family and parents. *Amer. J. Orthopsychiat.,* **29**: 172-179.

———. 1961. Kibbutz adolescents. *Amer. J. Orthopsychiat.,* **31**: 493-504.

RAFFERTY, F. T., and E. S. STEIN. 1958. Study of the relationship of early menarche to ego-development. *Amer. J. Orthopsychiat.,* **28**: 170-179.

RAINER, J. D. 1966a. The contributions of Franz Josef Kallmann to the genetics of schizophrenia. *Behav. Sci.,* **11**: 413-437.

———. 1966b. Genetic aspects of depression. *Canad. Psychiat. Ass. J. Suppl.,* **11**: 29-33.

———, A. HESNIKOFF, L. C. KOLB, and A. CARR. 1960. Homosexuality and heterosexuality in identical twins. *Psychosomat. Med.,* **22**: 251-259.

RAINWATER, L., and W. L. YANCEY. 1967. *The Moynihan Report and the politics of controversy.* Cambridge, Mass.: M.I.T. Press.

RAMSEY, A. O. 1951. Familial recognition in domestic birds. *Auk,* **68**: 1-16.

RANK, OTTO. 1907. *Der Künstler.* Vienna: Heller.

———. 1932. *Art and artist: creative urge and personality development.* Trans. from the German by C. F. Atkinson. New York: Knopf.

RAPAPORT, D. 1946. *Diagnostic psychological testing,* Vol. I. Chicago: Year Book.

RAPPORT, A., and A. M. CHAMMAH. 1965. Sex differences in factors contributing to the level of co-operation in the prisoners' dilemma game. *J. Pers. Soc. Psychol.,* **2**: 831-838.

RAUM, O. F. 1940. *Chaga childhood.* London: Oxford Univ. Press.

RAZRAN, G. H. S. 1933. Conditioned responses in children. *Arch. Psychol.,* **148**: 120.

———. 1936. Attitudinal control of human conditioning. *J. Psychol.,* **2**: 327-337.

———. 1957. The dominance-contiguity theory of the acquisition of classical conditioning. *Psychol. Bull.,* **54**: 1-46.

REED, M. R. 1957. The masculinity-femininity dimension in normal and psychotic subjects. *J. Abnorm. Social Psychol.,* **55**: 289-294.

REESE, H. W. 1960. Motor paired-associate learning and stimulus pretraining. *Child Develop.,* **31**: 505-513.

———. 1962. Verbal mediation as a function of age level. *Psychol. Bull.,* **59**: 502-509.

———. 1963a. Perceptual set in young children. I. *Child Develop.,* **34**: 151-159.

———. 1963b. Perceptual set in young children. II. *Child Develop.,* **34**: 451-454.

REICHARD, S., M. SCHNEIDER, and D. RAPAPORT. 1944. The development of concept formation in children. *Amer. J. Orthopsychiat.,* **14**: 156-161.

REIDER, N. 1959. Chess, oedipus and the *mater dolorosa. Int. J. Psychoanal.,* **40**: 1-14.

RENDLE-SHORT, J. 1961. The puff-test: an attempt to assess the intelligence of young children by use of a conditioned reflex. *Arch. Dis. Child.,* **36**: 50-57.

REYNOLDS, E. L., and J. V. WINER. 1951. Physical changes associated with adolescence in boys. *Amer. J. Dis. Child.,* **82**: 529-597.

RHEINGOLD, HARRIET L. 1956. The modification of social responsiveness in institutional babies. *Monogr. Soc. Res. Child Develop.,* **21**(2): Series No. 63.

————. 1969. The effects of a strange environment on the behavior of infants, in B. M. Foss, ed., *Determinants of infant behavior*. IV. London: Methuen.

RIBBLE, MARGARET A. 1944. Infantile experience in relation to personality development, in J. McV. Hunt, ed., *Personality and the behavior disorders*, Vol. II. New York: Ronald, 621-651.

————. 1965. *The rights of infants*, 2nd ed. New York: Columbia Univ. Press.

RIBOT, T. 1906. *Essay on the creative imagination*. London: Kegan Paul, Trench, Trubner.

RICHARDS, M. P., and HELEN E. ROSS. 1967. Developmental changes in children's drawings. *Brit. J. Educ. Psychol.*, **37**: 73-80.

RICHEY, H. G. 1937. The relation of accelerated, normal and retarded puberty to the height and weight of school children. *Monogr. Soc. Res. Child Develop.*, **2**(1): Series No. 8.

RICHMAN, B. J., H. N. KELLNER, and D. A. ALLEN. 1968. Size constancy in retarded versus normal children: a developmental hypothesis. *J. Consult. Clin. Psychol.*, **32**: 579-582.

RICHTER, C. P. 1927. Animal behavior and internal drives. *Quart. Rev. Biol.*, **2**: 307-313.

————, and E. H. UHLENHUTH. 1945. Comparison of the effects of gonadectomy on spontaneous activity of wild and domesticated Norway rats. *Endocrinology*, **54**: 311-322.

RICHTER, D. 1955. The metabolism of the developing brain, in H. Waelsch, ed., *Biochemistry of the developing nervous system*. New York: Academic Press.

RIERS, E., J. DANIELS, and J. L. QUACKENBUSH. 1960. The identification of creativity in adolescents. *J. Educ. Psychol.*, **51**: 346-351.

RIESEN, A. H. 1947. Visual discrimination by chimpanzees after rearing in darkness. *Amer. Psychol.*, **2**: 307.

————. 1958. Plasticity of behavior: psychological aspects, in H. F. Harlow and C. N. Woolsey, eds., *Biological and biochemical bases of behavior*. Madison: Univ. Wisconsin Press.

————. 1961a. Excessive arousal effects of stimulation after early sensory deprivation, in P. Solomon et al., eds., *Sensory deprivation*. Cambridge: Harvard Univ. Press.

————. 1961b. Stimulation as a requirement for growth and function in behavioral development, in D. W. Fiske and S. R. Maddi, eds., *Functions of varied experience*. Homewood, Ill.: Dorsey.

————, K. L. CHOW, J. SEMMES, and H. W. NISSEN. 1951. Chimpanzee vision after four conditions of light deprivation. *Amer. Psychol.*, **6**: 282 (abstract).

RIESEN, A. H., M. I. KURKE, and J. C. MELLINGER. 1953. Interocular transfer of habits learned monocularly in visually naive and visually experienced cats. *J. Comp. Physiol. Psychol.*, **46**: 166-172.

RIESMAN, D. 1950. *The lonely crowd*. New Haven: Yale Univ. Press.

RIMLAND, B. 1964. *Infantile autism*. New York: Appleton.

RISS, W., E. S. VALENSTEIN, J. SINKS, and W. C. YOUNG. 1955. Development of sexual behavior in male guinea pigs from genetically different stocks under controlled conditions of androgen treatment and caging. *Endocrinology*, **57**: 139-146.

RIVLIN, J. 1959. Creativity and the self-attitude and sociability of high-school students. *J. Educ. Psychol.*, **50**: 147-152.

ROBERTS, L. 1961. Activation and interference of cortical functions, in D. E. Sheer, ed., *Electrical stimulation of the brain*. Austin: Univ. Texas Press.

ROBERTSON, ANNE DE S., and J. YOUNISS. 1969. Anticipatory visual imagery in deaf and hearing children. *Child Develop.*, **40**: 123-135.

ROBSON, K. S. 1967. The role of eye-to-eye contact in maternal-infant attachment. *J. Child Psychol. Psychiat.*, **8**: 13-25.

ROE, ANNE. 1959. Personal problems and science, in C. W. Taylor, ed., The 3rd University of Utah Research Conference on the Identification of Creative Scientific Talent, Salt Lake City.

ROEDE, K. D., ed. 1953. *Insect physiology*. New York: Wiley.

RONGE, H. 1943. Altersveränderungen des Berührungssinnes. I. Druckpunktschwellen und Druckpunktfrequenz. (Modifications with age of the tactual sense.) *Acta Physiol. Scand.*, **6**: 343-352.

ROSENBERG, B. G., and B. SUTTON-SMITH. 1960. A revised conception of masculine-feminine differences in play activities. *J. Genet. Psychol.*, **96**: 165-170.

————. 1964a. The relationship of ordinal position and sibling sex status to cognitive abilities. *Psychon. Sci.*, **1**(4): 81-82.

————. 1964b. The measurement of masculinity

and femininity in children: an extension and revalidation. *J. Genet. Psychol.,* 104: 259-264.

ROSENBLATT, J. S., and L. R. ARONSON. 1958. The influence of experience on the behavioral effects of androgen in prepubertally castrated male cats. *Anim. Behav.,* 6: 171-182.

ROSENTHAL, R., and LENORE F. JACOBSON. 1968. Teacher expectations for the disadvantaged. *Sci. Amer.,* 218(4): 19-23.

ROSENZWEIG, M. R., D. KRECH, E. L. BENNETT, and MARIAN C. DIAMOND. 1962a. Effects of environmental complexity and training on brain chemistry and anatomy: a replication and extension. *J. Comp. Physiol. Psychol.,* 55: 429-437.

ROSENZWEIG, M. R., D. KRECH, E. L. BENNETT, and J. F. ZOLMAN. 1962b. Variations in environmental complexity and brain measures. *J. Comp. Physiol. Psychol.,* 55: 1029-1095.

ROSENZWEIG, S. 1945. Further comparative data on repetition—choice after success and failure as related to frustration tolerance. *J. Genet. Psychol.,* 66: 75-81.

ROSS, S., W. I. SMITH, and B. L. VOESSNER. 1955. Hoarding: an analysis of experiments and trends. *J. Genet. Psychol.,* 52: 307-326.

ROSSLER, R. H. 1966. Inherited environmental influences on the operant behavior of mice. *J. Comp. Physiol. Psychol.,* 61: 264-267.

ROWLAND, V. 1959. Conditioning and brain waves. *Sci. Amer.,* 201(2): 89-96.

RUBIN, BETTY L., H. J. STRECKER, and ELISSA B. KOFF. 1963. Further observations on sex-influenced activity of three beta-hydroxysteroid dehydrogenase of rat liver. *Endocrinology,* 72: 764-770.

RUCH, T. C., J. F. FULTON, and W. J. GERMAN. 1938. Sensory discrimination in the monkey, chimpanzee and man with lesions of the parietal lobe. *Arch. Neurol. Psychiat.,* 39: 919-937.

RUDEL, RITA G. and H. L. TEUBER. 1963a. Discrimination of direction of line in children. *J. Comp. Physiol. Psychol.,* 56: 892-898.

———. 1963b. Decrement of visual and haptic Muller-Lyer illusion on repeated trials: a study of cross-modal transfer. *Quart. J. Exp. Psychol.,* 15: 125-131.

RUDNICK, M., G. M. STERRITT, and M. FLAX. 1967. Auditory and visual rhythm perception and reading ability. *Child Develop.,* 38: 581-588.

RUEGEMAR, W. R., and F. R. SILVERMAN. 1956. Influence of gentling on physiology of the rat. *Proc. Soc. Exp. Biol. Med.,* 92: 170-174.

RUSSELL, B. 1961. *Has man a future?* London: Penguin.

RUSSELL, D. H. 1956. *Children's thinking.* Boston: Ginn.

RUSSELL, E. S. 1938. *The behavior of animals: an introduction to its study,* 2nd ed. London: Arnold.

RUSSELL, W. R. 1959. *Brain memory learning.* Oxford: Clarendon Press.

RYCHLAK, J. E., and A. LEGERSKI. 1967. A sociocultural theory of appropriate sexual role identification and level of personal adjustment. *J. Personality,* 35: 31-49.

SACKETT, G. P. 1963. A neural mechanism underlying unlearned, critical period, and developmental aspects of visually controlled behavior. *Psychol. Rev.,* 70: 40-50.

———. 1965. Effects of early rearing conditions upon the behavior of rhesus monkeys (Macaca mulatta). *Child Develop.,* 36: 855-868.

———. 1966. Monkeys reared in isolation with pictures as visual input: evidence for an innate releasing mechanism. *Science,* 154: 1468-1473.

SAHLINS, M. D. 1959. Social life of monkeys, apes and primitive men, in J. N. Spuhler, ed., *Symposium on evolution of man's capacity for culture.* Detroit: Wayne State Univ. Press, 54-73.

SALK, L. 1961. The importance of the heartbeat rhythm to human nature: theoretical, clinical and experimental observations, in *Proceedings of the 3rd World Congress of Psychiatry, Montreal and Toronto, 1961,* Vol. I. Toronto: Univ. Toronto Press and Montreal: McGill Univ. Press.

———. 1962. Mother's heartbeat as an imprinting stimulus. *Trans. N.Y. Acad. Sci.,* 24: 753-763.

———. 1966. Thoughts on the concept of imprinting and its place in early human development. *Canad. Psychiat. Ass. J.,* 11: 295-305.

SALMON, U. J. 1942. Rationale for androgen therapy in gynecology. *J. Clin. Endocrinol.,* 2: 162-179.

———, and S. H. GEIST. 1943. Effect of androgens upon libido in women. *J. Clin. Endocrinol.,* 3: 235-238.

SALTZSTEIN, H. D., and RHEA M. DIAMOND. 1967.

Transfer of social influence: effect of peers' sex. *Psychol. Rep.,* **20**: 343-350.

SALZBERGER, R. M., and L. F. JARVICK. 1963. Intelligence tests in deaf twins, in J. D. Rainer, ed., *Family and mental health problems in a deaf population.* New York: New York State Psychiatric Institute, Columbia Univ.

——, and A. SALEK. 1963. Deaf persons of outstanding achievement, in J. D. Rainer, ed., *Family and mental health problems in a deaf population.* New York: New York State Psychiatric Institute, Columbia Univ.

SALZEN, E. A. 1962. Imprinting and fear. *Symp. Zool. Soc. London,* **8**: 199-217.

——. 1963. Visual stimuli eliciting the smiling response in the human infant. *J. Genet. Psychol.,* **102**: 51-54.

——, and W. SLUCKIN. 1959. The incidence of the following response and the duration of responsiveness in domestic fowl. *Anim. Behav.,* **7**: 173-179.

SAMEROFF, A. J. 1965. An apparatus for recording sucking and controlling feeding in the first days of life. *Psychon. Sci.,* **2**: 355-356.

SAMUELS, INA. 1959. Reticular mechanisms and behavior. *Psychol. Bull.,* **56**: 1-25.

SAMUELS, S. J. 1967. The psychology of language. *Rev. Educ. Res.,* **37**: 109-119.

SANFORD, N. 1968. Education for individual development. *Amer. J. Orthopsychiat.,* **38**: 858-868.

——, M. B. FREEDMAN, H. WEBSTER, and D. BROWN. 1956. Personality development during the college years. *J. Sociol. Issues,* **12**(4): 3-70.

SANTOSTEFANO, S. 1963. A developmental study of the Delboeuf illusion. *Percept. Motor Skills,* **17**: 23-29.

——. 1964. A developmental study of the cognitive control "leveling-sharpening." *Merrill-Palmer Quart.,* **10**: 543-560.

——, and E. PALEY. 1964. Development of cognitive controls in children. *Child Develop.,* **35**: 939-949.

SARASON, S. B., K. S. DAVIDSON, F. F. LIGHTALL, R. R. WAITE, and B. K. RUEBUSH. 1960. *Anxiety in elementary school children.* New York: Wiley.

SARAVO, ANNE, and MAY KOLODNY. 1969. Learning set and shift behavior in children. *J. Exp. Child Psychol.,* **7**: 21-30.

SARNOFF, I. 1962. *Personality dynamics and development.* New York: Wiley.

SARTRE, J. P. 1962. *Sketch for a theory of the emotions.* London: Methuen.

SAWREY, W. L., and D. H. LONG. 1962. Strain and sex differences in ulceration in the rat. *J. Comp. Physiol. Psychol.,* **55**: 603-605.

SAYERS, G., and M. A. SAYERS. 1948. The pituitary adrenal system, in G. Pincus, ed., *Recent progress in hormone research,* Vol. II. New York: Academic Press.

SCARR, SANDRA. 1965. The inheritance of sociability. *Amer. Psychol.,* **20**: 524 (abstract).

——. 1966. Environmental bias in twin studies. Paper presented at 2nd Louisville Conference on Human Behavior Genetics, Louisville, Ky., May 1966. Quoted in Anne M. Brown, R. E. Stafford, and S. G. Vandenberg, 1967. Twins: behavioral differences. *Child Develop.,* **38**: 1055-1064.

SCHACHTEL, E. 1959. *Metamorphosis.* New York: Basic Books.

SCHACHTER, S. 1959. *The psychology of affiliation: experimental studies of the sources of gregariousness.* Stanford: Stanford Univ. Press.

——. 1963. Birth order, eminence and higher education. *Amer. Sociol. Rev.,* **28**: 757-768.

SCHADÉ, J. P. 1957. *Electro-area-grafie van de cortex cerebri.* Amsterdam: F. V. Rossen.

——. 1959. Maturational aspects of EEG and of spreading depression in rabbits. *J. Neurophysiol.,* **22**: 245-257.

SCHAEFER, E. S., and NANCY BAYLEY. 1963. Maternal behavior, child behavior, and their intercorrelations from infancy through adolescence. *Monogr. Soc. Res. Child Develop.,* **28**: Whole No. 87.

SCHAFFER, H. R. 1965a. Some issues for research in the study of attachment behaviour, in B. M. Foss, ed., *Determinants of infant behaviour. II.* London: Methuen.

——. 1965b. Changes in development quotient under two conditions of maternal separation. *Brit. J. Soc. Clin. Psychol.,* **4**: 39-46.

——. 1966. The onset of fear of strangers and the incongruity hypothesis. *J. Child Psychol. Psychiat.,* **7**: 95-106.

——, and PEGGY E. EMERSON. 1964a. Patterns of response to physical contact in early human development. *J. Child Psychol. Psychiat.,* **5**: 1-13.

——. 1964b. The development of social attachments in infancy. *Monogr. Soc. Res. Child Develop.,* **29** (3): Serial No. 94.

SCHAIE, K. W. 1966. Year-by-year changes in personality from six to eighteen years. *Multivariate Behav. Res.,* 1: 293-305.

SCHALLER, G. 1963. *The mountain gorilla: ecology and behavior.* Chicago: Univ. Chicago Press.

SCHEINFELD, A. 1944. *Women and men.* New York: Harcourt.

SCHIFF, W., J. A. CAVINESS, and J. J. GIBSON. 1962. Persistent fear responses in rhesus monkeys to the optical stimulus of looming. *Science,* 136: 982-983.

SCHILDER, P. 1950. *The image and appearance of the human body.* New York: International Univ. Press.

SCHMIDT, H. O. 1941. The effect of praise and blame as incentives to learning. *Psychol. Monogr.,* 53: Whole No. 240.

SCHNEIDER, R. A., and S. WOOLF. 1955. Olfactory perception thresholds for citral utilizing a new type olfactorium. *J. Appl. Physiol.,* 8: 337-342.

SCHNEIDER, S. F. 1964. Some comments on congenital insensitivity to pain: a critique. *Psychol. Bull.,* 62: 287-288.

SCHNEIRLA, T. C. 1957. The concept of development in comparative physiology, in D. B. Harris, ed., *The concept of development.* Minneapolis: Univ. Minnesota Press.

————, and JAY S. ROSENBLATT. 1961. Animal Research Panel 1960. *Amer. J. Orthopsychiat.,* 31: 223-291.

SCHOFIELD, M. 1965. *The sexual behavior of young people.* London: Longmans, Green.

SCHON, M. 1958. Physiological effects of hypophysectomy in women with metastatic breast cancer. *Cancer,* 11: 95-98.

————, and A. M. SUTHERLAND. 1960. The role of hormones in human behavior. III. Changes in female sexuality after hypophysectomy. *J. Clin. Endocrinol.,* 20: 833-841.

SCHOPLER, E. 1964. Visual and tactual receptor preference in normal and schizophrenic children. Unpublished doctoral dissertation, Univ. of Chicago.

SCHUELL, H. 1946. Sex differences in relation to stuttering. *I. J. Speech Disord.,* 11: 277-298.

SCHWARCZ, H. J. 1967. Machine animism in modern children's literature. *Library Quart.,* 37: 78-95.

SCOTT, J. H. 1955. Some effects of maturity of gentling, ignoring and checking rats during infancy. *J. Abnorm. Social Psychol.,* 51: 412-414.

SCOTT, J. P. 1937. The embryology of the guinea pig. III. The development of the polydactylous monster. *J. Exp. Zool.,* 77: 123-157.

————. 1945. Social behavior, organization and leadership in a small flock of domestic sheep. *Comp. Psychol. Monogr.,* 18 (4): 29.

————. 1953. New directions in the genetic study of personality and intelligence. *Eugen. News,* 38: 97-101.

————. 1957. Animal and human children. *Children,* 4: 163-168.

————. 1958. *Animal behavior.* Chicago: Univ. Chicago Press.

————. 1962. Critical periods in behavior development. *Science,* 138: 949-957.

————. 1963. The process of primary socialisation in canine and human infants. *Monogr. Soc. Res. Child Develop.,* 28 (1): Serial No. 85.

————, and M. S. CHARLES. 1953. Some problems of heredity and social behavior. *J. General Psychol.,* 48: 209-230.

————. 1954. Genetic differences in the behavior of dogs: a case of magnification by thresholds and by habit formation. *J. Genet. Psychol.,* 84: 175-188.

SCOTT, J. P., E. FREDERICSON, and J. FULLER. 1951. Experimental exploration of the critical period hypothesis. *Personality,* 1: 162-183.

SCOTT, J. P., and M. V. MARSTON. 1950. Critical periods affecting the development of normal and maladjustive social behavior in puppies. *J. Genet. Psychol.,* 77: 25-60.

SCOTT, T. H. 1954. *Intellectual effects of perceptual isolation.* Unpublished doctoral dissertation. Montreal: McGill Univ.

SCOTTISH COUNCIL FOR RESEARCH AND EDUCATION. 1933. *The intelligence of Scottish children: a national survey of an age group.* London: Univ. London Press.

————. 1949. *The trend of Scottish intelligence.* London: Univ. London Press.

SEARLE, L. V. 1949. The organization of hereditary maze-brightness and maze-dullness. *Genet. Psychol. Monogr.,* 39: 279-325.

SEARS, P. S. 1951. Doll play aggression in normal children: influence of sex, age, sibling status, father's absence. *Psychol. Monogr.,* 65(6).

————. 1953. Child-rearing factors related to the playing of sex-typed roles. *Amer. Psychol.,* 8: 431 (abstract).

SEARS, R. R. 1965a. Comparison of interview with questionnaires for measuring mother's attitudes toward sex and aggression. *J. Pers. Soc. Psychol.*, **2**: 37-44.

———. 1965b. Development of gender role, in F. A. Beach, ed., *Sex and behavior*. New York: Wiley.

———, E. MACCOBY, and H. LEVIN. 1957. *Patterns of child rearing*. New York: Harper & Row.

SEARS, R. R., M. H. PINTLER, and PAULINE S. SEARS. 1946. Effect of father separation on preschool children's doll-play aggression. *Child Develop.*, **17**: 219-243.

SEARS, R. R., LUCY RAU, and R. ALPERT. 1965. *Identification and child rearing*. Stanford: Stanford Univ. Press.

SEARS, R. R., I. W. WHITING, J. NOULIS, and P. S. SEARS. 1953. Some child rearing antecedents of aggression and dependency in young children. *Genet. Psychol. Monogr.*, **47**: 135-236.

SEASHORE, C. F. 1910. Measurement and pitch discrimination. *Psychol. Monogr.*, **13**: 21-59.

SELYE, H. 1955. Critical period for inhibition of inflammation by a primarily neurogenic stress situation. *Psychosomat. Med.*, **17**: 124-127.

SERGOVICH, F., G. H. VALENTINE, A. T. L. CHEN, R. A. H. KINCH, and M. S. SMOUT. 1969. Chromosome aberrations in 2159 consecutive newborn babies. *New England J. Med.*, **280**: 851-855.

SEWARD, G. H. 1940. Studies on the reproductive activities of the guinea pig. II. The role of hunger in filial behavior. *J. Comp. Psychol.*, **29**: 25-41.

SHAFFER, J. W. A. 1962. A specific cognitive deficit observed in gonadal aplasia (Turner's syndrome). *J. Clin. Psychol.*, **18**: 403-406.

———, S. MEDNICK, and JUDITH SEDER. 1957. Some developmental factors related to field independence in children. *Amer. Psychol.*, **12**: 399.

SHARPLESS, S., and H. JASPER. 1956. Habituation of the arousal reaction. *Brain*, **79**: 655-680.

SHEER, D. E., ed. 1961. *Electrical stimulation of the brain*. Austin, Texas: Hogg Foundation for Mental Health.

SHELDON, W. H., E. HARTT, and E. McDERMOTT. 1949. *Varieties of delinquent youth*. New York: Harper.

SHELDON, W. H., and S. S. STEVENS. 1942. *The varieties of temperament*. New York: Harper.

———, and W. B. TUCKER. 1940. *The varieties of human physique*. New York: Harper.

SHEPLER, B. F. 1951. A comparison of masculinity-femininity measures. *J. Consult. Psychol.*, **15**: 484-486.

SHEPPARD, W. C. 1969. Operant control of infant vocal and motor behavior. *J. Exp. Child Psychol.*, **7**: 36-51.

SHERMAN, JULIA A. 1967. Problem of sex differences in space perception and aspects of individual functioning. *Psychol. Rev.*, **74**: 290-299.

SHIELDE, J. 1962. *Monozygotic twins*. London: Oxford Univ. Press.

SHIPLEY, W. V. 1963. The demonstration in the domestic guinea pig of a process resembling classical imprinting. *Anim. Behav.*, **11**: 470-474.

SHIRLEY, MARY. 1933. *The first two years: a study of twenty-five babies. Vol. II. Intellectual development*. Inst. Child Welfare Monogr. Series 7. Minneapolis: Univ. Minnesota Press.

SHORR, E., G. N. PAPANICOLAOU, and B. F. STIMMEL. 1938. Neutralization of ovarian follicular hormone in women by simultaneous administration of male sex hormone. *Proc. Soc. Exp. Biol. Med.*, **38**: 759-762.

SHULMAN, D. 1966. Openness of perception as a condition for creativity. *Except. Child.*, **33**: 89-94.

SIEGAL, LINDA S. 1968. The development of the ability to process information. *J. Exp. Child Psychol.*, **6**: 368-383.

SIEGEL, A. W. 1968. Variables affecting incidental learning in children. *Child Develop.*, **39**: 957-968.

SIEGMANN, A. W. 1966. Father absence during early childhood and anti-social behaviour. *J. Abnorm. Psychol.*, **71**: 71-74.

SIGEL, I. E. 1953. Developmental trends in the abstraction ability of children. *Child Develop.*, **24**: 131-144.

———. 1961. Cognitive style and personality dynamics. Interim progress report. *Nat. Inst. Ment. Health*, M2983.

———. 1963. *Sex differences in cognitive functioning re-examined: a functional point of view*. Presented at the 1963 Biennial Meeting of the Society for Research in Child Development, Berkeley.

———. 1964. The attainment of concepts, in M. L. Hoffman and Lois W. Hoffman, eds., *Review of child development research*, Vol. I. New York: Russell Sage Foundation.

SILCOFF, CAROLE. 1966. Honours project, Department of Psychology, McGill Univ., Montreal.

SILFEN, C. K., and E. W. AMES. 1964. *Visual movement preference in the human infant.* Paper presented at the Eastern Psychological Association Meeting, Philadelphia.

SILLMAN, L. 1960. The evolution of vertebrate perception. *J. Genet. Psychol.,* **97**: 113-125.

SILVER, A. A., and ROSA A. HAGIN. 1967. The spectrum of communication defects in specific language disability. *Amer. J. Orthopsychiat.,* **37**: 370-371.

SILVERMAN, M., I. J. LASZLO, and JANE C. CRAMER. 1967. Deviant pre-school children: the contribution of constitutional predisposition and parental crisis. *Amer. J. Orthopsychiat.,* **37**: 330-331.

SIMMEL, M. L. 1962. Phantom experiences following amputation in childhood. *J. Neurol. Neurosurg. Psychiat.,* **25**: 69-78.

SIMON, MARIA D. 1959. Body configuration and school readiness. *Child Develop.,* **30**: 493-512.

SIMPSON, R. M. 1922. Creative imagination. *Amer. J. Psychol.,* **33**: 234-243.

SIMPSON, S. L. 1948. *Major endocrine disorders,* 2nd ed. London: Oxford Univ. Press.

SIQUELAND, E. R. 1968. Reinforcement patterns and extinction in human newborns. *J. Exp. Child Psychol.,* **6**: 431-442.

SKINNER, B. F. 1957. *Verbal behavior.* New York: Appleton.

SKODAK, H. M. 1966. Adult status of children with contrasting early life experiences. *Monogr. Soc. Res. Child Develop.,* **31** (3): Serial No. 105.

SKULTETY, F. M. 1961. Experimental mutism following electrolytic lesions of the peri-aqueductal grey matter in dogs. *Trans. Amer. Neurol. Ass.,* **86**: 245-246.

SLATER, P. E. 1961. Toward a dualistic theory of identification. *Merrill-Palmer Quart.,* **7**: 113-126.

SLOBIN, D. I. 1966. The acquisition of Russian as a native language, in F. Smith and G. A. Miller, eds., *The genesis of language: a psycholinguistic approach.* Cambridge: M.I.T. Press.

SLOVIC, P. 1966. Risk-taking in children: age and sex differences. *Child Develop.,* **37**: 169-176.

SLUCKIN, W. 1965. *Imprinting and early learning.* Chicago: Aldine.

———, and E. A. SALZEN. 1961. Imprinting and perceptual learning. *Quart. J. Exp. Psychol.,* **13**: 65-77.

SMEDSLUND, J. 1961. The acquisition of conservation of substance and weight in children. I-VI. *Scand. J. Psychol.,* **2**: 11-166.

SMITH, A. M. 1967. Infantile stimulation and the Yerkes-Dobson law. *Canad. J. Psychol.,* **21**: 285-293.

SMITH, C. G. 1942. Age incidence of atrophy of olfactory nerves in man. *J. Comp. Neurol.,* **77**: 589-595.

SMITH, J. M. 1936. The relative brightness values of three hues for newborn infants. *Univ. Iowa Studies Child Welfare,* **12**: 91-140.

SMITH, K. U., and P. GREENE. 1963. A critical period in maturation of performance with space-displaced vision. *Percept. Motor Skills,* **17**: 627-639.

SMITH, K. U., C. ZWERG, and N. J. SMITH. 1963. Sensory feedback analysis of infant control of the behavioral environment. *Percept. Motor Skills,* **16**: 725-732.

SMITH, O. W., and P. C. SMITH. 1963. A developmental study of the illusion of parallelism. *Percept. Motor Skills,* **16**: 871-878.

SMITH, R. M. 1962. *Perceptions of self, others and certain environmental aspects of high and low divergent intellectually superior children.* Unpublished doctoral dissertation. Urbana: Univ. Illinois.

SMITH, T. L., and MERLE E. MEYER. 1965. Preference of chicks in the original stimulus situation of imprinting. *Psychon. Sci.,* **2**: 121-122.

SNYDER, L. H., and P. R. DAVID. 1953. Penetrance and expression, in A. Sorsby, ed., *Clinical genetics.* London: Butterworth.

SOFFER, L. J., R. I. DORFMAN, and J. L. GABRILOVE. 1961. *The human adrenal gland.* Philadelphia: Lea & Febiger.

SOLLENBERGER, R. T. 1940. Some relationships between the urinary excretion of male hormone by maturing boys and their expressed interests and attitudes. *J. Psychol.,* **9**: 179-189.

SOLLEY, C. M., and G. MURPHY. 1960. *Development of the perceptual world.* New York: Basic Books.

SONTAG, L. W., C. T. BAKER, and VIRGINIA NELSON. 1955. Personality as a determinant of performance. *Amer. J. Orthopsychiat.,* **25**: 555-562.

———. 1958. Mental growth and personality development: a longitudinal study. *Monogr. Soc. Res. Child Develop.,* **23**(2): Whole No. 68.

SOPCHAK, A. L., and A. M. SUTHERLAND. 1960.

Psychological impact of cancer and its treatment. VII. Exogenous sex hormones and their relation to life-long adaptations in women with metastatic cancer of the breast. *Cancer,* **22:** 528-531.

SOUTH, E. B. 1927. Some psychological aspects of committee work. *J. Appl. Psychol.,* **11:** 348-368 and 437-464.

SOUTHWICK, C. H. 1963. *Primate social behavior.* Princeton, N.J.: Van Nostrand.

SPALDING, D. 1873. Instinct, with original observations on young animals. *MacMillan's Mag.,* **27:** 282-293.

SPEARS, W. C. 1964. Assessment of visual preference and discrimination in the four-month-old infant. *J. Comp. Physiol. Psychol.,* **57:** 381-386.

SPEMAN, H. 1938. *Embryonic development and induction.* New Haven: Yale Univ. Press.

SPENCE, K. W. 1937. Réactions des mères chimpanzés à l'égard des enfants chimpanzés après séparation. (The reaction of mother chimpanzees on seeing their baby chimpanzees after a separation.) *J. Psychol. Norm. Path.,* **34:** 475-493.

SPERRY, R. W. 1958. Developmental basis of behavior, in Anne Roe and G. G. Simpson, eds., *Behavior and evolution.* New Haven: Yale Univ. Press.

————. 1961. Cerebral organization and behavior. *Science,* **133:** 1749-1757.

————. 1963. Chemoaffinity in the orderly growth of nerve fiber patterns and connections. *Proc. Nat. Acad. Sci.,* **50**(4): 703-710.

SPERRY, W. M., FLORENCE C. BRAND, and M. WEBB. 1949. Composition of brain lipids in male and female rats. *Fed. Proc.,* **8:** 254-255.

SPIKER, C. C. 1960a. Associated transfer in verbal paired-associate learning. *Child Develop.,* **31:** 73-87.

————. 1960b. Research methods in children's learning, in P. H. Mussen, ed., *Handbook of research methods in child development.* New York: Wiley.

————. 1961. *Verbal factors in the discrimination learning of children.* Paper read at the Conference of Cognitive Processes, Minneapolis, April.

SPIRO, M. E. 1960. Is the family universal? The Israeli case, in N. W. Bell and E. F. Vogel, eds., *The family.* Toronto: Macmillan.

SPITZ, R. A. 1945. Hospitalism: an inquiry into the genesis of psychiatric conditions in early childhood. *Psychoanal. Stud. Child.,* **1:** 53-74.

————. 1946. Hospitalism: a follow-up report. *Psychoanal. Stud. Child.,* **2:** 113-117.

————. 1949. The role of ecological factors in emotional development in infancy. *Child Develop.,* **20:** 145-155.

————. 1957. *No and yes: on the genesis of human communication.* New York: International Univ. Press.

————, and K. M. WOLF. 1946a. Anaclitic depression: an enquiry into the genesis of psychiatric conditions in early childhood. *Psychoanal. Stud. Child.,* **2:** 313-342.

————. 1946b. The smiling response: a contribution to the ontogenesis of social relations. *Genet. Psychol. Monogr.,* **34:** 57-125.

SPOCK, B. 1963. The striving for autonomy and regressive object relationships. *Psychoanal. Stud. Child.,* **18:** 361-364.

STAATS, A. W. 1968. *Learning, language and cognition.* New York: Holt.

STAFFORD, R. E. 1961a. *Evidence for the sex-linked inheritance of spatial visualization.* Paper presented at the Eastern Psychological Association Meeting, Philadelphia.

————. 1961b. Sex differences in spatial visualization as evidence of sex-linked inheritance. *Percept. Motor Skills,* **13:** 428.

————. 1965. New techniques in analysing parent-child test scores for evidence of hereditary components, in S. G. Vandenberg, ed., *Methods and goals in human behavior genetics.* New York: Academic Press.

STAPLES, F. R. 1932. The responses of infants to color. *J. Exp. Psychol.,* **15:** 119-141.

————, and R. H. WALTERS. 1961. Anxiety, birth order and susceptibility to social influence. *J. Abnorm. Social Psychol.,* **62:** 616-619.

STASS, J. W., and F. N. WILLIS. 1967. Eye contact, pupil dilation and personal preference. *Psychon. Sci.,* **7:** 375-376.

STEIN, M. I. 1956. A transactional approach to creativity, in C. W. Taylor, ed., *The 1955 University of Utah Research Conference on the Identification of Creative Talent.* Salt Lake City: Univ. Utah Press.

STEINACH, E. 1912. Willkürliche Umwandlung von Säugetier Männchen in Tiere mit ausgeprägt weiblichen Geschlechtscharakteren und weiblicher Psyche. *Arch. Ges. Physiol.,* **144:** 71-108.

STEINMAN, ANN, and D. J. FOX. 1966. Male-female

perceptions of the female role in the U.S. *J. Psychol.*, 64: 265-276.

STENDLER, CELIA B. 1952. Critical periods in socialization and over-dependency. *Child Develop.*, 23: 3-12.

STERN, C. 1950. *Principles of human genetics.* San Francisco: Freeman.

——. 1960. *Principles of human genetics,* 2nd ed. San Francisco: Freeman.

STERNBACH, R. A. 1963. Congenital insensitivity to pain: a critique. *Psychol. Bull.*, 60: 252-266.

STETTNER, L. J., and K. A. MATYNIAK. 1968. The brain of birds. *Sci. Amer.*, 218(6): 64-77.

STEVEN, D. M. 1955. Transference of imprinting in a wild gosling. *Brit. J. Anim. Behav.*, 3: 14-16.

STEVENSON, H. W. 1962. Behavior theory and intelligence, in W. Kessen and Clementina Kuhlmann, eds., *Thought in the young child. Monogr. Soc. Res. Child Develop.*, 27(2): Series No. 83.

——, and R. D. ODOM. 1965. The relation of anxiety to children's performance on learning and problem-solving tasks. *Child Develop.*, 36: 1003-1012.

STINCHFIELD, S. N., and E. H. YOUNG. 1938. *Children with delayed and defective speech.* London: Oxford Univ. Press.

STOKE, S. M. 1950. An enquiry into the concept of identification. *J. Genet. Psychol.*, 76: 163-189.

STOLZ, H. R., and L. M. STOLZ. 1951. *Somatic development of adolescent boys. A study of the growth of boys during the second decade of life.* New York: Macmillan.

STOLZ, LOIS M. 1966. Old and new directions in child development. *Merrill-Palmer Quart.*, 12: 221-232.

—— et al. 1954. *Father relations of war-born children.* Stanford: Stanford Univ. Press.

STONE, C. P. 1924. A note on feminine behavior in adult male rats. *Amer. J. Psychol.*, 68: 39-41.

——. 1927. The retention of copulation ability in male rats following castration. *J. Comp. Psychol.*, 7: 369-387.

STOTT, D. H. 1966. Commentary on "The genetic determination of differences in intelligence: a study of monozygotic twins reared apart," by Cyril Burt: Congenital influences on the development of twins. *Brit. J. Psychol.*, 57: 423-429.

STRANGE, F. B., and J. O. PALMER. 1953. Note on

sex differences on the Wechsler Bellevue tests. *J. Clin. Psychol.*, 9: 85-87.

STRATTON, G. M. 1896. Some preliminary experiments in vision without inversion of the retinal image. *Psychol. Rev.*, 3: 611-617.

STRAUSS, A. A., and H. WERNER. 1942. Disorders of conceptual thinking in the brain-injured child. *J. Nerv. Ment. Dis.*, 96: 153-172.

SULLIVAN, H. S. 1953. *The interpersonal theory of psychiatry.* New York: Norton.

SULTAN, E. E. 1962. A factorial study in the domain of creative thinking. *Brit. J. Educ. Psychol.*, 32: 78-82.

SULZEN, E. A. 1967. Imprinting in birds and primates. *Behaviour*, 29: 232-254.

SUTHERLAND, N. S. 1957. Visual discrimination of orientation by octopus. *Brit. J. Psychol.*, 48: 55-71.

——. 1958. Visual discrimination of the orientation of rectangles by octopus vulgaris Lamark. *J. Comp. Physiol. Psychol.*, 51: 452-458.

——. 1960. Visual discrimination of orientation by octopus: mirror images. *Brit. J. Psychol.*, 51: 9-18.

TALLARICO, R. B. 1961. Studies of visual depth perception. III. Choice behavior of newly hatched chicks on a visual cliff. *Percept. Motor Skills*, 12: 259-262.

TANNER, J. M. 1955. *Growth at adolescence.* Oxford: Blackwell.

——. 1961. *Education and physical growth.* London: Univ. London Press.

——. 1962. *Growth at adolescence,* 2nd ed. Oxford: Blackwell.

——. 1968. Earlier maturation in man. *Sci. Amer.*, 218(1): 21-28.

TAPP, J. T., and H. MARKOWITZ. 1963. Infant handling: effects on avoidance learning, brain weight and cholinesterase. *Activity Sci.*, 140: 486-487.

TAUB, E., and A. J. BERMAN. 1968. Movement and learning in the absence of sensory feedback, in S. J. Freedman, ed., *The neurophysiology of spatially oriented behaviour.* Homewood, Ill.: Dorsey.

TAUB, E., S. J. ELLMAN, and A. J. BERMAN. 1966. Deafferentation in monkeys: effect on conditioned grasp response. *Science*, 151: 594-595.

TAUBER, E. S., and S. KOFFLER. 1966. Optomotor response in human infants to apparent motion: evidence of innateness. *Science,* **152:** 382-383.

TAYLOR, ANN. 1968. Deprived infants: potential for affective adjustment. *Amer. J. Orthopsychiat.,* **38:** 835-845.

TAYLOR, C. W. 1959. The 1955 and 1957 research conferences. The identification of creative scientific talent. *Amer. Psychol.,* **14:** 100-102.

TAYLOR, L. B. 1962. *Perception of digits presented to right and left ears in children with reading difficulties.* Paper read at Canadian Psychology Association Meeting, Hamilton.

TEILHARD DE CHARDIN, P. 1959. *The phenomenon of man.* London: Collins.

TELFER, MARY A., D. BAKER, G. R. CLARK, and C. E. RICHARDSON. 1968. Incidence of gross chromosomal errors among tall criminal American males. *Science,* **159:** 1249-1250.

TERMAN, L. M. 1938. Psychological factors in marital happiness. New York: McGraw-Hill.

———, and MAUDE A. MERRILL. 1937. *Measuring intelligence.* Boston: Houghton Mifflin.

TERMAN, L. M., and C. C. MILES. 1936. *Sex and personality.* New York: McGraw-Hill.

TERMAN, L. M., and LEONA E. TYLER. 1954. Psychological sex differences, in L. Carmichael, ed., *Manual of child psychology,* 2nd ed. New York: Wiley.

TERMAN, L. M., et al. 1925. *Genetic studies of genius, Vol. I. The mental and physical traits of a thousand gifted children.* Stanford: Stanford Univ. Press.

TEUBER, H. L. 1960. Perception, in J. Field, H. W. Magoun, and V. E. Hall, eds., *Handbook of physiology. Section 1. Neurophysiology,* Vol. III. New York: American Physiological Society.

——— et al. 1960. *Somato sensory changes after penetrating brain wounds.* Cambridge, Mass.: Harvard Univ. Press.

THISTLETHWAITE, D. 1951. A critical review of latent learning and related experiments. *Psychol. Bull.,* **48:** 97-129.

THOMAE, H. 1965. Objective socialization variables and personality development. *Hum. Develop.,* **8:** 87-116.

THOMAS, A., H. G. BIRCH, S. CHESS, and L. C. ROBBINS. 1960. Individuality in responses of children to similar environmental situations. *Amer. J. Psychiat.,* **117:** 789-803.

THOMAS, CAROLINE B. 1966. The precursors of hypertension and coronary artery disease: in-

sights from studies of biological variation. *Ann. N.Y. Acad. Sci.,* **134:** 1028-1039.

THOMAS, G. J. 1954. The effect on cortical flicker frequency of interocular differences in intensity and in phase relations of flashes of light. *Amer. J. Psychol.,* **67:** 632-646.

———. 1955. A comparison of uniocular and binocular cortical flicker frequencies: simultaneous and alternate flashes. *Amer. J. Psychol.,* **68:** 37-53.

THOMPSON, D'ARCY W. 1942. *On growth and form,* 2nd ed. London: Cambridge Univ. Press.

THOMPSON, H. B. 1903. *Mental traits of sex.* Chicago: Univ. Chicago Press.

THOMPSON, W. R. 1954. The inheritance and development of intelligence, in *Genetics and the inheritance of integrated neurological and psychiatric patterns,* Vol. XXXIII. Proceedings of the Association for Research of Nervous and Mental Diseases. Baltimore: Williams & Wilkins.

———. 1955. Early environment: its importance for later development, in P. H. Hoch and J. Zubin, eds., *Psychopathology of children.* New York: Grune & Stratton.

———. 1957. Influence of pre-natal maternal anxiety on emotionality in young rats. *Science,* **125:** 698-699.

———, and D. BINDRA. 1952. Motivational and emotional characteristics of "bright" and "dull" rats. *Canad. J. Psychol.,* **6:** 116-122.

THOMPSON, W. R., and R. A. DUBANOSKI. 1964. Imprinting and the law of effort. *Anim. Behav.,* **12:** 213-218.

THOMPSON, W. R., and R. MELZACK. 1956. Early environment. *Sci. Amer.,* **194**(1): 38-42.

THORPE, W. H. 1956. *Learning and instinct in animals.* London: Methuen.

———. 1958. The learning of song patterns by birds with especial reference to the song of the chaffinch, *Fringilla coelebs. Ibis,* **100:** 535-570.

———. 1965. *Science, man and morals.* London: Methuen.

THRASHER, F. M. 1927. *The gang.* Chicago: Univ. Chicago Press.

THRUM, M. E. 1935. The development of concepts of magnitude. *Child Develop.,* **6:** 120-140.

TIGHE, LOUISE S., and T. J. TIGHE. 1966a. Discrimination learning: two views in historical perspective. *Psychol. Bull.,* **66:** 353-370.

TIGHE, T. J., and LOUISE S. TIGHE. 1966b. Overtraining and optional shift behaviour in rats and children. *J. Comp. Physiol. Psychol.*, **62**: 49-54.

TILLICH, T. E. 1963. *Systematic theology*, Vol. III. Chicago: Univ. Chicago Press.

TIMASHEFF, N. S. 1960. The attempt to abolish the family in Russia, in N. W. Bell and E. F. Vogel, eds., *The family*. Toronto: Macmillan.

TINBERGEN, N. 1939a. On the analysis of social organization among vertebrates, with special reference to birds. *Amer. Midland Naturalist*, **21**: 210-234.

———. 1939b. The behavior of the snow bunting in spring. *Trans. Linn. Soc., N.Y.*, **5**: 1-94.

———. 1942. An objectivistic study of the innate behavior of animals. *Bibl. Biol. Theoret.*, Leiden, **1**: 39-98.

———. 1951. *The study of instinct*. London: Oxford Univ. Press.

———. 1953. *Social behaviour in animals*. London: Methuen.

———, and A. C. PERDECK. 1950. On the stimulus situation releasing the billing response in the newly hatched herring-gull chick. *Behaviour*, **3**: 1-39.

TINKLEPAUGH, O. L., and C. G. HARTMAN. 1930. Behavioral aspects of parturition in the monkey, M. rhesus. *J. Comp. Psychol.*, **11**: 63-98.

TISDALL, W. J. 1962. Productive thinking in retarded children. *Except. Child.*, **29**: 36-41.

TOGATZ, G. E. 1967. Effects of strategy, sex and age on conceptual behavior of elementary school children. *J. Educ. Psychol.*, **58**: 103-109.

TOMPSON, H. B. 1903. *The mental traits of sex*. Chicago: Univ. Chicago Press.

TORKELSON, H. P., L. B. FISK, and C. W. BROWN. 1941. Some results from the use of a glare recovery apparatus with college students. *J. Appl. Psychol.*, **25**: 447.

TORRANCE, E. P. 1960. Sex role identification and creative thinking. Research memo. Ber 59-10. Minneapolis: Univ. Minnesota Press.

———. 1962a. Cultural discontinuities and the development of originality of thinking. *Except. Child.*, **29**: 2-13.

———. 1962b. *Guiding creative talent*. Englewood Cliffs, N.J.: Prentice-Hall.

TRANKELL, A. 1955. Aspects of genetics in psychology. *Amer. J. Hum. Genet.*, **7**: 264-276.

———. 1956. Penetrance calculus in population genetics. *Amer. J. Hum. Genet.*, **8**: 44-48.

TREADWELL, YVONNE. 1967. Bibliography of empirical studies of wit and humor. *Psychol. Rep.*, **20**: 1074-1083.

TRYON, R. C. 1940. Genetic differences in maze learning ability in rats. *39th Yearbook Nat. Soc. Stud. Educ.* Bloomington: Public School Pub. Co., **39**: 111-119.

———. 1944. The adolescent peer culture. *43rd Yearbook Nat. Soc. Stud. Educ.*, Bloomington: Public School Pub. Co., **43**: 217-239.

TSANG, YÜ-CHÜAN. 1934. The function of the visual areas of the cortex of the rat in the learning and retention of the maze. *Comp. Psychol. Monogr.*, **10**: 1-56.

TUDDENHAM, R. D. 1966. Jean Piaget and the world of the child. *Amer. Psychol.*, **21**: 207-217.

TULKIN, S. R., J. P. MULLER, and L. K. CONN. 1969. Need for approval and popularity: sex differences in elementary school students. *J. Consult. Clin. Psychol.*, **33**: 35-39.

TURKEWITZ, G., TINA MOREAU, and H. G. BIRCH. 1966. Head position and receptor organization in the human neonate. *J. Exp. Child Psychol.*, **4**: 169-177.

TYLER, LEONA E. 1956. *The psychology of human differences*, 2nd ed. New York: Appleton.

———. 1965. *The psychology of individual differences*, 3rd ed. New York: Appleton.

UDRY, J. R., and NAOMI M. MORRIS. 1968. Distribution of coitus in the menstrual cycle. *Nature*, **220**: 593-596.

VALENTINE, C. W. 1930. The innate bases of fear. *J. Genet. Psychol.*, **37**: 394-420.

———. 1942. *The psychology of early childhood*. London: Methuen.

VAN DE CASTLE, R. L. 1965. Development and validation of a perceptual maturity scale using figure preferences. *J. Consult. Psychol.*, **29**: 314-319.

VANDENBERG, S. G. 1962. The hereditary abilities study: hereditary components in a psychological test battery. *Amer. J. Hum. Genet.*, **14**: 220-237.

———. 1966. Contributions of twin research to psychology. *Psychol. Bull.*, **66**: 327-352.

———, R. E. STAFFORD, A. BROWN, and J. GRESHAM. 1966. The Louisville twin study. Research Report No. 15. Univ. Louisville Medical School Twin Study. Quoted in S. G. Vandenberg, 1966. Contributions of twin research to psychology. *Psychol. Bull.*, **66:** 327-352.

VAN LAWICK-GOODALL, JANE. 1965. New discoveries among Africa's chimpanzees. *Nat. Geogr.*, **128:** 802-831.

VAN MONDFRANS, A. P., and R. W. TRAVERS. 1964. Learning of redundant material presented through two sensory modalities. *Percept. Motor Skills*, **19:** 743-751.

VERNON, M. D. 1948. The development of imaginative construction in children. *Brit. J. Psychol.*, **39:** 102-111.

VEST, S. A., and J. E. HOWARD. 1939. Clinical experiments with the use of male sex hormones. I. Use of a testosterone propionate in hypogonadism. *J. Urol.*, **40:** 154-183.

VOGEL, W. 1961. The relationship of age and intelligence to autonomic functioning. *J. Comp. Physiol. Psychol.*, **54:** 133-138.

———, and D. M. BROVERMAN. 1964. Relationship between E.E.G. and test intelligence: a critical review. *Psychol. Bull.*, **62:** 132-144.

———, J. G. DRAGUNS, and E. L. KLAIBER. 1966. The role of glutamic acid in cognitive behaviors. *Psychol. Bull.*, **6:** 367-382.

VON BERTALANFFY, L. 1952. *Problems of life.* New York: Wiley.

VON FRISCH, K. 1955. *The dancing bees.* New York: Harcourt.

VON HOLST, E. 1962. Electrically controlled behavior. *Sci. Amer.*, **206**(3): 50-60.

———, and URSULA E. V. SAINT PAUL. 1963. On the functional organization of drives. *Anim. Behav.*, **11:** 1-20.

VON HUMBOLDT, W. 1836. *Über die Verschiedenheit des Menschichen Sprachbanes.* Berlin.

VON SENDEN, M. 1932. *Raum und Gestaltauffessung bei oprierten Blindgeborenen vor und nach der Operation.* Leipzig: Barth.

VON UEXKÜLL, J. J. 1934. *Baron von Streifzuge durch die Unwelten von Tieren und Menschen: ein Bilderbuch unsichtbarer Welten.* Berlin: Springer.

VYGOTSKY, L. S. 1962. *Thought and language.* Trans. from the Russian and ed. by E. Hanfmann and Gertrude Vakan. Cambridge, Mass.: M.I.T. Press.

WAELCH, H. 1955. *Biochemistry of the developing nervous system.* First Neurochemical Symp. New York: Academic Press.

WAHLER, R. G. 1969. Infant social development: Some experimental analyses of an infant-mother interaction during the first year of life. *J. Exp. Child Psychol.*, **7:** 101-113.

WALK, R. D. 1965. The study of visual depth and distance perception in animals, in D. S. Lehrman, ed., *Advances in the study of behavior,* Vol. I. New York: Academic Press.

———, and ELEANOR J. GIBSON. 1961. A comparative and analytical study of visual depth perception. *Psychol. Monogr.*, **75** (15): Whole No. 519.

WALKER, R. N. 1962. Body build and behavior in young children. I. Body build and nursery school teachers' ratings. *Monogr. Soc. Res. Child Develop.*, **27**(3): 84.

WALLACH, M. A., and N. KOGAN. 1965. *Modes of thinking in young children: a study of creativity-intelligence distinction.* New York: Holt, Rinehart and Winston.

WALLAS, G. 1926. *The art of thought.* New York: Harcourt.

WALLER, PATRICIA F., and M. B. WALLER. 1963. Some relationships between early experience and late social behaviour in ducklings. *Behaviour*, **20:** 343-363.

WALLIN, J. E. 1916. A consensus of speech defectives among 89,157 public school pupils. *School Society*, **3:** 213-216.

WALLS, G. 1934a. The reptilian retina. I. A new concept of visual cell evolution. *Amer. J. Ophthalmol.*, **17:** 892-899.

———. 1934b. The significance of the reptilian Specticle. *Amer. J. Ophthalmol.*, **17:** 1045-1047.

WALSH, F. B. 1957. *Clinical neuro-ophthalmology,* 2nd ed. Baltimore: Williams & Wilkins.

WALTERS, CATHRYN, J. T. SHURLEY, and O. A. PARSONS. 1962. Differences in male and female responses to underwater sensory deprivation: an exploratory study. *J. Nerv. Ment. Dis.*, **135:** 302-310.

WAPNER, S., and H. WERNER, eds., 1965. *The body percept.* New York: Random House.

———, and MALLIPI LACIO. 1960. Perception of part-whole relationships in middle and old age. *J. Geront.*, **15:** 412-416.

WARD, W. C. 1968. Creativity in young children. *Child Develop.*, **39:** 737-754.

WARDLE, C. J. 1961. Two generations of broken homes in the genesis of conduct and behaviour disorders in childhood. *Brit. Med. J.*, **2**: 349-354.

WARNER, SILAS L., and L. J. SAUL. 1961. Evidence for the effects of child rearing on personality development, in *Proceedings of the 3rd World Congress of Psychiatry, Montreal and Toronto, 1961*. Toronto: Univ. Toronto Press and Montreal: McGill Univ. Press, 727-730.

WARREN, J. R. 1966. Birth order and social behavior. *Psychol. Bull.*, **65**: 38-49.

WARREN, R. M., C. J. OBUSEK, R. M. FARMER, and ROSLYN P. WARREN. 1969. Auditory sequence: a confusion of patterns other than speech or music. *Science*, **164**: 586-587.

WATERS, R. H., D. A. RETHINGHAFER, and W. E. CALDWELL. 1960. *Principles of comparative psychology*. New York: McGraw-Hill.

WATSON, J. B. 1925. *Behaviorism*. New York: Norton.

———. 1928. *Psychological care of the infant and child*. New York: Norton.

———, and J. J. B. MORGAN. 1917. Emotional reactions and psychological experimentation. *Amer. J. Psychol.*, **28**: 163-174.

WATSON, J. D., and F. H. C. CRICK. 1953. *Nature*, **171**: 737.

WATTENBERG, W. W., and CLARE CLIFFORD. 1964. Relation of self-concepts to beginning achievement in reading. *Child Develop.*, **35**: 461-467.

WATTS, A. 1966. *The book*. New York: Pantheon.

WAXENBERG, S. E., M. G. DRELLICH, and A. M. SUTHERLAND. 1959. The role of hormones, in A. M. Land, ed., *The role of hormones in human behavior. I. Changes in female sexuality after adrenalectomy. J. Clin. Endocrinol.*, **19**: 193-202.

WECHSLER, D. 1958. *The measurement and appraisal of adult intelligence*, 4th ed. Baltimore: Williams & Wilkins.

WEIDMAN, R., and U. WEIDMAN. 1958. An analysis of the stimulus situation releasing food begging in the Black-headed Gull. *Animal Behavior*, **6**: 114

WEIKART, D. P. 1967. Preliminary results from a longitudinal study of disadvantaged preschool children. Paper presented at the Convention of the Council for Exceptional Children, St. Louis, Mo.

———, CONSTANCE K. KAMII, and N. RADIN. 1964. *Perry pre-school project progress report*. Ypsilanti, Mich., Public Schools.

WEIL, A. 1943. The chemical growth of the brain of the white rat and its relation to sex. *Growth*, **7**: 257.

———. 1944. The influence of sex hormones upon the chemical growth of the brain of white rats. *Growth*, **8**: 107-115.

———, and E. LAMBERT. 1943. The correlation between sex and chemical constitution of the human brain. *Quart. Bull. Northwestern Univ. Med. School*, **17**: 117-120.

WEILAND, I. H., and R. RUDNICK. 1961. Consideration of the development and treatment of autistic childhood psychosis. *Psychoanal. Stud. Child.*, **16**: 555-556.

WEININGER, O. 1956. The effects of early experience on behavior and growth characteristics. *J. Comp. Physiol. Psychol.*, **49**: 1-9.

WEINSTEIN, S., and EUGENE A. SERSEN. 1961. Phantoms in cases of congenital absence of limbs. *Neurology*, **11**: 905-911.

———, and R. T. VETTER. 1964. Phantoms and somatic sensations in cases of congenital aplasia. *Cortex*, **1**: 276-290.

WEISBERG, P. 1969. Operant procedures for the establishment of stimulus control in two-year-old infants. *J. Exp. Child Psychol.*, **7**: 81-95.

WEISBERG, P. S., and KAYLA J. SPRINGER. Environmental factors in creative function: a study of gifted children. *Arch. Gen. Psychiat.*, **5**: 554-564.

WEISS, D. A. 1967. Central language imbalance (cluttering): a basic problem of the pathology of communication. *Amer. J. Orthopsychiat.*, **37**: 369-370.

WEISS, JAY M., B. S. MCEWEN, TERESA A. SILVA, and M. P. KALKUT. 1969. Pituitary-adrenal influences on fear responding. *Science*, **163**: 197-199.

WEISS, P. 1941. Autonomous versus reflexogenous activity of the central nervous system. *Proc. Amer. Phil. Soc.*, **84**: 53-64.

WELCH, L. 1940. A preliminary investigation of some aspects of the hierarchical development of concepts. *J. Genet. Psychol.*, **22**: 359-378.

WELKER, W. I. 1956a. Some determinants of play and exploration in chimpanzees. *J. Comp. Physiol. Psychol.*, **49**: 84-89.

———. 1956b. Variability of play and exploratory behavior in chimpanzees. *J. Comp. Physiol. Psychol.*, **49**: 181-185.

———. 1961. An analysis of exploratory and play behavior in animals, in D. W. Fiske and S. R.

Maddi, eds., *Functions of varied experience.* Homewood, Ill.: Dorsey.

WELLER, G. M., and R. Q. BELL. 1965. Basal skin conductance and neonatal state. *Child Develop.,* **36:** 647-651.

WELLER, L. 1962. The relationship of birth order to anxiety: a replication of the Schachter findings. *Sociometry,* **25:** 415-417.

WENAR, C., M. W. HANDLON, and A. M. GARNER. 1962. *Origins of psychosomatic and emotional disturbances.* New York: Hoeber.

WENNER, A. M., P. H. WELLS, and D. L. JOHNSON. 1969. Honey bee recruitment to food sources: olfaction or language? *Science,* **164:** 84-86.

WERNER, H. 1946. The concept of rigidity: a critical evaluation. *Psychol. Rev.,* **53:** 43-52.

———. 1948. *Comparative psychology of mental development,* rev. ed. Chicago: Follett.

———. 1957. *Comparative psychology of mental development,* rev. ed. New York: International Univ. Press.

WERTHEIMER, M. 1961. Psychomotor co-ordination of auditory and visual space at birth. *Amer. J. Psychol.,* **134:** 1692.

WEST, R., ed. 1931. A symposium on stuttering (stammering). Madison: Univ. Wisconsin, ms.

WHETNALL, EDITH. 1958. The deaf child, in D. Gairdner, ed., *Recent advances in paediatrics,* 2nd ed. London: Churchill.

WHIMBEY, A. E., and V. H. DENENBERG. 1966. Programming of life histories: creating individual differences by the experimental control of early experiences. *Multivariate Behav. Res.,* **1:** 279-286.

WHITE, B. L., and P. W. CASTLE. 1964. Visual exploratory behavior following postnatal handling of human infants. *Percept. Motor Skills,* **18:** 497-502.

WHITE HOUSE CONFERENCE ON CHILD HEALTH AND PROTECTION. 1933. *Growth and development of the child.* II. New York: Century.

WHITE, L. L. 1950. *The next development in man.* New York: New American Library.

WHITE, R. W. 1960. Competence and the psychosexual stages of development, in *Nebraska Symposium on Motivation.* Lincoln: Univ. Nebraska Press.

WHITE, S. H. 1965. Evidence for a hierarchical arrangement of learning processes, in L. P. Lipsitt and C. C. Spiker, eds., *Advances in child development and behavior,* Vol. II. New York: Academic Press.

WHITE, W. F., H. E. ANDERSON, and H. CRYDER. 1966. Allport's theory of emerging self-concept applied to secondary school students. *Proceedings of the 74th Annual Convention of the American Psychiatric Association.* **1:** 277-278.

———. 1967. The emerging self-concept in relation to selected variables of secondary school students. *J. Soc. Psychol.,* **72:** 81-88.

WHITEMAN, M. 1967. Children's conceptions of psychological causality. *Child Develop.,* **38:** 143-155.

WHITING, BEATRICE B., ed., 1963. *Six cultures: studies of child rearing.* New York: Wiley.

WHITING, G. W. M., and I. L. CHILD. 1953. *A cross-cultural study: Child training and personality.* New Haven: Yale Univ. Press.

WHITING, G. W. M., and BEATRICE B. WHITING. 1960. Contributions of anthropology to the methods of studying child rearing, in P. H. Mussen, ed., *Handbook of Research Methods in Child Development.* New York: Wiley.

WHORF, B. L. 1956. *Language, thought and reality.* New York: Wiley.

WICKLER, W. 1967. Socio-sexual signals and their intra-specific imitation among primates, in D. Morris, ed., *Primate ethology.* Chicago: Aldine.

WIENER, S., G. SUTHERLAND, A. A. BARTHOLOMEW, and B. HUDSON. 1968. XYY males in a Melbourne prison. *Lancet,* **1:** 150.

WIESEL, T. N., and D. H. HUBEL. 1963. Single-cell responses in striate cortex of kittens deprived of vision in one eye. *J. Neurophysiol.,* **26:** 1003-1017.

WIGGAM, A. E. 1923. *The new decalogue of science.* Indianapolis: Bobbs-Merrill.

WIGGLESWORTH, W. B. 1953. *Principles of insect physiology.* London: Methuen.

WILCOX, BARBARA M. 1969. Visual preferences of human infants for representation of the human face. *J. Exp. Child Psychol.,* **7:** 10-20.

———, and FRANCES L. CLAYTON. 1968. Infant visual fixation on motion pictures of the human face. *J. Exp. Child Psychol.,* **6:** 22-32.

WILE, I. S. 1942. Eye dominance: its nature and treatment. *Arch. Ophthalmol.,* **28:** 780-791.

WILLIAMS, R. J. 1946. *The human frontier.* New York: Harcourt.

———. 1956. *Biochemical individuality.* New York: Wiley.

———, R. B. PELTON, and F. L. SIEGEL. 1962. *Individuality as exhibited by inbred animals:*

its implication for human behavior. Paper read at Annual Meeting, National Academy of Sciences, Washington, D. C. *Science*, **136**: 330 (abstract).

WILSON, D. M. 1968. The flight control system of the locust. *Sci. Amer.*, **218**(5): 83-93.

WILSON, J. G., and W. C. YOUNG. 1941. Sensitivity to estrogen studied by means of experimentally induced mating responses in the female guinea pig and rat. *Endocrinology*, **29**: 779-783.

WILSON, M., J. M. WARREN, and L. ABBOTT. 1965. Infantile stimulation, activity and learning by cats. *Child Develop.*, **36**: 843-853.

WILSON, M., and W. A. WILSON. 1962. Intersensory facilitation of learning sets in normal and brain operated monkeys. *J. Comp. Physiol. Psychol.*, **55**: 931-934.

WILSON, W. A., and O. C. SHAFFER. 1963. Intermodality transfer of specific discriminations in the monkey. *Nature*, **197**: 107.

WILT, MIRIAM E. 1959. *Creativity in the elementary school*. New York: Appleton.

WINCOUR, C. G. 1965. Imprinting. Unpublished paper.

WINITZ, H. 1960. Spectrographic investigation of infant vowels. *J. Genet. Psychol.*, **96**: 171-181.

WINSTON, H. D. 1963. Influence of genotype and infantile trauma on adult learning in the mouse. *J. Comp. Physiol. Psychol.*, **56**: 630-635.

WITKIN, H. A. 1950. Individual differences in ease of perception of embedded figures. *J. Pers.* **19**: 1-15.

————. 1967. A cognitive-style approach to cross-cultural research. *Int. J. Psychol.*, **2**: 233-250.

————, RUTH B. DYKE, HANNA FATERSON, D. R. GOODENOUGH, and S. A. KARP. 1962. *Psychological differentiation: Studies of development*. New York: Wiley.

WITKIN, H. A., H. F. FATERSON, D. R. GOODENOUGH, and JUDITH BIRNBAUM. 1966. Cognitive patterning in mildly retarded boys. *Child Develop.*, **37**: 301-315.

WITKIN, H. A., H. B. LEWIS, M. HIRTZMAN, K. MACHOVER, P. B. MEISSNER, and S. WAPNER. 1954. *Personality through perception*. New York: Harper.

WITTY, P., and R. A. SIZEMORE. 1955. Phonics in the reading program: a review and an evaluation. *Elem. English*, **32**: 355-371.

WOHLWILL, J. F. 1960. Developmental studies of perception. *Psychol. Bull.*, **57**: 249-288.

————. 1962. From perception to inference: a dimension of cognitive development. *Monogr. Soc. Res. Child Develop.*, **27**(2): 87-107.

————. 1964. Development and measurement, in R. E. Ripple and V. N. Rockcastle, eds., *Piaget rediscovered: a report of the conference on cognitive studies and curriculum development*. Ithaca: School of Education, Cornell Univ.

————, and R. LOWE. 1962. Experimental analysis of the conservation of number. *Child Develop.*, **33**: 153-167.

WOLFENSTEIN, MARTHA. 1951. The emergence of fun morality. *J. Sociol. Issues*, **7**: 15-25.

WOLFF, J. L. 1967. Concept-shift and discrimination reversal learning in humans. *Psychol. Bull.*, **68**: 369-408.

WOLFF, P. 1963. Observations on the early development of smiling, in B. M. Foss, ed., *Determinants of infant behavior*. II. London: Methuen.

WOO, T. L., and K. PEARSON. 1927. Dextrality and sinistrality of hand and eye. *Biometrika*, **19**: 165-199.

WOODS, F. A. 1906. *Mental and moral heredity in royalty*. New York: Holt.

WOODWARD, M. 1961. Concepts of number of the mentally subnormal studied by Piaget's method. *J. Child Psychol. Psychiat.*, **2**: 249-259.

WOODWORTH, R. S. 1938. *Experimental psychology*. New York: Holt.

WOOLLEY, H. T. 1910. A review of the recent literature in the psychology of sex. *Psychol. Bull.*, **7**: 335-342.

————. 1914. General review and summaries: the psychology of sex. *Psychol. Bull.*, **11**: 353-379.

WORLD HEALTH ORGANIZATION. 1966. Technical report series No. 346. *Research on genetics in psychiatry*. Geneva: W.H.O.

WRIGHT, B., and SHIRLEY TUSKA. 1966. The nature and origin of feeling feminine. *Brit. J. Soc. Clin. Psychol.*, **5**: 140-149.

WRIGHT, J. C. 1969. Personal communication.

WRIGHT, M. J. 1956. *Sex differences in children: mental ability and certain types of behavior problems and personality disorders*. Report series, memo. No. 2 Mental Health Div., Dept. Nat. Hlth. and Welfare, Ottawa, March.

WYATT, RUTH F. 1945. Improvability of pitch discrimination. *Psychol. Monogr.*, **58**: Whole No. 2.

WYLIE, RUTH C. 1961. *The self concept: a critical*

survey of pertinent research literature. Lincoln: Univ. Nebraska Press.

YARROW, L. J. 1961. Maternal deprivation: toward an empirical and conceptual re-evaluation. *Psychol. Bull.,* **58:** 459-490.

YERKES, R. M. 1935. A second-generation captive-born chimpanzee. *Science,* 81: 542-543.

———, and D. BLOOMFIELD. 1910. Do kittens instinctively kill mice? *Psychol. Bull.,* 7: 253-263.

YERKES, R. M., and J. H. ELDER. 1936. Oestrus, receptivity and mating in the chimpanzee. *Comp. Psychol. Monogr.,* 13: 1-39.

———. 1937. Concerning reproduction in the chimpanzee. *Yale J. Biol. Med.,* 10: 41-48.

YERKES, R. M., and M. I. TOMILIN. 1935. Mother-infant relations in chimpanzee. *J. Comp. Psychol.,* **20:** 321-359.

YOUNG, H. H. 1937. *Genital abnormalities, hermaphroditism and related adrenal diseases.* Paris: Baillière.

YOUNG, P. T. 1961. *Motivation and emotion.* New York: Wiley.

YOUNG, W. C. 1961. The hormones and mating behavior, in W. C. Young, ed., *Sex and internal secretions,* 3rd ed., Vol. II. Baltimore: Williams & Wilkins.

———, R. W. GOY, and C. H. PHOENIX. 1964. Hormones and sexual behavior. *Science,* **143:** 212-218.

YOUNG, W. C., and W. D. ORBISON. 1944. Changes in features of behavior of chimpanzees during sexual cycle. *J. Comp. Psychol.,* **37:** 107-143.

YOUNG, W. C., and R. R. PETERSON. 1952. Reproductive performance in extremely hyperthyroid male guinea pigs. *Endocrinology,* **51:** 344-345.

ZANGWILL, O. L. 1960. *Cerebral dominance and its relation to psychological function.* Edinburgh: W. R. Henderson Trust (Oliver & Boyd).

ZAPOROZHETS, A. V. 1961. The origin and development of the conscious control of movements in man, in N. O'Connor, ed., *Recent soviet psychology.* New York: Liveright.

———. 1965. The development of perception in the preschool child, in European research in cognitive development. *Monogr. Soc. Res. Child Develop.,* 30(2): 82-101.

———, and V. P. ZINCHENKO. 1966. Development of perceptual activity and formation of a sensory image in the child, in *Psychological research in the U.S.S.R.,* Vol. I. Moscow: Progress.

ZEILER, M. D. 1964. Component and configurational learning in children. *J. Exp. Psychol.,* **68:** 292-296.

ZELLER, E. A. 1967. Personal communication to E. L. Klaiher.

ZELLER, W. 1936. *Der erste Gestaltwandel des Kindes.* (The first Gestalt transformations of the child.) Leipzig: Barth.

ZETTERSTRÖM, B. 1951. The clinical electroretinogram (IV). The electroretinogram in children during the first year of life. *Acta Ophthal. Kobenhavn,* 29: 295-304.

ZIELINSKI, K. 1960. Studies on higher nervous activity in chickens. II. The effect of sex on conditioned excitatory and inhibitory elementary reflexes. *Acta Biol. Exp.,* Warsaw, **20:** 79-90.

ZIGLER, E. F. 1963. Metatheoretical issues in developmental psychology, in M. H. Marx, ed., *Theories in contemporary psychology.* New York: Macmillan.

———, J. LEVINE, and L. GOULD. 1966. The humor response of normal institutionalized retarded and non-institutionalized retarded children. *Amer. J. Ment. Defic.,* **71:** 472-480.

———. 1967. Cognitive challenge as a factor in children's humor appreciation. *J. Pers. Soc. Psychol.,* **6:** 332-336.

ZONDEK, B., and I. TAMARI. 1960. Effect of audiogenic stimulation on genital function and reproduction. *Amer. J. Obstet. Gynecol.,* **80:** 1941-1948.

ZUCKERMAN, S. 1932. *The social life of monkeys and apes.* London: Kegan Paul.

Author Index

Bartley, S. H., 306, 507
Barton, W. H., 89, 527
Battle, Esther S., 327, 507
Bauer, J. A., 222-223, 525
Baum, M. J., 159, 507
Baumrind, Diana, 447, 507
Baxter, J. C., 418, 507
Bayer, E., 322, 507
Bayley, Nancy, 90-91, 143, 198, 251, 350, 507-508, 529, 546
Beach, F. A., 71, 155, 167, 175, 181, 191, 217, 508, 518, 529
Bean, L., 515
Beaton, L. E., 530
Beatty, R. T., 339, 508
Bechterev, V. M., 317, 508
Beck, E. C., 258, 516
Beck, L. F., 258, 529
Becker, W. C., 508
Beecher, H. K., 296, 508
Beery, Judith W., 286, 508
Beethoven, Ludwig van, 380, 403
Beilin, H., 369, 508
Bell, R. Q., 189, 192, 196, 508, 556
Bellugi, V., 511, 519
Belmont, Lillian, 286, 509
Beloff, J. R., 512
Bender, M. B., 251, 518
Benedict, Ruth, 427-428, 508
Bennett, E. L., 112-113, 218, 508, 531, 545
Bennett, O. K., 195, 508
Bentler, P. M., 522
Bentzen, Frances, 203, 508
Bereiter, C., 196, 508
Berlyne, D. E., 227, 291, 314, 508
Berman, A. J., 551
Berman, Phyllis, 508
Bernard, G., 277, 508
Berner, D. E., 114, 508
Berner, G. E., 114, 508
Bernstein, L., 263, 521
Berry, J. W., 374, 508
Bertalanffy, L. von, 335, 554
Bettelheim, Bruno, 415, 508
Bever, T. G., 365, 509, 537
Bexton, W. A., 464, 509
Bidney, D., 459, 509
Bierens de Haan, J. A., 329-330, 509
Bieri, J., 196, 208, 509
Biller, H. B., 423, 508
Bindra, D., 318, 321, 324, 509, 552
Bingham, W. E., 136, 509
Birch, H. G., 15, 284-286, 292, 509, 552-553
Birnbaum, Judith, 557
Bitterman, M. E., 96, 238, 509-510

Black, A. E., 447, 507
Blandau, R. J., 509
Blank, Marion, 401, 509
Blauvelt, H., 155, 509
Blewett, D. B., 509, 512
Bloomfield, D., 134, 558
Blum, A., 511
Blundell, J. E., 107, 115, 509
Blurton Jones, N. G., 55, 509
Boas, Franz, 355-356, 509
Boling, J. L., 509
Bolwig, N., 188, 509
Book, Hannah M., 190-191, 200, 509
Borstelman, L. J., 423, 509
Boss, W. R., 509
Boston, Mary, 510
Botkin, P. T., 518
Bouquet, A. C., 13, 509
Bousfield, W. I., 307-309, 509
Bouterline Young, H., 90, 509
Bovard, E. W., 218-219, 509
Bower, T. G. R., 261, 263-264, 300-301, 352, 509-510
Bowlby, J., 140, 142-143, 153-154, 157, 211-214, 472, 510
Bowles, J. W., 38, 510
Brachman, H. M., 208, 513
Brackbill, Yvonne, 236, 279, 510
Bradburn, Wendy M., 509
Bradley, N. C., 510
Bradway, Catherine P., 510
Brain, Russell, 102, 510
Braine, M. D. S., 193, 510
Brand, C. R., 507
Brand, Florence C., 550
Brandkamp, W. W., 538
Brazier, M. A. B., 338, 510
Bremer, J., 165, 510
Bressler, D. E., 96, 510
Brian, C. R., 510
Bridger, W. H., 509
Bridges, K. M. B., 307, 510
Bridgman, C. S., 528
Broadbent, D. E., 290, 510
Brodbeck, A. J., 157, 408, 510
Brodie, B. B., 372, 510
Brofenbrenner, U., 411-412, 451, 510
Bronson, G., 98, 117-122, 130-132, 140, 143, 197, 228, 249-252, 308, 314, 321, 510
Bronson, Wanda C., 203, 510
Brooks, R. M., 263, 510
Broom, L., 207, 510
Broverman, D. M., 89-90, 370-373, 376-378, 510-511, 530-531, 554
Broverman, I. K., 511
Brown, Anne M., 35, 511, 553-554

Brown, C. W., 553
Brown, D. G., 511, 546
Brown, J. S., 511
Brown, K. B., 541
Brown, M. H., 199, 511
Brown, R. W., 330, 332, 334, 336, 511, 519
Bruce, H. M., 541
Brügger, M., 526
Bruin, K., 541
Brun, R., 511
Bruner, J. S., 233, 247, 292, 301, 346, 351-356, 367-368, 380, 401, 486, 511
Brunswick, E., 263, 511
Bryan, G. Elizabeth, 199, 511
Buchanan, D. N., 507
Bucy, P. C., 507, 523
Budoff, M., 283, 510
Bugental, J. F. T., 511
Bühler, Charlotte, 121, 511
Bullock, T. H., 17, 511
Burchinal, L. G., 520
Burghardt, G. M., 147, 511
Burke, R. J., 202, 511, 536
Burks, B. S., 44, 511
Burney, Fanny, 347
Burt, C., 28, 36-37, 115, 189, 489, 511
Burton, D., 511-512
Burton, R. V., 412, 512
Butler, R. A., 314, 512

Calden, G., 534
Caldwell, W. E., 555
Campbell, B. A., 512
Candland, D. K., 512
Canelli, P. E., 512
Cannon, W. B., 309, 512
Cantor, T. N., 269, 537
Capra, P. C., 454, 512
Carlson, E. R., 512
Carlson, R., 512
Carmichael, L., 280, 512, 528
Carr, A., 543
Carr, H., 272, 512
Carrigan, W. C., 455, 512
Carroll, J. B., 340-341, 512
Carter, A. C., 512
Carter, H. B., 416, 512
Carterette, E. C., 283-284, 512
Cartledge, Connie J., 396, 512
Casper, Myra, 516
Cassen, D., 512
Castelli, C., 525-526
Castle, P. W., 288, 556
Cattell, Psyche, 512
Cattell, R. B., 28, 394, 512

Howard, K. I., 523
Hubby, J. L., 43, 533
Hubel, D. H., 225, 266, 274-275, 291, 303, 527, 556
Hudson, B., 556
Huizinga, J., 441, 527
Humboldt, W. von, 333, 554
Hunt, D. E., 525
Hunt, E. E., 89, 527
Hunt, J. McV., 227-228, 233, 245, 311, 387, 401, 527-528
Hunter, I. M. L., 275, 528
Hurley, W. P., 507
Hurlock, Elizabeth B., 317, 323, 326, 528
Hurst, C. C., 37-39, 528
Huston, Aletha C., 417, 422-423, 507
Hutt, Corinne, 68, 216, 224, 528
Hutt, S. J., 528
Huxley, Julian, 4, 22, 456-457, 497, 528
Huxley, Thomas H., 4
Hymovitch, B., 136, 528

Ibbolt, F., 527
Ilg, Frances, 506, 520
Imanishi, Kinji, 126-127, 528
Ingram, V. M., 528
Inhelder, Bärbel, 365-366, 380, 528, 542
Inman, O., 519
Irion, A. L., 283, 535
Itani, J., 188, 528

Jackson, P. W., 381-382, 387-388, 395, 397, 520-521
Jacob, F., 528
Jacobs, Patricia A., 535
Jacobsen, C. F., 112, 528
Jacobson, Edith, 412-413, 528
Jacobson, Lenore F., 99, 132, 402, 545
Jacobson, M., 520, 528
Jacques, L. B., 538
Jaensch, E. R., 380, 528
Jahoda, G., 528
James, Suzanne T., 512
James, William, 125, 128-129, 243, 248, 266, 477, 502, 528
Jarvik, Lissy F., 36-37, 517, 546
Jarvis, P. E., 518
Jasper, H. H., 99, 250, 528, 548
Jay, P., 188, 528
Jaynes, J., 128, 136, 155, 217, 508, 528
Jeffrey, W. E., 528, 531
Jersild, A. T., 121, 477, 528-529

Johnson, Beth, 258, 529
Johnson, D. L., 556
Johnson, D. M., 529
Johnson, Miriam M., 408, 472, 529
Johnson, R. C., 529
Johnson, R. W., 164, 176, 521
Johnson, T., 112, 524
Johnson, Virginia E., 173, 536
Jones, H. E., 38, 91, 206, 301, 513, 529
Jones, Margaret H., 283-284, 512, 514
Jones, Mary C., 91, 143, 301, 468, 529
Jonsson, G., 473-475, 529
Josey, C. C., 196, 529
Joss, Etienne, 529
Josso, Nathalie, 40, 529
Jouvet, M., 525
Julian, J. W., 455, 512
Jung, R., 120, 529

Kagan, J., 181, 269, 271, 284, 373, 378, 408, 412, 453, 475, 529, 533, 535
Kakolewski, J. W., 513
Kalafat, J., 533
Kalkut, M. P., 555
Kamii, Constance K., 555
Kanner, L., 225, 529
Kappas, Katherine H., 476, 529
Karas, G. G., 217, 224, 514-515, 529
Karas, S. S., 533
Karlsson, H., 508
Karnaby, K. J., 175, 529
Karp, S. A., 557
Katz, D., 262, 291, 426, 529-530
Katz, H., 531
Katz, Phyllis A., 286, 530
Kawamura, Syunze, 426-427, 530
Kaye, S. M., 149, 530
Kelleher, R. T., 248, 530
Kellner, H. N., 544
Kellogg, W. N., 330, 344, 530
Kelly, A. H., 107, 530
Kendler, H. H., 245-249, 251, 399, 530
Kendler, T. S., 245-249, 251, 399, 530
Kennard, M. A., 99, 530
Keppel, G., 247, 530
Kessen, W., 358, 524, 530
Kidd, D., 436, 530
Kimble, G. A., 237, 530
Kimmel, E., 192, 530
Kimmel, H. D., 192, 530
Kimura, Doreen, 115, 194, 530
Kinch, R. A. H., 548
Kinder, E. F., 540

King, C. D., 7-8, 530
King, J. A., 519
King, S. H., 519
Kinkle, E. C., 513
Kinsey, Alfred C., 173-174, 176, 181, 530
Kipnis, D., 513
Kirkpatrick, E. A., 384-385, 530
Kistyakovskaya, M. Yu., 153, 215, 530
Kitay, J. I., 159, 530
Klackenberg, G., 213, 530
Klaiber, E. L., 93, 371-372, 510, 530-531, 554
Klaus, R. A., 523
Klein, G. S., 370, 531
Klein, J. F., 332, 513
Kleitman, N., 531
Klineberg, O., 312, 531
Klopfer, P. H., 18, 148, 300, 531
Kluppel, D. D., 528, 531
Klüver, H., 380, 531
Knight, R. P., 409, 531
Kobayski, Y., 530-531
Koch, H. L., 453-454, 531
Koch, J., 531
Koegler, R. R., 516
Koff, Elissa B., 545
Koffka, K., 243, 263, 531
Koffler, S., 262, 551-552
Kogan, N., 381-382, 388-391, 396, 554
Kohlberg, L., 423, 531
Köhler, W., 295, 344, 531
Kohn, M., 453, 531
Kolb, L. C., 543
Kolodny, May, 247, 546
Kooistra, W. H., 365, 531
Koppenaal, R. J., 247, 531
Kostick, M. M., 200, 531
Kovach, J. K., 149-150, 531
Krauser, E. L., 396, 512
Krauss, P., 521
Krauss, R. M., 332, 531
Krech, D. R., 112-113, 218, 508, 531, 545
Kretschmer, E., 85, 531
Kris, E., 385, 390, 531
Krug, R. S., 508
Krull, A., 531
Kubie, L. S., 385, 395-396, 531
Kubzansky, P. E., 513
Kuenne, M. R., 399, 531
Kuhlman, Clementia, 299, 380, 531
Kun, H., 532
Kuo, Z. Y., 128, 532
Kurke, M. I., 544
Kutner, B., 532
Kvale, J. N., 39, 532

Labriola, J., 155, 532
Lacio, Mallipi, 554
Lack, D., 76, 169, 532
Lair, W. S., 413, 532
Lambert, E., 555
Landauer, T. K., 101, 217, 532
Landmark, Margrete, 532
Lang, T., 454, 532
Langham, W. H., 189, 506
Langworthy, O. R., 96, 532
Lanman, J., 309, 534
Lansdell, H., 194-195, 532
Lashley, K. S., 130, 234, 265, 532
Laszlo, I. J., 549
Laughlin, P. R., 386, 532
Laurendeau, Monique, 366, 532
Lawick-Goodall, Jane van, 188, 215, 443, 554
Lazarus, R. S., 370-371, 510
Lazuwick, L. M., 409, 413, 420, 422, 532
Leacock, Stephen, 476-477
Learnard, B., 530
Leeper, R. W., 292, 305, 307, 320-321, 532
Lefford, A., 284-285, 292, 509
Legerski, A., 545
Le Gross Clark, W. E., 96-97, 532
Lehninger, A. L., 532
Lehrman, D. S., 50, 168, 455, 532-533
Le Magnen, J., 195, 533
Lemkin, J., 529
Lenard, H. G., 528
Lenneberg, E. H., 105-107, 123, 330, 333-339, 341-342, 344-346, 352, 356, 533
Lennox, B., 40, 533
Lerner, I. M., 23, 533
Lester, D., 197, 533
Levene, H. I., 533
Levin, H. I., 323, 533, 548
Levine, Janet, 529, 558
Levine, S., 131, 135, 138, 192-193, 219, 223-224, 226, 311-312, 407, 533
Lévy-Bruhl, Lucien, 355, 533
Lewis, D. G., 37, 533
Lewis, G. W., 219, 533
Lewis, H. B., 557
Lewis, M., 190, 198, 290, 521, 529, 533
Lewontin, R. C., 43, 533
Leythan, G. W. H., 514
Lightall, F. F., 546
Ligon, E. M., 384, 533
Lilly, J. C., 330, 533
Lincoln, Abraham, 503

Lindholm, B. W., 533
Lindley, R. H., 526
Lindzey, G., 223, 445, 533
Lintz, L. M., 510
Lipsitt, L. P., 318, 533-534
Lipton, R. C., 227, 543
Lisk, R. D., 169, 534
Liss, P., 248, 522
Little, K., 435, 534
Livingston, W. K., 296, 534
Livson, N., 90, 534, 536
Locke, N. M., 263, 534
Lodge, Ann, 534
Loevinger, Jane, 354
London, I., 274, 534
Long, Barbara H., 534
Long, D. H., 197, 546
Long, L., 534
Lopez, S. P., 457-458, 534
Lorenz, Konrad Z., 46, 52-53, 61, 64-65, 67, 71-73, 76-77, 134, 137, 146-149, 155-156, 414, 534
Loughlin, L., 539
Louttit, C. M., 207, 534
Lovell, K., 365, 534
Lowe, R., 369, 557
Lowell, E. L., 535
Lowry, R. W., 385
Lubar, J. F., 107, 534
Ludwig, D. J., 534
Luff, M. C., 535
Lundy, R. M., 534
Lunneborg, Patricia W., 453, 534
Luria, A. R., 248, 344, 399, 534-535
Lynn, D. B., 417, 535
Lynn, R., 535

Maas, H. S., 222, 535
MacArthur, R. S., 389, 540
McCall, R. B., 269, 535
McCance, R. A., 535
McCarthy, Dorothea A., 194, 330, 332, 341, 535
McClearn, G. E., 23, 43, 535
McClelland, D. C., 315, 323, 535
McClelland, W. J., 135, 535
Maccoby, Eleanor E., 322, 521, 535 548
McCord, Joan, 474, 535
McCord, W., 535
McDermott, E., 548
MacDonald, G. E., 149, 535
McDougall, William, 22, 55, 59-60, 80-81, 233, 315, 328, 427, 477, 535
McEwen, B. S., 555
McFarland, W. J., 535

McFie, J., 114-115, 535
McGeoch, T. A., 242, 283, 535
McGraw, Myrtle B., 141, 535
Machover, K., 557
Machover, S., 540
McInnes, R. G., 514
Mackenberg, E. J., 522
MacKinnon, D. W., 386-387, 392-396, 535
McKissock, W., 114, 522
MacLean, N., 40, 535
MacLean, P. D., 170-171, 536
MacMeeken, A. M., 536
McMichael, R. E., 536
McMillan, Margaret, 383, 536
McMurray, G. A., 297, 536, 538
MacMurray, J., 481, 536
MacNamara, J., 342, 536
McNeil, J. D., 204, 536
McNeill, D., 90, 332, 334, 339, 346, 534, 536
MacNeill, M., 113, 536
McNiven, M. A., 65, 536
Maddock, W. O., 525
Maehr, M. L., 534
Magoun, H. W., 530
Maier, N. R. F., 201-202, 527, 536
Malinowski, Bronislaw, 436-437, 452, 536
Malmo, R. B., 311, 320, 536
Mamiya, Takeshi, 536
Mann, J. C., 260, 536
Manosevitz, M., 533
Mantle, D. J., 535
Markey, F. V., 384, 536
Markkanen, T., 541
Markowitz, H., 218, 551
Marler, P., 232, 536
Marouis, D. G., 110, 536
Marston, M. V., 137-138, 140, 547
Martin, C. E., 530
Maslow, A. H., 206, 317, 324, 390, 465, 480, 500-503, 536
Mason, W. A., 314, 536
Masters, W. H., 173, 536
Mathewson, Suzanne, 372, 536
Matter, Jean, 511
Matyniak, K. A., 96, 551
Maurer, Adah B., 478, 536
Mead, Margaret, 174, 206, 209, 212, 216, 427-429, 436-438, 452, 536-537
Meadows, Kathryn P., 345, 347, 537
Mearns, H., 384, 537
Medawar, P. B., 12, 22, 537
Mednick, S. A., 386, 537, 548
Meer, B., 388, 537

Pease, D., 520
Pechstein, L. A., 234, 541
Peiper, A., 260, 277, 541
Pelton, R. B., 556-557
Penfield, W., 101-103, 105-110, 114, 240, 462, 541
Penney, R. K., 319, 541
Perachio, A. A., 534
Perdeck, A. C., 266, 553
Perot, P., 109, 541
Peskin, H., 467-468, 541
Peters, R. S., 3, 541
Peters, W., 281, 541
Peterson, G. M., 114, 541
Peterson, K., 541
Peterson, R. R., 167, 558
Pettifor, J. L., 347, 541
Pfaff, D. W., 168, 541
Phillips, W., 529
Phoenix, C. H., 192, 541-542, 558
Piaget, Jean, 121, 133, 141, 145, 227, 247, 251, 254, 256, 286, 293-296, 298, 302-304, 344-346, 351-352, 355-370, 380, 399, 425, 431, 434, 463, 466, 478, 542
Pickford, R. W., 38, 542
Piddington, R., 206-207, 355, 429-430, 433, 438-440, 451, 542
Pinard, A., 366, 532
Pines, Maya, 401, 542
Pinneau, S. R., 214, 542
Pintler, M. H., 548
Pishkin, V., 542
Pistor, F., 542
Pitts, F. N., 185, 542
Pitz, G. R., 151, 542
Ploog, D. W., 536
Poffenberger, T., 416, 542
Polanyi, M., 541
Polt, J. M., 152, 542
Pomeroy, W. B., 530
Poole, E. W., 507
Poresky, R., 516
Powell, M., 539
Pratt, C. L., 451, 542
Pratt, J. P., 166, 543
Pratt, K. C., 279, 281, 543
Prechtl, H. F. R., 55, 528, 543
Prell, D. B., 28, 516
Pribram, K. H., 102-103, 113, 290, 543
Price, W. H., 40-41, 543
Pritchard, M., 454, 543
Pronko, N. H., 38, 510
Proshansky, H., 209, 515
Provence, S., 227, 543
Purohit, A. P., 192, 543

Quackenbush, J. L., 544
Quinlan, D., 283, 511

Rabin, A. I., 436-437, 543
Radin, N., 555
Rafferty, F. T., 175, 543
Rainer, J. D., 23-24, 543
Rainwater, L., 457, 543
Ramsey, A. O., 155, 543
Rank, Otto, 383, 543
Rapaport, D., 467-468, 543
Rapport, A., 205, 543
Rasmussen, Elizabeth, 542
Rau, Lucy, 548
Raum, O. F., 436, 452, 543
Rawson, R. A., 514
Razran, G. H. S., 236, 466, 543
Reed, Linda H., 527
Reed, M. R., 204, 543
Reese, H. W., 248, 296, 299-300, 399, 543
Reichard, S., 543
Reider, N., 208, 543
Rendle-Short, J., 236, 543
Rethinghafer, D. A., 555
Révész, G., 262, 291, 529-530
Reynolds, E. L., 90, 543
Rheingold, Harriet L., 215, 543-544
Ribble, Margaret A., 214, 216, 544
Ribot, T., 383, 544
Ricciuti, H. N., 539
Richards, M. P., 202, 544
Richardson, C. E., 552
Richey, H. G., 90, 544
Richman, B. J., 264, 544
Richmond, J. B., 526
Richter, C. P., 168, 193, 544
Richter, D., 544
Riers, E., 196, 544
Riesen, A. H., 120, 132, 219-220, 222, 225-227, 235, 239, 274-275, 286, 544
Riesman, David, 327, 431, 503, 544
Rimland, B., 225, 544
Riss, W., 544
Rivlin, J., 203, 544
Robbins, L. C., 552
Roberts, L., 101-103, 105-110, 114, 541, 544
Robertson, Anne de S., 380, 544
Robertson, J. B., 513
Robinson, B. W., 536
Robson, K. S., 69, 156, 544
Roe, Anne, 22, 395, 519, 544
Roede, K. D., 544
Rogers, C. M., 319, 465, 514
Ronge, H., 280, 544

Rosenberg, B. G., 204, 544-545
Rosenberg, K. M., 515
Rosenblatt, J. S., 155, 180, 545, 547
Rosenblut, B., 192, 522
Rosenbluth, Dina, 510
Rosenthal, R., 402, 545
Rosenzweig, M. R., 218, 226, 508, 531, 545
Rosenzweig, S., 314-315, 545
Rosman, B. L., 529
Ross, Helen E., 202, 544
Ross, R. B., 151, 542
Ross, S., 323, 545
Rossler, R. H., 22, 545
Rousseau, Jean Jacques, 2, 315, 439
Rowland, V., 101, 545
Rubin, Betty L., 545
Ruch, T. C., 111, 545
Rudel, Rita G., 265, 545
Rudnick, M., 286, 545
Rudnick, R., 146, 555
Ruebush, B. K., 546
Ruegemar, W. R., 135, 545
Rueping, R. R., 536
Russell, Bertrand, 456, 504, 545
Russell, D. H., 365, 545
Russell, E. S., 62, 545
Russell, W. R., 96, 112, 545
Rutherford, E., 408, 417, 472, 539
Rychlak, J. E., 545

Sackett, G. P., 57, 66-67, 120, 138, 215-216, 265, 291, 451, 542, 545
Sahlins, M. D., 438, 545
Sahs, A. L., 523
Saint Paul, Ursula E. V., 73, 554
Salek, A., 546
Salk, L., 152, 277, 279, 545
Salmon, U. J., 545
Salter, D., 505
Saltzstein, H. D., 205, 545-546
Salzberger, R. M., 36, 546
Salzen, E. A., 148-149, 153, 546, 549
Sameroff, A. J., 268, 546
Samuels, Ina, 118-119, 131, 289, 546
Samuels, S. J., 546
Sanford, N., 546
Santostefano, S., 294, 546
Sarason, S. B., 318, 526, 546
Saravo, Anne, 247, 546
Sarnoff, I., 412, 546
Sartre, Jean Paul, 306, 480, 500, 503, 546
Saul, L. J., 555
Sawrey, W. L., 197, 546
Sayers, G., 309, 546
Sayers, M. A., 309, 546

Subject Index

Eidetic imagery, 380
Electroencephalograms (see EEG)
Electroretinographic (ERG) technique, 258-259
Embryological development (see Prenatal development)
Emotion (see also Attachments; Anxiety; Fear response), 198, 487
  communication of, 342
  critical periods for, 131, 135, 137-138, 142
  early stimulation of, 211, 213, 215, 223-225, 227
  genetics of, 22-23, 310-311, 327, 483
  in identification process, 410, 416-420
  imprinting and, 151, 153
  innate behavior and, 57-59, 67
  neural basis of, 109, 119, 121-122
  perception influenced by, 288
  psychological efficiency of, 10
Emotional behavior, defined, 307
Emotional development, 305-328
  hormonal influence on, 308-313
  in infancy, 305-309, 311, 320-321, 327
  neural influence on, 307-308
Emotional disturbances (see Mental illness)
Enactive representation, 353
Endocrinology (see Glandular system)
Endomorphs, 85-89, 91, 94
England, 46, 89, 101, 278-279, 469, 495
  adolescent sex in, 173
  British culture, 428-429, 433, 451
  criminal population of, 41
  intelligence data from, 38
Environmental reactions (external events, nurture) (see also Culture; Learning), 5-6, 227, 481-487
  cognitive, 360, 368-369, 374-376, 383, 386, 401-402
  constitutional theory of, 87, 91-94
  in critical periods, 131, 136, 143
  heredity vs., 19-20, 22-23, 25, 27-30, 33-34, 36-37, 40-45, 483-484, 489
  in identification process, 407-408, 423, 425
  imprinting and, 147-148, 151-152, 154, 158

Environmental reactions (cont.)
  individual, 12-13, 15
  innate behavior and, 50, 53-54, 57-59, 62, 70, 79-80
  language and, 335, 338
  neural development and, 113, 116-118, 120-122
  to reduced or enriched environment, 228-230, 487
  sex behavior and, 159, 182, 184
  sex differences in, 9, 197-199, 206, 208, 210, 490
Environmentalism, 1-2, 30, 42, 70, 80-81, 184
  Bruner's, 352
Epigenetic theory, 53, 151
Epistemic behavior, 314
ERG technique, 258-259
Ergotropic functions, 376-377
Erotic impulse, strength of, 184
Eskimos, 354, 374, 446
Evolution (see also Natural selection), 1-2, 17-22, 146, 245, 481-483, 495-497
  cultural, 21-22, 491-492, 497
  of innate behavior, 54, 57, 60
  mammalian, 283
  neural, 110, 121, 191
  of self-concept, 459-460
  transcendencies in, 481
Experience, 2, 123, 199
  cognition influenced by, 368-369, 390, 400
  critical periods in, 127
  early stimulation by, 221
  imprinting affected by, 152
  individual response to, 14-15
  innate behavior and, 54, 57-59
  learning influenced by, 232, 245
  perception influenced by, 255, 292-297
  sex behavior influenced by, 159, 164, 172-173, 178-181, 184-185
Exploratory behavior (curiosity drive), 131, 499
  early stimulation of, 227-228
  as motivation, 313-315, 319, 325, 327-328
  neural basis of, 119-121
  sex differences in, 190-191, 193, 197
Expressivity (incomplete penetrance), 26, 29-30, 45
Extended family, 445-446
External factors (extrinsic factors) (see Environmental reactions)

Extinction, 151

Families (see also Parents; Siblings), 491-492
  authority structure in, 433-434
  of creative children, 394-395, 398
  personality influenced by, 427, 433-434, 436-438, 440, 442-457
  structure of, 442, 445-447
Fantasies, 418, 436-437
  critical periods for, 127
  sexual, 169, 172, 174-175
FAP (see Fixed action patterns)
Fathers, 214, 454-455
  as authority figures, 433
  identification with, 408, 413-418, 422-425
  inheritance from, 30-31, 33
  patriarchal societies, 445-446
  self-concept influenced by, 471-475, 479
Fear response (see also Anxiety), 185
  critical periods for, 128, 139-140, 142-143
  hereditary, 24, 35
  imprinting and, 149, 152
  innate, 57, 69, 75-77
  neural basis of, 118-121
Femininity (see also Sex differences; Sex roles):
  creativity and, 392-394
  feminine self-concept, 469-471
  measures of, 204, 209
  super, 39-40
Fetal development (see Prenatal development)
Field dependence, 9, 208, 210, 284, 295, 373-376
Field effects, 303
Fighting (see Aggression)
Filter hypothesis, 225-226
Fish (see also Sticklebacks), 17, 72, 280
  imprinting in, 146
  neural development in, 96, 110
Fixation, 224
  infantile, 120, 198, 257-258, 261, 267-269
Fixed action patterns (FAP's), 232, 239
  as innate behavior, 51-55, 66
  in perception, 291
Forebrain (see Hypothalamus)
Form perception, 264-272, 292
  sensitivity to form, 266-272

Maturation (cont.)
  instinctual, 58
  learning influenced by, 242-243,
    247, 249, 251-252
  neural, 97, 115-116, 118, 120-123
  perception and, 290-292
  rates of, 489
  sex behavior influenced by, 167,
    177
  sex differences in, 187, 189, 193,
    202
Meaning systems, 413
Mechanistic psychology, 13, 50
Memory, 101-103, 172, 225, 248-249
  auditory, 279
  short- and long-term, 9, 101, 116,
    133, 220
Mental defectives (deficiencies), 3,
    15
  genetic basis of, 18, 20, 26, 32-33,
    39-40, 496
Mental illness (emotional disturb-
    ances), 5-6, 16, 154, 158, 306,
    338, 385, 455, 487
  constitutional theory of, 85, 88
  of creative individuals, 395-396,
    398
  critical period to develop, 126,
    136
  deprivation causing, 213, 226
  hereditary, 20, 23-24, 29, 39-42,
    430
  neural basis of, 119
  self-concept and, 460-461
  sex behavior and, 170-172, 185,
    316
  sex differences in, 208
  treatment of (see Psychotherapy)
Mental processes (see Cognitive
    processes)
Mesomorphs, 85-91, 94
Methodology, 4-5
Mexico, 354, 437
Mice, 23, 131, 134
  early stimulation of, 217, 223-224
  innate response to, 67
  neural development of, 113
  sex differences in, 192
Modifier genes, 26-27
Monkeys, 314, 414
  critical periods in, 132, 138
  early stimulation of, 222-223, 226-
    228
  imprinting in, 154, 156-157
  innate behavior of, 57, 66-67, 78
  learning in, 249
  neural development of, 99, 110-112

Monkeys (cont.)
  perceptual development of, 288
  personality development of, 426-
    427, 451
  sex behavior of, 176-177
  sex differences in, 188-189, 193
Mothers, 24, 126
  cognitive style traced to, 374-375
  identification with, 408, 411, 413-
    414, 416, 423, 425, 427
  inheritance from, 30-31, 33, 35
  innate behavior of, 69-70, 73
  matriarchial societies, 206-207,
    445-446, 457
  muscle dominance of, 89-90
  personality influenced by, 427,
    438, 447-448, 450-452, 455,
    457
  self-concept influenced by, 472-
    474
  stimulation from (maternal depri-
    vation), 211-217, 225, 227
Motivation (see also Drives), 136,
    227-228, 404, 487
  anxiety as, 317-320
  development of, 99
  hierarchy of, 308
  instinctual, 57-61, 71
  intellectual, 36-37, 358
  for learning, 235-236, 314-315,
    317-318
  maturity and, 323-325
  neural basis of, 119, 121-122, 171-
    172
  nurturing of, 325-327
  origin of, 305-308
  perception influenced by, 221,
    228, 292, 297
  punishment as, 321-322
  sex differences in, 208, 313, 318,
    322-323, 327
  social influences on, 322-323, 328,
    436
Motor coordination, 222-223
Mundugumor people, 206, 427
Mutations, 19-20, 57, 93
Mutual (M) approach, 256
Myelination, 194, 219, 257
  process of, 96-97, 100

Natural selection, 21-23, 57, 69, 208
  in isolation, 429-430
Nature (see Genetics)
Needs (see also Drives):
  affiliative, 454-455
  motivation and, 306-307, 317, 323
  neural basis of, 121

Negativism, age of, 127, 466
Negroes, 401-402, 409, 456-457, 467-
    468, 492
Neovitalism, 12-13
Nervous system (see also Autonomic
    nervous system; Brain; Cen-
    tral nervous system; Neuro-
    chemistry; Neurology; Neuro-
    physiology; Sensory develop-
    ment), 93, 151, 483-486
  development of, 95-124
  early stimulation of, 214, 218-222,
    224-226, 228
  fundamental properties of, 9
  innate behavior due to, 51, 55,
    60-61, 65, 71-72, 74-75, 78-79,
    81-83, 168
  integrative function of, 65
  postnatal development of, 97-99
  sex differences based on, 33, 178,
    182, 189-197, 201-202, 209
Neurochemistry, 26, 101
Neurology (see also Nervous sys-
    tem), 164, 275
  of cognition, 376-377
  critical periods based on, 120,
    126, 129-133, 136, 144
  genetic influence on, 25-26, 29,
    36, 115
  of learning, 98, 101, 111-112, 116,
    119, 121-122, 235-237, 239-
    242, 249-253, 420, 485-486
  of pain perception, 120, 280-281
Neurophysiology (see also Body
    schema), 97, 182, 190
  of instinctive behavior, 50, 55,
    65, 73
  invertebrate, 17
  of vision, 259
New Guinea, 206, 426-427, 436, 444,
    452
Nomothetic discipline, 7
Nonanalytic approach, 284, 373
Nonlancement (NL) response, 256
Normality (norms), 7-10, 15, 29, 488
  disturbance of, 70, 92-93, 127
  problem of, 7-8
North America (see also United
    States), 14, 77, 133, 206, 401,
    426, 487, 491
  as advanced society, 354
  behaviorism in, 43-44
  developmental efficiency in, 9
  personality development in, 430,
    445, 451
  self-concept in, 468, 471
Nuclear family, 445-446

Nurture (see Child rearing; Environmental reactions; Learning)

Object choice (cathexis), 410-411
Object permanence, 363
Observation, problem of, 12
Oedipus complex, 399, 411-412
Olfaction (see Smell)
Ontogeny (see also Individual differences; Individuality), 1, 17, 19, 69, 160, 238, 481
  emotional, 307
Operational thought, 354, 361
Orientation reactions, 118, 120, 130-131
Orphanages (see Institutional rearing)
Other-directedness, 327, 431, 476
Owls, 61

Pain perception, 227, 232
  critical periods in, 132, 135
  development of, 280-281, 296-297
  neural basis of, 120, 280-281
  sex differences in, 196
Paradic, concept of, 8
Parents (see also Fathers; Identification; Mothers):
  bond between child and, 24
  emotions originating with, 310-311
  imprinting on, 147, 151, 155-157
  inheritance from, 19-20, 22, 28, 30-31, 33-35, 37-38, 42-44
  personality influenced by, 427, 433, 436-438, 440, 445-452, 454-455, 457
  self-concept influenced by, 471-475, 479
  sex differences traced to, 198, 202, 206-208
  social development due to, 142-143
Passing (P) response, 256
Pattern discrimination, 120, 131
Pattern norms, 8-10, 29, 488
Pecking order, 177, 426
Peer culture, 70, 143, 384
  function of, 451-453
  imprinting affected by, 152
  of infrahuman animals, 451
  maturation for, 91
  personality influenced by, 432, 450-456
  self-concept influenced by, 452, 473-475

Peer culture (cont.)
  sex behavior within, 174, 185, 451, 490-491
  sex differences in, 188, 199, 424, 452-455
  sex typing and, 453
Penetrance, 29-30, 35
  incomplete (expressivity), 26, 29-30, 45
Penis envy, 473
Perception (see also Chemical senses; Hearing; Innate releasing mechanisms; Intuition; Kinesthetic perception; Pain perception; Somaesthetic sense; Space perception; Touch; Vision), 362, 372, 486
  critical periods for, 130-133, 136, 139-140, 289
  genetic influence on, 34
  individual, 12-13, 284
  instinct modified by, 54, 57-59, 61-63
  learning influence and, 231, 243, 245, 253, 282-284
  neural basis of, 97, 115, 118, 120-121, 253-255
  sex differences in, 186, 190-191, 195-198, 201-202, 269, 284
Perceptual constancies, 262-264, 293, 304
Perceptual development, 138, 253-304
  attentional factors in, 289-290
  in child's phenomenal world, 255-257
  individual styles of, 284
  language influencing, 292
Perceptual learning, 149, 241-242, 272, 277, 297-304
Perceptual-motor dominance, 371, 378
"Perceptual openness," 386
Perceptual organization, 259, 261, 299
Permissiveness, 500
Personality (see also Temperament), 112, 143, 413-415, 467
  "affectionless," 211
  cognition influenced by, 368-369, 372-373, 404
  constitutional theory of, 86, 88-89
  of creative individuals, 382, 390-392, 398
  genetic basis of, 20, 24, 28, 31-33, 43, 45, 429-430, 444-445, 448-449, 484

Personality (cont.)
  interacting forces in, 481
  perceptual influence on, 297
  role of humor in, 476
  sex differences in, 188, 206, 208, 438, 447, 452-455
Personality development, 7
  eight stages of, 465
  global (uniform), 429-430, 448
  social influences on, 206, 426-458
Phantom-limb phenomenon, 296, 462-463
Phasic receptors, 190-191
Phenomenology, 465
Phenotypes, 18, 23, 27, 29-30, 36, 45
  deviant, 41
  individual, 42-43
  somatic, 88-89, 93
  stimulation of, 222
Phenylketonuria (PKU), 25-26, 36, 80
Phylogeny, 1, 17, 96, 118, 238, 257, 481
Physiognomy, 84-91
Physique and Character (Kretschmer), 85, 531
Pigeons (doves), 134, 455
PKU (phenylketonuria), 25-26, 36, 80
Pleasure, 174, 411
  neural basis of, 119, 170-172
Pleiotropism, 26-27
Postnatal development (see also Infancy):
  critical periods of, 125
  neurophysiological, 97-99
Postural receptors, 190-191
Prejudice, 82, 143, 409-410, 495
Prenatal development (embryology, fetal development), 17, 93, 152, 407
  of emotion, 309, 318
  of nervous system, 96, 117, 191
  of perception, 257, 277, 279-281
  sexual development, 160-164, 182, 193
Preprogrammed behaviors, 115-116, 173, 483, 488
Presets, 151, 233, 301
Primates (see also specific primates), 140, 313
  color vision of, 259
  imprinting in, 156-157
  innate behavior of, 55-56, 64, 66-67
  neural development of, 117